S0-AJE-264

Dear Reader

With the aim of giving a maximum amount of information in a limited number of pages Michelin has adopted a system of symbols which is today known the world over.

Failing this system the present publication would run to six volumes.

Judge for yourselves by comparing the descriptive text below with the equivalent extract from the Guide in symbol form.

🏨 ❀❀ **Continental** (Thomas) 🐟, ✆ 21 32 43, ≤ valley, 🏤 « Flowered garden » – 🛏 ☎ 🚗. **AE**
March-October – **M Gourmet** *(closed Sunday)* 300/550 – 🍽 75 – **35 rm** 485/780.
Spec. Ravioli de homard, Pigeonneau de Bresse aux pâtes fraîches, Soufflé au chocolat amer. **Wines.** Bourgueil, Vouvray.

A top class comfort hotel where you will enjoy a pleasant stay and be tempted to prolong your visit.

The excellence of the cuisine, which is personally supervised by the proprietor Mr Thomas, is worth a detour.

The hotel is in a quiet secluded setting, away from the built-up area.

To reserve phone 21 32 43.

The hotel affords a fine view of the valley ; in good weather it is possible to eat out of doors. The hotel is enhanced by an attractive flowered garden.

Smoking is not allowed in certain areas of the establishment.

Direct dialling telephone in room.

Parking facilities, under cover, are available to hotel guests.

The hotel accepts payment by American Express credit card.

The establishment is open from March to October but the restaurant "Gourmet" closes every Sunday.

The set meal prices range from 300 F for the lowest to 550 F for the highest.

The cost of continental breakfast served in the bedroom is 75 F.

35 bedroomed hotel. The charges vary from 485 F for a single to 780 F for the best twin bedded room.

Included for the gourmet are some culinary specialities, recommended by the hotelier : Ravioli de homard, Pigeonneau de Bresse aux pâtes fraîches, Soufflé au chocolat amer. In addition to the best quality wines you will find many of the local wines worth sampling : Vouvray, Bourgueil.

This demonstration clearly shows that each entry contains a great deal of information. The symbols are easily learnt and to know them will enable you to understand the Guide and to choose those establishments that you require.

Contents

In addition to those situated in the main cities, restaurants renowned for their exceptional cuisine will be found in the towns printed in light type in the list above.

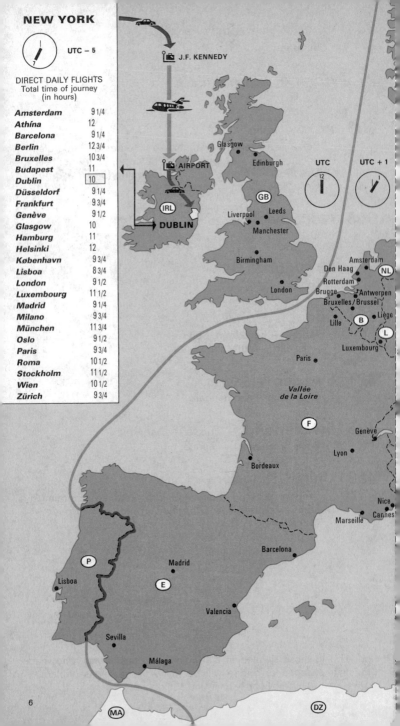

NEW YORK

UTC − 5

DIRECT DAILY FLIGHTS
Total time of journey
(in hours)

Amsterdam	9 1/4
Athína	12
Barcelona	9 1/4
Berlin	12 3/4
Bruxelles	10 3/4
Budapest	11
Dublin	10
Düsseldorf	9 1/4
Frankfurt	9 3/4
Genève	9 1/2
Glasgow	10
Hamburg	11
Helsinki	12
København	9 3/4
Lisboa	8 3/4
London	9 1/2
Luxembourg	11 1/2
Madrid	9 1/4
Milano	9 3/4
München	11 3/4
Oslo	9 1/2
Paris	9 3/4
Roma	10 1/2
Stockholm	11 1/2
Wien	10 1/2
Zürich	9 3/4

J.F. KENNEDY

AIRPORT

DUBLIN

IRL

Glasgow
Edinburgh

UTC

UTC + 1

GB

Liverpool Leeds
Manchester

Birmingham

London

Amsterdam
Den Haag
Rotterdam
Brugge   Antwerpen
Bruxelles/Brussel
Lille   Liège
B
Luxembourg

NL

L

Paris

Vallée de la Loire

F

Genève

Lyon

Bordeaux

Nice
Cannes
Marseille

Barcelona

P

Madrid

E

Lisboa

Valencia

Sevilla

Málaga

MA

DZ

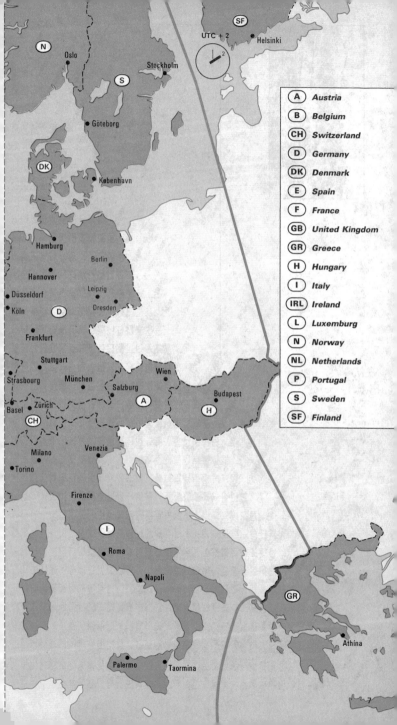

DISTANCES BY ROAD

(in kilometres)

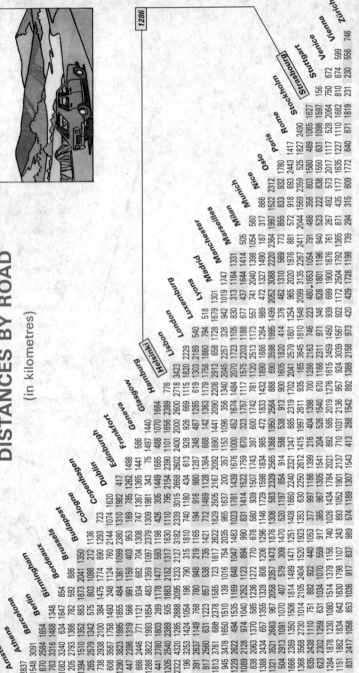

AIR LINKS (in hours)

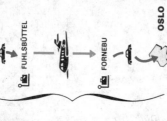

HAMBURG

FUHLSBÜTTEL

FORNEBU

OSLO

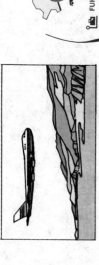

3 1/2 not daily

Amsterdam
Athens
Barcelona
Berlin
Birmingham
Bordeaux
Brussels
Budapest
Cologne
Copenhagen
Dublin
Edinburgh
Frankfort
Geneva
Glasgow
Hamburg
Helsinki
Lisbon
London
Luxemburg
Lyons
Madrid
Manchester
Marseilles
Milan
Munich
Nice
Oslo
Paris
Rome
Stockholm
Strasbourg
Stuttgart
Venice
Vienna
Zurich

9

This revised edition from
Michelin Tyre Company's Tourism Department
offers you a selection of
hotels and restaurants in the main European cities.
The latter have been chosen for
their business or tourist interest.

In addition the guide indicates establishments,
located in other towns,
renowned for the excellence of their cuisine.

Full colour has been introduced this year
throughout the guide in order to
make the presentation of the information
much clearer and more attractive.

We hope that the guide will help you
with your choice of a hotel or restaurant
and prove useful for your sightseeing.
Have an enjoyable stay.

Hotels
restaurants

CATEGORY, STANDARD OF COMFORT

🏨	Luxury in the traditional style	XXXXX
🏨	Top class comfort	XXXX
🏨	Very comfortable	XXX
🏨	Comfortable	XX
🏠	Quite comfortable	X
M	In its class, hotel with modern amenities	

ATMOSPHERE AND SETTING

🏨 ... 🏠	Pleasant hotels
XXXXX ... X	Pleasant restaurants
« Park »	Particularly attractive feature
🍃	Very quiet or quiet secluded hotel
🍃	Quiet hotel
≤ sea, ✳	Exceptional view, Panoramic view
≤	Interesting or extensive view

CUISINE

✿✿✿	Exceptional cuisine in the country, worth a special journey
✿✿	Excellent cooking : worth a detour
✿	A very good restaurant in its category
M	Other recommended carefully prepared meals

HOTEL FACILITIES

🛗 📺	Lift (elevator) – Television in room
⚞	Non-smoking areas
▤	Air conditioning
☎	Telephone in room: direct dialling for outside calls
☏	Telephone in room: outside calls connected by operator
🎾 ⌇ ⊠	Hotel tenis court(s) – Outdoor or indoor swimming pool
⊜ ꬵ	Sauna – Exercise room
🦌 🏖	Garden – Beach with bathing facilities
🍽	Meals served in garden or on terrace
🚗 🅿	Garage – Car park
♿	Bedrooms accessible to disabled people
🏛	Equipped conference hall
🐕̸	Dogs are not allowed
without rest.	The hotel has no restaurant

PRICES

These prices are given in the currency of the country in question. Valid for 1992 the rates shown should only vary if the cost of living changes to any great extent.

	Meals
M 115/230	Set meal prices
M à la carte 150/280	"a la carte" meals
b.i.	House wine included
🍷	Table wine available by the carafe
	Hôtels
30 rm 285/500	Lowest price for a comfortable single and highest price for the best double room.
	Breakfast
⊆ 55	Price of breakfast
Bb	Breakfast with choice from buffet
	Credit cards
🆑 AE CB 🅂 ⓞ E JCB VISA	Credit cards accepted

SERVICE and TAXES

Except in Greece, Portugal and Spain, prices shown are inclusive, that is to say service and V.A.T. included. In U.K. and Ireland, s = service only included, t = V.A.T. only included. In Italy, when not included, a percentage for service is shown after the meal prices.

Town Plans

Main conventional signs

🛈	Tourist Information Centre
□ ⊚ ● ● a	Hotel, restaurant – Reference letter on the town plan
⬛ ⬜ ◩	Place of interest and its main entrance ⎤ Reference letter on
🛉 🛉 ⸭ B	Interesting church or chapel ⎦ the town plan
Thiers (R.) 🅿	Shopping street – Public car park
•—•—•	Tram
⊚ ●	Underground station
→ ▶	One-way street
🛉 ♂	Church or chapel
⛫ ✉ 📞	Poste restante, telegraph – Telephone
⬜ ◩	Public buildings located by letters :
POL T M	Police (in large towns police headquaters) – Theatre – Museum
🚐 ✈ 🏥 🛒	Coach station – Airport – Hospital – Covered market
⁂ ■ ⊚	Ruins – Monument, statue – Fountain
🌳 ✝✝✝ ☖	Garden, park, wood – Cemetery, Jewish cemetery
⚳ 🏊 ⚳ 🏇	Outdoor or indoor swimming pool – Racecourse –
🏌	Golf course
⊶•⊶ ⊶⊶⊶	Cable-car – Funicular
⬭ ⪡ ❋	Sports ground, stadium – View – Panorama

Names shown on the street plans are in the language of the country to conform to local signposting.

SIGHTS

★★★	Worth a journey
★★	Worth a detour
★	Interesting

Avec cette nouvelle édition,
les Services de Tourisme du Pneu Michelin
vous proposent une sélection
d'hôtels et restaurants
des principales villes d'Europe,
choisies en raison de leur vocation internationale
sur le plan des affaires et du tourisme.

Vous y trouverez également les grandes tables
situées hors de ces grandes villes.

La couleur, introduite cette année
dans l'ensemble de l'ouvrage
est un nouveau pas vers la clarté
et l'agrément de son information.

Nous vous souhaitons d'agréables séjours
et espérons que ce guide vous aidera utilement
pour le choix d'un hôtel,
d'une bonne table
et pour la visite des principales curiosités.

Hôtels
restaurants

CLASSE ET CONFORT

🏰	Grand luxe et tradition	XXXXX
🏯	Grand confort	XXXX
🏛	Très confortable	XXX
🏚	Bon confort	XX
🏠	Assez confortable	X
M	Dans sa catégorie, hôtel d'équipement moderne	

L'AGRÉMENT

🏰 ... 🏠	Hôtels agréables
XXXXX ... X	Restaurants agréables
« Park »	Élément particulièrement agréable
🦢	Hôtel très tranquille, ou isolé et tranquille
🦢	Hôtel tranquille
⇐ sea, ❊	Vue exceptionnelle, panorama
⇐	Vue intéressante ou étendue

LA TABLE

❀❀❀	Une des meilleures tables du pays, vaut le voyage
❀❀	Table excellente, mérite un détour
❀	Une très bonne table dans sa catégorie
M	Autre table soignée

RESTAURANT
OUVERT
SAMEDI ET DIMANCHE
MENU

L'INSTALLATION

🛗 📺	Ascenseur – Télévision dans la chambre
🚭	Non-fumeurs
▤	Air conditionné
☎	Téléphone dans la chambre direct avec l'extérieur
🕿	Téléphone dans la chambre relié par standard
🎾 ⏋ 🏊	Tennis – Piscine : de plein air ou couverte
⛷ 🏋	Sauna – Salle de remise en forme
🌿 🏖	Jardin – Plage aménagée
🍴	Repas servis au jardin ou en terrasse
🚗 🅿	Garage – Parc à voitures
♿	Chambres accessibles aux handicapés physiques
🛎	L'hôtel reçoit les séminaires
🐕	Accès interdit aux chiens
without rest.	L'hôtel n'a pas de restaurant

LES PRIX

Les prix sont indiqués dans la monnaie du pays. Établis pour l'année 1992, ils ne doivent être modifiés que si le coût de la vie subit des variations importantes.

	Au restaurant
M 115/230	Prix des repas à prix fixes
M à la carte 150/280	Prix des repas à la carte
b.i.	Boisson comprise
🍷	Vin de table en carafe
	A l'hôtel
30 rm 285/500	Prix minimum pour une chambre d'une personne et maximum pour la plus belle chambre occupée par deux personnes
	Petit déjeuner
🍽 55	Prix du petit déjeuner
Bb	Petit déjeuner buffet
	Cartes de crédit
🆑 AE GB S D E JCB VISA	Cartes de crédit acceptées

SERVICE ET TAXES

A l'exception de la Grèce, du Portugal et de l'Espagne, les prix indiqués sont nets. Au Royaume Uni et en Irlande, s = service compris, t = T.V.A. comprise. En Italie, le service est parfois compté en supplément aux prix des repas. Ex. : (16 %).

Les Plans

Principaux signes conventionnels

🛈	Information touristique
□ ⊕ ● ● a	Hôtel, restaurant – Lettre les repérant sur le plan
	Monument intéressant et entrée principale ⎫ Lettre les repé-
	Église ou chapelle intéressante ⎭ rant sur le plan
Thiers (R.) 🅿	Rue commerçante – Parc de stationnement public
•—•—•	Tramway
◉ ●	Station de métro
→ ►	Sens unique
🛉 ŏ	Église ou chapelle
🖂 ⊗ 🕾	Poste restante, télégraphe – Téléphone
	Édifices publics repérés par des lettres :
POL T M	Police (dans les grandes villes commissariat central) – Théâtre – Musée
🚌 ✈ ⊞ ▭	Gare routière – Aéroport – Hôpital – Marché couvert
⁂ ▪ ◎	Ruines – Monument, statue – Fontaine
▦ t†t ⊡	Jardin, parc, bois – Cimetière, Cimetière israélite
⚊ ⌿ ▨ ▨ ⚞ 🏌	Piscine de plein air, couverte – Hippodrome – Golf
▯-▪-▪-▯ ▯·······▯	Téléphérique – Funiculaire
◯ ≼ ☀	Stade – Vue – Panorama

Les indications portées sur les plans sont dans la langue du pays, en conformité avec la dénomination locale.

LES CURIOSITÉS

★★★	Vaut le voyage
★★	Mérite un détour
★	Intéressante

Mit dieser Neuauflage
präsentieren Ihnen die Michelin-Touristikabteilungen
eine Auswahl von Hotels und Restaurants
in europäischen Hauptstädten
von internationaler Bedeutung
für Geschäftsreisende und Touristen.

Besonders gute Restaurants in der näheren Umgebung
dieser Städte wurden ebenfalls aufgenommen.

Die in diesem Jahr eingeführte
farbige Gestaltung des Führers
ist ein weiterer Schritt
in unserem Bemühen um
Modernisierung und Aktualisierung.

Wir wünschen einen angenehmen Aufenthalt
und hoffen, daß Ihnen dieser Führer
bei der Wahl eines Hotels, eines Restaurants
und beim Besuch der Hauptsehenswürdigkeiten
gute Dienste leisten wird.

Hotels
restaurants

KLASSENEINTEILUNG UND KOMFORT

⛪	Großer Luxus und Tradition	🍴🍴🍴🍴🍴
⛪	Großer Komfort	🍴🍴🍴🍴
⛪	Sehr komfortabel	🍴🍴🍴
🏠	Mit gutem Komfort	🍴🍴
🏠	Mit ausreichendem Komfort	🍴
M	Moderne Einrichtung	

ANNEHMLICHKEITEN

⛪ ... 🏠	Angenehme Hotels
🍴🍴🍴🍴🍴 ... 🍴	Angenehme Restaurants
« Park »	Besondere Annehmlichkeit
🦢	Sehr ruhiges oder abgelegenes und ruhiges Hotel
🦢	Ruhiges Hotel
≼ sea, ✳	Reizvolle Aussicht, Rundblick
≼	Interessante oder weite Sicht

KÜCHE

✿✿✿	Eine der besten Küchen des Landes : eine Reise wert
✿✿	Eine hervorragende Küche : verdient einen Umweg
✿	Eine sehr hute Küche : verdient Ihre besondere Beachtung
M	Andere sorgfältig zubereitete Mahlzeiten

19

EINRICHTUNG

📶 📺	Fahrstuhl – Fernsehen im Zimmer
🚭	Nichtraucher
▤	Klimaanlage
☎	Zimmertelefon mit direkter Außenverbindung
☏	Zimmertelefon mit Außenverbindung über Telefonzentrale
✗ ⌿ ▦	Tennis – Freibad – Hallenbad
⊆ ⌘	Sauna – Fitneß Center
⟿ ⛱	Garten – Strandbad
☂	Garten-, Terrassenrestaurant
⇌ Ⓟ	Garage – Parkplatz
♿	Für Körperbehinderte leicht zugängliche Zimmer
⚘	Konferenzraum
🐕	Das Mitführen von Hunden ist unerwünscht
without rest.	Hotel ohne Restaurant

DIE PREISE

Die Preise sind in der jeweiligen Landeswährung angegeben.
Sie gelten für das Jahr 1992 und können nur geändert werden, wenn die Lebenshaltungskosten starke Veränderungen erfahren.

	Im Restaurant
M 115/230	Feste Menupreise
M à la carte 150/280	Mahlzeiten "a la carte"
b.i.	Getränke inbegriffen
🍶	Preiswerter Tischwein in Karaffen
	Im Hotel
30 rm 285/500	Mindestpreis für ein Einzelzimmer und Höchstpreis für das schönste Doppelzimmer für zwei Personen.
	Frühstück
⌂ 55	Preis des Frühstücks
Bb	Frühstücksbuffet
	Kreditkarten
🅰 AE ⑤ 🅑 ① ⓔ JCB *VISA*	Akzeptierte Kreditkarten

BEDIENUNGSGELD UND GEBÜHREN

Mit Ausnahme von Griechenland, Portugal und Spanien sind die angegebenen Preise Inklusivpreise. In den Kapiteln über Großbritannien und Irland bedeutet s = Bedienungsgeld inbegriffen, t = MWSt inbegriffen. In Italien wird für die Bedienung gelegentlich ein Zuschlag zum Preis der Mahlzeit erhoben.

Stadtpläne

Erklärung der wichtigsten Zeichen

🛈	Informationsstelle
□ ⊙ ● ● a	Hotel, Restaurant – Referenzbuchstabe auf dem Plan
▬ ▭ ▨	Sehenswertes Gebäude mit Haupteingang ⎫ Referenzbuchstabe
⛪ ⛪ ⛪ B	Sehenswerte Kirche oder Kapelle ⎭ auf dem Plan
Thiers (R.) 🅿	Einkaufsstraße – Öffentlicher Parkplatz, Parkhaus
┼─┼─┼	Straßenbahn
◓ ●	U-Bahnstation
→ ►	Einbahnstraße
⛪ ♂	Kirche oder Kapelle
⛫ ⊠ ☎	Postlagernde Sendungen, Telegraph – Telefon
▭ ▨	Öffentliche Gebäude, durch Buchstaben gekennzeichnet :
POL T M	Polizei (in größeren Städten Polizeipräsidium) – Theater – Museum
🚌 ✈	Autobusbahnhof – Flughafen
⊞ ▭	Krankenhaus – Markthalle
⁂ ■ ◎	Ruine – Denkmal, Statue – Brunnen
▨ ₜᵗₜ ⌐	Garten, Park, Wald – Friedhof, Jüd. Friedhof
≋ ⌇ ▨ ⌐ 🐎 ⚑9	Freibad – Hallenbad – Pferderennbahn – Golfplatz und Lochzahl
□▬□▬□ ○┄┄┄○	Seilschwebebahn – Standseilbahn
⬭ ≼ ✳	Sportplatz – Aussicht – Rundblick

Die Angaben auf den Stadtplänen erfolgen, übereinstimmend
mit der örtlichen Beschilderung, in der Landessprache.

SEHENSWÜRDIGKEITEN

★★★	Eine Reise wert
★★	Verdient einen Umweg
★	Sehenswert

21

この改訂版ガイドブックはミシュラン・タイ
ヤ社観光部がおとどけするものです。

ビジネスに、観光に、国際的な拠点ヨーロッ
パ主要都市が誇る自慢のホテルとレストラン
を、そして郊外にたたずむ名うてのレストラ
ンをあわせて、御紹介いたします。

より美しく鮮明に旅の情報をお届けする為、
今年から、ガイドブックは全版色刷りとなり
ました。

このガイドブックが、より快適なホテル、味
わい深いレストランやあこがれの地と出逢う
きっかけとなり、皆さまの旅をより素晴らし
いものにするお手伝いができれば幸いです。

ホテル
レストラン

等級と快適さ

🏰	豪華で伝統的様式	XXXXX
🏨	トップクラス	XXXX
🏩	たいへん快適	XXX
🏘	快適	XX
🏠	割に快適	X
M	等級内での近代的設備のホテル	

居心地

🏰 … 🏠	居心地よいホテル
XXXXX … X	居心地よいレストラン
« Park »	特に魅力的な特徴
🕊	大変静かなホテルまたは人里離れた静かなホテル
🕊	静かなホテル
≤ sea ❉	見晴らしがよい展望(例：海)、パノラマ
≤	素晴らしい風景

料理

❉❉❉	最上の料理、出かける価値あり
❉❉	素晴らしい料理、寄り道の価値あり
❉	等級内では大変おいしい料理
M	その他の心のこもった料理

設備

🛗 📺	エレベーター、室内テレビ
🚭	非喫煙室
🖃	空調設備
☎	室内に電話あり、外線直通
☎	室内に電話あり、外線は交換台経由
✂ 🏊 🏊	テニスコート。屋外プール。屋内プール。
🧖ₛ 🏋	サウナ。トレーニングルーム。
🌳 🏖	くつろげる庭。整備された海水浴場
🍴	食事が庭またはテラスでできる。
🚗 🅿	駐車場、パーキング。
♿	体の不自由な方のための設備あり
🏛	会議又は研修会の出来るホテル
🐕	犬の連れ込みおことわり
without rest.	レストランの無いホテル

料金

料金は1992年のその国の貨幣単位で示してありますが、物価の変動などで変わる場合もあります。

レストラン

M 115/230
M à la carte
150/280

定食、ア・ラ・カルトそれぞれの最低料金と最高料金。

b.i. 飲物付

🍷 デカンター入りテーブルワイン有ります。

ホテル

30 rm 285/500 一人部屋の最低料金と二人部屋の最高料金。

朝食

🛏 55 朝食代

Bb 朝食はビュッフェ形式

クレジット・カード

🅰 AE CB 🅂
🅾 E JCB VISA

クレジット・カード使用可

サービス料と税金

ギリシャ、ポルトガル、スペイン以外の国に関しては正価料金。英国及びアイルランドでは、s.：サービス料込み、t.：付加価値税込み、を意味する。イタリアでは、サービス料が料金に加算されることがある。例: (16%)

地 図

主な記号

Z	ツーリストインフォメーション
□ ⊕ ● ● a	ホテル・レストラン — 地図上での目印番号
■ ▣ ▨	興味深い歴史的建造物と、その中央入口 ⎫ 地図上での
⬆ ⬆ ⓘ B	興味深い教会または聖堂 ⎭ 目印番号
Thiers (R.) 🅿	商店街　公共駐車場
·——·—·—	路面電車
◉ ●	地下鉄駅
→ ▶	一方通行路
⬆ ⓘ ⊠ ✉ ☏	教会または聖堂 —局留郵便、電報 —電話
▣ ▨	公共建造物、記号は下記の通り
POL T M	警察（大都市では、中央警察署）— 劇場 — 美術館、博物館
🚌 ✈ ✚ ▭	長距離バス発着所 — 空港 — 病院 — 屋内市場
⁘ ■ ◎	遺跡 — 歴史的建造物、像 — 泉
▦ ꜩ ▭	庭園、公園、森林 — 墓地 — ユダヤ教の墓地
⌇ ▨ ▨ ▨ 🐎 ⚑	屋外プール、屋内プール — 競馬場 — ゴルフ場
◦—◦—◦—◦ ◦—+—+—+—◦	ロープウェイ — ケーブルカー
◯ ≼ ❀	スタジアム — 風景 — パノラマ

地図上の名称は、地方の標識に合わせてその国の言葉で表記されています。

<table>
<tr><td colspan="2" align="center">名 所</td></tr>
<tr><td>★★★</td><td>出かける価値あり</td></tr>
<tr><td>★★</td><td>立ち寄る価値あり</td></tr>
<tr><td>★</td><td>興味深い</td></tr>
</table>

Austria

Österreich

PRACTICAL INFORMATION

LOCAL CURRENCY

Austrian Schilling; 100 S = 9,37 US $ (Jan. 92)

TOURIST INFORMATION

In Vienna: Österreich-Information, 1040 Wien, Margaretenstr. 1, ℘ (0222) 5 87 20 00
Niederösterreich-Information, 1010 Wien, Heidenschuß 2, ℘ (0222) 5 33 31 14 34
In Salzburg: Landesverkehrsamt, Sigmund-Haffner-Gasse 16, ℘ (0662) 80 42 23 27

AIRLINES

AUSTRIAN AIRLINES: 1010 Wien, Kärtner Ring 18, ℘ (0222) 7 17 99
AIR FRANCE: 1010 Wien, Kärntner Str. 49, ℘ (0222) 5 14 19
BRITISH AIRWAYS: 1010 Wien, Kärntner Ring 10, ℘ (0222) 65 76 91
DEUTSCHE LUFTHANSA: 1015 Wien, Kärntner Str. 42, ℘ (0222) 5 88 36
JAPAN AIRLINES: Stephansplatz 1, ℘ (0222) 535 51 25

FOREIGN EXCHANGE

Hotels, restaurants and shops do not always accept foreign currencies and it is wise, therefore, to change money and cheques at the banks and exchange offices which are found in the larger stations, airports and at the frontier.

SHOPPING and BANK HOURS

Shops are open from 9am to 6pm, but often close for a lunch break. They are closed Saturday afternoon, Sunday and Bank Holidays (except the shops in railway stations).
Branch offices of banks are open from Monday to Friday between 8am and 12.30pm (in Salzburg 12am) and from 1.30pm to 3pm (in Salzburg 2pm to 4.30pm), Thursday to 5.30pm (only in Vienna).
In the index of street names those printed in red are where the principal shops are found.

BREAKDOWN SERVICE

ÖAMTC: See addresses in the text of Vienna and Salzburg
ARBÖ: in Vienna: Mariahilfer Str. 180, ℘ (0222) 85 35 35
in Salzburg: Münchner Bundesstr. 9, ℘ (0662) 3 36 01
In Austria the ÖAMTC (emergency number ℘ 120) and the ARBÖ (emergency number ℘ 123) make a special point of assisting foreign motorists. They have motor patrols covering main roads.

TIPPING

Service is generally included in hotel and restaurant bills. But in Austria, it is usual to give more than the expected tip in hotels, restaurants and cafés. Taxi-drivers, porters, barbers and theatre attendants also expect tips.

SPEED LIMITS

The speed limit in built up areas (indicated by place name signs at the beginning and end of such areas) is 50 km/h - 31 mph; on motorways 130 km/h - 80 mph and on all other roads 100 km/h - 62 mph.

SEAT BELTS

The wearing of seat belts in Austria is compulsory for drivers and passengers.

Vienna

(WIEN) Austria 987 40, 426 12 – pop. 1 500 000 – alt. 156 m. – ⊙ 01.

HOFBURG★★★ FGY
Imperial Palace of the Habsburgs (Kaiserpalast der Habsburger) : Swiss Court – Royal Chapel – Amalienhof – Stallburg – Leopold Wing – Ballhausplatz – Imperial Chancellery – Spanish Riding School – Neue Burg – Josefsplatz – Michaelerplatz – In der Burg – Capuchins Crypt – Church of the Augustinians. Art Collections : Imperial Treasury★★★ – Imperial Apartments★★ – Austrian National Library (Great Hall★ – Frescoes★★) – Collection of Court Porcelain and Silver★★ – Collection of Arms and Armour★★ – Collection of Old Musical Instruments★ – Albertina (Dürer Collection★) – Museum of Ephesian Sculpture (Reliefs of Ephesus★★).

BUILDINGS AND MONUMENTS
St Stephen's Cathedral★★★ (Stephansdom) GY – Schönbrunn★★★ (Apartments★★★, Park★★, Gloriette★★, Coach Room★★) AS – Upper and Lower Belvedere★★ (Oberes und Unteres Belvedere) (Terraced Gardens and Art Collections★) HZ and DV – Opera★ (Staatsoper)★ GY – Church of St Charles★★ (Karlskirche) GZ – Church of St Michael (Michaeler Kirche) GY – Church of the Minor Friars (Minoritenkirche) FY – Church of the Teutonic Order (Deutschordenskirche) (Altarpiece★, Treasure★) GY **E** – Church of the Jesuits (Jesuitenkirche) HY **H** – Church of Our Lady of the River Bank (Maria am Gestade) GX – Church of the Faithful Virgin (Maria Treu) AR – Mozart Memorial (Mozart-Gedenkstätte) GY **F** – Dreimäderlhaus FX **W** – Pavilion Otto Wagner★ GZ **Q** – Pavilion of the Secession★ GZ **S**.

STREETS, PLACES, PARKS
The Tour of the Ring★ – The Old Town (Altstadt)★ – Kärntner Straße GY – Graben (Plague Column) GY – Am Hof (Column to the Virgin) GY – Herrengasse★ GY – Maria-Theresien-Platz FY – Prater★ (Giant Whell, ≼★) BR – Oberlaapark★ BS – Donner Fountain (Donnerbrunnen)★ GY **Y** – Heldenplatz FY – Burggarten GY – Volksgarten FY – Rathausplatz FY.

IMPORTANTS MUSEUMS (Hofburg and Belvedere see above)
Museum of Fine Arts★★★ (Kunsthistorisches Museum) FY – Historical Museum of the City of Vienna★★ (Historisches Museum der Stadt Wien) GZ **M6** – Austrian Folklore Museum★★ (Österreichisches Museum für Volkskunde) AR **M7** – Gallery of Painting and Fine Arts★ (Gemäldegalerie der Akademie der Bildenden Künste) GZ **M9** – Natural History Museum★ (Naturhistorisches Museum) FY **M1** – Birthplace of Schubert (Schubert-Museum) BR **M16** – Austrian Museum of Applied Arts★ (Österreichisches Museum für angewandte Kunst) HY **M10** – Clock Museum (Uhrenmuseum der Stadt Wien) GY **M3**.

EXCURSIONS
Danube Tower★★ (Donauturm) BR – Leopoldsberg ≼★★ AR – Kahlenberg ≼★ AR – Klosterneuburg Abbey (Stift Klosterneuburg) (Altarpiece by Nicolas of Verdun★) AR – Grinzing★ AR – Baden★ AS – Vienna Woods★ (Wienerwald) AS.

🇮🇸 Freudenau 65a, ℰ 2 18 95 64
🛬 Wien-Schwechat by ③, ℰ 77 70 and 5 05 57 57, Air Terminal, at Stadtpark (HY) ℰ 72 35 34
🚆 ℰ 56 50 29 89 and 56 50 56 85.

Exhibition Centre, Messeplatz 1, ℰ 9 31 52 40.

🅱 Tourist-information, ✉ A-1010, Kärtner Str. 38, ℰ 513 88 92 – ÖAMTC, ✉ A-1010, Schubertring 1, ℰ 71 19 90, Fax 7 13 18 07.

Budapest 208 ④ – München 435 ⑦ – Praha 292 ① – Salzburg 292 ⑦ – Zagreb 362 ⑥.

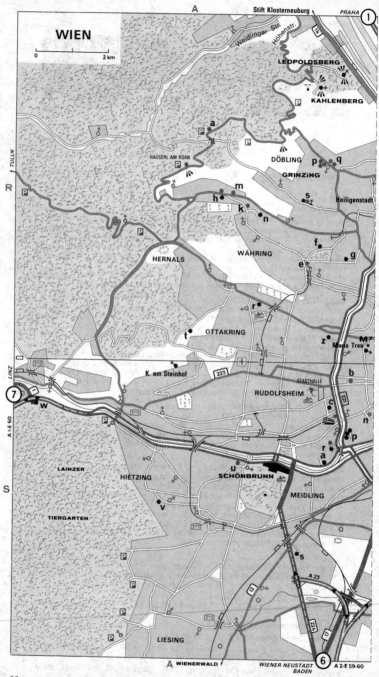

WIEN

0   2 km

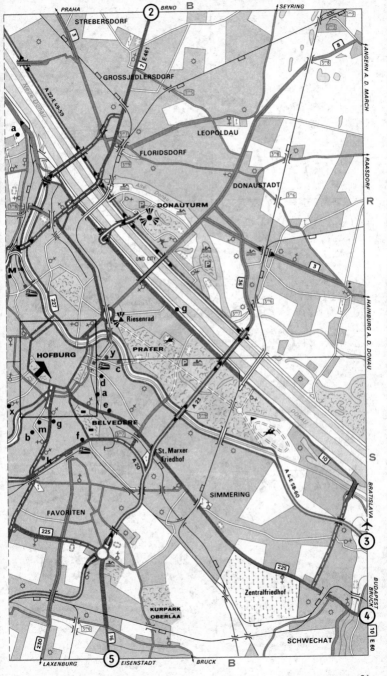

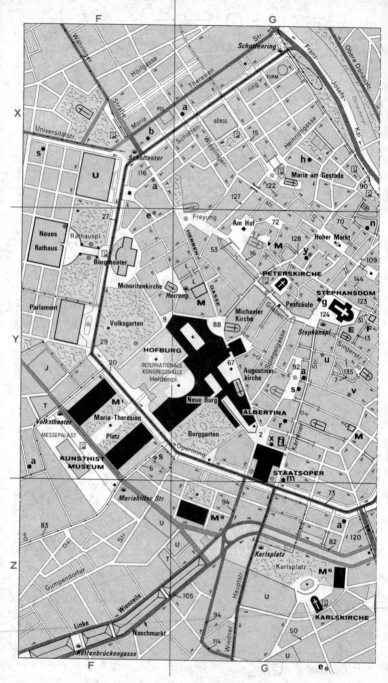

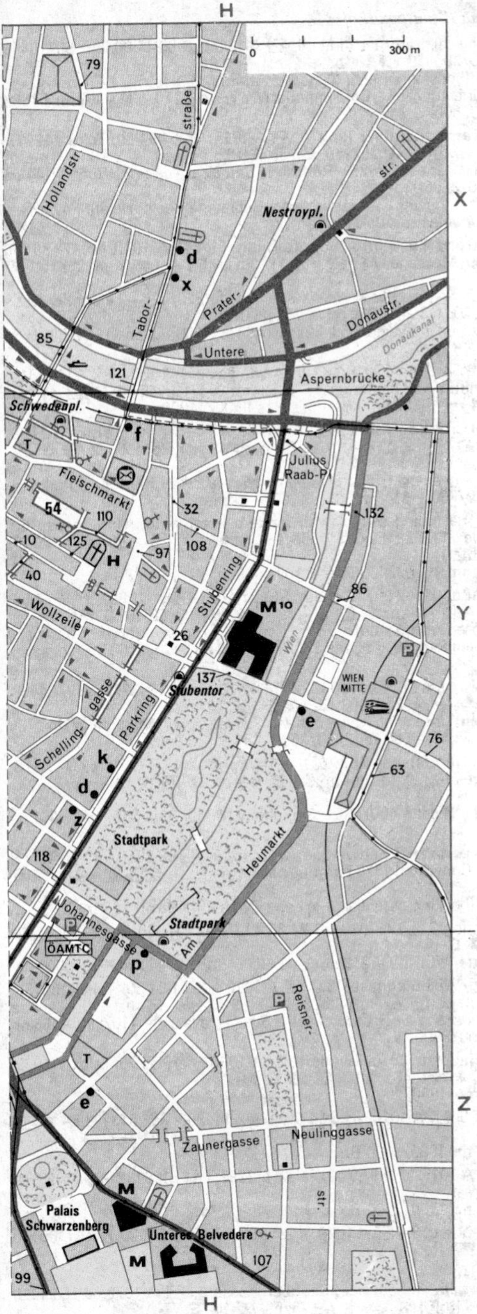

Write us...

*If you have any comments
on the contents
of this guide.*

*Your praise as well as
your criticisms will receive
careful consideration
and, with your assistance,
we will be able to add
to our stock of information
and, where necessary,
amend our judgments.*

Thank you in advance!

33

Town Centre, city districts (Stadtbezirke) 1-9 :

🏨🏨 **Imperial** (converted 19C palace), Kärntner Ring 16, ✉ A-1015, ☏ 50 11 00, Fax 50110410 – 🛗 ⇔ rm 📺 – 🏛 25/200. 🖭 ⓓ ⓔ 𝘝𝘐𝘚𝘈. ⚒ rest
GZ **a**
Restaurants : **Zur Majestät** (booking essential) *(closed Saturday lunch, 6 - 12 January and 13 July - 2 August)* **M** a la carte 405/755 – **Café Imperial M** a la carte 270/530 – **152 rm** 4 150/ 7 000 Bb – 22 suites 8500/32500.

🏨🏨 ✿ **Bristol - Restaurant Korso**, Kärntner Ring 1, ✉ A-1015, ☏ 51 51 60, Telex 112477, Fax 51516550 – 🛗 ⇔ rm 📺 – 🏛 25/150. 🖭 ⓓ ⓔ 𝘝𝘐𝘚𝘈 ⚒ rest
GYZ **m**
M *(closed Saturday lunch)* a la carte 395/825 – **Rôtisserie Sirk M** a la carte 320/550 – **144 rm** 3050/5100 – 13 suites 7800/8800
Spec. Marinierter Kalbskopf mit Ingwer und Balsamessig, Gebratene Seeforelle auf Petersilien-schaum, Soufflierter Scheiterhaufen mit Calvados-Äpfeln.

🏨🏨 ✿ **Plaza Wien - Restaurant La Scala**, Schottenring 11, ✉ A-1010, ☏ 31 39 00, Telex 135859, Fax 31390160, Massage, 🗜, ⇔ – 🛗 ⇔ rm 📺 ও ⇔ – 🏛 25/150.
🖭 ⓓ ⓔ 𝘝𝘐𝘚𝘈. ⚒ rest
GX **a**
M *(closed lunch Saturday, Sunday and Bank Holidays)* a la carte 390/725 – **Le Jardin** *(lunch only)* **M** a la carte approx. 370 (buffet) – **250 rm** 3675/4950 Bb – 37 suites 5950/30550
Spec. Variation von Meeresfischen in Seeigelfond, Medaillons vom Kalb "La Scala", Waldbeeren in Blätterkrokant.

🏨🏨 **Sacher**, Philharmonikerstr. 4, ✉ A-1010, ☏ 5 14 56, Telex 112520, Fax 51457810, « Collection of valuable furniture and paintings » – 🛗 ⇔ rm 📺 ও. 🖭 ⓓ ⓔ 𝘝𝘐𝘚𝘈 ⚒ rest
M a la carte 485/695 – **124 rm** 1600/4600 Bb – 3 suites 9500/14000.
GY **x**

🏨🏨 **Vienna Marriott Hotel**, Parkring 12a, ✉ A-1010, ☏ 51 51 80, Telex 112249, Fax 515186736, Massage, ⇔, 🖾 – 🛗 ⇔ rm 📺 ও ⇔ – 🏛 25/400. 🖭 ⓓ ⓔ 𝘝𝘐𝘚𝘈. ⚒ rest
HY **d**
Restaurants : **Symphonika** *(dinner only, closed Sunday)* **M** a la carte 500/790 – **Parkring-Restaurant M** a la carte 380/700 – **304 rm** 3050/4300 – 7 suites 5200/11900.

🏨🏨 **Penta Hotel** (former imperial riding school with modern hotel wing), Ungargasse 60, ✉ A-1030, ☏ 71 17 50, Telex 112529, Fax 7117590, Massage, ⇔, 🖾 – 🛗 ⇔ rm 📺 ও – 🏛 25/300. 🖭 ⓓ ⓔ 𝘝𝘐𝘚𝘈
BS **a**
M a la carte 295/565 – **342 rm** 1650/2600 Bb – 3 suites 6500.

🏨🏨 **Vienna Hilton**, Landstraßer Hauptstr. 2 (near Stadtpark), ✉ A-1030, ☏ 7 17 00, Telex 136799, Fax 7130691 – 🛗 ⇔ rm 📺 ও ⇔ – 🏛 25/700. 🖭 ⓓ ⓔ 𝘝𝘐𝘚𝘈. ⚒ rest
Restaurants : **Prinz Eugen** (closed lunch Saturday, Sunday and Bank Holidays) *(booking essential)* **M** a la carte 460/760 – **Café am Park M** a la carte 320/510 – **603 rm** 3100/3780 Bb – 25 suites 8640/25000.
HY **e**

🏨🏨 **Intercontinental**, Johannesgasse 28, ✉ A-1037, ☏ 71 12 20, Telex 131235, Fax 7134489, ⇔ – 🛗 ⇔ rm 📺 ও ⇔ – 🏛 25/1000. 🖭 ⓓ ⓔ 𝘝𝘐𝘚𝘈. ⚒ rest
HZ **p**
Restaurants : **Vier Jahreszeiten** *(closed Saturday lunch and Sunday dinner)* **M** a la carte 355/765 – **Brasserie M** a la carte 260/540 – **500 rm** 2250/3600 – 62 suites 8100.

🏨🏨 **Scandic Crown Hotel**, Handelskai 269, ✉ A-1020, ☏ 2 17 77, Telex 133318, Fax 21777199, ⇔, Massage, ⇔, 🔄 (heated), ⚒ – 🛗 ⇔ rm 📺 ও ⓟ – 🏛 25/300. 🖭 ⓓ ⓔ 𝘝𝘐𝘚𝘈. ⚒ rest
BR **g**
Restaurants : **Scandirama M** a la carte 400/635 – **Symphony M** a la carte 315/450 – **367 rm** 1900/4000 Bb

🏨🏨 **Hotel im Palais Schwarzenberg**, Schwarzenbergplatz 9, ✉ A-1030, ☏ 78 45 15, Telex 136124, Fax 784714, « Converted 1727 baroque palace, park » – 🛗 📺 ⓟ – 🏛 25/200. 🖭 ⓔ 🖭
HZ
M *(closed 2 - 17 February)* (booking essential) a la carte 510/880 – **38 rm** 3630/12260.

🏨🏨 **Hotel de France**, Schottenring 3, ✉ A-1010, ☏ 34 35 40, Telex 114360, Fax 315969, ⇔ – 🛗 📺 – 🏛 25/100. 🖭 ⓓ ⓔ 𝘝𝘐𝘚𝘈. ⚒ rest
FX **b**
M *(closed Saturday)* a la carte 275/400 – **218 rm** 2400/3600 Bb – 10 suites 4000/5000.

🏨🏨 **SAS-Palais-Hotel**, Parkring/Weihburggasse 32, ✉ A-1010, ☏ 51 51 70, Telex 136127, Fax 5122216, ⇔ – 🛗 ⇔ rm 📺 ও – 🏛 25/100. 🖭 ⓓ ⓔ 𝘝𝘐𝘚𝘈. ⚒ rest
HY **z**
M *(closed 2 weeks July - August and lunch Saturday and Sunday)* a la carte 410/610 – **165 rm** 2540/5240 Bb – 8 suites 5800/8800.

🏨🏨 **Biedermeier**, Landstraßer Hauptstr. 28 (at Sünnhof), ✉ A-1030, ☏ 75 55 75, Telex 111039, Fax 755575503, ⇔ – 🛗 📺 – 🏛 25/50. 🖭 ⓓ ⓔ 𝘝𝘐𝘚𝘈
BS **d**
M a la carte 280/425 – **204 rm** 1850/2900 – 18 suites 3600/4900.

🏨🏨 **Ambassador**, Neuer Markt 5, ✉ A-1010, ☏ 5 14 66, Telex 111906, Fax 5132999 – 🛗 📺. 🖭 ⓓ ⓔ 𝘝𝘐𝘚𝘈
GY **s**
M a la carte 320/690 – **107 rm** 1500/5000 Bb

🏨 **Europa**, Neuer Markt 3, ✉ A-1015, ☏ 51 59 40, Telex 112292, Fax 5138138 – 🛗 📺 ☎. – 🏛 30. 🖭 ⓓ ⓔ 𝘝𝘐𝘚𝘈 ⚒ rest
GY **a**
M a la carte 335/615 – **102 rm** 1500/2500 Bb

🏨 **City-Central** without rest, Taborstr. 8a, ✉ A-1020, ☏ 21 10 50, Telex 134570, Fax 21105140 – 🛗 📺 ☎ ও ⓟ. 🖭 ⓓ ⓔ 𝘝𝘐𝘚𝘈
HX **x**
58 rm 1460/1980 Bb

🏨 **K. u. K. Hotel Maria Theresia** without rest, Kirchberggasse 6, ✉ A-1070, ☏ 5 21 23, Telex 111530, Fax 5212370 – 🛗 📺 ☎ ⇔ – 🏛 25/50. 🖭 ⓓ ⓔ 𝘝𝘐𝘚𝘈
FY **a**
123 rm 1450/2870 Bb

🏨 **Pannonia**, Matrosengasse 6, ⊠ A-1060, ☎ 59 90 10, Telex 132940, Fax 5976940, ⇌ – |≑|
⟿ rm ▤ க ⇌ – ⚗ 25/80. ⚏ ⓪ ⋿ ꭟ
M a la carte 210/415 – **205 rm** 1290/1775 – 6 suites 2760.
AS **p**

🏨 **Rathauspark** without rest, Rathausstr. 17, ⊠ A-1010, ☎ 40 41 20, Telex 112817,
Fax 40412761 – |≑| �📺 ☎ – ⚗ 30. ⚏ ⓪ ⋿ ꭟ
117 rm 1200/2300 Bb
FX **s**

🏨 **K u. K Palais Hotel** without rest (modern hotel in a former palace), Rudolfsplatz 11, ⊠
A-1010, ☎ 5 33 13 53, Telex 134049, Fax 533135370 – |≑| �📺 ☎ – ⚗ 50. ⚏ ⓪ ⋿ ꭟ
66 rm 1390/1820 Bb
GX **h**

🏨 **Alba Hotel Palace**, Margaretenstr. 92, ⊠ A-1050, ☎ 55 46 86, Telex 114321,
Fax 55468686, ⇌ – |≑| ⚗ – ⚗ 25/130. ⚏ ⓪ ⋿ ꭟ. ⅍ rest
M a la carte 295/470 – **117 rm** 1300/2600 Bb
BS **b**

🏨 **Stefanie**, Taborstr. 12, ⊠ A-1020, ☎ 21 15 00, Telex 134589, Fax 21150160, 🍴 – |≑| �📺
☎ ⇌ – ⚗ 25/200. ⚏ ⓪ ⋿ ꭟ
M 200/300 and a la carte 240/400 – **130 rm** 1280/1980 Bb
HX **d**

🏨 **Amadeus** without rest, Wildpretmarkt 5, ⊠ A-1010, ☎ 63 87 38, Telex 111102, Fax 63873838
– |≑| �📺 ☎. ⚏ ⓪ ⋿ ꭟ – closed 22 to 28 December – **30 rm** 1050/1850 Bb
GY **y**

🏨 **Pullman Hotel Belvedere**, Am Heumarkt 35, ⊠ A-1030, ☎ 7 52 53 50, Telex 111822,
Fax 752535844 – |≑| �📺 ☎ ⇌ – ⚗ 30. ⚏ ⓪ ⋿ ꭟ. ⅍ rest
M a la carte 200/320 – **211 rm** 1290/2800 Bb
HZ **e**

🏨 **Alba-Accadia**, Margaretenstr. 53, ⊠ A-1050, ☎ 5 88 50, Telex 113264, Fax 58850899 –
|≑| �📺 ☎ ⇌. ⚏ ⓪ ⋿ ꭟ
M a la carte 285/425 – **104 rm** 1300/2600 Bb
BS **m**

🏨 **Capricorno** without rest, Schwedenplatz 3, ⊠ A-1010, ☎ 53 33 10 40, Telex 115266,
Fax 53376714 – |≑| �📺 ☎ ⇌ Ⓟ. ⚏ ⋿ ꭟ
46 rm 1120/1980 Bb
HY **f**

🏨 **President**, Wallgasse 23, ⊠ A-1060, ☎ 5 99 90, Telex 112523, Fax 567646 – |≑| ▤ �📺 ☎
⇌ – ⚗ 50. ⚏ ⓪ ⋿ ꭟ
M (closed Sunday) a la carte 250/400 – **77 rm** 1300/2300 Bb
AS **p**

🏨 **Astoria**, Führichgasse 1, ⊠ A-1015, ☎ 51 57 70, Telex 112856, Fax 5157782 – |≑| ⚗ ☎.
⚏ ⓪ ⋿ ꭟ
M (closed Saturday, Sunday and July) a la carte 305/500 – **108 rm** 1200/3200 Bb
GY **r**

🏨 **Kummer**, Mariahilfer Str. 71a, ⊠ A-1061, ☎ 5 88 95, Telex 111417, Fax 5878133 – |≑| ⟿ rm
�📺 ☎ ⚏ ⓪ ⋿ ꭟ
M a la carte 240/350 – **106 rm** 1200/2050 Bb
BS **x**

🏨 **Erzherzog Rainer**, Wiedner Hauptstr. 27, ⊠ A-1041, ☎ 50 11 10, Telex 132329,
Fax 50111350 – |≑| ▤ rest �📺 ☎ – ⚗ 50. ⚏ ꭟ
M a la carte 285/455 – **84 rm** 1100/2100 Bb
BS **g**

🏨 **Mercure**, Fleischmarkt 1a, ⊠ A-1010, ☎ 53 46 00, Telex 112048, Fax 53460232 – |≑| ⟿ rm
▤ �📺 ☎ க. ⚏ ⓪ ⋿ ꭟ
M a la carte 245/415 – **155 rm** 1450/2000 Bb
GY **n**

🏨 **Am Parkring**, Parkring 12, ⊠ A-1015, ☎ 5 14 80, Telex 113420, Fax 5148040 – |≑| ▤ �📺
☎ ⇌. ⚏ ⓪ ⋿ ꭟ
M (closed Sunday dinner) a la carte 275/445 – **64 rm** 1520/2180 Bb – 3 suites 2540.
HY **k**

🏨 **Am Stephansplatz**, Stephansplatz 9, ⊠ A-1010, ☎ 53 40 50, Telex 114334, Fax 53405711
– |≑| ▤ rest �📺 ☎. ⚏ ⓪ ⋿ ꭟ – (accepted by the hotel only)
M a la carte 230/375 – **62 rm** 1350/2060 Bb
GY **g**

🏠 **Prinz Eugen**, Wiedner Gürtel 14, ⊠ A-1040, ☎ 5 05 17 41, Telex 132483, Fax 5055308 –
|≑| ⟿ rm �📺 ☎. ⚏ ⓪ ⋿ ꭟ
M a la carte 240/400 – **112 rm** 1560/2500 Bb
BS **f**

🏠 **Ibis**, Mariahilfer Gürtel 22, ⊠ A-1060, ☎ 56 56 26, Telex 133833, Fax 564368 – |≑| ▤ �📺
☎ க ⇌ – ⚗ 25/180. ⚏ ⋿ ꭟ
M a la carte 210/370 – **341 rm** 990/1390 Bb
AS **p**

🏠 **Hungaria**, Rennweg 51, ⊠ A-1030, ☎ 7 13 25 21, Telex 131797, Fax 755930 – |≑| ⚏ ☎
⇌. ⚏ ⓪ ⋿ ꭟ
M a la carte 235/380 ⅋ – **168 rm** 1150/2550 Bb
BS **e**

✕✕✕✕ ❀❀ **Steirereck**, Rasumofskygasse 2 / Ecke Weißgerberlände, ⊠ A-1030, ☎ 7 13 31 68,
Fax 7135168 – ⚏ ⓪ ⋿ ꭟ – closed Saturday, Sunday and Bank Holidays – **M** (remarkable wine
list, visit of the wine cellar possible) (booking essential) a la carte 455/720
BS **c**
Spec. Avocadosalat mit Saibling, Lammrücken mit Liebstöcklsauce, Böhmisch-österreichische
Topfenmehlspeise.

✕✕✕ **Zu den drei Husaren**, Weihburggasse 4, ⊠ A-1010, ☎ 5 12 10 92, Fax 512109218 – ⚏
⓪ ⋿ ꭟ
GY **u**
closed mid July - mid August and 24 to 28 December - **M** a la carte 420/780.

✕✕✕ ❀ **Gottfried**, Untere Viaduktgasse 45/Marxergasse, ⊠ A-1030, ☎ 7 13 82 56,
Fax 713355130, remarkable wine list – ⚏ ꭟ
BRS **y**
closed Saturday lunch and Bank Holidays, May - September closed Saturday and Sunday - **M**
(booking essential) 350/550 (lunch) and a la carte 440/750
Spec. Variationen von der Gänseleber, Seewolf mit Kaviarbutter, Schokolademousseterrine mit
Moccasabayon.

35

XXX **Hauswirth**, Otto-Bauer-Gasse 20, ⊠ A-1060, ℰ 5 87 12 61, Fax 5860419 – 🝙 ⑩ 🝙 𝘝𝘐𝘚𝘈
closed Sunday, Bank Holidays and 24 - 30 December – **M** a la carte 360/540.   AS **n**

XXX **Steirer Stub'n**, Wiedner Hauptstr. 111, ⊠ A-1050, ℰ 55 43 49, Fax 550888 – 🝙 ⑩ 🝙
𝘝𝘐𝘚𝘈   BS **k**
closed Sunday and Bank Holidays – **M** (booking essential) a la carte 270/450.

XXX **Grotta Azzurra** (Italian rest.), Babenberger Str. 5, ⊠ A-1010, ℰ 5 86 10 44, Fax 586104415 –
🝙 ⑩ 🝙 𝘝𝘐𝘚𝘈 – closed Sunday and mid July - mid August – **M** a la carte 350/540.   FY **s**

XXX **Kupfertdachl**, Schottengasse 7 (entrance Mölker Bastei), ⊠ A-1010, ℰ 63 93 81,
Fax 5354042 – 🝙 ⑩ 🝙 𝘝𝘐𝘚𝘈   FX **a**
closed Saturday lunch, Sunday and 1 - 23 August – **M** a la carte 325/530.

XX **Schubertstüberln**, Schreyvogelgasse 4, ⊠ A-1010, ℰ 63 71 87, Fax 5353546, ☜ – 🝙 ⑩ 🝙
𝘝𝘐𝘚𝘈 – closed Saturday, Sunday and 23 December - 3 January – **M** a la carte 300/565.   FXY **e**

XX **Steinerne Eule**, Halbgasse 30, ⊠ A-1070, ℰ 93 22 50, ☜ – 🝙 𝘝𝘐𝘚𝘈   AS **b**
closed Sunday and Monday – **M** a la carte 360/630.

XX **Zum Kuckuck**, Himmelpfortgasse 15, ⊠ A-1010, ℰ 5 12 84 70, Fax 5233818 – 🝙 GY **v**
closed Saturday and Sunday – **M** a la carte 340/520.

XX **Wiener Rathauskeller** (vaults with murals), Rathausplatz 1, ⊠ A-1010, ℰ 4 21 21 90,
Fax 42121927 – 🝙 ⑩ 🝙 𝘝𝘐𝘚𝘈   FY
closed Sunday and Bank Holidays – **M** a la carte 205/380 ♨.

XX **Salut**, Wildpretmarkt 3, ⊠ A-1010, ℰ 5 33 13 22 – 🝙 ⑩ 🝙 𝘝𝘐𝘚𝘈   GY **y**
closed Sunday, Bank Holidays and 2 weeks August – **M** a la carte 330/495.

X Das Restaurant, Argentinierstr. 26, ⊠ A-1040, ℰ 5 05 40 37   GZ **e**

X **Leupold**, Schottengasse 7, ⊠ A-1010, ℰ 63 93 81 – 🝙 ⑩ 🝙 𝘝𝘐𝘚𝘈   FX **a**
closed Saturday lunch, Sunday and 1 - 23 August – **M** a la carte 260/440.

City districts (Stadtbezirke) 12 - 15 :

🏬 **Ramada Hotel**, Ullmannstr. 71, ⊠ A-1150, ℰ 8 50 40, Telex 112206, Fax 8504100, ☜,
⬛ – ∥ ☼ rm 🔲 🔲 ☜ – ♨ 25/200. 🝙 ⑩ 🝙 𝘝𝘐𝘚𝘈, ✂ rest   AS **a**
Restaurants : **Orangerie M** a la carte 265/580 – **Allegro M** 300 (lunch buffet only), a la carte
265/580 (dinner) – **309 rm** 2100/2450 Bb – 3 suites 5500.

🏨 **Garten Hotel Altmannsdorf** ⑤, Hoffingergasse 26, ⊠ A-1120, ℰ 8 04 75 27,
Telex 135327, Fax 804752751, ☜, Park, ☜ – ∥ 🔲 ☎ ☜ – ♨ 25/100. 🝙 ⑩ 🝙 𝘝𝘐𝘚𝘈   AS **s**
closed 23 to 29 December – **M** a la carte 255/415 – **41 rm** 1020/1700 Bb

🏨 **Austrotel**, Felberstr. 4, ⊠ A-1150, ℰ 98 11 10, Telex 115181, Fax 98111930, ☜ – ∥ 🔲
☎ ♨ – ♨ 25/260. 🝙 ⑩ 🝙 𝘝𝘐𝘚𝘈   AS **c**
M a la carte 245/470 – **254 rm** 1570/2800 Bb

🏨 **Reither** without rest, Graumanngasse 16, ⊠ A-1150, ℰ 85 61 65, Telex 136430, Fax 855244,
☜, ⬛ – ∥ 🔲 ☎ ☜. 🝙 ⑩ 🝙 𝘝𝘐𝘚𝘈 – closed 22 - 27 December – **50 rm** 950/1450 Bb   AS **r**

🏨 **Arabella - Hotel Jagdschloß** without rest, Jagdschloßgasse 79, ⊠ A-1130, ℰ 8 04 35 08,
Fax 8043500, ⬛ (heated), ☞ – ∥ 🔲 ☎ ☜   AS **v**
closed 3 January - 19 February – **48 rm** 760/1900 Bb

XX **Altwienerhof** with rm, Herklotzgasse 6, ⊠ A-1150, ℰ 83 71 45, Fax 85982532, « Winter
garden, court terrace » – ∥ 🔲 ☎. ⑩   AS **r**
M (closed Saturday lunch, Sunday, Bank Holidays and 2 - 16 February) a la carte 445/695 –
20 rm 520/1800 Bb

XX **Hietzinger Bräu**, Auhofstr. 1, ⊠ A-1130, ℰ 87 77 70 87, Fax 877708722   AS **u**
closed mid July - mid August and 24 to 27 December – **M** (mainly boiled beef dishes) a la carte
295/485.

City districts (Stadtbezirke) 16-19 :

🏬 **Modul**, Peter-Jordan-Str. 78, ⊠ A-1190, ℰ 47 66 00, Telex 116736, Fax 47660117 – ∥ 🔲
🔲 ☜ ☎ – ♨ 25/100. 🝙 ⑩ 🝙 𝘝𝘐𝘚𝘈   AR **f**
M (closed Saturday, Sunday and Bank Holidays) a la carte 330/550 – **43 rm** 1300/2500 Bb –
8 suites 2900.

🏨 **Clima Villenhotel** ⑤, Nussberggasse 2c, ⊠ A-1190, ℰ 37 15 16, Telex 115670,
Fax 371392, « Rest. Bockkeller, vaulted cellar with Tyrolian farmhouse furniture, closed
Sunday », ⬛, ⬛, ☞ – ∥ 🔲 ☎ ☜ ☎ – ♨ 25/70. 🝙 ⑩ 🝙 𝘝𝘐𝘚𝘈   BR **a**
closed 20 - 27 December – **M** (dinner only) a la carte 285/380 – **30 rm** 1590/2090 Bb

🏨 **Schloß Wilhelminenberg** ⑤, Savoyenstr. 2, ⊠ A-1160, ℰ 45 85 03, Telex 132008,
Fax 454876, « Terrace with < Vienna, Park » – ∥ ☎ ☎ – ♨ 30/120. 🝙 ⑩ 🝙 𝘝𝘐𝘚𝘈   AR **t**
M a la carte 145/360 – **90 rm** 675/1720 Bb

🏨 **Maté** (with guest house), Ottakringer Str. 34, ⊠ A-1170, ℰ 4 04 55, Telex 115485,
Fax 40455888, ☜, ⬛ – ∥ 🔲 ☎ ☜ ☎. 🝙 ⑩ 🝙 𝘝𝘐𝘚𝘈   AR **z**
M a la carte 225/445 ♨ – **125 rm** 980/2000 Bb

🏨 **Gartenhotel Glanzing** ⑤ without rest, Glanzinggasse 23, ⊠ A-1190, ℰ 47 04 27 20,
Fax 470427214, ☜ – ∥ 🔲 ☎ ☜. ⑩   AR **n**
20 rm 1180/2200 Bb

🏨 **Cottage** without rest, Hasenauerstr. 12, ⊠ A-1190, ℰ 31 25 71, Telex 134146, Fax 31257110
– ∥ 🔲 ☎. 🝙 ⑩ 🝙 𝘝𝘐𝘚𝘈   AR **g**
23 rm 1150/2600 Bb

🏠 **Jäger** without rest, Hernalser Hauptstr. 187, ⊠ A-1170, ℘ 46 66 20, Fax 4666208 – 📶 📺
☎ AR **r**
18 rm 960/1500.

🏠 **Schild** without rest, Neustift am Walde 97, ⊠ A-1190, ℘ 4 42 19 10, Fax 44219153, 🌷 –
📶 📺 ☎ ⚘ ⇌ AR **h**
33 rm 790/1220 Bb

XX **Fischerhaus**, an der Höhenstraße, ⊠ A-1190, ℘ 44 13 20, Fax 443533, ☜ – 🄿 AR **a**

XX **Eckel**, Sieveringer Str. 46, ⊠ A-1190, ℘ 32 32 18, Fax 326660, ☜ – ◑ AR **s**
closed Sunday, Monday, 9 - 24 August and 20 December - 18 January – **M** (remarkable wine-
list) a la carte 270/545 ⚘.

XX **Sailer**, Gersthofer Str. 14, ⊠ A-1180, ℘ 47 21 21, Fax 4721214, ☜, « Cellar » AR **e**
closed Sunday and Bank Holidays – **M** a la carte 260/430.

XX **Kirchenstöckl**, Himmelstr. 4, ⊠ A-1190, ℘ 32 15 71, Fax 32571322, self-grown wines only
– ◑ 🄴 *VISA* AR **p**
dinner only, closed Sunday and July - August – **M** a la carte 335/455.

X Römischer Kaiser, Neustift am Walde 2, ⊠ A-1190, ℘ 44 11 04, « Terraced garden with
≼ Vienna » AR **k**

Heurigen and Buschen-Schänken (wine gardens) – (mostly self-service, hot and cold
dishes from buffet, prices according to weight of chosen meals, therefore not shown below.
Buschen-Schänken sell their own wines only) :

X **Oppolzer**, Himmelstr. 22, ⊠ A-1190, ℘ 32 24 16, Fax 3224160, « Garden » – 🄰🄴 ◑ 🄴
VISA AR **p**
closed Sunday and 23 December - 6 January – **M** (dinner only).

X **Altes Preßhaus**, Cobenzlgasse 15, ⊠ A-1190, ℘ 32 23 93, Telex 132211, Fax 32234285,
☜, « Old vaulted wine cellar » – 🄰🄴 ◑ 🄴 *VISA* AR **p**
closed 5 January - 29 February – **M** (dinner only).

X **Wolff**, Rathstr. 44, ⊠ A-1190, ℘ 44 23 35, « Terraced garden » AR **m**
M (dinner only) (buffet).

X **Fuhrgassl Huber** (with guest house), Neustift am Walde 68, ⊠ A-1190, ℘ 44 14 05, (wine-
garden with Viennese Schrammelmusik), « Court-terrace » – 📺 ☎ AR **h**
Guest house closed 5 - 19 January – **M** (buffet) ⚘ – **22 rm** 980/1550 Bb

X **Grinzinger Hauermandl**, Cobenzlgasse 20, ⊠ A-1190, ℘ 3 22 04 44, Fax 32571322, ☜
– 🄰🄴 ◑ 🄴 *VISA* AR **q**
dinner only, closed Sunday – **M** a la carte 260/340.

X **Grinzinger Weinbottich**, Cobenzlgasse 28, ⊠ A-1190, ℘ 32 42 37, Fax 32571322,
« Shaded garden » – ◑ 🄴 *VISA* AR **q**
dinner only, closed Monday – **M** a la carte 260/340.

at Auhof motorway station W : 8 km :

🏨 Novotel Wien-West, Wientalstraße, ⊠ A-1140, ℘ (0222) 9 72 54 20, Telex 135584,
Fax 974140, ☜, ⴳ (heated), 🌷 – 📶 ⇌ rm 📺 ☎ ⚘ 🄿 – 🛦 25/300 AS **w**
115 rm Bb

at Vösendorf A-2334 S : 11 km by ⑥ or A 2 AS :

🏨 **City-Club-Hotel**, Parkallee 2 (Shopping City Süd), ℘ (0222) 69 35 35, Telex 132281,
Fax 693317 – 📶 ▤ 📺 🄿 – 🛦 25/280. 🄰🄴 ◑ 🄴 *VISA*
M (Restaurants and recreation - centre in a separate building) a la carte 230/450 – **471 rm**
2080/2570 Bb – 20 suites 3680/6000.

🏨 Novotel Wien-Süd, Nordring 4 (Shopping City Süd), ℘ (0222) 6 92 60 10, Telex 134793,
Fax 694859, ☜, ⴳ (heated) – 📶 ▤ rest 📺 ☎ ⚘ 🄿 – 🛦 25/250
102 rm Bb

at Schwechat-Mannswörth A-2323 SE : 15 km by ④ and B 9 :

🏠 Reinisch (with guest house, 📶), Mannswörther Str. 76, ℘ (0222) 77 72 90, Fax 773890, ☜
– 📺 ☎ 🄿
66 rm Bb

at Vienna-Schwechat airport ③ : 20 km :

🏨 **Novotel Wien Airport**, ⊠ A-1300 Schwechat, ℘ (0222) 7 01 07, Telex 111566,
Fax 773239, ☜, ⛱, ⴳ (heated) – 📶 ▤ 📺 ☎ ⚘ 🄿 – 🛦 25/300. 🄰🄴 ◑ 🄴 *VISA*
M a la carte 255/390 – **183 rm** 1350/1750 Bb

XX Le Gourmet, airport (2nd floor, 📶), ⊠ A-1300 Schwechat, ℘ (0222) 77 70 26 72, ≼.

at Groß-Enzersdorf A-2301 E : 16 km, by B 3 BR :

🏨 **Am Sachsengang**, Schloßhofer Str. 60 (B 3), ℘ (02249) 2 90 10, Telex 136236, Fax 2905,
« Terrace », Massage, ⛱, ▨, 🌷 – 📺 ☎ 🄿 – 🛦 25/120. 🄰🄴 ◑ 🄴 *VISA*
closed 20 - 26 December – **M** a la carte 315/480 – **102 rm** 780/2500 Bb

37

SALZBURG **5020**. Austria 🗺️ W 23, 🗺️ K 5, 🗺️ W 23 – pop. 140 000 – alt. 425 m – ✆ 0662.

See : ≤ ★★ on the town (from the Mönchsberg) X and ≤★★ (from Hettwer Bastei)Y – Hohensalzburg ★★ X, Z : ≤★★ (from the Kuenburg Bastion), ✴★★ (from the Reck Tower), Museum (Burgmuseum)★ – St. Peter's Churchyard (Petersfriedhof)★★ Z – St. Peter's Church (Stiftskirche St. Peter)★★ Z – Residenz★★ Z – Natural History Museum (Haus der Natur)★★ Y **M2** – Franciscan's Church (Franziskanerkirche)★ Z **A** – Getreidegasse★ Y – Mirabell Gardens (Mirabellgarten)★ V (Grand Staircase ★★ of the castle) – Baroquemuseum ★ V **M3** – Dom★ Z.

Envir. : Road to the Gaisberg (Gaisbergstraße)★★ (≤★) by ① – Untersberg★ by ② : 10 km (with 🚠) – Castle Hellbrunn (Schloß Hellbrunn) ★ by Nonntaler Hauptstraße X.

🛫 Salzburg-Wals, Schloß Klessheim, ✆ 85 08 51 ; 🛫 Hof (① : 20 km), ✆ (06229) 23 90 ; 🛫 St. Lorenz (① : 29 km), ✆ (06232) 38 35.

🚉 Innsbrucker Bundesstr. 95 (by ③), ✆ 85 12 23 - City Air Terminal, Südtiroler Platz (Autobus Station) V – 🚌 ✆ 71 54 14 22.

Exhibition Centre (Messegelände), Linke Glanzeile 65, ✆ 3 45 66.

🛈 Tourist Information, Mozartplatz 5, ✆ 84 75 68.

ÖAMTC, Alpenstr. 102 (by ②), ✆ 2 05 01, Fax 2050145.

Wien 292 ① – Innsbruck 177 ③ – München 140 ③.

SALZBURG					
Auerspergstraße	V 3	Bürglsteinstraße	X 5	Kaiserschützenstr.	V 20
		Erzabt-Klotz-Str.	X 9	Nonntaler Hauptstr.	X 29
		Gstättengasse	X 12	Spåthgasse	X 37

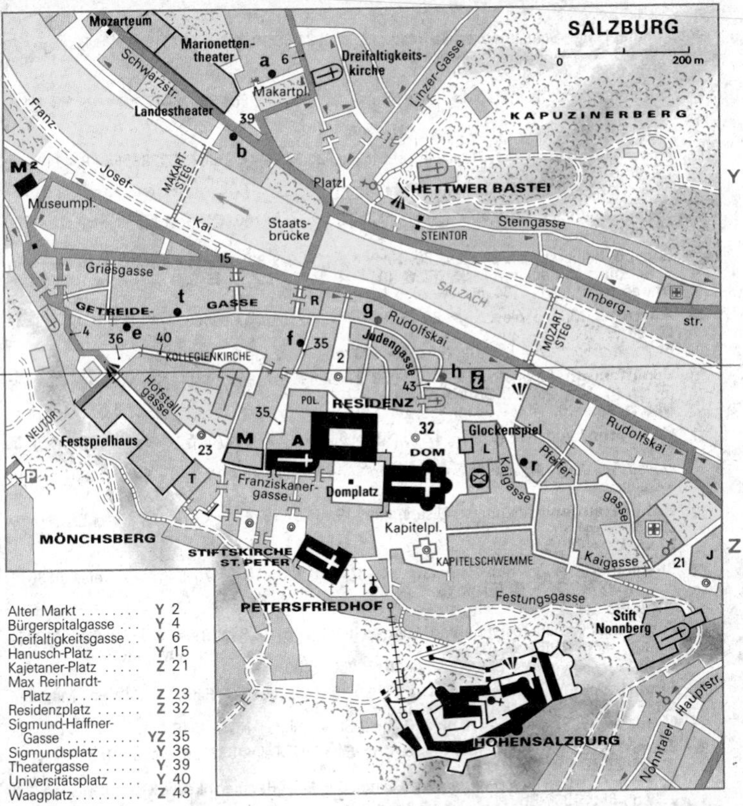

Alter Markt . . . . Y 2
Bürgerspitalgasse . . . Y 4
Dreifaltigkeitsgasse . . Y 6
Hanusch-Platz . . . . . . Y 15
Kajetaner-Platz . . . . . Z 21
Max Reinhardt-Platz . . . . Z 23
Residenzplatz . . . . . . Z 32
Sigmund-Haffner-Gasse . . . . YZ 35
Sigmundsplatz . . . . . Y 36
Theatergasse . . . . . . Y 39
Universitätsplatz . . . . Y 40
Waagplatz . . . . Z 43

Salzburg Sheraton Hotel, Auerspergstr. 4, 88 99 90, Telex 632518, Fax 881776, « Terrace in spa gardens », entrance to the spa facilities – rm – 25/150. AE E VISA. rest V **s**
Restaurants : **Mirabell M** a la carte 425/745 – **Bistro M** a la carte 180/420 – **165 rm** 2750/5050 Bb – 9 suites 5700/8300.

Österreichischer Hof, Schwarzstr. 5, 8 89 77, Telex 633590, Fax 8897714, « Salzach-side setting, terrace with < old town and castle » – rm – 25/70. AE E VISA Y **b**
Restaurants : **Zirbelzimmer M** a la carte 425/675 – **Salzach-Grill M** a la carte 230/455 – **119 rm** 2250/4900 – 3 suites.

Bristol, Makartplatz 4, 7 35 57, Telex 633337, Fax 8735576 – rest – 80. AE E VISA. rest – *mid April - December* – **M** 270 (lunch) and la carte 420/620 – **75 rm** 2250/5200 Bb – 10 suites 6900/8000. Y **a**

Schloß Mönchstein, Am Mönchsberg 26, 8 48 55 50, Telex 632080, Fax 848559, < Salzburg and environs, , « Small castle with elegant, stylish furnishings, wedding chapel, park », , – – 40. AE E VISA. rest X **e**
M a la carte 450/750 – **17 rm** 2000/8000.

Goldener Hirsch, Getreidegasse 37, 84 85 11, Telex 632967, Fax 848517845, « 15C Patrician house, tastefully furnished » – rm rest – 40. AE E VISA Y **e**
M a la carte 375/610 – **71 rm** 1950/7000 – 3 suites 7800.

Rosenberger, Bessarabierstr. 94, 4 35 46, Telex 3622405, Fax 43951095, – rm – 25/360. AE E VISA by ④
M a la carte 210/380 – **120 rm** 980/1500 Bb

Dorint-Hotel, Sterneckstr. 20, 88 20 31, Telex 631075, Fax 8820319, – rm rest – 25/300. AE E VISA V **z**
M a la carte 280/430 – **140 rm** 1100/2450 Bb

Mercure, Bayerhamerstr. 14, 88 14 38, Telex 632341, Fax 71111411, – rm – 25/200. AE E VISA V **t**
M a la carte 268/450 – **121 rm** 1800/2100 Bb

🏨 **Theater-Hotel**, Schallmooser Hauptstr. 13, ℰ 8 81 68 10, Telex 632319, 🍽, Massage, ⓢ – 🛗 📺 ☎ ⇄ – 🛎 40. ⚘ rest
58 rm Bb – 11 suites.
V y

🏨 **Carlton** without rest, Markus-Sittikus-Str. 3, ℰ 88 21 91, Fax 87478447, ⓢ – 🛗 ⇝ 📺 ☎
🅿 ⚙ 🆎 ⓞ 🇪 𝑽𝑰𝑺𝑨
40 rm 1400/2250 Bb – 13 suites 2200/2900.
V c

🏨 **Novotel Salzburg City**, Franz-Josef-Str. 26, ℰ 88 20 41, Telex 632886, Fax 874240 – 🛗
📺 ⚙ 🕭 ⇄ 🅿 – 🛎 25/140
M a la carte 260/430 – **140 rm** 1200/1950 Bb
V k

🏨 **Pitter**, Rainerstr. 6, ℰ 7 85 71, Telex 633532, Fax 7857190, 🍽 – 🛗 📺 ☎ – 🛎 25/150
200 rm Bb
V n

🏨 **Europa**, Rainerstr. 31, ℰ 88 99 30, Telex 633424, Fax 889938, rest. on the 14th floor with
⩽ Salzburg and environs – 🛗 📺 ☎ 🅿 – 🛎 25/80. 🆎 ⓞ 🇪 𝑽𝑰𝑺𝑨. ⚘ rest
M (residents only) – **104 rm** 930/2000 Bb
V b

🏨 **Austrotel**, Mirabellplatz 8, ℰ 88 16 88, Telex 632361, Fax 881687 – 🛗 📺 ☎ ⅙ – 🛎 45.
🆎 ⓞ 🇪 𝑽𝑰𝑺𝑨
M (closed Sunday) a la carte 225/330 – **73 rm** 1550/2400 Bb
V a

🏨 **Schaffenrath**, Alpenstr. 115, ℰ 2 31 53, Telex 633207, Fax 29314, 🍽, Massage, ⓢ – 🛗
📺 ☎ 🅿 – 🛎 25/100. 🆎 ⓞ 🇪 𝑽𝑰𝑺𝑨
M a la carte 200/400 – **50 rm** 990/2600 Bb
by ②

🏨 **Kasererhof**, Alpenstr. 6, ℰ 2 12 65, Telex 633477, Fax 28376, 🍽, 🚗 – 🛗 📺 ☎ 🅿. 🆎
🇪 𝑽𝑰𝑺𝑨
closed February – **M** (closed Saturday and Sunday) a la carte 310/540 – **54 rm** 1260/3515 Bb
– 6 suites.
by ②

🏨 **Hohenstauffen** without rest, Elisabethstr. 19, ℰ 87 76 69, Fax 87219351 – 🛗 📺 ☎ ⇄.
🆎 ⓞ 🇪 𝑽𝑰𝑺𝑨
27 rm 720/1640.
V e

🏨 **Stieglbräu** (Brewery-inn), Rainerstr. 14, ℰ 7 76 92(hotel) 7 76 94(rest.), Telex 633671,
Fax 7769271, 🍽 – 🛗 📺 ☎ 🅿 – 🛎 25
50 rm Bb
V g

🏨 **Fuggerhof** without rest, Eberhard-Fugger-Str. 9, ℰ 6 41 29 00, Telex 632533, Fax 6412904,
⩽, ⓢ, 🚗 – 🛗 📺 ☎ 🅿. ⚘
closed 20 December - 20 January – **20 rm** 950/2400.
by Bürglsteinstr. X

🏨 **Zum Hirschen**, St.-Julien-Str. 21, ℰ 88 90 30, Telex 632691, Fax 7314158, 🍽, Massage,
ⓢ – 🛗 📺 ☎ 🅿 – 🛎 25/50. ⚘ rest
M a la carte 185/345 🍸 – **70 rm** 710/1980 Bb – 5 suites 1920/2940.
V r

🏨 **Elefant** ⌕, Sigmund-Haffner-Gasse 4, ℰ 84 33 97, Telex 632725, Fax 84010928 – 🛗 📺
☎. 🆎 ⓞ 🇪 𝑽𝑰𝑺𝑨
M (closed Tuesday except August) a la carte 200/390 – **Ratsherrnkeller M** a la carte 195/375
– **38 rm** 650/1800 Bb
Y f

🏨 **Weiße Taube** ⌕ without rest, Kaigasse 9, ℰ 84 24 04, Telex 633065, Fax 84178350 – 🛗
☎. 🆎 ⓞ 🇪 𝑽𝑰𝑺𝑨. ⚘
33 rm 750/1600.
Z r

XX **Café Winkler** (modern café-rest. with casino), Mönchsberg 32 (access by 🛗, 19 A.S.),
ℰ 8 41 21 50, Telex 633967, Fax 84525830, ⩽ Salzburg, 🍽 – 🛎 25/120. 🆎 ⓞ 🇪 𝑽𝑰𝑺𝑨
closed Tuesday lunch and Monday – **M** 335/425 (lunch) and a la carte 450/645.
Y

XX K u. K Restaurant am Waagplatz, Waagplatz 2 (1st floor), ℰ 84 21 56, Fax 84215770, 🍽,
« Medieval dinner with period performance in the Freysauff-Keller (by arrangement) » 🍸
(booking essential) 🍸
Z h

XX **Mozart**, Getreidegasse 22 (1st floor, 🛗), ℰ 84 37 46, Fax 846852 – 🆎 ⓞ 🇪 𝑽𝑰𝑺𝑨
closed Thursday, Friday lunch and 11 June - 3 July – **M** (booking essential) a la carte 340/505.
Y t

XX **Zum Mohren**, Judengasse 9, ℰ 84 23 87 – ⚘
closed Sunday, Bank Holidays and 1 - 30 June **M** (booking essential) a la carte 240/370.
Y g

at Salzburg-Aigen A-5026 by Bürglsteinstr. X :

🏨 **Doktorwirt**, Glaser Str. 9, ℰ 2 29 73, Telex 632938, Fax 2897524, 🍽, ⓢ, 🏊 (heated), 🚗
– 🛗 📺 ☎ 🅿. 🆎 ⓞ 🇪 𝑽𝑰𝑺𝑨. ⚘ rest
closed 9 - 25 February and mid October - November – **M** (closed Monday) a la carte 180/370
🍸 – **39 rm** 750/1500.

X **Gasthof Schloß Aigen**, Schwarzenbergpromenade 37, ℰ 2 12 84, 🍽 – 🅿. 🆎 ⓞ 🇪 𝑽𝑰𝑺𝑨
closed Thursday lunch, Wednesday, 1 week February and 2 - 8 September – **M** a la carte
170/400 🍸.

at Salzburg-Liefering A-5020 by ④ :

🏨 **Brandstätter**, Münchner Bundesstr. 69, ℰ 83 45 35, Fax 83453590, 🍽, ⓢ, 🔲, 🚗 – 🛗
📺 ☎ 🅿 – 🛎 40
closed 22 to 27 December – **M** (closed 2 - 16 January) (booking essential) a la carte 255/
555 🍸 – **36 rm** 770/2380.

at Salzburg-Maria Plain A-5101 by Plainstr. V :

🏛 **Maria Plain** ⤳ (17C inn), Plainbergweg 41, ℘ 5 07 01, Telex 632801, Fax 507119, « Garden with ≼ » – |≣| 🆀 📺 ☎ ⇐⊃ 🅟 – 🕍 40. ⑩
closed 3 - 16 February and 13 - 23 July **M** *(closed October - March Wednesday and Tuesday lunch)* a la carte 230/325 – **30 rm** 748/1680 Bb – 3 suites 1848.

at Salzburg-Parsch A-5020 by Bürglsteinstr. X :

🏛🏛 **Fondachhof** ⤳, Gaisbergstr. 46, ℘ 64 13 31, Fax 641576, ≼, « 18C manor house in a park », ⇌s, ⤻ (heated), 🖛 – |≣| 📺 ⇐⊃ 🅟 – 🕍 25. 🆎 ⑩ 🅔 *VISA*, ⅏ rest
9 April - October – (rest. for residents only) – **28 rm** 1200/3600 – 4 suites 3600/5600.

🏛 **Villa Pace** ⤳, Sonnleitenweg 9, ℘ 64 15 01, Telex 631141, Fax 64150122, ≼ town and Hohensalzburg, ⇌s, ⤻ (heated), 🖛 – 📺 ☎ 🅟. 🆎 ⑩ 🅔 *VISA*
April - mid November (rest. for residents only) – **12 rm** 2300/3850 – 4 suites 4950/5450.

on the Heuberg NE : 3 km by ① - alt. 565 m

🏛 **Schöne Aussicht** ⤳, ✉ A-5023 Salzburg, ℘ (0662) 64 06 08, Telex 631153, Fax 6406902, « Garden with ≼ Salzburg and Alps », ⇌s, ⤻ (heated), 🖛, ⅏ – 📺 ☎ 🅟 – 🕍 40. 🆎 ⑩ 🅔 *VISA*
April - October – **M** *(closed Sunday)* a la carte 285/530 – **30 rm** 900/2000 Bb

on the Gaisberg by ① :

🏛🏛 **Kobenzl** ⤳, Gaisberg 11, alt. 750 m, ✉ A-5020 Salzburg, ℘ (0662) 64 15 10, Telex 633833, Fax 64223871, ☂, « Beautiful panoramic location with ≼ Salzburg and Alps », Massage, ⇌s, ⤻, 🖛 – 📺 ⇐⊃ 🅟 – 🕍 25/80. 🆎 ⑩ 🅔 *VISA*, ⅏ rest
mid March - mid November – **35 rm** 1450/5550 Bb – 4 suites 5900/6500.

🏛 **Romantik-Hotel Gersberg Alm** ⤳, Gaisberg 37, alt. alt. 800, ✉ A-5023 Salzburg-Gnigl, ℘ (0662) 64 12 57, Fax 64125780, ☂, ⇌s, ⤻, ⅏ – 📺 ☎ 🅟 – 🕍 25/60.
closed 8 January - February – **M** a la carte 265/450 – **36 rm** 1100/2900 Bb

🏛 **Berghotel Zistel-Alm** ⤳, Gaisberg 16, alt. 1 001 m, ✉ A-5026 Salzburg-Aigen, ℘ (0662) 64 10 67, Fax 20104200, ≼ Alps, ☂, ⤻, 🖛 – ☎ ⇐⊃ 🅟. ⅏ rest
24 rm

Beim Flughafen by ③ :

🏛🏛 **Airporthotel**, Loigstr. 20a, ✉ A-5020 Salzburg-Loig, ℘ (0662) 85 00 20, Telex 633634, Fax 85002044, ⇌s – 📺 ☎ 🅟 – 🕍 25. 🆎 ⑩ 🅔 *VISA*
(dinner only, residents only) – **34 rm** 1100/2500.

at Anif A-5081 ② : 7 km – ✿ 06246 :

🏛🏛 Point Hotel, Berchtesgadener Str.364, ℘ 42 56, Telex 631003, Fax 4256443, ☂, Massage, ⇌s, ⤻ (heated), 🖛 ⅏ (indoor court) – |≣| 📺 ☎ 🅟 – 🕍 25/100
62 rm Bb

🏛🏛 **Friesacher** (with guest-house Aniferhof), ℘ 20 75, Telex 632943, Fax 207549, ☂, ⇌s, 🖛 – |≣| 📺 ☎ 🅟 – 🕍 25
closed 2 to 22 January – **M** *(closed Wednesday)* a la carte 185/380 ⅊ – **70 rm** 680/1480 Bb

🏛🏛 **Hubertushof**, Neu Anif 4 (near motorway exit Salzburg Süd), ℘ 24 78, Telex 632684, Fax 421768, ☂ – |≣| 📺 ☎ 🅟 – 🕍 25/60. 🆎 *VISA*
M a la carte 275/475 – **70 rm** 700/1400 Bb

🏛🏛 **Romantik-Hotel Schloßwirt** (17C inn with Biedermeier furniture), Halleiner Bundesstr. 22, ℘ 21 75, Telex 631169, Fax 217580, ☂, 🖛 – |≣| 📺 ☎ ⇐⊃ 🅟. 🆎 ⑩ 🅔 *VISA*
closed February – **M** *(closed Tuesday)* a la carte 295/460 – **32 rm** 850/2500 Bb

at Hof A-5322 ① : 20 km :

🏛🏛🏛 **Schloß Fuschl** ⤳ (former 15C hunting seat with 3 guest houses), ℘ (06229) 2 25 30, Telex 633454, Fax 2253531, ≼, ☂, Massage, ⇌s, ⤻, 🐎, ⅏ – |≣| 📺 ⇐⊃ 🅟 – 🕍 25/100. 🆎 ⑩ 🅔 *VISA*, ⅏ rest
M 380/450 (lunch) and a la carte 475/750 – **84 rm** 1540/3640 Bb – 5 suites 3500/4550.

🏛🏛 **Jagdhof am Fuschlsee** (former 18C farm house with guest house), ℘ (06229) 2 37 20, Telex 633454, Fax 2253531, ≼, ☂, « Hunting museum », ⇌s, ⤻ – 📺 ☎ 🅟 – 🕍 25/180. ⅏ rest
50 rm Bb

at Fuschl am See A-5330 ① : 26 km :

🏛🏛 **Parkhotel Waldhof** ⤳, Seepromenade, ℘ (06226) 2 64, Telex 632487, Fax 644, ≼, ☂, Massage, ⇌s, ⤻, 🐎, 🖛, ⅏ – |≣| 📺 🅟 – 🕍 25/90. 🆎. ⅏ rest
closed 10 January - March – **M** a la carte 250/480 – **70 rm** 690/2200 Bb

XX **Brunnwirt**, ℘ (06226) 2 36, ☂ – 🅟. 🆎 ⑩ 🅔 *VISA*, ⅏
dinner only except during the festival, closed Sunday and 7 - 31 January – **M** (booking essential) a la carte 395/620.

at the Mondsee ① : 28 km (by motorway A 1) – ✿ 06232 :

🏛🏛 **Seehof** ⤳, (SE : 7 km), ✉ A-5311 Loibichl, ℘ 2 55 00, Fax 255051, ≼, ☂, Massage, ⇌s, 🐎, ⅏ – 📺 🅟
May - September – **M** a la carte 320/580 – **31 rm** 2000/3500 Bb – 10 suites.

41

🏛 ✿ **Weißes Kreuz**, Herzog-Odilo-Str. 25, ⊠ A-5310 Mondsee, ℘ 22 54, Fax 225434, ♨ –
🛗 📺 ☎ ⇔ 🅿
closed mid November - mid December – **M** *(closed Tuesday - Wednesday except August)*
(booking essential, remarkable wine-list) 307/760 – **10 rm** 500/1200
Spec. Marinierte Reinanke mit saurem Obers, Eierschwammerl-Rahmsuppe, Mondseefische mit
Schwammerlrisotto.

XXX ✿ **Landhaus Eschlböck-Plomberg** with rm, (S : 5 km), ⊠ A-5310 St. Lorenz - Plomberg,
℘ 35 72, Fax 316620, <, ♨, ⇌, ♠, ⚓ Landing jetty – 📺 ☎ ⇔ 🅿. 🆎 ⓪ ㄷ
VISA
closed 3 weeks January and 3 weeks November **M** *(closed Monday September - May)* (booking
essential) a la carte 452/695 – **14 rm** 750/2800
Spec. Parfait von Mondseefischen, Lachsforelle mit Selleriebutter, Zwetschkentartelle.

Benelux

Belgium
BRUSSELS - ANTWERP - BRUGES - LIÈGE

Grand Duchy of Luxemburg
LUXEMBURG

Netherlands
AMSTERDAM - The HAGUE - ROTTERDAM

PRACTICAL INFORMATION

LOCAL CURRENCY
Belgian Franc: 100 F = 3.20 US $ (Jan. 92) can also be used in Luxemburg
Dutch Florin: 100 Fl. = 58.55 US $ (Jan. 92)

TOURIST INFORMATION
Telephone numbers and addresses of Tourist Offices are given in the text of each city under 🆔.

FOREIGN EXCHANGE
In Belgium, banks close at 3.30pm and weekends;
in the Netherlands, banks close at 5.00pm and weekends, Schiphol Airport exchange offices open daily from 6.30am to 11.30pm.

TRANSPORT
Taxis: may be hailed in the street, at taxi ranks or called by telephone.
Bus, tramway: practical for long and short distances and good for sightseeing.

POSTAL SERVICES
Post offices open Monday to Friday from 9am to 5pm in Benelux.

SHOPPING
Shops and boutiques are generally open from 9am to 7pm in Belgium and Luxemburg, and from 9am to 6pm in the Netherlands. The main shopping areas are:
in Brussels: Rue Neuve, Porte de Namur, Avenue Louise - Also Brussels antique market on Saturday from 9am to 3pm, and Sunday from 9am to 1pm (around place du Grand-Sablon) - Flower market (Grand-Place) on Sunday morning.
in Antwerp: Bird Market: Sunday from 8.30am to 1pm - Antwerp diamond quarter.
in Bruges: Calashes on the Market Place for shopping and town sightseeing.
in Amsterdam: Kalverstraat, Leidsestraat, Nieuwendijk, P.C. Hoofstraat and Utrechtsestraat. Second-hand goods and antiques. Amsterdam Flea Market (near Waterlooplein).
in Den Haag: Hoogstraat, Korte Poten, Paleispromenade, De Passage and Spuistraat.
in Rotterdam: Binnenweg, Hoogstraat, Karel Koormanstraat, Lijnbaan and Stadhuisplein.

BREAKDOWN SERVICE
24 hour assistance:
Belgium: TCB, Brussels ✆ (0 2) 233 22 22 – VTB-VAB, Antwerp ✆ (0 3) 253 63 63 – RACB, Brussels ✆ (0 2) 287 09 00.
Luxemburg: ACL ✆ 45 00 45.
Netherlands: ANWB, The Hague ✆ (0 70) 314 71 47.

TIPPING
In Benelux, prices include service and taxes.

SPEED LIMITS
In Belgium and Luxemburg, the maximum speed limits are 120 km/h-74 mph on motorways and dual carriageways, 90 km/h-56 mph on all other roads and 50 km/h-31 mph in built-up areas.
In the Netherlands, 100/120 km/h-62/74 mph on motorways and "autowegen", 80 km/h-50 mph on other roads and 50 km/h-31 mph in built-up areas.

SEAT BELTS
In each country, the wearing of seat belts is compulsory.

Brussels

(BRUXELLES – BRUSSEL) 1000 Brabant 🔲🔲🔲 ⑱ and 🔲🔲🔲 ⑬ – Pop. 970 501 agglomeration – 🟢 0 2.

See : Market Square★★★ (Grand Palace) LZ – Manneken Pis★★ KZ – Rue des Bouchers LZ – St Michael's Cathedral★★ : stained glass★ FU – Place du Grand-Sablon★ and the Church of Notre-Dame du Sablon★ FV **D** – St Hubert Arcades★ LZ – Place Royale★ FV – Square du Petit Sablon★ FV – Royal Palace : Ballroom★ GV – Palais de la Nation : Senate Chamber★ GU – Notre Dame de la Chambre Abbey★ : Christ Reviled★ – La Cambre Wood★ – Atomium★ – Anderlecht : Erasmus's House★.

Museums : Ancient Art★★★ (Brueghel) FV – Royal Museum of Art and History★★★ (antiquities, Belgian decorative arts) – Musical Instruments★★ FV **M¹⁸** – Bellevue★ GV **M¹⁴** – Modern Art★★ FV **M³** – Auto world★★ – Natural Science (Royal Institute) : iguanodon skeletons★ HX **M⁸** – Belgian Centre of Comic Strips FU **M¹⁹** – Ixelles Municipal Museum★ – Horta Museum : staircase★ – Uccle : David and Alice van Buuren Museum★.

Env. Forest of Soignes★★ – Tervuren Park★ – Arboretum★ – Royal Museum of Central Africa★ ⑥ : 13 km : African art★, mineralogy★ – Beersel : castle★ S : 11 km – Gaasbeek : castle and grounds★, tapestrie★ SW : 12 km by rue de Lennick – Hoeilaart (Groenendaal) : site★ – Meise : Bouchout Estate★ ① : 13 km : Plant Houses★★ – Grimbergen ① : 18 km : confessional★ in the Abbey Church (Abdijkerk) – Vilvoorde : stalls in the Church of Our Lady (O.L.-Vrouwekerk).

⒙ ⒚ at Tervuren by ⑥ : 13 km, Château de Ravenstein ℰ (0 2) 767 58 01, ⒙ at Melsbroek NE : 15 km, Steenwagenstraat 11 ℰ (0 2) 751 82 05 – ⒚ at Anderlecht, Zone Sportive de la Pede, Drève Olympique 1 ℰ (0 2) 521 16 87 – ⒚ at Watermael-Boitsfort, chaussée de la Hulpe 53 ℰ (0 2) 672 22 22 – ⒚ at Overijse by ⑦ : 14 km, Gemslaan 55 ℰ (0 2) 687 50 30 – ⒚ at Itterbeek by ⑪ : 9 km, J.M. van Lierdelaan 28 b ℰ (0 2) 569 69 81.

✈ National NE : 12 km ℰ 722 31 11 – Air Terminal : Air Terminus, r. du Cardinal Mercier 35 LZ ℰ 511 90 30.

🚗 ℰ 218 60 50 ext. 4106.

🄸 Town Hall (Hôtel de Ville), Grand'Place, ✉ 1000 ℰ 513 89 40 – Tourist Association of the Province (closed Sunday from October to Easter), r. Marché-aux-Herbes 61, ✉ 1000 ℰ 504 04 00 and 504 04 55.

Paris 308 ⑨ – Amsterdam 204 ① – Düsseldorf 222 ⑤ – Lille 116 ⑫ – Luxembourg 219 ⑦.

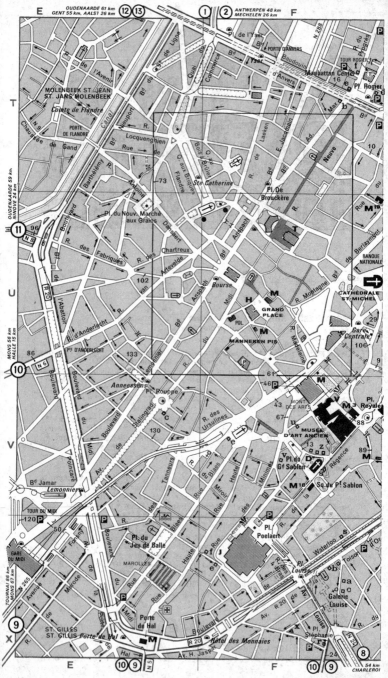

Pl. de l'Yser
PORTE D'ANVERS
Yser
d'Anvers
TOUR ROGIER
f
Manhattan Center
16
Pl. Rogier

MOLENBEEK ST. JEAN
ST. JANS MOLENBEEK
Cointe de Flandre
Canal
PORTE
DE FLANDRE
Chaussée de Gand
N 9

Nieuport
R.
Locquenghien
Rue de

R. de Laeken
E. Jacqmain
Nieuwe
10

73
Ste Catherine

Pl. De
Brouckère

BANQUE
NATIONALE

96
R. des Fabriques
R. des
Chartreux

CATHÉDRALE
ST-MICHEL

U

102
Anspach
Bourse
Midi
H
M
GRAND
PLACE
29
Gare
Centrale
106

86
Pl. D'ANDERLECHT
B⁴ d'Anderlecht
133
POL
MANNEKEN PIS

R. Madeleine
9

Anneessens
Pl. Rouppe
61
-46
M

130
R. des
Ursulines
43
MONT
DES ARTS
67
MUSÉE
D'ART ANCIEN
Pl. du
Gⁿ Sablon
M
Pl.
Royale
88
3
13
89
M

V

B⁴ Jamar
Lemonnier
TOUR DU MIDI
120

50
Pl. du
Jeu de Balle
MAROLLES
f
J
Pl.
Poelaert

Régence
M
Sq. du P⁴ Sablon

Waterloo
Pl.
Louise
Galerie
Louise

GARE
DU MIDI
265
Merode

ST. GILLES
ST. GILLIS Porte de Hal
M
Porte
de Hal
Hôtel des Monnaies
R 20
Av. H. Jaspar
Pl.
Stéphanie
R 24
8

Room prices are subject to the addition of a local tax of 6 %

BRUXELLES (BRUSSEL)

SAS Royal, r. Fossé-aux-Loups 47, ⊠ 1000, ℰ 219 28 28, Telex 22202, Fax 219 62 62, « Patio with vestige of 12C Brussels enclosure wall », ℐ₅, ⇌ – ⫯ �쬉 rm 🔲 🔟 ☎ ⊝
🅿 – 🔬 25-400. 🆎 ⓞ 🅴 𝘝𝘐𝘚𝘈
M see rest. **Sea Grill** below – **Atrium** a la carte 900/1300 – **256 rm** ⊇ 9900/16000. LY c

Pullman Astoria, r. Royale 103, ⊠ 1000, ℰ 217 62 90, Telex 25040, Fax 217 11 50, « Early 20C residence » – ⫯ ▤ rest 🔟 ☎ – 🔬 25-200. 🆎 ⓞ 🅴 𝘝𝘐𝘚𝘈 𝒮 rest GTU b
M **Palais Royal** *(closed Saturday lunch)* a la carte 1700/2300 – ⊇ 560 – **125 rm** 5400/7500.

Métropole, pl. de Brouckère 31, ⊠ 1000, ℰ 217 23 00, Telex 21234, Fax 218 02 20, « Late 19C hall and lounges », ℐ₅, ⇌ – ⫯ ﻣ쬉 rm ▤ rest 🔟 ☎ – 🔬 25-600. 🆎 ⓞ 🅴 𝘝𝘐𝘚𝘈 𝒮 rest
M **L'Alban Chambon** *(closed Saturday, Sunday and Bank Holidays)* 1300/1950 – **410 rm** ⊇ 5300/8500. LY r

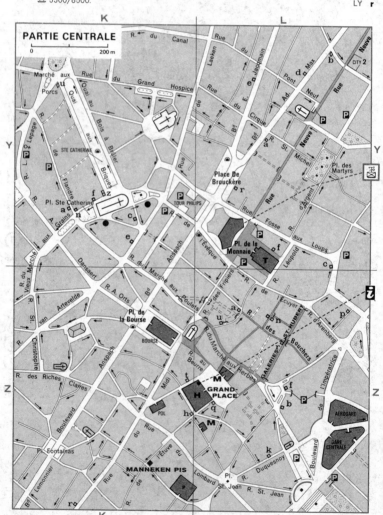

🏨🏨 **Bedford**, r. Midi 135, ✉ 1000, ℰ 512 78 40, Telex 24059, Fax 514 17 59 – 🛗 ▤ rest 📺
🕭 🚗 – 🛎 25-200. 🖭 ⓞ Ε 𝘝𝘐𝘚𝘈.
M a la carte 900/1500 – **275 rm** ⌂ 4900/5900.
KZ **r**

🏨🏨 **Jolly Atlanta**, bd A. Max 7, ✉ 1000, ℰ 217 01 20, Telex 21475, Fax 217 37 58 – 🛗 ▤ rest
📺 ☎ – 🛎 50. 🖭 ⓞ Ε 𝘝𝘐𝘚𝘈. ⅔ rest
M 1500/2300 – **241 rm** ⌂ 7500/8100.
LY **a**

🏨🏨 **Président Centre** without rest., r. Royale 160, ✉ 1000, ℰ 219 00 65, Telex 26784,
Fax 218 09 10 – 🛗 ▤ 📺 ☎. 🖭 ⓞ Ε 𝘝𝘐𝘚𝘈. ⅔
73 rm ⌂ 4900/6900.
GU **a**

🏨🏨 **Arenberg**, r. d'Assaut 15, ✉ 1000, ℰ 511 07 70, Telex 25660, Fax 514 19 76 – 🛗 ⅔← rm
📺 ☎ – 🛎 50-90. 🖭 ⓞ Ε 𝘝𝘐𝘚𝘈
M a la carte 750/1400 – **155 rm** ⌂ 4900/5500.
LZ **p**

🏨 **Chambord** without rest., r. Namur 82, ✉ 1000, ℰ 513 41 19, Telex 20373, Fax 514 08 47
– 🛗 📺 ☎ – 🛎 25. 🖭 ⓞ Ε 𝘝𝘐𝘚𝘈. ⅔
69 rm ⌂ 3395/4595.
GV **v**

🏨 **Vendôme** without rest., bd A. Max 98, ✉ 1000, ℰ 218 00 70, Telex 64460, Fax 218 06 83
– 🛗 📺 ☎ – 🛎 25. 🖭 ⓞ Ε 𝘝𝘐𝘚𝘈. ⅔
92 rm ⌂ 3175/3575.
LY **d**

🏨 **Queen Anne** without rest., bd E. Jacqmain 110, ✉ 1000, ℰ 217 16 00, Telex 22676,
Fax 217 18 38 – 🛗 📺 ☎. 🖭 ⓞ Ε 𝘝𝘐𝘚𝘈
60 rm ⌂ 2750/3425.
LY **e**

🏨 **Sabina** without rest., r. Nord 78, ✉ 1000, ℰ 218 26 37, Fax 219 32 39 – 🛗 📺 ☎. Ε 𝘝𝘐𝘚𝘈
24 rm ⌂ 1200/1850.
GU **e**

XXXX ❀ **Sea Grill** - (at SAS Royal H.), r. Fossé-aux-Loups 47, ✉ 1000, ℰ 219 28 28, Telex 22202,
Fax 219 62 62, Seafood – ▤ ℗. 🖭 ⓞ Ε 𝘝𝘐𝘚𝘈. ⅔
closed Saturday lunch, Sunday, Bank Holidays and 19 July-18 August – **M** a la carte 2100/2800
Spec. Saumon norvégien mariné à l'aneth et sauce moutarde, Salade de langoustines et foie gras
poêlé, Turbot rôti, sauce Choron.
LY **c**

XXX ❀❀❀ **Comme Chez Soi** (Wynants), pl. Rouppe 23, ✉ 1000, ℰ 512 29 21, Fax 511 80 52,
« Belle Epoque atmosphere in an Horta decor » – ▤ ℗. 🖭 ⓞ Ε
closed Sunday, Monday, 5 July-3 August and Christmas-New Year – **M** (booking essential) a
la carte 2100/4300
Spec. Emincé de St-Jacques et langoustines aux truffes blanches (November-December), Poussin
de Provence et béarnaise d'écrevisses, Vacherin aux fraises et son eau-de-vie.
EV **c**

XXX **Astrid "Chez Pierrot"**, r. Presse 21, ✉ 1000, ℰ 217 38 31, Fax 217 38 31 – 🖭 ⓞ Ε 𝘝𝘐𝘚𝘈
closed Sunday and 15 July-15 August – **M** 850.
GU **d**

XX **Roma,** r. Princes 12, ✉ 1000, ℰ 218 34 30, Partly Italian cuisine – ▤. 🖭 ⓞ Ε 𝘝𝘐𝘚𝘈. ⅔
closed Saturday lunch and Sunday – **M** 1400/3000.
LY **f**

Quartier de l'Europe

🏨🏨 **Europa,** r. Loi 107, ✉ 1040, ℰ 230 13 33, Telex 25121, Fax 230 36 82, 🏋, 🛋 – 🛗 ⅔← rm
▤ 📺 ℗ – 🛎 25-400. 🖭 ⓞ Ε 𝘝𝘐𝘚𝘈. ⅔
M Les Continents *(closed Saturday)* 1450/1850 – **240 rm** ⌂ 6700/9900.
HV **s**

🏨🏨 **Archimède** without rest., r. Archimède 22, ✉ 1040, ℰ 231 09 09, Telex 20420,
Fax 230 33 71 – 🛗 📺 ☎. 🖭 ⓞ Ε 𝘝𝘐𝘚𝘈. ⅔
closed 23 to 31 December – **56 rm** ⌂ 5800/6000.
HU **y**

🏨🏨 **Euro-flat** without rest., bd Charlemagne 50, ✉ 1040, ℰ 230 00 10, Telex 21120,
Fax 230 36 83, 🏋, 🛋 – 🛗 📺 ☎ – 🛎 25. 🖭 ⓞ Ε 𝘝𝘐𝘚𝘈. ⅔
135 rm ⌂ 5500/7200.
HU **y**

🏨🏨 **Eurovillage,** bd Charlemagne 80, ✉ 1040, ℰ 230 85 55, Telex 20927, Fax 230 56 35, 🏠,
🛋 – 🛗 ⅔← rm 📺 🕭 🚗 – 🛎 80-100. 🖭 ⓞ Ε 𝘝𝘐𝘚𝘈
M a la carte 1000/1600 – ⌂ 400 – **80 rm** 4500/5500.
GV **e**

🏨🏨 **City Garden** ⸚ without rest., with suites, r. Joseph II 59, ✉ 1040, ℰ 230 09 45, Telex 63570,
Fax 230 64 37 – 🛗 ⅔← 📺 ☎. 🖭 ⓞ Ε 𝘝𝘐𝘚𝘈. ⅔
95 rm ⌂ 4400/5350.
GU **r**

XX **Villa de Bruselas,** r. Archimède 65, ✉ 1040, ℰ 735 60 90, 🏠, Spanish cuisine – 🖭 ⓞ
Ε 𝘝𝘐𝘚𝘈. ⅔
closed Saturday lunch, Sunday, Bank Holidays and August – **M** a la carte 1250/1850.
HU **e**

X **Le Gigotin,** r. Stevin 102, ✉ 1040, ℰ 230 30 91, 🏠 – 🖭 ⓞ Ε 𝘝𝘐𝘚𝘈
closed Saturday, Sunday and Bank Holidays – **M** a la carte 950/1300.
HU **n**

X **La Maison Suisse,** r. Philippe le Bon 2, ✉ 1040, ℰ 230 43 41, Swiss specialities – ℗. 🖭
ⓞ Ε 𝘝𝘐𝘚𝘈
closed Saturday lunch, Sunday, Monday dinner and August – **M** a la carte approx. 1700.
HU **a**

Quartier Grand'Place (Ilot Sacré)

🏨🏨 **Royal Windsor**, r. Duquesnoy 5, ✉ 1000, ℰ 511 42 15, Telex 62905, Fax 511 60 04 – 🛗
⅔← rm ▤ 📺 ☎ 🚗 – 🛎 25-250. 🖭 ⓞ Ε 𝘝𝘐𝘚𝘈
M Les 4 Saisons *(closed 20 July-25 August)* a la carte 1300/2300 – **275 rm** ⌂ 8250/12000.
LZ **k**

🏨🏨 **Amigo,** r. Amigo 1, ✉ 1000, ℰ 511 59 10, Telex 21618, Fax 513 52 77, « Collection of works
of art » – 🛗 📺 ☎ – 🛎 25-150. 🖭 ⓞ Ε 𝘝𝘐𝘚𝘈. ⅔ rest
M a la carte 1350/1900 – **183 rm** ⌂ 5550/8050.
KZ **h**

🏨🏨 **Novotel Grand'Place,** r. Marché-aux-Herbes 120, ✉ 1000, ℰ 514 33 33, Telex 20377, Fax 511 77 23 – 🛗 📺 ☎ 🕭 ▣ **AE ⓪ E** *VISA*
M (open until midnight) a la carte 900/1400 – 🗇 460 – **136 rm** 4970.
LZ **b**

🏨 **Ibis Centre,** r. Marché-aux-Herbes 100, ✉ 1000, ℰ 514 40 40, Telex 25490, Fax 514 50 67 – 🛗 🕭 rest 📺 & 🕭 – 🔬 25-130. **AE ⓪ E** *VISA*
M a la carte approx. 1000 – **170 rm** 🗇 3650/4150.
LZ **f**

🗷🗷🗷🗷 ✸ **La Maison du Cygne,** Grand'Place 9, ✉ 1000, ℰ 511 82 44, Fax 514 31 48, « Former 17C guildhouse » – ▣ **℗. AE ⓪ E** *VISA*. 🌤
closed Saturday lunch, Sunday, 3 weeks August and Christmas-New Year – **M** a la carte 2250/2950
Spec. Salade tiède de langoustines, Turbot braisé au thym, Dos d'agneau "Cygne".
LZ **q**

🗷🗷 **La Tête d'Or,** r. Tête d'Or 9, ✉ 1000, ℰ 511 02 01, « Ancient Brussels residence » – **AE ⓪ E** *VISA*
closed Saturday and Sunday – **M** a la carte 1600/2300.
KZ **t**

🗷🗷 **La Table d'Or,** r. Fourche 50, ✉ 1000, ℰ 217 47 00, Fax 219 91 24, Open until 11 p.m. – **AE ⓪ E** *VISA*. 🌤
closed Saturday lunch, Sunday and 1 to 15 August – **M** 1165/1565.
LZ **a**

🗷🗷 **La Porte du Japon,** r. Fourche 9, ✉ 1000, ℰ 511 15 11, Fax 511 15 11, Japanese cuisine, open until 11.30 p.m. – ▣. **AE ⓪ E** *VISA*
closed Monday – **M** a la carte 1200/1800.
LZ **u**

🗷🗷 **Aux Armes de Bruxelles,** r. Bouchers 13, ✉ 1000, ℰ 511 55 98, Fax 514 33 81, Brussels atmosphere, open until 11 p.m. – ▣. **AE ⓪ E** *VISA*
closed Monday and June – **M** 925.
LZ **c**

🗷 **L'Ogenblik,** Galerie des Princes 1, ✉ 1000, ℰ 511 61 51, Fax 513 41 58, Open until midnight – **AE ⓪ E** *VISA*
closed Sunday – **M** a la carte 1450/2350.
LZ **n**

🗷 **Taverne du Passage,** Galerie de la Reine 30, ✉ 1000, ℰ 512 37 32, Fax 511 08 82, Brussels atmosphere, open until midnight – **AE ⓪ E** *VISA*
closed Wednesday and Thursday in June and July – **M** a la carte approx. 1000.
LZ **r**

🗷 **Rôtiss. Vincent,** r. Dominicains 8, ✉ 1000, ℰ 511 23 03, Fax 502 36 93, Brussels atmosphere, open until 11.30 p.m., « original ceramics » – ▣. **AE ⓪ E** *VISA*
closed August – **M** 1000/1500.
LZ **n**

Quartier Ste-Catherine (Marché-aux-Poissons)

🏨 **Sainte-Catherine** without rest., r. Joseph Plateau 2, ✉ 1000, ℰ 513 76 20, Telex 22476, Fax 514 22 14 – 🛗 📺 ☎ & – 🔬 80. **AE ⓪ E** *VISA*
235 rm 🗇 3600/5500.
KY **c**

🗷🗷 **La Sirène d'Or,** pl. Ste-Catherine 1a, ✉ 1000, ℰ 513 51 98, Fax 502 13 05, Seafood – ▣. **AE ⓪ E** *VISA*
closed Sunday, Monday, 22 July-11 August and 24 December-4 January – **M** a la carte 1700/2600.
KY **n**

🗷🗷 ✸ **François,** quai aux Briques 2, ✉ 1000, ℰ 511 60 89, Fax 512 06 67, Seafood – 🕭 ▣. **AE ⓪ E** *VISA*
closed Monday and June – **M** a la carte 1300/2100
Spec. Salade au tomate aux crevettes épluchées du jour, Moules au vin blanc (August-March), Bouillabaisse de la mer du Nord.
KY **z**

🗷🗷 ✸ **La Belle Maraîchère** (Devreker), pl. Ste-Catherine 11, ✉ 1000, ℰ 512 97 59, Fax 513 76 91, Seafood – ▣ **℗. AE ⓪ E** *VISA*
closed Wednesday and Thursday – **M** a la carte 1400/2200
Spec. Soupe de poissons, Fricassée de homard aux petits légumes, Suprême de turbot braisé "Sans Nom".
KY **f**

🗷🗷 **Au Cheval Marin,** Marché-aux-Porcs 25, ✉ 1000, ℰ 513 02 87, « Period decor » – **℗. AE ⓪ E** *VISA* – *closed Sunday and 15 to 31 August* – **M** 900/1750.
KY **u**

🗷🗷 **Café de Paris,** r. Vierge Noire 12, ✉ 1000, ℰ 512 39 40, Fax 344 02 45, Open until midnight « Art déco interior » – **AE ⓪ E** *VISA*
closed Sunday – **M** a la carte approx. 1300.
KY **e**

🗷🗷 **Le Bédouin,** r. Flandre 6, ✉ 1000, ℰ 502 35 73, Tunisian cuisine – **AE E** *VISA*
closed Tuesday lunch, Saturday and Monday – **M** a la carte 900/1250.
KY **a**

Quartier des Sablons

🏨🏨 **Jolly du Grand Sablon,** r. Bodenbroek 2, ✉ 1000, ℰ 512 88 00, Telex 20397, Fax 512 67 66 – 🛗 🕭 rm 🕭 📺 ☎ 🚗 – 🔬 50. **AE ⓪ E** *VISA*. 🌤 rest
M a la carte 1700/2400 – **203 rm** 🗇 7350/9400.
FV **z**

🗷🗷🗷 ✸✸ **L'Écailler du Palais Royal** (Basso), r. Bodenbroek 18, ✉ 1000, ℰ 512 87 51, Seafood – **℗. AE ⓪ E** *VISA*
closed Sunday, Bank Holidays, 1 to 10 March and August – **M** a la carte 2400/3000
Spec. Banc d'huîtres (October-April), Risotto de coquillages (October-April), Homard sauté à la crème d'oseille.
FV **z**

🗷🗷🗷 **En Provence "Chez Marius",** pl. du Petit Sablon 1, ✉ 1000, ℰ 511 12 08, Fax 512 27 89 – **AE E** *VISA*
closed Sunday – **M** 1300/1500.
FV **s**

XX **Les Brigittines,** pl. de la Chapelle 5, ✉ 1000, ℘ 512 68 91, Fax 512 41 30, 🏛, « Belle Epoque atmosphere » – AE ① E VISA FV **e**
closed Saturday lunch, Sunday and August – **M** a la carte 1500/2300.

XX ✿ **Trente rue de la Paille** (Martiny), r. Paille 30, ✉ 1000, ℘ 512 07 15, Fax 514 23 33 – AE ① E VISA FV **u**
closed Saturday, Sunday, Bank Holidays, July and Christmas-New Year – **M** a la carte 2000/2300
Spec. Salade de pigeon rôti, sauce au Porto, Poêlée de rouget-barbet en écailles de courgettes, Saumon aux trois cuissons, sauce au curry.

XX **Castello Banfi,** r. Bodenbroek 12, ✉ 1000, ℘ 512 87 94, Italian cuisine – AE ① E VISA
closed Sunday dinner and Monday – **M** 1495. FV **z**

X **L'Herbe Rouge,** r. Minimes 34, ✉ 1000, ℘ 512 48 34 – AE ① E VISA FV **v**
closed Saturday lunch and Sunday – **M** a la carte 1450/2000.

Quartier Palais de Justice

Hilton International, bd de Waterloo 38, ✉ 1000, ℘ 504 11 11, Telex 22744, Fax 504 21 11, ≦s – |¢| ⇆ rm ▤ TV ☎ ♿ ⇔ – 🔔 50-500. AE ① E VISA. ✗ FX **s**
M see rest. **Maison du Bœuf** below – **Plein Ciel** 27th floor ≤ town *(closed Saturday and July-August)* (lunch only) 950/1550 – **Café d'Egmont** a la carte 1100/1700 – ☕ 575 – **450 rm** 9000/14000.

XXXX **Maison du Bœuf** - (at Hilton H.), 1st floor, **bd de Waterloo 38,** ✉ 1000, ℘ 504 11 11, Telex 22744, Fax 504 21 11, ≤ – ▤ Ⓟ. AE ① E VISA. ✗ FX **s**
M a la carte 1600/2750.

X ✿ **Au Beurre Blanc** (Hella), r. Faucon 2a, ✉ 1000, ℘ 513 01 11 – AE ① E VISA FX **f**
closed Saturday, Sunday, 1 week Easter, last 2 weeks August and late December – **M** a la carte 1400/2100
Spec. Escalopes de foie de canard aux pommes caramélisées, Assiette du pêcheur au beurre blanc, Râble de lièvre poivrade aux mangues poêlées (15 October-December).

X **Les Larmes du Tigre,** r. Wynants 21, ✉ 1000, ℘ 512 18 77, Fax 502 10 03, 🏛, Thaï cuisine – AE ① E VISA FX **e**
closed Monday and Saturday lunch – **M** a la carte 850/1300.

Quartier Léopold (see also at Ixelles)

Stanhope, r. Commerce 9, ✉ 1040, ℘ 506 91 11, Fax 512 17 08, 🏛, ≦s – |¢| TV ☎ ⇔. AE E VISA. ✗ HU **b**
M *(closed Sunday)* a la carte 1750/2850 – **50 rm** ☕ 12500/14500.

Quartier Avenue Louise (see also at Ixelles)

Mayfair, av. Louise 381, ✉ 1050, ℘ 649 98 00, Telex 24821, Fax 640 17 64, « Opulent decor » – |¢| ⇆ rm ▤ TV ☎ ⇔ – 🔔 30. AE ① E VISA. ✗ rest
M *(closed Saturday)* a la carte 1700/2500 – ☕ 650 – **99 rm** 8200.

Copthorne Stéphanie, av. Louise 91, ✉ 1050, ℘ 539 02 40, Telex 25558, Fax 538 03 07, ▣ – |¢| ⇆ ▤ rest TV ☎ ⇔ – 🔔 50-200. AE ① E VISA. ✗ rest
M **L'Avenue Louise** *(closed Saturday, Sunday lunch, 25 July-23 August and 25 December-1 January)* a la carte 1100/2050 – ☕ 720 – **142 rm** 7300/10300.

Brussels President without rest., av. Louise 315, ✉ 1050, ℘ 640 24 15, Telex 25075, Fax 647 34 63 – |¢| TV ☎. AE ① E VISA. ✗
38 rm ☕ 4250/4700.

Club House without rest., r. Blanche 4, ✉ 1050, ℘ 537 92 10, Telex 62434, Fax 537 00 18 – |¢| TV ☎ ⇔ – 🔔 30. AE ① E VISA
82 rm ☕ 4500/6600.

L'Agenda without rest., r. Florence 6, ✉ 1050, ℘ 539 00 31, Telex 63947, Fax 539 00 63 – |¢| TV ☎ ⇔. AE ① E VISA
☕ 250 – **38 rm** 3000/3300.

XX **La Porte des Indes,** av. Louise 455, ✉ 1050, ℘ 647 86 51, Indian cuisine, « Exotic decor » – AE ① E VISA
closed Sunday – **M** 1850.

XX **Eastern Tandoori,** av. Louise 263, ✉ 1050, ℘ 646 09 41, Indian cuisine – ▤. AE ① E VISA
closed Sunday and lunch Bank Holidays – **M** a la carte 1000/1900.

Quartier Bois de la Cambre

XXXXX ✿✿ **Villa Lorraine** (Van de Casserie), av. du Vivier d'Oie 75, ✉ 1180, ℘ 374 31 63, 🏛 – Ⓟ. AE ① E VISA
closed Sunday and July – **M** a la carte 2550/3950
Spec. Foie de canard rôti aux reinettes, truffes et verjus (September-April), Queue de homard au Sauternes, Râble de lièvre des gourmets (October-January).

XXX ✿ **La Truffe Noire,** bd de la Cambre 12, ✉ 1050, ℘ 640 44 22, Fax 647 97 04, « Elegant interior » – AE ① E VISA
closed Saturday lunch, Sunday, 1 week Easter, last 2 weeks August and late December – **M** a la carte 2400/3300
Spec. Carpaccio aux truffes, Eclats de diamant noir en surprise, St-Pierre aux poireaux et truffes.

Quartier Atomium (Centenaire - Trade Mart)

XXX **Le Centenaire,** av. J. Sobieski 84, ✉ 1020, *£* 478 66 23 – AE ① E VISA
closed Tuesday, Monday, July and Christmas-New Year – **M** a la carte 1300/1800.

XX ۞ **Les Baguettes Impériales** (Mme Ma), av. J. Sobieski 70, ✉ 1020, *£* 479 67 32, Fax 479 67 32, 斎, Vietnamese cuisine, « Exotic decor » – AE. ﷼
closed Tuesday, Sunday dinner, Easter and August – **M** a la carte 2050/2900
Spec. Salade de crabe tiède à la vietnamienne, Pot-au-feu de pigeonneau, Magret d'oie à la moutarde de mangue.

X **Adrienne Atomium,** Square Atomium, ✉ 1020, *£* 478 30 00, ≼, Buffets – AE ① E VISA
closed Sunday, Bank Holidays and August – **M** 690.

Quartier Gare du Nord (Botanique)

🏨🏨🏨 **Sheraton Towers,** pl. Rogier 3, ✉ 1210, *£* 224 31 11, Telex 26887, Fax 224 34 56, 🗋, 😩, 🔲 – 🛗 ⤢ rm 🗐 🔲 ☎ 🄿 – 🕍 25-1500. AE ① E VISA. ﷼ rest   FT **e**
M Comtes de Flandre *(closed Saturday, Sunday and August)* a la carte 1800/2600 – 🍽 515
– **528 rm** 9600/13000.

🏨🏨 **President World Trade Center,** bd E. Jacqmain 180, ✉ 1210, *£* 217 20 20, Telex 21066, Fax 218 84 02, 🗋, 😩 – 🛗 🔲 ☎ ⟵⟶ – 🕍 25-400. AE ① E VISA. ﷼
M *(closed Saturday and Sunday)* a la carte 1100/1600 – **305 rm** 🍽 5000/8500.

🏨 **Le Dome,** bd du Jardin Botanique 13, ✉ 1000, *£* 218 06 80, Telex 61317, Fax 218 41 12 – 🛗 🔲 ☎ 🕭 – 🕍 25-100. AE ① E VISA   FT **b**
M *(closed Sunday and Monday dinner)* (open until 11 p.m.) a la carte 1100/1900 – **77 rm** 🍽 5500/6900.

🏨 **Président Nord** without rest., bd A. Max 107, ✉ 1000, *£* 219 00 60, Telex 61417, Fax 218 12 69 – 🛗 🔲 ☎. AE ① E VISA. ﷼   LY **b**
63 rm 🍽 4300/5400.

🏨 **Le Prince de Liège,** chaussée de Ninove 664, ✉ 1080, *£* 522 16 00, Fax 520 81 85 – 🛗 🔲 ☎ ⟵⟶ – 🕍 25. AE ① E VISA
M *(closed Sunday dinner and 12 July-5 August)* 785/1285 – **21 rm** 🍽 2350/2750.

XXX **Saint-Guidon** 2nd floor, av. Théo Verbeeck 2 (in the Constant Vanden Stock stadium), ✉ 1070, *£* 520 55 36, Fax 520 07 40 – 🄿 – 🕍 25-400. ① E VISA. ﷼
closed July, Christmas-New Year, Saturday, Sunday, first league match days and Bank Holidays – **M** (lunch only) a la carte approx. 2000.

XX **La Réserve,** chaussée de Ninove 675, ✉ 1080, *£* 522 26 53, 斎 – AE ① E VISA
closed Monday, Tuesday and Saturday lunch – **M** a la carte 1200/1900.

X **La Paix** r. Ropsy-Chaudron 49 (opposite slaughterhouse), ✉ 1070, *£* 523 09 58, Pub-rest. – AE E VISA
closed Saturday, Sunday and last 2 weeks July – **M** (lunch only) a la carte 900/1200.

XX ۞ **La Grignotière** (Chanson), chaussée de Wavre 2041, ✉ 1160, *£* 672 81 85 – AE ① E VISA
closed Sunday, Monday, Bank Holidays and 1 to 24 August – **M** 1600/2500
Spec. St-Jacques grillées au jus de truffes et épinards (October-March), Fondant de saumon sur coulis de basilic, Croustillant de pigeonneau et foie d'oie poêlé (March-September).

XX **L'Abbaye de Rouge Cloître,** r. Rouge Cloître 8, ✉ 1160, *£* 672 45 25, Fax 660 12 01, ≼, 斎, « Forest-side setting » – 🄿 – 🕍 25-55. AE ① E VISA
closed Saturday, Sunday and 23 December-6 January – **M** a la carte 1300/1800.

XX **New Asia,** chaussée de Wavre 1240, ✉ 1160, *£* 660 62 06, Chinese cuisine – ⤢. AE ① E VISA. ﷼
closed Monday and last 3 weeks July – **M** a la carte approx. 1000.

🏨 **Park** without rest., av. de l'Yser 21, ✉ 1040, *£* 735 74 00, Fax 735 19 67, 😩, 🌳 – 🛗 ⤢ 🔲 ☎ – 🕍 25. AE ① E VISA. ﷼
47 rm 🍽 5300/7200.

XX **La Fontaine de Jade,** av. de Tervuren 5, ✉ 1040, *£* 736 32 10, Chinese cuisine – AE ① E VISA
closed Tuesday – **M** a la carte approx. 1100.

X **Harry's Place,** r. Bataves 65, ✉ 1040, *£* 735 09 00 – AE ① E VISA
closed Thursday dinner, Saturday lunch, Sunday, 21 July-15 August and 24 December-1 January – **M** a la carte approx. 1400.

X **Le Pavillon d'Été,** av. de Tervuren 107, ✉ 1040, *£* 732 03 59, Fax 732 10 56, Pub rest., open until midnight – AE ① E VISA
closed Sunday, Monday and 26 July-17 August – **M** a la carte 1300/1900.

EVERE

Belson without rest., chaussée de Louvain 805, ⊠ 1140, ℰ 735 00 00, Telex 64921, Fax 735 60 43 – |自| 🌿 🔟 🕿 🅿 – 🔬 25. 🖭 ⓞ 🗲 ₩𝟷
≥ 580 – **90 rm** 5750/6350.

Mercure, av. J. Bordet 74, ⊠ 1140, ℰ 242 53 35, Telex 65460, Fax 245 05 95, ☆ – |自|
🌿 rm 🗏 rest 🔟 🕿 🕹 ⇔ – 🔬 30-60. 🖭 ⓞ 🗲 ₩𝟷
M *(closed lunch Saturday and Sunday)* a la carte 900/1600 – ≥ 495 – **120 rm** 3500/6000.

Evergreen, av. V. Day 1, ⊠ 1140, ℰ 732 15 15, Fax 732 16 60 – 🔟 🕿. 🖭 ⓞ 🗲 ₩𝟷
M (Pub-rest.) 650/1500 – **18 rm** ≥ 2650/3150.

Le Citron Vert, av. H. Conscience 242, ⊠ 1140, ℰ 241 12 57, Open until 11 p.m. – 🖭 ⓞ
🗲 ₩𝟷
closed Monday dinner, Tuesday and August – **M** 750.

FOREST (VORST)

Le Chouan, av. Brugmann 100, ⊠ 1060, ℰ 344 09 99, Seafood – 🖿. 🖭 ⓞ 🗲 ₩𝟷
closed Saturday lunch, Sunday dinner and July – **M** a la carte 1500/2150.

L'Abel Abbaye, pl. Saint-Denis 9, ⊠ 1190, ℰ 332 11 59, Fax 332 11 59, ≼, ☆ – 🅿. 🖭
ⓞ 🗲 ₩𝟷
closed Sunday dinner, Monday and August – **M** 795/1250.

GANSHOREN

❀❀❀ Bruneau, av. Broustin 73, ⊠ 1080, ℰ 427 69 78, Fax 425 97 26 – 🖭 ⓞ 🗲 ₩𝟷
closed holiday Thursdays, Tuesday dinner, Wednesday, mid June-late July and Christmas-New
Year – **M** a la carte 2600/3800
Spec. Carpaccio de langoustines à la crème de caviar, Fricassée de homard au jus de viande,
Pomme de terre de ris de veau aux truffes.

❀❀ Claude Dupont, av. Vital Riethuisen 46, ⊠ 1080, ℰ 426 00 00, Fax 426 65 40 – 🖭
ⓞ 🗲 ₩𝟷
closed Monday, Tuesday and 6 July-11 August – **M** a la carte 1800/2850
Spec. La crème mousseuse de langoustines, Aiguillettes de canard colvert au cidre bouché et
gingembre (September-January), Baluchon de raie et de homard au vinaigre balsamique.

Cambrils 1st floor, av. Charles-Quint 365, ⊠ 1080, ℰ 465 35 82, Fax 465 35 82, ☆ – 🖿.
🖭 🗲 ₩𝟷
closed Sunday, Monday dinner and 15 July-15 August – **M** 860/1500.

San Daniele, av. Charles-Quint 6, ⊠ 1080, ℰ 426 79 23, Italian cuisine – 🖭 ⓞ 🗲 ₩𝟷
closed Sunday and 15 July-15 August – **M** a la carte approx. 1500.

Le Claudalain, av. des Gloires Nationales 65, ⊠ 1080, ℰ 428 82 63 – 🖭 ⓞ 🗲
closed Sunday dinner, Monday, Tuesday, late August-early September and late January-early
February – **M** 740/1090.

IXELLES (ELSENE)

Aub. de Boendael, square du Vieux Tilleul 12, ⊠ 1050, ℰ 672 70 55, Fax 660 75 82, Grill
rest. Rustic – 🖿 🅿. 🖭 ⓞ 🗲 ₩𝟷
closed Saturday, Sunday, Bank Holidays, first 3 weeks August and Christmas-New Year –
M a la carte 1400/1950.

Les Foudres, r. Eugène Cattoir 14, ⊠ 1050, ℰ 647 36 36, ☆, « Former wine cellar » –
🅿. 🖭 ⓞ 🗲 ₩𝟷
closed Saturday lunch, Sunday and holiday Mondays – **M** 850/1250.

Le Chalet Rose, av. du Bois de la Cambre 49, ⊠ 1050, ℰ 672 78 64, ☆ – 🅿. 🖭 ⓞ 🗲
₩𝟷 – closed Saturday lunch, Sunday and Bank Holidays – **M** a la carte 1600/2200.

Quartier Léopold (see also at Bruxelles)

Leopold, r. Luxembourg 35, ⊠ 1040, ℰ 511 18 28, Telex 62804, Fax 514 19 39, ☆≋ – |自|
🔟 🕿 – 🔬 25-50. 🖭 ⓞ 🗲 ₩𝟷. 🌿 rm   GV **u**
M *(closed Saturday lunch and Sunday)* a la carte 1800/2300 – **33 rm** ≥ 3000/4100.

Quartier Bascule

Forum without rest., av. du Haut-Pont 2, ⊠ 1060, ℰ 343 01 00, Telex 62311, Fax 347 00 54
– |自| 🔟 🕿 ⇔ – 🔬 80. 🖭 ⓞ 🗲 ₩𝟷
77 rm ≥ 3500/4100.

La Mosaïque, r. Forestière 23, ⊠ 1050, ℰ 649 02 35, Fax 647 11 49 – 🖭 ⓞ 🗲 ₩𝟷
closed Saturday lunch and Sunday – **M** a la carte 1800/2500.

Maison Félix, r. Washington 149 (square Henri Michaux), ⊠ 1050, ℰ 345 66 93 – 🖭 ⓞ
🗲 ₩𝟷 – closed Sunday, Monday, 26 July-17 August and 21 December-8 January – **M** a la
carte 2050/2850.

La Charlotte aux Pommes, pl. du Châtelain 40, ⊠ 1050, ℰ 640 53 88 – 🖭 ⓞ 🗲 ₩𝟷
closed Saturday lunch, Sunday and August – **M** a la carte 1800/2700.

La Thaïlande, av. Legrand 29, ⊠ 1050, ℰ 640 24 62, ☆, Thaï cuisine – 🖭 ⓞ 🗲 ₩𝟷
closed Sunday and 15 July-15 August – **M** a la carte 1000/1400.

Quartier Avenue Louise (see also at Bruxelles)

🏨🏨 **Sofitel,** av. de la Toison d'Or 40, ✉ 1060, ☏ 514 22 00, Telex 63547, Fax 514 57 44 – 🛗
※ rm ▤ TV ☎ – 🔬 25-120. ⁂ ① Ⅽ VISA. ※ rest   FX **b**
M a la carte 1200/1800 – ☲ 580 – **171 rm** 6900/7400.

🏨🏨 **Cadett,** r. Paul Spaak 15, ✉ 1050, ☏ 645 61 11, Telex 20819, Fax 646 63 44, ⚏, 🚁 – 🛗
⁑ ▤ rest TV ☎ 🔬 🚗 – 🔬 25. ⁂ Ⅽ VISA
M (open until 11 p.m.) a la carte 800/1250 – ☲ 500 – **128 rm** 5600.

🏨 **Argus** without rest., r. Capitaine Crespel 6, ✉ 1050, ☏ 514 07 70, Telex 29393, Fax 514 12 22
– 🛗 TV ☎. ⁂ ① Ⅽ   FX **a**
41 rm ☲ 2650/2950.

✕✕ **Le Criterion,** av. de la Toison d'Or 7, ✉ 1060, ☏ 512 37 68, Pub-rest., open until midnight
– ⁂ Ⅽ VISA. ※   GX **p**
M a la carte 1100/1800.

✕ **Shogun,** r. Capitaine Crespel 10, ✉ 1050, ☏ 512 83 19, 🍴, Japanese cuisine, teppan-yaki,
open until 1 p.m. – ⁂ ① Ⅽ VISA   FX **c**
closed Saturday lunch, Sunday and 10 January-10 February – **M** 1300/1700.

JETTE

✕✕ ✿ **Le Sermon** (Kobs), av. Jacques Sermon 91, ✉ 1090, ☏ 426 89 35, Fax 426 70 90 – ⁂
Ⅽ VISA – *closed Sunday, Monday and 30 June-3 August* – **M** a la carte 1400/2300
Spec. Moules au Champagne (September-April), Sole "Sermon", Agneau persillé aux primeurs.

✕✕ **Rôtiss. Le Vieux Pannenhuis,** r. Léopold-Ier 317, ✉ 1090, ☏ 425 83 73, Fax 428 12 99,
🍴, « 17C inn » – ▤. ⁂ ① Ⅽ VISA
closed Saturday lunch, Sunday and July – **M** 895.

MOLENBEEK-ST-JEAN (SINT-JANS-MOLENBEEK)

✕✕✕ **Le Béarnais,** bd Louis Mettewie 318, ✉ 1080, ☏ 523 11 51, Fax 410 70 81 – ▤. ⁂ ①
Ⅽ VISA – *closed Sunday and Monday dinner* – **M** a la carte 1900/2600.

ST-GILLES (SINT-GILLIS)

🏨🏨 **Ramada,** chaussée de Charleroi 38, ✉ 1060, ☏ 539 30 00, Telex 25539, Fax 538 90 14 –
🛗 ※ rm ▤ TV ☎ 🚗 – 🔬 25-170. ⁂ ① Ⅽ VISA. ※ rest
M a la carte approx. 1100 – ☲ 600 – **201 rm** 6950/9850.

🏨 **Manos Stephanie,** chaussée de Charleroi 28, ✉ 1060, ☏ 539 02 50, Telex 20556,
Fax 537 57 29 – 🛗 TV ☎ 🚗 – 🔬 25. ⁂ ① Ⅽ VISA
M (residents only) – ☲ 550 – **48 rm** 4450/5750.

🏨 **Delta,** chaussée de Charleroi 17, ✉ 1060, ☏ 539 01 60, Telex 63225, Fax 537 90 11 – 🛗
▤ rest TV ☎ 🚗 – 🔬 60-100. ⁂ ① Ⅽ VISA. ※ rest   FX **r**
M a la carte 750/1050 – **246 rm** ☲ 4800/5400.

🏨 **Manos** without rest., chaussée de Charleroi 102, ✉ 1060, ☏ 537 96 82, Telex 65369,
Fax 539 36 55 – 🛗 TV ☎. ⁂ ① Ⅽ VISA
☲ 450 – **38 rm** 2975/3975.

🏨 **La Cascade** without rest., r. Source 14, ✉ 1060, ☏ 538 88 30, Telex 26637, Fax 538 92 79
– 🛗 TV ☎ 🚗 – 🔬 50. ⁂ ℗ Ⅽ VISA. ※
40 rm ☲ 2980/3710.

🏨 **Diplomat** without rest., r. Jean Stas 32, ✉ 1060, ☏ 537 42 50, Telex 61012, Fax 539 33 79
– 🛗 TV ☎. ⁂ ① Ⅽ VISA   FX **x**
68 rm ☲ 4800/5400.

✕✕ **L'Auvergne,** r. Aqueduc 61, ✉ 1050, ☏ 537 31 25, Rustic – ⁂ ① Ⅽ VISA
closed Sunday, Monday and 20 July-20 August – **M** 875.

✕✕ **Le Fronton Basque,** chaussée de Waterloo 361, ✉ 1060, ☏ 537 21 18, Oyster bar and
Seafood – ⁂ ① Ⅽ VISA
M a la carte 1100/1800.

✕✕ **Le Forcado,** chaussée de Charleroi 192, ✉ 1060, ☏ 537 92 20, Portuguese cuisine – ⁂ ①
Ⅽ VISA – *closed Sunday, Bank Holidays, August and carnival week* – **M** a la carte 1050/1600.

ST-JOSSE-TEN-NOODE (SINT-JOOST-TEN-NODE)

🏨🏨🏨 **Scandic Crown,** r. Royale 250, ✉ 1210, ☏ 220 66 11, Telex 61871, Fax 217 84 44, 🛁, ⚏
– 🛗 ※ rm ▤ TV ☎ 🚗 – 🔬 30-500. ⁂ ① Ⅽ VISA. ※ rest   GT **r**
M *(closed Saturday and mid July-mid August)* a la carte 1750/2300 – **315 rm** ☲ 8700/9500.

🏨 **New Siru,** pl. Rogier 1, ✉ 1210, ☏ 217 75 80 and 217 83 08 (rest.), Telex 21722,
Fax 218 33 03, « Every room decorated by a contemporary Belgian artist » – 🛗 ▤ rest TV
☎ ℗ – 🔬 70. ⁂ ① Ⅽ VISA   FT **f**
M (open until 11.30 p.m.) a la carte 900/1500 – ☲ 195 – **101 rm** 3200/5900.

🏨 **Albert Premier** without rest., pl. Rogier 20, ✉ 1210, ☏ 217 21 25, Telex 27111,
Fax 217 93 31 – 🛗 TV ☎ 🔬 – 🔬 25-70. ⁂ ① Ⅽ VISA   FT **d**
285 rm ☲ 3000/4500.

XX **De Ultieme Hallucinatie,** r. Royale 316, ✉ 1210, ℘ 217 06 14, Fax 217 72 40, « Art Nouveau interior » – AE ⓓ E VISA. ⛔ GT **u**
closed Saturday lunch and Sunday – **M** 1450/1950.

SCHAERBEEK (SCHAARBEEK)

XX **Den Botaniek,** r. Royale 328, ✉ 1210, ℘ 218 48 38, Fax 218 41 95, 🍴, « 1900 decor, garden » – AE ⓓ E VISA GT **n**
closed Saturday lunch, Sunday, Bank Holidays, last 2 weeks September and first week January – **M** a la carte 1650/2400.

Quartier Meiser

Lambermont without rest., bd Lambermont 322, ✉ 1030, ℘ 242 55 95, Telex 62220, Fax 242 55 95 – |♦| TV ☎. AE ⓓ E VISA
42 rm ☕ 3000/3500.

Reyers without rest., bd Aug. Reyers 40, ✉ 1040, ℘ 732 42 42, Fax 732 41 82, 🍴 – |♦| ☎ Ⓟ. AE ⓓ E VISA
49 rm ☕ 2600/2980.

XX **Philippe Riesen** 1st floor, bd Aug. Reyers 163, ✉ 1040, ℘ 736 41 38 – AE ⓓ E VISA
closed Saturday, Sunday and Bank Holidays – **M** a la carte 1400/2200.

UCCLE (UKKEL)

County House, square des Héros 2, ✉ 1180, ℘ 375 44 20, Telex 22392, Fax 375 31 22 – |♦| ▤ rest TV ☎ 🚗 Ⓟ – 🎤 25-80. AE ⓓ E VISA. ⛔ rest
M a la carte 1300/1750 – **96 rm** ☕ 4800.

XX ✿ **Villa d'Este,** r. Etoile 142, ✉ 1180, ℘ 376 48 48, 🍴, « Terrace » – Ⓟ. AE ⓓ E VISA
closed Sunday dinner, Monday, July and 23 December-5 January – **M** a la carte 1650/2300
Spec. Suprême de turbotin au basilic (summer), Cassolette de petits gris au chou vert, sauce cerfeuil (winter), Coquelet à la moutarde de Meaux.

XX **La Cité du Dragon,** chaussée de Waterloo 1024, ✉ 1180, ℘ 375 80 80, Fax 375 69 77, 🍴, Chinese cuisine, open until 11 p.m., « Exotic garden with fountains » – ⛔ Ⓟ. AE ⓓ E VISA – **M** 790/2200.

XX **Les Frères Romano,** av. de Fré 182, ✉ 1180, ℘ 374 70 98, 🍴 – AE ⓓ E VISA
closed Sunday, Bank Holidays and 3 August-1 September – **M** a la carte approx. 2000.

XX **L'Amandier,** av. de Fré 184, ✉ 1180, ℘ 374 03 95, Fax 374 86 92, 🍴, Open until 11 p.m. – AE ⓓ E VISA
closed Saturday lunch – **M** a la carte 1200/1900.

XX **A'mbriana,** r. Edith Cavell 151, ✉ 1180, ℘ 375 01 56, Italian cuisine – AE E VISA
closed Tuesday, Saturday lunch and 15 July-15 August – **M** a la carte approx. 1500.

XX **L'Éléphant Bleu,** chaussée de Waterloo 1120, ✉ 1180, ℘ 374 49 62, Fax 375 44 68, Thaï cuisine, « Exotic decor » – ▤. Ⓟ. AE ⓓ E VISA
closed Saturday lunch – **M** a la carte 1100/1900.

XX **La Feuille de Menthe,** r. Stalle 230, ✉ 1180, ℘ 332 24 97, Partly Moroccan cuisine – Ⓟ. AE ⓓ E VISA. ⛔
closed Saturday lunch, Sunday and August – **M** 1850/2500.

X **Brasseries Georges,** av. Winston Churchill 259, ✉ 1180, ℘ 347 21 00, Fax 344 02 45, 🍴, Open until midnight – ▤. AE ⓓ E VISA
closed Sunday – **M** a la carte 900/1500.

X **De Hoef,** r. Edith Cavell 218, ✉ 1180, ℘ 374 34 17, 🍴, 17C inn, Grill rest. – AE ⓓ E VISA
closed Wednesday and 10 to 31 July – **M** 625.

X **Willy et Marianne,** chaussée d'Alsemberg 705, ✉ 1180, ℘ 343 60 09 – AE ⓓ E VISA
closed Tuesday dinner, Wednesday, 3 weeks July and 3 weeks carnival – **M** 850.

WATERMAEL-BOITSFORT (WATERMAAL-BOSVOORDE)

XX **Host. Des 3 Tilleuls** 🐎 with rm, Berensheide 8, ✉ 1170, ℘ 672 30 14, Fax 673 65 52, 🍴 – TV ☎. AE ⓓ E VISA. ⛔ rm
M *(closed Sunday and 15 July-15 August)* a la carte 1600/2200 – **7 rm** ☕ 2700/4350.

XX **Le Canard Sauvage,** chaussée de La Hulpe 194, ✉ 1170, ℘ 673 09 75, Fax 675 21 45 – AE ⓓ E VISA
closed Saturday lunch, Sunday dinner and August – **M** a la carte 1200/1700.

XX **Nouveau Chez Nous,** r. Middelbourg 28, ✉ 1170, ℘ 673 53 93, Fax 673 53 93 – AE ⓓ E VISA
closed Sunday dinner, Monday and 6 to 27 August – **M** 1150.

XX **Samambaïa,** r. Philippe Dewolfs 7, ✉ 1170, ℘ 672 87 20, Fax 675 20 74, Brazilian cuisine – AE ⓓ E
closed Sunday, Monday and 19 July-19 August – **M** a la carte 1100/1500.

XX **Les Rives du Gange** with rm, av. de la Fauconnerie 1, ✉ 1170, ℘ 672 16 01, Telex 62661, Fax 672 43 30 – AE ⓓ E VISA
M (Indian cuisine, open until 11 p.m.) a la carte 1100/1750 – **19 rm** ☕ 1880/2280.

WOLUWÉ-ST-LAMBERT (SINT-LAMBRECHTS-WOLUWE)

🏨 **Sodehotel** ⌕, av. E. Mounier 5, ✉ 1200, ☎ 775 21 11, Telex 20170, Fax 770 47 80, 🏵
– 📳 ⇔ rm 🛏 📺 ☎ 🕭 ⇔ 🅿 – 🔒 25-200. 🆎 ⓞ 🖪 𝘝𝘐𝘚𝘈. ⅀ rest
M a la carte 1300/1900 – ⌷ 480 – **112 rm** 5600/6200.

🍴🍴🍴 ✿ **Mon Manège à Toi,** r. Neerveld 1, ✉ 1200, ☎ 770 02 38, Fax 762 95 80, « Flowered garden » – 🅿. 🆎 ⓞ 🖪 𝘝𝘐𝘚𝘈
closed Saturday, Sunday, Bank Holidays, 7 to 31 July and 23 December-1 January – **M** a la carte 2000/2900
Spec. Salade de homard à l'huile de noix, Soufflé d'huîtres et filets de sole au ratafia de Champagne, Filet d'agneau en croûte d'herbes fraîches.

🍴🍴🍴 **Lindekemale,** av. J.F. Debecker 6, ✉ 1200, ☎ 770 90 57, Fax 770 90 57, 🏵, « 15C watermill » – 🅿. 🆎 ⓞ 🖪 𝘝𝘐𝘚𝘈
closed Saturday, Sunday, Bank Holidays and August – **M** a la carte 1600/2300.

🍴🍴 **Le Relais de la Woluwe,** av. Georges Henri 1, ✉ 1200, ☎ 762 66 36, Fax 762 18 55, 🏵, « Terrace and garden » – 🆎 ⓞ 🖪 𝘝𝘐𝘚𝘈
closed Saturday lunch, Sunday, Bank Holidays, 1 week Easter and 1 week Christmas – **M** a la carte 1500/1900.

🍴🍴 **The Butterfly,** chaussée de Stockel 294, ✉ 1200, ☎ 763 22 16 – 🆎 ⓞ 🖪 𝘝𝘐𝘚𝘈
closed Tuesday and 1 week late September – **M** 750/1150.

WOLUWÉ-ST-PIERRE (SINT-PIETERS-WOLUWE)

🍴🍴🍴 ✿ **Des 3 Couleurs** (Tourneur), av. de Tervuren 453, ✉ 1150, ☎ 770 33 21, 🏵, « Terrace » – 🖪
closed 1 to 29 September, 21 to 31 December and Monday, Tuesday except Bank Holidays – **M** a la carte 1800/2250
Spec. Pigeonneau aux primeurs, Saumon "Liliane", Ris de veau du Père Gehain.

BRUSSELS ENVIRONS

at Diegem Brussels-Zaventem motorway Diegem exit Ⓒ Machelen pop. 11 177 – ✉ 1831 Diegem – ✿ 0 2 :

🏨 **Holiday Inn,** Holidaystraat 7, ☎ 720 58 65, Telex 24285, Fax 720 41 45, 𝕝ъ, ⇌, 🔲, ⅍
– 📳 ⇔ rm 🛏 📺 ☎ 🅿 – 🔒 25-500. 🆎 ⓞ 🖪 𝘝𝘐𝘚𝘈. ⅀ rest
M a la carte 1100/1700 – ⌷ 575 – **309 rm** 6500/7500.

🏨 **Sofitel Airport,** Bessenveldstraat 15, ☎ 725 11 60, Telex 26595, Fax 721 43 45, 🏵, ⇌, 🔲
– ⇔ rm 🛏 📺 ☎ 🅿 – 🔒 25-500
125 rm.

🏨 **Novotel Airport,** Olmenstraat, ☎ 725 30 50, Telex 26751, Fax 721 39 58, 🏵, ⍛ – 📳 ⇔ rm
🛏 📺 ☎ 🅿 – 🔒 25-250. 🆎 ⓞ 🖪 𝘝𝘐𝘚𝘈
M (open until midnight) a la carte 750/1100 – ⌷ 435 – **209 rm** 4500/4700.

🏨 **Ibis Airport,** Bessenveldstraat 17, ☎ 725 43 21, Telex 22062, Fax 725 40 40, 🏵 – 📳 📺
☎ 🕭 🅿 – 🔒 30-60. 🆎 ⓞ 🖪 𝘝𝘐𝘚𝘈
M 750/900 – **96 rm** ⌷ 3000/3450.

🏨 **Fimotel Airport,** Berkenlaan 5, ☎ 725 33 80, Telex 20906, Fax 725 38 10, 🏵 – 📳 📺 ☎
🕭 🅿 – 🔒 25-200. 🆎 ⓞ 🖪 𝘝𝘐𝘚𝘈
M 750 – **79 rm** ⌷ 3200/3700.

🍴🍴 **Diegemhof,** Calenbergstraat 51, ☎ 720 11 34, Fax 720 14 87, 🏵 – ⇔. 🆎 ⓞ 🖪 𝘝𝘐𝘚𝘈. ⅀
closed Saturday, Sunday and July – **M** a la carte 1450/2300.

at Dilbeek by ⑪ : 7 km – pop. 36 366 – ✉ 1700 Dilbeek – ✿ 0 2 :

🏨 **Relais Delbeccha** ⌕, Bodegemstraat 158, ☎ 569 44 30, Fax 569 75 30, 🏵, ⇌, 🔲, ⍛
– 📺 ☎ 🅿 – 🔒 30-100. 🆎 ⓞ 🖪 𝘝𝘐𝘚𝘈. ⅀ rest
M (closed Sunday dinner) a la carte 1300/1700 – ⌷ 350 – **14 rm** 3000/4800.

🍴🍴 **Host. d'Arconati** ⌕ with rm, d'Arconatistraat 77, ☎ 569 35 15, Fax 569 35 04, 🏵, « Flowered garden » – 📺 ☎ ⇔ 🅿 – 🔒 60. 🆎 🖪 𝘝𝘐𝘚𝘈. ⅀ rm
closed February – **M** (closed Sunday dinner, Monday and Tuesday) a la carte approx. 1700 – **6 rm** ⌷ 1500/2500.

at Dworp (Tourneppe) by ⑨ : 16 km Ⓒ Beersel pop. 21 747 – ✉ 1653 Dworp – ✿ 0 2 :

🏨 **Kasteel Gravenhof** ⌕, Alsembergsesteenweg 676, ☎ 380 44 99, Fax 380 40 60, « Woodland setting », ⍕ – 📳 🛏 📺 ☎ 🅿 – 🔒 25-120. 🆎 🖪 𝘝𝘐𝘚𝘈. ⅀ rest
M (closed Saturday, Sunday and Bank Holidays) (Pub-rest.) a la carte 1000/1550 – ⌷ 375 – **24 rm** 2950/3950.

at Groot-Bijgaarden Ⓒ Dilbeek pop. 36 366 – ✉ 1702 Groot-Bijgaarden – ✿ 0 2 :

🍴🍴🍴🍴🍴 ✿✿ **De Bijgaarden,** l. Van Beverenstraat 20 (near castle), ☎ 466 44 85, Fax 463 08 11, ⍖, 🏵 – 🆎 ⓞ 🖪 𝘝𝘐𝘚𝘈
closed Saturday lunch, Sunday, 19 to 27 April and 16 August-7 September – **M** a la carte 2600/3300
Spec. Marinière de langoustines au thym et aux algues, Pigeon sauvage au jus (15 September-December), Tranche d'ananas au four, crème Chiboust.

XXX ❀ **Michel** (Coppens), Schepen Gossetlaan 31, ☏ 466 65 91, Fax 466 90 07, 斉 – **ⓟ**. ⓞ **⑪** E VISA
closed Sunday, Monday and August – **M** a la carte 1650/2250
Spec. St-Jacques marinées aux pommes and witlof (October-March), Blanc de cabillaud rôti sur la peau, Filet d'agneau au gâteau de légumes et à l'ail doux.

at Hoeilaart – pop. 9 300 – ✉ 1560 Hoeilaart – ✿ 0 2 :

XXXXX ❀❀ **Romeyer,** Groenendaalsesteenweg 109 (at Groenendaal), ☏ 657 05 81, Fax 657 27 73, « ≤ garden and private lake » – **ⓟ**. 𝔸𝔼 ⓞ E VISA
closed 1 to 17 August, February, Sunday dinner and Monday – **M** a la carte 2450/3850
Spec. Quenelles de sandre et queues d'écrevisses sauce Nantua, Dos de turbot au four beurre au Bouzy, Côtes d'agneau poêlées sauce périgourdine.

XXX **Aloyse Kloos,** Terhulpsesteenweg 2 (at Groenendaal), ☏ 657 37 37, 斉 – **ⓟ**. ⓞ E VISA
closed Sunday dinner, Monday and mid August-mid September – **M** 1600/2100.

at Huizingen by ⑨ : 12 km ☪ Beersel pop. 21 747 – ✉ 1654 Huizingen – ✿ 0 2 :

XX **Terborght,** Oud Dorp 16 (near E 19), ☏ 380 10 10, Fax 380 10 97, « Rustic interior » – **ⓟ**. 𝔸𝔼 ⓞ E VISA. ⅏
closed dinner Sunday and Tuesday, Monday, 1 to 21 August and 15 to 28 February – **M** a la carte 1850/2200.

at Kobbegem by ⑬ : 11 km ☪ Asse pop. 26 890 – ✉ 1730 Kobbegem – ✿ 0 2 :

XXX **Chalet Rose,** Brusselsesteenweg 331, ☏ 452 60 41, Fax 452 60 41, 斉 – **ⓟ**. 𝔸𝔼 ⓞ E VISA
M 1750.

XXX **De Plezanten Hof,** Broekstraat 2, ☏ 452 89 39 – **ⓟ**. 𝔸𝔼 ⓞ E VISA
closed dinner Tuesday and Sunday, Wednesday, 22 July-20 August and 1 week February – **M** a la carte 1700/2000.

at Kraainem – pop. 12 409 – ✉ 1950 Kraainem – ✿ 0 2 :

XX **d'Oude Pastorie,** Pastoorkesweg 1 (Park Jourdain), ☏ 720 63 46, « Lakeside setting in park » – **ⓟ** 𝔸𝔼 ⓞ E VISA. ⅏
closed Monday dinner, Thursday, week after Easter and mid August-mid September – **M** a la carte 1500/2000.

at Linkebeek – pop. 4 541 – ✉ 1630 Linkebeek – ✿ 0 2 :

XXX **Le Saint-Sébastien,** r. Station 90, ☏ 380 54 90, Fax 380 54 41 – ⅏ **ⓟ**. ⓞ E VISA
closed Monday, Tuesday and August – **M** a la carte 1600/1900.

at Machelen – pop. 11 177 – ✉ 1830 Machelen – ✿ 0 2 :

XXX ❀ **André D'Haese,** Heirbaan 210, ☏ 252 50 72, Fax 252 50 72, « Modern decor » – **ⓟ**. 𝔸𝔼 ⓞ E VISA. ⅏
closed Saturday lunch, Sunday, Bank Holidays, 3 weeks July and Christmas-New Year – **M** a la carte 2000/2600
Spec. Foie d'oie du gastronome, Soupe de homard norvégien au pistou, Ris de veau braisé à brun et à blanc.

at Meise by ① : 14 km – pop. 16 460 – ✉ 1860 Meise – ✿ 0 2 :

XX **Aub. Napoléon,** Bouchoutlaan 1, ☏ 269 30 78, Fax 269 79 98 – ⅏ **ⓟ**. 𝔸𝔼 ⓞ E VISA
closed August – **M** a la carte 1700/2400.

XX **Koen Van Loven,** Brusselsesteenweg 11, ☏ 270 05 77 – **ⓟ**. 𝔸𝔼 ⓞ E VISA. ⅏
closed Sunday dinner and Monday – **M** a la carte 1700/2200.

at Melsbroek ☪ Steenokkerzeel pop. 9 848 – ✉ 1820 Melsbroek – ✿ 0 2 :

XX **Boetfort,** Sellaerstraat 42, ☏ 751 64 00, Fax 751 74 06, « 17C mansion, park » – **ⓟ** – ♨ 25. 𝔸𝔼 ⓞ E VISA. ⅏
closed Wednesday dinner, Saturday lunch, Sunday, 1 week August and carnival week – **M** a la carte 1900/2700.

at Overijse by ⑦ : 16 km – pop. 23 389 – ✉ 3090 Overijse – ✿ 0 2 :

XXXX ❀❀ **Barbizon** (Deluc), Welriekendedreef 95 (at Jezus-Eik), ☏ 657 04 62, Fax 657 40 66, 斉, « Terrace and garden » – **ⓟ**. 𝔸𝔼 ⓞ E VISA
closed Tuesday, Wednesday, 11 February-11 March and 14 July-5 August – **M** a la carte 2250/3300
Spec. Homard en chemise, beurre "Barbizon", Crêpes parmentières au saumon fumé et raifort, Gibiers (September-January).

X **Istas,** Brusselsesteenweg 652 (NW : 2 km at Jezus-Eik), ☏ 657 05 11, 斉, Pub-rest. – **ⓟ**
closed Wednesday, Thursday and August – **M** a la carte approx. 1000.

at Schepdaal by ⑪ : 12 km ☪ Dilbeek pop. 36 366 – ✉ 1703 Schepdaal – ✿ 0 2 :

🏠 **Lien Zana** without rest., Ninoofsesteenweg 209, ☏ 569 65 25, Fax 569 64 64, ⬓ – 🛗 📺 ☎ **ⓟ** – ♨ 25. 𝔸𝔼 ⓞ E VISA
closed 24 December-2 January – **27 rm** ⬓ 2350/2950.

at Sint-Genesius-Rode (Rhode-St-Genèse) by ⑧ : 13 km - pop. 17 443 - ✉ 1640 Sint-Genesius-Rode - ☎ 0 2 :

Aub. de Waterloo without rest., chaussée de Waterloo 212, ☎ 358 35 80, Telex 24042, Fax 358 38 06 - |♦| TV ☎ P - 25-80. AE ⓓ E VISA.
89 rm ☐ 4450/5980.

at Strombeek-Bever C Grimbergen pop. 31 817 - ✉ 1853 Strombeek-Bever - ☎ 0 2 :

XX **Le Val Joli,** Leestbeekstraat 16, ☎ 460 65 43, Fax 460 04 00, « Terrace and garden » - P. AE ⓓ VISA
closed Monday, Tuesday and first 3 weeks October - **M** 990/1290.

at Vilvoorde (Vilvorde) - pop. 32 852 - ✉ 1800 Vilvoorde - ☎ 0 2 :

XX **Barbay,** Romeinsesteenweg 220 (Koningslo), ☎ 267 00 45, Fax 267 00 45 - AE ⓓ E VISA
closed Saturday lunch, Sunday, 15 July-15 August and 1 week New-Year - **M** a la carte 1400/1900.

at Vlezenbeek by ⑩ : 11 km C Sint-Pieters-Leeuw pop. 28 456 - ✉ 1602 Vlezenbeek - ☎ 0 2 :

XX **Philippe Verbaeys,** Dorp 49, ☎ 569 05 25, Fax 569 05 25, - AE ⓓ E VISA
closed Sunday, Monday, 2 weeks Easter and 2 weeks July - **M** 850/1950.

X **Aub. Le St-Esprit,** Postweg 250 (road to the castle of Gaasbeek), ☎ 532 42 18 - AE ⓓ E VISA
closed Sunday dinner, Monday, September and first 2 weeks March - **M** a la carte 1400/2300.

at Wemmel - pop. 13 591 - ✉ 1780 Wemmel - ☎ 0 2 :

XX **Parkhof,** Parklaan 7, ☎ 460 42 89, Fax 460 25 10, « Terrace » - P. AE ⓓ E VISA
closed Wednesday, Thursday and 15 August-3 September - **M** 1000/2200.

at Wezembeek-Oppem by ⑤ : 11 km - pop. 13 026 - ✉ 1970 Wezembeek-Oppem - ☎ 0 2 :

XXX **L'Aub. Saint-Pierre,** Sint-Pietersplein 8, ☎ 731 21 79 - AE ⓓ E VISA
closed Saturday lunch, Sunday, Bank Holidays, mid July-mid August and 24 December-2 January - **M** a la carte approx. 1800.

at Zaventem - pop. 25 738 - ✉ 1930 Zaventem - ☎ 0 2 :

Sheraton Airport, at airport (NE by A 201), ☎ 725 10 00, Telex 27085, Fax 725 11 55 - |♦| rm TV ☎ ♿ P - 25-520. AE ⓓ E VISA. rest
M Concorde a la carte 1600/2550 - ☐ 650 - **290 rm** 7300/8800.

XX ✿ **Stockmansmolen** 1st floor, H. Henneaulaan 164, ☎ 725 34 34, Fax 725 75 05, « Former watermill » - P. AE ⓓ E VISA.
closed Saturday, Sunday and Bank Holidays - **M** a la carte 1800/2600
Spec. Ravioli de barbue sauce vanillée, Cassolette de homard aux perles de légumes, Tarte chaude de pêches à la crème d'amandes.

Berlare 9290 Oost-Vlaanderen 213 ⑤ and 409 ③ - pop. 12 670 - ☎ 0 52 - 38 km.

XXX ✿✿ **'t Laurierblad** (Van Cauteren) (new hotel planned in annex), Dorp 4, ☎ 42 48 01, Fax 42 59 97 - P. AE ⓓ E VISA
closed 3 weeks August and Monday March-August - **M** a la carte 1500/2700
Spec. Cabillaud rôti et pommes de terre à l'huile de truffes blanches, Salade de langoustines, foie de canard et filet d'Anvers, Fondant de ris et tête de veau aux truffes.

Genval 1322 Brabant C Rixensart pop. 20 611 213 ⑲ and 409 ⑬ - ☎ 0 2 - 21 km.

Château du Lac, av. du Lac 87, ☎ 654 11 22, Fax 653 62 00, ≤ lake and woodland, - |♦| TV ☎ P - 30-1000. AE ⓓ E VISA
M see rest. **Le Trèfle à 4** below - **38 rm** ☐ 7400/8600.

XXXX ✿✿ **Le Trèfle à 4** (Haquin) - at H. Château du Lac, av. du Lac 87, ☎ 654 07 98, Fax 653 62 00, ≤ lake and woodland - P. AE ⓓ E VISA
closed Monday, Tuesday and 12 January-13 February - **M** a la carte 2500/2900
Spec. Poêlée de langoustines, buisson de légumes et herbes frites, Côtelette de saumon au beurre d'olives, Mousse de homard en vinaigrette d'artichauts.

Michelin Green Guides in English

Austria
Canada
England : The West Country
France
Germany
Great Britain
Greece
Italy
London
Mexico
Netherlands
New England
New York City
Portugal
Rome
Scotland
Spain
Switzerland
Washington

See : Old Antwerp★★★ : Cathedral★★★ and Market Square★ (Grote Markt) FY – Rubens' House★★ (Rubenshuis) GZ – Butchers' House★ (Vleeshuis) : Musical instruments★ FY D – Interior★ of the St. James' church (St-Jacobskerk) GY – The port★★★ (Haven) 🚢 FY – Zoo★★ (Dierentuin) EU – St. Charles Borromeo's Church★ (St-Carolus-Borromeuskerk) GY – St. Paul's Church (St-Pauluskerk) : interior★ and wood-carving★ FY.

Museums : Royal Art Gallery★★★ (Koninklijk Museum voor Schone Kunsten) CV – Plantin-Moretus★★★ (ancient printing-office) FZ – Mayer Van den Bergh★★ (Brueghel) GZ – Maritime "Steen"★ (Nationaal Scheepvaartmuseum Steen) FY **M¹** – Rockox House★ (Rockoxhuis) GY **M²** – Open-air Museum of Sculpture Middelheim★ (Openluchtmuseum voor Beeldhouwkunst) – Museum of Photography★ – Etnographic Museum★ FY **M¹⁰**.

🏌 🏌 at Kapellen by ② : 22 km, G. Capiaulei 2, ℘ (0 3) 666 84 56 - 🏌 at Aartselaar by ⑩ : 10 km, Kasteel Cleydael, ℘ (0 3) 887 00 79 - 🏌 at Wommelgem by ⑥ : 9 km, Uilenbaan 15, ℘ (0 3) 353 02 92 - 🏌 🏌 at Broechem by ⑥ : 12 km, Kasteel Bossenstein, ℘ (0 3) 485 64 46.

🛈 Grote Markt 15, ℘ 232 01 03 – Koningin Astridplein (Pavilion), ℘ 233 05 70 – Tourist association of the province, Karel Oomsstraat 11, ⊠ 216 28 10.

Brussels 48 ⑩ – Amsterdam 159 ④ – Luxemburg 261 ⑨ – Rotterdam 103 ④.

Plans on following pages

Room prices are subject to the addition of a local tax of 6 %

Town Centre

Alfa De Keyser, De Keyserlei 66, ⊠ 2018, ℘ 234 01 35, Telex 34219, Fax 232 39 70, 𝄠, ⇌, 🅜 - 🔋 ⇆ rm 🔲 🕿 - 🔏 25-120. 🕮 ⓞ 🈁 𝗩𝗜𝗦𝗔. ✄ rest EU **b**
M a la carte 1300/1750 – **117 rm** ⊊ 5050/7600.

Pullman Park, Desguinlei 94, ⊠ 2018, ℘ 216 48 00, Telex 33368, Fax 216 47 12, 𝄠, ⇌ - 🔋 ⇆ rm 🔲 🕿 ⇌ - 🔏 25-450. 🕮 ⓞ 🈁 𝗩𝗜𝗦𝗔. ✄ rest
M Tiffany's *(closed Saturday lunch)* a la carte 1800/2400 – ⊊ 525 – **216 rm** 3700/7000.

Switel, Copernicuslaan 2, ⊠ 2018, ℘ 231 67 80, Telex 33965, Fax 233 02 90, 𝄠, ⇌, 🅂, ✄ - 🔋 ⇆ rm 🔲 🕿 ⇌ - 🔏 25-1000. 🕮 ⓞ 🈁 𝗩𝗜𝗦𝗔 EV **a**
M a la carte 1300/2400 – ⊊ 510 – **310 rm** 5045/5800.

Carlton, Quinten Matsijslei 25, ⊠ 2018, ℘ 231 15 15, Telex 31072, Fax 225 30 90, ⇐ - 🔋 ⇆ rm 🔲 🔲 🕿 ⇌ - 🔏 30-100. 🕮 ⓞ 🈁 𝗩𝗜𝗦𝗔. ✄ rest DV **v**
M *(closed 1 to 21 August, 24 December-3 January, dinner Friday and Sunday and Saturday lunch)* a la carte approx. 1900 – **127 rm** ⊊ 4850/6250.

Plaza without rest., Charlottalei 43, ⊠ 2018, ℘ 218 92 40, Telex 31531, Fax 218 88 23 – 🔋 🔲 🕿. 🕮 ⓞ 🈁 𝗩𝗜𝗦𝗔 EV **v**
⊊ 350 – **79 rm** 3100/3900.

Alfa Empire without rest., Appelmansstraat 31, ⊠ 2018, ℘ 231 47 55, Telex 33909, Fax 233 40 60 – 🔋 ⇆ 🔲 🕿. 🕮 ⓞ 🈁 𝗩𝗜𝗦𝗔 DU **s**
70 rm ⊊ 5450/6550.

Alfa Congress, Plantin en Moretuslei 136, ⊠ 2018, ℘ 235 30 00, Telex 31959, Fax 235 52 31 – 🔋 ⇆ rm 🔲 🕿 ⇌ ⓟ – 🔏 30-70. 🕮 ⓞ 🈁 𝗩𝗜𝗦𝗔. ✄ EV **s**
M *(closed Saturday, Sunday, Bank Holidays and late December)* a la carte 1200/1500 – **66 rm** ⊊ 3850/4300.

Firean ✄ without rest., Karel Oomsstraat 6, ⊠ 2018, ℘ 237 02 60, Fax 238 11 68, « Period residence, Art-Deco style » – 🔋 🔲 🕿 ⇌. 🕮 ⓞ 🈁 𝗩𝗜𝗦𝗔. ✄
closed 1 to 20 August and Christmas-New Year – **12 rm** ⊊ 3100/4100.

Residence without rest., St-Jacobsmarkt 85, ℘ 232 76 75, Fax 233 73 28 – 🔋 🔲 🕿 ⇌ ⓟ. 🕮 ⓞ 🈁 𝗩𝗜𝗦𝗔. ✄ DU **f**
⊊ 400 – **19 rm** 3500/6000.

Antwerp Tower without rest, with 11 suites in annexe, Van Ertbornstraat 10, ⊠ 2018, ℘ 234 01 20, Telex 34478, Fax 233 39 43 – 🔋 🔲 🖨 ⇌. 🕮 ⓞ 🈁 𝗩𝗜𝗦𝗔. ✄ DU **b**
39 rm ⊊ 3050/3800.

Fouquets 1st floor, De Keyserlei 17, ⊠ 2018, ℘ 233 97 42, Fax 226 16 88, 🍽, Open until 11 p.m. – 🔲. 🕮 ⓞ 🈁 𝗩𝗜𝗦𝗔 DU **a**
closed 15 July-August – **M** a la carte 1300/2000.

Loncin, Markgravelei 127, ℘ 248 29 89, Fax 248 38 66, Open until midnight – 🔲. ⓞ 🈁 𝗩𝗜𝗦𝗔
closed 1 to 15 July, lunch Saturday and Sunday, Tuesday and Wednesday – **M** a la carte 1850/2600.

Corum, Italiëlei 177, ℘ 232 23 44, Fax 232 24 41 – ⓟ. 🕮 ⓞ 🈁 𝗩𝗜𝗦𝗔 DT **b**
closed lunch Saturday and Sunday, Monday and July – **M** a la carte 1300/2050.

Sawadee, 1st floor, Britselei 16, ℘ 233 08 59, Telex 71068, Fax 231 37 59, Thaï cuisine, « Ancient residence » – 🕮 ⓞ 🈁 𝗩𝗜𝗦𝗔. ✄ DV **b**
closed Tuesday and August – **M** a la carte approx. 1100.

De Poterne, Desguinlei 186, ⊠ 2018, ℘ 238 28 24, Fax 238 28 24 – 🕮 ⓞ 🈁
closed Saturday lunch, Sunday, Bank Holidays, 21 July-15 August and 24 December-1 January – **M** a la carte 1800/2300.

Liang's Garden, Markgravelei 141, ⊠ 2018, ℘ 237 22 22, Fax 248 38 34, Chinese cuisine – 🔲. 🕮 ⓞ 🈁 𝗩𝗜𝗦𝗔. ✄
closed 2 to 19 August, 24 December-1 January and Sunday – **M** a la carte 1200/1850.

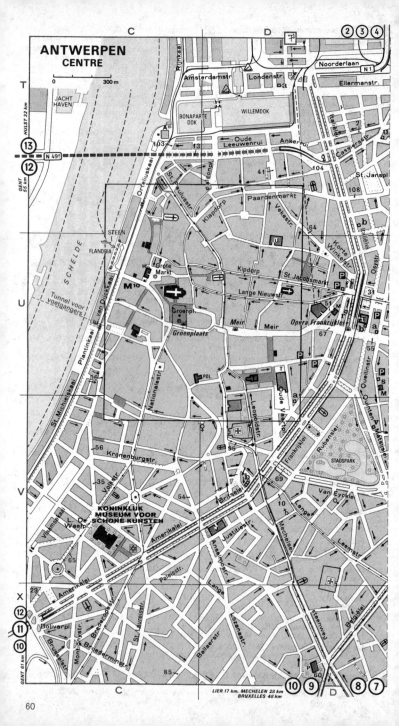

Continued on next page

61

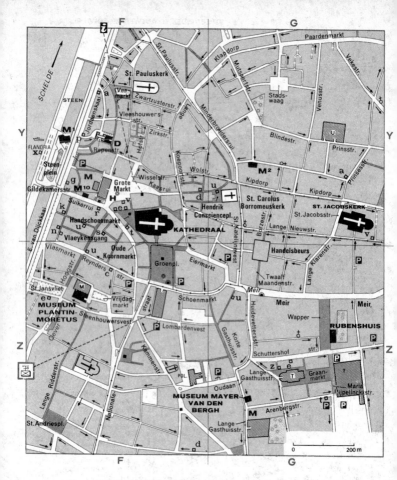

XX **De Barbarie,** Van Breestraat 4, ✉ 2018, ℰ 232 81 98, � – 🖭 **E** 𝘝𝘐𝘚𝘈
closed Sunday, Monday and September – **M** a la carte 1750/2500.
DV **b**

XX **Blue Phoenix,** Frankrijklei 14, ℰ 233 33 77, Fax 233 88 46, Chinese cuisine – ▤. 🖭 **E** 𝘝𝘐𝘚𝘈.
🌺
closed Monday and August – **M** 750/1500.
DU **r**

X ⊛ **De Zeste** (Garnich R.), Lange Dijkstraat 36, ✉ 2060, ℰ 233 45 49 – ▤. 🖭 ⊙ **E** 𝘝𝘐𝘚𝘈
closed Saturday lunch, Sunday, Monday, 3 weeks August, Christmas and New Year – **M** (booking essential) a la carte 1750/2350
DT **u**
Spec. St-Jacques aux poireaux, Ris de veau aux champignons des bois, St-Pierre à la tomate et au basilic.

X **Milano,** Statiestraat 15, ✉ 2018, ℰ 232 67 43, Partly Italian cuisine, open until 2 a.m. – ▤. 🖭 ⊙ **E** 𝘝𝘐𝘚𝘈
EU **q**
closed July – **M** a la carte 800/1700.

X **'t Lammeke,** Lange Lobroekstraat 51 (opposite slaughterhouse), ✉ 2060, ℰ 236 79 86, Fax 271 05 16 – ▤. 🖭 ⊙ **E** 𝘝𝘐𝘚𝘈
closed 10 to 30 August, 21 to 31 December, lunch Saturday and Monday, Sunday and Bank Holidays – **M** a la carte 1000/1850.

Old Antwerp

🏠 **De Rosier** ⅏ without rest., Rosier 23, ℰ 225 01 40, Telex 33697, Fax 231 41 11, « Former 17C residence », ⩲, 🏊, 🌳 – 🛗 📺 ☎ 🚗. 🖭 ⊙ **E** 𝘝𝘐𝘚𝘈
FZ **d**
closed late December – ☲ 600 – **12 rm** 6500/15000.

🏠 **Alfa Theater,** Arenbergstraat 30, ℰ 231 17 20, Telex 33910, Fax 233 88 58 – 🛗 ↔ rm ▤ rest 📺 ☎ – 🔒 25. 🖭 ⊙ **E** 𝘝𝘐𝘚𝘈. 🌺
GZ **t**
M *(closed Saturday, Sunday and Bank Holidays)* a la carte 1400/1800 – **85 rm** ☲ 4400/6800.

🏠 **Villa Mozart,** Handschoenmarkt 3, ℰ 231 30 31, Fax 231 56 85, �, ⩲ – 🛗 📺 ☎ – 🔒 25. 🖭 ⊙ **E** 𝘝𝘐𝘚𝘈
FY **e**
M a la carte 1300/1800 – **25 rm** ☲ 5500/8500.

🏠 **Prinse** ⅏ without rest., Keizerstraat 63, ℰ 226 40 50, Fax 225 11 48 – 🛗 ▤ 📺 ☎ 🚗 – 🔒 25-120. 🖭 𝘝𝘐𝘚𝘈. 🌺
GY **a**
30 rm ☲ 2900/5000.

🏠 **Antigone** without rest., Jordaenskaai 11, ℰ 231 66 77, Fax 231 37 74 – 🛗 📺 ☎. 🖭 ⊙ **E** 𝘝𝘐𝘚𝘈. 🌺
FY **a**
17 rm ☲ 3000/3500.

🏠 **Arcade** without rest., Meistraat 39 (Theaterplein), ℰ 231 88 30, Telex 31104, Fax 234 29 21 – 🛗 📺 ☎ 🚫 – 🔒 75. 🖭 **E** 𝘝𝘐𝘚𝘈
DV **a**
150 rm ☲ 2650/3200.

XXXX ⊛⊛ **La Pérouse,** Steenplein (pontoon), ℰ 231 31 51, Telex 35529, Fax 231 31 02, ≼, « Anchored vessel » – ▤ 🅿. 🖭 ⊙ **E** 𝘝𝘐𝘚𝘈. 🌺
FY **x**
closed Sunday, Monday and 15 July - August – **M** a la carte 2100/2900
Spec. Parmentier de ris et langue de veau confite, Rouelle de sandre, bouillon beurré aux aromates, Filet d'agneau cuit à l'orange et au basilic.

XXX ⊛⊛ **Sir Anthony Van Dijck** (Paesbrugghe), Oude Koornmarkt 16 (Vlaeykensgang), ℰ 231 61 70, Fax 225 11 69, « Situated in a 16C lane » – 🖭 ⊙ **E** 𝘝𝘐𝘚𝘈. 🌺
FY **s**
closed Saturday, Sunday, Bank Holidays and 20 to 24 April, 3 to 21 August, 24 to 31 December – **M** a la carte 2100/3050
Spec. Blanc de poularde farci au foie gras et truffes, Matelote de filets de sole aux artichauts et champignons, Potage léger de langoustines au curry.

XXX **Den Gulden Greffoen,** Hoogstraat 37, ℰ 231 50 46, Fax 233 20 39, « In a 15C house » – ▤. 🖭 ⊙ **E** 𝘝𝘐𝘚𝘈. 🌺
FZ **u**
closed Sunday except Bank Holidays, lunch Monday and Tuesday and 3 weeks August – **M** 1750/2500.

XXX **La Rade,** 1st floor, Van Dijckkaai 8, ℰ 233 37 37, Fax 233 49 63, « Former 19C freemason's lodge » – 🖭 ⊙ **E** 𝘝𝘐𝘚𝘈
FY **g**
closed Saturday lunch, Sunday, Bank Holidays, 22 February-1 March and 6 to 26 July – **M** a la carte 1800/2600.

XXX ⊛ **'t Fornuis** (Segers), Reyndersstraat 24, ℰ 233 62 70, « 17C house, rustic interior » – 🖭 ⊙ **E** 𝘝𝘐𝘚𝘈. 🌺
FZ **c**
closed Saturday, Sunday, last 3 weeks August and Christmas-New Year – **M** a la carte 2000/2500
Spec. Sole à la rhubarbe, Escalope de saumon au miel, Rognon de veau rôti à la crème de thym.

XX **Petrus,** Kelderstraat 1, ℰ 225 27 34 – ▤. 🖭 ⊙ **E** 𝘝𝘐𝘚𝘈
GZ **z**
closed lunch Saturday and Sunday, Monday, 3 weeks July and carnival week – **M** a la carte 1600/2100.

XX **Neuze Neuze,** Wijngaardstraat 19, ℰ 232 57 83, Fax 225 27 38 – 🖭 ⊙ **E** 𝘝𝘐𝘚𝘈. 🌺 FY **d**
closed Sunday and 20 July-9 August – **M** a la carte 1650/2000.

XX **De Kerselaar,** Grote Pieter Potstraat 22, ℰ 233 59 69, Fax 233 11 49 – ▤. 🖭 ⊙ **E** 𝘝𝘐𝘚𝘈
closed lunch Saturday and Monday, Sunday, 6 to 26 July and 23 to 30 December – **M** a la carte 1800/2250.
FY **n**

XX **'t Silveren Claverblat,** Grote Pieter Potstraat 16, ℰ 231 33 88 – 🖭 ⊙ **E** 𝘝𝘐𝘚𝘈. 🌺
closed 1 to 10 March, 1 to 15 September, Tuesday and Saturday lunch – **M** 1950. FY **k**

XX **De Koperen Ketel,** Wiegstraat 5, ℰ 233 12 74 – 🆎 ⓞ ⋐ 𝘝𝘐𝘚𝘈 GZ **u**
closed Sunday and Bank Holidays – **M** 1200/2000.

XX **P. Preud'homme,** Suikerrui 28, ℰ 233 42 00, Fax 233 42 00, Open until 11 p.m. – ⋙ ▤
🆎 ⓞ ⋐ 𝘝𝘐𝘚𝘈. ⋘ FY **r**
closed Tuesday October-May – **M** a la carte 1500/3100.

XX **De Gulden Beer,** Grote Markt 14, ℰ 226 08 41, ⋒, Partly Italian cuisine – ▤. 🆎 ⓞ ⋐
𝘝𝘐𝘚𝘈. ⋘ FY **v**
closed Wednesday – **M** a la carte 1150/1850.

XX **De Manie,** H. Conscienceplein 3, ℰ 232 64 38 – 🆎 ⓞ ⋐ 𝘝𝘐𝘚𝘈 GY **u**
closed Wednesday, Sunday and 16 August-2 September – **M** a la carte 1600/2000.

XX **Les Larmes du Tigre,** Vleeshuisstraat 1, ℰ 226 21 90, Thaï cuisine, « Elegant Asiatic
installation » – 🆎 ⓞ ⋐ 𝘝𝘐𝘚𝘈 FY **p**
closed Monday and Saturday lunch – **M** a la carte 850/1300.

XX **VIP Diners,** Lange Nieuwstraat 95, ℰ 233 13 17 – 🆎 ⓞ ⋐ 𝘝𝘐𝘚𝘈 GY **v**
closed 2 weeks Easter and last 2 weeks July – **M** a la carte 1100/1700.

XX **Het Nieuwe Palinghuis,** St-Jansvliet 14, ℰ 231 74 45, Seafood – ▤. 🆎 ⓞ ⋐ 𝘝𝘐𝘚𝘈
closed Monday, Tuesday, June and first 2 weeks January – **M** a la carte 1300/2200. FZ **e**

XX **Fourchette,** Schuttershofstraat 28, ℰ 231 33 35 – 🆎 ⓞ ⋐ 𝘝𝘐𝘚𝘈 GZ **e**
closed Saturday lunch, Sunday, Monday and last 2 weeks July-first 2 weeks August – **M** a la
carte 1200/1700.

XX ⊛ **De Matelote** (Garnich D.), Haarstraat 9, ℰ 231 32 07, Seafood – 🆎 ⓞ ⋐ 𝘝𝘐𝘚𝘈 FY **u**
closed lunch Saturday and Monday, Sunday and July – **M** a la carte 1500/2900
Spec. "Steak"de saumon fumé maison, Sole à la vinaigrette de pommes de terre écrasées, Fruits
rouges à la meringue gratinée (July-October).

X **In de Schaduw van de Kathedraal,** Handschoenmarkt 17, ℰ 232 40 14, Fax 231 78 47,
⋒, Mussels in season – 🆎 ⓞ ⋐ 𝘝𝘐𝘚𝘈. ⋘ FY **e**
closed Monday October-May, Tuesday and February – **M** a la carte 1400/2300.

X **Rooden Hoed,** Oude Koornmarkt 25, ℰ 233 28 44, Mussels in season, Antwerp atmosphere – 🆎 𝘝𝘐𝘚𝘈. ⋘ FY **t**
closed Wednesday, Thursday, 16 June-16 July and 26 February-8 March – **M** a la carte
1100/1800.

Suburbs

North – ✉ 2030 :

🏨 **Novotel,** Luithagen-Haven 6, ℰ 542 03 20, Telex 32488, Fax 541 70 93, ⋝, ⋘ – ▮ ⋙ rm
📺 ☎ ⅍ ℗ – 🏛 25-200. 🆎 ⓞ ⋐ 𝘝𝘐𝘚𝘈. ⋘ rest
M (open until midnight) a la carte 800/1650 – ⋤ 375 – **119 rm** 3200/3850.

South – ✉ 2020 :

🏨 **Holiday Inn Crowne Plaza,** G. Legrellelaan 10, ℰ 237 29 00, Telex 33843, Fax 216 02 96,
⌶ – ▮ ⋙ rm ▤ 📺 ☎ ⟿ ℗ – 🏛 25-750. 🆎 ⓞ ⋐ 𝘝𝘐𝘚𝘈
M (open until 11 p.m.) a la carte 1700/2200 – ⋤ 850 – **254 rm** 7500/8000.

at Borgerhout ⓒ Antwerpen – ✉ 2140 Borgerhout – ✆ 03 :

🏨 **Scandic Crown,** Luitenant Lippenslaan 66, ℰ 235 91 91, Telex 34479, Fax 235 08 96, ⋸s,
▧ – ▮ ⋙ rm 📺 ☎ ℗ – 🏛 25-100. 🆎 ⓞ ⋐ 𝘝𝘐𝘚𝘈. ⋘ rest
M 750/2500 – ⋤ 450 – **203 rm** 4200/5000.

at Deurne ⓒ Antwerpen – ✉ 2100 Deurne – ✆ 03 :

XX **Périgord,** Turnhoutsebaan 273, ℰ 325 52 00 – ℗. 🆎 ⓞ ⋐ 𝘝𝘐𝘚𝘈. ⋘
closed Tuesday dinner, Wednesday, Saturday lunch, July and carnival week – **M** 1250.

at Ekeren ⓒ Antwerpen – ✉ 2180 Ekeren – ✆ 03 :

XX ⊛ **Hof de Bist** (Mme Vercammen), Veltwijcklaan 258, ℰ 664 61 30, Fax 664 67 24 – ℗. 🆎
ⓞ ⋐
closed Sunday, Monday and August – **M** (booking essential) a la carte 2000/2400
Spec. Foie d'oie maison aux raisins, Lasagne de homard sauce aux truffes, Selle d'agneau fumée
aux petits oignons et lardons.

at Merksem ⓒ Antwerpen – ✉ 2170 Merksem – ✆ 03 :

XXX **Maritime,** Bredabaan 978, ℰ 646 22 23, Fax 646 22 71, ⋒, Seafood – ℗. 🆎 ⓞ ⋐ 𝘝𝘐𝘚𝘈.
⋘
closed Sunday – **M** a la carte 1050/2000.

at Wilrijk ⓒ Antwerpen – ✉ 2610 Wilrijk – ✆ 03 :

XX **Schans XV,** Moerelei 155, ℰ 828 45 64, Fax 828 93 29, ⋒, « Early 20C redoubt » – ⋙
℗. 🆎 ⓞ ⋐ 𝘝𝘐𝘚𝘈. ⋘
*closed Thursday dinner, Saturday lunch, Sunday, Bank Holidays, 2 weeks August, 2 weeks
February and after 8.30 p.m.* – **M** a la carte 2000/2600.

XX **Bistrot,** Doornstraat 186, ℰ 829 17 29 – 🆎 ⓞ ⋐ 𝘝𝘐𝘚𝘈
closed Monday, Tuesday, Saturday lunch and late July-late August – **M** 795.

Environs

at Aartselaar : by ⑩ : 10 km – pop. 13 700 – ✉ 2630 Aartselaar – ☻ 0 3 :

XXXX **Host. Kasteelhoeve Groeninghe** with rm, Kontichsesteenweg 78, ☎ 457 95 86, Fax 458 13 68, ≤, ☞, « Restored Flemish farm, country atmosphere », ☞ – 📺 ☎ 🅿 – 🄰 25-120. 🄰🄴 ⑩ 🄴 ⱽⁱˢᵃ ※
closed 15 to 31 July and 20 December-4 January – **M** *(closed Saturday lunch and Sunday)*
a la carte 2100/2700 – ☲ 500 – **8 rm** 3900/6000.

XXX **Lindenbos,** Boomsesteenweg 139, ☎ 888 09 65, Fax 844 47 58, « Converted mansion with park and lake » – 🅿. 🄰🄴 ⑩ 🄴 ⱽⁱˢᵃ ※
closed Monday and August – **M** a la carte 1800/2400.

at Brasschaat : by ② and ③ : 11 km – pop. 34 065 – ✉ 2930 Brasschaat – ☻ 0 3 :

XXX ❀ **Het Villasdal** (Van Raes), Kapelsesteenweg 480, ☎ 664 58 21, Fax 605 08 42, ☞ – 🅿. 🄰🄴 ⑩ 🄴 ⱽⁱˢᵃ
closed Saturday lunch, Sunday dinner, Monday, 13 July-4 August and 20 January-4 February – **M** a la carte 1900/2500
Spec. Petit gâteau de saumon fumé et saumon frais au caviar, Sole farcie aux poireaux, crevettes grises et moules au safran, Ris de veau aux champignons sauvages et jus de truffes.

XXX **Halewijn,** Donksesteenweg 212 (Ekeren-Donk), ☎ 647 20 10, ☞ – ⑩ 🄴 ⱽⁱˢᵃ
closed Monday – **M** a la carte 1400/2100.

at Kapellen : by ② : 15,5 km – pop. 23 683 – ✉ 2950 Kapellen – ☻ 0 3 :

XXX ❀ **De Bellefleur** (Buytaert), Antwerpsesteenweg 253, ☎ 664 67 19, Fax 665 02 01, ☞, « Winter garden » – 🅿. 🄰🄴 ⑩ 🄴 ⱽⁱˢᵃ
closed Saturday, Sunday, July and 2 weeks February – **M** a la carte 1700/2700
Spec. Crabe farci "Kwan Yu", Rôti de turbot aux champignons des bois, Soufflé chaud au chocolat amer et aux poires.

at Kontich : by ⑧ : 12 km – pop. 18 530 – ✉ 2550 Kontich – ☻ 0 3 :

XXX **Carême,** Koningin Astridlaan 114, ☎ 457 63 04, Fax 457 93 02, ☞ – 🅿. 🄰🄴 ⑩ 🄴 ⱽⁱˢᵃ
closed Saturday lunch, Sunday, Monday dinner and July – **M** a la carte 2050/2750.

XXX **Alexander's,** Mechelsesteenweg 318, ☎ 457 26 31, Fax 457 26 31 – 🅿. 🄰🄴 ⑩ 🄴 ⱽⁱˢᵃ ※
closed Sunday dinner and Monday – **M** 1595.

at Schoten 10 km – pop. 31 042 – ✉ 2900 Schoten – ☻ 0 3 :

XXX **Uilenspiegel,** Brechtsebaan 277 (on N 115), ☎ 651 61 45, ☞, « Terrace and garden » – 🅿. 🄰🄴 🄴 ⱽⁱˢᵃ
closed Sunday, Monday and 1 week January – **M** a la carte 1600/2300.

XXX **Kleine Barreel,** Bredabaan 1147, ☎ 645 85 84, Fax 645 85 03 – 🍽 🅿. 🄰🄴 ⑩ 🄴 ⱽⁱˢᵃ ※ **M** 1100/1900.

XX **De Witte Raaf,** Horstebaan 97, ☎ 658 86 64, ☞ – 🅿. 🄰🄴 ⑩ 🄴 ⱽⁱˢᵃ
closed Tuesday dinner, Wednesday, Saturday lunch, 17 August-3 September and 1 to 10 January – **M** 1500/2000.

at Wijnegem by ⑤ : 10 km – pop. 8 302 – ✉ 2110 Wijnegem – ☻ 0 3 :

XXX **Ter Vennen,** Merksemsebaan 278, ☎ 326 20 60, Fax 326 38 47, ☞, « Small farmhouse with elegant interior » – 🅿. 🄰🄴 ⑩ 🄴 ⱽⁱˢᵃ
closed Sunday – **M** a la carte 1750/2700.

Kruiningen Zeeland (Netherlands) © Reimerswaal pop. 19 434 ②①② ⑬ ⑭ and ④⓪⑧ ⑯ – ☻ 0 1130 – 56 km.

🏤 **Le Manoir** ⬠, Zandweg 2 (W : 1 km), ✉ 4416 NA, ☎ 17 53 (will be 8 17 53), Fax 17 63 (will be 8 17 63), ≤, ☞ – 📺 ☎ 🅿. 🄰🄴 ⑩ 🄴 ⱽⁱˢᵃ
closed 15 January-15 February – **M** see rest. **Inter Scaldes** below – ☲ 10 – **12 rm** 350/400.

XXX ❀❀ **Inter Scaldes** (Mme Boudeling) – at H. Le Manoir, Zandweg 2 (W : 1 km), ✉ 4416 NA, ☎ 17 53 (will be 8 17 53), Fax 17 63 (will be 8 17 63), ☞, « Terrace-veranda overlooking English-style garden » – 🅿. 🄰🄴 ⑩ 🄴 ⱽⁱˢᵃ
closed Monday, Tuesday and 15 January-15 February – **M** a la carte 132/185
Spec. Homard fumé, sauce au caviar, Bar légèrement fumé à la tomate et basilic, Turbot en robe de truffes et son beurre.

Pleasant hotels and restaurants are shown in the Guide by a red sign.
Please send us the names of any where you have enjoyed your stay.
Your **Michelin Guide** will be even better.

🏤🏤 ... 🏠
XXXXX ... X

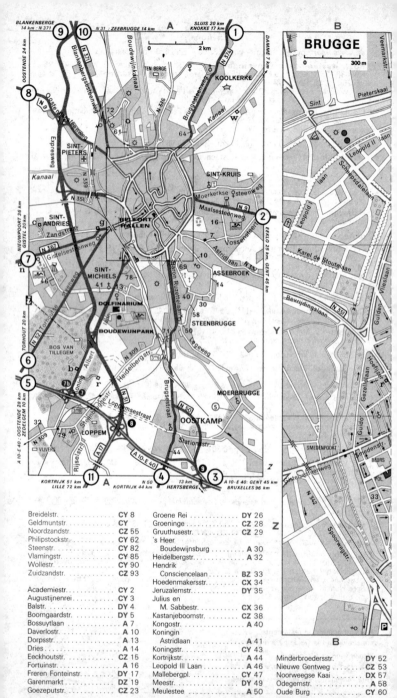

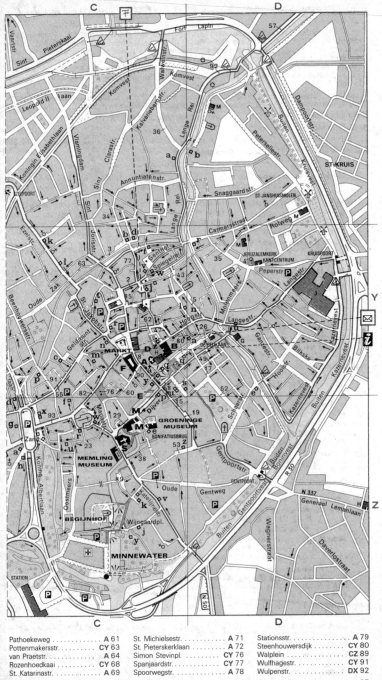

BRUGES (BRUGGE) 8000 West-Vlaanderen 🄩🄩🄩 ③ and 🄰🄾🄾 ② – pop. 117 653 agglomeration – 🅶 🔾 50.

See : Trips on the canals★★★ (Boottocht) CY E – Historic centre and canals★★★ – Procession of the Holy Blood★★★ – Market square★★ (Markt) : Belfry and Halles★★★ (Belfort-Hallen) CY F – Market-town★★ (Burg) CY D – Beguinage★★ (Begijnhof) CZ – Basilica of the Holy Blood★ CY A – Church of Our Lady★ (O.L. Vrouwekerk) : tower★★, statue of the Madonna★★, tombstone of Mary of Burgundy★★ CZ S – Rosery quay (Rozenhoedkaai) ≤★★ CY – Dijver ≤★★ CZ – St. Boniface bridge (Bonifaciusbrug) : site★★ CZ – Chimney of the "Brugse Vrije" in the Court of Justice (Gerechtshof) CY B.

Museums : Groeninge★★★ (Stedelijk Museum voor Schone Kunsten) CZ – Memling★★★ (St. John's Hospital) CZ – Gruuthuse★ CZ M¹ – Brangwyn★ (Brangwynmuseum) CZ M⁴.

Envir : Zedelgem : baptismal font★ in the St. Lawrence's church by ⑥ : 10,5 km.

🄸🄸 at Damme NE : 7 km, Doornstraat 16, 🅶 (0 50) 33 35 72.

🄱 Burg 11, 🅶 44 86 86 – Tourist association of the province, Kasteel Tillegem ✉ 8200, 🅶 38 02 96.

Brussels 96 ③ – Ghent 45 ③ – Lille 72 ⑪ – Ostend 28 ⑤.

Plans on preceding pages

🄰🄰🄰🄰 **Holiday Inn Crowne Plaza** ⑤, Burg 10, 🅶 34 58 34, Telex 81461, Fax 34 56 15, ≤, « Interesting medieval remains and objects in basement », 🄵🄳, ⇌, 🔲 – 🄸 🈺 rm 🟦 📺 🍴 🅖 ♿ ♿ – 🄰 65-420. 🄰🄴 ⑩ 🄴 🆅🆂🄰. 🈺 CY **z**
M 't Kapittel *(closed Sunday dinner and Monday)* a la carte 950/1750 – ⌷ 475 – **96 rm** 6200.

🄰🄰🄰🄰 **Pullman,** Boeveriestraat 2, 🅶 34 09 71, Telex 81369, Fax 34 40 53, ⇌, 🔲, 🍴 – 🄸 🈺 🟦 📺 🍴 🅖 ♿ – 🄰 35-200. 🄰🄴 ⑩ 🄴 🆅🆂🄰. 🈺 rest CZ **a**
M 950/2350 – **155 rm** 4500/5500.

🄰🄰🄰 **De Tuilerieën** without rest., Dijver 7, 🅶 34 36 91, Fax 34 04 00, ≤, ⇌, 🔲 – 🄸 📺 🍴 ♿ – 🄰 45. 🄰🄴 ⑩ 🄴 🆅🆂🄰. CYZ **p**
26 rm ⌷ 5100/10250.

🄰🄰🄰 **Oud Huis Amsterdam** ⑤ without rest., Spiegelrei 3, 🅶 34 18 10, Telex 83121, Fax 33 88 91, ≤, « 17C residence, former Dutch trading post » – 🄸 📺 🍴 ♿ – 🄰 25. 🄰🄴 ⑩ 🄴 🆅🆂🄰. 🈺 CY **w**
22 rm ⌷ 3750/7500.

🄰🄰🄰 **De Orangerie** ⑤ without rest., Karthuizerinnenstraat 10, 🅶 34 16 49, Telex 82443, Fax 33 30 16, « Period canalside residence » – 🄸 📺 🍴 ♿. 🄰🄴 ⑩ 🄴 🆅🆂🄰. CY **y**
18 rm ⌷ 5100/8250.

🄰🄰🄰 **Academie,** Wijngaardstraat 7, 🅶 33 22 66, Fax 33 21 66 – 🄸 🟦 rest 📺 🍴 ♿ ↩ – 🄰 30-300. 🄰🄴 ⑩ 🄴 🆅🆂🄰. 🈺 CZ **k**
M a la carte approx. 750 – **34 rm** ⌷ 3700/4350.

🄰🄰🄰 **Karos** without rest., Hoefijzerlaan 37, 🅶 34 14 48, Telex 82377, Fax 34 00 91, ⇌, 🔲 – 🄸 🍴 🅖 ♿. 🄰🄴 ⑩ 🄴 🆅🆂🄰. BY **r**
closed last 3 weeks January-first 2 weeks February – **60 rm** ⌷ 3500.

🄰🄰🄰 **de' Medici** ⑤ without rest., Potterierei 15, 🅶 33 98 33, Telex 82227, Fax 33 07 64, « Modern style », 🍴 – 🄸 📺 🍴 ♿ – 🄰 35. 🄰🄴 ⑩ 🄴 🆅🆂🄰. DX **b**
28 rm ⌷ 4700/5200.

🄰🄰🄰 **Novotel Centrum,** Katelijnestraat 65b, 🅶 33 75 33, Telex 81799, Fax 33 65 56, 🔅, 🍴 – 🄸 🈺 rm 🟦 📺 🍴 ♿ – 🄰 50-400. 🄰🄴 ⑩ 🄴 🆅🆂🄰. CZ **v**
M (open until midnight) a la carte 900/1400 – ⌷ 425 – **126 rm** 3650/4360.

🄰🄰🄰 **Parkhotel** without rest., Vrijdagmarkt 5, 🅶 33 33 64, Telex 81686, Fax 33 47 63 – 🄸 📺 🍴 ↩ – 🄰 25-115. 🄰🄴 ⑩ 🄴 🆅🆂🄰. CZ **g**
56 rm ⌷ 3000/3600.

🄰🄰🄰 **Portinari** ⑤ without rest., 't Zand 15, 🅶 34 10 34, Telex 82400, Fax 34 41 80 – 🄸 📺 🍴 ♿ ♿ – 🄰 80. 🄰🄴 ⑩ 🄴 🆅🆂🄰. CZ **x**
closed 2 to 25 January – **37 rm** ⌷ 3000/4500.

🄰🄰🄰 **Alfa Dante** without rest., Coupure 29, 🅶 34 01 94, Telex 81452, Fax 34 35 39, ≤ – 🄸 📺 🍴 – 🄰 25-60. 🄰🄴 ⑩ 🄴 🆅🆂🄰. DY **e**
22 rm ⌷ 4000/5500.

🄰🄰🄰 **Acacia** without rest., Korte Zilverstraat 3a, 🅶 34 44 11, Fax 33 88 17, 🄵🄳, ⇌, 🔲 – 🄸 📺 ↩ – 🄰 40. 🄰🄴 ⑩ 🄴 🆅🆂🄰. 🈺 CY **m**
closed January – **30 rm** ⌷ 3600/5400.

🄰🄰 **Die Swaene** ⑤, Steenhouwersdijk 1, 🅶 34 27 98, Telex 82446, Fax 33 66 74, ≤, « Stylish furnishing » – 🄸 📺 🍴 – 🄰 30. 🄰🄴 ⑩ 🄴 🆅🆂🄰. 🈺 CY **g**
M *(closed Wednesday, Thursday lunch, 1 to 22 July and 2 weeks January)* a la carte 1700/2300 – **24 rm** ⌷ 4050/5900.

🄰🄰 **Pandhotel** ⑤ without rest., Pandreitje 16, 🅶 34 06 66, Telex 81018, Fax 34 05 56 – 🄸 📺 🍴. 🄰🄴 🄴 🆅🆂🄰 – **24 rm** ⌷ 3200/4200. **u**

🄰🄰 **De Castillion,** Heilige Geeststraat 1, 🅶 34 30 01, Telex 83252, Fax 33 94 75, 🄵🄳, ⇌ – 🈺 rest 📺 🍴 – 🄰 50. 🄰🄴 ⑩ 🄴 🆅🆂🄰. 🈺 rest CZ **w**
M *(closed Tuesday November-April)* 1895 – **20 rm** ⌷ 3650/5300.

🄰🄰 **Prinsenhof** ⑤ without rest., Ontvangersstraat 9, 🅶 34 26 90, Telex 81315, Fax 34 23 21 – 🄸 📺 🍴 🅖 ♿. 🄰🄴 ⑩ 🄴 🆅🆂🄰. CY **c**
16 rm ⌷ 3200/6000.

🏠 **Bryghia** without rest., Oosterlingenplein 4, ℰ 33 80 59, Fax 34 14 30 – 🛗 📺 ☎. 🆎 ⓪ 🇪 VISA. 🛇 CY **f**
closed 4 January-15 February – **18 rm** ⊇ 3240/3750.

🏠 **Adornes** without rest., St-Annarei 26, ℰ 34 13 36, Fax 34 20 85, ≼, « Period vaulted cellars » – 🛗 📺 ☎ 🚗. 🆎 🇪 VISA DY **r**
closed 2 January-13 February – **20 rm** ⊇ 2100/3200.

🏠 **Aragon** without rest., Naaldenstraat 24, ℰ 33 35 33, Telex 81593, Fax 34 28 05 – 🛗 📺 ☎ 🚗. 🆎 ⓪ 🇪 VISA CY **t**
closed January – **18 rm** ⊇ 2750/3750.

🏠 **Biskajer** 🛇 without rest., Biskajersplein 4, ℰ 34 15 06, Telex 81874, Fax 34 39 11 – 🛗 ☎. 🆎 ⓪ 🇪 VISA CY **j**
17 rm ⊇ 2700/3700.

🏠 **Ter Duinen** without rest., Langerei 52, ℰ 33 04 37, Fax 34 42 16 – 🛗 📺 ☎. 🆎 ⓪ 🇪 VISA. 🛇 CX **a**
closed 3 to 31 January – **18 rm** ⊇ 2200/3300.

🏠 **Azalea** without rest., Wulfhagestraat 43, ℰ 33 14 78, Telex 81282, Fax 33 97 00, ⇌ – 🛗 📺 ☎ ⅙ 🚗. 🆎 ⓪ 🇪 VISA CY **p**
25 rm ⊇ 3000/3950.

🏠 **Europ** 🛇 without rest., Augustijnenrei 18, ℰ 33 79 75, Fax 34 52 66 – 🛗 📺 ☎ 🚗 – 🏛 30. 🆎 ⓪ 🇪 VISA. 🛇 CY **b**
closed January – **31 rm** ⊇ 2600/3700.

🏠 **Ter Brughe** without rest., Oost-Gistelhof 2, ℰ 34 03 24, Telex 82265, Fax 33 88 73 – 📺 ☎. 🆎 ⓪ 🇪 VISA CY **d**
23 rm ⊇ 2550/4400.

🏠 **Boudewijn I** 🛇 without rest., 't Zand 21, ℰ 33 69 62, Telex 81163, Fax 34 44 57 – 🛗 📺 ☎ – 🏛 25. 🆎 ⓪ 🇪 VISA CZ **t**
closed last 2 weeks January – **M** *(closed Tuesday)* 750/1500 – **11 rm** ⊇ 2050/3700.

🏠 **Patritius** without rest., Riddersstraat 11, ℰ 33 84 54, Fax 33 96 34, ⇝ – 🛗 📺 ☎ ⓟ – 🏛 25. 🆎 ⓪ 🇪 VISA CY **l**
closed January-14 February – **16 rm** ⊇ 2900/4500.

🏠 **Bourgoensch Hof,** Wollestraat 39, ℰ 33 16 45, Fax 34 63 78, ≼ canals and old Flemish houses – 🛗 📺 🚗. 🛇 CY **a**
M *(closed Tuesday 15 September-15 March, Wednesday, Thursday lunch and January)* (Pub-rest.) a la carte 900/1200 – **11 rm** *(12 November-15 March open weekend only)* ⊇ 2600/5300.

🏠 **Albert I** without rest., Koning Albertlaan 2, ℰ 34 09 30, Fax 34 09 30 – 📺 ☎. 🆎 ⓪ 🇪 VISA CZ **h**
11 rm ⊇ 2350/2750.

🏠 ✿ **Maraboe** (De Smedt), Hoefijzerlaan 9, ℰ 33 81 55, Fax 33 29 28 – 📺 ☎. 🆎 ⓪ 🇪 VISA CZ **d**
M *(closed Saturday lunch, Sunday dinner, Monday, 3 weeks after carnival, last week June and last week November)* (booking essential) a la carte 1650/2250 – **9 rm** *(closed 3 weeks after carnival, last week November and Sunday dinner and Monday out of season)* ⊇ 1800/2500
Spec. Terrine de foie gras, Homard au four au basilic (July-November), Coucou de Malines aux asperges sauce moutardée (May-July).

🏠 **Egmond** 🛇 without rest., Minnewater 15, ℰ 34 14 45, Fax 34 29 40, « Garden setting » – 📺 ☎ ⓟ. VISA CZ **y**
closed January – **9 rm** ⊇ 2500/3100.

XXX ✿ **De Snippe** (Huysentruyt) 🛇 with rm, Nieuwe Gentweg 53, ℰ 33 70 70, Fax 33 76 62, « 18C house with wall paintings » – 🛗 📺 ☎ ⓟ. 🆎 ⓪ 🇪 VISA CZ **z**
closed 3 weeks March – **M** *(closed Sunday and Monday lunch)* a la carte 2200/2800 – **11 rm** ⊇ 3750/6000
Spec. Lotus de coquilles St-Jacques aux pistils de safran (October-March), Langoustines aux cornes de Florenville et caviar osciétre, Parmentier de ris de veau persillé.

XXX **Vasquez,** Zilverstraat 38, ℰ 34 08 45, Fax 33 52 41, ⇷, « 15C residence, flowered inner courtyard » – 🆎 ⓪ 🇪 VISA. 🛇 CZ **f**
closed Wednesday, Thursday lunch, 1 to 12 March and 19 July-August – **M** a la carte 2100/2800.

XXX **De Witte Poorte,** Jan Van Eyckplein 6, ℰ 33 08 83, Telex 82232, « Vaulted dining room, garden » – 🆎 ⓪ 🇪 VISA CY **v**
closed Sunday, Monday, 2 weeks July and 2 weeks January – **M** a la carte 1800/2500.

XXX **Duc de Bourgogne** with rm, Huidenvettersplein 12, ℰ 33 20 38, Fax 34 40 37, ≼ canals, « Rustic decor and wall paintings of late medieval style » – 🍽 rest 📺 ☎. 🆎 ⓪ 🇪 CY **q**
closed 3 weeks July and 3 weeks January – **M** *(closed Monday and Tuesday lunch)* a la carte 1900/2700 – **9 rm** ⊇ 3250/4600.

XXX **Den Braamberg,** Pandreitje 11, ℰ 33 73 70, Fax 33 99 73 – 🆎 ⓪ 🇪 VISA CY **u**
closed Sunday dinner, Thursday, 15 to 31 August and 1 to 10 January – **M** a la carte 1700/2550.

XXX **Huyze Die Maene** 1st floor, Markt 17, ℰ 33 39 59, Fax 33 44 60 – 🆎 ⓪ 🇪 VISA CY **n**
closed Tuesday, Wednesday, last week June-first 2 weeks July and 2 weeks February – **M** a la carte approx. 2000.

4 69

XXX **Den Gouden Harynck,** Groeninge 25, ℰ 33 76 37, Fax 34 42 70 – **ⓟ**, **ⒶⒺ ⓄⒹ Ⓔ VISA**
closed Sunday, Monday, 7 to 13 April, 20 July-10 August and last week December – **M** a la carte 2050/2600.
CZ **e**

XXX **'t Pandreitje,** Pandreitje 6, ℰ 33 11 90, Fax 34 00 70 – **ⒶⒺ ⓄⒹ Ⓔ VISA**
closed Wednesday, Sunday, first 2 weeks March and first 2 weeks July – **M** a la carte 2000/2950.
CDY **s**

XXX ✿✿ **De Karmeliet** (Van Hecke), Langestraat 19, ℰ 33 82 59 – ⇔, **ⓟ**, **ⒶⒺ ⓄⒹ Ⓔ VISA**. ✺
closed Sunday dinner, Monday and 2 weeks February – **M** a la carte 2200/3000
Spec. Papillote fine de pommes de terre, escargots et gésiers de canard confits, Rôti de turbot piqué aux lardons, Pigeon aux truffes, raviolis au foie d'oie.
DY **u**

XX ✿ **Hermitage** (Dryepondt), Ezelstraat 18, ℰ 34 41 73 – **ⓄⒹ Ⓔ VISA**
closed Sunday, Monday, July and August – **M** (dinner only) (booking essential) a la carte 1650/2400.
Spec. Aile de raie poêlée au vieux vinaigre, Suprême de turbotin au Champagne, Pigeonneau rôti à la chiffonade de chou et jus de truffes.
CY **i**

XX **Ambrosius,** Arsenaalstraat 53, ℰ 34 41 57, 🌴, « Rustic » – VISA. ✺
closed Monday, Tuesday, 2 weeks September and 2 weeks February – **M** (dinner only) a la carte 1650/2150.
CZ **j**

XX **'t Bourgoensche Cruyce,** Wollestraat 41, ℰ 33 79 26, Telex 83121, Fax 33 88 91, ⩽ canals and old Flemish houses – **ⒶⒺ VISA**. ✺
closed Tuesday May-October, Sunday and Monday lunch October-May, first 2 weeks November and February – **M** a la carte 2000/2850.
CY **a**

XX **René Van Puyenbroeck,** 't Zand 13, ℰ 33 30 35 – **ⒶⒺ ⓄⒹ Ⓔ VISA**. ✺
closed Sunday dinner, Monday and 1 to 25 July – **M** 1200.
CZ **x**

XX **Kardinaalshof,** Sint-Salvatorkerkhof 14, ℰ 34 16 91, Fax 34 20 62, Seafood – **ⒶⒺ ⓄⒹ Ⓔ VISA**
closed Wednesday, Saturday lunch and 2 weeks January – **M** a la carte 1600/2000.
CZ **r**

XX **Spinola,** Spinolarei 1, ℰ 34 17 85, Fax 39 12 01, « Rustic » – **ⒶⒺ ⓄⒹ Ⓔ VISA**
closed Sunday and Monday lunch except Bank Holidays – **M** a la carte 1100/1600.
CY **j**

XX **De Lotteburg,** Goezeputstraat 43, ℰ 33 75 35, Fax 33 75 35, 🌴 – **ⒶⒺ ⓄⒹ Ⓔ VISA** CZ **u**
closed Monday and Tuesday except Bank Holidays, 20 July-6 August and 1 week February – **M** a la carte 1400/2100.

XX **De Zinc,** A. Van Ackerplein 2, ℰ 33 64 65, Open until midnight – **ⒶⒺ ⓄⒹ Ⓔ VISA**
closed Wednesday, first 2 weeks July and first week January – **M** a la carte 850/1150.
CY **k**

X **Chez Olivier,** Meestraat 9, ℰ 33 36 59, ⩽
closed Thursday and Friday lunch – **M** 1500/2500.
DY **a**

X **Tanuki,** Noordstraat 3, ℰ 31 75 12, Fax 31 75 12, Japanese cuisine – **Ⓔ VISA**. ✺
closed Monday and Tuesday – **M** a la carte 950/1150.
CZ **k**

X **Malpertuus,** Eiermarkt 9, ℰ 33 30 38 – 🍽, **ⒶⒺ ⓄⒹ Ⓔ VISA**
closed Wednesday dinner, Thursday and July – **M** 490/975.
CY **r**

South – ✉ 8200 – ☎ 0 50 :

🏨 **Novotel Zuid,** Chartreuseweg 20, ℰ 38 28 51, Telex 81507, Fax 38 79 03, 🌴, 🏊, 🌳 – 📺 ⇔ rm ▤ rest 📺 ☎ & **ⓟ** – 🔔 25-230. **ⒶⒺ ⓄⒹ VISA**
M (open until midnight) a la carte 900/1400 – ⥮ 400 – **101 rm** 3100/3900.
A **r**

XXXX ✿ **Weinebrugge** (Galens), Koning Albertlaan 242, ℰ 38 44 40, Fax 38 72 67, Seafood – ⇔ **ⓟ**. **ⒶⒺ Ⓔ**
closed Sunday dinner in winter, Wednesday, Thursday, last week June, first 2 weeks September and first 2 weeks January – **M** a la carte approx. 3500
Spec. Création de foie gras d'oie frais au "Vintage Port", Homard rôti au four aux épices douces, Javanais de saumon aux langoustines.
A **b**

South-West – ✉ 8200 – ☎ 0 50 :

🏨 **Host. Pannenhuis** ⊗, Zandstraat 2, ℰ 31 19 07, Telex 82345, Fax 31 77 66, ⩽, 🌴, « Terrace and garden » – 📺 ☎ & **ⓟ** – 🔔 25. **ⒶⒺ ⓄⒹ Ⓔ VISA**. ✺ rest
M (*closed Tuesday dinner, Wednesday, 1 to 16 July and 15 January-1 February*) a la carte approx. 1800 – **20 rm** (*closed 15 January-1 February*) ⥮ 2800/4600.
A **g**

XX **Vossenburg** ⊗ with rm, Zandstraat 272 (Coude Ceucen), ℰ 31 70 26, Fax 32 08 65, ⩽, « Converted mansion in a park » – 📺 ☎ **ⓟ** **ⒶⒺ ⓄⒹ Ⓔ VISA**. ✺
closed 9 to 26 March and 16 to 26 November – **M** (*closed Monday dinner and Tuesday*) a la carte 1350/1800 – **7 rm** ⥮ 2975/3950.
A **c**

at Hertsberge by ④ : 12,5 km © Oostkamp pop. 20 167 – ✉ 8020 Hertsberge – ☎ 0 50 :

XXX **Manderley,** Kruisstraat 13, ℰ 27 80 51, 🌴, « Terrace and garden » – **ⓟ**. **ⒶⒺ ⓄⒹ Ⓔ VISA**
closed Sunday dinner, Monday, first week October and last 3 weeks January – **M** a la carte 1600/2200.

at Ruddervoorde by ④ : 12 km © Oostkamp pop. 20 167 – ✉ 8020 Ruddervoorde – ☎ 0 50 :

XXX **Host. Leegendael** ⊗ with rm, Kortrijkstraat 498 (N 50), ℰ 27 76 99, Fax 27 58 80, « Period residence, country atmosphere » – 📺 ☎ **ⓟ** **ⒶⒺ ⓄⒹ Ⓔ VISA**
closed last 2 weeks August-early September and carnival week – **M** (*closed Wednesday and Sunday dinner*) a la carte 1650/2300 – **7 rm** ⥮ 1750/2550.

at Sint-Kruis by ② : 6 km 🄲 Bruges – ✉ 8310 Sint-Kruis – ☎ 0 50 :

Wilgenhof without rest., Polderstraat 151, ☎ 36 27 44, Fax 36 28 21, ←, « Polder surroundings » – TV ☎ P. AE ⓓ E VISA A w
closed last week January – **6 rm** ☕ 2400/4000.

XXX **Jonkman,** Maalsesteenweg 438, ☎ 36 07 67, Fax 35 76 96, 🏠, « Terrace » – P. AE ⓓ E VISA
closed Sunday, Monday, 1 week Easter, first week July and 1 to 15 October – **M** a la carte 1900/2700.

at Varsenare by ⑦ : 6,5 km 🄲 Jabbeke pop. 11 887 – ✉ 8490 Varsenare – ☎ 0 50 :

XXX **Manoir Stuivenberg** with rm, Gistelsteenweg 27, ☎ 38 15 02, Fax 38 28 92, 🏠, Ⅰ₆, ≘s – |‡| TV ☎ P. AE ⓓ E VISA. ✱ rm A n
M *(closed Sunday dinner and Monday)* a la carte 2000/2500 – **9 rm** ☕ 3500/12500.

at Waardamme by ④ : 11 km 🄲 Oostkamp pop. 20 167 – ✉ 8020 Waardamme – ☎ 0 50 :

XXX **Ter Talinge,** Rooiveldstraat 46, ☎ 27 90 61, « Terrace » – P. AE VISA
closed Wednesday, Thursday, 20 to 31 August and late February-early March – **M** a la carte 1200/1700.

at Zedelgem by ⑥ : 10,5 km – pop. 19 992 – ✉ 8210 Zedelgem – ☎ 0 50 :

Zuidwege without rest., Torhoutsesteenweg 126, ☎ 20 13 39, Fax 20 17 39 – TV ☎ P. AE ⓓ E VISA. ✱
closed 25 December-6 January – **17 rm** ☕ 2380.

XX **Ter Leepe,** Torhoutsesteenweg 168, ☎ 20 01 97 – P. AE ⓓ E VISA
closed Wednesday dinner, Sunday, 15 to 31 July and 1 to 12 February – **M** a la carte 1350/1800.

Gent 9000 Oost-Vlaanderen 213 ④ and 409 ③ – pop. 230 822 – ☎ 0 91 – 45 km.

South :

XXX ✿✿ **Apicius** (Slawinsky), Maurice Maeterlinckstraat 8, ☎ 22 46 00, « Garden » – AE ⓓ E VISA. ✱
closed lunch Saturday and Thursday, Sunday, Bank Holidays, 1 week Easter, 20 July-10 August and 1 week New Year – **M** a la carte 2500/3500
Spec. Salade d'huîtres au mirepoix de légumes (15 September-April), Ecrevisses aux lentilles à la sauge, Rognon de veau à la boulangère de légumes.

Kortrijk 8500 West-Vlaanderen 213 ⑮ and 409 ⑪ – pop. 76 279 – ☎ 0 56 – 51 km.

XXX ✿✿ **Filip Bogaert,** Minister Tacklaan 5, ☎ 20 30 34, Fax 20 30 75, « Late 19C residence » – P. AE ⓓ E VISA
closed Wednesday, Sunday dinner and 1 to 21 August – **M** a la carte 2100/3200
Spec. Foie d'oie au torchon, Navarin de homard aux morilles et asperges, Pigeonneau rôti à l'échalote.

Waregem 8790 West-Vlaanderen 213 ⑮ and 409 ⑪ – pop. 34 250 – ☎ 0 56 – 47 km.

XXXX ✿✿ **'t Oud Konijntje** (Mme Desmedt), Bosstraat 53 (S : 2 km near E 17), ☎ 60 19 37, Telex 86350, Fax 60 92 12, 🏠, « Flowered terrace » – P. AE ⓓ E VISA
closed dinner Thursday and Sunday, Friday, 22 July-13 August and 22 December-4 January – **M** a la carte 1900/2500
Spec. Mousseline de homard au chou, Canette de Barbarie aux échalotes et au poivre vert, Le délice de Mélanie.

LIÈGE 4000 Liège 213 ㉒ and 409 ⑮ – pop. 199 020 – ☎ 0 41.

See : Old town★★ – Baptismal font★★★ of St. Bartholomew's church DX – Citadel ←★★ DX – Treasury★★ of St. Paul's Cathedral FZ – Palace of the Prince-Bishops★ : court of honour★★ GY J – The Perron★ (market cross) GY A – Aquarium★ DY D – St. James church★ DY – Cointe Park ←★ CZ – Altarpiece★ in the St. Denis church GZ – Church of St. John : Wooden Calvary Statues★ FZ.

Museums : Life in Wallonia★★ GY – Curtius★ : evangelistary★★★, glassware Museum : collection★ EX M1 – Ansembourg★ DX M2 – Arms★ DX M3 – Religious and Roman Art Museum★ GY M5.

Envir : Baptismal font★ in the church★ of St. Severin-en-Condroz by ⑥ : 23 km.

18 at Ougrée by ⑥ : 7 km, rte du Condroz 541, ☎ (0 41) 36 20 21 - 18 at Gomzé-Andoumont by ⑤ : 17 km, Sur Counachamps, ☎ (0 41) 60 92 07.

☎ 42 52 14.

i En Féronstrée 92, ☎ 22 24 56 and Gare des Guillemins, ☎ 52 44 19 – Tourist association of the province, bd de la Sauvenière 77, ☎ 22 42 10.

Brussels 97 ⑨ – Amsterdam 242 ① – Antwerp 119 ⑫ – Köln 122 ② – Luxemburg 159 ⑤.

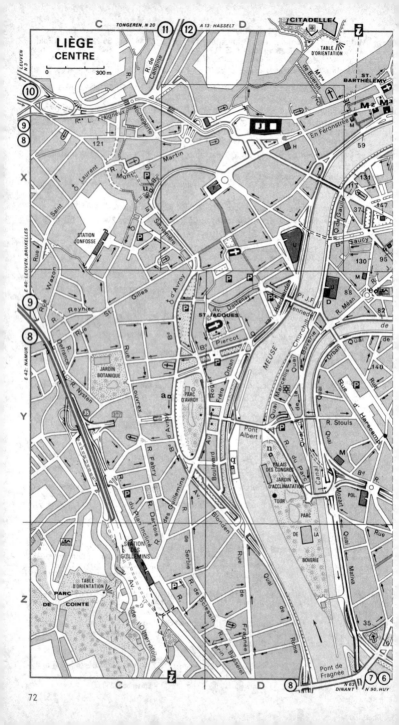

To obtain a general view of Benelux,
use the Michelin Map 987
Germany – Austria – Benelux
(1 in: 16 miles)

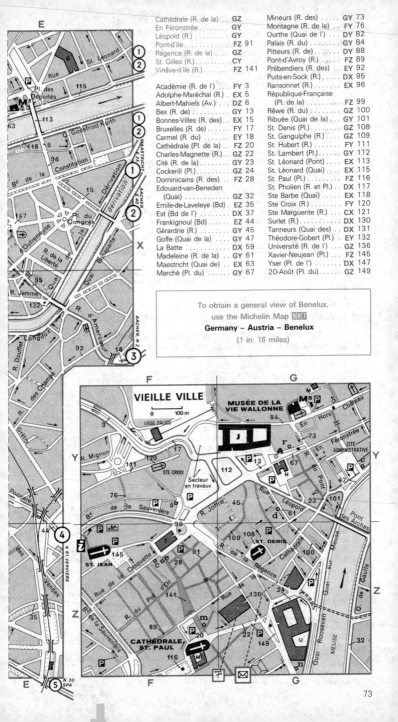

Room prices are subject to the addition of a local tax of 6 %

🏨 **Holiday Inn,** Esplanade de l'Europe 2, ✉ 4020, ☎ 42 60 20, Telex 41156, Fax 43 48 10, ⬱, ☎, ▨, - 🕼 ⇔ rm 🗐 📺 ☎ ₠, ⇔ 🅿 - 🔬 25-40. 🆎 ⓓ ⋿ 𝘝𝘐𝘚𝘈. ✻ rest   DY **n**
M Ile de Meuse a la carte 1300/1900 - **219 rm** � 4750/6500.

🏨 **Ramada,** bd de la Sauveniere 100, ☎ 22 49 10, Telex 41896, Fax 22 39 83 - 🕼 ⇔ 🗐 📺 ☎ ⇔ - 🔬 25-100. 🆎 ⓓ ⋿ 𝘝𝘐𝘚𝘈   CX **u**
M a la carte 1100/1900 - � 540 - **105 rm** 5000/6000.

XXX **Vieux Liège,** quai Goffe 41, ☎ 23 77 48, « 16C house » - 🆎 ⓓ ⋿ 𝘝𝘐𝘚𝘈   GY **c**
closed Wednesday dinner, Sunday, Bank Holidays, 1 week Easter, mid July-mid August and 24 December - **M** a la carte 1700/2200.

XXX **L'Héliport,** bd Frère-Orban, ☎ 52 13 21, ⬱, 🌳 - 🅿. ⋿ 𝘝𝘐𝘚𝘈   DY **q**
closed Sunday, Monday dinner and last 3 weeks July - **M** a la carte 1600/2300.

XX **François** r. Casquette 5, ☎ 22 92 34, Fax 22 92 34, Open until 11 p.m. - 🆎 𝘝𝘐𝘚𝘈 FZ **c**
closed Saturday lunch, Sunday and 27 July-16 August - **M** a la carte 1650/2450.

XX **As Ouhès,** pl. du Marché 21, ☎ 23 32 25, 🌳, Open until 11 p.m. - 🆎 ⓓ ⋿ 𝘝𝘐𝘚𝘈 GY **r**
closed Sunday and last 3 weeks July - **M** a la carte 900/1600.

XX **Le Shanghai** 1st floor, Galeries Cathédrale 104, ☎ 22 22 63, Fax 23 00 50, Chinese cuisine - 🗐. 🆎 ⓓ ⋿ 𝘝𝘐𝘚𝘈. ✻   FZ **m**
closed Tuesday, 17 August-8 September and 1 week February - **M** a la carte 750/1300.

X **Chez Max,** pl. de la République Française 12, ☎ 22 08 59, Fax 22 90 02, 🌳, Open until 11 p.m. - 🆎 ⓓ ⋿ 𝘝𝘐𝘚𝘈   FY **s**
closed Saturday lunch and Sunday - **M** a la carte 1200/2000.

X **L'Ecailler,** r. Dominicains 26, ☎ 22 17 49, Fax 21 10 09, Seafood - 🗐. 🆎 ⓓ ⋿ 𝘝𝘐𝘚𝘈   FZ **e**
M a la carte 1100/2000.

X **Lalo's Bar,** r. Madeleine 18, ☎ 23 22 57, Italian cuisine - 🆎 ⓓ ⋿ 𝘝𝘐𝘚𝘈. ✻   GY **d**
closed Saturday lunch, Sunday, Bank Holidays, Easter, August and Christmas-New Year - **M** 750/990.

at Ans - pop. 27 381 - ✉ 4430 Ans - ✪ 0 41 :

XX **La Fontaine de Jade,** r. Yser 321, ☎ 46 49 72, Fax 63 39 53, Chinese cuisine, open until 11 p.m. - 🗐. 🆎 ⓓ ⋿ 𝘝𝘐𝘚𝘈. ✻
closed Monday except Bank Holidays and mid August-early September - **M** a la carte 900/1200.

X **Le Marguerite,** r. Walthère Jamar 171, ☎ 26 43 46 - 🆎 ⓓ ⋿ 𝘝𝘐𝘚𝘈
closed Saturday lunch, Sunday, Monday, 1 week Easter, 15 July-15 August and 23 December-2 January - **M** a la carte 1200/1700.

at Argenteau by ① : 13 km 🅲 Visé pop. 17 175 - ✉ 4601 Argenteau - ✪ 0 41 :

X **Le Tourne-Bride,** chaussée d'Argenteau 42, ☎ 79 17 11 - 🅿. 🆎 ⓓ ⋿ 𝘝𝘐𝘚𝘈
closed dinner Sunday and Bank Holidays and August - **M** a la carte 1000/2100.

at Chênée 🅲 Liège - ✉ 4032 Chênée - ✪ 0 41 :

XX **Le Gourmet,** r. Large 91, ☎ 65 87 97, 🌳 - 🆎 ⓓ ⋿ 𝘝𝘐𝘚𝘈
closed Monday dinner, Wednesday, Saturday lunch and 15 to 31 July - **M** a la carte 1200/1750.

XX **Le Vieux Chênée,** r. Gravier 45, ☎ 67 00 92 - 🆎 ⓓ ⋿ 𝘝𝘐𝘚𝘈
closed Thursday, 2 weeks July and 1 week end January - **M** a la carte 1100/1600.

at Engis by ⑦ : 10 km - pop. 5 884 - ✉ 4480 Engis - ✪ 0 41 :

XX **La Ciboulette,** quai Herten 11, ☎ 75 19 65, 🌳 - 🆎 ⓓ ⋿ 𝘝𝘐𝘚𝘈
closed Saturday lunch, dinner Sunday and Wednesday and Monday - **M** a la carte 1500/2400.

at Hermalle-sous-Argenteau by ① : 14 km 🅲 Oupeye pop. 23 286 - ✉ 4681 Hermalle-sous-Argenteau - ✪ 0 41 :

XXX **Au Comte de Mercy** ⇓ with rm, r. Tilleul 5, ☎ 79 35 35, 🌳, « Rustic » - ☎ 🅿. 🆎 ⓓ ⋿ 𝘝𝘐𝘚𝘈. ✻ rm
closed Sunday, Monday, 3 days after Easter, July and first 2 weeks January - **M** *(closed Monday and Sunday except May and Easter)* a la carte 1250/2200 - � 350 - **8 rm** 1500/1800.

at Herstal - pop. 36 343 - ✉ 4040 Herstal - ✪ 0 41 :

🏨 **Post House** ⇓, r. Hurbise (by motorway E 40 exit 34), ☎ 64 64 00, Telex 41103, Fax 48 06 90, 🌳, ⅀, - 🕼 ⇔ rest 🗐 rest 📺 ☎ 🅿 - 🔬 25-60. 🆎 ⓓ ⋿ 𝘝𝘐𝘚𝘈
M 1150 - **94 rm** � 3740/4870.

at Neuville-en-Condroz by ⑥ : 18 km 🅲 Neupré pop. 8 619 - ✉ 4121 Neuville-en-Condroz - ✪ 0 41 :

XXXX ✿✿ **Le Chêne Madame** (Mme Tilkin), av. de la Chevauchée 70 (in Rognacs wood SE : 2 km), ☎ 71 41 27, Fax 71 29 43 - 🅿. 🆎 ⓓ ⋿ 𝘝𝘐𝘚𝘈. ✻
closed Monday, dinner Sunday and Thursday, August and 22 December-4 January - **M** a la carte 1600/2700
Spec. Filets de sole farcis sauce à la badiane et à l'orange, Petite salade de caille à l'huile de noix et lentins, Gibiers en saison.

at Rotheux-Rimière by ⑥ : 16 km Ⓒ Neupré pop. 8 619 – ✉ 4120 Rotheux-Rimière – ☎ 0 41 :

XX **Le Vieux Chêne,** r. Bonry 146 (near N 63), ☎ 71 46 51 – P. AE ① E VISA. ✻
closed Wednesday, dinner Monday and Tuesday, August and 24 December-5 January – **M** a la carte 850/1400.

at Tilff S : 12 km by N 633 Ⓒ Esneux pop. 12 571 – ✉ 4130 Tilff – ☎ 0 41 :

XXX **Casino** with rm, pl. du Roi Albert 3, ☎ 88 10 15, Fax 88 33 16 – ☎. ✻ rm
closed 15 December-15 January – **M** *(closed Monday)* a la carte 1350/2100 – **6 rm** ☕ 1600/2300.

Hasselt **3500** Limburg 213 ⑨ and 409 ⑥ – pop. 65 861 – ☎ 0 11 – 42 km.

at Stevoort by N 2 : 5 km to Kermt, then road on the left Ⓒ Hasselt – ✉ 3512 Stevoort – ☎ 0 11 :

✿✿ **Scholteshof** (Souvereyns) ⛰, Kermtstraat 130, ☎ 25 02 02, Telex 39684, Fax 25 43 28, ←, ⛱, « 18C farmhouse with English-style garden, country atmosphere », ✻ – TV ☎ P – 🏛 25-60. AE ① E VISA
closed 13 to 31 July and 1 to 18 January – **M** *(closed Wednesday)* a la carte 3100/3950 – ☕ 450 – **18 rm** 4000/14000
Spec. Homard aux épices et à l'estragon, Turbot à la fleur de lavande (June-October), Délice praliné sauce aux noisettes grillées.

St-Vith 4780 Liège 214 ⑨ and 409 ⑯ – pop. 8 548 – ☎ 0 80 – 78 km.

XXX ✿✿ **Zur Post** (Pankert) with rm, Hauptstr. 39, ☎ 22 80 27, Fax 22 93 10 – TV ☎. E VISA. ✻
closed Sunday dinner and Monday except Bank Holidays, 30 June-10 July and January – **M** a la carte 2000/2700 – ☕ 350 – **8 rm** 1800/2500
Spec. Langoustines grillées aux graines de sésame, Nage de St-Pierre aux lentins et cardamone, Côtelettes de pigeonneau farcies et foie gras (February-September).

Valkenburg Limburg (Netherlands) Ⓒ Valkenburg aan de Geul pop. 17 842 212 ① and 408 ㉖ – ☎ 0 4406 – 47 km.

✿✿ **Prinses Juliana** (annexe Residentie ⛰ - 8 rm 200/350), Broekhem 11, ✉ 63011 HD, ☎ 1 22 44, Fax 1 44 05, ⛱, « Terrace and flowered garden » – |‡| ▤ rest TV ☎ 🚗 P – 🏛 50. AE ① E VISA. ✻ rest
M *(closed Saturday lunch)* a la carte 93/132 – ☕ 25 – **17 rm** 200/250
Spec. Dégustation de foies gras maison, Langue confite au jus de truffes, Pigeon fermier à l'estragon.

Weert Limburg (Netherlands) 212 ⑲ and 408 ⑲ – pop. 40 262 – ☎ 0 4950 – 90 km.

XX ✿✿ **L'Auberge** (Mertens) Parallelweg 101, ✉ 6001 HM, ☎ 3 10 57, Fax 3 10 57 – AE E VISA. ✻
closed 7 to 27 August, 22 December-2 January, Sunday and Monday – **M** a la carte 74/115
Spec. Canard rôti et son foie aux raisins, Croustade de langoustines au romarin et chips d'ail, Canard sauvage au hachis de champignons (July-January).

Luxemburg

(LUXEMBOURG) 215 ⑤ and 409 ㉖ – pop. 74 400.

See : Site★★ – Old Luxemburg★★ DY – "Chemin de la Corniche"★★ and the rocks
DY **29** – The Bock cliff ≤★★, Bock Casemates★★ DY **A** – Place de la Constitution
≤★★ DY **28** – Grand-Ducal Palace★ DY **K** – Our Lady's Cathedral (Notre Dame)★
DY **L** – Grand-Duchess Charlotte Bridge★ DY – Boulevard Victor Thorn ≤★ DY **97**.
Museum : State (Musée de l'État)★★ DY **M¹**.

Senningerberg, near Airport ℘ 3 40 90.

Findel by ③ : 6 km ℘ 40 08 08 – Air Terminal : pl. de la Gare ℘ 48 11 99.

pl. d'Armes. ✉ 2011, ℘ 22 28 09 and 22 75 65 – Air Terminus (closed Sunday
from December to March), pl. de la Gare ℘ 48 11 99 – Findel, Airport ℘ 40 08 08.

Amsterdam 391 ⑧ – Bonn 190 ③ – Bruxelles 219 ⑧.

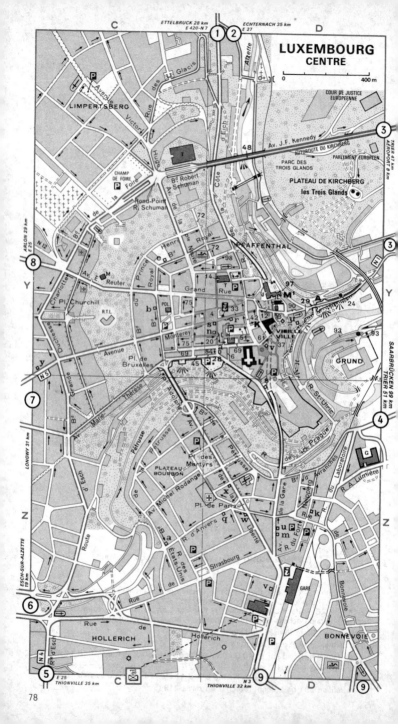

Luxembourg-Centre :

🏨🏨 **Le Royal**, bd Royal 12, ⊠ 2449, ℰ 4 16 16, Telex 2979, Fax 22 59 48, ℉ӧ, ≘ȿ, ◪ – ⫞ ⤬⫟ rm CY e
🔲 ☎ 🕭 ⚑ ⊖ – 🔏 25-350. 🖭 ◑ ☰ 𝘝𝘐𝘚𝘈. ⫟ rest
M Le Relais Royal *(closed Saturday lunch, Bank Holidays and 3 weeks August)* 2250 - **Le Jardin**
a la carte 1100/1600 – **170 rm** ⊇ 7200/11800.

🏨🏨 **Cravat**, bd Roosevelt 29, ⊠ 2450, ℰ 22 19 75, Telex 2846, Fax 22 67 11 – ⫞ 🔲 ☎ –
🔏 25-70. 🖭 ◑ ☰ 𝘝𝘐𝘚𝘈 DY a
M a la carte 1400/1800 – **59 rm** ⊇ 5200/6500.

🏨 **Rix** without rest., bd Royal 20, ⊠ 2449, ℰ 47 16 66, Fax 22 75 35 – ⫞ 🔲 ☎ ⚑. 𝘝𝘐𝘚𝘈. ⫟
closed 19 December-4 January – **21 rm** ⊇ 3460/5340. CY b

🍴🍴🍴🍴 **Clairefontaine**, pl. de Clairefontaine 9, ⊠ 1341, ℰ 46 22 11, Fax 47 08 21 – ▤. 🖭 ◑ ☰ 𝘝𝘐𝘚𝘈
closed Saturday lunch, Sunday, Bank Holidays, 1 to 8 March, 1, 2 and 3 May, 9 to 31 August
and 1 to 8 November – **M** a la carte 2300/3200. DY v

🍴🍴🍴 ☆☆ **St-Michel** (Guillou) 1st floor, r. Eau 32, ⊠ 1449, ℰ 22 32 15, Fax 46 25 93, « In the old
city, rustic interior » – 🖭 ◑ ☰ 𝘝𝘐𝘚𝘈 DY e
closed Saturday, Sunday, August and 26 December-5 January – **M** *(booking essential)* a la carte
2550/3500
Spec. Foie gras en robe des champs, Cotriade aux trois poissons, Pot-au-feu de pigeonneau. Wines
Pinot gris, Pinot noir.

🍴🍴🍴 **Astoria**, av. du X-Septembre 14, ⊠ 2550, ℰ 44 62 23, Fax 45 82 96 – 🖭 ◑ ☰ 𝘝𝘐𝘚𝘈 CY y
closed Saturday and 26 December-5 January – **M** *(lunch only)* a la carte 1800/2250.

🍴🍴🍴 **Hemmen**, Plateau du St-Esprit 5, ⊠ 1475, ℰ 47 00 23, Fax 46 64 02, ⩔ – ▤. 🖭 ◑ ☰ 𝘝𝘐𝘚𝘈
closed Sunday dinner and 1 week January – **M** a la carte 2000/3000. DZ s

🍴🍴🍴 **Speltz**, r. Chimay 8, ⊠ 1333, ℰ 47 49 50, Fax 47 46 77 – 🖭 ◑ ☰ 𝘝𝘐𝘚𝘈 DY n
closed Saturday, Sunday, Bank Holidays, 20 to 26 April, 3 to 16 August and 25 December-
3 January – **M** 1100/1450.

🍴🍴🍴 **La Cigogne**, r. Curé 24, ⊠ 1368, ℰ 22 82 50, Fax 46 51 21 – ◑ ☰ 𝘝𝘐𝘚𝘈. ⫟ DY r
closed Saturday, Sunday, Monday and August – **M** a la carte approx. 2300.

🍴🍴 **La Lorraine**, pl. d'Armes 7, ⊠ 1136, ℰ 47 46 20, Fax 47 09 64, ⩔, Oyster bar and Seafood
– ▤. 🖭 ◑ ☰ 𝘝𝘐𝘚𝘈. ⫟ DY s
closed Saturday lunch, Sunday, Bank Holidays, 29 August-14 September, 1 to 5 January and
8 to 16 February – **M** a la carte 1650/3450.

🍴 **Brédewée**, r. Large/Corniche 9, ⊠ 1917, ℰ 22 26 96, Fax 22 08 63, ⩔ – 🖭 ◑ ☰ 𝘝𝘐𝘚𝘈
closed Sunday and first week January – **M** a la carte 1300/2000. DY u

Luxembourg-Station :

🏨🏨 **President**, pl. de la Gare 32, ⊠ 1616, ℰ 48 61 61, Telex 1510, Fax 48 61 80 – ⫞ ▤ rm
🔲 ☎ – 🔏 40. 🖭 ◑ ☰ 𝘝𝘐𝘚𝘈. ⫟ DZ v
M *(closed August)* (dinner only) 1300 – **35 rm** ⊇ 4000/6400.

🏨 **Arcotel** without rest., av. de la Gare 43, ⊠ 1611, ℰ 49 40 01, Telex 3776, Fax 40 56 24 –
⫞ 🔲 ☎. 🖭 ◑ ☰ 𝘝𝘐𝘚𝘈. ⫟ DZ u
30 rm ⊇ 3800/4400.

🏨 **Central Molitor**, av. de la Liberté 28, ⊠ 1930, ℰ 48 99 11, Telex 2613, Fax 48 33 82 – ⫞
🔲 ☎. 🖭 ◑ ☰ 𝘝𝘐𝘚𝘈 DZ x
M *(closed Friday and mid December-mid January)* 900/1500 – **36 rm** ⊇ 3200/4200.

🏨 **Nobilis**, av. de la Gare 47, ⊠ 1611, ℰ 49 49 71, Telex 3212, Fax 40 31 01 – ⫞ ▤ 🔲 ☎
⩔ – 🔏 70. 🖭 ◑ ☰ 𝘝𝘐𝘚𝘈 DZ m
M 750/1900 – ⊇ 410 – **43 rm** 3370/3670.

🏨 **Aub. du Coin**, bd de la Pétrusse 2, ⊠ 2320, ℰ 40 21 01, Fax 40 36 66 – ⫞ 🔲 ☎ – 🔏 30.
🖭 ◑ ☰ 𝘝𝘐𝘚𝘈. ⫟ rest CZ a
closed 15 December-15 January – **M** *(closed Sunday and Bank Holidays)* a la carte 1750/2400
– **23 rm** ⊇ 2300/3100.

🏨 **Marco Polo** without rest., r. Fort Neipperg 27, ⊠ 2230, ℰ 406 41 41, Fax 40 48 84 – ⫞ 🔲
☎ ⩔. 🖭 ◑ ☰ 𝘝𝘐𝘚𝘈 – **18 rm** ⊇ 2700/3700. DZ k

XXX **Cordial** 1st floor, pl. de Paris 1, ⊠ 2314, ☎ 48 85 38 – E VISA   DZ **w**
closed Friday, Saturday lunch, 1 to 8 March, 8 to 13 June and 14 July-8 August – **M** a la carte
2050/2850.

XX **Italia** with rm, r. Anvers 15, ⊠ 1130, ☎ 48 66 26, Telex 3644, Fax 48 08 07, 🍽 – 📺 ☎.
AE ◑ E VISA – **M** a la carte 1100/1800 – **20 rm** ⊇ 2300/2700.
                                                                                                                         DZ **q**

Airport by ③ : 8 km :

🏨 **Sheraton Aérogolf** ⑤, rte de Trèves, ⊠ 1019, ☎ 3 45 71, Telex 2662, Fax 3 42 17, ≤ –
🛗 ⇄ rm 🗏 📺 ☎ ❷ – 🔬 25-120. AE ◑ E VISA
M Le Montgolfier (open until 11.30 p.m.) a la carte 1200/2100 – ⊇ 525 – **146 rm** 7500/8200.

🏨 **Ibis**, rte de Trèves, ⊠ 2632, ☎ 43 88 01, Telex 60790, Fax 43 88 02, ≤ – 🛗 🗏 📺 ☎ ♿
❷ – 🔬 25-80. AE ◑ E VISA – **M** 690/1500 – **120 rm** ⊇ 2800/4300.

XX **Le Grimpereau,** r. Cents 140, ⊠ 1319, ☎ 43 67 87 – ❷. AE E VISA. ⋘
closed 13 to 18 April, 27 July-17 August, 1 to 8 November, Sunday dinner and Monday –
M a la carte 1200/2000.

at Dommeldange Ⓖ Luxembourg :

🏨 **Inter.Continental** ⑤, r. Jean Engling 12, ⊠ 1466, ☎ 4 37 81, Telex 3754, Fax 43 60 95,
≤, 🍽, 🔥, ≦s, 🔲 – 🛗 ⇄ rm 🗏 📺 ☎ ♿ ❷ – 🔬 25-360. AE ◑ E VISA. ⋘ rest
M (closed lunch Saturday and Sunday and August) a la carte approx. 2300 – **344 rm**
⊇ 5300/8550.

🏨 **Parc**, rte d'Echternach 120, ⊠ 1453, ☎ 43 56 43, Telex 1418, Fax 43 69 03, 🔥, ≦s, 🔲,
🌳, ⋇ – 🛗 📺 ☎ ♿ ❷ – 🔬 40-2000. ◑ E VISA
M a la carte 1500/2000 – **271 rm** ⊇ 3500/4200.

🏨 **Host. du Grünewald**, rte d'Echternach 10, ⊠ 1453, ☎ 43 18 82 and 42 03 14 (rest.),
Telex 60543, Fax 42 06 46, 🌳 – 🛗 📺 ☎ ❷ – 🔬 40. AE ◑ E VISA. ⋘ rest
M (closed Saturday lunch, Sunday, Bank Holidays except weekends and 1 to 22 January) a
la carte 2100/2700 – **28 rm** ⊇ 3250/4600.

at Hesperange – pop. 9 660 :

XXX ⊛ **L'Agath** (Steichen) with rm, rte de Thionville 274 (Howald), ⊠ 5884, ☎ 48 86 87,
Fax 48 55 05, 🍽, 🌳 – 📺 ☎ ❷ – 🔬 60. AE ◑ E VISA
closed Sunday, Monday, Bank Holidays, 15 July-1 August and 22 December-4 January –
M a la carte 2100/3100 – **6 rm** ⊇ 2200/3500
Spec. Terrine de queue de bœuf aux légumes et graines de moutarde, Saumon et turbotin en
feuilleté, Suprême de poularde aux ravioles de foie gras. Wines Riesling.

Upland of Kirchberg :

🏨 **Pullman**, r. Fort Niedergrünewald 6 (European Centre), ⊠ 2226, ☎ 43 77 61, Telex 2751,
Fax 43 86 58, ≦s, 🔲 – 🛗 ⇄ rm 🗏 📺 ☎ ♿ ❷ – 🔬 50-450. AE ◑ E VISA. ⋘ rest
M Les Trois Glands (closed Saturday lunch) a la carte 1400/2000 – **260 rm** ⊇ 5100/7000.

at the skating-rink of Kockelscheuer :   ♥

XXX ⊛⊛ **Patin d'Or** (Berring), r. Bettembourg 40, ⊠ 1899, ☎ 22 64 99, Fax 40 40 11 – 🗏 ❷.
◑ E VISA. ⋘
closed Saturday lunch, Sunday, Bank Holidays, 1 week Easter, 1 week Whitsun, late August-early
September and late December-early January – **M** a la carte 2400/2800
Spec. Salade de homard au beurre de Sauternes, St-Jacques et langoustines en chartreuse
(21 September-21 June), Pigeonneau avec sa cuisse en crépinette (February-September). Wines
Pinot gris, Riesling Koëppchen.

at Sandweiler by ④ : 7 km – pop. 2 110 :

XX **Hoffmann,** r. Principale 21, ⊠ 5240, ☎ 3 51 80, Fax 35 79 36 – E VISA. ⋘
closed 2 to 24 August, 25 January-18 March, Monday dinner and Tuesday – **M** a la carte
1300/2050.

Echternach 215 ③ and 409 ㉗ – pop. 4 360 – 35 km.

at Geyershof SW : 6,5 km by E 27 Ⓖ Bech pop. 800 :

XXX ⊛⊛ **La Bergerie** (Phal), ⊠ 6251, ☎ 7 94 64, Fax 7 97 71, ≤, 🍽, « Floral country setting »
– ❷. ◑ E VISA
closed Sunday dinner, Monday and 5 January-12 February – **M** a la carte 2200/3000
Spec. Ballottine de pigeonneau, Feuillantine de langoustines aux artichauts, Sandre au sabayon
de moutarde à l'ancienne. Wines Riesling, Pinot gris.

Paliseul 6850 Luxembourg belge (Belgium) 214 ⑯ and 409 ㉔ – pop. 4 843 – ⊛ 061 –
94 km.

XXX ⊛⊛ **Au Gastronome** (Libotte) with rm, r. Bouillon 2 (Paliseul-Gare), ☎ 53 30 64, « Flowered
garden » – 📺 ⇌ ❷. AE ◑ E VISA. ⋘ rest
closed Sunday dinner and Monday except Bank Holidays, February, carnival and last week
June-first week July – **M** a la carte 1900/2700 – **9 rm** ⊇ 2250/2500
Spec. Ravioli de langoustines aux champignons des bois, Pastilla de homard au pied de porc,
Croustillant de cochon de lait au poivre et citron vert.

Amsterdam

Noord-Holland 𝟜𝟘𝟠 ⑩ ㉗ ㉘ – Pop. 695 162 – ✪ 0 20.

See : Old Amsterdam★★★ : the canals★★★ (Grachten) : Singel ; Herengracht
Cromhout Houses (Cromhouthuizen) ; Reguliersgracht ≼★ ; Keizersgracht – Boat
trips★ (Rond-vaart) – Beguine Convent★★ (Begijnhof) LY – Dam : pulpit★ in the
New Church★ (Nieuwe Kerk) LXY – Flower market★ (Bloemenmarkt) LY –
Rembrandt Square (Rembrandtsplein) MY – Thin Bridge★ (Magere Brug) MZ –
Leeuwenburg House ≼★ MX – Artis★ (Zoological Garden) – Royal Palace★
(Koninklijk Paleis) LY **B**.

Museums : Rijksmuseum★★★ KZ – Vincent van Gogh National Museum★★★
(Rijksmuseum) – Municipal★★ (Stedelijk Museum) : Modern Art – Amsterdam
Historical Museum★★ (Amsterdams Historisch Museum) LY – Madame Tussaud's :
wax museum LY **M¹** – Amstelkring Museum "Our Dear Lord in the Attic" (Museum
Amstelkring Ons'Lieve Heer op Solder) : clandestine chapel MX **M⁴** – Rembrandt's
House★ (Rembrandthuis) : works by the master MY **M⁵** – Netherlands Maritime
History Museum★ (Nederlands Scheepvaart Museum) – Tropical Museum★
(Tropenmuseum) – Allard Pierson★ : antiquities LY **M²** – Jewish Museum★ (Joods
Historisch Museum) MY **M¹⁵**.

Casino **KZ**, Max Euweplein 62 (near Leidseplein) ✆ 620 10 06

🏌 Bauduinlaan 35 at Halfweg ✆ (0 2907)78 66 – 🏌 Zwarte Laantje 4 at
Duivendrecht ✆ (0 20) 694 36 50.

✈ at Schiphol SW : 9,5 km ✆ (0 20) 601 09 66 (information) and 674 77 47
(reservations).

🚗 (Departure from's-Hertogenbosch) ✆ 620 22 66 and 601 05 41 (Schiphol).

🚢 to Göteborg : Scandinavian Seaways Cie ✆ 611 66 15.

🛈 Stationsplein, ✉ 1012 AB ✆ 626 64 44.

Bruxelles 204 – Düsseldorf 227 – Den Haag 60 – Luxembourg 419 – Rotterdam 76.

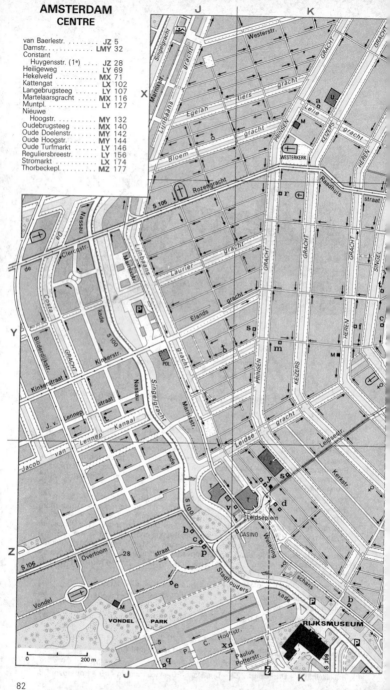

AMSTERDAM
CENTRE

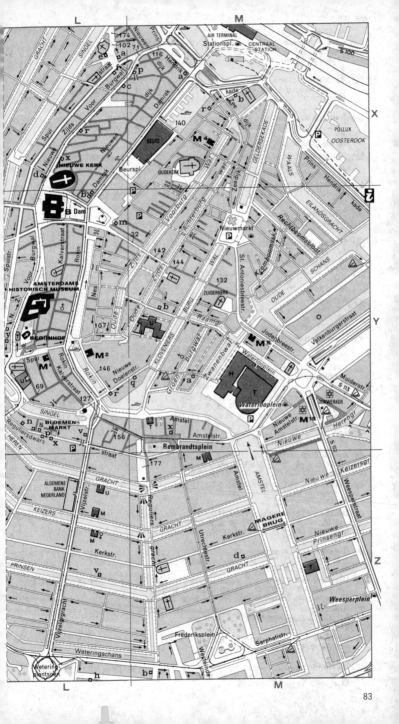

Europe, Nieuwe Doelenstraat 2, ⌧ 1012 CP, ℰ 623 48 36, Telex 12081, Fax 624 29 62, ≤,
ƒ6, ⇌, 🖵 – |≣| 🛏 📺 ☎ 🅿 – 🏛 25-250. 🕮 ⓞ ⅀ 𝘝𝘐𝘚𝘈
LY **r**
M see rest. **Excelsior** below – **Le Relais** (open until midnight) a la carte 62/84 – ⌸ 29 – **101 rm**
385/610.

Barbizon Palace, Prins Hendrikkade 59, ⌧ 1012 AD, ℰ 556 45 64, Telex 10187,
Fax 624 33 53, *ƒ6*, ⇌ – |≣| 🛏 rm ≣ 📺 ☎ & 🅿 – 🏛 25-210. 🕮 ⓞ ⅀ 𝘝𝘐𝘚𝘈. 🍴 rest
M Vermeer *(closed Sunday and mid July-mid August)* (dinner only) 75/90 – ⌸ 30 – **268 rm**
405/525.
MX **b**

Ramada Renaissance, Kattengat 1, ⌧ 1012 SZ, ℰ 621 22 23, Telex 17149, Fax 627 52 45,
« Contemporary art collection », *ƒ6*, ⇌ – |≣| 🛏 ≣ 📺 ☎ & ⇌ – 🏛 25-400. 🕮 ⓞ ⅀
𝘝𝘐𝘚𝘈. 🍴 rest
LX **a**
M a la carte approx. 60 – ⌸ 34 – **425 rm** 425/525.

Marriott, Stadhouderskade 21, ⌧ 1054 ES, ℰ 607 55 55, Telex 15087, Fax 607 55 11, *ƒ6*,
⇌ – |≣| 🛏 rm ≣ 📺 ☎ & ⇌ – 🏛 25-360. 🕮 ⓞ ⅀ 𝘝𝘐𝘚𝘈. 🍴 rest
M (open until 11 p.m.) a la carte approx. 65 – ⌸ 35 – **393 rm** 500.
p

Holiday Inn Crowne Plaza, N.Z. Voorburgwal 5, ⌧ 1012 RC, ℰ 620 05 00, Telex 15183,
Fax 620 11 73, *ƒ6*, ⇌, 🖵 – |≣| 🛏 rm ≣ 📺 ☎ & ⇌ – 🏛 25-260. 🕮 ⓞ ⅀ 𝘝𝘐𝘚𝘈. 🍴
M 7-Seas (dinner only) 50 – ⌸ 28 – **270 rm** 350/475.
MX **p**

SAS Royal ⌁, Rusland 17, ⌧ 1012 CK, ℰ 623 12 31, Telex 10365, Fax 520 82 00, *ƒ6*, ⇌
– |≣| 🛏 rm ≣ 📺 ☎ & ⇌ – 🏛 25-180. 🕮 ⓞ ⅀ 𝘝𝘐𝘚𝘈. 🍴
MY **b**
M a la carte 40/94 – ⌸ 30 – **247 rm** 340/410.

Scandic Crown Victoria, Damrak 1, ⌧ 1012 LG, ℰ 623 42 55, Telex 16625, Fax 625 29 97,
ƒ6, ⇌, 🖵 – |≣| 🛏 ≣ rest 📺 ☎ & 🅿 – 🏛 25-250. 🕮 ⅀ 𝘝𝘐𝘚𝘈
MX **a**
M 40/120 – ⌸ 25 – **305 rm** 300/375.

Gd H. Krasnapolsky, Dam 9, ⌧ 1012 JS, ℰ 554 91 11, Telex 12262, Fax 622 86 07 – |≣|
🛏 rm ≣ 📺 ☎ & ⇌ – 🏛 25-1500. 🕮 ⓞ ⅀ 𝘝𝘐𝘚𝘈. 🍴
LY **m**
M Le Reflet d'Or (dinner only) 55/88 – ⌸ 33 – **317 rm** ⌸ 350/425.

Pulitzer, Prinsengracht 323, ⌧ 1016 GZ, ℰ 523 52 35, Telex 16508, Fax 627 67 53, 🌫,
« Contemporary art collection », ⇌ – |≣| 🛏 rm ≣ rest 📺 ☎ ⇌ – 🏛 25-160. 🕮 ⓞ ⅀
𝘝𝘐𝘚𝘈. 🍴 rest
KY **r**
M De Goudsbloem (dinner only) a la carte 81/105 – ⌸ 33 – **236 rm** 325/445.

Jolly Carlton, Vijzelstraat 4, ⌧ 1017 HK, ℰ 622 22 66, Telex 11670, Fax 626 61 83 – |≣|
🛏 rm ≣ rest 📺 ☎ 🅿 – 🏛 25-80. 🕮 ⓞ ⅀ 𝘝𝘐𝘚𝘈. 🍴
LY **v**
M *(closed Sunday)* (dinner only) a la carte 62/82 – ⌸ 34 – **219 rm** 280/500.

Barbizon Centre, Stadhouderskade 7, ⌧ 1054 ES, ℰ 685 13 51, Telex 12601,
Fax 685 16 11, *ƒ6*, ⇌ – |≣| 🛏 rm ≣ 📺 ☎ & – 🏛 150. 🕮 ⓞ ⅀ 𝘝𝘐𝘚𝘈. 🍴
JZ **c**
M a la carte 63/105 – ⌸ 30 – **236 rm** 370/525.

American, Leidsekade 97, ⌧ 1017 PN, ℰ 624 53 22, Telex 12545, Fax 625 32 36, 🌫, *ƒ6*,
⇌ – |≣| 🛏 ≣ – 🏛 80-200. 🕮 ⓞ ⅀ 𝘝𝘐𝘚𝘈
JKZ **v**
M Café Américain (open until 11 p.m.) a la carte 60/80 – ⌸ 29 – **188 rm** 325/450.

Capitool, N.Z. Voorburgwal 67, ⌧ 1012 RE, ℰ 627 59 00, Telex 14494, Fax 623 89 32, *ƒ6*,
⇌ – |≣| 🛏 rm ≣ 📺 ☎ ⇌ – 🏛 30-100. 🕮 ⓞ ⅀ 𝘝𝘐𝘚𝘈. 🍴 rest
LX **r**
M (dinner only) a la carte 49/83 – **148 rm** ⌸ 270/325.

Ascot, Damrak 95, ⌧ 1012 LP, ℰ 626 00 66, Telex 16620, Fax 627 09 82 – |≣| 🛏 rm ≣
📺 ☎ & – 🏛 25-70. 🕮 ⓞ ⅀ 𝘝𝘐𝘚𝘈. 🍴 rest
LY **b**
M a la carte 60/100 – ⌸ 25 – **110 rm** 280/360.

Doelen, Nieuwe Doelenstraat 24, ⌧ 1012 CP, ℰ 622 07 22, Telex 14399, Fax 622 10 84, ≤
– |≣| 🛏 rm ≣ rest 📺 ☎ – 🏛 25-150
MY **q**
M (dinner only) – **85 rm**.

Dikker en Thijs, Prinsengracht 444, ⌧ 1017 KE, ℰ 626 77 21, Telex 13161, Fax 625 89 86
– |≣| 📺 ☎ ⇌ – 🏛 25. 🕮 ⓞ ⅀ 𝘝𝘐𝘚𝘈. 🍴 rest
KZ **s**
M see rest. **Dikker en Thijs** below – **De Prinsenkelder** (dinner only) a la carte 54/86 – ⌸ 23
– **25 rm** 240/350.

Caransa, Rembrandtsplein 19, ⌧ 1017 CT, ℰ 622 94 55, Telex 13342, Fax 622 27 73, 🌫
– |≣| 🛏 rm ≣ 📺 ☎ – 🏛 30-150. 🕮 ⓞ ⅀ 𝘝𝘐𝘚𝘈
MY **x**
M 35 – **66 rm** ⌸ 265/335.

Die Port van Cleve, N.Z. Voorburgwal 178, ⌧ 1012 SJ, ℰ 624 48 60, Telex 13129,
Fax 622 02 40 – |≣| 📺 ☎ – 🏛 25-50. 🕮 ⓞ ⅀ 𝘝𝘐𝘚𝘈
LX **d**
M see rest. De Blauwe Parade below – **98 rm** ⌸ 245/310.

Ambassade without rest., Herengracht 341, ⌧ 1016 AZ, ℰ 626 23 33, Telex 10158,
Fax 624 53 21, ≤ – |≣| 📺 ☎. 🕮 ⓞ ⅀ 𝘝𝘐𝘚𝘈
KY **f**
47 rm ⌸ 190/250.

Estheréa without rest., Singel 305, ⌧ 1012 WJ, ℰ 624 51 46, Telex 14019, Fax 623 90 01
– |≣| 📺 ☎. 🕮 ⓞ ⅀ 𝘝𝘐𝘚𝘈. 🍴
KY **t**
75 rm ⌸ 250/275.

De Roode Leeuw, Damrak 93, ⌧ 1012 LP, ℰ 624 03 96, Telex 10569, Fax 620 47 16 –
|≣| ≣ rest 📺 ☎ – 🏛 25-50. 🕮 ⓞ ⅀ 𝘝𝘐𝘚𝘈
LXY **b**
M 40/48 – **78 rm** ⌸ 145/285.

🏨 **Avenue** without rest., N.Z. Voorburgwal 27, ⊠ 1012 RD, ℰ 623 83 07, Fax 638 39 46 – 🛗
📺 ☎. 🖭 ⓞ 🖃 𝘝𝘐𝘚𝘈. 🞕 – **50 rm** ☑ 150/190.
LX **c**

🏨 **Owl** without rest., Roemer Visscherstraat 1, ⊠ 1054 EV, ℰ 618 94 84, Telex 13360,
Fax 618 94 41 – 🛗 📺 ☎. 🖭 ⓞ 🖃 𝘝𝘐𝘚𝘈 – **34 rm** ☑ 130/175.
JZ **e**

🏨 **Nicolaas Witsen** without rest., Nicolaas Witsenstraat 4, ⊠ 1017 ZH, ℰ 626 65 46,
Fax 620 51 13 – 🛗 📺 ☎. 🖃 𝘝𝘐𝘚𝘈 – **31 rm** ☑ 80/170.
MZ **b**

🏨 **Wiechmann** without rest., Prinsengracht 328, ⊠ 1016 HX, ℰ 626 33 21, Fax 626 89 62 –
📺 ☎
38 rm ☑ 150/225.
KY **s**

🏨 **Asterisk** without rest., Den Texstraat 16, ⊠ 1017 ZA, ℰ 626 23 96, Fax 638 27 90 – 🛗 📺
☎. 🖃 𝘝𝘐𝘚𝘈
25 rm ☑ 60/175.
LZ **h**

🍴🍴🍴🍴 ❀ **Excelsior** - (at Europe H.), Nieuwe Doelenstraat 2, ⊠ 1012 CP, ℰ 623 48 36, Telex 12081,
Fax 624 29 62, ≤, 🏤 – 🗐. 🅿 🖭 ⓞ 🖃 𝘝𝘐𝘚𝘈
LY **r**
closed Saturday lunch – **M** a la carte 105/145
Spec. Langoustines au curry et pommes à la crème, Turbot enrobé de pommes de terre crous-
tillantes à l'huile de truffes, Perdreau choucroute à la crème de foie d'oie (September-January).

🍴🍴🍴 **Dikker en Thijs** 1st floor, Prinsengracht 444, ⊠ 1017 KE, ℰ 626 77 21, Telex 13161,
Fax 625 89 86 – 🖭 ⓞ 🖃 𝘝𝘐𝘚𝘈
KZ **s**
closed Sunday and 27 July-10 August – **M** (dinner only) 90/105.

🍴🍴🍴 **D'Vijff Vlieghen,** Spuistraat 294, ⊠ 1012 VX, ℰ 624 83 69, Fax 623 64 04, « Typical
17C houses » – 🞕. 🖭 ⓞ 🖃 𝘝𝘐𝘚𝘈
KY **c**
closed 1 January – **M** (dinner only) a la carte 67/114.

🍴🍴🍴 **Radèn Mas,** Stadhouderskade 6, ⊠ 1054 ES, ℰ 685 40 41, Fax 685 39 81, Indonesian cuisine, « Exotic decor » – 🗐.
JZ **b**

🍴🍴🍴 **De Blauwe Parade** - (at Die Port van Cleve H.), N.Z. Voorburgwal 178, ⊠ 1012 SJ,
ℰ 624 00 47, Telex 13129, Fax 622 02 40, « Delftware » – 🖭 ⓞ 🖃 𝘝𝘐𝘚𝘈. 🞕
LX **d**
closed lunch Saturday and Sunday – **M** 65/80.

🍴🍴 **Dynasty,** Reguliersdwarsstraat 30, ⊠ 1017 BM, ℰ 626 84 00, Fax 620 32 38, 🏤, Oriental
cuisine – 🗐. 🖭 ⓞ 🖃 𝘝𝘐𝘚𝘈. 🞕
LY **p**
closed Tuesday – **M** (dinner only) a la carte 55/95.

🍴🍴 **'t Swarte Schaep** 1st floor, Korte Leidsedwarsstraat 24, ⊠ 1017 RC, ℰ 622 30 21,
Fax 624 82 68, Open until 11 p.m., « 17C, old Dutch interior » – 🗐. 🖭 ⓞ 🖃 𝘝𝘐𝘚𝘈 KZ **d**
closed 25, 26 and 31 December and 1 January – **M** a la carte 90/125.

🍴🍴 **Les Quatre Canetons,** Prinsengracht 1111, ⊠ 1017 JJ, ℰ 624 63 07, Fax 638 45 99 – 🖭
ⓞ 🖃 𝘝𝘐𝘚𝘈. 🞕
MZ **d**
closed Saturday lunch, Sunday, Easter, Whitsun and 31 December-1 January – **M** 78/140.

🍴🍴 **Tout Court,** Runstraat 13, ⊠ 1016 GJ, ℰ 625 86 37 – 🖭 ⓞ 🖃 𝘝𝘐𝘚𝘈
KY **m**
closed Sunday and Monday – **M** (dinner only until 11.30 p.m.) 50/90.

🍴🍴 **Sichuan Food,** Reguliersdwarsstraat 35, ⊠ 1017 BK, ℰ 626 93 27, Chinese cuisine – 🗐.
🖭 ⓞ 🖃 𝘝𝘐𝘚𝘈. 🞕
LY **s**
M (dinner only until 11.30 p.m.) a la carte 59/83.

🍴🍴 **De Oesterbar,** Leidseplein 10, ⊠ 1017 PT, ℰ 623 29 88, Seafood, open until midnight –
🗐. 🖭 ⓞ 🖃. 🞕
KZ **y**
M 40/80.

🍴🍴 **Treasure,** N.Z. Voorburgwal 115, ⊠ 1012 RH, ℰ 626 09 15, Fax 640 12 02, Chinese cuisine
– 🗐. 🞕
LX **x**
M a la carte 40/68.

🍴🍴 **Manchurian,** Leidseplein 10a, ⊠ 1017 PT, ℰ 623 13 30, Fax 622 30 38, Oriental cuisine
– 🗐. 🖭 ⓞ 🖃 𝘝𝘐𝘚𝘈. 🞕
KZ **y**
closed late December-early February – **M** a la carte approx. 50.

🍴🍴 **Les Trois Neufs,** Prinsengracht 999, ⊠ 1017 KM, ℰ 622 90 44 – 🖭 ⓞ 🖃 𝘝𝘐𝘚𝘈 LZ **v**
closed Monday, mid July-mid August and 25 December-2 January – **M** (dinner only) 45/70.

🍴🍴 **Lana Thai,** Warmoesstraat 10, ⊠ 1012 JD, ℰ 624 21 79, Thaï cuisine – 🖭 ⓞ 🖃 𝘝𝘐𝘚𝘈. 🞕
MX **r**
M (dinner only until 11 p.m.) a la carte approx. 65.

🍴🍴 **La Camargue,** Reguliersdwarsstraat 7, ⊠ 1017 BJ, ℰ 623 93 52, Open until 11 p.m. – 🗐.
🖭 ⓞ 🖃 𝘝𝘐𝘚𝘈. 🞕
LY **n**
closed 31 December and 1 January – **M** 43/60.

🍴🍴 **Het Amsterdamse Wijnhuis,** Reguliersdwarsstraat 23, ⊠ 1017 BJ, ℰ 623 42 59 – 🖭
ⓞ 🖃 𝘝𝘐𝘚𝘈
LY **n**
closed Sunday, Monday and 23 December-8 January – **M** 40.

🍴🍴 **Sea Palace,** Oosterdokskade 8, ⊠ 1011 AE, ℰ 626 47 77, Fax 620 42 66, Asian cuisine,
open until 11 p.m., « Floating restaurant with ≤ town » – 🖭 ⓞ 🖃 𝘝𝘐𝘚𝘈. 🞕
M a la carte approx. 55.

🍴🍴 ❀ **Christophe** (Royer), Leliegracht 46, ⊠ 1015 DH, ℰ 625 08 07 – 🗐. 🖭 ⓞ 🖃 𝘝𝘐𝘚𝘈
closed 19 July-11 August, 1 to 4 January, Sunday and Monday – **M** (dinner only until 11 p.m.)
a la carte 85/130
KX **a**
Spec. Compote de figues fraîches et la glace au thym, Rougets grillés aux artichauts "barigoule",
Pigeonneau à la marocaine.

✗ **Le Provençal,** Weteringschans 91, ✉ 1017 RZ, ☎ 623 96 19 – ▤. 🅰🅴 ⓪ 🄴 𝖵𝖨𝖲𝖠 KZ **b**
M 55/80.

✗ **Tom Yam,** Staalstraat 22, ✉ 1011 JM, ☎ 622 95 33, Fax 624 90 62, Thaï cuisine – 🅰🅴 🄴
𝖵𝖨𝖲𝖠   MY **a**
closed Monday – **M** (dinner only) a la carte 64/89.

✗ **Bistro La Forge,** Korte Leidsedwarsstraat 26, ✉ 1017 RC, ☎ 624 00 95 – 🅰🅴 ⓪ 🄴
𝖵𝖨𝖲𝖠   KZ **d**
closed 24, 31 December and 1 January – **M** (dinner only until 11 p.m.) 43/75.

✗ **Lucius,** Spuistraat 247, ✉ 1012 VP, ☎ 624 18 31, Fax 627 61 53, Seafood – 🅰🅴 ⓪ 🄴
𝖵𝖨𝖲𝖠   LY **e**
closed 31 December – **M** (dinner only until 11 p.m.) 60.

✗ **Haesje Claes,** Spuistraat 273, ✉ 1012 RV, ☎ 624 99 98, Fax 627 48 17, « Typical
atmosphere » – 🅰🅴 🄴 𝖵𝖨𝖲𝖠. ⌘   LY **y**
closed lunch Sunday and Bank Holidays – **M** a la carte 40/57.

✗ **Kantjil,** Spuistraat 291, ✉ 1012 VS, ☎ 620 09 94, Fax 623 21 66, 🍴, Pub-rest., Indonesian
cuisine, open until 11 p.m. – ⤬. 🅰🅴 🄴 𝖵𝖨𝖲𝖠. ⌘   LY **y**
M a la carte 40/87.

South and West Quarters

🏨🏨 **Okura,** Ferdinand Bolstraat 333, ✉ 1072 LH, ☎ 678 71 11, Telex 16182, Fax 671 23 44, ⇔s
– 🛗 ▤ 📺 ☎ ⇔ ℗ – 🔬 25-600. 🅰🅴 ⓪ 🄴 𝖵𝖨𝖲𝖠. ⌘
M see rest. **Ciel Bleu** below – **Yamazato** (Japanese cuisine) 100/150 – ☲ 32 – **370 rm** 430/480.

🏨🏨 **Garden,** Dijsselhofplantsoen 7, ✉ 1077 BJ, ☎ 664 21 21, Telex 15453, Fax 679 93 56 – 🛗
⤬ 📺 ☎ ℗ – 🔬 25-150. 🅰🅴 ⓪ 🄴 𝖵𝖨𝖲𝖠
M see rest. **De Kersentuin** below – ☲ – **96 rm** 340/420.

🏨🏨 **Apollo,** Apollolaan 2, ✉ 1077 BA, ☎ 673 59 22, Telex 14084, Fax 570 57 44, 🍴, « Terrace
with ⩽ canal » – 🛗 ⤬ rm 📺 ☎ ℗ – 🔬 25-200. 🅰🅴 ⓪ 🄴 𝖵𝖨𝖲𝖠. ⌘
M a la carte 79/105 – ☲ 30 – **219 rm** 380/450.

🏨🏨 **Hilton,** Apollolaan 138, ✉ 1077 BG, ☎ 678 07 80, Telex 11025, Fax 662 66 88 – 🛗 ⤬ rm
▤ rest 📺 ☎ ℗ – 🔬 25-325. 🅰🅴 ⓪ 🄴 𝖵𝖨𝖲𝖠
M 50/85 – ☲ 36 – **265 rm** 390/630.

🏨 **Novotel,** Europaboulevard 10, ✉ 1083 AD, ☎ 541 11 23, Telex 13375, Fax 646 28 23 – 🛗
⤬ rm 📺 ☎ ℗ – 🔬 25-300. 🅰🅴 ⓪ 🄴 𝖵𝖨𝖲𝖠
M (open until midnight) a la carte approx. 50 – ☲ 23 – **600 rm** 240/270.

🏨 **Altea,** Joan Muyskenweg 10, ✉ 1096 CJ, ☎ 665 81 81, Telex 13382, Fax 694 87 35, 🛋,
⇔s – 🛗 ⤬ rm 📺 ☎ 🕭 ℗ – 🔬 25-250. 🅰🅴 ⓪ 🄴 𝖵𝖨𝖲𝖠. ⌘ rm
M a la carte 40/90 – **178 rm** ☲ 205/240.

🏨 **Memphis** without rest., De Lairessestraat 87, ✉ 1071 NX, ☎ 673 31 41, Telex 12450,
Fax 673 73 12 – 🛗 ⤬ rm 📺 ☎ ℗ – 🔬 25-45. 🅰🅴 ⓪ 🄴 𝖵𝖨𝖲𝖠
74 rm ☲ 325/360.

🏨 **Cok Hotels,** Koninginneweg 34, ✉ 1075 CZ, ☎ 664 61 11 – 🛗 📺 ☎ – 🔬 25-80
159 rm.

🏨 **Toro** ⌖ without rest., Koningslaan 64, ✉ 1075 AG, ☎ 673 72 23, Fax 675 00 31 – 🛗 📺
☎. 🅰🅴 ⓪ 🄴 𝖵𝖨𝖲𝖠
22 rm ☲ 115/190.

🏨 **Jan Luyken** without rest., Jan Luykenstraat 58, ✉ 1071 CS, ☎ 573 07 30, Telex 16254,
Fax 676 38 41 – 🛗 📺 ☎ – 🔬 25-150. 🅰🅴 ⓪ 🄴 𝖵𝖨𝖲𝖠. ⌘   JZ **x**
63 rm ☲ 240/300.

🏨 **Borgmann** without rest., Koningslaan 48, ✉ 1075 AE, ☎ 673 52 52, Fax 676 25 80 – 🛗 📺
☎. 🅰🅴 ⓪ 🄴 𝖵𝖨𝖲𝖠. ⌘
15 rm ☲ 115/205.

🏨 **Apollofirst,** Apollolaan 123, ✉ 1077 AP, ☎ 673 03 33 and 679 79 71 (rest.), Telex 13446,
Fax 675 03 48, 🍴 – 🛗 ▤ rest 📺 ☎ 🅰🅴 ⓪ 🄴 𝖵𝖨𝖲𝖠. ⌘ rest
M *(closed Saturday lunch, Sunday and 27 December-1 January)* a la carte 71/85 – **40 rm**
☲ 250/275.

🏨 **Delphi** without rest., Apollolaan 105, ✉ 1077 AN, ☎ 679 51 52, Telex 16659, Fax 675 29 41
– 🛗 📺 ☎ 🅰🅴 ⓪ 🄴 𝖵𝖨𝖲𝖠
closed 24 December-2 January – **50 rm** ☲ 165/225.

✗✗✗ ❀ **De Kersentuin** - (at Garden H.), Dijsselhofplantsoen 7, ✉ 1077 BJ, ☎ 664 21 21,
Telex 15453, Fax 679 93 56 – ℗. 🅰🅴 ⓪ 🄴 𝖵𝖨𝖲𝖠
closed Saturday lunch, Sunday, 31 December and 1 January – **M** a la carte 117/153
Spec. Flétan braisé à l'huile d'olives et crème de pommes de terre, Raviolis de truffes et carpaccio
de canette au romarin, Poularde de Malines en demi-deuil à la moutarde régionale.

✗✗✗ **Ciel Bleu** 23rd floor - (at Okura H.), Ferdinand Bolstraat 333, ✉ 1072 LH, ☎ 678 71 11,
Telex 16182, Fax 671 23 44, ⩽ town, Partly Asian cuisine – ▤ ℗. 🅰🅴 ⓪ 🄴 𝖵𝖨𝖲𝖠. ⌘
closed 1 to 15 August – **M** (dinner only) 83/130.

✗✗✗ **Parkrest. Rosarium,** Amstelpark 1, Europaboulevard, ✉ 1083 HZ, ☎ 644 40 85,
Fax 646 60 04, 🍴, « Floral park » – ℗. 🅰🅴 ⓪ 🄴 𝖵𝖨𝖲𝖠
closed Sunday – **M** a la carte 85/120.

XX ✿ **De Trechter** (de Wit), Hobbemakade 63, ✉ 1071 XL, ✆ 671 12 63, Fax 685 25 71 – AE ⓓ E VISA. ✼
closed Sunday, Monday, Bank Holidays, 14 July-5 August and 25 December-8 January –
M (dinner only, booking essential) a la carte 90/118
Spec. Terrine d'anguille au vert aux tomates confites (April-Nov.), Terrine de foie gras d'oie, filet de bœuf et persil, Pêche au four au jus de menthe et crème anglaise (August-October).

XX ✿ **Halvemaan,** van Leyenberghlaan 20 (Gijsbrecht van Aemstelpark), ✉ 1082 GM, ✆ 644 03 48, Fax 644 17 77, ☂, « Terrace with ≤ private lake » – Ⓟ. AE ⓓ E VISA. ✼
closed Saturday lunch, Sunday and 24 December-2 January – **M** a la carte 96/142
Spec. Soupe de homard et crevettes au basilic, Homard à l'ail, Bread and Butter pudding.

XX **De Graaf** 1st floor, Emmalaan 25, ✉ 1075 AT, ✆ 662 48 84, Fax 675 60 91 – AE ⓓ E VISA. ✼
closed 28 December-11 January – **M** 79/125.

XX **Bartholdy,** Van Baerlestraat 35, ✉ 1071 AP, ✆ 662 26 55, Fax 671 09 19, ☂ – ▤. AE E VISA. ✼ – *closed Monday* – **M** a la carte 74/112.

XX **Le Garage,** Ruysdaelstraat 54, ✉ 1071 XE, ✆ 679 71 76, Fax 662 22 49 – AE ⓓ E VISA. ✼
M (dinner only, open until midnight) a la carte approx. 60.

XX **Beddington's,** Roelof Hartstraat 6, ✉ 1071 VH, ✆ 676 52 01 – AE ⓓ E VISA. ✼
closed Sunday and 20 December-4 January – **M** a la carte 70/89.

XX **Keyzer,** Van Baerlestraat 96, ✉ 1071 BB, ✆ 671 14 41, Fax 673 73 53, Open until 11.30 p.m. – AE ⓓ E VISA. ✼
closed Sunday and Bank Holidays – **M** 40/80.

XX **Het Bosch,** Jollenpad 10 (by Amstelveenseweg), ✉ 1081 KC, ✆ 644 58 00, Fax 644 19 64, ≤, ☂, « Terrace overlooking lake » – ▤ Ⓟ. AE ⓓ E VISA. ✼
closed Sunday October-March – **M** a la carte 70/105.

X **Ravel,** Gelderlandplein 2, ✉ 1082 LA, ✆ 644 16 43, Fax 642 86 84, Pub-rest. – ▤. AE ⓓ E VISA – *closed Sunday lunch* – **M** 43/63.

X **Brasserie Van Baerle,** Van Baerlestraat 158, ✉ 1071 BG, ✆ 679 15 32, Fax 671 71 96, ☂, Pub-rest., open until 11 p.m. – ✼
closed Saturday and 25 December-2 January – **M** 55.

X **Oriënt,** Van Baerlestraat 21, ✉ 1071 AN, ✆ 673 49 58, Indonesian cuisine – ▤. AE ⓓ E VISA
closed 27 to 31 December – **M** (dinner only) a la carte 40/62. JZ **q**

North

🏨 **Galaxy,** Distelkade 21, ✉ 1031 XP, ✆ 634 43 66, Telex 18607, Fax 636 03 45 – ▥ TV ☎ Ⓟ – 🏛 25-250. AE ⓓ E VISA
M a la carte approx. 55 – **280 rm** ☕ 205/240.

🏨 **Bastion Noord** without rest., Rode Kruisstraat 28 (by Nieuwe Purmerweg), ✉ 1025 KN, ✆ 632 31 31, Fax 634 44 96 – TV ☎ Ⓟ. AE ⓓ E VISA. ✼
40 rm ☕ 106/134.

Environs

at Schiphol (international airport) Ⓒ Haarlemmermeer pop. 95 782 – ☎ 0 20 :

🏨 **Hilton International,** Herbergierstraat 1, ✉ 1118 ZK, ✆ 603 45 67, Telex 15186, Fax 648 09 17, 🏋, ≘ – ▥ ⇎ rm ▤ TV ☎ ♿ Ⓟ – 🏛 25-110. AE ⓓ E VISA. ✼ rest
M a la carte 81/114 – ☕ 33 – **275 rm** 415/590.

by motorway The Hague (A 4) – ☎ 0 20 :

🏨 **Pullman,** Oude Haagseweg 20, ✉ 1066 BW, ✆ 617 90 05, Telex 15524, Fax 615 90 27 – ▥ ⇎ rm ▤ rest TV ☎ Ⓟ – 🏛 25-250. AE ⓓ E VISA. ✼
M a la carte 60/81 – **151 rm** ☕ 225/260.

🏨 **Barbizon,** Kruisweg 495, ✉ 2132 NA Hoofddorp (15 km), ✆ (0 20) 655 05 55, Telex 74546, Fax (0 20) 653 49 99, ☂, 🏋, ≘ – ▥ ⇎ rm ▤ TV ☎ ♿ Ⓟ – 🏛 25-500. AE ⓓ E VISA
M *(closed lunch Saturday and Sunday and late December)* a la carte 80/119 – ☕ 29 – **244 rm** 350/395.

Amstelveen

Noord-Holland 408 ⑩ ㉗ – pop. 69 982 – ☎ 0 20 – 11 km.

XXX ✿ **Molen "De Dikkert",** Amsterdamseweg 104a, ✉ 1182 HG, ✆ 641 13 78, Fax 647 54 67, « 17C windmill » – Ⓟ. AE ⓓ E VISA
closed Sunday except Bank Holidays and last week July-first 2 weeks August – **M** a la carte 78/125
Spec. Brandade glacée de turbot, Foie gras de canard braisé enrobé de chou, Râble de lièvre aux pruneaux sauce poivrade (15 Oct.-Dec.).

Blokzijl

Overijssel Ⓒ Brederwiede pop. 11 907 408 ⑫ – ☎ 0 5272 – 102 km.

🏨 ✿✿ **Kaatje bij de Sluis** ⛵, Brouwerstraat 20, ✉ 8356 DV, ✆ 18 33, Fax 18 36, ≤, 🪑 – ▤ rest TV ☎ Ⓟ. AE ⓓ E VISA
closed Monday, Tuesday and February – **M** *(closed Monday, Tuesday and Saturday lunch)* a la carte 99/139 – ☕ 28 – **8 rm** 185/240
Spec. Homard gratiné aux tomates et basilic, Feuilleté de saumon cru à l'aneth, Canard sauvage au vin rouge (August-15 November).

Haarlem Noord-Holland 408 ⑩ – pop. 149 269 – ✪ 0 23 – 24 km.

at Overveen W : 4 km Ⓒ Bloemendaal pop. 17 369 – ✪ 0 23 :

XXX ✿✿ **De Bokkedoorns,** Zeeweg 53 (by ①), ⊠ 2051 EB, ✆ 26 36 00, Fax 27 31 43, 舎 « Terrace with ≤ dunes » – ▤ Ⓟ 🝙 ⓪ Ⅎ VISA ✂
closed Monday, Saturday lunch, 5, 24 and 31 December-13 January – **M** a la carte 109/158
Spec. Salade de homard à l'huile de homard, Waterzooi de coquelet, Grand dessert.

Hoorn Noord-Holland 408 ⑩ ⑪ – pop. 57 384 – ✪ 0 2290 – 43 km.

XX ✿✿ **De Oude Rosmolen** (Fonk), Duinsteeg 1, ⊠ 1621 ER, ✆ 1 47 52, Fax 1 49 38 – ▤ 🝙
Ⅎ VISA
closed Thursday, 10 to 27 August, 28 December-7 January and 2 weeks February – **M** (dinner only, booking essential) a la carte 92/135
Spec. Profiterolles à la mousse de foie gras, St-Pierre au court-bouillon à l'huile parfumée, Pâtisseries maison.

Zaandam Noord-Holland Ⓒ Zaanstad pop. 130 007 408 ⑩ – ✪ 0 75 – 16 km.

XXX ✿ **De Hoop op d'Swarte Walvis,** Kalverringdijk 15 (Zaanse Schans), ⊠ 1509 BT, ✆ 16 55 40, Fax 16 24 76, 舎, « 18C residence in a museum village » – ✂ Ⓟ 🝙 ⓪ Ⅎ
VISA ✂
closed 28 December-3 January, Saturday lunch and Sunday – **M** a la carte 95/128
Spec. Petits gâteaux de pommes de terre farcis de saumon et couvert de foie d'oie, Bar grillé sauce au verjus, foie d'oie sauté au jus de truffes.

If you intend staying in a resort or hotel
off the beaten track, telephone in advance,
especially during the season.

The HAGUE (Den HAAG or 's-GRAVENHAGE) Zuid-Holland 408 ⑨ – pop. 441 506 – ✪ 0 70.
See : Scheveningen★★ – Binnenhof★ : The Knights' Room★ (Ridderzaal) JV **A** – Hofvijver (Court pool) ≤★ JV – Lange Voorhout★ JV – Panorama Mesdag★ HV **B** – Madurodam★.
Museums : Mauritshuis★★★ JV **D** – Municipal★★ (Gemeentemuseum) – Mesdag★ HU **M²** – Prince William V painting gallery★ (Schilderijengalerij Prins Willem V).
🛆 at Wassenaar N : 4 km, Gr. Haesebroekseweg 22 ✆ (0 1751) 7 96 07 – 🛆 at Wassenaar, Hoge klei 1 ✆ (0 1751) 1 78 46 – 🛆 at Rijswijk SE : 5 km, Delftweg 59 ✆ (0 70) 399 50 40.
🛪 Amsterdam-Schiphol NE : 37 km ✆ (0 20) 601 09 66 (information) and (0 20) 674 77 47 (reservations) – Rotterdam-Zestienhoven SE : 17 km ✆ (0 10) 446 34 44 (information) and 437 27 45, 415 54 30 (reservations).
🚄 (departs from 's-Hertogenbosch) ✆ 347 16 81.
🛈 Kon. Julianaplein 30, ⊠ 2595 AA, ✆ 354 62 00.
Amsterdam 55 – Brussels 182 – Rotterdam 24 – Delft 13.

Plan opposite

🏨 **Des Indes,** Lange Voorhout 54, ⊠ 2514 EG, ✆ 363 29 32, Telex 31196, Fax 345 17 21, « Late 19C residence » – 🛗 ✂ rm ▤ rest 📺 🕾 Ⓟ – 🔏 25-250. 🝙 ⓪ Ⅎ VISA JV **s**
M Le Restaurant a la carte approx. 65 – ⊇ 36 – **76 rm** 360/460.

🏨 **Sofitel,** Koningin Julianaplein 35, ⊠ 2595 AA, ✆ 381 49 01, Telex 34001, Fax 382 59 27 – 🛗 ✂ rm ▤ 📺 🕾 Ⓟ 🕭 – 🔏 25-100. 🝙 ⓪ Ⅎ VISA
M a la carte approx. 90 – ⊇ 30 – **144 rm** 300/375.

🏨 **Promenade,** van Stolkweg 1, ⊠ 2585 JL, ✆ 352 51 61, Telex 31162, Fax 354 10 46, ≤, « Collection of modern Dutch paintings » – 🛗 ▤ rest 📺 🕾 🛆 Ⓟ – 🔏 25-160. 🝙 ⓪ Ⅎ VISA
M La Cigogne *(closed Saturday and Sunday)* a la carte 49/93 – ⊇ 28 – **101 rm** 315/345.

🏨 **Pullman Central,** Spui 180, ⊠ 2511 BW, ✆ 363 67 00, Telex 32000, Fax 363 93 98, 🛋, 🕾 – 🛗 ✂ rm ▤ rest 📺 🕾 Ⓟ – 🔏 25-110. 🝙 ⓪ Ⅎ VISA JX **v**
M 40 – **159 rm** ⊇ 260.

🏨 ✿ **Corona,** Buitenhof 42, ⊠ 2513 AH, ✆ 363 79 30, Telex 31418, Fax 361 57 85 – 🛗 ▤ rest 📺 📺 🕾 🝙 ⓪ Ⅎ VISA HV **v**
M *(closed last 2 weeks July)* a la carte 115/145 – ⊇ 15 – **26 rm** 230/455
Spec. Langoustines en chaud-froid à l'orientale, Bar et poivrons grillés aux filets d'anchois et thym.

🏨 **Bel Air,** Johan de Wittlaan 30, ⊠ 2517 JR, ✆ 350 20 21, Telex 31444, Fax 351 26 82, ≤, ⛆ – 🛗 📺 🕾 Ⓟ – 🔏 25-250. 🝙 ⓪ Ⅎ VISA ✂ rest
M a la carte 42/86 – ⊇ 25 – **350 rm** 210/250.

🏨 **Parkhotel** without rest., Molenstraat 53, ⊠ 2513 BJ, ✆ 362 43 71, Telex 33005, Fax 361 45 25 – 🛗 📺 🕾 – 🔏 25-100. 🝙 ⓪ Ⅎ VISA HV **a**
114 rm ⊇ 133/225.

🏨 **Paleis** without rest., Molenstraat 26, ⊠ 2513 BL, ✆ 362 46 21, Telex 34349, Fax 361 45 33, 🕾 – 🛗 📺 🝙 ⓪ Ⅎ VISA HV **r**
⊇ 13 – **20 rm** 149/209.

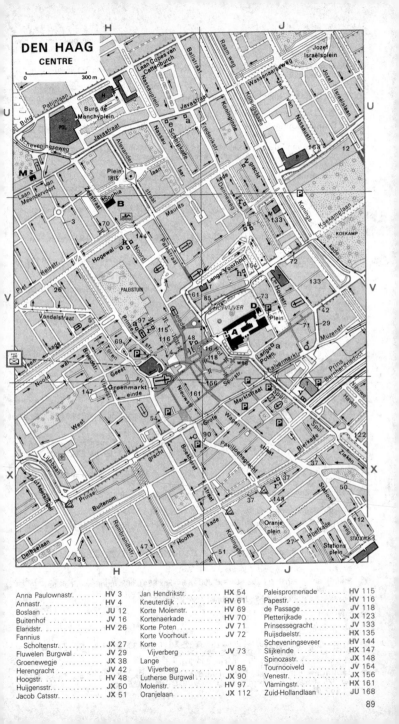

XXX **Da Roberto,** Noordeinde 196, ⊠ 2514 GS, ℰ 346 49 77, Italian cuisine, open until 11 p.m.
– AE ⓪ E   HV **k**
closed Tuesday and lunch Saturday and Sunday – **M** a la carte 75/93.

XXX **De Hoogwerf,** Zijdelaan 20 (by N 44), ⊠ 2594 BV, ℰ 347 55 14, Fax 381 95 96, 斎, « 17C
farmhouse, garden » – AE ⓪ E VISA ✸
closed Sunday and Bank Holidays except 30 April and 25 and 26 December – **M** 75.

XXX **Royal Dynasty,** Noordeinde 123, ⊠ 2514 GG, ℰ 365 25 98, Asian cuisine – ▤. AE ⓪ E
VISA   HV **k**
closed Monday and 27 December – **M** a la carte 49/65.

XX **La Grande Bouffe,** Maziestraat 10, ⊠ 2514 GT, ℰ 365 42 74, Fax 356 28 28 – AE E VISA
closed Monday and 27 July-19 August – **M** 60/87.   HV **k**

XX **Rousseau,** Van Boetzelaerlaan 134, ⊠ 2581 AX, ℰ 355 47 43, 斎 – AE ⓪ E VISA
closed 24 February-9 March, 1 to 21 September, Monday and lunch Saturday and Sunday –
M a la carte 72/105.

XX **'t Ganzenest,** Groenewegje 115, ⊠ 2515 LP, ℰ 389 67 09 – AE ⓪ E. ✸   JX **r**
*closed Sunday, Monday, late August-early September, 31 December-2 January and first week
February* – **M** (dinner only, open until 11.30 p.m.) 53/80.

XX **Shirasagi,** Spui 170, ⊠ 2511 BW, ℰ 346 47 00, Fax 346 26 01, Japanese cuisine, teppan-
yaki – ▤ Ⓟ. AE ⓪ E VISA. ✸   JX **v**
closed lunch Saturday and Sunday – **M** 45/125.

XX Radèn Ajoe, Lange Poten 31, ⊠ 2511 CM, ℰ 364 56 13, Fax 364 45 92, Indonesian cuisine.   JV **a**

X **Les Ombrelles,** Hooistraat 4a, ⊠ 2514 BM, ℰ 365 87 89, 斎, Seafood, open until 11 p.m.
– AE ⓪ E VISA. ✸   JV **r**
closed late December-early January and lunch Saturday and Sunday – **M** 50.

X **Saur,** Lange Voorhout 47, ⊠ 2514 EC, ℰ 346 25 65, Fax 365 86 14, Seafood – ▤. AE ⓪
E VISA.   JV **h**
closed Sunday and Bank Holidays – **M** a la carte 54/89.

at Scheveningen Ⓒ *'s-Gravenhage* – ✪ 0 70 – Casino Kurhaus, Gevers Deijnootplein ℰ 351 26 21.
🛈 Gevers Deijnootweg 126, ⊠ 2586 BP, ℰ 354 62 00

🏨 **Kurhaus,** Gevers Deijnootplein 30, ⊠ 2586 CK, ℰ 352 00 52, Telex 33295, Fax 350 09 11,
≤, 斎, « Former late 19C concert hall », 🗜, ⩫, 🎱 – 🛗 ⩫ rm 📺 ☎ ⏦ Ⓟ – 🔬 35-480.
AE ⓪ E VISA. ✸ rest
M see rest. **Kandinsky** below – **Kurzaal** (Buffets) a la carte approx. 40 – ⊡ 33 – **231 rm** 345/440.

🏨 **Carlton Beach,** Gevers Deijnootweg 201, ⊠ 2586 HZ, ℰ 354 14 14, Telex 33687,
Fax 352 00 20, ≤, 🗜, ⩫, 🗜 – 🛗 📺 ☎ Ⓟ – 🔬 45-280. AE ⓪ E VISA
M 55 – ⊡ 18 – **182 rm** 195/235.

🏨 **Europa,** Zwolsestraat 2, ⊠ 2587 VJ, ℰ 351 26 51, Telex 33138, Fax 350 64 73, 🗜, ⩫,
🗜 – 🛗 ⩫ rm 📺 ☎ Ⓟ – 🔬 400. AE ⓪ E VISA
M (dinner only until 11 p.m.) 40/95 – ⊡ 26 – **174 rm** 200/285.

XXXX **Kandinsky** - (at Kurhaus H.), Gevers Deijnootplein 30, ⊠ 2586 CK, ℰ 352 00 52,
Telex 33295, Fax 350 09 11, ≤, Open until 11.30 p.m. – ▤ Ⓟ. AE ⓪ E VISA. ✸
M a la carte 94/138.

XXX Radèn Mas, Gevers Deijnootplein 125, ⊠ 2586 CR, ℰ 354 54 32, Fax 354 54 32, Indonesian
cuisine – ▤.

XXX **Seinpost,** Zeekant 60, ⊠ 2586 AD, ℰ 355 52 50, Fax 355 50 93, ≤, Seafood – ▤. AE ⓪
E VISA
closed Saturday lunch, Sunday and 24 December – **M** a la carte 54/77.

XX **China Delight,** Dr Lelykade 118, ⊠ 2583 CN, ℰ 355 54 50, Fax 354 66 52, Chinese cuisine,
open until 11 p.m. – ▤. ⓪ E VISA
M a la carte 50/78.

XX **Ducdalf,** Dr Lelykade 5, ⊠ 2583 CL, ℰ 355 76 92, Fax 355 15 28, ≤, Seafood, Mussels in
season – Ⓟ. AE ⓪ E VISA
closed 31 December and 1 January – **M** 50/83.

XX **Bali,** Badhuisweg 1, ⊠ 2587 CA, ℰ 350 24 34, Fax 354 03 63, Indonesian cuisine – Ⓟ. AE
⓪ E VISA. ✸
closed 31 December – **M** (dinner only) 40/63.

Environs

at Kijkduin W : 4 km Ⓒ *'s-Gravenhage* – ✪ 0 70 :

🏨 **Atlantic,** Deltaplein 200, ⊠ 2554 EJ, ℰ 325 40 25, Fax 368 67 21, ≤, 斎, 🗜, ⩫, 🗜 –
🛗 📺 ☎ Ⓟ – 🔬 25-300. AE ⓪ E VISA. ✸ rest
M a la carte 55/98 – ⊡ 20 – **120 rm** 200/275.

🏨 **Zeehaghe** without rest., Deltaplein 675, ⊠ 2554 GK, ℰ 325 62 62, Telex 34186,
Fax 325 40 69, ≤, ⩫ rm 📺 ☎ Ⓟ – 🔬 30. AE ⓪ E VISA
⊡ 18 – **75 rm** 125/165.

at Leidschendam E : 6 km – pop. 32 992 – ✪ 0 70 :

🏨 **Green Park,** Weigelia 22, ✉ 2262 AB, ☎ 320 92 80, Telex 33090, Fax 327 49 07, ≤, *Fᴓ* – 🛗 ⇔ rm 🍴 rest 📺 ☎ 🅿 – 🛇 25-250. 🆎 ① 🗲 *VISA*
M Brasserie The Greenery a la carte 43/76 – 🖃 28 – **96 rm** 225/250.

ᕽᕽᕽ **Villa Rozenrust,** Veursestraatweg 104, ✉ 2265 CG, ☎ 327 74 60, Fax 327 50 62, ☞ –
🅿. 🆎 ① 🗲 *VISA*
closed Saturday lunch, Sunday and 3 to 15 August – **M** a la carte approx. 110.

at Voorburg E : 5 km – pop. 40 116 – ✪ 0 70 :

ᕽᕽᕽᕽ ✿ **Vreugd en Rust** (Savelberg) ⅌ with rm, Oosteinde 14, ✉ 2271 EH, ☎ 387 20 81, Fax 387 77 15, ≤, ☞, « 17C residence with terrace in public park » – 🛗 ⇔ rm 📺 ☎ 🅿 – 🛇 35. 🆎 ① 🗲 *VISA*
M *(closed dinner 24 and 31 December)* a la carte 115/144 – **14 rm** 🖃 200/495
Spec. Salade de homard, Pigeon de Bresse à la sauge, Huîtres chaudes au safran (October-April).

ᕽᕽ **Villa la Ruche,** Prinses Mariannelaan 71, ✉ 2275 BB, ☎ 386 01 10, Fax 386 50 64 – 🍽.
🆎 ① 🗲 *VISA*
closed 27 December-6 January – **M** a la carte 80/109.

at Wassenaar NE : 11 km – pop. 26 159 – ✪ 0 1751 :

🏨 **Aub. De Kieviet** ⅌, Stoeplaan 27, ✉ 2243 CX, ☎ 1 92 32, Fax 1 09 69, ☞, « Floral terrace » – 🛗 ⇔ rm 📺 ☎ 🅿 – 🛇 50. 🆎 ① 🗲 *VISA*
M a la carte 78/141 – 🖃 23 – **24 rm** 295/395.

🏨 **Wassenaar,** Katwijkseweg 33 (N : 2 km), ✉ 2242 PC, ☎ 1 92 18, Telex 32087, Fax 7 64 81 – 🛗 ⇔ rm 📺 ☎ 🅿 – 🛇 60. 🆎 ① 🗲 *VISA*
M a la carte 50/83 – **57 rm** 🖃 110/190.

ROTTERDAM Zuid-Holland 🗺 ⑤ and 🗺 ㉔ ㉕ – pop. 579 179 – ✪ 0 10 – Casino JKY, Weena 10 ☎ 414 77 99.

See : The harbour★★★ ⏴ KZ – Lijnbaan★ (Shopping centre) JKY – St. Laurence Church (Grote-of St. Laurenskerk) : interior★ KY D – Euromast★ (tower) (☀★★, ≤★) JZ.

Museums : Boymans-van Beuningen★★★ JZ – "De Dubbele Palmboom"★ – Het Schielandshuis★ (History Museum) KY.

🏌 Kralingseweg 200 ☎ 452 22 83 – 🏌 at Rhoon SW : 11 km, Veerweg 2a ☎ (0 1890) 1 61 65.

✈ Zestienhoven ☎ 446 34 44 (information) and 415 54 30, 437 27 45 (reservations).

🚗 (departs from 's-Hertogenbosch) ☎ 411 71 00.

⛴ Europoort to Kingston-upon-Hull : North Sea Ferries ☎ (0 1819) 5 55 55.

🛈 Coolsingel 67, ✉ 3012 AC, ☎ 06-34 03 40 65 and Central Station ☎ 413 60 06 – at Schiedam W : 6 km, Buitenhavenweg 9, ✉ 3113 BC, ☎ (0 10) 473 30 00.

Amsterdam 76 – The Hague 24 – Antwerp 103 – Brussels 149 – Utrecht 57.

Plan on next page

🏨 **Hilton International,** Weena 10, ✉ 3012 CM, ☎ 414 40 44, Telex 22666, Fax 411 88 84 – 🛗 ⇔ rm 🍴 📺 ☎ 🕭 🅿 – 🛇 80/250. 🆎 ① 🗲 *VISA*. ✾
M a la carte 48/110 – 🖃 35 – **252 rm** 365/465. JKY **a**

🏨 **Parkhotel,** Westersingel 70, ✉ 3015 LB, ☎ 436 36 11, Telex 22020, Fax 436 42 12, *Fᴓ*, ≘s, – 🛗 ⇔ rm 📺 ☎ ⇔ 🅿 – 🛇 25-50. 🆎 ① 🗲 *VISA*. ✾ JZ **a**
M a la carte 57/86 – **199 rm** 🖃 155/305.

🏨 **Rijnhotel,** Schouwburgplein 1, ✉ 3012 CK, ☎ 433 38 00, Telex 21640, Fax 414 54 82 – 🛗 🍴 rest 📺 ☎ – 🛇 25-220. 🆎 ① 🗲 *VISA*. ✾ JY **e**
M *(closed lunch Saturday and Sunday)* (dinner only 15 July-15 August) a la carte 45/70 – 🖃 28 – **100 rm** 200/275.

🏨 **Atlanta,** Aert van Nesstraat 4, ✉ 3012 CA, ☎ 411 04 20, Telex 21595, Fax 413 53 20 – 🛗 ⇔ rm 📺 ☎ ⇔ – 🛇 25-400. 🆎 ① 🗲 *VISA* KY **e**
M (dinner only) 40/75 – 🖃 20 – **164 rm** 180/240.

🏨 **Inntel,** Leuvehaven 80, ✉ 3011 EA, ☎ 413 41 39, Fax 413 32 22, ≤, *Fᴓ*, ≘s, 🔲 – 🛗 ⇔ rm 🍴 rest ☎ 🅿 – 🛇 25-220. 🆎 ① 🗲 *VISA* KZ **d**
M (open until 11 p.m.) a la carte 44/76 – 🖃 20 – **150 rm** 159/250.

🏨 **Zuiderparkhotel,** Dordtsestraatweg 285, ✉ 3083 AJ, ☎ 485 00 55, Telex 28755, Fax 485 63 04, ≘s, 🔲 – 🛗 🍴 rest 📺 ☎ 🅿 – 🛇 25-200. 🆎 ① 🗲 *VISA*
M a la carte 56/103 – 🖃 24 – **113 rm** 120/205.

🏨 **Savoy,** Hoogstraat 81, ✉ 3011 PJ, ☎ 413 92 80, Telex 21525, Fax 404 57 12 – 🛗 📺 ☎. 🆎 ① 🗲 *VISA* KY **n**
M a la carte 52/80 – 🖃 20 – **94 rm** 150/165.

🏨 **Pax** without rest., Schiekade 658, ✉ 3032 AK, ☎ 466 33 44, Fax 467 52 78 – 🛗 📺 ☎. 🆎 ① 🗲 *VISA*. ✾ JY **m**
45 rm 🖃 145/200.

🏨 **Van Walsum,** Mathenesserlaan 199, ✉ 3014 HC, ☎ 436 32 75, Telex 20010, Fax 436 44 10 – 🛗 ☎ 🅿. 🆎 ① 🗲 *VISA*. ✾ rest JZ **e**
closed 21 December-1 January – **M** (residents only) – **26 rm** 🖃 80/150.

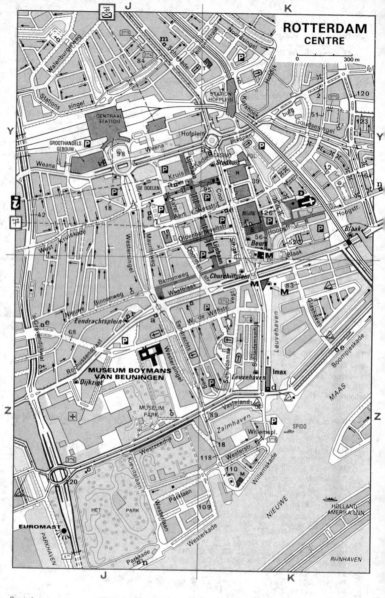

ROTTERDAM
CENTRE

0   300 m

XXX ❀ **Parkheuvel** (Helder), Heuvellaan 21, ⊠ 3016 GL, ℰ 436 05 30, Fax 436 71 40, ≼, 佘,
« Terrace » – ⓟ. ᴬᴱ ⓞ ᴇ ᴠɪꜱᴀ   JZ **n**
closed Saturday lunch, Sunday and 27 December-2 January – **M** a la carte 95/140
Spec. Pot-au-feu à la vinaigrette de moutarde, Melon et langoustines au curry, Barbue au caviar
et aux légumes.

XXX **Old Dutch,** Rochussenstraat 20, ⊠ 3015 EK, ℰ 436 03 44, Fax 436 78 26, 佘 – ▤ ⓟ. ᴬᴱ
ⓞ ᴇ ᴠɪꜱᴀ   JZ **r**
closed Saturday, Sunday and Bank Holidays – **M** 63/78.

XXX **World Trade Center** 23rd floor, Beursplein 37, ⊠ 3011 AA, ℰ 405 44 65, Fax 405 51 20,
❊ city – ▐ ▤ ⓟ. ᴬᴱ ⓞ ᴇ ᴠɪꜱᴀ. ❉   KY **r**
closed Saturday, Sunday and 3 to 30 August – **M** a la carte 66/123.

XXX **Radèn Mas** 1st floor, Kruiskade 72, ⊠ 3012 EH, ℰ 411 72 44, Fax 411 97 11, Indonesian
cuisine, « Exotic decor » – ▤.   JY **a**

XXX **Regent Palace,** Oosterkade 5, ⊠ 3011 TV, ℰ 414 19 11, Fax 414 32 05, ≼, Chinese cuisine
– ▤. ᴬᴱ ⓞ ᴇ ᴠɪꜱᴀ. ❉ – **M** 50/125.

XX **Brasserie La Vilette,** Westblaak 160, ⊠ 3012 KM, ℰ 414 86 92, Fax 414 13 91 – ▤. ᴬᴱ
ⓞ ᴇ ᴠɪꜱᴀ   JZ **t**
closed Sunday, Bank Holidays and 3 to 23 August – **M** 40/55.

XX **Boompjes,** Boompjes 701, ⊠ 3011 XZ, ℰ 413 60 70, Fax 413 70 87, ≼ Nieuwe Maas
(Meuse), Open until 11 p.m. – ▤ ᴬᴱ ⓞ ᴇ ᴠɪꜱᴀ. ❉   KZ **e**
closed lunch Saturday and Sunday – **M** a la carte 61/104.

XX **Silhouet** Euromast tower (Admission charge), Parkhaven 20, ⊠ 3016 GM, ℰ 436 48 11,
Fax 436 22 80, ❊ city and port – ▤ ⓟ. ᴬᴱ ⓞ ᴇ ᴠɪꜱᴀ. ❉   JZ
closed Saturday lunch, Sunday and Monday – **M** a la carte 58/97.

XX **Engels,** Stationsplein 45, ⊠ 3013 AK, ℰ 411 95 50, Fax 413 94 21, Multinational cuisines
– ▤ ⓟ. – ♨ 25-800. ᴬᴱ ⓞ ᴇ ᴠɪꜱᴀ. ❉   JY **v**
M a la carte approx. 60.

Airport ⒸRotterdam – ❀ 0 10 :

🏨 **Airport,** Vliegveldweg 59, ⊠ 3043 NT, ℰ 462 55 66, Telex 25785, Fax 462 22 66 – ▐ ❊ rm
ᴛᴠ ☎ ♿ ⓟ – ♨ 25-300. ᴬᴱ ⓞ ᴇ ᴠɪꜱᴀ
M a la carte 64/83 – **98 rm** ⊑ 195/245.

at Hillegersberg ⒸRotterdam – ❀ 0 10 :

XXX **Beau Rivage,** Weissenbruchlaan 149, ⊠ 3054 LM, ℰ 418 40 40, Fax 418 64 65, ≼, 佘,
« Terrace overlooking the lake » – ᴬᴱ ⓞ ᴇ ᴠɪꜱᴀ. ❉
M a la carte 92/135.

XX **Senang,** Grindweg 650, ⊠ 3055 VD, ℰ 422 25 02, 佘, Indonesian cuisine – ▤ ⓟ. ᴬᴱ ⓞ
ᴇ ᴠɪꜱᴀ – **M** 34/63.

at Kralingen ⒸRotterdam – ❀ 0 10 :

🏨 **Novotel,** K.P. van der Mandelelaan 130 (near A 16), ⊠ 3062 MB, ℰ 453 07 77, Telex 24109,
Fax 453 15 03 – ▐ ❊ rm ▤ ᴛᴠ ☎ ♿ ⓟ – ♨ 25-625. ᴬᴱ ⓞ ᴇ ᴠɪꜱᴀ
M (open until midnight) 65/82 – ⊑ 20 – **196 rm** 205/235.

XXX **In den Rustwat,** Honingerdijk 96, ⊠ 3062 NX, ℰ 413 41 10, Fax 404 85 40, 佘,
« 16C house » – ᴬᴱ ⓞ ᴇ ᴠɪꜱᴀ.
closed Saturday lunch, Sunday and Bank Holidays – **M** a la carte 73/108.

at Ommoord ⒸRotterdam – ❀ 0 10 :

XXX **Keizershof,** Martin Luther Kingweg 7, ⊠ 3069 EW, ℰ 455 13 33, Fax 456 80 23, 佘 – ▤
ⓟ. ᴬᴱ ⓞ ᴇ ᴠɪꜱᴀ – closed 24 and 31 December – **M** 40/90.

at Rhoon ⒸAlbrandswaard pop. 13 913 – ❀ 0 1890 :

XX **Het Kasteel van Rhoon,** Dorpsdijk 63, ⊠ 3161 KD, ℰ 1 88 84, Fax 1 24 18, ≼, 佘, « In
the grounds of the chateau » – ⓟ. ᴬᴱ ⓞ ᴇ ᴠɪꜱᴀ
closed Saturday lunch, 25 and 26 December – **M** a la carte 80/104.

at Schiedam – pop. 69 417 – ❀ 0 10 :

🏨 **Novotel,** Hargalaan 2 (near A 20), ⊠ 3118 JA, ℰ 471 33 22, Telex 22582, Fax 470 06 56,
♨, ⌇, 佘 – ▐ ❊ rm ▤ rest ᴛᴠ ☎ ♿ ⓟ – ♨ 25-150. ᴬᴱ ⓞ ᴇ ᴠɪꜱᴀ. ❉ rest
M (open until midnight) a la carte 40/80 – ⊑ 20 – **138 rm** 190/210.

XXX **La Duchesse,** Maasboulevard 9, ⊠ 3114 HB, ℰ 426 46 26, Fax 473 25 01, ≼ Nieuwe Maas
(Meuse), 佘 – ⓟ. ᴬᴱ ⓞ ᴇ ᴠɪꜱᴀ
closed Saturday lunch, Sunday and 31 December – **M** a la carte 90/117.

XXX **Aub. Hosman Frères** 1st floor, Korte Dam 10, ⊠ 3111 BG, ℰ 426 40 96, Fax 473 00 08
– ▤. ᴬᴱ ⓞ ᴇ ᴠɪꜱᴀ – closed Sunday, Monday and 24, 30 and 31 December – **M** 60/99.

Europoort zone by ⑥ : 25 km – ❀ 0 1819 :

🏨 **De Beer Europoort,** Europaweg 210 (N 15), ⊠ 3198 LD, ℰ 6 23 77, Telex 29979,
Fax 6 29 23, ≼, 佘, ⌇, ❊ – ▐ ᴛᴠ ☎ ⓟ – ♨ 25-250. ᴬᴱ ⓞ ᴇ ᴠɪꜱᴀ
M a la carte 68/106 – **78 rm** ⊑ 135/180.

Denmark

Danmark

COPENHAGEN

PRACTICAL INFORMATION

LOCAL CURRENCY

Danish Kroner: 100 D.Kr = 16.95 US $ (Jan. 92)

TOURIST INFORMATION

The telephone number and address of the Tourist Information office is given in the text under ␃.

FOREIGN EXCHANGE

Banks are open between 9.30am and 4.00pm (6.00pm on Thursdays) on weekdays except Saturdays. The main banks in the centre of Copenhagen, the Central Station and the Airport have exchange facilities outside these hours.

MEALS

At lunchtime, follow the custom of the country and try the typical buffets of Scandinavian specialities.
At dinner, the a la carte and the menus will offer you more conventional cooking.

SHOPPING IN COPENHAGEN

Strøget (Department stores, exclusive shops, boutiques).
Kompagnistræde (Antiques).
See also in the index of street names, those printed in red are where the principal shops are found.

CAR HIRE

The international car hire companies have branches in Copenhagen – Your hotel porter should be able to give details and help you with your arrangements.

TIPPING

In Denmark, all hotels and restaurants include a service charge. As for the taxis, there is no extra charge to the amount shown on the meter.

SPEED LIMITS

The maximum permitted speed in cities is 50 km/h - 31mph, outside cities 80 km/h - 50mph and 100 km/h - 62mph on motorways.

SEAT BELTS

The wearing of seat belts is compulsory for drivers and all passengers except children under the age of 3 and taxi passengers.

Copenhagen

(KØBENHAVN) Danmark 985 Q 9 - pop. 650 590 - ✪ 01.

See : Tivoli★★★ : May 1 to September 15 BZ - Harbour and Canal Tour★★★ (Kanaltur) : May to September 15 (Gammel Strand and Nyhavn) - Little Mermaid★★★ (Den Lille Havfrue) DX - Strøget★★ BCYZ - Nyhavn★★ DY - Amalienborg★★ : Changing of the Guard at noon DY - Rosenborg Castle★★ (Rosenborg Slot) CX - Christiansborg Palace★★ (Christiansborg Slot) CZ - Old Stock Exchange★★ (Børsen) CZ - Round Tower★★ (Rundetårn) CY **D** - Gråbrødretorv★ CY **28** - Gammel Strand★ CZ **26** - Marble Church★ (Marmorkirke) DY **E** - Royal Chapel and Naval Church★ (Holmen's Kirke) CZ **B** - King's Square★ (Kongens Nytorv) DY - Charlottenborg Palace★ (Charlottenborg Slot) DY **F** - Citadel★ (Kastellet) DX - Christianhavn★ DZ - Botanical Garden★ (Botanisk Have) BX - Frederiksberg Garden★ (Frederiksberg Have) AZ - Town Hall (Rådhus) : World Clock★ (Jens Olsen's Verdensur) BZ **H.** Breweries - Porcelain Factories.

Museums : Ny Carlsberg Glyptotek★★★ (Glyptoteket) BZ - National Museum★★ (Nationalmuseet) CZ - Royal Museum of Fine Arts★★ (Statens Museum for Kunst) CX - Thorvaldsen Museum★ CZ **M1** Royal Arsenal Museum★ (Tøjhusmuseet) CZ **M2** - Royal Theatre Museum★ (Teaterhistorisk Museum) CZ **M3** - Copenhagen City Museum★ (Bymuseet) AZ **M4**.

Outskirts : Open Air Museum★★ (Frilandsmuseet) NW : 12 km BX - Ordrupgaard Museum★ (Ordrupgaardsamlingen) N : 10 km CX - Dragør★ SW : 13 km DZ.

Dansk Golf Union 56 ✆ 42 64 06 66.

Copenhagen/Kastrup SE : 10 km ✆ 31 54 17 01 - Air Terminal : main railway station.

Motorail for Southern Europe : ✆ 33 14 17 01.

Further information from the D S B, main railway station or tourist information centre (see below).

Danmarks Turistråd, H.C. Andersens Bould. 22 A - 1553 København, V ✆ 33 11 13 25.

Berlin 385 - Hamburg 305 - Oslo 583 - Stockholm 630.

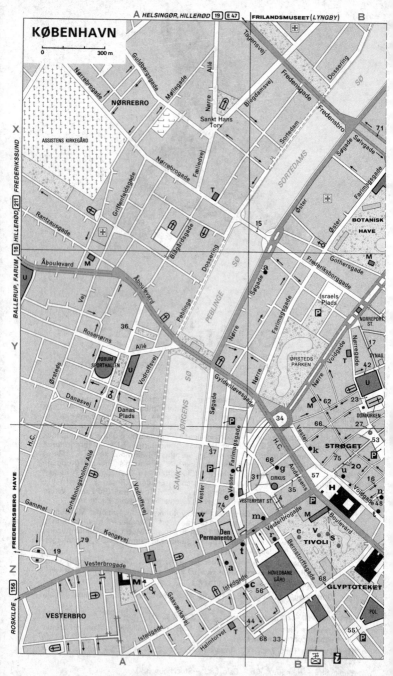

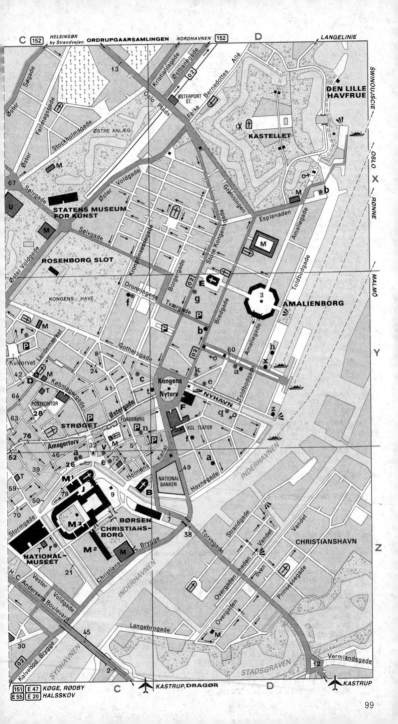

STREET INDEX TO KØBENHAVN TOWN PLAN

Angleterre, Kongens Nytorv 34, ⊠ 1050 K, ℰ 33 12 00 95, Telex 15877, Fax 33 12 11 18
– 📶 🖪 📺 ☎ ⇦ – 🛋 250. 🆎 ◑ 🅴 𝑉𝐼𝑆𝐴   CDY **t**
M 178/445 and a la carte – ☲ 120 – **118 rm** 1750/2800, **12 suites** 4100/9500.

Sheraton - Copenhagen 🅼, 6 Vester Søgade, ⊠ 1601 K, ℰ 33 14 35 35, Telex 27450,
Fax 33 32 12 23, ⇐, ⇔ – 📶 🖪 📺 ☎ – 🛋 1 000. 🆎 ◑ 🅴 𝑉𝐼𝑆𝐴   AZ **w**
M 300/500 and a la carte – **469 rm** ☲ 2100/2400, **2 suites** 2600/10000.

SAS Scandinavia, Amager Boulevard 70, ⊠ 2300 S, ℰ 33 11 23 24, Telex 31330,
Fax 31 57 01 93, ⇐ Copenhagen, « Panoramic restaurant on 25th floor », 🎠, ⇔s,
🔲, squash – 📶 ↦ rm 🖪 📺 ☎ 🅿 – 🛋 1 500. 🆎 ◑ 🅴 𝑉𝐼𝑆𝐴
M – Top of Town – ☲ 115 – **506 rm** 1670/1890, **36 suites** 2110.
                                                          by Amager Boulevard CZ

SAS Royal, Hammerichsgade 1, ⊠ 1611 V, ℰ 33 14 14 12, Telex 27155, Fax 33 14 14 21, ⇐,
« Panoramic restaurant on 20th floor ». ⇔s – 📶 ↦ rm 🖪 📺 ☎ ⇦ 🅿 – 🛋 200. 🆎 ◑
🅴   BZ **m**
M 195/440 and a la carte – ☲ 115 – **264 rm** 1795/2395, **2 suites** 2495/12375.

Plaza, Bernstorffsgade 4, ⊠ 1577 V, ℰ 33 14 92 62, Telex 15330, Fax 33 93 93 62, « Library
bar » – 📶 🖪 📺 ☎ – 🛋 60. 🆎 ◑ 🅴 𝑉𝐼𝑆𝐴. ⬚
closed Christmas - New Year – **M** – **Alesandra Newski** (Russian rest.) 128/225 and a la carte
– ☲ 105 – **87 rm** 1325/1925, **6 suites** 2750/5750.   BZ **r**

Kong Frederik, Vester Voldgade 25, ⊠ 1552 V, ℰ 33 12 59 02, Telex 19702, Fax 33 93 59 01,
« Victorian pub, antiques » – 📶 📺 ☎ – 🛋 80. 🆎 ◑ 🅴 𝑉𝐼𝑆𝐴. ⬚
closed 22 December-2 January – **M** 195/380 and a la carte – ☲ 95 – **107 rm** 1300/1850,
3 suites 2100/6000.   BZ **k**

Phoenix, Bredgade 37, ⊠ 1260 K, ℰ 33 95 95 00, Telex 40068, Fax 33 33 98 33 – ↦ rm
🖪 ☎ – 🛋 60. 🆎 ◑ 🅴 𝑉𝐼𝑆𝐴
M – **Guldensten** (closed until summer 1992) – **Von Plessen** 225/275 and a la carte – ☲ 95
– **209 rm** 990/2050, **3 suites** 5000.   DY **b**

Palace, Raadhuspladsen 57, ⊠ 1550 V, ℰ 33 14 40 50, Telex 19693, Fax 33 14 52 79, ⇔s
– 📶 📺 ☎ – 🛋 50. 🆎 ◑ 🅴 𝑉𝐼𝑆𝐴   BZ **u**
156 rm ☲ 1290/1490, **3 suites** 1940/2390.

Imperial, Vester Farimagsgade 9, ⊠ 1606 V, ℰ 33 12 80 00, Telex 15556, Fax 33 93 80 31
– 📶 ↦ rm 📺 ☎ ♿ – 🛋 100. 🆎 ◑ 🅴 𝑉𝐼𝑆𝐴. ⬚   AZ **e**
M 230/275 and a la carte – **163 rm** ☲ 1075/2140.

🏨 **Copenhagen Admiral**, Toldbodgade 24-28, ⊠ 1253 K, ℰ 33 11 82 82, Telex 15941, Fax 33 32 55 42, ≼, « Former 18C warehouse », 🛏s – |🕽| 📺 ☎ 🅟 – 🖭 180   DY **h**
363 rm, 2 suites.

🏨 **Sophie Amalie** Ⓜ, Sankt Annae Plads 21, ⊠ 1250 K, ℰ 33 13 34 00, Telex 15815, Fax 33 32 55 42, 🛏s – |🕽| ▤ 📺 ☎ – 🖭 180   DY **x**
M (see **Copenhagen Admiral** H.) – **130 rm, 4 suites.**

🏨 **Neptun**, Sankt Annae Plads 18-20, ⊠ 1250 K, ℰ 33 13 89 00, Telex 19554, Fax 33 14 12 50 – |🕽| 📺 ☎ – 🖭 60. 🖭 ⓸ 🗲 𝗩𝗜𝗦𝗔   DY **a**
closed 22 December-2 January – **M** 160/300 and a la carte – **119 rm** ⊑ 1070/1440, **10 suites** 1800.

🏨 **Kong Arthur** without rest., Nørre Søgade 11, ⊠ 1370 K, ℰ 33 11 12 12, Telex 16512, Fax 33 32 61 30, 🛏s – |🕽| 📺 ☎ 🚗 🅟 🖭 ⓸ 🗲 𝗩𝗜𝗦𝗔   BY **a**
90 rm ⊑ 845/1095, **1 suite** 1800/2700.

🏨 **Mayfair** without rest., Helgolandsgade 3-5, ⊠ 1653 V, ℰ 31 31 48 01, Telex 27468, Fax 31 23 96 86 – |🕽| 📺 ☎. 🖭 ⓸ 🗲 𝗩𝗜𝗦𝗔   AZ **a**
102 rm ⊑ 805/1300, **4 suites** 1500/1900.

🏨 **Mercur**, Vester Farimagsgade 17, ⊠ 1780 V, ℰ 33 12 57 11, Telex 19767, Fax 33 12 57 17, ✖ – |🕽| 📺 ☎. 🖭 ⓸ 🗲 𝗩𝗜𝗦𝗔   AZ **d**
M (closed Sunday and Bank Holidays) 155/198 and a la carte – **108 rm** ⊑ 995/1650, **1 suite** 1900.

🏨 **71 Nyhavn**, Nyhavn 71, ⊠ 1051 K, ℰ 33 11 85 85, Telex 27558, Fax 33 93 15 85, ≼, « Former warehouse » – |🕽| 📺 ☎   DY **z**
76 rm, 6 suites.

🏨 **Grand**, Vesterbrogade 9, ⊠ 1620 V, ℰ 31 31 36 00, Telex 15343, Fax 31 31 33 50 – |🕽| ✖ rm 📺 ☎ – 🖭 120. 🖭 ⓸ 🗲 𝗩𝗜𝗦𝗔   AZ **t**
M (closed Sunday) 198/445 – **147 rm** ⊑ 685/1280 1900/2300.

🏨 **Scala - Copenhagen** Ⓜ without rest., Colbjørnsensgade 13, ⊠ 1652 V, ℰ 31 22 11 00, Fax 31 22 21 99 – 📺 ☎ – 🖭 35. 🖭 ⓸ 🗲 𝗩𝗜𝗦𝗔   ABZ **c**
closed Christmas and New Year – **131 rm** ⊑ 890/1120, **3 suites** 1280.

🏨 **City** without rest., Peder Skramsgade 24, ⊠ 1054 K, ℰ 33 13 06 66, Telex 19258, Fax 33 13 06 67 – |🕽| ✖ ☎ – 🖭 20. 🖭 ⓸ 🗲 𝗩𝗜𝗦𝗔. ✖   DZ **a**
85 rm ⊑ 870/1170.

🏨 **Ascot** without rest., Studiestraede 57, ⊠ 1554 V, ℰ 33 12 60 00, Telex 15730, Fax 33 14 60 40 – |🕽| 📺 ☎ 🅟. 🖭 ⓸ 🗲 𝗩𝗜𝗦𝗔   BZ **g**
117rm ⊑ 670/1090, **3 suites** 1220/1980.

🏨 **Komfort**, Løngangstraede 27, ⊠ 14 68 K, ℰ 33 12 65 70, Telex 16488, Fax 33 15 28 99 – |🕽| 📺 ☎ 🚗. 🖭 ⓸ 🗲 𝗩𝗜𝗦𝗔   BZ **n**
closed 23 December-2 January – **201 rm** ⊑ 780/1080.

🏨 **Opera** without rest., Tordenskjoldsgade 15, ⊠ 1055 K, ℰ 33 12 15 19, Telex 15812, Fax 33 32 12 82 – |🕽| 📺 ☎ – 🖭 25   DY **f**
85 rm, 2 suites.

🏨 **Christian IV** without rest., Dronningens Tvaergade 45, ⊠ 1302 K, ℰ 33 32 10 44, Fax 33 32 07 06 – |🕽| 📺 ☎   CY **f**
42 rm.

🏨 **Danmark** without rest., Vester Voldgade 89, ⊠ 1552 V, ℰ 33 11 48 06, Telex 15518, Fax 33 14 36 30 – |🕽| 📺 ☎ 🚗. 🖭 ⓸ 🗲 𝗩𝗜𝗦𝗔   BZ **t**
closed 23 December-4 January – **49 rm** ⊑ 675/950, **2 suites** 1175/1300.

XXX ⸙ **Kong Hans Kaelder**, Vingardsstraede 6, ⊠ 1070 K, ℰ 33 11 68 68, Telex 50404, Fax 33 32 67 68, « Vaulted Gothic cellar » – 🖭 ⓸ 🗲 𝗩𝗜𝗦𝗔   CY **n**
closed Sunday, first week July-first week August and Bank Holidays – **M** (booking essential) (dinner only) 350/640 and a la carte 545/615
Spec. Home smoked salmon, Lobster "Tiger Lee", Wild duck with autumn berries (October-January).

XX ⸙ **Nouvelle**, Gammel Strand 34 (1st floor), ⊠ 1202 K, ℰ 33 13 50 18 – 🖭 ⓸ 🗲 𝗩𝗜𝗦𝗔   CZ **a**
closed Sunday, 23 December-5 January and Bank Holidays – **M** 225/385 and a la carte 365/515
Spec. Skagerak lobster bisque, Russian caviar on lemon pancakes with herbs, Poached North Sea turbot with squash and fried mussels.

XX ⸙ **Kommandanten**, NY Adelgade 7, ⊠ 1104 K, ℰ 33 12 09 90, Fax 33 93 12 23, « 17C town house, contemporary furnishings » – 🖭 ⓸ 🗲 𝗩𝗜𝗦𝗔   CY **c**
closed lunch 15 April-1 September, Saturday lunch, Sunday and Bank Holidays – **M** 215/450 and a la carte 280/490
Spec. Lobster consommé with rice noodles and summer truffles, Saddle of Danish spring lamb baked in parsley dough with a basil sauce, "Bag of pancake" with fresh berries and a warm Champagne sabayon (season).

XX ⸙ **Les Etoiles et une Rose**, Dronningens Tvaergade 43, ⊠ 1302 K, ℰ 33 15 05 54, Fax 33 32 07 06 – 🖭 ⓸ 🗲 𝗩𝗜𝗦𝗔   CY **f**
closed Saturday lunch, Sunday and 1 to 14 January – **M** 245/495 and a la carte 318/497
Spec. Three kinds of fish, pressed with savoy cabbage, tomato beurre blanc, The very best of veal garnished with quail breast and sweetbreads, Pear with nougat filling baked in a pancake.

XX **Leonore Christine,** Nyhavn 9, ✉ 1051 K, ✆ 33 13 50 40 – AE ① E VISA DY **e**
closed Sunday except April-23 December, 23 December-30 January and Bank Holidays – **M** 225/358 and a la carte.

XX Krogs, Gammel Strand 38, ✉ 1202 K, ✆ 33 15 89 15, Seafood CZ **a**

XX **St. Gertruds Kloster,** 32 Hauser Plads, ✉ 1127 K, ✆ 33 14 66 30, Fax 33 93 93 65, « Part 14C monastic cellars » – ▤. AE ① E VISA CY **r**
closed 31 May and Christmas-New Year – **M** (dinner only) 366/445 and a la carte.

X **Lille Laekkerbisken,** Gammel Strand 34 (ground floor), ✉ 1202 K, ✆ 33 32 04 00 – AE ① E VISA CZ **a**
closed Sunday, 23 December-5 January and Bank Holidays – **M** (lunch only) 165 and a la carte.

X **Els,** Store Strandstraede 3, ✉ 1255 K, ✆ 33 14 13 41, Fax 33 91 07 00, « 19C murals » AE ① E VISA DY **k**
closed 24-25 and 31 December and 1 January – **M** 296 (dinner) and a la carte.

X Lumskebugten, Esplanaden 21, ✉ 1263 K, ✆ 33 15 60 29, 🏖, « Mid 19C café-pavilion » DX

X **Den Gyldne Fortun,** Ved Stranden 18, ✉ 1061 K, ✆ 33 12 20 11, Fax 33 93 35 11, Seafood – AE ① E VISA CZ **e**
closed 15 to 20 April, 15 and 28 May, 6 to 8 June, 24 December-1 January and Bank Holidays – **M** *(closed lunch Saturday and Sunday)* 145/285 and a la carte.

X **Den Sorte Ravn,** Nyhavn 14, ✉ 1051 K, ✆ 33 13 12 33 – AE ① E VISA DY **q**
closed 16 to 20 April, 6 to 8 June and 24 to 27 December – **M** 210/425 and a la carte.

in Tivoli : (Entrance fee payable)

XXX **Divan 2,** Vesterbrogade 3, ✉ 1620 V, ✆ 33 12 51 51, Fax 33 91 08 82, ≤, 🏖, « Floral decoration and terrace » – ① E VISA BZ **a**
29 April-13 September – **M** 450/525 and a la carte.

XXX **Divan 1,** Vesterbrogade 3, ✉ 1620 V, ✆ 33 11 42 42, Fax 33 11 74 07, ≤, 🏖, « Floral decoration and terrace » – AE ① E VISA BZ **v**
closed 14 September – **M** 235/395 and a la carte 362/600.

XX **La Crevette,** Vesterbrogade 3, ✉ 1620 V, ✆ 33 14 68 47, Fax 33 14 60 06, ≤, 🏖, Seafood, « Part mid 19C pavilion and terrace » – AE ① E VISA BZ **e**
29 April-13 September – **M** 225/350 and a la carte.

XX **Belle Terrasse,** Vesterbrogade 3, ✉ 1620 V, ✆ 33 12 11 36, Fax 33 15 00 31, ≤, 🏖, « Floral decoration and terrace » – AE ① E VISA BZ **s**
29 April-September – **M** 315/495 and a la carte.

SMØRREBRØD RESTAURANTS

The following list of simpler restaurants and cafés/bars specialize in Danish open sandwiches and are generally open from 10.00am to 4.00pm.

X **Ida Davidsen,** St. Kongensgade 70, ✉ 1264 K, ✆ 33 91 36 55 – ① E VISA DY **g**
closed Saturday and Sunday – **M** 110/655.

X **Slotskaelderen-Hos Gitte Kik,** Fortunstraede 4, ✉ 1065 K, ✆ 33 11 15 37 – ① E VISA CYZ **v**
closed Sunday, Monday and Easter – **M** (lunch only) approx. 65.

X Kanal Caféen, Frederiksholms Kanal 18, ✉ 1220 K, ✆ 33 11 57 70 CZ **r**

X Sankt Annae, Sankt Annae Plads 12, ✉ 1250 K, ✆ 33 12 54 97 DY **a**

at Skovshoved N : 10 km – ✉ Charlottenlund :

XX **Saison and Skovshoved Hotel** with rm, Strandvejen 267, ✉ 2920 K, ✆ 31 64 00 28, Fax 31 64 06 72 – 📺 ☎ – 🏛 70. AE ① E VISA
closed 24 to 26 December and 1 January – **M** *(closed Sunday and Bank Holidays)* 300/495 and a la carte – **19 rm** ☕ 695/950**1 suite** 950/1150.

at Klampenborg N : 12 km by Østbanegade –DX – on coast rd :

X **Den Gule Cottage,** Staunings Plaene, Strandvejen 506, ✉ 2930, ✆ 31 64 06 91, ≤, « Thatched cottage beside the sea » – Ⓟ. AE ① E VISA
M (booking essential) 250/425 and a la carte.

at Søllerød N : 16 km by Tagensvej – BX – Lyngbyvej and Road 19 – ✉ 2840 Holte

XXX ✿ **Søllerød Kro,** Søllerødvej 35, ✉ 2840, ✆ 42 80 25 05, Fax 42 80 22 70, 🏖, « 17C thatched inn, terrace » – Ⓟ. AE ① E VISA
M 210/575 and a la carte
Spec. Salad with medallions of smoked salmon and pickled foie gras de canard, Small whole turbot served with fennel and lemon flavoured tomatoes, Young pigeon in gravy with grapes, crayfish and grilled potatoes.

at Kastrup Airport SE : 10 km – ✉ 2300 S :

🏨 SAS Globetrotter, Engvej 171, ✉ 2300 S, NW : 2 ½ km ✆ 31 55 14 33, Telex 31222, Fax 31 55 81 45, 🏋, 🏊 – 🛗 ⅟ rm 📺 ☎ Ⓟ – 🏛 350 by Amager Boulevard CZ
196 rm.

Finland

Suomi

PRACTICAL INFORMATION

LOCAL CURRENCY

Finnish Mark: 100 FIM = 24.26 $ (Jan. 92)

TOURIST INFORMATION

The Tourist Office is situated near the Market Square, Pohjoisesplanadi 19 ☎ 169 3757 and 174 088. Open from 15 May to 15 September, Monday to Friday 8.30am - 6pm, Saturday 8.30am - 1pm, and from 16 September to 14 May, Monday 8.30am - 4.30pm and Tuesday to Friday 8.30am - 4.00pm. Hotel bookings are possible from a reservation board situated in airport arrival lounge; information also available free.

FOREIGN EXCHANGE

Banks are open between 9.15am and 4.15pm on weekdays only. Exchange office at Helsinki-Vantaa airport open daily between 6.30am and 11pm.

MEALS

At lunchtime, follow the custom of the country and try the typical buffets of Scandinavian specialities.
At dinner, the a la carte and the menus will offer you more conventionnal cooking.
A lot of city centre restaurants are closed for a few days over the Midsummer Day period.

SHOPPING IN HELSINKI

Furs, jewelry, china, glass and ceramics, Finnish handicraft and wood. In the index of street names, those printed in red are where the principal shops are found. Your hotel porter will be able to help you and give you information.

THEATRE BOOKINGS

A ticket service - Lippupalvelu, Mannerheimintie 5, is selling tickets for cinema, concert and theatre performances - Telephone 664 466, open Mon-Fri 9am to 5pm, Sat. 9am to 2pm (except July).

CAR HIRE

The international car hire companies have branches in Helsinki city and at Vantaa airport. Your hotel porter should be able to help you with your arrangements.

TIPPING

Service is normally included in hotel and restaurant bills - Doormen, baggage porters etc. are generally given a gratuity; taxi drivers are usually not tipped.

SPEED LIMITS

The maximum permitted speed on motorways is 120 km/h - 74 mph (in winter 100 km/h - 62 mph), 80 km/h - 50 mph on other roads and 50 km/h - 31 mph in built-up areas.

SEAT BELTS

The wearing of seat belts in Finland is compulsory for drivers and for front and rear seat passagers.

Helsinki

Finland 985 L 21 – Pop. 491 777 – ✪ 90.

See : Senate Square★★★ (Senaatintori) DY 53 : Lutheran Cathedral (Tuomiokirkko) DY, University Library (Yliopiston kirjasto) CY B, Senate House (Valtioneuvosto) DY C, Sederholm House DY E – Market Square★★ (Kauppatori) DY 26 : Uspensky Cathedral (Uspenskin katedraali) DY, Presidential Palace (Presidentinlinna) DY F, Havis Amanda Fountain DY K – Spa Park★ (Kaivopuisto) DZ ; Esplanade★★ (Eteläesplanadi CY 8, Pohjoisesplanadi CY 43 ; Aleksanterinkatu★ CDY 2 ; Atheneum Art Museum★★ (Ateneumintaidemuseo) CY M¹ – Mannerheimintie★★ BCXY : Parliament House (Eduskuntatalo) BX, Rock Church (Temppeliaukion kirkko) BX, National Museum (Kansallismuseo) BX M², Helsinki City Museum (Helsingin kaupunginmuseo) BX M³, Finlandia Hall (Finlandiatalo) BX – Sibelius Monument★★ (Sibeliuksen puisto) AX ; Stadium tower (Olympia-stadion) BX : view★★.

Sightseeing by sea : Fortress of Suomenlinna★★ ; Seurasaari Open-Air Museum★ (from Kauppatori) ; Helsinki zoo★ (Korkeasaari).

Entertainment : Helsinki Festival★★ (20 August to 6 September).

ⓘ₈ Tali Manor ℘ 550 235.

✈ Helsinki-Vantaa N : 19 km ℘ 821 122 – Finnair Head Office, Mannerheimintie 102 ℘ 822 414, Telex 124 404, Fax 818 87 36 – Air Terminal : Hotel Intercontinental, Mannerheimintie 46.

⛴ To Sweden, USSR and boat excursions : contact the City Tourist Office (see below) – Car Ferry : Silja Line – Finnjet Line ℘ 180 41.

🅱 City Tourist Office Pohjoisesplanadi 19 ℘ 169 37 60, Fax 169 38 39 – Automobile and Touring Club of Finland : Autoliitto ℘ 694 00 22, Telex 124 839, Fax 693 25 78.

Lahti 103 – Tampere 176 – Turku 165.

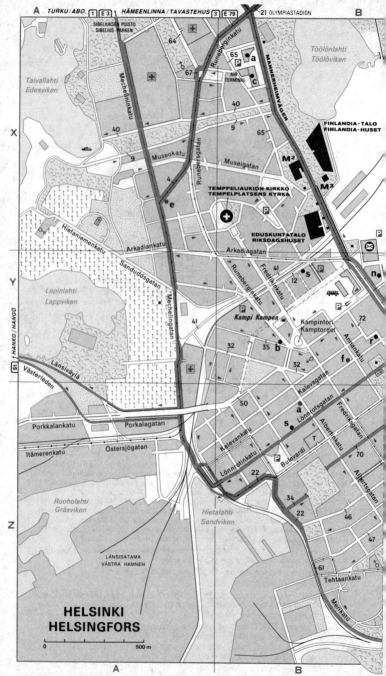

HELSINKI
HELSINGFORS

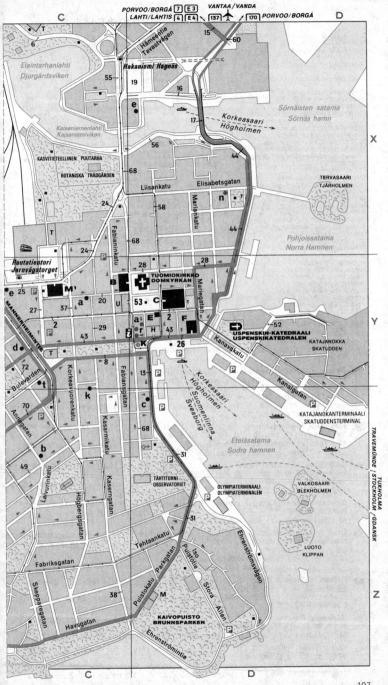

STREET INDEX TO HELSINKI/HELSINGFORS TOWN PLAN

Inter-Continental, Mannerheimintie 46, 00260, ℰ 40551, Telex 122159, Fax 4055255, ⇔s, ▯ – ⌷ ✳ rm ▤ ▥ ☎ ⅙ ⟅⟆ ℗ – ⅍ 400. ஃ ⑩ E VISA
closed 1 to 28 July, 23 to 29 December and 24 to 28 February – **M** – **Galatea** (Seafood) (dinner only) 350 and a la carte – **Brasserie** 150/250 and a la carte – **543 rm** ⊑ 780/1140, **12 suites** 2000/4000.
BX **c**

Strand Intercontinental, John Stenbergin Ranta 4, 00530, ℰ 39351, Telex 126202, Fax 393255, ≤, « Contemporary decor, modern art collection », ⇔s, ▯ – ⌷ ✳ rm ▤ ▥ ☎ ⅙ ⟅⟆ – ⅍ 300. ஃ E VISA
closed Christmas – **M Atrium Plaza** *(closed Christmas)* a la carte 203/235 – **Pamir** *(closed Saturday, Sunday, Easter, 22 June-16 August and Christmas)* 290/340 (dinner) – ⊑ 65 – **192 rm** 920/1140, **8 suites** 2100/4600.
DX **e**

Hesperia, Mannerheimintie 50, 00260, ℰ 43101, Telex 122117, Fax 4310995, ⇔s, ▯ – ⌷ ✳ rm ▤ ▥ ☎ ⟅⟆ ℗ – ⅍ 400. ஃ ⑩ E VISA
BX **a**
M – **Russian Room** *(closed Saturday and Sunday)* (dinner only) a la carte approx. 380 – ⊑ 40 – **372 rm** 780/1020, **4 suites** 1800/3600.

SAS Royal, Runeberginkatu 2, 00100, ℰ 69580, Telex 122112, Fax 69587100, ⇔s – ⌷ ✳ rm ▤ ▥ ⟅⟆ – ⅍ 250. ஃ E VISA. ⅏
BY **b**
closed Christmas – **M** 130/250 and a la carte – ⊑ 45 – **253 rm** 820/1160, **7 suites** 1800/4000.

Ramada Presidentti, Eteläinen Rautatiekatu 4, 00100, ℰ 6911, Telex 121953, Fax 6947886, ⇔s, ▯ – ⌷ ✳ rm ▤ ▥ ☎ ⅙ – ⅍ 400. ஃ ⑩ E VISA
BY **s**
M 165/175 – ⊑ 40 – **495 rm** 800/920, **5 suites** 3000/3500.

Lord ⅊, Lönnrotinkatu 29, 00180, ℰ 680 1680, Fax 680 1315, « Part Jugendstil (Art Nouveau) building, fireplaces », ▯ – ⌷ ✳ rm ▤ ▥ ☎ ⅙ ⟅⟆ – ⅍ 100. ஃ ⑩ E VISA
BZ **s**
closed 23 to 27 December – **M** *(closed Sunday and Bank Holidays)* 130/250 and a la carte – **35 rm** ⊑ 650/800, **1 suite** 1000/1500.

Palace, Eteläranta 10, 00130, ℰ 134 561, Telex 121570, Fax 654 786, ⇔s – ⌷ ✳ rm ▤ ▥ ☎ ⅙ – ⅍ 40. ஃ ⑩ E VISA
closed Christmas and Easter – **M** – (see also **Palace Gourmet** below) – **44 rm** ⊑ 820/1160, **6 suites** 1400/2400.
DZ **c**

Vaakuna, Asema-ankio 2, 00100, ℰ 131 181, Telex 121381, Fax 13118234, ⇔s – ✳ rm ▤ ☎ ⅙ – ⅍ 80. ஃ ⑩ E VISA
BY **n**
M 180 (lunch) and a la carte 96/119 – ⊑ 35 – **278 rm** 780/880, **10 suites** 1400/3000.

Klaus Kurki, Bulevardi 2, 00120, ℰ 618 911, Telex 121670, Fax 608 538, ⇔s – ⌷ ✳ rm ▤ ▥ ☎ ⅙ E VISA
CY **t**
closed 23 December-3 January – **M** *(closed Saturday lunch, Sunday and Bank Holidays)* 140/180 (lunch) and dinner a la carte 96/155 – ⊑ 35 – **133 rm** 680/840, **2 suites** 1200.

🏨 **Seurahuone** without rest., Kaivokatu 12, 00100, ℰ 170 441, Telex 122234, Fax 664 170, ⇔
– 🛗 ⇔ 🔲 📺 ☎. 🆎 ① 🔄 *VISA*   CY **e**
⬜ 40 – **118 rm** 680/1300.

🏨 **Arctia Hotel Marski,** Mannerheimintie 10, 00100, ℰ 68061, Telex 121240, Fax 642377,
⇔ – 🛗 ⇔ rm 🔲 📺 ☎ ⟐ – 🛁 300. 🆎 ① 🔄 *VISA*   CY **d**
M 130/190 and a la carte – ⬜ 35 – **158 rm** 790/990, **6 suites** 1800.

🏨 **Pasila** Ⓜ, Maistraatinportti 3, 00240, ℰ 148 841, Telex 125809, Fax 143 771, ⇔, squash
– 🛗 ⇔ rm ▣ rest 📺 ☎ 👐 ⟐ 🅿 – 🛁 80. 🆎 🔄 *VISA*
M 135/200 and a la carte – ⬜ 30 – **252 rm** 510/650, **1 suite** 1300.
                                                                    N : 3 km by Mannerheimintie BX

🏨 **Rivoli Jardin** Ⓜ ⌕ without rest., Kasarmikatu 40, 00130, ℰ 177 880, Telex 125881,
Fax 656 988, ⇔ – 🛗 ▣ 📺 ☎ 🛁 – 🛁 20. 🆎 ① 🔄 *VISA*   CYZ **k**
53 rm ⬜ 710/820, **1 suite** 1800.

🏨 **Helsinki** without rest., Hallituskatu 12, 00100, ℰ 131 401, Telex 121022, Fax 176 014, ⇔
– 🛗 ⇔ 📺 ☎ – 🛁 30. 🆎 ① 🔄 *VISA*. ⌗   CY **a**
⬜ 30 – **129 rm** 540/850.

🏨 **Torni,** Yrjönkatu 26, 00100, ℰ 131 131, Telex 125153, Fax 1311361, ⇔ – 🛗 ⇔ rm ▣ rest
📺 ☎ – 🛁 30. 🆎 ① 🔄 *VISA*. ⌗   BY **r**
closed Christmas – **M** – Ritarisali (closed Sunday) 220/350 and a la carte – ⬜ 35 – **146 rm**
660/790, **9 suites** 1000.

🏨 **Aurora** without rest., Helsinginkatu 50, 00530, ℰ 717 400, Telex 125643, Fax 714 240, 🛁,
⇔, ▣, squash – 🛗 ⇔ ▣ 📺 ☎ 🅿 – 🛁 80. 🆎 ① 🔄 *VISA*
70 rm ⬜ 430/530.   NE : 2 km by Helsinginkatu BX

🏨 **Anna** without rest., Annankatu 1, 00120, ℰ 648 011, Telex 125514, Fax 602 664, ⇔ – 🛗
⇔ 📺 ☎. 🆎 🔄 *VISA*. ⌗   CZ **b**
closed 10 days Christmas-New Year – **59 rm** ⬜ 420/570, **1 suite** 850/950.

🍽🍽🍽 **Havis Amanda,** Unioninkatu 23, 00170, ℰ 666 882, Fax 631 435, Seafood – 🆎 ① 🔄 *VISA*
closed lunch in July, Saturday dinner, Sunday and Bank Holidays – **M** (booking essential) (restricted lunch) 165/295 and a la carte.   DY **r**

🍽🍽🍽 **Palace Gourmet,** (at Palace H.), Eteläranta 10 (10th floor), 00130, ℰ 134 561, Telex 121570,
Fax 657 474, ≼ harbour and city – 🛗 ▣. 🆎 ① 🔄 *VISA*   DZ **c**
closed Saturday, Sunday, July and Bank Holidays – **M** 220/395 and dinner a la carte.

🍽🍽🍽 **Alexander Nevski,** Pohjoisesplanadi 17, 00170, ℰ 639 610, Fax 6164252, Russian rest. –
▣. 🆎 ① 🔄 *VISA*   DY **r**
closed lunch in July, Sunday and Bank Holidays except Easter – **M** 120/310 and a la carte.

🍽🍽 **Svenska Klubben,** Maurinkatu 6, 00170, ℰ 1354706, Fax 1354896, « Scottish
style house » – ▣. 🆎 ① 🔄 *VISA*   DX **n**
closed Sunday – **M** 140/320 and a la carte.

🍽🍽 **Rivoli (Kala and Cheri),** Albertinkatu 38, 00180, ℰ 643 455, Fax 647 780, « Nautical
decor » – ▣. 🆎 ① 🔄 *VISA*   BZ **a**
closed lunch Saturday and Sunday, 16 to 20 April, 19 to 21 July, 24 to 27 December and
Bank Holidays – **M** (restricted lunch)/dinner a la carte 112/213.

🍽🍽 **Piekka,** Sibeliuksenkatu 2, 00260, ℰ 493 591, Fax 495 664, Finnish rest. – 🆎 ① 🔄 *VISA*
closed Christmas – **M** (dinner only) a la carte 163/222.   by Mannerheimintie BX

🍽🍽 **Amadeus,** Sofiankatu 4, 00170, ℰ 626 676, Fax 636 064 – 🆎 ① 🔄 *VISA*   DY **a**
closed Saturday lunch, Saturday dinner in July, Sunday and Christmas – **M** 130/170 (lunch)
dinner a la carte 190/293.

🍽 **Troikka,** Caloniuksenkatu 3, 00100, ℰ 445 229, Fax 445 037, Russian rest. – ▣. 🆎 ① 🔄
VISA   AX **e**
closed Saturday and Sunday – **M** a la carte 129/240.

on 137 N : 15 km – ✉ Vanta – 🍽 90 Helsinki :

🏨 **Airport Hotel Rantasipi** Ⓜ, Takamaantie 4, Box 53, 01510, ℰ 87051, Telex 121812,
Fax 822 846, ⇔, ▣ – 🛗 ⇔ rm ▣ rm 📺 ☎ 🛁 🅿 – 🛁 150. 🆎 ① 🔄 *VISA*
M 130 (lunch) and dinner a la carte 87/151 – **296 rm** ⬜ 640/730, **4 suites** 1200/1700.
                                                                          by Helsinginkatu BX

France

PARIS AND ENVIRONS - BORDEAUX
CANNES - LILLE - LYONS
MARSEILLES - PRINCIPALITY OF MONACO
NICE - STRASBOURG
VALLEY OF THE LOIRE

PRACTICAL INFORMATION

LOCAL CURRENCY

French Franc: 100 F = 19.31 US $ (Jan. 92)

TOURIST INFORMATION IN PARIS

Paris "Welcome" Office (Office du Tourisme et des Congrès de Paris - Accueil de France): 127 Champs-Élysées, 8th, ℰ 47 23 61 72, Telex 611984
American Express 11 Rue Scribe, 9th, ℰ 42 66 09 99

AIRLINES

T.W.A.: 101 Champs-Élysées, 8th, ℰ 47 20 62 11
DELTA AIRLINES: 4 pl. des Vosges Immeuble Lavoisier Cédex 64 – Paris 92052 La défense ℰ 47 68 92 92
BRITISH AIRWAYS: 91 Champs-Élysées, 8th, ℰ 47 78 14 14
AIR FRANCE: 119 Champs-Élysées, 8th, ℰ 45 35 61 61
AIR INTER: 1 Avenue Mar. Devaux, 91551 Paray-Vieille-Poste Cedex, ℰ 46 75 12 12
UTA: 3 Boulevard Malesherbes, 8th, ℰ 40 17 46 46

FOREIGN EXCHANGE OFFICES

Banks: close at 5pm and at weekends
Orly Airport: daily 6.30am to 11.30pm
Charles de Gaulle Airport: daily 6am to 11.30pm

TRANSPORT IN PARIS

Taxis: may be hailed in the street when showing the illuminated sign-available day and night at taxi ranks or called by telephone
Bus-Métro (subway): for full details see the Michelin Plan de Paris n° 11. The metro is quicker but the bus is good for sightseeing and practical for short distances.

POSTAL SERVICES

Local post offices: open Mondays to Fridays 8am to 7pm; Saturdays 8am to noon
General Post Office: 52 rue du Louvre, 1st: open 24 hours

SHOPPING IN PARIS

Department stores: Boulevard Haussmann, Rue de Rivoli and Rue de Sèvres
Exclusive shops and boutiques: Faubourg St-Honoré, Rue de la Paix and Rue Royale, Avenue Montaigne.
Antiques and second-hand goods: Swiss Village (Avenue de la Motte Picquet), Louvre des Antiquaires (Place du Palais Royal), Flea Market (Porte Clignancourt).

TIPPING

Service is generally included in hotel and restaurants bills. But you may choose to leave more than the expected tip to the staff. Taxi-drivers, porters, barbers and theatre or cinema attendants also expect a small gratuity.

BREAKDOWN SERVICE

Certain garages in central and outer Paris operate a 24 hour breakdown service. If you breakdown the police are usually able to help by indicating the nearest one.

SPEED LIMITS

The maximum permitted speed in built up areas is 50 km/h - 31 mph; on motorways the speed limit is 130 km/h - 80 mph and 110 km/h - 68 mph on dual carriageways. On all other roads 90 km/h - 56 mph.

SEAT BELTS

The wearing of seat belts is compulsory for drivers and passengers.

Paris and environs

75 Maps : 10, 11, 12 G. Paris – ⚙ 1.

Population : Paris 2 152 333 ; Ile-de-France region : 10 651 000.

Altitude : Observatory : 60 m ; Place Concorde : 34 m

Air Terminals : Esplanade des Invalides, 7th, ℘ 43 23 97 10 – Palais des Congrès, Porte Maillot, 17th, ℘ 42 99 20 18

Paris'Airports : see Orly and Charles de Gaulle (Roissy)

Railways, motorail : information ℘ 45 82 50 50.

ARRONDISSEMENTS

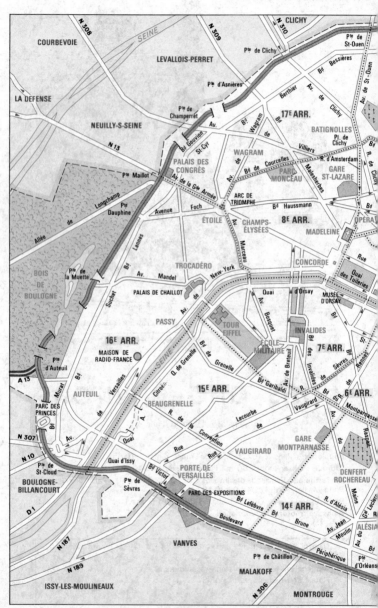

AND DISTRICTS

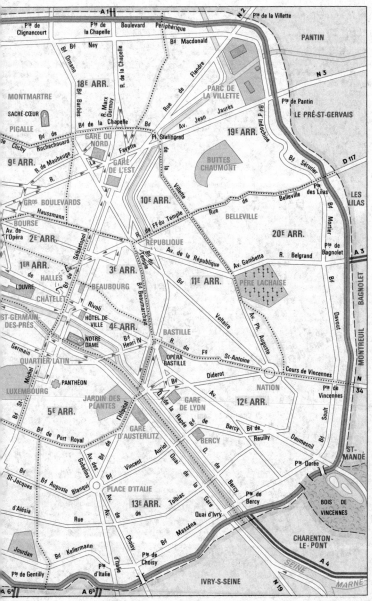

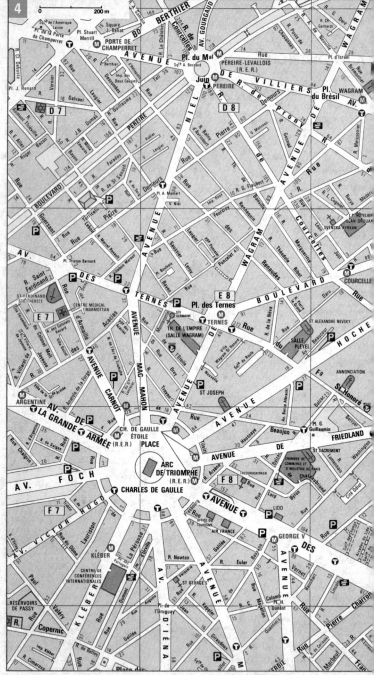

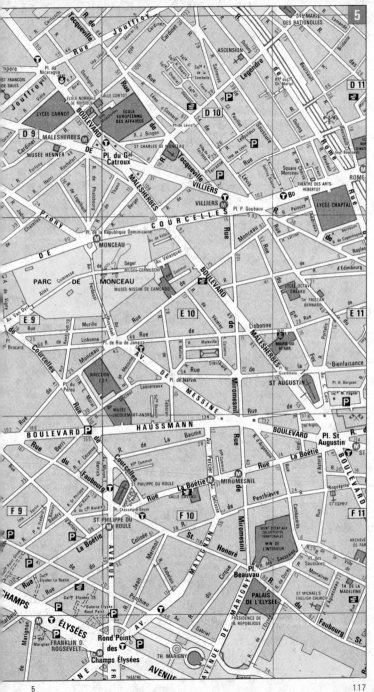

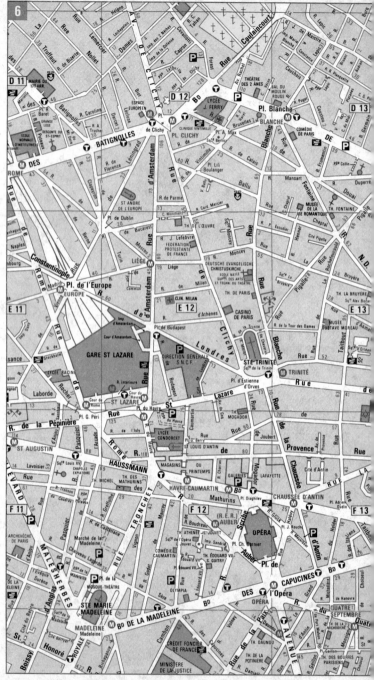

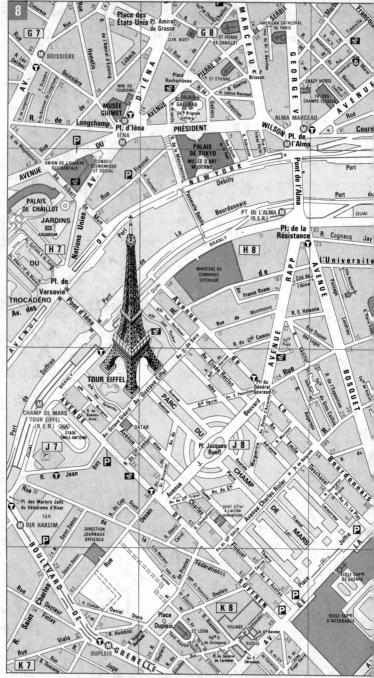

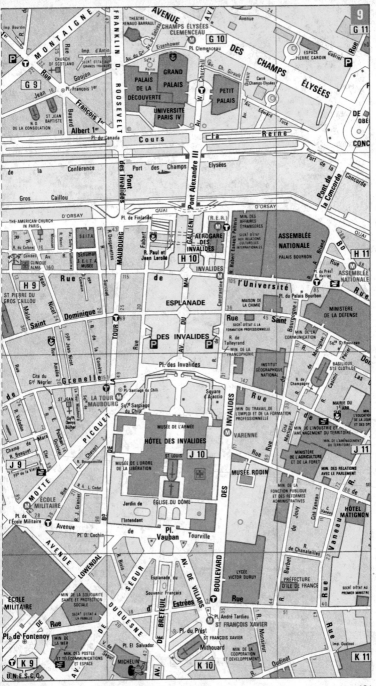

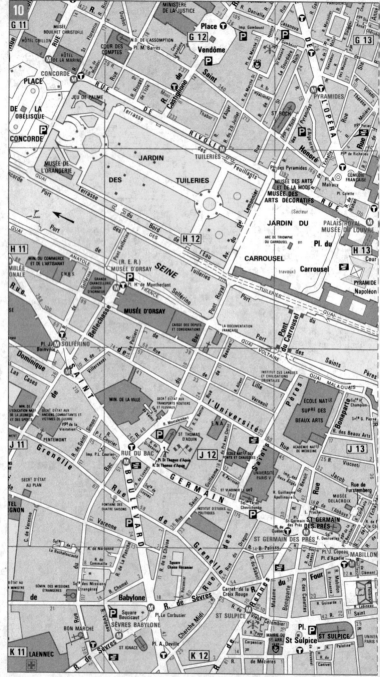

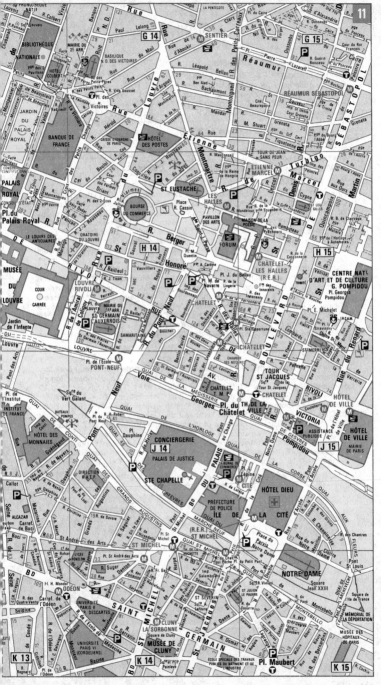

Sights

STREETS – SQUARES – GARDENS

Champs-Élysées★★★ F 8, F 9, G 10 – Place de la Concorde★★★ (Obelisk of Luxor) G 11 – Tuileries Gardens★★ (Jardin des Tuileries) H 12 – Rue du Faubourg St-Honoré★★ G 11, G 12 – Avenue de l'Opéra★★ G 13 – Place Vendôme★★ G 12 – Place des Vosges★★ J 17 – Place du Tertre★★ D 14 – Botanical Gardens★★ (Jardin des Plantes) L 16 – Avenue Foch★ F 6, F 7 – Rue de Rivoli★ G 12 – Rue Mouffetard★ M 15 – Place de la Bastille (July Column : Colonne de Juillet) – Place de la République – Grands Boulevards F 13, F 14.

OLD QUARTERS

Cité★★★ (Ile St-Louis, The Quays) J 14, J 15 – Le Marais★★★ – Montmartre★★★ D 14 – Montagne Ste Geneviève★★ (Latin Quarter : Quartier Latin) K 14.

MAIN MONUMENTS

Louvre★★★ (Royal Palace : Palais des Rois de France★★★ ; Cour Carrée, Perrault's Colonnade, Embankment Façade : façade sur le quai, the "two arms" of the Louvre : les "bras" du Louvre, Carrousel Triumphal Arch : Arc de Triomphe du Carrousel, and the Pyramid.) H 13 – Notre Dame Cathedral★★★ K 15 – Sainte Chapelle★★★ J 14 – Arc de Triomphe★★★ F 8 (Place Charles de Gaulle) – Eiffel Tower★★★ (Tour Eiffel) J 7 – The Invalides★★★ (Dôme Church : Napoléon's Tomb) J 10 – Palais Royal★★ H 13 – Madeleine★★ G 11 – Opéra★★ F 12 – St. Germain l'Auxerrois Church★★ H 14 – Conciergerie★★ J 14 – Ecole Militaire★★ K 9 – Luxembourg★★ (Palace, gardens) KL 13 – Panthéon★★ L 14 – St. Séverin Church★★ K 14 – St. Germain des Prés Church★★ J 13 – St. Etienne du Mont Church★★ – St. Sulpice Church★★ K 13 – Hôtel de Lamoignon★★ J 16 – Hôtel Guénégaud★★ (Museum of the Chase) H 16 – Hôtel de Rohan★★ H 16 – Soubise Palace★★ (Historical Museum of France) H 16 – The Sacré Cœur Basilica★★ D 14 – Montparnasse Tower★★ LM 11 – Institute of France★ (Institut de France) J 13 – Radio France House★ (Maison de Radio France) – Palais des Congrès★ – St. Roch Church★ G 13 – Alexandre III Bridge★ (Pont Alexandre III) H 10 – Pont Neuf J 14 – Pont des Arts J 13.

MAIN MUSEUMS

Louvre★★★ : Freize of the Archers, Seated Scribe, Vénus de Milo, Winged Victory of Samothrace, Nymphs of Jean Goujon, Mona Lisa : La Joconde, Regent diamond... H 13 – Orsay★★★ H 12 – Army Museum★★★ (The Invalides★★★) J 10 – Centre for Science and Industry★★★ (La Vilette★★) BC 20 – Modern Art Museum★★★ (Georges Pompidou Centre★★) H 15 – Decorative Arts★★ H 13 – Hôtel de Cluny and its Museum★★ (The Lady and the Unicorn) K 14 – Rodin★★ (Hôtel de Biron) J 10 – Historical Museum of Paris★★ (Hôtel Carnavalet★ J 17 – Picasso★ (Hôtel Salé) H 17 – Museum of French Monuments★★, Museum of Man★★, Maritime Museum★★ (Chaillot Palace) H 7 – Science Museum★★ (Palais de la Découverte★★) G 10 – National Technical Museum★★ (Conservatoire des Arts et Métiers★) G 16 – Marmottan Museum★★ H 4 – Orangery★ H 11.

K 14, G 10 : *Reference letters and numbers on the Michelin town plans* 🔟, 🔟, 🔟, 🔟 *or* 🔟.

Alphabetical list
(Hotels and Restaurants)

HOTELS, RESTAURANTS

Listed by districts and arrondissements

(List of Hotels and Restaurants in alphabetical order, see pp 5 to 8)

G 12: These reference letters and numbers correspond to the squares on the Michelin Map of Paris no ▮▮. Paris Atlas no ▮▮. Map with street index no ▮▮ and Map of Paris no ▮▮.

Consult any of the above publications when looking for a car park nearest to a listed establishment.

Opéra, Palais-Royal, Halles, Bourse.

1st and 2nd arrondissements - 1st: ✉ *75001 - 2nd:* ✉ *75002*

Ritz ⌕, 15 pl. Vendôme (1st) ✆ 42 60 38 30, Telex 220262, Fax 42 60 23 71, ☂, « Attractive pool and luxurious fitness centre » – ▯ ▤ 🖵 ☎ ᓬ – ⚿ 30 - 80. 🝰 ⓪ 🝳 🝮. ⅏ rest
M see **Espadon** below – ☲ 160 – **142 rm** 2750/4100, 45 suites.   G 12

Meurice, 228 r. Rivoli (1st) ✆ 42 60 38 60, Telex 230673, Fax 49 27 94 97 – ▯ ▤ 🖵 ☎ ᓬ – ⚿ 40 - 100. 🝰 ⓪ 🝳. ⅏ rest
M see **Meurice** below – ☲ 130 – **148 rm** 2200/2900, 40 suites.   G 12

Inter-Continental, 3 r. Castiglione (1st) ✆ 44 77 11 11, Telex 220114, Fax 44 77 14 60, ☂ – ▯ ⅏ rm ▤ 🖵 ☎ ᓬ – ⚿ 500. 🝰 ⓪ 🝳. ⅏ rest   G 12
Café Tuileries (coffee shop) **M** a la carte 215/295 – **La Terrasse Fleurie M** a la carte 340/540 – ☲ 120 – **435 rm** 1650/2450, 16 suites.

Lotti, 7 r. Castiglione (1st) ✆ 42 60 37 34, Telex 240066, Fax 40 15 93 56 – ▯ ⅏ rm ▤ 🖵 ☎ ᓬ – ⚿ 25. 🝰 ⓪ 🝳 🝮. ⅏ rest   G 12
M 230 and a la carte 260/410 ᓬ – ☲ 120 – **129 rm** 1600/3000.

Westminster, 13 r. Paix (2nd) ✆ 42 61 57 46, Telex 680035, Fax 42 60 30 66 – ▯ ⅏ rm ▤ rm 🖵 ☎ ᓬ – ⚿ 40. 🝰 ⓪ 🝳 🝮. ⅏ rest   G 12
M see **Le Céladon** below – ☲ 110 – **101 rm** 1900/2400, 18 suites 2600/4200.

du Louvre, pl. A. Malraux (1st) ✆ 44 58 38 38, Telex 240412, Fax 44 58 38 01 – ▯ ▤ 🖵 ☎ ☎ ᓬ – ⚿ 100. 🝰 ⓪ 🝳 🝮   H 13
Brasserie Le Louvre M a la carte 190/330 ᓬ – ☲ 90 – **179 rm** 1200/2000, 21 suites.

Edouard VII and rest. Le Delmonico, 39 av. Opéra (2nd) ✆ 42 61 56 90, Telex 680217, Fax 42 61 47 73 – ▯ ▤ rest 🖵 ☎ – ⚿ 45. 🝰 ⓪ 🝳 🝮   G 13
M (closed 25 July-25 August, Saturday and Sunday) 250 b.i./350 – ☲ 30 – **68 rm** 750/1290, 4 suites 1800.

Normandy, 7 r. Échelle (1st) ✆ 42 60 30 21, Telex 670250, Fax 42 60 45 81 – ▯ 🖵 ☎ – ⚿ 50. 🝰 ⓪ 🝳 🝮   H 13
L'Echelle (closed Saturday and Sunday) **M** 180 and a la carte 230/320 – ☲ 68 – **123 rm** 920/1490, 8 suites 1770/2500.

Cambon without rest, 3 r. Cambon (1st) ✆ 42 60 38 09, Telex 240814, Fax 42 60 30 59 – ▯ ▤ 🖵 ☎. 🝰 ⓪ 🝳 🝮   G 12
☲ 70 – **43 rm** 880/1380.

Mayfair without rest, 3 r. Rouget-de-Lisle (1st) ✆ 42 60 38 14, Telex 240037, Fax 40 15 04 78 – ▯ ▤ 🖵 ☎. 🝰 ⓪ 🝳 🝮. ⅏   G 12
☲ 70 – **53 rm** 850/1555.

Novotel Paris Halles Ⓜ, 8 pl. M.-de-Navarre (1st) ✆ 42 21 31 31, Telex 216389, Fax 40 26 05 79, ☂ – ▯ ⅏ ▤ 🖵 ☎ ᓬ – ⚿ 40 - 100. 🝰 ⓪ 🝳   H 14
M a la carte approx. 150 – ☲ 55 – **280 rm** 790/860, 5 suites 1500.

Royal St Honoré without rest, 13 r. Alger (1st) ✆ 42 60 32 79, Telex 680429, Fax 42 61 21 49 – ▯ 🖵 ☎ – ⚿ 25. 🝰 ⓪ 🝳 🝮   G 12
☲ 60 – **71 rm** 700/900, 3 suites 1650.

🏠 **de Noailles** Ⓜ without rest, 9 r. Michodière (2nd) ℰ 47 42 92 90, Telex 290644, Fax 49 24 92 71 – |≣| 🆃🆅 ☎. 🅰🅴 🇬🇧
⌷ 35 – **58 rm** 800.　　　　　　　　　　　　　　　　　　　　　　　　　　　G 13

🏠 **Favart** without rest, 5 r. Marivaux (2nd) ℰ 42 97 59 83, Telex 213126, Fax 40 15 95 58 – |≣|
🆃🆅 ☎ 🕭. 🅰🅴 🇬🇧　　　　　　　　　　　　　　　　　　　　　　　　　　　F 13
⌷ 20 – **37 rm** 490/590.

🏠 **François** without rest, 3 bd Montmartre (2nd) ℰ 42 33 51 53, Telex 211097, Fax 40 26 29 90
– |≣| 🆃🆅 ☎. 🅰🅴 ⓪ 🇬🇧. 🦜　　　　　　　　　　　　　　　　　　　　　　　F 14
⌷ 48 – **61 rm** 680/820, 11 suites 795/930.

🏠 **Montana Tuileries** without rest, 12 r. St-Roch (1st) ℰ 42 60 35 10, Telex 214404, Fax 42 61 12 28 – |≣| 🆃🆅 ☎. 🅰🅴 ⓪ 🇬🇧 🇯🇨🇧　　　　　　　　　　　　　　G 12
⌷ 48 – **25 rm** 690/990.

🏠 **Duminy Vendôme** without rest, 3 r. Mont-Thabor (1st) ℰ 42 60 32 80, Telex 213492, Fax 42 96 07 83 – |≣| 🆃🆅 ☎ – 🔬 30. 🅰🅴 ⓪ 🇬🇧 🇯🇨🇧. 🦜　　　　　　　G 12
79 rm ⌷ 780/850.

🏠 **Louvre St-Honoré** Ⓜ without rest, 141 r. St-Honoré (1st) ℰ 42 96 23 23, Telex 215044, Fax 42 96 21 61 – |≣| 🆃🆅 ☎. 🅰🅴 ⓪ 🇬🇧 🇯🇨🇧　　　　　　　　　　　　H 14
⌷ 45 – **40 rm** 450/945.

🏠 **Molière** without rest, 21 r. Molière (1st) ℰ 42 96 22 01, Telex 213292, Fax 42 60 48 68 – |≣|
🆃🆅 ☎. 🅰🅴 ⓪ 🇬🇧. 🦜　　　　　　　　　　　　　　　　　　　　　　　　G 13
⌷ 35 – **29 rm** 430/650, 3 suites.

🏠 **Lautrec Opéra** without rest, 8 r. Ambroise (2nd) ℰ 42 96 67 90, Telex 216502, Fax 42 96 06 83 – |≣| 🆃🆅 ☎. 🅰🅴 🇬🇧. 🦜　　　　　　　　　　　　　F 13
⌷ 25 – **30 rm** 500/800.

🏠 **Baudelaire Opéra** Ⓜ without rest, 61 r. Ste Anne (2nd) ℰ 42 97 50 62, Telex 216116, Fax 42 86 85 85 – |≣| 🆃🆅 ☎. 🅰🅴 ⓪ 🇬🇧 🇯🇨🇧　　　　　　　　　　　G 13
⌷ 30 – **29 rm** 420/570, 5 duplex 680.

🏠 **Ducs d'Anjou** without rest, 1 r. Ste-Opportune (1st) ℰ 42 36 92 24, Telex 218681, Fax 42 36 16 63 – |≣| 🆃🆅 ☎. 🅰🅴 🇬🇧 🇯🇨🇧　　　　　　　　　　　　　H 14
⌷ 42 – **38 rm** 410/565.

🏠 **Timhôtel Le Louvre** without rest, 4 r. Croix des Petits Champs (1st) ℰ 42 60 34 86, Telex 216405, Fax 42 60 10 39 – |≣| 🆃🆅 ☎ 🕭. 🅰🅴 ⓪ 🇬🇧 🇯🇨🇧　　　　　　　H 13
⌷ 45 – **56 rm** 389/523.

XXXXX ✿✿ **Espadon** - Hôtel Ritz, 15 pl. Vendôme (1st) ℰ 42 60 38 30, Telex 220262, Fax 42 60 23 71, 🌤 – ▣. 🅰🅴 ⓪ 🇬🇧 🇯🇨🇧. 🦜　　　　　　　　　　　　　　　　　　　G 12
closed August – **M** 340 (lunch)/560 and a la carte 450/750
Spec. Foie gras de canard au Médoc, Omble chevalier du lac Pavin (November-December), Canette de Barbarie.

XXXXX ✿✿ **Grand Vefour,** 17 r. Beaujolais (1st) ℰ 42 96 56 27, Fax 42 86 80 71, « Pre-Revolutionary (late 18C) Café Style » – ▣. 🅰🅴 ⓪ 🇬🇧 🇯🇨🇧. 🦜　　　　G 13
closed August, Saturday and Sunday – **M** 305 (lunch) and a la carte 510/720
Spec. Saumon mi-cuit en terrine, Pigeon de Bresse rôti, Déclinaison de pomme.

XXXX ✿ **Le Meurice** - Hôtel Meurice, 228 r. Rivoli (1st) ℰ 42 60 38 60, Telex 230673, Fax 49 27 94 97
– ▣. 🅰🅴 ⓪ 🇬🇧 – **M** 300 (lunch) and a la carte 355/460
Spec. Crêpes de maïs fourrées au foie de canard, Filets de sole en bouillon d'écrevisses, Pomme de ris de veau truffée au Vin Jaune.

XXXX ✿✿ **Carré des Feuillants** (Dutournier), 14 r. Castiglione (1st) ℰ 42 86 82 82, Fax 42 86 07 71 – ▣. 🅰🅴 ⓪ 🇬🇧 🇯🇨🇧　　　　　　　　　　　　　　　　　G 12
closed Saturday (except dinner September-June) and Sunday – **M** 250 (lunch) and a la carte 410/570
Spec. Gaspacho blanc de homard (summer), Merlu poêlé, Jarret de veau de lait à la daube de cèpes (autumn-winter).

XXXX ✿ **Drouant,** pl. Gaillon (2nd) ℰ 42 65 15 16, Fax 49 24 02 15 – ▣. 🅰🅴 ⓪ 🇬🇧 🇯🇨🇧　　G 13
M 320 (lunch) and a la carte 405/550 - **Café Drouant M** 200 b.i. (dinner and Sunday) and a la carte 245/340
Spec. Charlotte de langoustines aux aubergines confites, Aile de raie en papillote aux aromates, Filet de veau à la ficelle.

XXXX ✿ **Goumard-Prunier,** 9 r. Duphot (1st) ℰ 42 60 36 07, Fax 42 60 04 54, Seafood – ▣. 🅰🅴 ⓪ 🇬🇧 🇯🇨🇧 – *closed Sunday and Monday* – **M** a la carte 410/560　　　　　G 12
Spec. Friture de petits calamars, Carpaccio de Saint-Jacques et truffes (October-May), Poissons de roche en soupe safranée.

XXXX ✿ **Gérard Besson,** 5 r. Coq Héron (1st) ℰ 42 33 14 74, Fax 42 33 85 71 – ▣. 🅰🅴 ⓪ 🇬🇧
closed 11 July-2 August, 25 December-2 January, Saturday and Sunday – **M** 260 (lunch) and a la carte 335/520　　　　　　　　　　　　　　　　　　　　　　　　　　　H 14
Spec. Homard et poissons de la baie d'Erquy, Champignons et truffes (season), Gibier (season).

XXX ✿ **Mercure Galant**, 15 r. Petits-Champs (1st) ℰ 42 96 98 89, Fax 42 96 08 89 – GB
closed Saturday lunch, Sunday and Bank Holidays – **M** 250 (lunch)/400   G 13
Spec. Tournedos de saumon fumé, Cœur de Charolais à la moelle en papillote, Mille et une feuilles.

XXX ✿ **Le Céladon** - Hôtel Westminster, 15 r. Daunou (2nd) ℰ 42 61 57 46, Telex 680035,
Fax 42 60 30 66 – ⇆ ■, AE ⓞ GB   G 12
closed August, Saturday, Sunday and Bank Holidays – **M** 290 and a la carte 420/545
Spec. Œufs brouillés aux oursins en coque (October-March), Saint-Jacques grillées bardées de magret de canard (October-March), Escalope de ris de veau panée.

XXX **Pierre " A la Fontaine Gaillon ",** pl. Gaillon (2nd) ℰ 42 65 87 04, ⛱ – ■, AE ⓞ GB
JCB   G 13
closed August, Saturday lunch and Sunday – **M** a la carte 200/360.

XXX **Serge Granger**, 36 pl. Marché St-Honoré (1st) ℰ 42 60 03 00, Fax 42 60 00 89, ⛱ – ■.
AE ⓞ GB. ❀ – *closed mid-August-mid-September, Saturday lunch, Sunday and Bank Holidays*
– **M** 170/220 b.i.   G 13

XXX **La Corbeille**, 154 r. Montmartre (2nd) ℰ 40 26 30 87 – AE GB   G 14
closed 10 to 20 August, Saturday and Sunday – **M** 150/280.

XXX **Chez Vong**, 10 r. Grande-Truanderie (1st) ℰ 40 39 99 89, Chinese and Vietnamese rest. –
■, AE ⓞ GB   H 15
closed Sunday – **M** a la carte 170/340.

XX **Au Pied de Cochon**, 6 r. Coquillière (1st) ℰ 42 36 11 75, Fax 45 08 48 90 – ■, AE ⓞ GB
JCB   H 14
M a la carte 170/310.

XX **Gaya**, 17 r. Duphot (1st) ℰ 42 60 43 03, Fax 42 60 39 57, « Attractive glazed tile panels »
– ■, AE ⓞ GB JCB   G 12
closed Sunday and Monday – **M** a la carte approx. 250.

XX ✿ **Chez Pauline** (Génin), 5 r. Villédo (1st) ℰ 42 96 20 70, Fax 49 27 99 89 – AE GB
*closed 9 to 27 August, 20 to 27 December, Saturday (except lunch from October-April) and
Sunday* – **M** (■ 1st floor) 190 (lunch) and a la carte 290/480   G 13
Spec. Salade tiède de tête de veau, Terrine de lapereau en gelée de Pouilly, Ris de veau en croûte.

XX ✿ **Pierre Au Palais Royal**, 10 r. Richelieu (1st) ℰ 42 96 09 17 – ⓞ GB   H 13
closed August, Saturday, Sunday and Bank Holidays – **M** a la carte 215/380
Spec. Escalopes de foie gras de canard chaud, Quenelles de brochet, Rognon de veau rôti.

XX **Saudade**, 34 r. Bourdonnais (1st) ℰ 42 36 30 71, Portuguese rest. – ■, AE ⓞ GB. ❀
closed Sunday dinner – **M** a la carte 170/270.   H 14

XX **Kinugawa**, 9 r. Mont-Thabor (1st) ℰ 42 60 65 07, Fax 42 60 45 21, Japanese rest. – ■, AE
GB JCB. ❀   G 12
M a la carte 175/310 ♨.

XX ✿ **Pharamond**, 24 r. Grande-Truanderie (1st) ℰ 42 33 06 72 – AE ⓞ GB   H 15
closed 19 July-17 August, Monday lunch and Sunday – **M** a la carte 210/360
Spec. Tripes à la mode de Caen, Coquilles Saint-Jacques au cidre (15 October-15 May), Dodine de caneton au Saumur-Champigny.

XX **Palais Cardinal**, 43 r. Montpensier (1st) ℰ 42 61 20 23 – GB   G 13
closed 1 to 25 August, Sunday and Monday – **M** a la carte 195/315.

XX ✿ **Pile ou Face**, 52bis r. N.-D.-des-Victoires (2nd) ℰ 42 33 64 33, Fax 42 36 61 09 – ■, GB
closed 27 July-23 August, 23 December-1 January, Saturday, Sunday and Bank Holidays – **M**
a la carte 285/435   G 14
Spec. Pigeonneau rôti à l'huile de truffe, Fricassée de ris de veau et coques à l'oseille, Mousse de thé "Earl Grey".

XX **Bernard Chirent**, 28 r. Mont-Thabor (1st) ℰ 42 86 80 05 – GB   G 12
closed Saturday lunch and Sunday – **M** 170 b.i./450.

XX **Velloni**, 22 r. des Halles (1st) ℰ 42 21 12 50, Italian rest. – AE ⓞ GB JCB. ❀   H 14
closed August and Sunday – **M** a la carte 180/290.

XX **A la Grille St-Honoré**, 15 pl. Marché St-Honoré (1st) ℰ 42 61 00 93, Fax 47 03 31 64 – AE
GB   G 12
closed 30 July-19 August, 24 December-2 January, Sunday and Monday – **M** 180 and a la
carte 260/395 ♨.

XX **La Passion**, 41 r. Petits Champs (1st) ℰ 42 97 53 41 – ■, GB. ❀   G 13
closed 26 July-26 August, Saturday and Sunday – **M** 170/360.

XX **Vaudeville**, 29 r. Vivienne (2nd) ℰ 40 20 04 62, Fax 49 27 08 78, Brasserie – AE ⓞ GB
M a la carte 150/290 ♨.   G 14

XX **Chatelet Gourmand**, 13 r. Lavandières Ste-Opportune (1st) ℰ 40 26 45 00 – AE ⓞ GB
closed August, Saturday lunch and Sunday – **M** 160 and a la carte 245/335.   J 14

XX **Le Grand Colbert**, 2 r. Vivienne (2nd) ℰ 42 86 87 88, Brasserie – ■, AE ⓞ GB   G 13
closed August – **M** a la carte 160/240 ♨.

XX **Coup de Cœur**, 19 r. St-Augustin (2nd) ℰ 47 03 45 70 – AE ⓞ GB   G 13
closed 8 to 23 August, Saturday lunch and Sunday – **M** 130/165 b.i.

XX **Le Soufflé**, 36 r. Mont-Thabor (1st) ℰ 42 60 27 19 – ■, AE ⓞ GB JCB   G 12
closed Sunday and Bank Holidays – **M** 200.

XX **Les Cartes Postales,** 7 r. Gomboust (1st) ✆ 42 61 02 93 – ⚏. ✼   G 13
closed 2 to 23 August, 20 December-3 January, Saturday lunch, Sunday and Bank Holidays
– **M** (booking essential) a la carte 220/330.

XX **Chez Gabriel,** 123 r. St-Honoré (1st) ✆ 42 33 02 99 – ⚏. ⬛ ⓪ ⚏ ⌷⌷⌷. ✼   H 14
closed 1 to 20 August, 24 December – 4 January, Sunday and Bank Holidays – **M** 145/235.

XX **Le Saint Amour,** 8 r. Port Mahon (2nd) ✆ 47 42 63 82 – ⚏. ⬛ ⓪ ⚏   G 13
closed 13 July-15 August, Saturday (except dinner from 16 September-14 June), Sunday and
Bank Holidays – **M** 165 and a la carte 200/315.

XX **Escargot Montorgueil,** 38 r. Montorgueil (1st) ✆ 42 36 83 51, Fax 42 36 35 05, « Bistro
with 1830 decor » – ⬛ ⓪ ⚏   H 14
closed 2 to 17 August and Monday – **M** a la carte 240/380.

XX **Caveau du Palais,** 19 pl. Dauphine (1st) ✆ 43 26 04 28, Fax 43 26 81 84 – ⬛ ⚏   J 14
closed Saturday October-May and Sunday – **M** a la carte 190/335.

XX **Bonne Fourchette,** 320 r. St-Honoré, in the backyard (1st) ✆ 42 60 45 27 – ⚏. ⓪ ⚏.
✼   G 12
closed 1 to 30 August, Sunday lunch and Saturday – **M** 105/145 🍴.

X **La Main à la Pâte,** 35 r. St-Honoré (1st) ✆ 45 08 85 73, Italian rest. – ⬛ ⓪ ⚏   H 14
closed Sunday – **M** 168 and a la carte 180/310.

X **Aux Petits Pères " Chez Yvonne ",** 8 r. N.-D.-des-Victoires (2nd) ✆ 42 60 91 73 – ⚏.
⬛ ⚏   G 14
closed 2 to 8 March, August, Saturday, Sunday and Bank Holidays – **M** 158 and a la carte
170/315.

X **Chez Georges,** 1 r. Mail (2nd) ✆ 42 60 07 11 – ⚏. ⬛ ⚏   G 14
closed 6 to 20 August, Sunday and Bank Holidays – **M** a la carte 195/335.

X **La Clef du Périgord,** 38 r. Croix des Petits Champs (1st) ✆ 40 20 06 46 – ⚏   G 14
closed 1 to 15 May, 15 to 31 August, Saturday lunch and Sunday – **M** 145/198 b.i.

X **Joss Dumoulin,** 16 r. St-Augustin (2nd) ✆ 49 27 09 90 – ⚏. ⚏   G 13
closed August, Saturday (except dinner 1 October-30 June) and Sunday – **M** a la carte 145/230.

X **Cochon Doré,** 16 r. Thorel (2nd) ✆ 42 33 29 70 – ⚏. ⚏   F 15
closed 1 to 16 August and Monday – **M** 78/150.

X **Paul,** 15 pl. Dauphine (1st) ✆ 43 54 21 48 – ⚏. ✼   J 14
closed 2 to 10 March, 3 to 27 August, Monday and Tuesday – **M** a la carte 185/310.

X **La Poule au Pot,** 9 r. Vauvilliers (1st) ✆ 42 36 32 96 – ⚏   H 14
closed Monday – **M** (dinner only) a la carte 210/360.

Bastille,
République,
Hôtel de Ville.

3rd, 4th and 11th arrondissements.
        3rd: ✉ *75003*
        4th: ✉ *75004*
      11th: ✉ *75011*

🏨 **Pavillon de la Reine** Ⓜ ⚘ without rest, 28 pl. Vosges (3rd) ✆ 42 77 96 40, Telex 216160,
Fax 42 77 63 06 – 🛗 ⚏ ☎ & ⟵⟶. ⬛ ⓪ ⚏   J 17
⛐ 85 – **31 rm** 1150/1600, 24 suites 1600/2800.

🏨 **Holiday Inn** Ⓜ, 10 pl. République (11th) ✆ 43 55 44 34, Telex 210651, Fax 47 00 32 34, ⟲
– 🛗 ⚞⚟ rm ⚏ ⚏ ☎ & Ⓟ – 🔥 200. ⬛ ⓪ ⚏ ⌷⌷⌷. ✼ rest   G 17
Belle Époque *(closed 1 to 30 August, Saturday lunch and Sunday)* **M** a la carte 240/335 –
⛐ **304 rm** 1150/1590, 7 suites 1950/2800.

🏨 **Jeu de Paume** Ⓜ without rest, 54 r. St-Louis-en-l'Ile (4th) ✆ 43 26 14 18, Telex 205160,
Fax 43 26 14 18, « 17C tennis court » – 🛗 ⚏ ☎ – 🔥 30. ⬛ ⓪ ⚏ ⌷⌷⌷   K 16
⛐ 70 – **32 rm** 820/1070, 8 duplex.

🏨 **Atlantide République** Ⓜ without rest, 114 bd Richard-Lenoir (11th) ✆ 43 38 29 29,
Telex 216907, Fax 43 38 03 18 – 🛗 ⚏ ☎. ⬛ ⓪ ⚏   H 18
⛐ 35 – **27 rm** 420/630.

🏨 **Beaubourg** Ⓜ without rest, 11 r. S. Le Franc (4th) ✆ 42 74 34 24, Fax 42 78 68 11 – 🛗 ⚏
☎. ⬛ ⓪ ⚏. ✼   H 15
⛐ 35 – **28 rm** 450/650.

🏨 **Bretonnerie** Ⓜ without rest, 22 r. Ste-Croix-de-la-Bretonnerie (4th) ✆ 48 87 77 63,
Fax 42 77 26 78 – 🛗 ⚏ ☎. ⚏. ✼   J 16
closed 26 July-23 August – ⛐ 40 – **30 rm** 500/700.

🏨 **Méridional** Ⓜ without rest, 36 bd Richard-Lenoir (11th) ✆ 48 05 75 00, Telex 211324,
Fax 43 57 42 85 – 🛗 ⚏ ☎. ⬛ ⓪ ⚏ ⌷⌷⌷   J 18
⛐ 40 – **36 rm** 600.

🏠 **Lutèce** without rest, 65 r. St-Louis-en-l'Ile (4th) ℰ 43 26 23 52, Fax 43 29 60 25 – 🛗 📺 ☎.
  K 16
  ⌷ 37 – **23 rm** 690/710.

🏠 **Bastille Spéria** Ⓜ without rest, 1 r. Bastille (4th) ℰ 42 72 04 01, Telex 214327,
  Fax 42 72 56 38 – 🛗 📺 ☎. ⒶⒺ ① ⒼⒷ. ⌘
  J 17
  ⌷ 35 – **42 rm** 490/580.

🏠 **Rivoli Notre Dame** without rest, 19 r. Bourg Tibourg (4th) ℰ 42 78 47 39, Telex 215314,
  Fax 40 29 07 00 – 🛗 📺 ☎. ⒶⒺ ① ⒼⒷ. ⌘
  J 16
  ⌷ 38 – **31 rm** 480/590.

🏠 **Paris Voltaire** Ⓜ without rest, 79 r. Sedaine (11th) ℰ 48 05 44 66, Telex 215401,
  Fax 48 07 87 96 – 🛗 📺 ☎. ⒶⒺ ① ⒼⒷ ⒿⒸⒷ. ⌘
  J 9
  closed 15 to 31 August and 23 to 28 December – ⌷ 35 – **28 rm** 350/500.

🏠 **Mondia** without rest, 22 r. Gd Prieuré (11th) ℰ 47 00 93 44, Fax 43 38 66 14 – 🛗 📺 ☎. ⒶⒺ
  ① ⒼⒷ
  G 17
  ⌷ 35 – **23 rm** 310/420.

🏠 **Place des Vosges** without rest, 12 r. Birague (4th) ℰ 42 72 60 46, Fax 42 72 02 64 – 🛗 ☎.
  ⒶⒺ ① ⒼⒷ
  J 17
  ⌷ 32 – **16 rm** 275/400.

XXXX ❀❀❀ **L'Ambroisie** (Pacaud), 9 pl. des Vosges (4th) ℰ 42 78 51 45 – ⒼⒷ. ⌘
  J 17
  closed 1 to 16 March, 3 to 23 August, Sunday and Monday – **M** a la carte 550/810
  Spec. Feuillantine de queues de langoustines, Foie de veau fermier en persillade, Tarte fine sablée
  au cacao amer et glace vanille.

XXX ❀ **Miraville** (Épié), 72 quai Hôtel de Ville (4th) ℰ 42 74 72 22, Fax 42 74 64 85 – ⒺⒶⒺ ⒼⒷ
  J 15
  closed Saturday lunch and Sunday – **M** 150 (lunch)/500
  Spec. Beignet de foie gras au Porto, Pissalat de loup à la mozzarella, Tournedos de pied de cochon
  aux truffes.

XXX **Ambassade d'Auvergne**, 22 r. Grenier St-Lazare (3rd) ℰ 42 72 31 22, Fax 42 78 85 47 –
  ⌘ Ⓔ ⒼⒷ
  H 15
  closed 26 July-11 August – **M** a la carte 175/275.

XXX **Le Péché Mignon**, 5 r. Guillaume-Bertrand (11th) ℰ 43 57 02 51 – Ⓔ ⒶⒺ ⒼⒷ
  H 19
  closed 1 (lunch) and a la carte 220/325.

XX **Bofinger**, 5 r. Bastille (4th) ℰ 42 72 87 82, Fax 42 72 97 68, brasserie, « Belle Epoque
  decor » – ⒶⒺ ① ⒼⒷ
  J 17
  M 160 b.i. and a la carte 200/320 ⓖ.

XX ❀ **Benoît** (4th), 20 r. St-Martin (4th) ℰ 42 72 25 76
  J 15
  closed August, Saturday and Sunday – **M** a la carte 325/460
  Spec. Langue de bœuf Lucullus, Selle d'agneau en rognonnade, Bœuf mode braisé à l'ancienne.

XX ❀ **A Sousceyrac** (Asfaux), 35 r. Faidherbe (11th) ℰ 43 71 65 30, Fax 40 09 79 75 – Ⓔ ⒶⒺ
  ⒼⒷ
  J 19
  closed August, Saturday and Sunday – **M** a la carte 185/345
  Spec. Les foies gras en terrine, Ris de veau aux pleurotes, Lièvre à la royale (season).

XX **Blue Elephant**, 43 r. Roquette (11th) ℰ 47 00 42 00, Fax 47 00 45 44, « Thaï decor » – ⒶⒺ
  ① ⒼⒷ
  J 18
  closed 24 to 28 December and Saturday lunch – **M** a la carte 180/260 ⓖ.

XX **Repaire de Cartouche**, 8 bd Filles-du-Calvaire (11th) ℰ 47 00 25 86 – ⒶⒺ ① ⒼⒷ
  H 17
  closed 25 July-25 August, Saturday lunch and Sunday – **M** 140/350.

XX **L'Aiguière**, 37bis r. Montreuil (11th) ℰ 43 72 42 32 – Ⓔ ⒶⒺ ① ⒼⒷ
  K 20
  closed Saturday lunch and Sunday – **M** 120 (lunch) and a la carte 240/340.

XX **Coconnas**, 2bis pl. Vosges (4th) ℰ 42 78 58 16, 🍴 – ⒼⒷ
  J 17
  closed mid January-mid February, Monday lunch and Tuesday – **M** a la carte 230/350.

XX **L'Alisier**, 26 r. Montmorency (3rd) ℰ 42 72 31 04, Fax 42 72 74 83 – ⒶⒺ ⒼⒷ. ⌘
  H 16
  closed 3 to 30 August, Saturday lunch and Sunday – **M** 145/195.

XX **La Table Richelieu**, 276 bd Voltaire (11th) ℰ 43 72 31 23 – Ⓔ ⒶⒺ ⒼⒷ
  K 21
  M a la carte 220/320.

XX **Wally**, 16 r. Le Regrattier (4th) ℰ 43 25 01 39, Fax 45 86 08 35, North African rest. – ⌘
  ① ⒼⒷ. ⌘
  K 15
  closed Monday lunch and Sunday – **M** 300.

XX **Les Amognes**, 243 r. Fg St-Antoine (11th) ℰ 43 72 73 05 – ⒼⒷ
  K 20
  closed August, Sunday dinner and Monday – **M** 160.

XX **Pyrénées Cévennes**, 106 r. Folie-Méricourt (11th) ℰ 43 57 33 78 – ⒶⒺ ⒼⒷ
  G 17
  closed August, Saturday and Sunday – **M** a la carte 190/370.

XX **Guirlande de Julie**, 25 pl. des Vosges (3rd) ℰ 48 87 94 07, 🍴 – Ⓔ ⒼⒷ
  J 17
  M 200/250.

✗ **Le Navarin,** 3 av. Philippe Auguste (11th) ✆ 43 67 17 49 – **GB**. ✁ – *closed 14 to 18 August, 23 to 26 December, Saturday lunch and Sunday dinner* – **M** 117 (lunch) and a la carte 175/335.　　K 21

✗ **Le Monde des Chimères,** 69 r. St-Louis-en-l'Ile (4th) ✆ 43 54 45 27 – **GB**　　K 16
closed February Holidays, Sunday and Monday – **M** a la carte 230/340 🍴.

✗ **Le Grizzli,** 7 r. St-Martin (4th) ✆ 48 87 77 56 – **GB** – *closed 20 December-3 January, Monday lunch and Sunday* – **M** 110 (lunch) and a la carte 145/225.　　J 15

✗ **Astier,** 44 r. J.-P. Timbaud (11th) ✆ 43 57 16 35 – ▤. **GB** – *closed 24 April-11 May, 31 July-7 September, 18 December-4 January, Saturday, Sunday and Bank Holidays* – **M** 125.　　G 18

✗ **Le Maraicher,** 5 r. Beautreillis (4th) ✆ 42 71 42 49 – **GB**　　K 17
closed 2 to 30 August, Saturday lunch and Sunday – **M** a la carte 195/270.

✗ **Chez Fernand,** 17 r. Fontaine au Roi (11th) ✆ 43 57 46 25 – **GB**　　G 18
closed 3 to 24 August, Sunday and Monday – **M** 100 (lunch) and a la carte 155/250 - **Les Fernandises M** 100 (lunch) and a la carte 115/170.

Quartier Latin, Luxembourg, Jardin des Plantes.

5th and 6th arrondissements.
　　5th: ✉ 75005
　　6th: ✉ 75006

🏨 **Lutétia,** 45 bd Raspail (6th) ✆ 49 54 46 46, Telex 270424, Fax 49 54 46 00 – 🛗 ▤ 📺 ☎ – 🔬 400. **AE** ⓞ **GB** ✁　　K 12
M see Le Paris below - Brasserie Lutétia **M** 105/175 🍴 – �`□` 85 – **232 rm** 1400/2050, 39 suites.

🏨 **Relais Christine** **M** ⚜ without rest, 3 r. Christine (6th) ✆ 43 26 71 80, Telex 202606, Fax 43 26 89 38, « Attractive installation » – 🛗 ▤ 📺 ☎ ⟺. **AE** ⓞ **GB**　　J 14
�`□` **38 rm** 1300/1700, 13 suites 1800/2500.

🏨 **Quality Inn** **M** without rest, 92 r. Vaugirard (6th) ✆ 42 22 00 56, Telex 206900, Fax 42 22 05 39 – 🛗 ✂ ▤ 📺 ☎ & ⟺. **AE** ⓞ **GB** **JCB**　　L 12
�`□` 60 – **134 rm** 660/825.

🏨 **Latitudes St Germain** **M** without rest, 7-11 r. St-Benoit (6th) ✆ 42 61 53 53, Telex 213531, Fax 49 27 09 33 – 🛗 ▤ 📺 ☎ &. **AE** ⓞ **GB**　　J 13
�`□` 58 – **117 rm** 790/890.

🏨 **Victoria Palace** ⚜ without rest, 6 r. Blaise-Desgoffe (6th) ✆ 45 44 38 16, Telex 270557, Fax 45 49 23 75 – 🛗 📺 ☎. **AE** ⓞ **GB**. ✁ – **110 rm** �`□` 780/1320.　　L 11

🏨 **Littré** ⚜ without rest, 9 r. Littré (6th) ✆ 45 44 38 68, Telex 203852, Fax 45 44 88 13 – 🛗 📺 ☎ – 🔬 25. **AE** ⓞ **GB** **JCB**. ✁　　L 11
�`□` 50 – **93 rm** 660/875, 4 suites 1345.

🏨 **Madison H.** without rest, 143 bd St-Germain (6th) ✆ 40 51 60 00, Telex 201628, Fax 40 51 60 01 – 🛗 ▤ 📺 ☎. **AE** ⓞ **GB**　　J 13
55 rm �`□` 700/1200.

🏨 **St-Grégoire** **M** without rest, 43 r. Abbé Grégoire (6th) ✆ 45 48 23 23, Telex 205343, Fax 45 48 33 95 – 🛗 📺 ☎. **AE** ⓞ **GB** **JCB**. ✁　　L 12
�`□` 55 – **20 rm** 830/1160.

🏨 **Abbaye St-Germain** ⚜ without rest, 10 r. Cassette (6th) ✆ 45 44 38 11, Fax 45 48 07 86 – 🛗. **GB**. ✁　　K 12
44 rm �`□` 760/1200, 4 duplex 1780.

🏨 **Relais St Germain** **M** without rest, 9 carrefour de l'Odéon (6th) ✆ 43 29 12 05, Telex 201889, Fax 46 33 45 30, « Fine setting » – 🛗 ▤ 📺 ☎. **AE** ⓞ **GB**　　K 13
10 rm �`□` 1190/1380.

🏨 **Sainte Beuve** **M** without rest, 9 r. Ste Beuve (6th) ✆ 45 48 20 07, Telex 270182, Fax 45 48 67 52 – 🛗 📺 ☎. **AE** **GB** **JCB**. ✁　　L 12
�`□` 70 – **22 rm** 650/1150.

🏨 **Left Bank H.** **M** without rest, 11 r. Ancienne Comédie (6th) ✆ 43 54 01 70, Telex 200502, Fax 43 26 17 14 – 🛗 📺 ☎. **AE** ⓞ **GB** **JCB**　　K 13
�`□` 25 – **31 rm** 875/950.

🏨 **La Villa** **M** without rest, 29 r. Jacob (6th) ✆ 43 26 60 00, Telex 202437, Fax 46 34 63 63, « Contemporary decor » – 🛗 ▤ 📺 ☎. **AE** **GB**. ✁　　J 13
�`□` 80 – **28 rm** 800/1250, 4 suites 1950.

🏨 **Angleterre** without rest, 44 r. Jacob (6th) ✆ 42 60 34 72, Fax 42 60 16 93 – 🛗 📺 ☎. **AE** ⓞ **GB**. ✁　　J 13
�`□` 40 – **29 rm** 750/1100.

🏨 **St-Germain-des-Prés** without rest, 36 r. Bonaparte (6th) ✆ 43 26 00 19, Telex 200409, Fax 40 46 83 63, « Attractive installation » – 🛗 📺 ☎. **GB**. ✁　　J 13
30 rm �`□` 780/1200.

🏨 **Villa des Artistes** Ⓜ ⮟ without rest, 9 r. Grande Chaumière (6th) ☏ 43 26 60 86, Telex 204080, Fax 43 54 73 70 – 🛗 📺 ☎. ℻ ⑩ GB. ❊
L 12
59 rm 🍽 580/780.

🏨 **Ferrandi** without rest, 92 r. Cherche-Midi (6th) ☏ 42 22 97 40, Telex 205201, Fax 45 44 89 97
– 🛗 📺 ☎. ℻ ⑩ GB
L 11
🍽 60 – **40 rm** 400/850.

🏨 **Panthéon** Ⓜ without rest, 19 pl. Panthéon (5th) ☏ 43 54 32 95, Telex 206435, Fax 43 26 64 65, ← – 🛗 📺 ☎. ℻ ⑩ GB. ❊
L 14
🍽 35 – **34 rm** 600/700.

🏨 **Grands Hommes** Ⓜ without rest, 17 pl. Panthéon (5th) ☏ 46 34 19 60, Telex 200185, Fax 43 26 67 32, ← – 🛗 📺 ☎. ℻ ⑩ GB. ❊
L 14
🍽 35 – **32 rm** 600/700.

🏨 **des Saints-Pères** without rest, 65 r. Sts-Pères (6th) ☏ 45 44 50 00, Telex 205424, Fax 45 44 90 83 – 🛗 📺 ☎. GB. ❊
J 12
🍽 45 – **34 rm** 450/1500, 3 suites 1500.

🏨 **Odéon H.,** Ⓜ without rest, 3 r. Odéon (6th) ☏ 43 25 90 67, Telex 202943, Fax 43 25 55 98
– 🛗 🍴 📺 ☎. ℻ ⑩ GB. ❊
K 13
🍽 50 – **34 rm** 700/900.

🏨 **de Fleurie** without rest, 32 r. Grégoire de Tours (6th) ☏ 43 29 59 81, Telex 206153, Fax 43 29 68 44 – 🛗 📺 ☎. ℻ ⑩ GB. ❊
K 13
🍽 45 – **29 rm** 550/950.

🏨 **Le Régent** Ⓜ without rest, 61 r. Dauphine (6th) ☏ 46 34 59 80, Telex 206257, Fax 40 51 05 07 – 🛗 🍴 📺 ☎ &. ℻ ⑩ GB ⒿⒸⒷ
J 13
🍽 50 – **25 rm** 600/900.

🏨 **Parc St-Séverin** Ⓜ without rest, 22 r. Parcheminerie (5th) ☏ 43 54 32 17, Telex 270905, Fax 43 54 70 71 – 🛗 📺 ☎. ℻ ❊
K 14
🍽 45 – **27 rm** 500/1500.

🏨 **St Christophe** Ⓜ without rest, 17 r. Lacépède (5th) ☏ 43 31 81 54, Telex 204304, Fax 43 31 12 54 – 🛗 📺 ☎. ℻ ⑩ GB ⒿⒸⒷ
L 15
🍽 40 – **31 rm** 650.

🏨 **Select** Ⓜ without rest, 1 pl. Sorbonne (5th) ☏ 46 34 14 80, Telex 201207, Fax 46 34 51 79
– 🛗 🍴 📺 ☎. ℻ ⑩ GB
K 14
🍽 30 – **67 rm** 590/750.

🏨 **Elysa Luxembourg** Ⓜ without rest, 6 r. Gay-Lussac (5th) ☏ 43 25 31 74, Telex 206881 –
🛗 📺 ☎. ℻ ⑩ GB ⒿⒸⒷ. ❊
🍽 35 – **30 rm** 560/660.

🏨 **Aramis St Germain** without rest, 124 r. Rennes (6th) ☏ 45 48 03 75, Telex 205098, Fax 45 44 99 29 – 🛗 📺 ☎ – 🔬 30. ℻ ⑩ GB ⒿⒸⒷ. ❊
L 12
🍽 45 – **42 rm** 550/750.

🏨 **de l'Odéon** without rest, 13 r. St-Sulpice (6th) ☏ 43 25 70 11, Telex 206731, Fax 43 29 97 34, « 16C setting » – 🛗 📺 ☎. ℻ ⑩ GB
K 13
🍽 39 – **29 rm** 520/760.

🏨 **Jardin des Plantes** Ⓜ without rest, 5 r. Linné (5th) ☏ 47 07 06 20, Telex 203684, Fax 47 07 62 74 – 🛗 📺 ☎. ℻ ⑩ GB
L 15
🍽 40 – **33 rm** 390/640.

🏨 **Jardin de Cluny** without rest, 9 r. Sommerard (5th) ☏ 43 54 22 66, Telex 206975, Fax 40 51 03 36 – 🛗 📺 ☎. ℻ ⑩ GB ⒿⒸⒷ. ❊
K 14
🍽 30 – **40 rm** 500/600.

🏨 **Notre Dame** Ⓜ without rest, 1 quai St-Michel (5th) ☏ 43 54 20 43, Telex 206650, Fax 43 26 61 75, ← – 🛗 📺 ☎. ℻ ⑩ GB ⒿⒸⒷ
K 14
🍽 35 – **23 rm** 470/770, 3 duplex 1030.

🏨 **Albe** Ⓜ without rest, 1 r. Harpe (5th) ☏ 46 34 09 70, Telex 203328, Fax 40 46 85 70 – 🛗 📺 ☎. ℻ GB ⒿⒸⒷ. ❊
K 14
🍽 33 – **45 rm** 436/554.

🏨 **Louis II** without rest, 2 r. St-Sulpice (6th) ☏ 46 33 13 80, Telex 206561, Fax 46 33 17 29 –
🛗 📺 ☎. ℻ ⑩ GB
K 13
🍽 35 – **22 rm** 415/620.

🏨 **Marronniers** ⮟ without rest, 21 r. Jacob (6th) ☏ 43 25 30 60, Fax 40 46 83 56 – 🛗 ☎. ❊
J 13
🍽 45 – **37 rm** 650/690.

🏨 **Nations** without rest, 54 r. Monge (5th) ☏ 43 26 45 24, Telex 200397, Fax 46 34 00 13 – 🛗 📺 ☎. ℻ ⑩ GB
L 15
🍽 50 – **38 rm** 520/550.

🏨 **La Sorbonne** without rest, 6 r. Victor Cousin (5th) ☏ 43 54 58 08, Telex 206373, Fax 40 51 05 18 – 🛗 📺 ☎. GB
K 14
🍽 35 – **37 rm** 380/500.

🏨 **Gd H. Suez** without rest, 31 bd St-Michel (5th) ☏ 46 34 08 02, Telex 202019, Fax 40 51 79 44
– 🛗 📺 ☎. ℻ ⑩ GB ⒿⒸⒷ. ❊
K 14
49 rm 🍽 345/475.

XXXXX ❀❀❀ **Tour d'Argent** (Terrail), 15 quai Tournelle (5th) ℰ 43 54 23 31, Fax 44 07 12 04,
« ≤ Notre Dame - little museum showing the development of eating utensils. In the cellar:
an illustrated history of wine » – ▦ 🆔 🔵 ⬛ 　　　　　　　　　　　　　　　 K 16
closed Monday – ▦ 375 (lunch except Sunday) and a la carte 700/880
Spec. Quenelles de brochet André Terrail, Caneton Tour d'Argent, Poire "Vie Parisienne".

XXX ❀❀ **Jacques Cagna**, 14 r. Gds Augustins (6th) ℰ 43 26 49 39, Fax 43 54 54 48, « Old
Parisian house » – ▦ 🆔 🔵 ⬛ ⬛　　　　　　　　　　　　　　　　　　 J 14
closed Saturday and Sunday – ▦ 260 (lunch) and a la carte 460/690
Spec. Petits escargots frais en surprise, Goujonnettes de sole et rouget de roche, Côte de veau
mijotée à l'ancienne.

XXX ❀ **Paris** - Hôtel Lutétia, 45 bd Raspail (6th) ℰ 49 54 46 90, Telex 270424, Fax 49 54 46 00,
« Transatlantic liner theme in Art Deco style » – ▦ 🆔 🔵 ⬛ ⬛　　　　　　　 K 12
closed August, February Holidays, Saturday, Sunday and Bank Holidays – ▦ 395 (lunch) and
a la carte 380/470
Spec. Ravioles de tourteau et chou vert, Tronçon de turbot rôti au lard, Feuilles de chocolat noir
et blanc.

XXX ❀ **Relais Louis XIII**, 1 r. Pont de Lodi (6th) ℰ 43 26 75 96, Fax 44 07 07 80, « 16C cellar,
fine furniture » – ▦ 🆔 🔵 ⬛ ⬛　　　　　　　　　　　　　　　　　　 J 14
closed 26 July-25 August, Monday lunch and Sunday – ▦ 240 (lunch) and a la carte 375/580
Spec. Ravioli de langoustines, Panaché de poissons de petite pêche, Filet de bœuf aux truffes
du Périgord.

XXX **Lapérouse**, 51 quai Gds Augustins (6th) ℰ 43 26 68 04, Fax 43 26 99 39, « Belle Epoque
decor » – ✂ ▦ 🆔 🔵 ⬛ ⬛ ❀　　　　　　　　　　　　　　　　　　 J 14
closed August, Monday lunch and Sunday – ▦ 250 (lunch) and a la carte 375/550.

XXX **Le Procope**, 13 r. Ancienne Comédie (6th) ℰ 43 26 99 20, Fax 43 54 16 86, « Former 18C
literary café » – 🆔 🔵　　　　　　　　　　　　　　　　　　　　　　 K 13
▦ 128 b.i./289 b.i.

XX **Aub. des Deux Signes**, 46 r. Galande (5th) ℰ 43 25 46 56, Fax 46 33 20 49, « Medieval
decor » – 🆔 🔵 ⬛ ⬛　　　　　　　　　　　　　　　　　　　　　　 K 14
closed August, Saturday lunch and Sunday – ▦ 140 (lunch) and a la carte 310/490.

XX **Au Pactole**, 44 bd St-Germain (5th) ℰ 46 33 31 31 – 🆔 🔵　　　　　 K 15
closed Saturday lunch and Sunday – ▦ 139/279.

XX ❀ **Dodin-Bouffant**, 25 r. F.-Sauton (5th) ℰ 43 25 25 14, ☂ – ▦ 🆔 🔵 🔵　 K 15
closed 10 to 23 August and Sunday – ▦ 170 and a la carte 230/370
Spec. Daube d'huîtres et pieds de porc, Ragoût de canard et ris de veau, Soufflé chaud aux fruits
de saison.

XX **Calvet**, 165 bd St-Germain (6th) ℰ 45 48 93 51 – ▦ 🆔 🔵 🔵 ⬛　　　 J 12
closed August – ▦ 139/195.

XX **Quai de la Tournelle**, 25 quai Tournelle (5th) ℰ 43 54 05 17 – ▦ 🔵 ❀　 K 15
closed Saturday lunch and Sunday – ▦ a la carte 260/430.

XX **Diapason**, 30 r. Bernardins (5th) ℰ 43 54 21 13 – 🆔 🔵 🔵 ⬛　　　　 K 15
closed 1 to 15 August, Saturday lunch and Sunday – ▦ 165/300.

XX ❀ **Clavel**, 65 quai Tournelle (5th) ℰ 46 33 18 65 – ▦ 🔵 ❀　　　　　　 K 15
closed 3 to 24 August, Sunday dinner and Monday – ▦ 160/450 b.i.
Spec. Feuilleté de haddock aux poireaux, Tourte de canard sauvage (season), Gâteau au chocolat
noir.

XX **Yugaraj**, 14 r. Dauphine (6th) ℰ 43 26 44 91, Indian rest. – ▦ 🆔 🔵 🔵 ❀　 J 14
closed Monday – ▦ 196/230.

XX **L'Arrosée**, 12 r. Guisarde (6th) ℰ 43 54 66 59 – ▦ 🆔 🔵 🔵 ⬛ ❀　　 K 13
closed 2 to 8 January and Sunday – ▦ 145/450.

XX **La Truffière**, 4 r. Blainville (5th) ℰ 46 33 29 82 – ▦ 🆔 🔵 🔵　　　　 L 15
closed 10 to 24 August, Saturday lunch and Monday – ▦ 162/210.

XX **La Petite Cour**, 8 r. Mabillon (6th) ℰ 43 26 52 26, ☂ – 🔵　　　　　 K 13
▦ 180/250.

XX **Marty**, 20 av. Gobelins (5th) ℰ 43 31 39 51, Fax 43 37 63 70 – 🆔 🔵 🔵　 M 15
▦ 159 b.i. and a la carte 175/320 ♪.

XX ❀ **La Timonerie** (de Givenchy), 35 quai Tournelle (5th) ℰ 43 25 44 42 – ▦ 🔵　 K 15
closed 24 to 30 August, 22 to 28 February, Sunday and Monday – ▦ a la carte 260/425
Spec. Fleurs de courgettes farcies aux aubergines (May-September), Sandre rôti au céleri frit
(October-June), Tarte fine au chocolat.

XX **La Marlotte**, 55 r. Cherche Midi (6th) ℰ 45 48 86 79 – 🆔 🔵 🔵　　　　 K 12
closed August, Saturday and Sunday – ▦ a la carte 185/320.

XX **Bistrot d'Alex**, 2 r. Clément (6th) ℰ 43 25 77 66 – ▦ 🆔 🔵 🔵 ⬛　　　 K 13
closed 24 December-2 January, Monday lunch and Sunday – ▦ 140/190 ♪.

XX **Au Régent,** 97 r. Cherche Midi (6th) ✆ 42 22 32 44 – AE ◑ GB L 11
closed August, Sunday and Monday – **M** 125/170.

XX **Petit Germain,** 11 r. Dupin (6th) ✆ 42 22 64 56 – GB K 12
closed 3 to 24 August, Saturday and Sunday – **M** a la carte 170/230.

XX **Le Sybarite,** 6 r. Sabot (6th) ✆ 42 22 21 56, Fax 42 22 26 21 – ▤. AE ◑ GB K 12
closed Saturday lunch and Sunday – **M** 75 (lunch)/168 ♁.

XX **Joséphine** "Chez Dumonet", 117 r. Cherche Midi (6th) ✆ 45 48 52 40, Fax 42 84 06 83 – GB L 11
closed 4 July-2 August, 19 to 27 December, Saturday and Sunday – **M** 170 b.i. (lunch) and a la carte 215/350 **La Rôtisserie** ✆ 42 22 81 19 *closed 3-31 August, 28 December-5 January, Saturday and Sunday in July, Tuesday and Monday* **M** 140 b.i. (lunch) and a la carte 185/285.

XX **Chez Maître Paul,** 12 r. Monsieur-le-Prince (6th) ✆ 43 54 74 59 – AE ◑ GB K 13
closed Saturday lunch and Sunday – **M** 180 and a la carte 170/285.

XX **Au Grilladin,** 13 r. Mézières (6th) ✆ 45 48 30 38 – AE GB K 12
closed August, 23 December-3 January, Monday lunch and Sunday – **M** 149 and a la carte 170/250.

X **Allard,** 41 r. St-André-des-Arts (6th) ✆ 43 26 48 23 – AE ◑ GB K 14
closed 31 July-3 September, 23 December-3 January, Saturday and Sunday – **M** a la carte 215/395.

X **Moissonnier,** 28 r. Fossés-St-Bernard (5th) ✆ 43 29 87 65 – GB K 15
closed 24 July-2 September, Sunday dinner and Monday – **M** a la carte 170/270.

X **Moulin à Vent "Chez Henri",** 20 r. Fossés-St-Bernard (5th) ✆ 43 54 99 37 – GB. ✻ K 15
closed August, Sunday and Monday – **M** a la carte 225/340.

X **Rôtisserie du Beaujolais,** 19 quai Tournelle (5th) ✆ 43 54 17 47 – GB K 15
closed Monday – **M** a la carte 165/260.

X **Le Palanquin,** 12 r. Princesse (6th) ✆ 43 29 77 66, Vietnamese rest. – GB K 13
closed Sunday – **M** 118 and a la carte 145/240.

X **Balzar,** 49 r. Écoles (5th) ✆ 43 54 13 67, ☂, Brasserie – AE GB K 14
closed August and Christmas-New Year – **M** a la carte 145/275.

X **La Vigneraie,** 16 r. Dragon (6th) ✆ 45 48 57 04 – AE ◑ GB JCB J 12
closed 10 to 20 August and Sunday lunch – **M** 130 and a la carte 190/290.

Faubourg-St-Germain, Invalides, École Militaire.

7th arrondissement.
7th: ✉ 75007

Pont Royal and rest. Les Antiquaires, 7 r. Montalembert ✆ 45 44 38 27, Telex 270113, Fax 45 44 92 07 – ⧆ kitchenette ▤ TV ☎ – 🏛 30. AE ◑ GB JCB J 12
M *(closed August, Saturday and Sunday)* 160 – **73 rm** ☕ 850/1550, 5 suites 2800.

Montalembert, 3 r. Montalembert ✆ 45 48 68 11, Telex 200132, Fax 42 22 58 19, « Original decor » – ⧆ ▤ rm TV ☎ – 🏛 25. AE ◑ GB J 12
M 165 (lunch) and a la carte 195/320 – ☕ 90 – **51 rm** 1450/1850, 5 suites 3000.

Duc de Saint Simon without rest, 14 r. St-Simon ✆ 45 48 35 66, Telex 203277, Fax 45 48 68 25, « Tastefully furnished interior » – ⧆ TV ☎. ✻ J 11
☕ 70 – **29 rm** 950/1500, 5 suites 1900.

Cayré M without rest, 4 bd Raspail ✆ 45 44 38 88, Telex 270577, Fax 45 44 98 13 – ⧆ TV ☎ – 🏛 30. AE ◑ GB JCB J 12
126 rm ☕ 920/1400.

La Bourdonnais, 111 av. La Bourdonnais ✆ 47 05 45 42, Telex 201416, Fax 45 55 75 54 – ⧆ TV ☎ ♿. ◑ GB JCB J 9
M see rest. **La Cantine des Gourmets** below – **60 rm** ☕ 445/615.

Eiffel Park H. M without rest, 17bis r. Amélie ✆ 45 55 10 01, Telex 202950, Fax 47 05 28 68 – ⧆ TV ☎ ♿ – 🏛 40. AE ◑ GB JCB. ✻ J 9
☕ 49 – **36 rm** 695/900.

Université without rest, 22 r. Université ✆ 42 61 09 39, Fax 42 60 40 84, « Fine furniture » – ⧆ TV ☎. ✻ – ☕ 50 – **27 rm** 600/1350. J 12

Les Jardins d'Eiffel M without rest, 8 r. Amélie ✆ 47 05 46 21, Telex 206582, Fax 45 55 28 08 – ⧆ ⊁ TV ☎ 🚗. AE ◑ GB JCB H 9
44 rm ☕ 690/850.

🏨 **Élysées Maubourg** Ⓜ without rest, 35 bd La Tour-Maubourg ℘ 45 56 10 78, Telex 206227, Fax 47 05 65 08 – 🛗 📺 ☎. 🖭 ⓄⒹ 🆎 ⒿⒸⒷ
☐ 35 – **30 rm** 520/800.   H 10

🏨 **Beaugency** Ⓜ without rest, 21 r. Duvivier ℘ 47 05 01 63, Telex 201494, Fax 45 51 04 96 – 🛗 📺 ☎. 🖭 ⓄⒹ 🆎
30 rm ☐ 580.   J 9

🏨 **Lenox Saint-Germain** without rest, 9 r. Université ℘ 42 96 10 95, Fax 42 61 52 83 – 🛗 📺 ☎. 🖭 ⓄⒹ 🆎 ⒿⒸⒷ
☐ 40 – **32 rm** 490/690.   J 12

🏨 **De Varenne** Ⓜ 🍽 without rest, 44 r. Bourgogne ℘ 45 51 45 55, Telex 205329, Fax 45 51 86 63 – 🛗 📺 ☎. 🖭 🆎
☐ 37 – **24 rm** 450/610.   J 10

🏨 **Londres** without rest, 1 r. Augereau ℘ 45 51 63 02, Telex 206398, Fax 47 05 28 96 – 🛗 📺 ☎. 🖭 ⓄⒹ 🆎 ⒿⒸⒷ, 🍽
☐ 35 – **30 rm** 440/560.   J 8

🏨 **Suède** without rest, 31 r. Vaneau ℘ 47 05 00 08, Telex 200596, Fax 47 05 69 27 – 🛗 ☎. 🖭 🆎 🍽
40 rm ☐ 540/850.   K 11

🏨 **Bourgogne et Montana,** 3 r. Bourgogne ℘ 45 51 20 22, Telex 270854, Fax 45 56 11 98 – 🛗 ▤ rest 📺 ☎. 🖭 ⓄⒹ 🆎
M *(closed August, Saturday and Sunday)* 160 – **30 rm** ☐ 600/950, 5 suites 1200.   H 11

🏨 **St-Germain** without rest, 88 r. Bac ℘ 45 48 62 92, Fax 45 48 26 89 – 🛗 📺 ☎. 🖭 🆎 🍽
☐ 36 – **29 rm** 330/640.   J 11

🏨 **France** Ⓜ without rest, 102 bd La Tour-Maubourg ℘ 47 05 40 49, Telex 205020, Fax 45 56 96 78 – 🛗 📺 ☎ 🐾. 🖭 🆎
☐ 30 – **60 rm** 310/440.   J 9

🏨 **Bersoly's** without rest, 28 r. Lille ℘ 42 60 73 79, Telex 217505, Fax 49 27 05 55 – 🛗 📺 ☎. 🆎
closed August – ☐ 45 – **16 rm** 550/650.   J 13

🏨 **Solférino** without rest, 91 r. Lille ℘ 47 05 85 54, Telex 203865, Fax 45 55 51 16 – 🛗 ☎. 🖭 🆎 🍽
closed 23 December-3 January – **33 rm** ☐ 265/650.   H 11

🏠 **L'Empereur** without rest, 2 r. Chevert ℘ 45 55 88 02, Fax 45 51 88 54 – 🛗 📺 ☎. 🆎
☐ 34 – **34 rm** 390/430.   J 9

🏠 **Tour Eiffel** without rest, 17 r. Exposition ℘ 47 05 14 75, Fax 47 53 99 46 – 🛗 📺 ☎. 🆎
☐ 25 – **22 rm** 320/420.   J 9

🏠 **Turenne** without rest, 20 av. Tourville ℘ 47 05 99 92, Telex 203407, Fax 45 56 06 04 – 🛗 ☎. 🖭 ⓄⒹ 🆎
☐ 30 – **34 rm** 290/500.   J 9

🏠 **Mars H.** without rest, 117 av. La Bourdonnais ℘ 47 05 42 30, Fax 47 05 45 91 – 🛗 📺 ☎. 🆎 🍽
☐ 30 – **24 rm** 290/350.   J 9

🏠 **Champ de Mars** without rest, 7 r. Champ de Mars ℘ 45 51 52 30 – 🛗 ☎. 🆎
closed 10 to 25 August – ☐ 35 – **25 rm** 320/380.   J 9

🏠 **Résidence Orsay** without rest, 93 r. Lille ℘ 47 05 05 27 – 🛗 ☎. 🆎
closed August – ☐ 30 – **32 rm** 190/400.   H 11

ⅩⅩⅩⅩ **Jules Verne,** Eiffel Tower : 2nd platform, lift in south leg ℘ 45 55 61 44, Telex 205789, Fax 47 05 94 40, ≤ Paris – ▤. 🖭 ⓄⒹ 🆎 🍽
M 290 (lunch) and a la carte 450/600   J 7

ⅩⅩⅩⅩ ❀❀ **Le Divellec,** 107 r. Université ℘ 45 51 91 96, Fax 45 51 31 75, Seafood – ▤. 🖭 ⓄⒹ 🆎 ⒿⒸⒷ, 🍽
closed August, Sunday and Monday – **M** 270 (lunch) and a la carte 440/730   H 10
Spec. Homard à la presse et son corail, Filet de Saint-Pierre poêlé aux chicons, Merlu braisé à la lie de vin.

ⅩⅩⅩⅩ ❀❀ **Arpège** (Passard), 84 r. Varenne ℘ 45 51 47 33, Fax 44 18 98 39 – ▤. 🖭 ⓄⒹ 🆎
closed Sunday lunch and Saturday – **M** 240 (lunch) and a la carte 430/570   J 10
Spec. Homard et navet à la vinaigrette aigre douce, Canard "Louise Passard", Feuilletage au chocolat.

ⅩⅩⅩⅩ ❀❀ **Duquesnoy,** 6 av. Bosquet ℘ 47 05 96 78, Fax 44 18 90 57 – ▤. 🖭 🆎
closed August, Saturday lunch and Sunday – **M** 250 (lunch) and a la carte 400/590   H 9
Spec. Croustillants d'escargots frais, Noix de ris de veau rôtie au "caramel poivré", Millefeuille aux poires.

XXX ✿ **La Cantine des Gourmets,** 113 av. La Bourdonnais ✆ 47 05 47 96, Fax 45 51 09 29 – ▤. AE ① GB JCB J 9
M 220 b.i. and a la carte 280/450
Spec. Soufflé d'artichaut au foie gras de canard poêlé, Petit ragoût de homard au curry, Tourte de pigeonneau au foie gras.

XXX ✿ **Regain** (Delaveyne), 135 r. St-Dominique ✆ 47 53 09 85, Fax 45 56 96 16 – ▤. AE GB JCB. ✻ J 9
closed August, Saturday and Sunday – **M** 240 (lunch) and a la carte 335/470
Spec. Soupière de palourdes, Friandise de merlan "Plein Ciel", Tomate farcie fondante à la Brivadoise.

XXX **Chez les Anges,** 54 bd La Tour-Maubourg ✆ 47 05 89 86, Fax 45 56 03 83 – ▤. AE ① GB JCB J 9
closed Sunday dinner – **M** 230/320 b.i.

XXX **La Flamberge,** 12 av. Rapp ✆ 47 05 91 37 – ▤. AE ① GB H 8
closed 1 to 21 August, Christmas-New Year, Saturday lunch and Sunday – **M** 230 and a la carte 260/455.

XXX ✿ **La Boule d'Or,** 13 bd La Tour-Maubourg ✆ 47 05 50 18 – ▤. AE ① GB JCB H 10
closed Saturday lunch and Monday – **M** 195 and a la carte 250/360
Spec. Foie gras frais de canard, Saumon piqué au lard fumé, Soufflé chaud au citron.

XXX **Beato,** 8 r. Malar ✆ 47 05 94 27, Italian rest. – ▤. AE GB. ✻ H 9
closed August, Christmas-New Year, Sunday and Monday – **M** 145 (lunch) and a la carte 215/315 ♫.

XXX **Focly,** 71 av. Suffren ✆ 47 83 27 12, Chinese and Thai rest. – ▤. AE GB K 8
closed 6 to 19 July – **M** 130 b.i./160 b.i.

XX ✿ **Ferme St-Simon** (Vandenhende), 6 r. St-Simon ✆ 45 48 35 74 – ▤. GB J 11
closed 1 to 23 August, Saturday lunch and Sunday – **M** 160 (lunch) and a la carte 250/370
Spec. Gâteau de cèpes aux petits gris (October-January), Saint-Jacques poêlées en feuilleté (October-March), Pêche rôtie aux fraises (June-October).

XX ✿ **Récamier** (Cantegrit), 4 r. Récamier ✆ 45 48 86 58, Fax 42 22 84 76, 🏛 – ▤. ① GB K 12
closed Sunday – **M** a la carte 290/475
Spec. Œufs en meurette, Mousse de brochet sauce Nantua, Sauté de bœuf Bourguignon.

XX **Au Quai d'Orsay,** 49 quai d'Orsay ✆ 45 51 58 58 – AE GB H 9
M a la carte 225/365.

XX **Le Petit Laurent,** 38 r. Varenne ✆ 45 48 79 64, Fax 42 66 68 59 – AE ① GB J 11
closed 9 to 22 August, Saturday lunch and Sunday – **M** 175.

XX **Le Florence,** 22 r. Champ-de-Mars ✆ 45 51 52 69, Italian rest. – ▤. AE GB J 9
closed August, Sunday and Monday – **M** a la carte 215/355.

XX ✿ **Le Bellecour** (Goutagny), 22 r. Surcouf ✆ 45 51 46 93 – AE ① GB H 9
closed August, Monday (except June-September), Saturday and Sunday – **M** 180 (lunch) and a la carte 285/450
Spec. Langoustines rôties aux poireaux frits (March-October), Lotte rôtie à l'ail en chemise, Pigeonneau fermier à la moelle.

XX **D'Chez Eux,** 2 av. Lowendal ✆ 47 05 52 55 – ▤. ① GB J 9
closed 3 July-3 September and Sunday – **M** a la carte 270/425.

XX **Giulio Rebellato,** 20 r. Monttessuy ✆ 45 55 79 01, Italian rest. – ▤. AE GB. ✻ H 8
closed 25 July-18 August, Saturday lunch and Sunday – **M** a la carte 240/340.

XX **Vert Bocage,** 96 bd La Tour-Maubourg ✆ 45 51 48 64 – ▤. AE ① GB J 9
closed Saturday and Sunday – **M** a la carte 245/370.

XX **Le Luz,** 4 r. Pierre-Leroux ✆ 43 06 99 39 – ▤. AE ① GB K 11
closed 9 to 23 August, Saturday lunch and Sunday – **M** 150 and a la carte 190/325.

XX **Les Glénan,** 54 r. Bourgogne ✆ 47 05 96 65 – ▤. GB J 10
closed 10 to 20 August, Sunday lunch and Saturday – **M** a la carte 240/310.

XX **Aux Délices de Szechuen,** 40 av. Duquesne ✆ 43 06 22 55, 🏛, Chinese rest. – ▤. AE GB K 10
closed 27 July-24 August and Monday – **M** 96 (except Sunday) and a la carte 155/260 ♫.

XX **Le Club,** (Au Bon Marché) 38 r. Sèvres - 1st floor building 2 ✆ 45 48 95 25, Fax 45 49 27 99 – ▤. AE ① GB K 11
closed August and Sunday – **M** (lunch only) 149 and a la carte 170/290 ♫.

XX **Chez Ribe,** 15 av. Suffren ✆ 45 66 53 79 – AE ① GB J 7
closed August, 23 December-4 January, Saturday lunch and Sunday – **M** 168.

XX **Gildo,** 153 r. Grenelle ✆ 45 51 54 12, Fax 45 51 57 42, Italian rest. – ▤. GB J 9
closed 20 July-30 August, 24 December-3 January, Monday lunch and Sunday – **M** a la carte 210/330.

XX **Tan Dinh,** 60 r. Verneuil ✆ 45 44 04 84, Vietnamese rest. J 12
closed August and Sunday – **M** a la carte 225/300.

XX **Le Champ de Mars,** 17 av. La Motte-Picquet ✆ 47 05 57 99 – AE ① GB J 9
closed 13 July-20 August, Tuesday dinner and Monday – **M** 118/159.

XX **Clémentine,** 62 av. Bosquet ✆ 45 51 41 16 – GB J 9
M 168.

X ✿ **Vin sur Vin** (Vidal), 20 r. Monttessuy *𝄇* 47 05 14 20 – **GB**　　　　　　　　　　　H 8
　　*closed 1 to 8 May, 12 to 31 August, 22 December-3 January, Saturday lunch, Monday lunch
　　and Sunday* – **M** a la carte 230/345
　　Spec. Salade de ris de veau aux noisettes (October-January), Raquette de bœuf (June-September),
　　Crème brûlée à la vergeoise.

X **L'Oeillade**, 10 r. St-Simon *𝄇* 42 22 01 60 – **▤**. **GB**　　　　　　　　　　　　　J 11
　　closed 15 August-1 September, 22 December-2 January, Saturday lunch and Sunday – **M** 152.

X **Le Maupertu**, 94 bd La Tour Maubourg *𝄇* 45 51 37 96 – **GB**　　　　　　　　　J 10
　　closed 3 to 24 August, Saturday lunch and Sunday – **M** 130 and a la carte 190/280.

X **Bistrot de Breteuil**, 3 pl. Breteuil *𝄇* 45 67 07 27, 🌫 – **GB**　　　　　　　　　L 10
　　M 170 b.i.

X **Chez Collinot**, 1 r. P. Leroux *𝄇* 45 67 66 42 – **GB**　　　　　　　　　　　　K 11
　　closed August, Saturday (except dinner in winter) and Sunday – **M** 120 and a la carte 165/285.

X **Clos de l'Alma**, 17 r. Malar *𝄇* 45 55 79 77 – **GB**　　　　　　　　　　　　H 9
　　closed 10 to 25 August, Saturday lunch and Sunday – **M** a la carte 150/230.

X **Nuit de St Jean**, 29 r. Surcouf *𝄇* 45 51 61 49, Fax 47 05 36 40 – **AE ⓞ GB**. 🍽　H 9
　　*closed 7 to 15 March, 1 to 10 May, 1 to 16 August, 23 December-4 January, Saturday lunch
　　and Sunday* – **M** 120 and a la carte 145/270 🍴.

X **Pantagruel**, 20 r. Exposition *𝄇* 45 51 79 96 – **AE ⓞ GB**　　　　　　　　　J 9
　　closed Saturday lunch – **M** a la carte 190/325.

X **La Calèche**, 8 r. Lille *𝄇* 42 60 24 76 – **AE ⓞ GB JCB**　　　　　　　　　J 12
　　closed 5 to 31 August, 26 December-1 January, Saturday and Sunday – **M** 130/170.

X **Thoumieux**, 79 r. St Dominique *𝄇* 47 05 49 75, Fax 47 05 36 96 – **▤**. **GB**　　H 9
　　M a la carte 145/250 🍴.

Champs-Élysées, St-Lazare, Madeleine.

8th arrondissement.
8th: ✉ *75008*

🏨🏨🏨🏨 **Plaza-Athénée**, 25 av. Montaigne *𝄇* 47 23 78 33, Telex 650092, Fax 47 20 20 70 – 🛗 ▤
　　📺 ☎ – 🔔 30 - 100. **AE ⓞ GB JCB**　　　　　　　　　　　　　　　　　　G 9
　　M see rest. **Régence and Relais Plaza** below – 🍴 115 – **215 rm** 2890/4610, 41 suites.

🏨🏨🏨🏨 **Crillon**, 10 pl. Concorde *𝄇* 44 71 15 00, Telex 290204, Fax 44 71 15 02 – 🛗 ▤ rm 📺 ☎
　　– 🔔 30 - 60. **AE ⓞ GB JCB**. 🍽 rest　　　　　　　　　　　　　　　　　G 11
　　M see **Les Ambassadeurs** below - **L'Obélisque** *𝄇* 44 71 15 15 *(closed August and Bank Holi-
　　days)* **M** 220 – 🍴 130 – **117 rm** 2300/3800, 46 suites.

🏨🏨🏨🏨 **Bristol**, 112 r. Fg St-Honoré *𝄇* 42 66 91 45, Telex 280961, Fax 42 66 68 68, 🔲, 🌫 – 🛗 ▤
　　📺 ☎ – 🔔 40 - 150. **AE ⓞ GB JCB**. 🍽　　　　　　　　　　　　　　　F 10
　　M see **Bristol** below – 🍴 130 – **152 rm** 2300/3300, 45 suites.

🏨🏨🏨🏨 **George V**, 31 av. George-V *𝄇* 47 23 54 00, Telex 650082, Fax 47 20 40 00, 🌫 – 🛗 ▤ rm
　　📺 ☎ – 🔔 600. **AE ⓞ GB JCB**　　　　　　　　　　　　　　　　　　G 8
　　M see **Les Princes** and **Le Grill** below – 🍴 115 – **298 rm** 2150/3850, 53 suites.

🏨🏨🏨 **Royal Monceau**, 37 av. Hoche *𝄇* 45 61 98 00, Telex 650361, Fax 45 63 28 93, 🌫, « Pool
　　and fitness centre » – 🛗 ▤ 📺 ☎ – 🔔 30 - 300. **AE ⓞ GB JCB**. 🍽　　　　E 8
　　Le Jardin M 270 (lunch) and a la carte 340/570 – **Le Carpaccio** *(closed August)* **M** 270 (lunch)
　　and a la carte 300/430 – 🍴 130 – **180 rm** 1950/2650, 39 suites.

🏨🏨🏨 **Prince de Galles**, 33 av. George-V *𝄇* 47 23 55 11, Telex 651627, Fax 47 20 96 92, 🌫 –
　　🛗 🍽 rm ▤ 📺 ☎ – 🔔 40 - 200. **AE ⓞ GB**. 🍽 rest　　　　　　　　　G 8
　　M (Sunday Brunch only 240) 235/575 – 🍴 95 – **141 rm** 1700/2400, 30 suites.

🏨🏨 **Vernet** Ⓜ, 25 r. Vernet *𝄇* 47 23 43 10, Telex 290347, Fax 40 70 10 14 – 🛗 ▤ 📺 ☎. **AE**
　　ⓞ GB. 🍽 rest　　　　　　　　　　　　　　　　　　　　　　　　　F 8
　　Les Élysées *(closed 23 July-26 August, Saturday and Sunday)* **M** a la carte 320/410 – 🍴 100
　　– **54 rm** 1400/1950, 3 suites.

🏨🏨 **San Régis** Ⓜ, 12 r. J. Goujon *𝄇* 43 59 41 90, Telex 643637, Fax 45 61 05 48, « Tasteful
　　decor » – 🛗 ▤ rm 📺 ☎. **AE ⓞ GB JCB**　　　　　　　　　　　　　　G 9
　　M a la carte 265/415 – 🍴 100 – **34 rm** 1325/2525, 10 suites 2800/4800.

🏨🏨 **Balzac** Ⓜ, 6 r. Balzac *𝄇* 45 61 97 22, Telex 290298, Fax 42 25 24 82 – 🛗 ▤ 📺 ☎. **AE ⓞ GB**
　　M see **Bice** below – 🍴 90 – **56 rm** 1320/1730, 14 suites.　　　　　　　　F 8

🏨🏨 **De Vigny** Ⓜ without rest, 9 r. Balzac *𝄇* 40 75 04 39, Telex 651822, Fax 40 75 05 81,
　　« Tasteful decor » – 🛗 🍽 rm ▤ 📺 ☎ 🛏. **AE ⓞ GB**　　　　　　　　　F 8
　　🍴 90 – **25 rm** 1900/2600, 12 suites.

🏨🏨 **La Trémoille**, 14 r. La Trémoille *𝄇* 47 23 34 20, Telex 640344, Fax 40 70 01 08 – 🛗 ▤ 📺
　　☎. **AE ⓞ GB JCB**　　　　　　　　　　　　　　　　　　　　　　G 9
　　M *(closed Saturday)* a la carte 235/380 – 🍴 80 – **96 rm** 1770/2760, 14 suites 2760.

🏨 **Warwick** 🅼, 5 r. Berri ℰ 45 63 14 11, Telex 642295, Fax 45 63 75 81 – 🛗 ⤬ rm 🗏 📺 ☎ – 🔏 30 – 120. 🖭 ⓞ ☒ 🃏
M see La Couronne below – ⌓ 100 – **144 rm** 1920/2420, 4 suites.
F 9

🏨 **Golden Tulip St-Honoré** 🅼, 220 r. Fg St-Honoré ℰ 49 53 03 03, Telex 650657, Fax 40 75 02 00, ⟁ – 🛗 kitchenette 🗏 📺 ☎ ᰔ ᐸᐳ – 🔏 200. 🖭 ⓞ ☒ 🃏 ⚘ rest
Relais Vermeer (closed Sunday) **M** 195 and a la carte 270/450 – ⌓ 95 – **52 rm** 1550/1750, 20 suites.
E 8

🏨 **Lancaster,** 7 r. Berri ℰ 43 59 90 43, Telex 640991, Fax 42 89 22 71, ᱤ – 🛗 🗏 rm 📺 ☎. 🖭 ⓞ ☒ 🃏
M 230 – ⌓ 110 – **52 rm** 1890/2500, 7 suites.
F 9

🏨 **Pullman Windsor** 🅼, 14 r. Beaujon ℰ 45 63 04 04, Telex 650902, Fax 42 25 36 81 – 🛗 🗏 📺 ☎ – 🔏 130. 🖭 ⓞ ☒ 🃏
M see Le Clovis below – ⌓ 90 – **135 rm** 1250/1600, 7 suites 1900/3200.
F 8

🏨 **Relais Carré d'Or** 🅼, 46 av. George V ℰ 40 70 05 05, Telex 640561, Fax 47 23 30 90, ᱤ – 🛗 kitchenette 🗏 📺 ☎ ᐸᐳ. 🖭 ⓞ ☒ 🃏
M a la carte 195/370 – ⌓ 95, 23 suites 2350/16550.
F 8

🏨 **Château Frontenac,** 54 r. P.-Charron ℰ 47 23 55 85, Telex 644994, Fax 47 23 03 32 – 🛗 📺 ☎ – 🔏 30. ⓞ ☒ 🃏
Pavillon Frontenac (closed August, Saturday lunch and Sunday) **M** 190 and a la carte 210/295 – ⌓ 75 – **102 rm** 850/1300, 4 suites 1480.
G 9

🏨 **Bedford,** 17 r. Arcade ℰ 42 66 22 32, Telex 290506, Fax 42 66 51 56 – 🛗 🗏 ☎ – 🔏 80. ☒ ⚘ rest
M (closed 1 to 30 August, Saturday and Sunday) a la carte 210/335 – **137 rm** ⌓ 680/980, 10 suites 1425/1750.
F 11

🏨 **Résidence du Roy** 🅼 without rest, 8 r. François 1ᵉʳ ℰ 42 89 59 59, Telex 648452, Fax 40 74 07 92 – 🛗 kitchenette 🗏 📺 ☎ ᰔ ᐸᐳ – 🔏 25. 🖭 ⓞ ☒ 🃏
⌓ 65 – **5 rm** 1140, 31 suites.
G 9

🏨 **Élysées Star** 🅼 without rest, 19 r. Vernet ℰ 47 20 41 73, Telex 651153, Fax 47 23 32 15 – 🛗 🗏 📺 ☎ – 🔏 30. 🖭 ⓞ ☒ 🃏
⌓ 80 – **39 rm** 1300/1900, 4 suites 3500.
F 8

🏨 **Claridge Bellman,** 37 r. François 1ᵉʳ ℰ 47 23 54 42, Telex 641150, Fax 47 23 08 84 – 🛗 🗏 📺 ☎. 🖭 ⓞ ☒. ⚘
M (closed August, 25 December-2 January, Saturday and Sunday) a la carte 230/380 ⅓ – ⌓ 70 – **42 rm** 950/1300.
G 9

🏨 **Napoléon,** 40 av. Friedland ℰ 47 66 02 02, Telex 640609, Fax 47 66 82 33 – 🛗 📺 ☎ – 🔏 130. 🖭 ⓞ ☒ 🃏
Le Napoléon ℰ 42 27 99 50 (closed 8 to 16 August, Saturday and Sunday) **M** a la carte 265/430 – ⌓ 70 – **70 rm** 1100/1550, 32 suites.
F 8

🏨 **California,** 16 r. Berri ℰ 43 59 93 00, Telex 644634, Fax 45 61 03 62 – 🛗 ⤬ rm 🗏 📺 ☎ – 🔏 40. 🖭 ⓞ ☒ 🃏
M a la carte 220/290 – ⌓ 100 – **154 rm** 1400/1900, 18 suites.
F 9

🏨 **Concorde-St-Lazare,** 108 r. St-Lazare ℰ 40 08 44 44, Telex 650442, Fax 42 93 01 20 – 🛗 🗏 📺 ☎ – 🔏 95. 🖭 ⓞ ☒ 🃏 ⚘ rest
Café Terminus M 140/195 – ⌓ 90 – **298 rm** 950/1650, 13 suites 1950/2450.
E 12

🏨 **Queen Elizabeth,** 41 av. Pierre-1ᵉʳ-de-Serbie ℰ 47 20 80 56, Telex 641179, Fax 47 20 89 19 – 🛗 🗏 📺 ☎ – 🔏 25 – 30. 🖭 ⓞ ☒ 🃏
M (closed August and Sunday) (lunch only) 150 b.i./210 ⅓ – ⌓ 85 – **54 rm** 1000/1750, 12 suites 1900/2600.
G 8

🏨 **La Maison des Centraliens** 🅼, 8 r. J. Goujon ℰ 43 59 52 41, Telex 651838, Fax 42 25 06 59 – 🛗 ⤬ rm 🗏 📺 ☎ ᰔ ᐸᐳ – 🔏 150. 🖭 ⓞ ☒ 🃏
M 150 b.i./220 – ⌓ 100 – **40 rm** 1200/1400.
G 9

🏨 **Pullman St-Honoré** without rest, 15 r. Boissy d'Anglas ℰ 42 66 93 62, Telex 240366, Fax 42 66 14 98 – 🛗 🗏 📺 ☎. 🖭 ⓞ ☒ 🃏
⌓ 90 – **104 rm** 790/1050, 8 suites 1650.
G 11

🏨 **Chateaubriand** 🅼 without rest, 6 r. Chateaubriand ℰ 40 76 00 50, Telex 641012, Fax 40 76 09 22 – 🛗 🗏 📺 ☎. 🖭 ⓞ ☒ 🃏
⌓ 65 – **28 rm** 1600.
F 9

🏨 **L'Horset Astor,** 11 r. Astorg ℰ 42 66 56 56, Telex 642737, Fax 42 65 18 37 – 🛗 🗏 rest 📺 ☎ – 🔏 25. 🖭 ⓞ ☒ 🃏
M (closed July-August, Saturday and Sunday) (lunch only) 190/210 – ⌓ 70 – **128 rm** 920.
F 11

🏨 **Royal Alma** 🅼 without rest, 35 r. J. Goujon ℰ 42 25 83 30, Telex 641428, Fax 45 63 68 64 – 🛗 📺 ☎. 🖭 ⓞ ☒ 🃏 ⚘
⌓ 85 – **58 rm** 1100/1600, 7 suites 1600/2500.
G 9

🏨 **Montaigne** 🅼 without rest, 6 av. Montaigne ℰ 47 20 30 50, Telex 648051, Fax 47 20 94 12 – 🛗 🗏 📺 ☎ ᰔ. 🖭 ⓞ ☒. ⚘
⌓ 80 – **29 rm** 1300/1800.
G 9

🏨 **François 1ᵉʳ** 🅼, 7 r. Magellan ℰ 47 23 44 04, Telex 648880, Fax 47 23 93 43 – 🛗 ⤬ rm 🗏 📺 ☎. 🖭 ⓞ ☒ 🃏
M 165/380 – ⌓ 90 – **36 rm** 1250/1380, 4 suites 2160.
F 8

🏥 **de l'Élysée** M without rest, 12 r. Saussaies ℰ 42 65 29 25, Telex 281665, Fax 42 65 64 28
– 🛗 📺 ☎ 🌆 ⓪ 🌮
☑ 60 – **30 rm** 620/880. F 11

🏥 **Marignan,** 12 r. Marignan ℰ 40 76 34 56, Telex 644018, Fax 40 76 34 34 – 🛗 ⟷ rm 📺
☎ – 🔥 80. 🌆 ⓪ 🌮 🌐 🌮 – **M** *(closed August, Saturday, Sunday and Bank Holidays)* a la
carte 250/300 – ☑ 95 – **55 rm** 1900/2200, 18 suites 2500. G 9

🏥 **Élysées Ponthieu and Résidence Le Cid** M without rest, 24 r. Ponthieu ℰ 42 25 68 70,
Telex 640053, Fax 42 25 80 82 – 🛗 kitchenette 🔲 📺 ☎ 🌆 ⓪ 🌮 🌐
☑ 65 – **92 rm** 610/1600, 6 suites 1800/2500. F 9

🏥 **Royal H.** without rest, 33 av. Friedland ℰ 43 59 08 14, Telex 651465, Fax 45 63 69 92 – 🛗
📺 ☎ 🌆 ⓪ 🌐
☑ 60 – **58 rm** 810/1100. F 8

🏥 **Résidence Champs-Elysées** M without rest, 92 r. La Boétie ℰ 43 59 96 15, Telex 650695,
Fax 42 56 01 38 – 🛗 📺 ☎ 🌆 ⓪ 🌮 🌮
☑ 70 – **83 rm** 740/1200. F 9

🏥 **Résidence Monceau** M without rest, 85 r. Rocher ℰ 45 22 75 11, Telex 280671,
Fax 45 22 30 88 – 🛗 📺 ☎ ♿ 🌆 ⓪ 🌮 🌮
☑ 42 – **50 rm** 585. E 11

🏥 **Concortel** without rest, 19 r. Pasquier ℰ 42 65 45 44, Telex 660228, Fax 42 65 18 33 – 🛗
📺 ☎ 🌆 ⓪ 🌮
☑ 35 – **46 rm** 550/700. F 11

🏥 **Résidence St-Honoré** without rest, 214 r. Fg-St-Honoré ℰ 42 25 26 27, Telex 640524,
Fax 45 63 30 67 – 🛗 ⟷ 📺 ☎ 🌆 ⓪ 🌮 🌐
☑ 40 – **89 rm** 650/1000. E 9

🏥 **Powers** without rest, 52 r. François-1ᵉʳ ℰ 47 23 91 05, Telex 642051, Fax 49 52 04 63 – 🛗
📺 ☎ 🌆 ⓪ 🌮 🌮
☑ 50 – **53 rm** 720/980. G 9

🏥 **Beau Manoir** without rest, 6 r. Arcade ℰ 42 66 03 07, Fax 42 68 03 00 – 🛗 🔲 📺 ☎ ♿
🌆 ⓪ 🌮 🌐
☑ 30 – **29 rm** 820/890, 3 suites 1240. F 11

🏥 **Castiglione,** 40 r. Fg-St-Honoré ℰ 42 65 07 50, Telex 240362, Fax 42 65 12 27 – 🛗 🔲 rest
📺 ☎ – ♿ 50. 🌆 ⓪ 🌮 🌐
M 160 and a la carte 250/400 – **119 rm** ☑ 930/1800, 10 suites 2100/2800. G 11

🏥 **Printemps and rest. Chez Martin,** 1 r. Isly ℰ 42 94 12 12, Telex 290744, Fax 42 94 05 02
– 🛗 📺 ☎ – ♿ 25 - 35. 🌮
M *(closed 20 July-9 August, Saturday and Sunday)* 108/160 ♨ – **67 rm** ☑ 444/928. F 12

🏥 **New Roblin and rest. Le Mazagran,** 6 r. Chauveau-Lagarde ℰ 44 71 20 80, Telex 640154,
Fax 42 65 19 49 – 🛗 🔲 📺 ☎ 🌆 ⓪ 🌮 🌐 🌮 rest
M *(closed Saturday, Sunday and Bank Holidays)* 140/150 ♨ – ☑ 55 – **74 rm** 600/790, 3 suites
1350. F 11

🏨 **West End** without rest, 7 r. Clément-Marot ℰ 47 20 30 78, Telex 611972, Fax 47 20 34 42
– 🛗 📺 ☎ 🌆 ⓪ 🌮 🌐
☑ 40 – **47 rm** 650/1450. G 9

🏨 **Lido** M without rest, 4 passage Madeleine ℰ 42 66 27 37, Telex 281039, Fax 42 66 61 23
– 🛗 📺 ☎ 🌆 ⓪ 🌮 🌐
☑ 25 – **32 rm** 555/780. F 11

🏨 **Cordélia** M without rest, 11 r. Greffulhe ℰ 42 65 42 40, Telex 281760, Fax 42 65 11 81 –
🛗 📺 ☎ 🌆 ⓪ 🌮
☑ 45 – **30 rm** 630/680. F 11

🏨 **Newton Opéra** M without rest, 11bis r. Arcade ℰ 42 65 32 13, Telex 280340,
Fax 42 65 30 90 – 🛗 📺 ☎ 🌆 ⓪ 🌮
☑ 45 – **31 rm** 660/830. F 11

🏨 **Franklin Roosevelt** without rest, 18 r. Clément-Marot ℰ 47 23 61 66, Telex 614797,
Fax 47 20 44 30 – 🛗 📺 ☎ 🌆 ⓪ 🌮 🌮
☑ 45 – **45 rm** 650/800. G 9

🏨 **Colisée** without rest, 6 r. Colisée ℰ 43 59 95 25, Telex 643101, Fax 45 63 26 54 – 🛗 📺 ☎
🌆 ⓪ 🌮
☑ 30 – **44 rm** 490/780. F 9

🏨 **Rochambeau** without rest, 4 r. La Boétie ℰ 42 65 27 54, Telex 640030, Fax 42 66 03 81 –
🛗 📺 ☎ 🌆 ⓪ 🌮 🌐
50 rm ☑ 745/1200. F 11

🏨 **Atlantic** without rest, 44 r. Londres ℰ 43 87 45 40, Telex 650477, Fax 42 93 06 26 – 🛗 📺
☎ 🌆 🌮 🌐 🌮
☑ 45 – **93 rm** 410/660. E 12

🏨 **L'Orangerie** M without rest, 9 r. Constantinople ℰ 45 22 07 51, Telex 650294,
Fax 45 22 16 49 – 🛗 📺 ☎ 🌆 ⓪ 🌮 🌮
☑ 30 – **29 rm** 450/635. E 11

🏨 **St Augustin** without rest, 9 r. Roy ℰ 42 93 32 17, Telex 283919, Fax 42 93 19 34 – 🛗 📺
☎ 🌆 ⓪ 🌮 🌐
☑ 37 – **62 rm** 550/760. F 11

🏬 **Queen Mary** without rest, 9 r. Greffulhe ℰ 42 66 40 50, Telex 640419, Fax 42 66 94 92 –
|\$| 📺 ☎. GB – 🖙 40 – **36 rm** 550/730.　　　　　　　　　　　　　　　　F 12

🏬 **Waldorf Florida** without rest, 12 bd Malesherbes ℰ 42 65 72 06, Telex 650557,
Fax 40 07 10 45 – |\$| 📺 ☎. ⅎ ⓪ GB 📖 – **44 rm** 🖙 725/1130.　　　　　　　　F 11

🏬 **Résidence Saint-Philippe** without rest, 123 r. Fg-St-Honoré ℰ 43 59 86 99, Telex 650837,
Fax 45 61 09 07 – |\$| 📺 ☎. ⅎ ⓪ GB 📖 – 🖙 40 – **38 rm** 430/700.　　　　F 9-10

🏬 **Élysées** without rest, 100 r. La Boétie ℰ 43 59 23 46, Telex 648572, Fax 42 56 33 80 – |\$|
📺 ☎. ⅎ ⓪ GB. ⅍ – 🖙 25 – **28 rm** 525/605.　　　　　　　　　　　　　　　F 9

🏬 **Angleterre-Champs-Élysées** without rest, 91 r. La Boétie ℰ 43 59 35 45, Telex 640317,
Fax 45 63 22 22 – |\$| 📺 ☎. GB – 🖙 30 – **40 rm** 450/580.　　　　　　　　　　F 9

🏬 **Plaza Haussmann** without rest, 177 bd Haussmann ℰ 45 63 93 83, Telex 643716,
Fax 45 61 14 30 – |\$| 📺 ☎. GB 📖. ⅍ – 🖙 30 – **41 rm** 620/730.　　　　　F 9

🏠 **Charing Cross** Ⓜ without rest, 39 r. Pasquier ℰ 43 87 41 04, Telex 290681, Fax 42 93 70 45
– |\$| 📺 ☎. ⅎ ⓪ GB 📖　　　　　　　　　　　　　　　　　　　　　　　　　　　F 11
31 rm 🖙 385/485.

XXXXX ✿✿✿ **Lucas-Carton** (Senderens), 9 pl. Madeleine ℰ 42 65 22 90, Telex 281088,
Fax 42 65 06 23, « 1900 attractive decor » – ▤. GB 📖. ⅍　　　　　　　　　　G 11
closed 1 to 25 August, 24 December-3 January, Saturday and Sunday – **M** 375 (lunch) and
a la carte 560/980
Spec. Risotto de riz sauvage aux girolles, Turbot à l'encre de seiche, Pigeon rôti au vermicelle
à la coriandre.

XXXXX ✿✿ **Lasserre**, 17 av. F.-D.-Roosevelt ℰ 43 59 53 43, Fax 45 63 72 23, Open roof in fine weather – ▤. GB. ⅍　　　　　　　　　　　　　　　　　　　　　　　　　　　　　G 10
closed 2 to 31 August, Monday lunch and Sunday – **M** a la carte 415/555
Spec. Salade tiède de ris de veau et langoustines, Parmentier de morue fraîche, Soufflé glacé
menthe-chocolat.

XXXXX ✿✿✿ **Taillevent**, 15 r. Lamennais ℰ 45 61 12 90, Fax 42 25 95 18 – ▤. GB. ⅍　　F 9
closed 26 July-26 August, February Holidays, Saturday, Sunday and Bank Holidays – **M** (booking
essential) a la carte 550/750
Spec. Ravioli d'escargots au curry, Côtes d'agneau aux olives noires, Fantaisie au caramel et au
pain d'épices.

XXXXX ✿✿ **Les Ambassadeurs** - Hôtel Crillon, 10 pl. Concorde ℰ 44 71 16 16, Telex 290204,
Fax 44 71 15 02, « 18C decor » – ▤. ⅎ ⓪ GB 📖. ⅍　　　　　　　　　　　　G 11
M 310 (lunch) and a la carte 400/680
Spec. Moelleux de pommes rattes et médaillon de homard à la civette, Bar croustillant aux graines
de sésame, Carré d'agneau de Pauillac rôti sous la cendre.

XXXXX ✿✿ **Laurent**, 41 av. Gabriel ℰ 42 25 00 39, Fax 45 62 45 21, « Attractive summer terrace »
– ⅎ ⓪ GB. ⅍　　　　　　　　　　　　　　　　　　　　　　　　　　　　　G 10
closed Saturday lunch, Sunday and Bank Holidays – **M** 400 (lunch) and a la carte 480/800
Spec. "Minestrone" aux écrevisses, Gambas tièdes à la fine semoule épicée, Rognon de veau
entier rôti.

XXXXX ✿ **Bristol** - Hôtel Bristol, 112 r. Fg St-Honoré ℰ 42 66 91 45, Telex 280961, Fax 42 66 68 68
– ▤. ⅎ ⓪ GB 📖. ⅍ – **M** a la carte 480/630　　　　　　　　　　　　　　　F 10
Spec. Blanc de barbue et langoustines aux épinards, Escalope de turbot au Sauternes, Feuillantine
de rognon de veau.

XXXXX ✿ **Régence** - Hôtel Plaza Athénée, 25 av. Montaigne ℰ 47 23 78 33, Telex 650092,
Fax 47 20 20 70, ⇔ – ▤. ⅎ ⓪ GB 📖 – **M** a la carte 400/620　　　　　　　G 9
Spec. Soufflé de homard "Plaza", Duo de langoustines et Saint-Jacques, Piccata de veau au
citron.

XXXXX ✿ **Ledoyen**, carré Champs-Élysées ℰ 47 42 23 23, Telex 282358, Fax 47 42 55 01, ⇔ – ▤.
Ⓟ. ⅎ ⓪ GB. ⅍　　　　　　　　　　　　　　　　　　　　　　　　　　　　G 10
closed August and Sunday – **M** 350 (lunch) and a la carte 480/650 – **Le Carré M** 250 and
a la carte 280/420
Spec. Terrine de ris de veau et crustacés, Pot-au-feu de pigeon, Velours au chocolat.

XXXX ✿ **Élysée Lenôtre**, 10 av. Champs-Élysées ℰ 42 65 85 10, Fax 42 65 76 23, ⇔ – |\$| ▤. Ⓟ.
ⅎ ⓪ GB　　　　　　　　　　　　　　　　　　　　　　　　　　　　　　　　G 10
Rez-de-Chaussée (lunch only) *(closed Saturday and Sunday)* **M** 350 – **1ᵉʳ étage** (dinner only)
(closed Sunday) **M** a la carte 380/670
Spec. Homard tiède verdurette, Saint Pierre à la nage de palourdes, Millefeuille au chocolat et
glace à la chicorée.

XXXXX ✿ **Les Princes** - Hôtel George V, 31 av. George V ℰ 47 23 54 00, Telex 650082, Fax 47 20 40 00,
⇔ – ▤. ⅎ ⓪ GB 📖　　　　　　　　　　　　　　　　　　　　　　　　　　G 8
closed 25 July-23 August – **M** 350 b.i. and a la carte 400/670
Spec. Tartare d'huîtres (October-April), Daurade aux épices et ses "pailles" de crevettes, Millefeuille caramélisé aux noix.

XXXX ۞۞ **Chiberta,** 3 r. Arsène-Houssaye ℰ 45 63 77 90, Fax 45 62 85 08 – 🔳. 🔟 ⓪ ⊖⊖
JCB
F 8
closed 1 to 30 August, 24 December-3 January, Saturday, Sunday and Bank Holidays – **M** a
la carte 415/585
Spec. Salade d'anguille de Loire au caviar (October-January), Bar croustillant au jus truffé (October-January), Ris de veau braisé au cidre.

XXXX ۞ **La Marée,** 1 r. Daru ℰ 43 80 20 00, Fax 48 88 04 04, Seafood – 🔳. 🔟 ⓪ ⊖⊖   E 8
closed August, Saturday and Sunday – **M** a la carte 410/640
Spec. Cassolette de homard et langouste, Tronçon de turbot rôti à la sauge, Fricassée de rognons de veau aux choux.

XXXX **Fouquet's,** 99 av. Champs-Élysées ℰ 47 23 70 60, Fax 47 20 08 69 – 🔟 ⓪ ⊖⊖ JCB
Rez-de-Chaussée (grill) **M** 250 and a la carte 260/410 – **1ᵉʳ étage** *(closed Saturday lunch and Sunday)* **M** a la carte 290/510.   F 8

XXX ۞ **15 Montaigne Maison Blanche,** 15 av. Montaigne (6th floor) ℰ 47 23 55 99,
Fax 47 20 09 56, <, 🛒, « Contemporary decor » – 🔾 🔳. 🔟 ⓪ ⊖⊖   G 9
closed Saturday lunch and Sunday – **M** 295 (lunch) and a la carte 335/550
Spec. Gâteau landais, Risotto de langoustines, Sablé de pommes au romarin et à la cannelle.

XXX ۞ **La Couronne** - Hôtel Warwick, 5 r. Berri ℰ 45 63 78 49, Telex 642295, Fax 45 63 75 81 –
🔳. 🔟 ⓪ ⊖⊖ JCB
F 9
closed August, Saturday lunch, Sunday and Bank Holidays – **M** 260 and a la carte 300/440
Spec. Marbré de langoustines et ris de veau, Matelote d'anguilles au Saumur, Rosace de selle d'agneau à la graine de semoule.

XXX ۞ **Le Clovis** - Hôtel Pullman Windsor, 4 r. B.-Albrecht ℰ 45 61 15 32, Telex 650902,
Fax 42 25 36 81 – 🔳. 🔟 ⓪ ⊖⊖
F 8
closed 3 to 28 August, 28 December-1 January, Saturday, Sunday and Bank Holidays – **M** 245 (lunch) and a la carte 320/460
Spec. Tartare de dorade rose et saumon mariné, Médaillon de veau aux grains de café écrasés, Assiette des quatre douceurs.

XXX **Le 30 - Fauchon,** pl. Madeleine ℰ 47 42 56 58, Fax 47 42 83 75, 🛒 – 🔳. 🔟 ⓪ ⊖⊖ JCB
closed Sunday – **M** a la carte 255/415.   F 12

XXX ۞ **Copenhague,** 142 av. Champs-Élysées (1st floor) ℰ 43 59 20 41, Fax 42 25 83 10, 🛒,
Danish rest. – 🔳. 🔟 ⓪ ⊖⊖ JCB. 🛠   F 8
closed 3 to 30 August, 1 to 7 January, Saturday lunch and Bank Holidays in summer and Sunday
– **M** a la carte 265/450 - **Flora Danica M** a la carte 200/360
Spec. Saumon mariné à l'aneth, Mignon de renne aux mûres jaunes, Mandelrand avec sorbets et fruits.

XXX **Relais-Plaza** - Hôtel Plaza Athénée, 21 av. Montaigne ℰ 47 23 46 36, Telex 650092,
Fax 47 20 20 70 – 🔳. 🔟 ⓪ ⊖⊖
G 9
M 285 b.i. and a la carte 300/580.

XXX **Le Grill** - Hôtel George V, 31 av. George V ℰ 47 23 54 00, Fax 47 30 04 49 – 🔳. 🔟 ⓪ ⊖⊖
JCB
G 8
M 198 and a la carte 210/360.

XXX **Yvan,** 1bis r. J. Mermoz ℰ 43 59 18 40, Fax 45 63 78 69 – 🔳. 🔟 ⓪ ⊖⊖   F-G 10
closed Saturday lunch and Sunday – **M** 168/285.

XXX **Les Géorgiques,** 36 av. George V ℰ 40 70 10 49 – 🔳. 🔟 ⓪ ⊖⊖ JCB. 🛠   G 8
closed Saturday lunch and Sunday – **M** 180 (lunch) and a la carte 275/465.

XXX **Vancouver,** 4 r. Arsène Houssaye ℰ 42 56 77 77, Fax 42 56 50 52, Seafood – 🔳. ⊖⊖
closed August, Christmas-New Years, Saturday, Sunday and Bank Holidays – **M** a la carte 255/360.

XXX **Le Jardin Violet,** 19 r. Bayard ℰ 47 20 55 11, Chinese rest. – 🔳. 🔟 ⓪ ⊖⊖   G 9
M 150 b.i./350 b.i.

XXX **Indra,** 10 r. Cdt-Rivière ℰ 43 59 46 40, Fax 42 89 90 18, Indian rest. – 🔳. 🔟 ⓪ ⊖⊖
closed Saturday lunch and Sunday – **M** 220/300.   F 9

XX **Baumann Marbeuf,** 15 r. Marbeuf ℰ 47 20 11 11, Fax 47 23 69 65 – 🔟 ⓪ ⊖⊖   G 9
closed 13 to 19 August, Saturday lunch and Sunday from 18 July-31 August – **M** a la carte 175/300 🍴.

XX **Fermette Marbeuf,** 5 r. Marbeuf ℰ 47 23 31 31, Fax 40 70 02 11, « 1900 decor with genuine ceramics and leaded glass windows » – 🔳. 🔟 ⓪ ⊖⊖   G 9
M 160 and a la carte 185/315 🍴.

XX **Bice** - Hôtel Balzac, 6 r. Balzac ℰ 42 89 86 34, Fax 42 25 24 82, Italian rest. – 🔳. ⊖⊖   F 8
closed 14 to 31 August and 22 December-3 January – **M** a la carte 220/370.

XX **Chez Tante Louise,** 41 r. Boissy d'Anglas ℰ 42 65 06 85 – 🔳. 🔟 ⓪ ⊖⊖ JCB   F 11
closed August, Saturday and Sunday – **M** 190 and a la carte 245/405.

XX **Le Bœuf sur le Toit,** 34 r. Colisée ℰ 43 59 83 80, Fax 45 63 45 40, brasserie – 🔟 ⓪ ⊖⊖
M a la carte 170/295 🍴.   F 10

XX **Le Grenadin,** 46 r. Naples ℰ 45 63 28 92 – 🔳. 🔟 ⊖⊖   E 11
closed 11 to 19 July, 8 to 16 August, Christmas-New Year, Saturday, Sunday and Bank Holidays
– **M** 200/370.

XX **Le Sarladais,** 2 r. Vienne ℰ 45 22 23 62 – 🔳. 🔟 ⊖⊖   E 11
closed August, Saturday (except dinner in winter) and Sunday – **M** 145 (dinner) and a la carte 205/355.

XX **Androuët,** 41 r. Amsterdam *&* 48 74 26 93, Telex 280466, Fax 49 95 02 54, Cheese specialities – ▤. AE ⓞ GB JCB   E 12
closed Sunday – **M** 175 (lunch)/240.

XX **Marius et Janette,** 4 av. George V *&* 47 23 41 88, Fax 47 23 07 19, 斎, Seafood – ▤. AE
GB   G 8
closed 24 to 31 December – **M** a la carte 320/480.

XX **L'Avenue,** 41 av. Montaigne *&* 40 70 14 91 brasserie – ▤. AE GB   G 9
M a la carte 180/290.

XX **Finzi,** 24 av. George V *&* 47 20 14 78, Fax 47 20 10 08, Italian cuisine – ▤. AE ⓞ
GB   G 8
closed Saturday lunch in July-August and Sunday lunch – **M** a la carte 160/300 ⅃.

XX **Le Pichet,** 68 r. P. Charron *&* 43 59 50 34 – ▤. AE ⓞ GB   GF 9
closed 23 December-6 January, Saturday and Sunday – **M** a la carte 260/370.

XX **Le Lloyd's,** 23 r. Treilhard *&* 45 63 21 23 – AE GB   E 10
closed 25 December-2 January, Saturday and Sunday – **M** 200 (lunch) and a la carte 260/
385.

XX **Artois,** 13 r. Artois *&* 42 25 01 10 – GB   F 9
closed August, Saturday and Sunday – **M** (booking essential) a la carte 220/330.

XX **Stresa,** 7 r. Chambiges *&* 47 23 51 62, Italian rest. – AE ⓞ   G 9
closed August, 20 December-3 January, Saturday dinner and Sunday – **M** 250/400.

XX **L'Étoile Marocaine,** 56 r. Galilée *&* 47 20 54 45, Morrocan rest. – ▤. AE ⓞ GB.
%   F 8
M 180/450.

XX **Tong Yen,** 1bis r. J. Mermoz *&* 42 25 04 23, Fax 45 63 51 57, Chinese rest. with Vietnamese
and Thai specialities – ▤. AE ⓞ GB   F 10
closed 1 to 25 August – **M** a la carte 190/340.

XX **Chez Bosc,** 7 r. Richepanse *&* 42 60 10 27 – ⓞ GB   G 12
closed 1 to 16 August, Saturday lunch and Sunday – **M** 190 ⅃.

X **Le Bouchon Gourmand,** 25 r. Colisée *&* 43 59 25 29, Fax 42 56 33 97 – AE ⓞ
GB   F 9
closed August, Saturday lunch and Sunday – **M** 130.

X **Bistrot de Marius,** 6 av. George V *&* 40 70 11 76, 斎, Seafood – AE GB   G 8
M a la carte 200/300.

X **La Petite Auberge,** 48 r. Moscou *&* 43 87 91 84 – GB   D 11
closed 8 to 24 August, Saturday and Sunday – **M** 140 and a la carte 190/290.

X **Ferme des Mathurins,** 17 r. Vignon *&* 42 66 46 39 – GB   F 12
closed August, Sunday and Bank Holidays – **M** 150/250.

X **Finzi,** 182 bd Haussmann *&* 45 62 88 68, Fax 47 20 10 08, Italian rest. – ▤. AE GB   F 8
closed Sunday lunch – **M** a la carte 175/300.

Opéra, Gare du Nord,
Gare de l'Est,
Grands Boulevards.

9th and 10th arrondissements.
   9th: ✉ 75009
   10th: ✉ 75010

🏨 **Grand Hôtel Inter-Continental,** 2 r. Scribe (9th) *&* 40 07 32 32, Telex 220875,
Fax 42 66 12 51, 斤 – 劇 ⅍ rm ▤ TV ☎ 👌 – 🔏 350. AE ⓞ GB JCB ⅍ rest   F 12
M see Opéra and Brasserie Café de la Paix below - **La Verrière** *&* 40 07 31 00 *(closed August)*
M (lunch only) 275 – 🖂 140 - **470 rm** 1650/3500, 23 suites.

🏨 **Scribe** Ⓜ, 1 r. Scribe (9th) *&* 44 71 24 24, Telex 214653, Fax 42 65 39 97 – 劇 ⅍ rm ▤
TV ☎ 👌 – 🔏 80. AE ⓞ GB JCB ⅍ rest   F 12
Le Jardin des Muses *&* 44 71 24 24 (coffee shop) **M** a la carte 155/250 ⅃ - **Les Muses** *(closed
August, Saturday, Sunday and Bank Holidays)* **M** 210 (lunch)/350 – 🖂 105 - **206 rm** 1450/1950,
11 suites.

🏨 **Ambassador,** 16 bd Haussmann (9th) *&* 42 46 92 63, Telex 650912, Fax 40 22 08 74 – 劇
▤ TV ☎ – 🔏 110. AE ⓞ GB JCB ⅍ rest   F 13
M 250/400 – 🖂 100 - **298 rm** 1300/2000.

🏨 **Commodore,** 12 bd Haussmann (9th) *&* 42 46 72 82, Telex 280601, Fax 47 70 23 81 – 劇
TV ☎ – 🔏 25. AE ⓞ GB JCB   F 13
M 240 - **Cancans** (coffee shop) **M** a la carte 150/245 - **Le Carvery** (lunch only)
(closed July-August, Saturday and Sunday) **M** 240 – 🖂 80 - **151 rm** 1000/1800, 11 suites
2150/2900.

🏨 **L'Horset Pavillon** M, 38 r. Échiquier (10th) 𝄞 42 46 92 75, Telex 283905, Fax 42 47 03 97
– 📶 🗏 📺 ☎. ⁂ 🆎 GB �📇
M 110 – 🖵 65 – **92 rm** 660/760.
F 15

🏨 **Blanche Fontaine** M 🍴 without rest, 34 r. Fontaine (9th) 𝄞 45 26 72 32, Telex 660311,
Fax 42 81 05 52 – 📶 📺 ☎ ⏪. 🆎 GB. ⁂
🖵 38 – **45 rm** 395/465.
D 13

🏨 **Cidotel Lafayette** M without rest, 49 r. Lafayette (9th) 𝄞 42 85 05 44, Telex 283025,
Fax 49 95 06 60 – 📶 📺 ☎. 🆎 ⓞ GB �📇. ⁂
🖵 65 – **75 rm** 800.
F 14

🏨 **Brébant,** 32 bd Poissonnière (9th) 𝄞 47 70 25 55, Telex 280127, Fax 42 46 65 70 – 📶 🗏 rest
📺 ☎ – 🔏 60. 🆎 ⓞ GB �📇
M 89/198 – **122 rm** 🖵 690/850.
F 14

🏨 **St-Pétersbourg** without rest, 33 r. Caumartin (9th) 𝄞 42 66 60 38, Telex 680001,
Fax 42 66 53 54 – 📶 📺 ☎ – 🔏 100. 🆎 ⓞ GB �📇
100 rm 🖵 473/915.
F 12

🏨 **Astra** M without rest, 29 r. Caumartin (9th) 𝄞 42 66 15 15, Telex 210408, Fax 42 66 98 05
– 📶 ⁂ 🗏 📺 ☎. 🆎 ⓞ GB �📇. ⁂
🖵 45 – **85 rm** 790/980.
F 15

🏨 **Opéra Cadet** M without rest, 24 r. Cadet (9th) 𝄞 48 24 05 26, Telex 282287, Fax 42 46 68 09
– 📶 📺 ☎ ⅔ ⏪. 🆎 ⓞ GB
🖵 48 – **90 rm** 690/695.
F 14

🏨 **Bergère** without rest, 34 r. Bergère (9th) 𝄞 47 70 34 34, Telex 290668, Fax 47 70 36 36 –
📶 📺 ☎. 🆎 ⓞ GB �📇
🖵 45 – **131 rm** 850/890.
F 14

🏨 **Altéa Ronceray** M without rest, 10 bd Montmartre (9th) 𝄞 42 47 13 45, Telex 283906,
Fax 42 47 13 63 – 📶 📺 ☎ – 🔏 65. 🆎 ⓞ GB
🖵 59 – **117 rm** 680/1250, 7 duplex.
F 14

🏨 **Trinité Plaza** M without rest, 41 r. Pigalle (9th) 𝄞 42 85 57 00, Telex 280110, Fax 45 26 41 20
– 📶 📺 ☎. 🆎 ⓞ GB. ⁂
42 rm 🖵 525/650.
E 13

🏨 **Paix République** without rest, 2bis bd St Martin (10th) 𝄞 42 08 96 95, Telex 680632,
Fax 42 06 36 30 – 📶 📺 ☎. 🆎 ⓞ GB. ⁂
🖵 35 – **45 rm** 540/950.
G 16

🏨 **Anjou-Lafayette** M without rest, 4 r. Riboutté (9th) 𝄞 42 46 83 44, Telex 281001,
Fax 48 00 08 97 – 📶 📺 ☎. 🆎 ⓞ GB �📇
🖵 30 – **39 rm** 450/660.
E 14

🏨 **Carlton's H.** without rest, 55 bd Rochechouart (9th) 𝄞 42 81 91 00, Telex 640649,
Fax 42 81 97 04 – 📶 📺 ☎. 🆎 ⓞ GB
🖵 45 – **103 rm** 575/785.
D 14

🏨 **Frantour Paris Est** M, cour d'Honneur (10th) 𝄞 42 05 00 33, Telex 217916, Fax 42 09 91 60
– 📶 📺 ☎. GB �📇
M a la carte 100/170 🍷 – 🖵 39 – **34 rm** 385/880.
E 16

🏨 **Mercure Monty** M, 5 r. Monthyon (9th) 𝄞 47 70 26 10, Telex 660677, Fax 42 46 55 10 –
📶 📺 ☎ – 🔏 50. 🆎 ⓞ GB
M (closed Saturday and Sunday) 82/160 – 🖵 55 – **71 rm** 470/710.
F 14

🏨 **Printania** without rest, 19 r. Château d'Eau (10th) 𝄞 42 01 84 20, Telex 215425,
Fax 42 39 55 12 – 📶 📺 ☎. 🆎 ⓞ GB. ⁂
🖵 39 – **51 rm** 460/545.
F 16

🏨 **Caumartin** M without rest, 27 r. Caumartin (9th) 𝄞 47 42 95 95, Telex 680702,
Fax 47 42 88 19 – 📶 📺 ☎. 🆎 ⓞ GB �📇
🖵 65 – **40 rm** 760/790.
F 12

🏨 **Albert 1er** M without rest, 162 r. La Fayette (10th) 𝄞 40 36 82 40, Telex 212887,
Fax 40 35 72 52 – 📶 🗏 📺 ☎. 🆎 ⓞ GB
🖵 35 – **59 rm** 400/550.
E 16

🏨 **La Tour d'Auvergne** without rest, 10 r. La Tour d'Auvergne (9th) 𝄞 48 78 61 60,
Telex 281604, Fax 49 95 99 00 – 📶 ⁂ 📺 ☎. 🆎 ⓞ GB. ⁂
🖵 35 – **24 rm** 500/650.
E 14

🏨 **Celte La Fayette** M without rest, 25 r. Buffault (9th) 𝄞 49 95 09 49, Fax 49 95 01 88 – 📶
📺 ☎. 🆎 ⓞ GB. ⁂
🖵 35 – **50 rm** 480/630.
E 14

🏨 **Corona** 🍴 without rest, 8 cité Bergère (9th) 𝄞 47 70 52 96, Telex 281081, Fax 42 46 83 49
– 📶 📺 ☎. 🆎 ⓞ GB
🖵 40 – **56 rm** 490/710, 4 suites 990.
F 14

🏨 **Résidence du Pré** without rest, 15 r. P. Sémard (9th) 𝄞 48 78 26 72, Telex 660549,
Fax 42 80 64 83 – 📶 📺 ☎. 🆎 GB
🖵 30 – **40 rm** 395/435.
E 15

🏨 **du Pré** without rest, 10 r. P. Sémard (9th) 𝄞 42 81 37 11, Telex 660549, Fax 40 23 98 28 –
📶 📺 ☎. 🆎 GB
🖵 35 – **41 rm** 395/495.
E 15

🏨 **Gd H. Montmartre** Ⓜ without rest, 2 r. Calais (9th) ℰ 48 74 87 76, Telex 649906, Fax 42 81 31 31 – |🛗 📺 ☎. 𝔸𝔼 ⓄⒹ 𝔾𝔹
D 12
🛏 60 – **40 rm** 550/750.

🏨 **Libertel du Moulin** Ⓜ without rest, 39 r. Fontaine (9th) ℰ 42 81 93 25, Telex 660055, Fax 40 16 09 90 – |🛗 📺 ☎. 𝔸𝔼 ⓄⒹ 𝔾𝔹 ⒿⒸⒷ. ✀
D 13
🛏 50 – **50 rm** 620/840.

🏩 **Montréal** without rest, 23 r. Godot-de-Mauroy (9th) ℰ 42 65 99 54, Fax 49 24 07 33 – |🛗 📺 ☎. 𝔸𝔼 ⓄⒹ 𝔾𝔹
F 12
closed August – 🛏 35 – **14 rm** 285/550, 5 suites 600.

🏩 **Modern' Est** without rest, 91 bd Strasbourg (10th) ℰ 40 37 77 20, Fax 40 37 17 55 – |🛗 📺 ☎. 𝔾𝔹. ✀
E 16
🛏 28 – **30 rm** 320/400.

🏩 **Capucines** without rest, 6 r. Godot de Mauroy (9th) ℰ 47 42 06 37, Fax 42 68 05 05 – |🛗 ✀ ☎. 𝔸𝔼 𝔾𝔹
F 12
🛏 25 – **47 rm** 390/580.

🏩 **D'Estrées** Ⓜ ॐ without rest, 2bis cité Pigalle (9th) ℰ 48 74 39 22, Telex 290609, Fax 45 96 04 09 – |🛗 📺 ☎. 𝔸𝔼 ⓄⒹ 𝔾𝔹
E 13
🛏 40 – **23 rm** 540/570.

🏩 **Urbis Lafayette** without rest, 122 r. Lafayette (10th) ℰ 45 23 27 27, Telex 290272, Fax 42 46 73 79 – |🛗 📺 ☎ &. 𝔾𝔹
E 16
🛏 35 – **70 rm** 372/415.

XXXXX ❀ **Rest. Opéra-Café de la Paix** - Le Grand Hôtel, pl. Opéra (9th) ℰ 40 07 30 10, Telex 220875, Fax 42 66 12 51, « Second Empire decor » – 🍽. 𝔸𝔼 ⓄⒹ 𝔾𝔹 ⒿⒸⒷ
F 12
closed August – **M** a la carte 370/600
Spec. Salade de canette rouennaise à la coriandre, Boudin blanc truffé à l'ancienne (autumn-winter), Filet mignon de veau aux morilles (spring).

XXX ❀ **La Table d'Anvers** (Conticini), 2 pl. Anvers (9th) ℰ 48 78 35 21, Fax 45 26 66 67 – 🍽. 𝔸𝔼 𝔾𝔹
D 14
closed 10 to 20 August, Saturday lunch and Sunday – **M** 240/490
Spec. Chausson de langoustines aux girolles, Filet de bar au thym et citron, Croquettes au chocolat fondant.

XXX **Charlot "Roi des Coquillages"**, 81 bd Clichy (9th) ℰ 48 74 49 64, Fax 40 16 11 00, Seafood – 🍽. 𝔸𝔼 ⓄⒹ 𝔾𝔹
D 12
M a la carte 230/390.

XXX **Le Louis XIV**, 8 bd St-Denis (10th) ℰ 42 08 56 56 – 𝔸𝔼 ⓄⒹ 𝔾𝔹
G 15
closed May-August – **M** a la carte 230/450.

XX **Au Chateaubriant**, 23 r. Chabrol (10th) ℰ 48 24 58 94, Italian rest., Paintings Collection – 🍽. 𝔸𝔼 𝔾𝔹. ✀
E 15
closed August, 14 to 22 February, Sunday and Monday – **M** a la carte 205/370.

XX **Chez Michel**, 10 r. Belzunce (10th) ℰ 48 78 44 14 – 🍽. 𝔸𝔼 ⓄⒹ 𝔾𝔹
E 15
closed August, 25 December-1 January, Saturday and Sunday – **M** (booking essential) 250 (lunch) and a la carte 300/455.

XX **Brasserie Flo Printemps**, (Printemps de la Mode - 6th floor) 64 bd Haussman (9th) ℰ 42 82 58 81, Fax 45 26 31 24 – 🍽. 𝔸𝔼 ⓄⒹ 𝔾𝔹
F 12
closed Sunday and Bank Holidays – **M** (lunch only) a la carte 160/265 ♨.

XX **Brasserie Café de la Paix** - Le Grand Hôtel, 12 bd Capucines (9th) ℰ 40 07 30 20, Telex 220875, Fax 42 66 12 51 – ✀. 𝔸𝔼 ⓄⒹ 𝔾𝔹 ⒿⒸⒷ
F 12
M 180 and a la carte 185/300 ♨.

XX **Grand Café Capucines** (24 hr service), 4 bd Capucines (9th) ℰ 47 42 19 00, Fax 47 42 74 22, « Early 20C decor » – 𝔸𝔼 ⓄⒹ 𝔾𝔹
F 13
M a la carte 175/320 ♨.

XX **Le Quercy**, 36 r. Condorcet (9th) ℰ 48 78 30 61 – 𝔸𝔼 ⓄⒹ 𝔾𝔹
E 14
closed August, Sunday and Bank Holidays – **M** 158 and a la carte 175/310.

XX **Comme Chez Soi**, 20 r. Lamartine (9th) ℰ 48 78 00 02 – 🍽. ⓄⒹ 𝔾𝔹 ⒿⒸⒷ
E 14
closed August, Saturday and Sunday – **M** 170/220.

XX **Le Saintongeais**, 62 r. Fg Montmartre (9th) ℰ 42 80 39 92 – 𝔸𝔼 ⓄⒹ 𝔾𝔹
E 14
closed 8 to 30 August, 25 December-4 January, Saturday and Sunday – **M** a la carte 180/260.

XX **Julien**, 16 r. Fg St-Denis (10th) ℰ 47 70 12 06, Fax 42 47 00 65, « Early 20C brasserie » – 🍽. 𝔸𝔼 ⓄⒹ 𝔾𝔹
F 15
M a la carte 155/290 ♨.

XX **Le Franche-Comté**, 2 bd Madeleine (Maison de la Franche-Comté) (9th) ℰ 49 24 99 09, Fax 49 24 96 56 – 𝔸𝔼 𝔾𝔹
F 12
closed Sunday – **M** 90/150.

XX **Petit Riche,** 25 r. Le Peletier (9th) ℰ 47 70 68 68, Fax 48 24 10 79, « Late 19C decor »
🆎 ⓪ 🆒 🇯🇨🇧
closed Saturday from 15 July-31 August and Sunday – **M** 180 and a la carte 170/300 ◊. F 13

XX **Bistrot Papillon,** 6 r. Papillon (9th) ℰ 47 70 90 03 – 🆎 ⓪ 🆒
closed 1 to 10 May, 8 to 30 August, Saturday, Sunday and Bank Holidays – **M** 135 and a la carte 210/300. E 15

XX **Aux Deux Canards,** 8 r. Fg Poissonnière (10th) ℰ 47 70 03 23, restaurant for no-smokers
– 🔳 🆎 ⓪ 🆒
closed Saturday lunch and Sunday – **M** a la carte 230/330 ◊. F 15

XX **Brasserie Flo,** 7 cour Petites-Écuries (10th) ℰ 47 70 13 59, Fax 42 47 00 80, « 1900 decor »
– 🔳 🆎 ⓪ 🆒 🇯🇨🇧
M a la carte 155/290 ◊. F 15

XX **Gokado,** 18 r. Caumartin (9th) ℰ 47 42 08 82, Fax 47 42 76 19, Japanese cuisine – 🔳 🆎
🆒 🇯🇨🇧
closed Christmas-New Year, lunch Saturday and Sunday – **M** a la carte 270/335. F 12

XX **Terminus Nord,** 23 r. Dunkerque (10th) ℰ 42 85 05 15, Fax 40 16 13 98, Brasserie – 🆎 ⓪
🆒
M a la carte 155/290 ◊. E 16

XX **La P'tite Tonkinoise,** 56 r. Fg Poissonnière (10th) ℰ 42 46 85 98, Vietnamese rest. –
🆒
closed 1 August-15 September, 22 December-5 January, Sunday and Monday – **M** a la carte 150/235. F 15

X **Relais Beaujolais,** 3 r. Milton (9th) ℰ 48 78 77 91 – 🆒
closed Saturday and Sunday – **M** 130 (lunch) and a la carte 135/290. E 14

X **Petit Batailley,** 26 r. Bergère (9th) ℰ 47 70 85 81 – 🆎 ⓪ 🆒 🇯🇨🇧
closed 1 to 21 August, 1 to 8 January, Saturday lunch, Sunday and Bank Holidays – **M** 100/205 ◊. F 14

X **La Grille,** 80 r. Fg Poissonnière (10th) ℰ 47 70 89 73 – 🆎 ⓪ 🆒
closed August, February Holidays, Saturday and Sunday – **M** a la carte 190/280. E 15

X **Chez Jean l'Auvergnat,** 52 r. Lamartine (9th) ℰ 48 78 62 73, Fax 48 78 39 29 –
🆒
closed Saturday lunch and Sunday – **M** a la carte 135/235. E 14

X **Bistro des Deux Théâtres,** 18 r. Blanche (9th) ℰ 45 26 41 43 – 🔳 🆒
M 162. E 12

Bastille, Gare de Lyon,
Place d'Italie,
Bois de Vincennes.

12th and 13th arrondissements.
12th: ✉ 75012
13th: ✉ 75013

🏨 **Pavillon Bastille** Ⓜ without rest, 65 r. Lyon (12th) ℰ 43 43 65 65, Fax 43 43 96 52 – 🛗 ↦
📺 ☎ ໒, 🆎 ⓪ 🆒 🇯🇨🇧
☲ 65 – **25 rm** 890. K 18

🏨 **Novotel Paris Bercy** Ⓜ, 86 r. Bercy (12th) ℰ 43 42 30 00, Telex 218332, Fax 43 45 30 60,
⛲ – 🛗 ↦ 🔳 📺 ☎ ໒ – 🔏 30 - 100. 🆎 ⓪ 🆒
M a la carte approx. 150 ◊ – ☲ 55 – **129 rm** 700/1090. M 19

🏨 **Altéa Place d'Italie** Ⓜ without rest, 178 bd Vincent Auriol (13th) ℰ 44 24 01 01,
Telex 203424, Fax 44 24 07 07 – 🛗 📺 ☎ – 🔏 25. 🆎 ⓪ 🆒
☲ 60 – **70 rm** 630/1000. N 16

🏨 **Mercure Pont de Bercy** Ⓜ, 6 bd Vincent Auriol (13th) ℰ 45 82 48 00, Telex 205010,
Fax 45 82 19 16 – 🛗 ↦ rm 🔳 rest 📺 ☎ ໒ – 🔏 40. 🆎 ⓪ 🆒
M *(closed 27 July-23 August, 24 December-3 January, Saturday and Sunday)* a la carte approx.
250 – ☲ 53 – **89 rm** 620/690. M 18

🏨 **Mercure Paris Tolbiac** Ⓜ without rest, 21 r. Tolbiac (13th) ℰ 45 84 61 61, Telex 250822,
Fax 45 84 43 38 – 🛗 ↦ 📺 ☎ ໒ 🅿 – 🔏 25. 🆎 ⓪ 🆒
☲ 55 – **71 rm** 590/670. P 18

🏨 **Équinoxe** without rest, 40 r. Le Brun (13th) ℰ 43 37 56 56, Telex 201476, Fax 45 35 52 42
– 🛗 📺 ☎ ⇦ 🆎 ⓪ 🆒 🇯🇨🇧
☲ 30 – **49 rm** 450/590. N 15

🏨 **Relais de Lyon** without rest, 64 r. Crozatier (12th) ℰ 43 44 22 50, Telex 216690,
Fax 43 41 55 12 – 🛗 📺 ☎ ⇦ 🆎 ⓪ 🆒 🇯🇨🇧 ⚹
☲ 30 – **34 rm** 400/498. K 19

🏥 **Quatre Saisons Bastille** Ⓜ without rest, 67 r. Lyon (12th) ℰ 40 01 07 17, Telex 214223, Fax 40 01 07 27 – |🛗| 📺 ☎ – 🔬 25. ℄ ① ☐
K 18
☐ 40 – **36 rm** 550/900.

🏥 **Modern H. Lyon** without rest, 3 r. Parrot (12th) ℰ 43 43 41 52, Telex 220083, Fax 43 43 81 16 – |🛗| 📺 ☎. ℄ ☐ ⬚. ⌘
L 18
☐ 37 – **49 rm** 500/640.

🏥 **Média** Ⓜ without rest, 22 r. Reine Blanche (13th) ℰ 45 35 72 72, Telex 206702, Fax 43 31 43 31 – |🛗| 📺 ☎ – 🔬 25. ℄ ①
M 15
☐ 30 – **19 rm** 450/520.

🏥 **de Weha** Ⓜ without rest, 205 av. Choisy (13th) ℰ 45 86 06 06, Telex 206898, Fax 43 31 42 06 – |🛗| ⬚ 📺 ☎. ℄ ① ☐
P 16
☐ 40 – **34 rm** 539/649.

🏥 **Terminus-Lyon** without rest, 19 bd Diderot (12th) ℰ 43 43 24 03, Telex 220117, Fax 43 44 09 00 – |🛗| 📺 ☎. ℄ ① ☐ ⬚
L 18
☐ 35 – **61 rm** 470/550.

🏥 **Slavia** with rest, 51 bd St-Marcel (13th) ℰ 43 37 81 25, Telex 205542, Fax 45 87 05 03 – |🛗| 📺 ☎. ℄ ☐. ⌘
M 16
☐ 28 – **37 rm** 300/340, 6 suites 405.

🏥 **Midi** without rest, 114 av. Daumesnil (12th) ℰ 43 07 72 03, Telex 215917, Fax 43 43 21 75 – 📺 ☎. ℄ ① ☐
L 20
☐ 30 – **36 rm** 350/440.

🏥 **Résidence Vert Galant** Ⓜ ⌖, 43 r. Croulebarbe (13th) ℰ 43 36 22 41, Telex 202371 – 📺 ☎ 🔬. ℄ ① ☐ ⬚. ⌘ rm
N 15
M see rest. **Etchegory** below – ☐ 35 – **15 rm** 400/500.

🏥 **Ibis Paris Bercy** Ⓜ, 77 r. Bercy (12th) ℰ 43 42 91 91, Telex 216391, Fax 43 42 34 79, 🍴 – |🛗| ⬚ rm ▤ rest 📺 ☎ 🔬 – 🔬 25 - 180. ℄ ☐
M 19
M 135 🍴 – ☐ 32 – **368 rm** 455.

🏨 **Corail** without rest, 23 r. Lyon (12th) ℰ 43 43 23 54, Telex 212002, Fax 43 43 82 55 – |🛗| 📺 ☎. ℄ ① ☐ ⬚
L 18
☐ 31 – **50 rm** 310/400.

🏨 **Marceau** without rest, 13 r. J. César (12th) ℰ 43 43 11 65, Telex 214006, Fax 43 41 67 70 – |🛗| 📺 ☎. ☐. ⌘
K 17
closed 20 July-20 August – ☐ 30 – **53 rm** 335/380.

🏨 **Campanile** without rest, 15bis av. Italie (13th) ℰ 45 84 95 95, Telex 205256, Fax 45 70 73 06 – |🛗| 📺 ☎. ℄ ① ☐
P 16
☐ 29 – **122 rm** 350/395.

🏨 **Nouvel H.** without rest, 24 av. Bel Air (12th) ℰ 43 43 01 81, Telex 240139, Fax 43 44 64 13, 🍴 – 📺 ☎. ℄ ① ☐
L 21
☐ 40 – **28 rm** 245/550.

🏨 **Gd H. Gobelins** without rest, 57 bd St-Marcel (13th) ℰ 43 31 79 89, Fax 45 35 43 56 – |🛗| 📺 ☎
M 16
☐ 30 – **45 rm** 240/350.

🏨 **des Trois Gares** without rest, 1 r. J. César (12th) ℰ 43 43 01 70, Telex 216392, Fax 43 41 36 58 – |🛗| 📺 ☎. ☐. ⌘
K 17
☐ 30 – **36 rm** 220/400.

🏨 **Viator** without rest, 1 r. Parrot (12th) ℰ 43 43 11 00, Telex 216236, Fax 43 43 10 89 – |🛗| 📺 ☎. ☐. ⌘
L 18
☐ 32 – **45 rm** 310/360.

🏨 **Palym H.** without rest, 4 r. E.-Gilbert (12th) ℰ 43 43 24 48, Fax 43 41 69 47 – |🛗| 📺 ☎. ☐
L 18
☐ 30 – **51 rm** 300/380.

🏨 **Urbis Paris Tolbiac** without rest, 177 r. Tolbiac (13th) ℰ 45 80 16 60, Telex 200821, Fax 45 80 95 80 – |🛗| 📺 ☎ 🔬. ☐
P 15
☐ 32 – **60 rm** 360/390.

🏨 **Résidence Les Gobelins** without rest, 9 r. Gobelins (13th) ℰ 47 07 26 90, Telex 206566, Fax 43 31 44 05 – |🛗| 📺 ☎. ℄ ① ☐. ⌘
N 15
☐ 32 – **32 rm** 320/400.

🏨 **Timhôtel** without rest, 22 r. Barrault (13th) ℰ 45 80 67 67, Telex 205461, Fax 45 89 36 93 – |🛗| 📺 ☎. ℄ ① ☐ ⬚
P 15
☐ 45 – **73 rm** 343/425.

When driving through towns
*use the plans in the **Michelin Red Guide**.*
Features indicated include :
throughroutes and by-passes,
traffic junctions and major squares,
new streets, car parks, pedestrian streets...
All this information is revised annually.

XXXX Fouquet's Bastille, 130 r. Lyon (12th) ℰ 43 42 18 18, Fax 43 42 08 20 – ▤. ☒ ◉ ☒ ☒
closed August and Sunday – **Rez-de-Chaussée M** 165 b.i. – **1ᵉʳ étage M** a la carte 300/430
M 22

XXX ✿ Au Pressoir (Séguin), 257 av. Daumesnil (12th) ℰ 43 44 38 21, Fax 43 43 81 77 – ▤. ☒
closed August, February Holidays, Saturday and Sunday – **M** 360 and a la carte 330/490
Spec. Fricassée de Saint-Jacques aux cèpes (October-December), Bar à l'écaille au beurre à la
badiane, Ris de veau aux noix et au lard.
M 22

XXX Train Bleu, Gare de Lyon (12th) ℰ 43 43 38 39, Telex 240788, Fax 43 43 97 96, « Murals
recalling the journey from Paris to the Mediterranean » – ☒ ◉ ☒
M (1st floor) 220 b.i. (lunch) and a la carte 260/360.
L 18

XX ✿ Au Trou Gascon, 40 r. Taine (12th) ℰ 43 44 34 26, Fax 43 07 80 55 – ▤. ☒ ◉ ☒ ☒
closed August, 25 December-3 January, Saturday and Sunday – **M** (booking essential) 200 and
a la carte 295/400
M 21
Spec. Bouillon de châtaignes au blanc de poule faisanne (autumn-winter), Pâté chaud de cèpes,
Volaille de Chalosse truffée.

XX La Gourmandise, 271 av. Daumesnil (12th) ℰ 43 43 94 41 – ☒ ☒
M 22
closed 1 to 8 May, 2 to 24 August, Sunday and Monday – **M** 188 and a la carte 260/400.

XX L'Oulette, 15 pl. Lachambeaudie (12th) ℰ 40 02 02 12, Fax 40 02 02 13, ☞ – ▤. ☒
closed August, February Holidays, Saturday lunch and Bank Holidays – **M** 170 (lunch)
and a la carte 250/345.
N 20

XX Au Petit Marguery, 9 bd Port-Royal (13th) ℰ 43 31 58 59 – ☒ ◉ ☒
M 15
closed August, 24 December-2 January, Sunday and Monday – **M** a la carte 300/435.

XX Les Vieux Métiers de France, 13 bd A. Blanqui (13th) ℰ 45 88 90 03 – ▤. ☒ ◉ ☒ ☒
closed Sunday and Monday – **M** 165/290.
P 15

XX Le Luneau, 5 r. Lyon (12th) ℰ 43 43 90 85 – ☒ ◉ ☒
L 18
M 139 and a la carte 240/300 ♨.

XX La Flambée, 4 r. Taine (12th) ℰ 43 43 21 80 – ☒ ◉ ☒
M 20
closed 2 to 23 August, 20 to 28 December, Sunday dinner and Monday – **M** 119/169.

XX La Frégate, 30 av. Ledru-Rollin (12th) ℰ 43 43 90 32, Seafood – ▤. ☒ ☒
L 18
closed 1 to 23 August, Saturday and Sunday – **M** 200/290.

XX Le Traversière, 40 r. Traversière (12th) ℰ 43 44 02 10 – ☒ ◉ ☒ ☒
K 18
closed 1 to 30 August, Sunday dinner and Bank Holidays – **M** 150 and a la carte 180/350.

XX La Sologne, 164 av. Daumesnil (12th) ℰ 43 07 68 97 – ☒
M 21
closed Saturday lunch and Sunday – **M** 135/250.

XX L'Escapade en Touraine, 24 r. Traversière (12th) ℰ 43 43 14 96 – ☒ ☒
L 18
closed August, Saturday, Sunday and Bank Holidays – **M** 140 and a la carte 130/220.

X Mange Tout, 24 bd Bastille (12th) ℰ 43 43 95 15 – ☒ ☒
K 17
closed 10 to 16 August, 21 to 27 December and Sunday – **M** 98 and a la carte 150/245 ♨.

X Le Quincy, 28 av. Ledru-Rollin (12th) ℰ 46 28 46 76 – ▤
L 17
closed 10 August-10 September, Saturday, Sunday and Monday – **M** a la carte 200/345.

X Etchegorry, 41 r. Croulebarbe (13th) ℰ 43 31 63 05, Telex 202371 – ☒ ◉ ☒
N 15
closed Sunday – **M** 140 b.i./200 b.i.

X Le Rhône, 40 bd Arago (13th) ℰ 47 07 33 57, ☞ – ☒
N 14
closed August, Saturday, Sunday and Bank Holidays – **M** 75/155 ♨.

X Chez Françoise, 12 r. Butte aux Cailles (13th) ℰ 45 80 12 02 – ☒ ◉ ☒. ✻
P 15
closed 1 to 8 March, 30 July-26 August, Saturday lunch and Sunday – **M** 88/128.

Vaugirard, Gare Montparnasse, Grenelle, Denfert-Rochereau.

14th and 15th arrondissements.
14th: ✉ 75014
15th: ✉ 75015

Hilton ▥, 18 av. Suffren (15th) ℰ 42 73 92 00, Telex 200955, Fax 47 83 62 66, ☞ – ▮ ☒
▤ ▥ ☎ ♨ – ▵ 100. ☒ ◉ ☒
J 7
Western M a la carte 230/405 ♨ – **La Terrasse M** a la carte 185/300 ♨ – ☲ 120 – **455 rm**
1450/2150, 22 suites.

Nikko ▥, 61 quai Grenelle (15th) ℰ 40 58 20 00, Telex 205811, Fax 45 75 42 35, ≤, ♨, ▨
– ▮ ☒ rm ▤ ▥ ☎ ☜ – ▵ 800. ☒ ◉ ☒ ☒
K 6
M see **Les Célébrités** below - **Brasserie Pont Mirabeau M** a la carte 195/340 - **Rest. japonais
Benkay M** 300/650 – ☲ 75 – **761 rm** 1260/1880, 7 suites.

Méridien Montparnasse ▥, 19 r. Cdt-Mouchotte (14th) ℰ 44 36 44 36, Telex 200135,
Fax 44 36 49 00, ≤ – ▮ ☒ rm ▤ ▥ ☎ ♨ – ▵ 1 400. ☒ ◉ ☒ ☒ ☒ ✻ rest
M 11
M see **Montparnasse 25** below - **Justine** ℰ 44 36 44 00 **M** 185 – ☲ 98 – **950 rm** 1150/2200,
34 suites.

Sofitel Paris Porte de Sèvres M, 8 r. L.-Armand (15th) ℰ 40 60 30 30, Telex 200484, Fax 45 57 04 22, ≼, indoor pool overlooking Paris, 🖽 – 🖨 ⩲ rm 🔲 📺 & ⩘ – 🕰 1 200. 🖽 ⓞ ⒼⒷ
N 5
M see Le Relais de Sèvres below - **La Tonnelle** (brasserie) **M** 145 🔔 – ⬚ 80 – **601 rm** 750/950, 14 suites 1500/1900.

Pullman St-Jacques M, 17 bd St-Jacques (14th) ℰ 40 78 79 80, Telex 270740, Fax 45 88 43 93 – 🖨 ⩲ 🔲 📺 ☎ ⩘ – 🕰 40 - 1 200. 🖽 ⓞ ⒼⒷ 🅙ⒸⒷ
N 13-14
Brasserie Le Français **M** 182 b.i. – ⬚ 90 – **783 rm** 1095/1360, 14 suites 1825/2200.

Adagio Paris Vaugirard M, 253 r. Vaugirard (15th) ℰ 40 45 10 00, Telex 250709, Fax 40 45 10 10, 🖽 – 🖨 ⩲ rm 🔲 ☎ rest – 🕰 400. 🖽 ⓞ ⒼⒷ
M 9
Le Transatlantique **M** 120 – ⬚ 65 – **185 rm** 850/930.

Mercure Paris Vaugirard M, porte de Versailles (15th) ℰ 45 33 74 63, Telex 205628, Fax 48 28 22 11 – 🖨 ⩲ rm 🔲 📺 ☎ & ⩘ – 🕰 120. 🖽 ⓞ ⒼⒷ 🅙ⒸⒷ
N 7
M 130 – ⬚ 55 – **91 rm** 980/1400.

Mercure Paris Montparnasse M, 20 r. Gaîté (14th) ℰ 43 35 28 28, Telex 201532, Fax 43 27 98 64 – 🖨 🔲 📺 ☎ & ⩘ – 🕰 100. 🖽 ⓞ ⒼⒷ
M 11
Bistrot de la Gaîté **M** a la carte approx. 180 – ⬚ 65 – **177 rm** 770/900, 8 suites 1200.

L'Aiglon without rest, 232 bd Raspail (14th) ℰ 43 20 82 42, Telex 206038, Fax 43 20 98 72 – 🖨 kitchenette ☎. 🖽 ⓞ ⒼⒷ 🅙ⒸⒷ
M 12
⬚ 33 – **40 rm** 450/670, 9 suites 750/950.

Lenox Montparnasse M without rest, 15 r. Delambre (14th) ℰ 43 35 34 50, Telex 205937, Fax 43 20 46 64 – 🖨 🔲 📺 ☎. 🖽 ⓞ ⒼⒷ 🅙ⒸⒷ. ⅀
M 12
⬚ 40 – **46 rm** 460/890.

Orléans Palace H. without rest, 185 bd Brune (14th) ℰ 45 39 68 50, Telex 205490, Fax 45 43 65 64 – 🖨 🔲 📺 ☎ – 🕰 35. 🖽 ⓞ ⒼⒷ
R 11
⬚ 40 – **92 rm** 450/500.

Mercure Paris XV M without rest, 6 r. St-Lambert (15th) ℰ 45 58 61 00, Telex 206936, Fax 45 54 10 43 – 🖨 🔲 📺 ☎ & ⩘. 🖽 ⓞ ⒼⒷ
M 7
⬚ 50 – **56 rm** 550/650.

Capitol M without rest, 9 r. Viala (15th) ℰ 45 78 61 00, Telex 202881, Fax 45 79 32 51 – 🖨 🔲 📺 ☎. 🖽 ⓞ ⒼⒷ 🅙ⒸⒷ. ⅀
K 7
⬚ 65 – **42 rm** 590/690, 4 suites 1080.

Messidor without rest, 330 r. Vaugirard (15th) ℰ 48 28 03 74, Telex 204606, Fax 48 28 75 17, ⌖ – 🖨 🔲 ☎. 🖽 ⓞ ⒼⒷ
M 8
⬚ 48 – **72 rm** 475/950.

Waldorf M without rest, 17 r. Départ (14th) ℰ 43 20 64 79, Telex 201677, Fax 43 35 17 52 – 🖨 🔲 📺 ☎. 🖽 ⓞ ⒼⒷ 🅙ⒸⒷ. ⅀
L 11
⬚ 40 – **30 rm** 520/720.

Raspail M without rest, 203 bd Raspail (14th) ℰ 43 20 62 86, Fax 43 20 50 79 – 🖨 🔲 📺 ☎. 🖽 ⓞ ⒼⒷ. ⅀
M 12
⬚ 40 – **36 rm** 495/790.

Alizé Grenelle M without rest, 87 av. É. Zola (15th) ℰ 45 78 08 22, Telex 250095, Fax 40 59 03 06 – 🖨 📺 ☎. 🖽 ⓞ ⒼⒷ 🅙ⒸⒷ
L 7
⬚ 30 – **50 rm** 360/400.

Beaugrenelle St-Charles M without rest, 82 r. St-Charles (15th) ℰ 45 78 61 63, Telex 270263, Fax 45 79 04 38 – 📺 ☎. 🖽 ⓞ ⒼⒷ 🅙ⒸⒷ
K 7
⬚ 30 – **51 rm** 330/400.

Renoir M without rest, 39 r. Montparnasse (14th) ℰ 43 21 72 50, Telex 205436, Fax 43 21 68 72 – 🖨 📺 ☎. 🖽 ⓞ ⒼⒷ. ⅀
L 12
⬚ 32 – **29 rm** 470/580.

Versailles M without rest, 213 r. Croix Nivert (15th) ℰ 48 28 48 66, Telex 200473, Fax 45 30 16 22 – 🖨 📺 ☎. 🖽 ⒼⒷ
N 7
⬚ 40 – **41 rm** 455/680.

Châtillon H. without rest, 11 square Châtillon (14th) ℰ 45 42 31 17, Fax 45 42 72 09 – 🖨 📺 ☎. ⒼⒷ. ⅀
P 11
⬚ 25 – **31 rm** 270/310.

Terminus Vaugirard without rest, 403 r. Vaugirard (15th) ℰ 48 28 18 72, Telex 206562, Fax 48 28 56 34 – 🖨 📺 ☎. ⒼⒷ. ⅀
N 7
⬚ 30 – **89 rm** 400/600.

Wallace without rest, 89 r. Fondary (15th) ℰ 45 78 83 30, Telex 205277, Fax 40 58 19 43 – 🖨 📺 ☎. 🖽 ⓞ ⒼⒷ 🅙ⒸⒷ
L 8
⬚ 35 – **35 rm** 500.

Acropole without rest, 199 bd Brune (14th) ℰ 45 39 64 17, Telex 203131, Fax 45 42 18 21 – 🖨 📺 ☎. 🖽 ⓞ ⒼⒷ. ⅀
R 12
⬚ 30 – **41 rm** 340/450.

L'Alligator without rest, 39 r. Delambre (14th) ℰ 43 35 18 40, Telex 270545, Fax 43 35 30 71 – 🖨 📺 ☎. 🖽 ⓞ ⒼⒷ. ⅀
M 12
⬚ 40 – **35 rm** 395/620.

🏨 **Résidence St-Lambert** without rest, 5 r. E. Gibez (15th) ✆ 48 28 63 14, Telex 205459, Fax 45 33 45 50 – 🛗 📺 ☎. ⬛ ⓞ 🆑 🄹🄲🄱
☲ 32 – **48 rm** 390/550.
N 8

🏨 **Alésia Montparnasse** without rest, 84 r. R. Losserand (14th) ✆ 45 42 16 03, Fax 45 42 11 60 – 🛗 ⇅ 📺 ☎. ⬛ ⓞ 🆑 🄹🄲🄱
☲ 35 – **45 rm** 450/490.
N 10

🏨 **Lilas Blanc** Ⓜ without rest, 5 r. Avre (15th) ✆ 45 75 30 07, Fax 45 78 66 65 – 🛗 📺 ☎. ⬛ ⓞ 🆑. ⇅
☲ 30 – **32 rm** 375/420.
K 8

🏨 **Ariane Montparnasse** without rest, 35 r. Sablière (14th) ✆ 45 45 67 13, Telex 203554, Fax 45 45 39 49 – 🛗 📺 ☎. ⬛ 🆑. ⇅
☲ 35 – **30 rm** 370/500.
N 11

🏨 **Fondary** without rest, 30 r. Fondary (15th) ✆ 45 75 14 75, Telex 206761, Fax 45 75 84 42 – 🛗 📺 ☎. ⬛ 🆑
☲ 38 – **20 rm** 365/405.
L 8

🏨 **Istria** without rest, 29 r. Campagne Première (14th) ✆ 43 20 91 82, Telex 203618, Fax 43 22 48 45 – 🛗 📺 ☎. ⬛ 🆑 🄹🄲🄱
☲ 40 – **26 rm** 440/540.
M 12

🏨 **Pasteur** without rest, 33 r. Dr.-Roux (15th) ✆ 47 83 53 17, Fax 45 66 62 39 – 🛗 📺 ☎. 🆑
closed August – ☲ 35 – **19 rm** 310/430.
M 10

XXXX ❀ **Les Célébrités** - Hôtel Nikko, 61 quai Grenelle (15th) ✆ 40 58 20 00, Telex 205811, Fax 45 75 42 35, < – ⬛. ⬛ ⓞ 🆑 🄹🄲🄱
M 250 (lunch) and a la carte 420/690
K 6
Spec. Langoustines rôties au basilic, Bar grillé sur peau au beurre rouge, Canette de Bresse rôtie.

XXXX ❀ **Montparnasse 25** - Hôtel Méridien Montparnasse, ✆ 44 36 44 25, Telex 200135, Fax 44 36 49 00 – ⬛ ⓟ. ⬛ ⓞ 🆑 🄹🄲🄱. ⇅
M 11
M *(closed August, 19 to 27 December, Saturday and Sunday)* 230 (lunch) and a la carte 270/360
Spec. Galette de petits gris et grenouilles au persil, Effiloché de raie aux pommes de terre tièdes, Royal de lapereau et gratin de pâtes fraîches au foie gras.

XXXX ❀ **Relais de Sèvres** - Hôtel Sofitel Paris, 8 r. L.-Armand (15th) ✆ 40 60 33 66, Telex 200432, Fax 45 57 04 22 – ⇅ ⬛. ⬛ ⓞ 🆑
N 5
closed August, 24 December-2 January, Saturday and Sunday – **M** 320 and a la carte 280/430
Spec. Tartare de poisson à l'huile douce, Fricassée de sole à l'aigre doux, Hochepot d'aiguillette de boeuf aux pieds de mouton.

XXX ❀ **Morot Gaudry**, 6 r. Cavalerie (15th) (8th floor) ✆ 45 67 06 85, Fax 45 67 55 72, 🍽 – ⬛. ⬛ 🆑 🄹🄲🄱
K 8
closed Saturday and Sunday – **M** 200 (lunch) and a la carte 280/460
Spec. Salade de rougets et langoustines au safran, Sandre en écailles de pommes de terre, Grouse rôtie (15 September-28 February).

XXX **Armes de Bretagne**, 108 av. Maine (14th) ✆ 43 20 29 50 – ⬛. ⬛ ⓞ 🆑 🄹🄲🄱
N 11
closed August, Sunday dinner and Monday – **M** 200 and a la carte 245/505.

XXX **Pavillon Montsouris**, 20 r. Gazan (14th) ✆ 45 88 38 52, Fax 45 88 63 40, <, 🍽, « 1900 Pavilion beside the park » – ⓟ. ⬛ ⓞ 🆑
R 14
M 255.

XXX **Moniage Guillaume** with rm, 88 r. Tombe-Issoire (14th) ✆ 43 22 96 15, Fax 43 27 11 79 – 📺 ☎. ⬛ ⓞ 🆑 🄹🄲🄱
P 12
closed August and Sunday – **M** 195 b.i. (lunch) and a la carte 260/460 – ☲ 30 – **5 rm** 240/320.

XXX **Lous Landès**, 157 av. Maine (14th) ✆ 45 43 08 04 – ⬛. ⬛ ⓞ 🆑
N 11
closed August, Saturday lunch and Sunday – **M** a la carte 255/430.

XXX **Olympe**, 8 r. Nicolas Charlet (15th) ✆ 47 34 86 08 – ⬛. ⬛ ⓞ 🆑 🄹🄲🄱
L 10
closed Saturday lunch, Sunday lunch and Monday – **M** 200 and a la carte 230/345.

XX **Lal Qila**, 88 av. É. Zola (15th) ✆ 45 75 68 40, Indian rest., « Unusual decor » – ⬛. ⬛ ⓞ 🆑. ⇅
L 7
M 185/400.

XX ❀ **Jacques Hébert,** 38 r. Sébastien Mercier (15th) ✆ 45 57 77 88 – 🆑
L 5
closed Sunday and Monday – **M** 185/260
Spec. Marinière de poissons à la tomate et basilic, Crépinette de pied de porc farci, Symphonie gourmande.

XX **L'Aubergade**, 53 av. La Motte-Picquet (15th) ✆ 47 83 23 85, 🍽 – ⬛ 🆑
J 9
closed 13 to 23 April, 27 July-27 August, 21 December-5 January, Sunday dinner and Monday – **M** 150 b.i. (lunch) and a la carte 235/355.

XX **La Chaumière des Gourmets,** 22 pl. Denfert-Rochereau (14th) ✆ 43 21 22 59 – ⬛ 🆑
N 12
closed August, Saturday lunch and Sunday – **M** 240 and a la carte 245/385.

XX ✿ **Bistro 121,** 121 r. Convention (15th) ℰ 45 57 52 90 – 𝔸𝔼 ⓪ 𝖦𝖡   M 7
   M 200 b.i./450 b.i.
   Spec. Foie gras de canard chaud au verjus, Marmite de poissons au fumet de homard, Pou
   au pot farcie.

XX ✿ **Le Dôme,** 108 bd Montparnasse (14th) ℰ 43 35 25 81, Fax 42 79 01 19, Seafood – 🍽 𝔸
   ⓪ 𝖦𝖡   LM 12
   closed Monday – **M** a la carte 270/400
   Spec. Saint-Jacques crues aux truffes, Queues de langoustines aux girolles, Curry de filets de
   sole.

XX **La Coupole,** 102 bd Montparnasse (14th) ℰ 43 20 14 20, Fax 43 35 46 14, « 1920 Parisian
   brasserie » – 𝔸𝔼 ⓪ 𝖦𝖡 – **M** a la carte 170/310 ⅃   L 12

XX ✿ **Petite Bretonnière** (Lamaison), 2 r. Cadix (15th) ℰ 48 28 34 39 – 𝔸𝔼 𝖦𝖡   N 7
   closed August, Saturday lunch and Sunday – **M** 220 and a la carte 280/440
   Spec. Terrine de tête de veau a la tomate confite, Croustillant de pieds de veau farcis (October-
   January), Magret de canard farci (October-March).

XX **Yves Quintard,** 99 r. Blomet (15th) ℰ 42 50 22 27 – 𝖦𝖡   M 8
   closed August, Monday lunch and Sunday – **M** 145 and a la carte 225/325.

XX **Didier Délu,** 85 r. Leblanc (15th) ℰ 45 54 20 49 – 𝔸𝔼 ⓪ 𝖦𝖡   M 5
   closed 1 to 16 August, Christmas-New Year, Saturday and Sunday – **M** 170 (lunch) and a la
   carte 250/360.

XX **La Roseraie,** 15 r. Ferdinand Fabre (15th) ℰ 48 28 60 24 – 𝔸𝔼 𝖦𝖡   M 8
   closed August, Saturday lunch and Sunday – **M** 160 and a la carte 170/250.

XX **L'Entre Siècle,** 29 av. Lowendal (15th) ℰ 47 83 51 22 – 𝔸𝔼 𝖦𝖡   K 9
   closed August, Saturday lunch, Sunday and Bank Holidays – **M** 160 (lunch) and a la carte
   240/330.

XX **Senteurs de Provence,** 295 r. Lecourbe (15th) ℰ 45 57 11 98, Seafood – 𝔸𝔼 ⓪
   𝖦𝖡   M 6
   closed 1 to 11 May, 3 to 24 August, Sunday and Monday – **M** 225 and a la carte 200/340.

XX **Napoléon et Chaix,** 46 r. Balard (15th) ℰ 45 54 09 00 – 🍽 𝖦𝖡   M 5
   closed 1 to 30 August, Saturday lunch and Sunday – **M** a la carte 210/325.

XX **Monsieur Lapin,** 11 r. R. Losserand (14th) ℰ 43 20 21 39 – 𝔸𝔼 𝖦𝖡   N 11
   closed August, Saturday lunch and Monday – **M** 200 (lunch) and a la carte 265/410.

XX **Le Croquant,** 28 r. J. Maridor (15th) ℰ 45 58 50 83 – 𝖦𝖡. ✻   M 6
   closed 1 to 11 May, 1 to 30 August, Sunday and Monday – **M** a la carte 290/440.

XX **Le Copreaux,** 15 r. Copreaux (15th) ℰ 43 06 83 35 – 𝖦𝖡   M 9
   closed Saturday except dinner September-July and Sunday – **M** 145/255.

XX **L'Étape,** 89 r. Convention (15th) ℰ 45 54 73 49 – 𝖦𝖡   M 6
   closed Christmas Holidays, Saturday (except dinner September-June) and Sunday – **M** 150 and
   a la carte 180/325.

XX **La Chaumière,** 54 av. F.-Faure (15th) ℰ 45 54 13 91 – 𝔸𝔼 𝖦𝖡   M 7
   closed August, Monday dinner and Tuesday – **M** a la carte 200/305.

XX **La Giberne,** 42bis av. Suffren (15th) ℰ 47 34 82 18 – 𝔸𝔼 ⓪ 𝖦𝖡   J 8
   closed 25 July-23 August, Saturday lunch and Sunday – **M** 115 b.i./350 ⅃.

XX **Le Clos Morillons,** 50 r. Morillons (15th) ℰ 48 28 04 37 – 𝖦𝖡   N 8
   closed 1 to 21 August, Saturday lunch and Sunday – **M** 220 (lunch)/285.

XX **Filoche,** 34 r. Laos (15th) ℰ 45 66 44 60 – 𝖦𝖡. ✻   K 8
   closed 15 July-20 August, 23 December-4 January, Saturday and Sunday – **M** a la carte
   190/285.

XX **Les Vendanges,** 40 r. Friant (14th) ℰ 45 39 59 98 – 𝖦𝖡   R 11
   closed August, Saturday lunch, Sunday and Bank Holidays – **M** 155 and a la carte 205/310.

XX **Pierre Vedel,** 19 r. Duranton (15th) ℰ 45 58 43 17, Fax 45 58 42 65 – 𝖦𝖡. ✻   M 6
   closed Saturday and Sunday – **M** a la carte 210/315.

XX **Mina Mahal,** 25 r. Cambronne (15th) ℰ 47 34 19 88, Indian rest. – 🍽. 𝔸𝔼 ⓪ 𝖦𝖡.
   ✻   L 8
   M 160/350.

XX ✿ **La Cagouille** (Allemandou), 10 pl. Constantin Brancusi (14th) ℰ 43 22 09 01,
   Fax 45 38 57 29, 🍴, Seafood – 𝖦𝖡   M 11
   closed 5 to 11 May, 9 to 31 August, 27 December-4 January, Sunday and Monday – **M** a
   la carte 295/440
   Spec. Chaudrée charentaise (November-March), Céteaux à la poêle (April-October), Moules de
   bouchot "brûle-doigts" (June-October).

XX **de la Tour,** 6 r. Desaix (15th) ℰ 43 06 04 24 – 𝖦𝖡   J 8
   closed August, Saturday lunch and Sunday – **M** 168 and a la carte 185/300.

X **Bistrot du Dôme,** 1 r. Delambre (1st) ℰ 43 35 32 00, Seafood – 𝔸𝔼 𝖦𝖡   M 12
   M a la carte 150/200.

X **Oh ! Duo,** 54 av. E. Zola (15th) ℰ 45 77 28 82 – 𝖦𝖡   L 6
   closed August, Saturday and Sunday – **M** 127/135 ⅃.

X **La Bonne Table,** 42 r. Friant (14th) ℰ 45 39 74 91 – 𝖦𝖡   R 11
   closed 4 July-4 August, 24 December-5 January, Saturday and Sunday – **M** a la carte 180/295.

✕ **La Datcha Lydie,** 7 r. Dupleix (15th) ℘ 45 66 67 77, Russian rest. - GB K 8
closed 12 July-31 August and Wednesday - **M** 125 b.i. and a la carte 120/200.

✕ **Le Gastroquet,** 10 r. Desnouettes (15th) ℘ 48 28 60 91 - GB N 7
closed 11 July-3 August, Saturday and Sunday - **M** 140 and a la carte 160/245.

✕ **Chez Pierre,** 117 r. Vaugirard (15th) ℘ 47 34 96 12 - ▤. AE GB JCB L 11
closed 25 July-25 August, Saturday lunch, Monday lunch and Sunday - **M** 120 (lunch)/ 195.

✕ **L'Armoise,** 67 r. Entrepreneurs (15th) ℘ 45 79 03 31 - GB L 7
closed 5 to 26 August, February Holidays, Saturday lunch and Sunday dinner - **M** 125/163 b.i.

✕ **La Gitane,** 53bis av. La Motte-Picquet (15th) ℘ 47 34 62 92, ☂ - GB K 8
closed Saturday and Sunday - **M** a la carte 130/190.

✕ **Chez Yvette,** 46bis bd Montparnasse (15th) ℘ 42 22 45 54 - GB L 11
closed 18 to 26 April, August, Saturday and Sunday - **M** a la carte 155/250.

✕ **L'Amuse Bouche,** 186 r. Château (14th) ℘ 43 35 31 60 - GB N 11
closed 14 to 21 August, Saturday lunch and Sunday - **M** (booking essential) 145 (lunch) and a la carte 210/335.

✕ **St-Vincent,** 26 r. Croix-Nivert (15th) ℘ 47 34 14 94 - ▤. GB. ⋙ L 8
closed Sunday - **M** a la carte 160/230 ♁.

✕ **Fellini,** 58 r. Croix-Nivert (15th) ℘ 45 77 40 77, Italian rest. - ▤. GB. ⋙ L 8
closed August, Saturday lunch and Sunday - **M** a la carte 180/300.

Passy, Auteuil, Bois de Boulogne, Chaillot, Porte Maillot.

16th arrondissement.
16th: ✉ 75016

Park Avenue et Central Park [M] (due to re-open in May), 55 av. Poincaré ✉ 75116 ℘ 45 53 44 60, Telex 643862, Fax 47 27 53 04, ☂ - |‡| kitchenette ⋇ rm ▤ TV ☎ - 🏃 400. AE ◑ GB JCB. ⋙ rest G 6
M *(closed Saturday, Sunday and Bank Holidays)* 190 and a la carte 280/460 - ☕ 95 - **99 rm** 1600/2200, 13 suites 2200/2800.

Raphaël, 17 av. Kléber ✉ 75116 ℘ 44 28 00 28, Telex 645356, Fax 45 01 21 50, « Tasteful old decor » - |‡| TV ☎ - 🏃 50. AE ◑ GB JCB F 7
M 220 and a la carte 320/400 - ☕ 95 - **87 rm** 1600/2600, 23 suites.

Baltimore [M], 88bis av. Kléber ✉ 75116 ℘ 44 34 54 54, Telex 611591, Fax 45 34 54 44 - |‡| ▤ TV ☎ - 🏃 30 - 100. AE ◑ GB JCB. ⋙ G 7
L'Estournel *(closed August, Saturday, Sunday and Bank Holidays)* **M** 250 and a la carte 310/440 - ☕ 90 - **104 rm** 1600/2200.

Villa Maillot [M] without rest, 143 av. Malakoff ✉ 75116 ℘ 45 01 25 22, Telex 649808, Fax 45 00 60 61 - |‡| ▤ TV ☎ ♿. AE ◑ GB JCB F 6
☕ 100 - **39 rm** 900/1600, 3 suites 2400.

Garden Elysée [M] ⛰, 12 r. St-Didier ✉ 75116 ℘ 47 55 01 11, Telex 648157, Fax 47 27 79 24, ☂ - |‡| ▤ TV ☎ ♿. AE ◑ GB JCB. ⋙ G 7
M *(closed August, Saturday and Sunday)* 160/250 - ☕ 80 - **48 rm** 1350/1550.

Résidence Bassano [M] without rest, 15 r. Bassano ✉ 75116 ℘ 47 23 78 23, Telex 649872, Fax 47 20 41 22 - |‡| kitchenette ▤ TV ☎. AE ◑ GB G 8
☕ 65 - **28 rm** 750/1150, 3 suites 1950.

Majestic without rest, 29 r. Dumont d'Urville ✉ 75116 ℘ 45 00 83 70, Telex 640034, Fax 45 00 29 48 - |‡| ▤ TV ☎. AE ◑ GB JCB F 7
☕ 55 - **27 rm** 900/1250, 3 suites 1700.

Pergolèse [M] without rest, 3 r. Pergolèse ✉ 75116 ℘ 40 67 96 77, Telex 651618, Fax 45 00 12 11 - |‡| ▤ TV ☎. AE ◑ GB E 6
☕ 70 - **40 rm** 1200/1500.

Rond-Point de Longchamp [M], 86 r. Longchamp ✉ 75116 ℘ 45 05 13 63, Telex 640883, Fax 47 55 12 80 - |‡| ⋇ rest ▤ TV ☎ - 🏃 40. AE ◑ GB JCB G 6
M (snack) a la carte approx. 160 - ☕ 45 - **56 rm** 760/850.

🏨 **Alexander** without rest, 102 av. V. Hugo ⊠ 75116 ℰ 45 53 64 65, Telex 610373, Fax 45 53 12 51 – 🛗 📺 🆔 🅐🅔 🅞 🅖🅑 🅙🅒🅑. ⌖
⌖ 60 – **59 rm** 790/1140, 3 suites 1870. G 6

🏨 **Union H. Étoile** without rest, 44 r. Hamelin ⊠ 75116 ℰ 45 53 14 95, Telex 611394, Fax 47 55 94 79 – 🛗 kitchenette 📺 🆔 🅐🅔 🅞
⌖ 40 – **29 rm** 680/790, 13 suites 1050/1200. G 7

🏨 **Elysées Bassano** without rest, 24 r. Bassano ⊠ 75116 ℰ 47 20 49 03, Telex 611559, Fax 47 23 06 72 – 🛗 📺 🆔 🅐🅔 🅞 🅖🅑 🅙🅒🅑
⌖ 65 – **40 rm** 600/760. G 8

🏨 **Victor Hugo** without rest, 19 r. Copernic ⊠ 75116 ℰ 45 53 76 01, Telex 630939, Fax 45 53 69 93 – 🛗 📺 🆔 🅐🅔 🅞 🅖🅑. ⌖
⌖ 40 – **75 rm** 610/730. G 7

🏨 **Sévigné** without rest, 6 r. Belloy ⊠ 75116 ℰ 47 20 88 90, Telex 645219, Fax 40 70 98 73 – 🛗 📺 🆔 🅐🅔 🅞 🅖🅑 🅙🅒🅑
⌖ 30 – **30 rm** 600/720. G 7

🏨 **Frémiet** without rest, 6 av. Frémiet ⊠ 75016 ℰ 45 24 52 06, Telex 630329, Fax 42 88 77 46 – 🛗 🍽 📺 🆔 🅐🅔 🅞 🅖🅑 🅙🅒🅑
⌖ 40 – **34 rm** 625/850. J 6

🏨 **Floride Etoile** Ⓜ without rest, 14 r. St-Didier ⊠ 75116 ℰ 47 27 23 36, Telex 643715, Fax 47 27 82 87 – 🛗 ⧖ 📺 🆔 – ⚒ 40. 🅐🅔 🅞 🅖🅑 🅙🅒🅑. ⌖
⌖ 45 – **60 rm** 780/800. G 7

🏨 **Massenet** without rest, 5bis r. Massenet ⊠ 75116 ℰ 45 24 43 03, Telex 640196, Fax 45 24 41 39 – 🛗 📺 🆔 🅐🅔 🅞 🅖🅑 🅙🅒🅑
⌖ 40 – **41 rm** 460/700. J 6

🏨 **Résidence Foch** without rest, 10 r. Marbeau ⊠ 75116 ℰ 45 00 46 50, Telex 645886, Fax 45 01 98 68 – 🛗 📺 🆔 🅐🅔 🅞 🅖🅑
⌖ 40 – **21 rm** 610/690, 4 suites 890. F 6

🏨 **Kléber** without rest, 7 r. Belloy ⊠ 75116 ℰ 47 23 80 22, Telex 612830, Fax 49 52 07 20 – 🛗 ⧖ 📺 🆔 🅐🅔 🅞 🅖🅑 🅙🅒🅑
⌖ 45 – **23 rm** 670/950. G 7

🏨 **Murat** Ⓜ without rest, 119bis bd Murat ⊠ 75016 ℰ 46 51 12 32, Telex 648963, Fax 46 51 70 01 – 🛗 📺 🆔 🅐🅔 🅞 🅖🅑. ⌖
⌖ 45 – **28 rm** 500/650. M 3

🏨 **Résidence Chambellan Morgane** Ⓜ without rest, 6 r. Keppler ⊠ 75116 ℰ 47 20 35 72, Telex 613682, Fax 47 20 95 69 – 🛗 📺 🆔 🅐🅔 🅞 🅖🅑. ⌖
closed 20 to 27 December – ⌖ 40 – **20 rm** 600/800. GF 8

🏨 **Résidence Impériale** without rest, 155 av. Malakoff ⊠ 75116 ℰ 45 00 23 45, Telex 651158, Fax 45 01 88 82 – 🛗 ▤ 📺 🆔 🅐🅔 🅞 🅖🅑 🅙🅒🅑
⌖ 35 – **37 rm** 790/870. E 6

🏨 **Résidence Kléber** Ⓜ without rest, 97 r. Lauriston ⊠ 75016 ℰ 45 53 83 30, Telex 642707, Fax 47 55 92 52 – 🛗 📺 🆔 🅐🅔 🅞 🅖🅑 🅙🅒🅑
⌖ 40 – **51 rm** 750. G 7

🏨 **Étoile Maillot** without rest, 10 r. Bois de Boulogne (angle r. Duret) ⊠ 75116 ℰ 45 00 42 60, Telex 613936, Fax 45 00 55 89 – 🛗 📺 🆔 🅐🅔 🅖🅑
27 rm ⌖ 530/690. F 6

🏨 **Passy Eiffel** without rest, 10 r. Passy ⊠ 75016 ℰ 45 25 55 66, Fax 42 88 89 88 – 🛗 📺 🆔 🅐🅔 🅞 🅖🅑 🅙🅒🅑
⌖ 35 – **50 rm** 550/600. J 6

🏨 **Résidence Marceau** without rest, 37 av. Marceau ⊠ 75116 ℰ 47 20 43 37, Telex 648509, Fax 47 20 14 76 – 🛗 📺 🆔 🅐🅔 🅞 🅖🅑. ⌖
closed 5 to 25 August – ⌖ 32 – **30 rm** 500/580. G 8

🏨 **Ambassade** without rest, 79 r. Lauriston ⊠ 75116 ℰ 45 53 41 15, Telex 613643, Fax 45 53 30 80 – 🛗 📺 🆔 🅐🅔 🅞 🅖🅑. ⌖
⌖ 40 – **38 rm** 440/560. G 7

🏨 **Beauséjour Ranelagh** without rest, 99 r. Ranelagh ⊠ 75016 ℰ 42 88 14 39, Telex 614072, Fax 40 50 81 21 – 🛗 📺 🆔 🅐🅔
⌖ 30 – **30 rm** 370/600. J 4

🏨 **Longchamp** without rest, 68 r. Longchamp ⊠ 75116 ℰ 47 27 13 48, Telex 610342, Fax 47 55 68 26 – 🛗 📺 🆔 🅐🅔 🅞 🅖🅑
⌖ 40 – **23 rm** 580/750. G 6

🏨 **Hameau de Passy** Ⓜ ⌖ without rest, 48 r. Passy ⊠ 75016 ℰ 42 88 47 55, Telex 651469, Fax 42 30 83 72 – 🛗 📺 🆔 🅐🅔 🅖🅑
32 rm ⌖ 480/550. J 5-6

🏨 **Queen's H.** without rest, 4 r. Bastien Lepage ⊠ 75016 ℰ 42 88 89 85, Fax 40 50 67 52 – 🛗 ⧖ 📺 🆔 🅐🅔 🅞 🅖🅑. ⌖
⌖ 35 – **23 rm** 275/490. K 4

🏨 **Keppler** without rest, 12 r. Keppler ⊠ 75116 ℰ 47 20 65 05, Telex 640544, Fax 47 23 02 29 – 🛗 📺 🆔 🅐🅔 🅖🅑. ⌖
⌖ 28 – **49 rm** 380/400. F 8

XXXX ✿✿ **Faugeron**, 52 r. Longchamp ⊠ 75116 ℰ 47 04 24 53, Fax 47 55 62 90 – ▤. GB. ✺
closed August, 23 December-2 January, Saturday and Sunday – **M** 310 (lunch) and a la carte
415/585   G 7
Spec. Parmentier de truffes aux fines épices (January-March), Croustillant de ris de veau (May-July), Millefeuille "Amadeus".

XXXX ✿✿✿ **Jamin** (Robuchon), 32 r. Longchamp ⊠ 75116 ℰ 47 27 12 27 – ▤. GB   G 7
closed July, Saturday and Sunday – **M** (booking essential) a la carte 600/900
Spec. Tarte friande de truffes aux oignons et lard fumé (December-March), Pièce de saumon rôti (March-September), Lièvre à la royale (October-December).

XXXX ✿✿ **Vivarois** (Peyrot), 192 av. V.-Hugo ⊠ 75116 ℰ 45 04 04 31, Fax 45 03 09 84 – ▤. AE
① GB. ✺   G 5
closed August, Saturday and Sunday – **M** 345 (lunch) and a la carte 480/650
Spec. Fondant de légumes à la purée d'olives, Dartois de sole, Salade de pigeon au soja.

XXX ✿ **Toit de Passy** (Jacquot), 94 av. P. Doumer (6th floor) ⊠ 75016 ℰ 45 24 55 37,
Fax 45 20 94 57, ☎ – ▤ P. AE GB   HJ 5
closed 24 December-4 January, Saturday lunch, Sunday and Bank Holidays – **M** 265 (lunch)
and a la carte 375/540
Spec. Foie gras froid poché au vin de Graves, Pigeonneau cuit dans sa croûte de sel, Tarte au chocolat sans sucre (15 September-15 April).

XXX **Tsé-Yang**, 25 av. Pierre 1ᵉʳ de Serbie ⊠ 75016 ℰ 47 20 68 02, Chinese rest., « Tasteful
decor » – ▤, AE ① GB   G 8
M 225/275.

XXX **Sully d'Auteuil**, 78 r. Auteuil ⊠ 75016 ℰ 46 51 71 18, Fax 46 51 70 60 – ▤. AE GB
closed 10 to 31 August, Saturday lunch and Sunday – **M** a la carte 315/460.   K 3

XXX **Jean-Claude Ferrero**, 38 r. Vital ⊠ 75016 ℰ 45 04 42 42, Fax 45 04 67 71 – AE GB
closed 1 to 15 May, 10 August-5 September, Saturday (except dinner from 10 November-1 March) and Sunday – **M** 220 (lunch) and a la carte 315/500.   H 5

XXX **Le Petit Bedon**, 38 r. Pergolèse ⊠ 75116 ℰ 45 00 23 66, Fax 45 01 96 29 – ▤. AE ① GB
closed August, Saturday (except dinner from October-April) and Sunday – **M** a la carte 305/
505.   F 6

XXX ✿ **Port Alma** (Canal), 10 av. New-York ⊠ 75116 ℰ 47 23 75 11 – ▤. AE ① GB   H 8
closed August and Sunday – **M** 200 (lunch) and a la carte 260/425
Spec. Gaspacho de tourteau (June-September), Fricassée de sole poêlée au foie gras, Soufflé au chocolat.

XXX **Chez Ngo**, 70 r. Longchamp ⊠ 75116 ℰ 47 04 53 20, Chinese and Thai rest. – ▤. AE GB. ✺
M a la carte 160/225.   G 6

XXX **Le Pergolèse**, 40 r. Pergolèse ⊠ 75016 ℰ 45 00 21 40, Fax 45 00 81 31 – AE GB   F 6
closed 8 to 24 August, Saturday and Sunday – **M** a la carte 275/390.

XXX **Pavillon Noura**, 21 av. Marceau ⊠ 75116 ℰ 47 20 33 33, Fax 47 20 60 31, Lebanese rest.
– AE ① GB   G 8
M a la carte 165/225.

XX ✿ **Relais d'Auteuil** (Pignol), 31 bd Murat ⊠ 75016 ℰ 46 51 09 54, Fax 40 71 05 03 – ▤. AE GB
closed August, Saturday lunch and Sunday – **M** 180 (lunch)/390   L 3
Spec. Amandine de foie gras de canard, Gibier (season), Madeleines au miel de bruyère avec glace miel et noix.

XX **Al Mounia**, 16 r. Magdebourg ⊠ 75116 ℰ 47 27 57 28, Moroccan rest. – ▤. AE GB. ✺
closed 12 July-31 August and Sunday – **M** a la carte 200/280.   G 7

XX **Giulio Rebellato**, 136 r. Pompe ⊠ 75116 ℰ 47 27 50 26, Italian rest. – AE GB. ✺
closed August, Saturday lunch and Sunday – **M** a la carte 245/380.   G 6

XX ✿ **Fontaine d'Auteuil** (Grégoire), 35bis r. La Fontaine ℰ 42 88 04 47 – AE ① GB   K 5
closed 2 to 30 August, 9 to 16 February, Saturday lunch and Sunday – **M** 180 (lunch) and
a la carte 255/385
Spec. Pommes de terre lardées aux huîtres "Spéciales" (15 October-1 March), Pavé de cabillaud, Mitonnée de joue de boeuf au vin de Graves.

XX ✿ **Conti**, 72 r. Lauriston ⊠ 75116 ℰ 47 27 74 67 – ▤. AE ① GB   G 7
closed 10 to 31 August, Saturday and Sunday – **M** 265 b.i. (lunch) and a la carte 265/400
Spec. Carpaccio de Saint-Jacques (November-March), Tagliatelles aux truffes blanches (October-December), Rognon de veau rôti au romarin (June-September).

XX **Villa Vinci**, 23 r. P. Valéry ⊠ 75116 ℰ 45 01 68 18, Italian rest. – ▤. GB. ✺   F 7
closed August, 25 December-1 January, Saturday and Sunday – **M** 170 (lunch) and a la carte
225/405.

XX **Paul Chêne**, 123 r. Lauriston ⊠ 75116 ℰ 47 27 63 17 – ▤. AE ① GB   G 6
closed August, 24 December-4 January, Saturday and Sunday – **M** 250 and a la carte 245/
420.

XX ❀ **La Petite Tour** (Israël), 11 r. Tour ⌧ 75116 ℰ 45 20 09 31 – 🆎 ⓞ 🇬🇧   H 6
closed August and Sunday – **M** a la carte 225/410
Spec. Mousse de Saint-Jacques aux huîtres (October-March), Noisettes de chevreuil Grand Veneur (October-December), Tête de veau sauce ravigote.

XX **Sous l'Olivier**, 15 r. Goethe ⌧ 75116 ℰ 47 20 84 81, � – 🇬🇧   G 8
closed Saturday, Sunday and Bank Holidays – **M** a la carte 210/315.

XX **Palais du Trocadéro**, 7 av. Eylau ⌧ 75016 ℰ 47 27 05 02, Chinese rest. – 🔳. 🆎 🇬🇧
M a la carte 175/290.   H 6

XX **Le Grand Chinois**, 6 av. New York ⌧ 75116 ℰ 47 23 98 21, Chinese rest. – 🆎 ⓞ
closed 3 August-2 September and Monday – **M** a la carte 185/290.   H 8

XX **Marius**, 82 bd Murat ⌧ 75016 ℰ 46 51 67 80 – 🇬🇧   M 2
closed August, 21 December-2 January, Saturday lunch and Sunday – **M** a la carte 195/280.

X **Chez Géraud**, 31 r. Vital ⌧ 75016 ℰ 45 20 46 60, « Attractive Longwy porcelain mural »
– 🇬🇧   H 5
closed August, Saturday lunch from 16 November-25 April and Sunday – **M** a la carte 200/325.

X **Bistrot de l'Étoile**, 19 r. Lauriston ⌧ 75016 ℰ 40 67 11 16 – 🔳. 🇬🇧   F 7
closed Saturday lunch and Sunday – **M** a la carte 180/245.

X **Brasserie de la Poste**, 54 r. Longchamp ⌧ 75116 ℰ 47 55 01 31, Fax 39 50 74 32 – 🇬🇧
M a la carte 130/270 ♨.   G 7

X **Beaujolais d'Auteuil**, 99 bd Montmorency ⌧ 75016 ℰ 47 43 03 56 – 🆎 🇬🇧   K 3
closed Saturday lunch, Sunday and Bank Holidays – **M** 109 and a la carte 160/265.

in the Bois de Boulogne :

XXXX ❀ **Pré Catelan**, rte de Suresnes ⌧ 75016 ℰ 45 24 55 58, Telex 614983, Fax 45 24 43 25,
��, 🌳 – 🅿. 🆎 ⓞ 🇬🇧 🇯🇨🇧   H 2
closed 1 to 16 March, February Holidays, Sunday dinner and Monday – **M** 650/800
Spec. Soufflé d'oursins (October-March), Saint-Pierre aux truffes et céleri rave (October-March), Canard de Duclair aux épices.

XXXX ❀ **Grande Cascade**, allée de Longchamp (opposite the hippodrome) ⌧ 75016
ℰ 45 27 33 51, Fax 42 88 99 06, � – 🅿. 🆎 ⓞ 🇬🇧 – *closed 20 December-20 January and dinner 1 November-15 April* – **M** 270 (lunch) and a la carte 400/690
Spec. Délice des Landes, Homard étuvé aux algues bretonnes, Filet de bœuf à la fricassée de champignons.

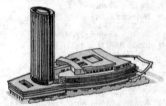

Clichy, Ternes, Wagram.

17th arrondissement.
17th: ⌧ 75017

🏨 **Concorde La Fayette** Ⓜ, 3 pl. Gén.-Koenig ℰ 40 68 50 68, Telex 650892, Fax 40 68 50 43,
« Bar with ≤ Paris on 34th floor » – 🛗 🔳 📺 ☎ – 🚪 40. 🆎 ⓞ 🇬🇧 🇯🇨🇧   E 6
M see Etoile d'Or below – **L'Arc-en-Ciel M** 175/280 ♨ – **Les Saisons** (coffee shop) **M** 115/180
♨ – ⊆ 90 – **935 rm** 1500/2100, 44 suites.

🏨 **Méridien** Ⓜ, 81 bd Gouvion St Cyr ℰ 40 68 34 34, Telex 651952, Fax 40 68 31 31 – 🛗 🔳
📺 ☎ – 🚪 50 - 800. 🆎 ⓞ 🇬🇧 🇯🇨🇧   E 6
M see **Clos de Longchamp** below - **Café l'Arlequin M** a la carte 175/305 – **Le Yamato** (Japanese rest.) *(closed August, 3 to 11 January, Sunday and Monday)* **M** a la carte 150/260 – **La Maison Beaujolaise** *(closed August, 21 to 28 December and Sunday)* **M** a la carte approx. 180 –
⊆ 95 – **989 rm** 1600/1950, 17 suites.

🏨 **Splendid Etoile** without rest, 1bis av. Carnot ℰ 43 80 14 56, Telex 651773, Fax 47 64 05 09
– 🛗 🔳 📺 ⓞ 🇬🇧. 🌳   F 7
⊆ 70 – **50 rm** 850/1100, 7 suites 1320.

🏨 **Regent's Garden** ⑤ without rest, 6 r. P.-Demours ℰ 45 74 07 30, Telex 640127,
Fax 40 55 01 42, « Garden » – 🛗 📺 ☎. 🆎 ⓞ 🇬🇧 🇯🇨🇧   E 7
⊆ 35 – **40 rm** 630/880.

🏨 **Pierre** Ⓜ without rest, 25 r. Th.-de-Banville ℰ 47 63 76 69, Telex 643003, Fax 43 80 63 96
– 🛗 🌳 📺 ☎ ♿ – 🚪 30. 🆎 ⓞ 🇬🇧 🇯🇨🇧   D 8
⊆ 60 – **50 rm** 630/900.

🏨 **Balmoral** without rest, 6 r. Gén.-Lanrezac ℰ 43 80 30 50, Telex 642435, Fax 43 80 51 56 –
🛗 📺 ☎. 🆎 ⓞ 🇬🇧   E 7
⊆ 38 – **57 rm** 500/700.

🏨 **Magellan** ⑤ without rest, 17 r. J.B.-Dumas ℰ 45 72 44 51, Telex 644728, Fax 40 68 90 36,
🌳 – 🛗 📺 ☎. 🆎 ⓞ 🇬🇧. 🌳   D 7
⊆ 30 – **75 rm** 490.

🏨🏨 **Mercure Paris Etoile** Ⓜ without rest, 27 av. Ternes ℰ 47 66 49 18, Telex 650679, Fax 47 63 77 91 – 🛗 🗐 📺 ☎. 🖭 ⑩ 🅖🅑   E 8
⌁ 55 – **56 rm** 660/790.

🏨🏨 **Résidence St-Ferdinand** Ⓜ without rest, 36 r. St-Ferdinand ℰ 45 72 66 66, Telex 649565, Fax 45 74 12 92 – 🛗 🗐 📺 ☎. 🖭 ⑩ 🅖🅑 🅙🅒🅑   E 6-7
⌁ 40 – **42 rm** 620/790.

🏨 **Banville** without rest, 166 bd Berthier ℰ 42 67 70 16, Telex 643025, Fax 44 40 42 77 – 🛗 📺 ☎. 🖭 🅖🅑   D 8
⌁ 35 – **39 rm** 535/600.

🏨 **Mercédès** Ⓜ without rest, 128 av. Wagram ℰ 42 27 77 82, Telex 644751, Fax 40 53 09 89 – 🛗 🗐 📺 ☎. 🖭 🅖🅑. ✳   D 9
⌁ 45 – **35 rm** 580/650.

🏨 **De Neuville**, 3 r. Verniquet ℰ 43 80 26 30, Telex 648822, Fax 43 80 38 55 – 🛗 📺 ☎. 🖭 ⑩ 🅖🅑 🅙🅒🅑 – Ⓜ *(closed Saturday and Sunday)* à la carte 160/220 ♟ – ⌁ 38 – **28 rm** 540/670.   C 8

🏨 **Harvey** Ⓜ without rest, 7bis r. Débarcadère ℰ 45 74 27 19, Telex 650855, Fax 40 68 03 56 – 🛗 📺 ☎. 🖭 ⑩ 🅖🅑   E 6
⌁ 35 – **32 rm** 480/680.

🏨 **Cheverny** Ⓜ without rest, 7 villa Berthier ℰ 43 80 46 42, Telex 648848, Fax 47 63 26 62 – 🛗 📺 ☎. 🖭 ⑩ 🅖🅑   D 7
⌁ 35 – **50 rm** 450/750.

🏨 **Étoile Pereire** ⌂ without rest, 146 bd Péreire ℰ 42 67 60 00, Fax 42 67 02 90 – 🛗 📺 ☎. 🖭 ⑩ 🅖🅑. ✳   D 7
⌁ 50 – **21 rm** 460/650, 5 suites 900.

🏨 **Royal Magda** without rest, 7 r. Troyon ℰ 47 64 10 19, Telex 641068, Fax 47 64 02 12 – 🛗 📺 ☎. 🖭 ⑩ 🅖🅑   E 8
⌁ 35 – **26 rm** 565/630, 11 suites 700/900.

🏨 **Belfast** without rest, 10 av. Carnot ℰ 43 80 12 10, Telex 642777, Fax 43 80 34 93 – 🛗 📺 ☎. 🖭 ⑩ 🅖🅑 🅙🅒🅑   E 7
⌁ 40 – **54 rm** 570/740.

🏨 **Abrial** Ⓜ without rest, 176 r. Cardinet ℰ 42 63 50 00, Fax 42 63 50 03 – 🛗 📺 ☎ ♿. 🖭 🅖🅑 🅙🅒🅑   C 11
⌁ 42 – **80 rm** 550/590.

🏨 **Star H. Étoile** without rest, 18 r. Arc de Triomphe ℰ 43 80 27 69, Telex 643569, Fax 40 54 94 84 – 🛗 📺 ☎. 🖭 ⑩ 🅖🅑   E 7
⌁ 38 – **62 rm** 440/580.

🏨 **Monceau** without rest, 7 r. Rennequin ℰ 47 63 07 52, Telex 649094, Fax 47 66 84 44 – 🛗 📺 ☎. 🖭 🅖🅑   E 8
⌁ 35 – **25 rm** 530/700.

🏨 **Étoile Park H.** without rest, 10 av. Mac Mahon ℰ 42 67 69 63, Telex 649266, Fax 43 80 18 99 – 🛗 📺 ☎. 🖭 ⑩ 🅖🅑   E 8
⌁ 47 – **28 rm** 440/700.

🏨 **Monceau Étoile** without rest, 64 r. Levis ℰ 42 27 33 10, Telex 643170, Fax 42 27 59 58 – 🛗 📺 ☎. 🅖🅑. ✳   D 10
⌁ 30 – **26 rm** 470/530.

🏨 **Acacias Étoile** without rest, 11 r. Acacias ℰ 43 80 60 22, Telex 643551, Fax 48 88 96 40 – 🛗 📺 ☎. 🖭 ⑩ 🅖🅑 🅙🅒🅑   E 7
⌁ 35 – **37 rm** 480/610.

🏨 **Prima H.**, 167 r. Rome ℰ 46 22 21 09, Telex 642186, Fax 46 22 21 09 – 🛗 🗐 rest 📺 ☎. 🖭 ⑩ 🅖🅑   C 10
Ⓜ *(closed 10 to 20 August and Sunday)* à la carte 140/270 ♟ – ⌁ 28 – **30 rm** 300/380.

🍴🍴🍴🍴 ✿✿ **Guy Savoy**, 18 r. Troyon ℰ 43 80 40 61, Fax 46 22 43 09 – 🗐. 🖭 🅖🅑   E 8
closed Saturday (except dinner October to Easter) and Sunday – **M** 650 and a la carte 490/680
Spec. Suprême de volaille de Bresse au foie gras, Crème légère de lentilles et langoustines, Bar en écailles grillées.

🍴🍴🍴🍴 ✿✿ **Michel Rostang**, 20 r. Rennequin ℰ 47 63 40 77, Fax 47 63 82 75 – 🗐. 🖭 🅖🅑   D 8
closed 1 to 10 May, 1 to 15 August, Saturday except dinner September-June and Sunday – **M** 260 (lunch)/660 and a la carte 480/700
Spec. Œufs de caille en coque d'oursins (October-April), Canette de Bresse au sang, Tarte au chocolat amer.

🍴🍴🍴🍴 ✿✿ **Le Clos Longchamp** - Hôtel Méridien, 81 bd Gouvion-St-Cyr (Pte Maillot) ℰ 40 68 00 70, Telex 651952, Fax 40 68 30 81 – 🗐. 🖭 ⑩ 🅖🅑 🅙🅒🅑   E 6
closed 8 to 16 August, Saturday and Sunday – **M** 250 (lunch) and a la carte 425/550
Spec. Echaudé de caille aux grenouilles (March-October), Marbré de foie de canard au Beaumes de Venise, Noisettes d'agneau au café (March-October).

XXXX ✿ **Étoile d'Or** - Hôtel Concorde La Fayette, 3 pl. Gén.-Koenig ✆ 40 68 51 28, Fax 40 68 50 43 – ▤. AE ① GB JCB E 6
closed 29 February-8 March, August, Saturday lunch and Sunday – **M** a la carte 310/540
Spec. Maraîchère de homard au miel de romarin, Turbot vapeur à l'infusion de coriandre, Fin ragoût du Gâtinais en ravioles.

XXXX ✿ **Manoir de Paris,** 6 r. P. Demours ✆ 45 72 25 25, Fax 45 74 80 98 – ▤. AE ① GB JCB
closed Saturday lunch and Sunday – **M** 290 (lunch) and a la carte 365/560 E 7
Spec. Ravioli de scampi de Méditerranée, Ris et onglet de veau de lait en cocotte, Douceur tiède au chocolat.

XXX ✿✿ **Apicius** (Vigato), 122 av. Villiers ✆ 43 80 19 66, Fax 44 40 09 57 – ▤. AE GB D 8
closed August, Saturday and Sunday – **M** a la carte 350/540
Spec. Grosses langoustines façon "Tempura", Pied de porc en crépinette rôti et jus de truffe au persil, Grand dessert au chocolat amer.

XXX ✿✿ **Amphyclès** (Groult), 78 av. Ternes ✆ 40 68 01 01, Fax 40 68 91 88 – ▤. ① GB
closed 7 to 28 July, Saturday lunch and Sunday – **M** 240/580 and a la carte E 7
Spec. Gelée de pied de veau, Canette de Challans à la coriandre, Joue de bœuf braisée.

XXX **Maître Corbeau,** 6 r. Armaillé ✆ 42 27 19 20 – ▤. AE ① GB JCB E 7
closed 3 to 20 August, 21 February-3 March, Saturday lunch and Sunday – **M** a la carte 305/440.

XXX ✿ **Timgad** (Laasri), 21 r. Brunel ✆ 45 74 23 70, Telex 649239, Fax 40 68 76 46, Maghreb rest., « Moorish decor » – ▤. AE ① GB. ✗ – **M** 230/510 E 7
Spec. Couscous, Pastilla.

XXX ✿ **Sormani** (Fayet), 4 r. Gén.-Lanrezac ✆ 43 80 13 91 – ▤. GB E 7
closed 25 April-5 May, 1 to 23 August, 23 December-3 January, Saturday, Sunday and Bank Holidays – **M** a la carte 290/470
Spec. Chou vert au mascarpone (October-March), Friture de cervelles, ris de veau, rognons et amourettes d'agneau (November-April), Risotto aux truffes blanches (season).

XXX ✿ **Faucher,** 123 av. Wagram ✆ 42 27 61 50, Fax 46 22 25 72, 帀 – AE GB D 8
closed 8 to 16 August, Saturday lunch and Sunday – **M** 180 (lunch) and a la carte 255/460
Spec. Millefeuille de boeuf cru, Filet de rouget au foie gras à la provençale, Ris de veau croustillant.

XXX **La Table de Pierre,** 116 bd Péreire ✆ 43 80 88 68, Fax 47 66 53 02 – AE GB D 8
closed Saturday lunch and Monday – **M** 220 and a la carte 250/370.

XXX **Chez Augusta,** 98 r. Tocqueville ✆ 47 63 39 97, Fax 42 27 21 71, Seafood – ▤. GB
closed 9 to 24 August, Saturday (except dinner from October-end April) and Sunday – **M** a la carte 370/480. C 9

XXX ✿ **Paul et France** (Romano), 27 av. Niel ✆ 47 63 04 24 – ▤. AE ① GB JCB. ✗ D 8
closed 14 July-15 August, Saturday and Sunday – **M** 290 (lunch) and a la carte 330/530
Spec. Ravioli de tourteaux, Rougets de roche au beurre de pistou, Rognon de veau au jus de truffe.

XXX **Il Ristorante,** 22 r. Fourcroy ✆ 47 63 34 00, Italian rest. – ▤. AE GB D 8
closed 10 to 24 August and Sunday – **M** 158 (lunch) and a la carte 185/305.

XX **Le Madigan,** 22 r. Terrasse ✆ 42 27 31 51, Fax 42 67 70 29, 帀 – ▤. AE ① GB JCB. ✗
closed Saturday lunch, Sunday and Bank Holidays – **M** 170/250 ♁. D 10

XX **L'Introuvable,** 15 r. Arc de Triomphe ✆ 47 54 00 28 – AE GB E 7
closed August, Saturday lunch and Sunday – **M** 145 (lunch) and a la carte 250/350.

XX ✿ **Le Petit Colombier** (Fournier), 42 r. Acacias ✆ 43 80 28 54, Fax 44 40 04 29 – ▤. AE GB
closed 18 July-17 August, Sunday lunch and Saturday – **M** 200 (lunch) and a la carte 310/440
Spec. Œufs rôtis à la broche aux truffes fraîches (November-February), Côte de veau en cocotte, Grouse d'Ecosse rôtie (August-November). E 7

XX **Andrée Baumann,** 64 av. Ternes ✆ 45 74 16 66, Fax 45 72 44 32 – ▤. AE ① GB JCB
M a la carte 190/335 ♁. E 7

XX **La Braisière,** 54 r. Cardinet ✆ 47 63 40 37, Fax 47 63 04 76 – AE GB D 9
closed spring Holidays, August, Saturday and Sunday – **M** a la carte 185/390.

XX **Gourmand Candide,** 6 pl. Mar. Juin ✆ 43 80 01 41, Fax 46 22 82 66, 帀 – AE ① GB
closed 1 to 10 May, August, Saturday (except dinner September-May) and Sunday – **M** a la carte 255/380. D 8

XX **Billy Gourmand,** 20 r. Tocqueville ✆ 42 27 03 71 – GB D 10
closed 3 to 23 August, Saturday except dinner from September-June, Sunday and Bank Holidays – **M** a la carte 220/360.

XX **La Soupière,** 154 av. Wagram ✆ 42 27 00 73 – ▤. AE GB D 9
closed 8 to 18 August, Saturday lunch and Sunday – **M** 160 and a la carte 210/360.

XX **Le Beudant,** 97 r. des Dames ✆ 43 87 11 20 – ⇹ ▤. AE GB D 11
closed 15 to 31 August, Saturday lunch and Sunday – **M** 140/285.

XX **La Coquille,** 6 r. Débarcadère ✆ 45 74 25 95 – ▤. AE GB E 7
closed August, 23 December-4 January, Sunday and Monday – **M** a la carte 270/390.

XX **Ballon des Ternes,** 103 av. Ternes ✆ 45 74 17 98, Fax 45 72 18 84 – AE GB E 6
closed August – **M** a la carte 180/305.

XX **Chez Laudrin,** 154 bd Péreire ✆ 43 80 87 40 – ▤. AE GB D 7
closed 1 to 9 May, Saturday lunch and Sunday – **M** a la carte 280/390.

XX **La Truite Vagabonde,** 17 r. Batignolles ✆ 43 87 77 80, 帀 – AE GB D 11
closed Sunday dinner – **M** 210/320.

XX **La Petite Auberge,** 38 r. Laugier ✆ 47 63 85 51 – ⊕   D 7-8
closed August, September, Sunday dinner and Monday – **M** (booking essential) 160 and a la carte 230/350.

XX **L'Écrevisse,** 212bis bd Péreire ✆ 45 72 17 60 – ▤. 🆎 ⓞ ⊕   E 6
closed Saturday lunch and Sunday – **M** a la carte 180/340.

XX **Chez Guyvonne,** 14 r. Thann ✆ 42 27 25 43 – ⊕   D 10
closed 13 July-3 August, 24 December-4 January, Saturday and Sunday – **M** 230 and a la carte 250/390.

XX **Chez Georges,** 273 bd Péreire ✆ 45 74 31 00, Fax 45 74 02 58 – ⊕. ⚝   E 6
closed August – **M** a la carte 150/300.

XX **Epicure 108,** 108 r. Cardinet ✆ 47 63 50 91 – ⊕   D 10
closed 15 July-15 August, Saturday lunch, Sunday and Bank Holidays – **M** 175/300.

XX **La Niçoise,** 4 r. P. Demours ✆ 45 74 42 41, Fax 45 74 80 98 – ▤. 🆎 ⓞ ⊕ ⓙⓒⓑ   E 7
closed Saturday lunch and Sunday – **M** a la carte 170/230.

XX **Le Cougar,** 10 r. Acacias ✆ 47 66 74 14, Fax 47 66 74 14 – ▤. 🆎 ⓞ ⊕   E 7
closed Saturday lunch and Sunday – **M** a la carte 255/390.

XX **Le Gouberville,** 1 pl. Ch. Fillon ✆ 46 27 33 37, 斎 – ⊕   C 10-11
closed August, February Holidays, Sunday and Monday – **M** a la carte 220/330.

XX **Chez Léon,** 32 r. Legendre ✆ 42 27 06 82 – ⓞ ⊕   D 10
closed 31 July-1 September, February Holidays, Saturday, Sunday and Bank Holidays – **M** 160 and a la carte 185/330.

XX **L'Écailler du Palais,** 101 av. Ternes ✆ 45 74 87 07, Seafood – ▤. 🆎 ⓞ ⊕   E 6
M 155 and a la carte 215/350.

XX **Le Troyon,** 4 r. Troyon ✆ 43 80 57 02 – ⊕   E 8
closed Saturday lunch and Sunday – **M** a la carte 165/245.

XX **La Toque,** 16 r. Tocqueville ✆ 42 27 97 75 – ▤. ⊕   D 10
closed 25 July-25 August, Saturday and Sunday – **M** 160 and a la carte 210/325.

X **Bistrot de l'Étoile,** 75 av. Niel ✆ 42 27 88 44 – ▤. ⊕   D 8
closed Sunday – **M** a la carte 200/275.

X **Bistrot d'à Côté Villiers,** 16 av. Villiers ✆ 47 63 25 61 – 🆎 ⊕   D 10
closed 1 to 10 May, 1 to 18 August, Saturday (except dinner September-June) and Sunday – **M** 115 and a la carte 170/245.

X **Bistrot d'à Côté Flaubert,** 10 r. G. Flaubert ✆ 42 67 05 81, Fax 47 63 82 75 – 🆎 ⊕   D 8
closed 1 to 10 May, 1 to 15 August, Saturday (except dinner September-June) and Sunday – **M** 115 and a la carte 170/245.

X **Les Béatilles,** 127 r. Cardinet ✆ 42 27 95 64 – ⊕   D 10
closed 30 July-24 August, Saturday and Sunday – **M** 130 (lunch) and a la carte 230/330.

X **Mère Michel,** 5 r. Rennequin ✆ 47 63 59 80 – 🆎 ⊕   E 8
closed August, Saturday and Sunday – **M** (booking essential) a la carte 215/365.

X **Le Champart,** 132 r. Cardinet ✆ 42 27 36 78 – 🆎 ⊕   C 10
closed 11 to 19 August, February Holidays, Saturday lunch and Sunday – **M** 130 and a la carte 140/230.

X **L'Oeuf à la Neige,** 16 r. Salneuve ✆ 47 63 45 43 – 🆎 ⓞ ⊕   D 10
closed 1 to 25 August, 24 December-2 January, Saturday lunch and Sunday – **M** 135 and a la carte 175/320.

X **Bistrot de l'Étoile,** 13 r. Troyon ✆ 42 67 25 95 – ▤. ⊕   E 8
closed Saturday and Sunday – **M** 200 b.i./250 🍸.

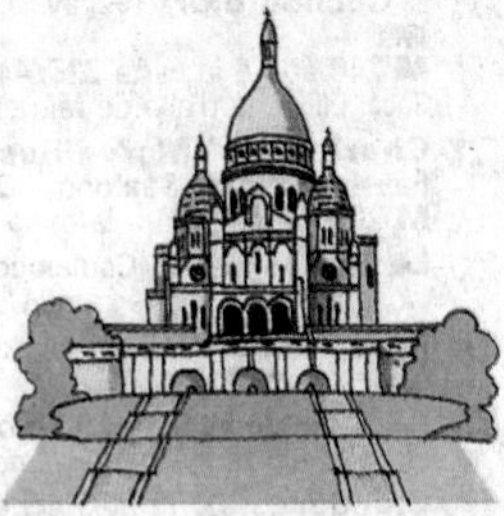

Montmartre, La Villette, Belleville.

18th, 19th and 20th arrondissements.
18th: ✉ 75018
19th: ✉ 75019
20th: ✉ 75020

Terrass'H. M, 12 r. J. de Maistre (18th) ☎ 46 06 72 85, Telex 280830, Fax 42 52 29 11 – rest TV ☎ – 30. AE ⓓ GB JCB C 13
M *(closed August)* a la carte approx. 200 – **88 rm** ☕ 800/1200, 13 suites 1330.

Mercure Paris Montmartre M without rest, 1 r. Caulaincourt (18th) ☎ 42 94 17 17, Telex 640605, Fax 42 93 66 14 – TV ☎ ♿ – 120. AE ⓓ GB JCB D 12
☕ 68 – **308 rm** 760/940.

Palma M without rest, 77 av. Gambetta (20th) ☎ 46 36 13 65, Telex 216056, Fax 46 36 03 27 – TV ☎. AE ⓓ GB. G 21
☕ 27 – **32 rm** 315/365.

Belgrand M without rest, 60 r. Belgrand (20th) ☎ 43 61 28 38, Telex 233620 – TV ☎. AE ⓓ GB G 22
☕ 30 – **27 rm** 360/400.

Regyn's Montmartre without rest, 18 pl. Abbesses (18th) ☎ 42 54 45 21, Fax 42 54 45 21 – TV ☎. ⓓ GB D 13
☕ 36 – **22 rm** 335/420.

Résidence Montmartre without rest, 10 r. Burq (18th) ☎ 46 06 51 91, Telex 282779, Fax 42 52 82 59 – TV ☎. AE ⓓ GB D 13
☕ 45 – **50 rm** 445/520.

Super H. without rest, 208 r. Pyrénées (20th) ☎ 46 36 97 48, Telex 215588, Fax 46 36 26 10 – TV ☎. GB – *closed August* – ☕ 27 – **28 rm** 255/430. G 21

Roma Sacré Cœur M without rest, 101 r. Caulaincourt (18th) ☎ 42 62 02 02, Telex 643492, Fax 42 54 34 92 – TV ☎. AE ⓓ GB JCB C 14
☕ 35 – **57 rm** 390/460.

Eden H. without rest, 90 r. Ordener (18th) ☎ 42 64 61 63, Telex 290504, Fax 42 64 11 43 – TV ☎. AE ⓓ GB. B 14
☕ 28 – **35 rm** 340/370.

Pyrénées Gambetta without rest, 12 av. Père Lachaise (20th) ☎ 47 97 76 57, Fax 47 97 17 61 – TV ☎. AE GB H 21
☕ 28 – **32 rm** 164/400.

H. Le Laumière without rest, 4 r. Petit (19th) ☎ 42 06 10 77, Fax 42 06 72 50 – TV ☎. GB D 19
☕ 27 – **54 rm** 220/340.

Arts without rest, 5 r. Tholozé (18th) ☎ 46 06 30 52, Fax 46 06 10 83 – TV ☎ ♿. AE GB. D 13
☕ 30 – **50 rm** 310/420.

Prima-Lepic without rest, 29 r. Lepic (18th) ☎ 46 06 44 64, Telex 281162, Fax 46 06 66 11 – TV ☎. GB. D 13
☕ 32 – **38 rm** 260/600.

Climat de France M, 2 av. Prof. A. Lemierre (20th) ☎ 40 31 08 80, Telex 232711, Fax 40 31 09 66 – TV ☎ ♿ – 150. AE ⓓ GB J 23
M 90/130 – ☕ 40 – **325 rm** 425.

Capucines Montmartre without rest, 5 r. A.-Bruant (18th) ☎ 42 52 89 80, Telex 281648, Fax 42 52 29 57 – TV ☎. AE ⓓ GB JCB D 13
☕ 30 – **29 rm** 290/380.

XXX ✿ **Beauvilliers,** 52 r. Lamarck (18th) ☎ 42 54 54 42, Fax 42 62 70 30, , « 1900 decor, terrace » – . AE GB. – *closed 30 August-15 September, Monday lunch and Sunday* – **M** 185 (lunch) and a la carte 390/520 C 14
Spec. Rognonnade de veau au jus de truffes, Sauté de homard aux "billes du jardin", Gâteau au chocolat.

XXX **Pavillon Puebla,** Parc Buttes-Chaumont, entrance : av. Bolivar, r. Botzaris (19th) ☎ 42 08 92 62, Fax 42 39 83 16, , « Pleasant situation in the park » – GB E 19
closed Sunday and Monday – **M** 230 and a la carte 300/430.

XXX ✿ **Cochon d'Or,** 192 av. J.-Jaurès (19th) ✆ 42 45 46 46, Fax 42 40 43 90 – 🖬. ＡＥ ⓞ
GB   C 20
M 240 and a la carte 225/445
Spec. Effiloché d'aile de raie en salade, Tête de veau ravigote, Grillades.

XXX **Charlot 1ᵉʳ ''Merveilles des Mers'',** 128bis bd Clichy (18th) ✆ 45 22 47 08,
Fax 44 70 07 50, Seafood – ＡＥ ⓞ GB   D 12
M 200 (lunch) and a la carte 250/410.

XX **Le Clodenis,** 57 r. Caulaincourt (18th) ✆ 46 06 20 26 – GB   C 13
closed Sunday dinner and Monday – **M** 200 (lunch) and a la carte 220/310.

XX **Deux Taureaux,** 206 av. J.-Jaurès (19th) ✆ 42 02 12 40 – ＡＥ GB   C 21
closed Saturday and Sunday – **M** 250/280.

XX **Au Clair de la Lune,** 9 r. Poulbot (18th) ✆ 42 58 97 03 – ＡＥ GB   D 14
closed February, Monday lunch and Sunday – **M** 170/300.

XX **Grandgousier,** 17 av. Rachel (18th) ✆ 43 87 66 12 – ＡＥ ⓞ GB   D 12
closed 10 to 23 August, Saturday lunch, Sunday and Bank Holidays – **M** 145 and a la carte
180/270.

XX **La Chaumière,** 46 av. Secrétan (19th) ✆ 42 06 54 69 – ＡＥ ⓞ GB   E 18
closed 8 to 25 August – **M** 143.

XX **Cottage Marcadet,** 151 bis r. Marcadet (18th) ✆ 42 57 71 22 – 🖬. GB. ❀   C 13
closed 30 April-19 May, 8 to 31 August and Sunday – **M** 195 b.i. and a la carte 200/300.

XX **Les Chants du Piano,** 10 r. Lambert (18th) ✆ 42 62 02 14, Fax 42 54 98 52 – ＡＥ ⓞ GB   C 14
closed 16 to 26 August, Sunday dinner and Monday lunch – **M** 149/319.

XX **Poulbot Gourmet,** 39 r. Lamarck (18th) ✆ 46 06 86 00   C 14
closed Sunday – **M** a la carte 195/270.

XX **Clap 49ᵉ,** 49 quai Seine (19th) ✆ 42 09 01 70 – GB   C 18
closed 1 to 15 September, 1 to 15 February, Saturday lunch and Sunday – **M** 59/170 b.i. ♨.

X **Marie-Louise,** 52 r. Championnet (18th) ✆ 46 06 86 55 – ⓞ GB   B 15
closed 31 July-3 September, Sunday, Monday and Bank Holidays – **M** 110 and a la carte
140/235.

X **Le Sancerre,** 13 av. Corentin Cariou (19th) ✆ 40 36 80 44 – ＡＥ ⓞ GB   B 19
closed Saturday and Sunday – **M** 110/169 ♨.

X **Aucune Idée,** 2 pl. St-Blaise (20th) ✆ 40 09 70 67 – GB   H 22
closed 3 to 23 August, Sunday dinner and Monday – **M** 110/215 ♨.

ENVIRONS

The outskirts of Paris up to 25Km

When calling the following places from the provinces dial 1 + eight-digit number.

K 11: These reference letters and numbers correspond to the squares on the Michelin plans of Parisian suburbs nos 18, 20, 22, 24.

La Défense 92 Hauts-de-Seine 101 ⑭. 18 – ⊠ 92400 Courbevoie.
See : Quarter★★ : perspective★ from the parvis.
Paris 8,5.

Sofitel Paris CNIT M ⑤, 2 pl. Défense ℰ 46 92 10 10, Telex 613782, Fax 46 92 10 50 –
🛗 ⇔ rm 📺 ☎ ఉ ⇔. 𝔸𝔼 ⓪ ☰ 𝒥𝒞ℬ. ⅘ rest   U-V 19
M see **Les Communautés** below – � 90 – **141 rm** 1300/1600, 6 suites 2500/3000.

Sofitel Paris La Défense M ⑤, 34 cours Michelet by ring road, exit La Défense 4
ℰ 47 76 44 43, Telex 612189, Fax 47 73 72 74, 🌁 – 🛗 ⇔ rm ☰ 📺 ☎ ఉ ⇔ – 🔏 50.
𝔸𝔼 ⓪ ☰. ⅘ rest   V 20
Les 2 Arcs **M** 325 (lunch) except Sunday and a la carte 260/420 – � 90 – **150 rm** 1200.

Novotel Paris La Défense M, 2 bd Neuilly ℰ 47 78 16 68, Telex 630288, Fax 47 78 84 71,
⇐ – 🛗 ☰ 📺 ☎ ఉ. – 🔏 25 - 150. 𝔸𝔼 ⓪ ☰ 𝒥𝒞ℬ   V 21
M a la carte approx. 150 ⅊ – ⊂ 55 – **278 rm** 720/750.

Ibis Paris La Défense M, 4 bd Neuilly ℰ 47 78 15 60, Telex 611555, Fax 47 78 94 16 –
🛗 ☰ 📺 ☎ ఉ. – 🔏 120. ☰ – **M** 77/98 ⅊ – ⊂ 35 – **284 rm** 455.   V 21

Fouquet's Europe, au CNIT, 2 pl. Défense, (5th floor) ℰ 46 92 28 04, Fax 46 92 28 16
– ☰. 𝔸𝔼 ⓪ ☰ 𝒥𝒞ℬ. ⅘   V 19
closed Saturday lunch and Sunday – **M** a la carte 270/430
Spec. Petits gris des Charentes en meurette, Blanc de Saint-Pierre au fumet de bigorneaux, Tarte
aux pommes paysanne et glace vanille.

Les Communautés - Hôtel Sofitel Paris CNIT, 2 pl. Défense ℰ 46 92 10 10, Fax 46 92 10 50
– ☰. 𝔸𝔼 ⓪ ☰ 𝒥𝒞ℬ   U19-V19
closed Saturday and Sunday – **M** a la carte 300/420
Spec. Foie gras chaud aux lentilles, Duo de turbot et barbue aux rattes, Nougat glacé à l'ancienne.

Enghien-les-Bains 95880 Val-d'Oise 101 ⑤. 18 – pop. 10 077 alt. 50 – Spa (closed
January) – Casino.
🏌 of Domont Montmorency ℰ 39 91 07 50, N : 8 km.
🅱 Office de Tourisme 2 bd Cotte ℰ 34 12 41 15.
Paris 19.

Grand Hôtel M ⑤, 85 r. Gén.-de-Gaulle ℰ 34 12 80 00, Telex 607842, Fax 34 12 73 81, 🌁,
🌊 – 🛗 ☰ rm 📺 ☎ �|– 🔏 25. 𝔸𝔼 ⓪ ☰   K 25
M 210/450 – ⊂ 70 – **48 rm** 980/1100, 3 suites 1400.

Duc d'Enghien, au Casino ℰ 34 12 90 00, ⇐ lake, 🌁 – ☰. 𝔸𝔼 ⓪ ☰   J 25
closed August, 2 to 10 January, Sunday dinner and Monday – **M** 325 (lunch) and a la carte 460/655
Spec. Langoustines à la vanille et menthe fraîche, Turbot rôti clouté au laurier, Ris de veau rôti
jus de persil (October-May).

Aub. Landaise, 32 bd d'Ormesson ⊠ 95880 ℰ 34 12 78 36 – ☰. 𝔸𝔼 ☰   J 26
closed August, Sunday dinner and Wednesday – **M** a la carte 150/265.

Maisons-Laffitte 78600 Yvelines 101 ⑬. 18 – pop. 22 173 alt. 40.
See : Château★.
Paris 21.

Le Tastevin (Blanchet), 9 av. Eglé ℰ 39 62 11 67, Fax 39 62 73 09, 🌁, 🌊 – 𝔸𝔼 ⓪ ☰
𝒥𝒞ℬ
closed 18 August-10 September, February Holidays, Monday dinner and Tuesday – **M** a la carte
400/525   M 11
Spec. Saint-Jacques rôties aux endives (October-March), Ris de veau rôti dans son jus, Millefeuille
au caramel et noix (September-March).

Vieille Fontaine (Clerc), 8 av. Gretry ℰ 39 62 01 78, 🌁, 🌊 – ☰. 𝔸𝔼 ⓪ ☰   L 12
closed 30 July-30 August, Sunday and Monday – **M** 230 and a la carte 400/570
Spec. Terrine de pieds de mouton "Poulette", Langoustines à la vanille et au gingembre, Ris de
veau, ail et échalotes confites à la cannelle.

Le Laffitte, 5 av. St-Germain ℰ 39 62 01 53 – 𝔸𝔼 ☰   M 11
closed August, Sunday dinner, Tuesday dinner and Wednesday – **M** a la carte 210/315.

6   165

Marne-la-Vallée 77206 S.-et-M. 🔟🔟🔟 ⑲

Paris 28.

at Collégien - pop. 2 331 - ✉ 77080 :

🏨 **Novotel** M, at the A4 Lagny intersection ℘ 64 80 53 53, Telex 691990, Fax 64 80 48 37, ☞, ⌘, ☞ – 🛗 ⇔ rest 🍽 ☎ 🅟 – 🕍 130. 🆎 ⓪ ☒
M a la carte approx. 150 🍷 – ☲ 52 – **200 rm** 450/490.

at Euro Disney access by Highway A 4 and Euro Disney exit

🏨 **Disneyland** M, ℘ 60 45 65 00, Fax 60 45 65 33, ≤, ☞, « Victorian style architecture, at the entrance to the Euro Disneyland Theme Park », 🐾, 🔲 – 🛗 ⇔ rm 🍽 📺 ☎ 🅟. 🆎 ☒. ⅍
California Grill M a la carte 300/375 – **Inventions M** a la carte 200/250 – ☲ 140 – **479 rm** 1950/2750, 21 suites.

🏨 **New-York** M, ℘ 60 45 73 00, Fax 60 45 73 33, ≤, ☞, « Resembling the architecture of Manhattan », 🐾, ⌘, 🔲, 🅟 – 🛗 ⇔ rm 🍽 rest 📺 ☎ 🅟 – 🕍 120. 🆎 ⓪ ☒. ⅍
Rainbow Room (dinner and dancing) **M** a la carte 300/450 – **Parkside Diner M** 235 – ☲ 110 – **554 rm** 1600/2400, 19 suites.

🏨 **Newport Bay Club** M, ℘ 60 45 55 00, Fax 60 45 55 33, ≤, ☞, « In the style of a New England seaside resort », 🐾, ⌘, 🔲 – 🛗 ⇔ rm 🍽 📺 ☎ 🅟. 🆎 ☒. ⅍
Cape Cod M 170/350 – **Yacht Club M** 110 b.i./175 b.i. – ☲ 60 – **1 093 rm** 1100/1350, 5 suites 2000.

🏨 **Séquoia Lodge** M, ℘ 60 45 51 00, Fax 60 45 51 33, ≤, ☞, « The atmosphere of an American mountain Lodge », 🐾, 🔲 – 🛗 ⇔ rm 🍽 📺 ☎ 🅟. 🆎 ☒. ⅍ rm
Hunter's Grill M 165 – **Beaver Creek Tavern M** a la carte 125/270 – ☲ 100 – **1 007 rm** 1100/1700, 4 suites 1900.

🏨 **Santa Fé** M, ℘ 60 45 78 00, Fax 60 45 78 33, ☞, « Evokes the fravour of New Mexico » – 🛗 ⇔ rm 🍽 rest 📺 ☎ 🅟 🆎 ☒. ⅍ rm
La Cantina M a la carte 110/160 – ☲ 60 – **1 000 rm** 750.

🏨 **Cheyenne** M, ℘ 60 45 62 00, Fax 60 45 62 33, ☞, « Resembles a frontier town of the American Wild West » – ⇔ rm 🍽 rest 📺 ☎ 🅟. 🆎 ☒. ⅍ rm
Chuck Wagon Café M a la carte 110/160 – ☲ 60 – **1 000 rm** 750.

Neuilly-sur-Seine 92200 Hauts-de-Seine 🔟🔟🔟 ⑮. 🔟🔟 – pop. 61 768 alt. 36.

See : Bois de Boulogne★★, Bagatelle★ (Park and Garden), National Museum of Popular Art and Traditions★★

Paris 7,5.

🏨 **L'Hôtel International de Paris** M, 58 bd V.-Hugo ℘ 47 58 11 00, Telex 610971, Fax 47 58 75 52, ☞ – 🛗 🍽 rm 📺 ☎ 🅟 – 🕍 120. 🆎 ⓪ ☒   V 23
M a la carte 150/250 – ☲ 75 – **318 rm** 780/1300, 3 suites.

🏨 **Paris Neuilly** M without rest, 1 av. Madrid ℘ 47 47 14 67, Telex 613170, Fax 47 47 97 42 – 🛗 🍽 📺 ☎. 🆎 ⓪ ☒ ⱼⱼⱼ   W 21
☲ 50 – **74 rm** 555/810, 6 suites 995.

🏨 **Jardin de Neuilly** without rest, 5 r. P. Déroulède ℘ 46 24 51 62, Telex 612004, Fax 46 37 14 60 – 🛗 📺 ☎. 🆎 ⓪ ☒. ⅍   W 23
☲ 50 – **30 rm** 700/1200.

🏨 **Parc Neuilly** without rest, 4 bd Parc ℘ 46 24 32 62, Telex 613689, Fax 46 40 77 31 – 🛗 📺 ☎. ☒   U 22
☲ 25 – **71 rm** 285/480.

XXX ❀ **Jacqueline Fénix,** 42 av. Ch. de Gaulle ℘ 46 24 42 61 – 🍽. 🆎 ☒   W 23
closed August, 24 December-2 January, Saturday and Sunday – **M** (booking essential) 330 and a la carte 310/430
Spec. Vinaigrette de cresson et langoustines aux nouilles "grillotées", Dos de turbotin rôti, Cocotte de pigeon en ravioli de champignons des bois.

XXX ❀ **Truffe Noire** (Jacquet), 2 pl. Parmentier ℘ 46 24 94 14, Fax 46 37 27 02 – ☒. ⅍
closed 8 to 31 August, Saturday and Sunday – **M** 225 and a la carte 265/335   W 23
Spec. Mousseline de brochet beurre blanc, Beuchelle à la tourangelle (September-November), Gratin de coquilles Saint-Jacques (October-March).

XXX **Focly,** 79 av. Ch. de Gaulle ℘ 46 24 43 36, Chinese rest. – 🍽. 🆎 ☒   V 21
closed 9 to 23 August – **M** 105 (lunch) and a la carte 150/250.

XX **Jarrasse,** 4 av. Madrid ℘ 46 24 07 56 – 🆎 ⓪ ☒   W 21
closed August and Sunday dinner – **M** a la carte 285/490.

XX **San Valero,** 209 ter av. Ch. de Gaulle ℘ 46 24 07 87, Spanish rest. – 🆎 ⓪ ☒. ⅍
closed 24 December-1 January, Saturday lunch, Sunday and Bank Holidays – **M** 140 (except Saturday)/190.   V 21

X **Bistrot d'à Côté Neuilly,** 4 r. Boutard ℘ 47 45 34 55 – 🆎 ☒   W 21
closed 1 to 10 May, 1 to 15 August, Saturday (except dinner September June) and Sunday – **M** 160 and a la carte 170/245.

X **La Catounière,** 4 r. Poissonniers ℘ 47 47 14 33 – 🍽. ☒   V 22
closed 1 to 13 May, 1 August-2 September, Saturday lunch and Sunday – **M** 173 b.i.

Orly (Paris Airports) **94396** Val-de-Marne 101 ㉖, 24 – pop. 21 646 alt. 89.

✈ ☎ 49 75 15 15.

Paris 15.

Hilton Orly M, near airport station ✉ 94544 ☎ 46 87 33 88, Telex 265971, Fax 49 78 06 75 – 🛗 ⇝ rm ▤ TV ☎ ♿ P – 🏢 300. AE ⓓ GB JCB AR 31
M 190/250 – ☕ 90 – **359 rm** 880/1500.

Altéa Paris Orly M, N 7, Z.I. Nord ✉ 94547 ☎ 46 87 23 37, Telex 265665, Fax 46 87 71 92 – 🛗 ▤ TV ☎ ♿ P – 🏢 30. AE ⓓ GB
M a la carte 180/290 – ☕ 55 – **193 rm** 620/790.

Orly Airport South :

Le Grillardin, 3rd floor ✉ 94542 ☎ 49 75 78 23, Fax 49 75 36 69, ← – ▤. AE ⓓ GB
M (lunch only) 180 and a la carte 190/300.

Orly Airport West :

Maxim's, 2nd floor ✉ 94546 ☎ 46 86 87 84, Telex 265247, Fax 46 87 05 39, ← – ▤. AE ⓓ GB
closed August, Saturday and Sunday – **M** (lunch only) a la carte 390/530.

Grill Maxim's, 2nd floor ✉ 94546 ☎ 46 87 16 16, Telex 265247, Fax 46 87 05 39, ← – ▤. AE ⓓ GB
M 250 b.i. and a la carte 235/330.

See also ***Rungis***

Roissy-en-France (Paris Airports) **95700** Val-d'Oise 101 ⑧ – pop. 2 054 alt. 85.

✈ ☎ 48 62 22 80 – Paris 26.

at Roissy-Town :

Holiday Inn M, allée Verger ☎ 34 29 30 00, Telex 605143, Fax 34 29 90 52, 🏋 – 🛗 ⇝ ▤ TV ☎ P – 🏢 25 - 200. AE ⓓ GB JCB
M 135/205 – ☕ 75 – **240 rm** 760/980.

Altéa, allée Verger ☎ 34 29 40 00, Telex 605205, Fax 34 29 00 18 – 🛗 ▤ TV ☎ ♿ P – 🏢 30 - 160. AE ⓓ GB JCB
Brasserie **M** 110/165 – ☕ 60 – **198 rm** 640/910, 4 suites 1070.

Ibis M, av. Raperie ☎ 34 29 34 34, Telex 699083, Fax 34 29 34 19 – 🛗 ▤ TV ☎ ♿ P – 🏢 25 - 80. AE ⓓ GB
M 91 – ☕ 34 – **200 rm** 415/470.

in the airport area :

Sofitel M, ☎ 48 62 23 23, Telex 230166, Fax 48 62 78 49, 🏊, 🎾 – 🛗 ⇝ ▤ TV ☎ ♿ P – 🏢 25 - 180. AE ⓓ GB
Les Valois panoramic rest. *(dinner only on Saturday, Sunday, Bank Holidays and August)* **M** a la carte 200/370 – **Le Jardin** Brasserie (ground floor) **M** a la carte 130/220 – ☕ 70 – **344 rm** 780/880, 8 suites 1300.

Novotel M, ☎ 48 62 00 53, Telex 232397, Fax 48 62 00 11 – 🛗 ⇝ rm ▤ TV ☎ ♿ P – 🏢 25 - 70. AE ⓓ GB JCB
M a la carte approx. 160 – ☕ 52 – **201 rm** 640/690.

in Terminal 1 :

Maxim's, ☎ 48 62 16 16, Telex 236356, Fax 48 62 45 96 – ▤. AE ⓓ GB
M (lunch only) 250 and a la carte 280/440.

Grill Maxim's, ☎ 48 62 16 16, Telex 236356, Fax 48 62 45 96 – ▤. AE ⓓ GB
M 220 b.i. and a la carte 160/310.

Rungis **94150** Val-de-Marne 101 ㉖, 24 – pop. 2 939 alt. 80.

Paris 14.

at Pondorly : Access : from Paris, Highway A 6 and take Orly Airport exit ; from outside of Paris, A 6 and Rungis exit :

Pullman Orly M, 20 av. Ch. Lindbergh ✉ 94656 ☎ 46 87 36 36, Telex 260738, Fax 46 87 08 48, 🏊 – 🛗 ▤ TV ☎ 🚗 P – 🏢 25 - 250. AE ⓓ GB AM 29
La Rungisserie M 135/185 b.i. – ☕ 75 – **196 rm** 600/780.

Holiday Inn M, 4 av. Ch. Lindbergh ✉ 94656 ☎ 46 87 26 66, Telex 265803, Fax 45 60 91 25, 🎾 – 🛗 ⇝ rm ▤ TV ☎ ♿ P – 🏢 50 - 200. AE ⓓ GB JCB AM 29
M 130/180 – ☕ 70 – **168 rm** 795/995.

Ibis M, 1 r. Mondétour ✉ 94656 ☎ 46 87 22 45, Telex 261173, Fax 46 87 84 72, 🏠 – 🛗 TV ☎ ♿ P – 🏢 80. GB AM 29
M 91 – ☕ 35 – **119 rm** 330.

St-Germain-en-Laye 78100 Yvelines 101 ⑫, 18 – pop. 39 926 alt. 78.

See : Terrace★★ BY – English Garden★ BY – Castel★ BZ : Museum of National Antiquities★★ – Priory Museum★ AZ.

9 18 (private) ✆ 34 51 75 90 by ④ : 3 km ; 9 9 9 of Fourqueux (private) ✆ 34 51 41 47 by r. de Mareil AZ.

Office Municipal de Tourisme 38 r. au Pain ✆ 34 51 05 12.

Paris 23 ③.

ST-GERMAIN EN-LAYE

Bonnenfant (R. A.) .... AZ 3
Marché-Neuf (Pl. du) . AZ 17
Pain (R. au) .... AZ 20
Paris (R. de) .... AZ
Poissy (R. de) .... AZ 22

Vieux-Marché (R. du) .. AZ 33

Alain (Pl. Jéhan) ...... AY 2
Coches (R. des) ...... AZ 4
Denis (R. M.) .... AZ 5
Detaille (Pl.) .... AY 6
Gaulle (Pl. Ch. de) ..... BZ 7
Giraud-Teulon (R.) ..... BZ 9
Gde-Fontaine (R.) ..... AZ 10
Gréban (R. R.) .... AZ 12

Lattre-de-T. (Av. Mar. de) . BZ 13
Loges (Av. des) .... AY 14
Lyautey (R. Mar.) ...... BZ 15
Malraux (Pl. A.) .... BZ 16
Mareil (Pl.) .... AZ 19
Pologne (R. de) .... AY 23
Pontoise (R. de) ...... AY 25
St-Louis (R.) .... BZ 26
Victoire (Pl. de la) ..... AY 30
Vieil-Abreuvoir (R. du) .. AZ 32

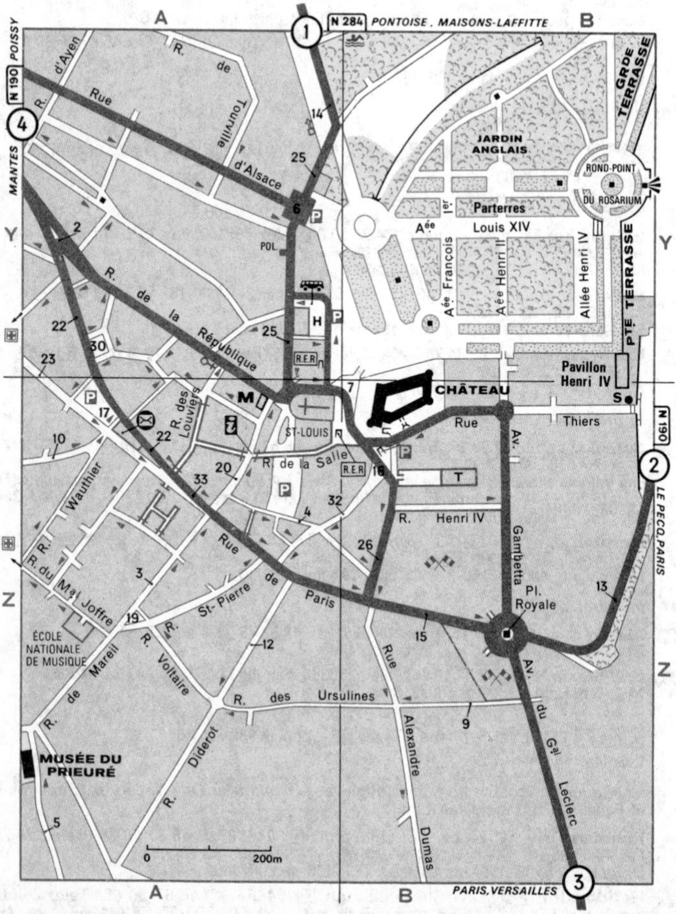

Pavillon Henri IV , 21 r. Thiers ✆ 34 51 62 62, Telex 695822, Fax 39 73 93 73, ≤ Paris and the River Seine, , – rest – 200. BZ s

M a la carte 190/290 – 50 – **42 rm** 500/1300.

to the NW by ① : 2,5 km on N 284 and rte des Mares – ⊠ 78100 St-Germain-en-Laye :

La Forestière Ⓜ 🔊, 1 av. Prés.-Kennedy ☎ 39 73 36 60, Telex 696055, Fax 39 73 73 88, 🎠 – 🛗 📺 ☎ 🅿 – 🔏 30. 🖸 🃏
M see Cazaudehore below – ⊡ 58 – **24 rm** 650/780, 6 suites 950/1200.

Cazaudehore, 1 av. Prés.-Kennedy ☎ 34 51 93 80, Telex 696055, Fax 39 73 73 88, 🌳, « Flowered garden in woods » – 🅿. 🖸 🃏
closed Monday except Bank Holidays – **M** a la carte 290/440.

When driving through towns
use the plans in the Michelin Red Guide.
Features indicated include :
throughroutes and by-passes,
traffic junctions and major squares,
new streets, car parks, pedestrian streets...
All this information is revised annually.

Versailles 🅿 78000 Yvelines 📖 ② ㉒ – pop. 87 789 alt. 132.

See : Castel★★★ Y – Gardens★★★ (fountain display★★★ (grandes eaux) and illuminated night performances★★★ (fêtes de nuit) in summer) – Ecuries Royales★ Y – The Trianons★★ – Lambinet Museum★ Y **M**.

🏌 🏌 🏌 Racing Club France (private) ☎ 39 50 59 41 by ③ : 2,5 km.
🛈 Office de Tourisme 7 r. Réservoirs ☎ 39 50 36 22.
Paris 20 ①.

Plan on next page

Trianon Palace Ⓜ 🔊, 1 bd Reine ☎ 30 84 38 00, Telex 698863, Fax 39 49 00 77, ≤, park, « Tasteful early 20C decor », 🛁, 🏊, 🛠 – 🛗 🗐 rm 📺 ☎ 🚗 🅿. 🖭 ⓪ 🖸 🃏 — X r
🛠 rest
M see **Les Trois Marches** below – ⊡ 95 – **69 rm** 850/2200, 25 suites.

Pullman Place d'Armes Ⓜ, 2 av. Paris ☎ 39 53 30 31, Telex 697042, Fax 39 53 87 20 – 🛗 🗐 rest 📺 ☎ 🕭 🚗 – 🔏 150. 🖭 ⓪ 🖸 🃏 — Y a
M 185/320 – ⊡ 65 – **146 rm** 690, 6 suites 1300.

Trianon Hôtel Ⓜ 🔊, 1 bd Reine ☎ 30 84 38 00, Telex 699210, Fax 39 51 57 79, 🛁, 🏊, 🛠 – 🛗 📺 ☎ 🕭 🚗 🅿 – 🔏 400. 🖭 ⓪ 🖸 🃏 🛠 rest — X r
M 195 – ⊡ 85 – **97 rm** 850/1050.

Novotel Ⓜ, 4 bd St-Antoine at Le Chesnay ⊠ 78150 ☎ 39 54 96 96, Telex 689624, Fax 39 54 94 40 – 🛗 🕭 rm 🗐 📺 ☎ 🕭 🚗 – 🔏 25 - 150. 🖭 ⓪ 🖸 🃏 — X z
M a la carte approx. 150 🍷 – ⊡ 49 – **103 rm** 510/540.

Mercure Ⓜ without rest, r. Marly-le-Roi at Le Chesnay, in front of the Commercial Centre Parly II ⊠ 78150 ☎ 39 55 11 41, Telex 695205, Fax 39 55 06 22 – 🛗 🗐 📺 ☎ 🅿. 🖭 ⓪ 🖸
⊡ 48 – **78 rm** 495/550.

Résidence du Berry Ⓜ without rest, 14 r. Anjou ☎ 39 49 07 07, Telex 689058, Fax 39 50 59 40 – 🛗 📺 ☎ 🕭. 🖭 🖸 — Z s
closed 20 December-5 January – ⊡ 35 – **38 rm** 360/430.

Arcade Ⓜ without rest, 4 av. Gén. de Gaulle ☎ 39 53 03 30, Telex 695652, Fax 39 50 06 31 – 🛗 📺 ☎ 🕭 🅿 – 🔏 25. 🖭 🖸 — Y u
⊡ 40 – **85 rm** 360/470.

Urbis Ⓜ without rest, av. Dutartre at Le Chesnay, Commercial Centre Parly II ⊠ 78150 ☎ 39 63 37 93, Telex 689188, Fax 39 55 18 66 – 🛗 🕭 📺 ☎ 🕭. 🖸
⊡ 32 – **72 rm** 345/370.

❀❀ ❀❀ **Les Trois Marches** (Vié), 1 bd Reine ☎ 39 50 13 21, Fax 30 21 01 25, ≤, 🌳 – 🗐. 🖭 ⓪ 🖸 🛠 — X r
closed Sunday and Monday – **M** 260 (lunch) (except Saturday)/595 and a la carte 380/600
Spec. Assiette de foie gras au vin de Maury et à la croque au sel, Turbot au jus de viande, Crème Chiboust caramélisée aux fruits.

❀ **La Grande Sirène,** 25 r. Mar. Foch ☎ 39 53 08 08, Fax 39 53 37 15 – 🗐. 🖭 ⓪ 🖸 — Y v
closed 1 to 9 May, 9 to 31 August, Sunday and Monday – **M** 148 b.i. (lunch)/240
Spec. Trilogie de canard, Saint-Pierre rôti au jus de veau, Millefeuille aux noix chocolatées.

Rescatore, 27 av. St-Cloud ☎ 39 50 23 60, Seafood – 🗐. 🖭 🖸 — Y s
closed Saturday lunch and Sunday – **M** 200/375.

Le Chesnoy, 24 r. Pottier au Chesnay ⊠ 78150 ☎ 39 54 01 01 – 🗐. 🖭 ⓪ 🖸
closed 6 to 27 August, Sunday dinner and Monday – **M** a la carte 200/290.

Potager du Roy, 1 r. Mar.-Joffre ☎ 39 50 35 34, Fax 30 21 69 30 – 🗐. 🖸 — Z r
closed Sunday and Monday – **M** 115/160.

VERSAILLES

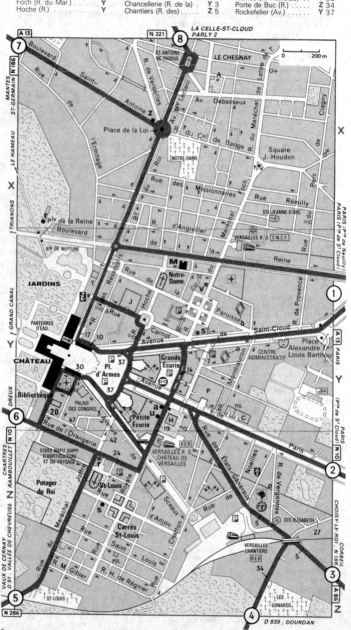

AND BEYOND...

Joigny 89300 Yonne 🔟 ④ – pop. 9 697 alt. 101.

🛈 Office de Tourisme quai H.-Ragobert ℘ 86 62 11 05.

Paris 147 – Auxerre 27 – Gien 75 – Montargis 62 – Sens 31 – Troyes 77.

🛖 ✿✿✿ **A la Côte St-Jacques** (Lorain) Ⓜ ⌁, 14 fg Paris ℘ 86 62 09 70, Telex 801458, Fax 86 91 49 70, ≼, « Tasteful decor », ⌧, ⌖ – ⧈ ☰ rm ⎘ ☎ ⟵ ⊘ – 🅐 30. 🆎 ⓞ ☞
closed 4 January-4 February – **M** (Sunday booking essential) 300 (lunch)/620 and a la carte 480/660 – ⌁ 90 – **25 rm** 690/1650, 4 suites 2500
Spec. Huîtres arcachonnaises en petite terrine océane, Bar légèrement fumé à la sauce au caviar, Filet de canard rôti et endives braisées. Wines Chablis, Irancy.

Pontoise ⬇ 95300 Val d'Oise 🔟🔟🔟 ⑤ – pop. 27 150 alt. 27.

🛈 Office de Tourisme 6 pl. Petit-Martroy ℘ (1) 30 38 24 45.

Paris 36 – Beauvais 50 – Dieppe 135 – Mantes-la-Jolie 39 – Rouen 91.

at Cormeilles-en-Vexin NW by D 915 – ⬚ 95830 :

XXX ✿✿✿ **Relais Ste-Jeanne** (Cagna), on D 915 ℘ (1) 34 66 61 56, Fax (1) 34 66 40 31, ⌖, « Garden » – ⊘. 🆎 ⓞ ☞ – *closed 1 to 25 August, 23 to 28 December, February Holidays, Sunday dinner, Tuesday dinner and Monday* – **M** 260 (lunch)/480 and a la carte
Spec. Salade de pigeon aux navets et griottes, Filets de sole au foie gras, Rêve au chocolat.

Rheims ⬇ 51100 Marne 🔟🔟 ⑥ ⑯ – pop. 180 620 alt. 83.

See : Cathedral★★★ : tapestries★★ – St-Remi Basilica★★ : interior★★★ – Palais du Tau★★ – Champagne cellars★ – Place Royale★ – Porte Mars★ – Hôtel de la Salle★ – Foujita Chapel★ – Library★ of Ancient College des Jésuites – St-Remi Museum★★ – Hôtel le Vergeur Museum★★ – St-Denis Museum★ – Historical centre of the French motor industry★.

Envir. : Fort de la Pompelle : German helmets★ 9 km to the SE by N 44.

🛫 Rheims-Champagne ℘ 26 03 60 14 at Gueux ; to the NW by N 31-E 46 : 9,5 km.

🚗 ℘ 26 88 50 50.

🛈 Office de Tourisme and Accueil de France (Information facilities and hotel reservations - not more than 5 days in advance) 2 r. Guillaume-de-Machault ℘ 26 47 25 69, Telex 840890 – A.C. 7 bd Lundy ℘ 26 47 34 76.

Paris 144 – Bruxelles 214 – Châlons-sur-Marne 48 – Lille 203 – Luxembourg 232.

🛖 ✿✿✿ **Boyer "Les Crayères"** Ⓜ ⌁, 64 bd Vasnier ℘ 26 82 80 80, Telex 830959, Fax 26 82 65 52, ≼, ⌖, « Elegant mansion in park », ⚒ – ⧈ ☰ ⎘ ☎ ⊘. 🆎 ⓞ ☞
closed 21 December-12 January – **M** *(closed Tuesday lunch and Monday)* (booking essential) a la carte 450/650 – ⌁ 85 – **16 rm** 990/1690, 3 suites 1790
Spec. Pied de porc farci au foie gras, Filet de Saint-Pierre grillé au concassé de tomate et flan de Bouchot, Grenadin de veau de lait au jus de truffe. Wines Champagne.

Saulieu 21210 Côte-d'Or 🔟🔟 ⑰ – pop. 2 917 alt. 514.

See : Capitals★ in the basilica of St-Andoche.

Paris 249 – Autun 41 – Avallon 38 – Beaune 64 – Clamecy 76 – Dijon 73.

🛖 ✿✿✿ **Côte d'Or** (Loiseau) Ⓜ ⌁, 2 r. Argentine ℘ 80 64 07 66, Telex 350778, Fax 80 64 08 92, « Tasteful Inn », ⌖ – ⧊ rest ⎘ ☎ ⟵ – 🅐 25. 🆎 ⓞ ☞
closed 2 to 13 March, 23 November-17 December, Tuesday lunch and Monday 1 November-31 March – **M** 390/690 and a la carte 500/850 – ⌁ 90 – **16 rm** 260/600, 4 suites, 3 duplex
Spec. Jambonnettes de grenouilles à la purée d'ail, Sandre à la fondue d'échalote sauce au vin rouge, Blanc de volaille au foie gras chaud et aux truffes. Wines Chablis, Savigny-les-Beaune.

Vézelay 89450 Yonne 🔟🔟 ⑮ – pop. 571 alt. 302 pilgrimage (22 July).

See : Ste-Madeleine Basilica★★★ : tower ❊★.

Envir. : Site★ of Pierre-Perthuis SE : 6 km.

🛈 Syndicat d'Initiative r. St-Pierre (April-October) ℘ 86 33 23 69.

Paris 223 – Auxerre 51 – Avallon 15 – Château-Chinon 60 – Clamecy 22.

at St-Père : SE : 3 km by D 957 – alt. 148 – ⬚ 89450.

See : Church of N.-Dame★

🛖 ✿✿✿ **L'Espérance** (Meneau) ⌁, ℘ 86 33 20 45, Telex 800005, Fax 86 33 26 15, ≼, « Country garden » – ☰ rest ⎘ ☎ ⊘. 🆎 ⓞ ☞
closed early January-early February – **M** *(closed Wednesday lunch and Tuesday)* (booking essential) 300 (lunch)/780 and a la carte 450/750 – ⌁ 100 – **33 rm** 350/1300, 8 suites
Spec. Tourte de pommes de terre au caviar, Homard pané au riz sauce safran, Cromesquis de foie gras. Wines Vézelay, Irancy.

171

BORDEAUX Ⓟ 33000 Gironde **171** ⑨ – pop. 210 336 alt. 5 Greater Bordeaux 624 286.

See : Grand Théâtre★★ DX – Cathedral★ and Pey Berland Belfry★ DY **E** – Place de la Bourse★ EX – St-Michel Basilica★ EY **F** – Place du Parlement★ EX **66** – Church of N.-Dame★ DX **D** – Fountain★ of the Monument to the Girondins DX **R** – Great Bell★ (Grosse cloche) DZ **D** – Fine Arts Museum★★ (Musée des Beaux Arts) CDY **M1** Decorative Arts★ DY **M2**

🖾 Golf Bordelais ℰ 56 28 56 04, to the NW by D109 : 4 km ; 🖾 🖾 de Bordeaux Lac ℰ 56 50 92 72, to the N by D 2 : 10 km ; 🖾 🖾 of Cameyrac ℰ 56 72 96 79, to the NE by N 89 : 18 km ; 🖾 🖾 🖾 Internat. of Bordeaux-Pessac ℰ 56 36 24 47 to the SW by N 150.

✈ of Bordeaux-Mérignac : ℰ 56 34 50 00 to the W : 11 km. 🚗 ℰ 56 92 50 50.

🛈 Office de Tourisme and Accueil de France, (Information, exchange facilities and hotel reservations - not more than 5 days in advance) 12 cours 30-Juillet ℰ 56 44 28 41, Telex 570362 at the Gare St-Jean ℰ 56 91 64 70 and the airport, Arrivals Hall ℰ 52 34 39 39 - A.C. du Sud-Ouest 8 pl. Quinconces ℰ 56 44 22 92 – Bordeaux wine Exhibition (Maison du vin de Bordeaux), 3 cours 30-Juillet (Information, wine-tasting - closed weekends from 16 Oct.-14 May) ℰ 56 00 22 66 DX **z**.

Paris 579 – Lyons 531 – Nantes 324 – Strasbourg 919 – Toulouse 245.

Plan on next page.

🏨 **Château Chartron** Ⓜ, 81 cours St-Louis ✉ 33300 ℰ 56 43 15 00, Telex 573938, Fax 56 69 15 21, ☞, ⚗ – 🛗 ⛌ ☰ rm 🔟 ☎ 🕭 ⟷ – 🛃 30 - 200. ☒ ⑩ ☞ **Novamagus** *(closed Saturday and Sunday)* Ⓜ 350 – **Le Cabernet** Ⓜ a la carte approx. 140 – ☳ 60 – **130 rm** 650/850, 15 suites 1100/1500.

🏨 **Burdigala** Ⓜ, 115 r. G. Bonnac ℰ 56 90 16 16, Telex 572981, Fax 56 93 15 06 – 🛗 ☰ 🔟 ☎ 🕭 🚗 – 🛃 100. ☒ ⑩ ☞ ☷ CX **r** Ⓜ 140/340 – ☳ 65 – **68 rm** 720/1300, 7 duplex 1100/1900.

🏨 **Pullman Mériadeck** Ⓜ, 5 r. R. Lateulade ℰ 56 56 43 43, Telex 540565, Fax 56 96 50 59 – 🛗 ☰ 🔟 ☎ 🕭 – 🛃 350. ☒ ⑩ ☞ ✂ rest CY **w** **Le Mériadeck** Ⓜ 140/210 b.i. – ☳ 65 – **192 rm** 520/750.

🏨 **Alliance** Ⓜ, 30 r. de Tauzia ✉ 33800 ℰ 56 92 21 21, Telex 573848, Fax 56 91 08 06, ☞ 🛗 ⛌ rm 🔟 ☎ 🕭 🚗 – 🛃 80. ☒ ⑩ ☞ FZ **v** Ⓜ *(closed Sunday)* 90/120 – ☳ 50 – **90 rm** 450/500.

🏨 **Novotel Bordeaux-Centre** Ⓜ, 45 cours Maréchal Juin ℰ 56 51 46 46, Telex 573749, Fax 56 98 25 56, ☞ – 🛗 ⛌ rm 🔟 ☎ 🕭 🚗 – 🛃 80. ☒ ⑩ ☞ ☷ CY **m** Ⓜ a la carte approx. 160 – ☳ 48 – **136 rm** 480/530.

🏨 **Sainte-Catherine** Ⓜ without rest, 27 r. Parlement Ste-Catherine ℰ 56 81 95 12, Telex 573215, Fax 56 44 50 51 – 🛗 ☰ 🔟 ☎ – 🛃 45. ☒ ⑩ ☞ ☷ DX **m** ☳ 65 – **82 rm** 510/810.

🏨 **Normandie** without rest, 7 cours 30-Juillet ℰ 56 52 16 80, Telex 570481, Fax 56 51 68 91 – 🛗 🔟 ☎ ☒ ⑩ ☷ DX **z** ☳ 37 – **100 rm** 280/530.

🏨 **Majestic** without rest, 2 r. Condé ℰ 56 52 60 44, Telex 572938, Fax 56 79 26 70 – 🛗 ☰ 🔟 ☎. ☒ ⑩ ☞ ☷ DX **a** ☳ 32 – **49 rm** 310/440.

🏨 **Gd H. Français** Ⓜ without rest, 12 r. Temple ℰ 56 48 10 35, Telex 550587, Fax 56 81 76 18 – 🛗 ☰ 🔟 ☎ 🕭. ☒ ⑩ ☷ DX **v** ☳ 45 – **35 rm** 330/550.

🏨 **Royal St Jean** Ⓜ without rest, 15 r. Ch. Domercq ✉ 33800 ℰ 56 91 72 16, Telex 570468, Fax 56 94 08 32 – 🛗 🔟 ☎ 🕭. ☒ ⑩ ☷ FZ **u** ☳ 40 – **37 rm** 250/410.

🏨 **Ibis Mériadeck** Ⓜ, 35 cours Mar. Juin ℰ 56 90 10 33, Telex 572918, Fax 56 96 33 15 – 🛗 ☰ 🔟 ☎ 🕭 🅟 – 🛃 250. ☒ ☷ CY **m** Ⓜ 80/155 ♨ – ☳ 32 – **210 rm** 306/389.

🏨 **Relais Bleus** Ⓜ, 68 r. Tauzia ✉ 33800 ℰ 56 91 55 50, Fax 56 91 08 41 – 🛗 ☰ rest 🔟 ☎ 🕭 🅟 – 🛃 60. ☒ ⑩ ☷ FZ **b** Ⓜ 68 b.i./120 b.i. – ☳ 32 – **88 rm** 280/350.

🏨 **Presse** Ⓜ without rest, 6 r. Porte Dijeaux ℰ 56 48 53 88, Fax 56 01 05 82 – 🛗 🔟 ☎. ☒ ⑩ ☷ DX **k** ☳ 29 – **30 rm** 185/340.

🍴🍴🍴🍴 ❀ **Le Chapon Fin** (Garcia), 5 r. Montesquieu ℰ 56 79 10 10, Fax 56 79 09 10, « Unusual Rococo decor 1900 » – ☰. ☒ ⑩ ☷ ☷ – *closed Sunday and Monday* – Ⓜ 140 (lunch)/ 400
Spec. Ravioles de langoustines au citron vert, Lamproie à la bordelaise, Tournedos de homard aux chips d'artichaut. DX **p**

🍴🍴🍴 ❀ **Le Rouzic** (Gautier), 34 cours Chapeau Rouge ℰ 56 44 39 11, Fax 56 40 55 10 – ☰. ☒ ⑩ ☷ ☷ – *closed Saturday lunch and Sunday* – Ⓜ 195/420
Spec. Terrine de foie de canard aux morilles, Lamproie à la bordelaise, La marée du jour en tamis. Wines St-Julien. DX **b**

🍴🍴🍴 ❀ **La Chamade** (Carrère), 20 r. Piliers de Tutelle ℰ 56 48 13 74 – ☰. ☷ DX **d** *closed 7 to 14 August, weekends July-August and Saturday lunch* – Ⓜ 180/280
Spec. Foie de canard en terrine à l'Armagnac, Salade de goujonnettes de sole et foie gras poêlé, Noix de ris de veau grillée et raviole de morilles. Wines Graves, Saint-Julien.

172

XXX ✿ **Jean Ramet**, 7 pl. J. Jaurès ℰ 56 44 12 51 – ▣. ⚏   EX **u**
closed 10 to 30 August, Saturday and Sunday – **M** a la carte 240/440
Spec. Salade de Saint-Jacques crues aux épinards et champignons (November-February), Blanc de turbot braisé au Médoc, Aumonières de crêpes en chaud et froid. **Wines** Moulis.

XXX ✿ **Pavillon des Boulevards** (Franc), 120 r. Croix de Seguey ℰ 56 81 51 02, Fax 56 51 14 58,
🌂 – ▣. ⓐ ⓪ ⚏ ⚏
closed 1 to 10 May, 8 to 16 August, Saturday lunch and Sunday – **M** 280/350
Spec. Poêlée de homard au chou, Chinoiseries de pigeonneau, Millefeuille chocolat à la sauce Malaga. **Wines** Bordeaux Côtes de Francs, Pessac Léognan.

XXX **Le Cailhau**, 3 pl. Palais ℰ 56 81 79 91, Fax 56 44 86 58 – ▣. ⓐ ⓪ ⚏. ⚙   EY **m**
closed 1 to 25 August, Saturday lunch and Sunday – **M** 160/370.

XXX ✿ **Le Vieux Bordeaux** (Bordage), 27 r. Buhan ℰ 56 52 94 36, 🌂 – ⓐ ⓪ ⚏   EY **a**
closed 1 to 24 August, February Holidays, Saturday lunch, Sunday and Bank Holidays –
M 145/250
Spec. Omelette aux truffes et lard fumé, Homard sauté et gratin dauphinois, Canard rosé et son foie gras aux pêches. **Wines** Canon-Fronsac.

XXX **Villa Carnot**, 335 bd Wilson ✉ 33200 ℰ 56 08 04 21, 🌂 – ⓐ ⓪ ⚏. ⚙
closed 31 August-15 September, Sunday and Monday – **M** 166/350.

XX **Les Plaisirs d'Ausone**, 10 r. Ausone ℰ 56 79 30 30, Fax 56 51 38 16 – ⓐ ⚏   EY **t**
closed 4 to 26 August, Monday lunch, Saturday lunch and Sunday – **M** 150/250.

XX **Le Buhan**, 28 r. Buhan ℰ 56 52 80 86 – ⓐ ⓪   EY **a**
closed Monday – **M** 130/230.

XX **Les Provinces**, 41 r. St-Rémi ℰ 56 81 74 30, Fax 56 48 05 05 – ⚏   DX **t**
closed Saturday lunch and Sunday – **M** 115/280.

XX **Didier Gélineau**, 26 r. Pas St Georges ℰ 56 52 84 25 – ⓐ ⓪ ⚏   EX **n**
closed Saturday lunch and Sunday 16 April-14 October, Sunday dinner and Monday out of season – **M** a la carte 175/300.

at Parc des Expositions : North of the town – ✉ 33300 Bordeaux :

🏨 **Sofitel Aquitania** Ⓜ, ℰ 56 50 83 80, Telex 570557, Fax 56 39 73 75, <, ⚊, ⚙ – 🛗 ⚑ rm ▣
📺 ☎ ⓟ – 🔔 25 - 250. ⓐ ⓪ ⚏. ⚙ rest
Le Flore **M** 110/160 – ⚌ 65 – **212 rm** 575.

🏨 **Mercure Pont d'Aquitaine** Ⓜ, ℰ 56 43 36 72, Telex 540097, Fax 56 50 23 95, 🌂, ⚊, ⚙
– 🛗 ⚑ rm ▣ 📺 ☎ ⓟ – 🔔 80 - 120. ⓐ ⓪ ⚏. ⚙ rest
M 98 – ⚌ 48 – **100 rm** 420/550.

🏨 **Novotel-Bordeaux le Lac** Ⓜ, ℰ 56 50 99 70, Telex 570274, Fax 56 43 00 66, <, 🌂, ⚊
– 🛗 ⚑ rm ▣ 📺 ☎ ⓟ. ⓐ ⓪ ⚏
M a la carte approx. 180 ⚖ – ⚌ 48 – **176 rm** 440.

🏨 **Mercure Bordeaux le Lac** Ⓜ, ℰ 56 50 90 30, Telex 540077, Fax 56 43 07 55, 🌂 – 🛗
⚑ rm ▣ 📺 ☎ ⓟ – 🔔 250. ⓐ ⓪ ⚏ ⓙⓒⒷ
M 95 b.i./145 – ⚌ 48 – **108 rm** 420/550.

at Carbon-Blanc NE : 8 km – pop. 5 842 – ✉ 33560 :

XXX **Marc Demund**, av. Gardette ℰ 56 74 72 28, Fax 56 06 55 40, 🌂, park – ⓟ. ⓐ ⓪ ⚏
closed 14 to 26 August, Sunday dinner and Monday – **M** 160/340.

at Bouliac – ✉ 33270 :

🏨 ✿ **Le St-James** (Amat) Ⓜ ⚲, pl. C. Hosteins, near church ℰ 56 20 52 19, Telex 573001,
Fax 56 20 92 58, < Bordeaux, « Original contemporary decor », ☀ – 📺 ☎ ⓟ. ⓐ ⓪ ⚏
ⓙⒸⒷ. ⚙
M 300 b.i./450 – **Le Bistroy M** a la carte 120/170 – ⚌ 70 – **18 rm** 750/1350
Spec. Alose à la bordelaise (May-June), Lamproie à la bordelaise, Noisette d'agneau de Pauillac à la crème d'ail. **Wines** Premières Côtes de Bordeaux-Cadillac, Médoc.

to the W :

at Pessac : 9 km – pop. 51 055 – ✉ 33600 :

🏨 **La Réserve** Ⓜ ⚲, av. Bourgailh ℰ 56 07 13 28, Telex 560585, Fax 56 36 31 02, 🌂,
« Park », ⚊, 🌂 – 📺 ☎ ⓟ – 🔔 60. ⓐ ⓪ ⚏
25 February-25 November – **M** 250 – ⚌ 58 – **19 rm** 530/900.

🏨 **Royal Brion** ⚲ without rest, 10 r. Pin Vert ℰ 56 45 07 72, Fax 56 46 13 75 – 📺 ☎ ⇔
ⓟ. ⓐ ⓪ ⚏
closed 22 December-5 January – ⚌ 35 – **25 rm** 260/340.

at the airport : 11 km by D 106E – ✉ 33700 Mérignac :

🏨 **Novotel-Mérignac** Ⓜ, av. Kennedy ℰ 56 34 10 25, Telex 540320, Fax 56 55 99 64, 🌂, ⚊,
☀ – 🛗 ▣ 📺 ☎ ⓟ – 🔔 25 - 100. ⓐ ⓪ ⚏ ⓙⒸⒷ
M a la carte approx. 180 ⚖ – ⚌ 48 – **149 rm** 450.

🏨 **Mercure Aéroport** Ⓜ, 1 av. Ch. Lindbergh ℰ 56 34 74 74, Telex 573953, Fax 56 34 30 84,
⚊, 🌂 – 🛗 ⚑ rm ▣ 📺 ☎ ⓟ – 🔔 200. ⓐ ⓪ ⚏
M a la carte 160/230 – ⚌ 48 – **105 rm** 295/550.

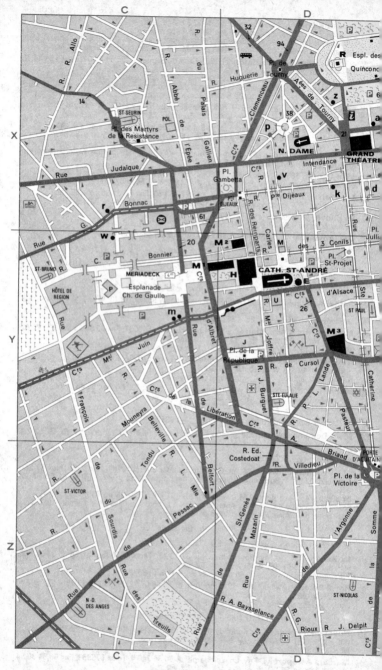

To go a long way quickly, use **Michelin Maps** at scale of 1: 1 000 000.

174

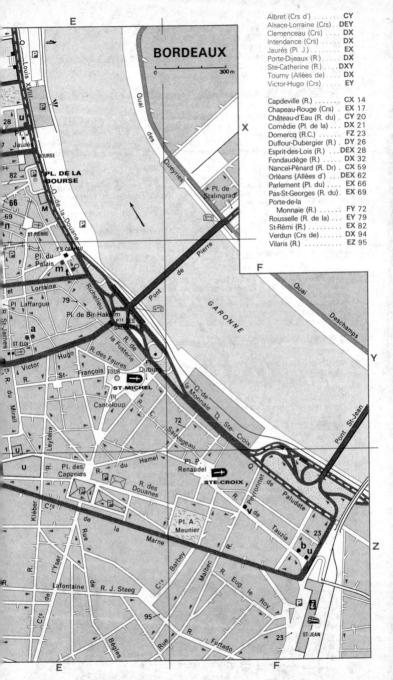

BORDEAUX

300 m

Ensure that you have up to date **Michelin maps** in your car.

175

Le Patio Ⓜ, av. J.-F. Kennedy at Mérignac ℰ 56 55 93 42, Telex 540183, Fax 56 47 64 94,  –  rm Ⓣⓥ ☎ & Ⓟ – 🔬 60. ⒶⒺ Ⓞ ⒼⒷ
M 125 – ⋍ 48 – **81 rm** 395/445.

Fimotel Ⓜ, 97 av. J.-F. Kennedy ℰ 56 34 33 08, Telex 541315, Fax 56 34 01 90, ☕, ⤳ –
▯ Ⓣⓥ ☎ & Ⓟ – 🔬 35. ⒶⒺ Ⓞ ⒼⒷ
M 80/120 ⅄ – ⋍ 35 – **60 rm** 300/330.

Eugénie-les-Bains 40320 Landes ⑧② ① – pop. 467 alt. 90 – Spa (15 February-November).
Bordeaux 151.

Les Prés d'Eugénie et le Couvent des Herbes (Guérard) Ⓜ ⟋, ℰ 58 05 06 07,
Telex 540470, Fax 58 51 13 59, « 19C mansion, elegant decor, park », ⤳, ⁇ – ▯ Ⓣⓥ ☎
Ⓟ. ⒶⒺ Ⓞ ⒼⒷ ⒿⒸⒷ. ⅋
closed 1 December-13 February – **M** (low-calorie menu for residents only) 270/350 and a la
carte - **rest. Michel Guérard** (booking essential) **M** 360/560 and a la carte 400/540 – ⋍ 95
- 28 rm 1250/1450, 7 suites 1650/1800
Spec. Rillettes de lapereau en venaison, Cannelloni aux herbes "cueillies à la rosée", Gâteau mollet
du Marquis de Béchamel. Wines Tursan blanc, Côtes de Gascogne.
Le Couvent des Herbes Ⓜ ⟋, « 18C Convent » – Ⓣⓥ ☎ Ⓟ. ⒶⒺ Ⓞ ⒼⒷ. ⅋ rest
closed 1 December-13 February – **M** see **Les Prés d'Eugénie** and **Michel Guérard** – ⋍ 95
- 5 rm 1450/1650, 3 suites 2000.
Maison Rose ⏡, ℰ 58 05 05 05, Telex 540470, Fax 58 51 13 59, ☕, guesthouse atmosphere, ⤳ – Ⓣⓥ ☎ & Ⓟ. ⒶⒺ Ⓞ ⒼⒷ. ⅋ rest
closed 1 December-13 February – **M** (residents only) (booking allowed) 170 – ⋍ 60 – **26 rm**
420/550.

Grenade-sur-l'Adour 40270 Landes ⑧② ① – pop. 2 187 alt. 55.
Bordeaux 140.

Pain Adour et Fantaisie (Oudill) Ⓜ with rm, 7 pl. Tilleuls ℰ 58 45 18 80,
Fax 58 45 16 57, ☕, « Riverside terrace » – ▤ rm Ⓣⓥ ☎ Ⓟ – 🔬 25. ⒶⒺ Ⓞ ⒼⒷ. ⅋ rm
closed 4 to 8 January, Monday (except hotel) and Sunday dinner except July-August and Bank
Holidays – **M** 170/390 and a la carte – ⋍ 80 – **11 rm** 480/780
Spec. Cruchade de foie gras à la poêlée de champignons, Cannelon d'oie fondante au bouillon
de légumes confits, Tourte chaude au chocolat amer. Wines Tursan, Madiran.

Langon ⓼ 33210 Gironde ⑦⑨ ② – pop. 5 842 alt. 22.
Bordeaux 48.

Claude Darroze Ⓜ, 95 cours Gén. Leclerc ℰ 56 63 00 48, Fax 56 63 41 15, ☕ – Ⓣⓥ
☎ ⟋ Ⓟ – 🔬 25. ⒶⒺ Ⓞ ⒼⒷ. ⅋ rm
closed 15 October-5 November and 5 to 25 January – **M** 200/500 and a la carte – ⋍ 65 –
16 rm 320/420
Spec. Salade de petits artichauts aux queues de langoustines, Plateau de fruits de mer chauds,
Gibier (season). Wines Entre-Deux-Mers, Graves rouge.

Pons 17800 Char.-Mar. ⑰① ⑤ – pop. 4 412 alt. 20.
Bordeaux 95.

at **Mosnac** S : 11 km by Bordeaux road and D 134 – ✉ 17240 :

Moulin de Marcouze (Bouchet) Ⓜ ⟋, ℰ 46 70 46 16, Telex 793453, Fax 46 70 48 14,
park, « Tasteful mansion on the banks of the River Seugne », ⤳ – ▤ Ⓣⓥ ☎ & Ⓟ. ⒶⒺ ⒼⒷ ⒿⒸⒷ
closed 17 to 30 November, February, Wednesday lunch and Tuesday from 15 September-
15 June except Bank Holidays – **M** 190/400 and a la carte – ⋍ 70 – **9 rm** 500/670
Spec. Tarte aux pommes de terre au saumon fumé, Gigot d'agneau de sept heures, Soufflé chaud
au Grand Marnier.

See : Site★★ - Sea-Front★★ : boulevard★★ BCDZ – and pointe★ de la Croisette X – ≤★ from the Mount Chevalier Tower AZ V – The Castre Museum★ (Musée de la Castre) AZ M – Tour into the Hills★ (Chemin des Collines) NE : 4 km V – The Croix des Gardes X E ≤★ W : 5 km then 15 mn.

☒ Country-Club of Cannes-Mougins ℘ 93 75 79 13 by ⑤ : 9 km ; ☒ Golf-Club of Cannes-Mandelieu ℘ 93 49 55 39 by ② : 6,5 km ; ☒ Biot ℘ 93 65 08 48 by ⑤ : 14 km ; ☒ Opio-Valbonne ℘ 93 42 00 08 by ⑤ : 15 km ; ☒ Val Martin ℘ 93 42 07 98 by ⑤ : 12 km by N 285, D 3 and D 103.

🛈 Direction Générale du Tourisme et des Congrès and Accueil de France (Information, exchange facilities and hotel reservations not more than 5 days in advance), espl. Prés. Georges-Pompidou ℘ 93 39 01 01, Telex 470749 (Welcome Office ℘ 93 39 24 53) and Railway Station ℘ 93 99 19 77, Telex 470795 – A.C. 12bis r. L. Blanc ℘ 93 39 38 94.

Paris 903 ⑤ – Aix-en-Provence 146 ⑤ – Grenoble 312 ⑤ – Marseille 159 ⑤ – Nice 32 ⑤ – Toulon 121 ⑤.

Plans on following pages

Carlton Intercontinental, 58 bd Croisette ℘ 93 68 91 68, Telex 470720, Fax 93 38 20 90, ≤, ⅃₀, ☂₀ – ፤ 🔟 ☎ ⬩ ⬤ – 🏛 30 - 250. 🖭 ⑩ 🞉 ⎀
CZ e
M see La Côte below- Café Carlton M a la carte 295/465 – 立 140 – **298 rm** 2000/3250, 28 suites.

Martinez, 73 bd Croisette ℘ 93 94 30 30, Telex 470708, Fax 93 39 67 82, ≤, 🕼, ⅃, ☂₀, ⚘ – ፤ 🔟 ☎ 🅟 ⬩ – 🏛 60 - 700. 🖭 ⑩ 🞉 ⎀
DZ n
closed mid November-mid January – M see La Palme d'Or below - L'Orangeraie ℘ 92 98 30 17 M 195 Ⅰ – 立 95 – **417 rm** 1250/3150, 13 suites.

Majestic, 14 bd Croisette ℘ 92 98 77 00, Telex 470787, Fax 93 38 97 90, ≤, 🕼, ⅃, ☂₀, ⚘ – ፤ 🔟 ☎ 🛦 ⬩ – 🏛 400. 🖭 ⑩ 🞉
BZ n
closed 10 November-20 December – Le Sunset M a la carte 260/430 – 立 100 – **258 rm** 1070/3410, 24 suites.

Gray d'Albion M, 38 r. Serbes ℘ 92 99 79 79, Telex 470744, Fax 93 99 26 10, ☂₀ – ፤ 🔟 rm 🔟 ☎ 🛦 – 🏛 30 - 200. 🖭 ⑩ 🞉 ⎀ ⚘ rm
BZ d
M see Royal Gray below – Les 4 Saisons M a la carte 155/250 – 立 85 – **172 rm** 800/1550, 14 suites.

L'Horset-Savoy M, 5 r. F. Einessy ℘ 92 99 72 00, Telex 461873, Fax 93 68 25 59, 🕼, ☂₀ – ፤ 🔟 ☎ 🛦 ⬩ – 🏛 120. 🖭 ⑩ 🞉
CZ u
M (closed Saturday and Sunday 1 November-31 March) 160 b.i. – 立 70 – **101 rm** 820/1150, 5 suites.

Pullman Beach M without rest, 13 r. Canada ℘ 93 94 50 50, Telex 470034, Fax 93 68 35 38, ☂₀ – 🏛 40. 🖭 ⑩ 🞉
DZ y
closed 20 November-26 December – 立 80 – **93 rm** 810/1590.

Sofitel Méditerranée M, 2 bd J. Hibert ℘ 92 99 73 00, Telex 470728, Fax 92 99 73 29, 🕼, « Roof-top swimming pool and terrace ≤ bay of Cannes » – ፤ ⚘ rm 🔟 ☎ ⬩ – 🏛 150. 🖭 ⑩ 🞉
AZ n
closed 17 November-18 December – Le Palmyre M 170/250 Ⅰ – 立 80 – **150 rm** 850/1250, 5 suites 1820.

Grand Hôtel, 45 bd Croisette ℘ 93 38 15 45, Telex 470727, Fax 93 68 97 45, ≤, 🕼, ☂₀, ⚘ – ፤ rm 🔟 ☎ 🅟 – 🏛 30. 🖭 ⑩ 🞉. ⚘ rest
CZ q
M 190 – 立 60 – **74 rm** 730/1460.

Cristal M, 15 rd-pt Duboys d'Angers ℘ 93 39 45 45, Telex 470844, Fax 93 38 64 66, 🕼 – ፤ 🔟 ☎ ⬩. 🖭 ⑩ 🞉 ⚘ rest
CZ s
M (closed November) a la carte 180/290 – 立 65 – **51 rm** 745/1050, 4 suites 1730.

Novotel M 🕉, 25 av. Beauséjour ℘ 93 68 91 50, Telex 470039, Fax 93 38 37 08, ≤, 🕼, « Garden », ⅃₀, ⅃ – ፤ ⚘ rm 🔟 ☎ ⬩ – 🏛 400. 🖭 ⑩ 🞉
DY r
M a la carte approx. 150 – 立 60 – **180 rm** 850/1100.

Splendid without rest, 4 r. F. Faure ℘ 93 99 53 11, Telex 470990, Fax 93 99 55 02, ≤ – ፤ kitchenette 🔟 🔟 ☎ 🖭 ⑩ 🞉
BZ a
立 50 – **63 rm** 500/830.

Victoria M without rest, rd-pt Duboys d'Angers ℘ 93 99 36 36, Fax 93 38 03 91, ⅃ – ፤ 🔟 ☎ ⬩. 🖭 ⑩ 🞉 ⎀. ⚘
CZ x
closed 10 November-20 December – 立 45 – **25 rm** 600/1200.

Canberra without rest, rd-pt Duboys d'Angers ℘ 93 38 20 70, Telex 470817, Fax 92 98 03 47 – ፤ 🔟 ☎ 🅟. 🖭 ⑩ 🞉
CZ h
立 38 – **45 rm** 423/741.

Fouquet's M without rest, 2 rd-pt Duboys d'Angers ℘ 93 38 75 81, Fax 92 98 03 39 – 🔟 ☎ ⬩. 🖭 ⑩ 🞉 ⎀
CZ y
closed 26 October-26 December – 立 60 – **10 rm** 950/1300.

Paris without rest, 34 bd Alsace ℘ 93 38 30 89, Telex 470995, Fax 93 39 04 61, ⅃, 🕼 – ፤ 🔟 ☎ ⬩ – 🏛 40. 🖭 ⑩ 🞉 ⎀. ⚘
CY a
closed 15 November-15 January – 立 60 – **45 rm** 550/980, 5 suites 1800.

Embassy, 6 r. Bône ℘ 93 38 79 02, Telex 470081, Fax 93 99 07 98 – ፤ 🔟 ☎. 🖭 ⑩ 🞉
DY j
M (closed Monday lunch and Tuesday lunch from 1 September-30 April) 115 – **60 rm** 立 610/735.

CANNES – LE CANNET – VALLAURIS

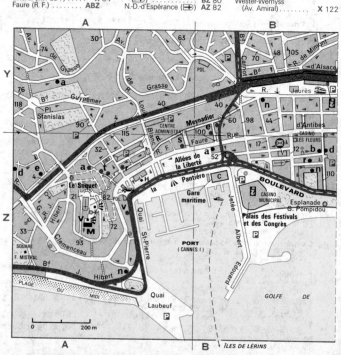

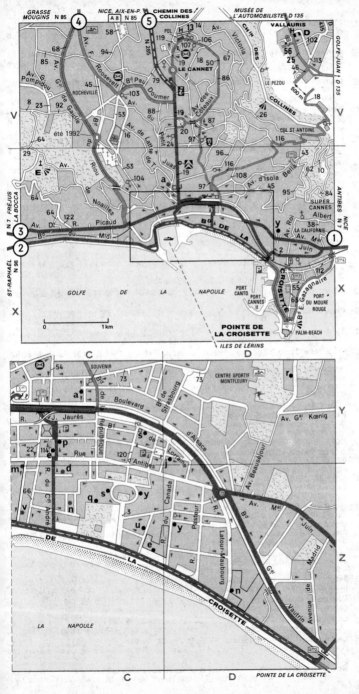

🏨 **Mondial** Ⓜ without rest, 77 r. d'Antibes ℰ 93 68 70 00, Telex 462918, Fax 93 99 39 11 –
📶 ✿✖ 🗏 📺 ♿ 🔓 – 🔬 30. 🆎 ⓪ 🇬🇧   CY **e**
⌑ 40 – **56 rm** 500/700.

🏨 **Abrial** without rest, 24 bd Lorraine ℰ 93 38 78 82, Telex 470761, Fax 92 98 67 41 – 📶 🗏
📺 ☎ ⟷ – 🔬 30. 🆎 ⓪ 🇬🇧 ⌚   CY **s**
⌑ 48 – **50 rm** 569/610.

🏨 **Ligure** without rest, 5 pl. Gare ℰ 93 39 03 11, Telex 970275, Fax 93 39 19 48 – 📶 🗏 📺 ☎.
🆎 ⓪ 🇬🇧   BY **n**
⌑ 30 – **36 rm** 595/650.

🏨 **Beau Séjour,** 5 r. Fauvettes ℰ 93 39 63 00, Telex 470975, Fax 92 98 64 66, 🛋, 🏊, 🌿 –
📶 🗏 rm 📺 ☎ ⟷ – 🔬 30. 🆎 ⓪ 🇬🇧. 🌫 rest   AZ **d**
closed 1 November-14 December – **M** 140 – **46 rm** ⌑ 660/750.

🏨 **La Madone** 🕭 without rest, 5 av. Justinia ℰ 93 43 57 87, Fax 93 43 22 79, 🏊, 🌿 –
kitchenette 📺 ☎. 🆎 ⓪ 🇬🇧   X **y**
⌑ 40 – **25 rm** 410/640.

🏨 **Château de la Tour** 🕭, 10 av. Font-de-Veyre by ③ ⊠ 06150 Cannes-La-Bocca
ℰ 93 47 34 64, Telex 470906, Fax 93 47 86 61, 🏊 – 📶 📺 ☎ ℗. 🆎 ⓪ 🇬🇧 ⌚ 🌫 rest
M *(closed 15 November-15 December, Saturday January-March and Monday April-December)*
80/110 – **42 rm** ⌑ 520/680.

🏨 **America** Ⓜ without rest, 13 r. St-Honoré ℰ 93 68 36 36, Fax 93 68 04 58 – 📶 🗏 📺 ☎. 🆎
🇬🇧 ⌚ 🌫   BZ **r**
⌑ 50 – **30 rm** 500/800.

🏨 **Host. de l'Olivier** without rest, 5 r. Tambourinaires ℰ 93 39 53 28, Telex 970902,
Fax 93 39 55 85, 🏊 – 📺 ☎ ℗. 🆎 🇬🇧.   AZ **e**
closed 23 November-28 December – ⌑ 35 – **23 rm** 475/565.

🏨 **Des Congrès et Festivals** without rest, 12 r. Teisseire ℰ 93 39 13 81, Fax 93 39 56 28 –
📶 🗏 📺 ☎. 🆎 ⓪ 🇬🇧 ⌚   CY **p**
closed 1 November-20 January – ⌑ 35 – **20 rm** 420/650.

🏠 **Albert 1ᵉʳ** Ⓜ without rest, 68 av. Grasse ℰ 93 39 24 04, Fax 93 38 83 75 – 📺 ☎ ℗. 🇬🇧
⌑ 27 – **11 rm** 280/320.   AY **d**

🏠 **Cheval Blanc** without rest, 3 r. Maupassant ℰ 93 39 88 60 – 📺 ☎. 🇬🇧   AY **a**
⌑ 27 – **16 rm** 220/300.

🏠 **Modern** without rest, 11 r. Serbes ℰ 93 39 09 87 – 📶 📺 ☎   BZ **b**
closed 1 November-23 December – ⌑ 28 – **19 rm** 210/500.

🍴🍴🍴🍴🍴 ✿ **La Belle Otéro,** 58 bd Croisette, (at Carlton H.-7th floor) ℰ 93 68 00 33, Fax 92 98 90 92,
🛋 – 🗏. 🆎 ⓪ 🇬🇧   CZ **e**
closed 1 to 16 November, February and Monday – **M** (dinner only) a la carte 490/670
Spec. Poêlée de langoustines aux farcis de jeunes légumes (July-September), Rougets en filets
sur une fondue provençale, Carré d'agneau rôti aux fines épices. **Wines** Muscat des coteaux varois,
Côtes de Provence.

🍴🍴🍴🍴🍴 ✿ **La Côte** - Hôtel Carlton Intercontinental, 58 bd Croisette ℰ 93 68 91 68, Telex 470720,
Fax 93 68 91 68 – 🗏. 🆎 ⓪ 🇬🇧 ⌚ 🌫   CZ **e**
closed 18 November-17 December, Tuesday and Wednesday – **M** a la carte 360/600
Spec. Tagliatelles aux pieds d'agneau en daubière, Chapon de Méditerranée à la fleur de sel,
Pigeon fermier rôti et ravioli de potiron au cerfeuil. **Wines** Côtes de Provence.

🍴🍴🍴🍴🍴 ✿✿ **La Palme d'Or** - Hôtel Martinez, 73 bd Croisette ℰ 92 98 30 18, Telex 470708,
Fax 93 39 67 82, ≼, 🛋 – 🗏 ℗. 🆎 ⓪ 🇬🇧 ⌚   DZ **n**
*closed mid November-mid January, Tuesday (except dinner 12 May-13 September) and Mon-
day* – **M** 310/530 and a la carte
Spec. Confit de lapin au foie gras, Rougets aux palets d'ail et fondue d'olives, Festin d'agneau
en trilogie. **Wines** Côtes de Provence.

🍴🍴🍴🍴 ✿✿ **Royal Gray** - Hôtel Gray d'Albion, 6 r. Etats-Unis ℰ 92 99 79 60, Telex 470744,
Fax 93 99 26 10, 🛋, « Tasteful, contemporary decor » – 🗏. 🆎 ⓪ 🇬🇧 ⌚   CYZ **m**
closed February – **M** 500/580 and a la carte
Spec. Aïgo de homard aux langoustines et supions, Saint Pierre rôti au fumet de fenouil, Palmier
de pamplemousse rôti au miel. **Wines** Côtes de Provence.

🍴🍴🍴 ✿ **Poêle d'Or** (Leclerc), 23 r. États-Unis ℰ 93 39 77 65 – 🆎 ⓪ 🇬🇧   CZ **v**
closed 22 to 30 March, 29 June-6 July, 22 November-7 December, Tuesday lunch and Monday
– **M** (weekends : booking essential) 170/290
Spec. Salade de truffes et parmesan frais (summer), Sabayon de queues d'écrevisses en gratin
(season), Sablé de fruits rouges au coulis de framboises. **Wines** Côtes de Provence, Bellet.

🍴🍴🍴 **Gaston et Gastounette,** 7 quai St-Pierre ℰ 93 39 47 92, 🛋 – 🆎 ⓪ 🇬🇧   AZ **v**
closed 4 to 19 January – **M** a la carte 270/430.

🍴🍴 **La Mirabelle,** 24 r. St Antoine ℰ 93 38 72 75 – 🗏. 🆎 ⓪ 🇬🇧   AZ **a**
closed 15 to 30 November, 15 to 28 February and Tuesday – **M** (dinner only) 195/255.

🍴🍴 **Le Mesclun,** 16 r. St Antoine ℰ 93 99 45 19 – 🗏. 🆎 🇬🇧   AZ **t**
closed 1 to 20 December, 15 February-10 March and Wednesday dinner out of season – **M**
(dinner only) 170.

🍴🍴 **Relais des Semailles,** 9 r. St Antoine ℰ 93 39 22 32 – 🆎 🇬🇧   AZ **t**
closed March, 1 to 18 December and Sunday out of season – **M** (dinner only) 210/320.

XX **Maître-Pierre,** 6 r. Mar. Joffre ℰ 93 99 36 30 – 🍽. 🆎 🇬🇧
BY **r**
closed July and Sunday except Bank Holidays – **M** *(dinner only in season)* 95/195.

XX **St-Benoit,** 9 r. Bateguier ℰ 93 39 04 17 – 🇬🇧
CZ **n**
closed Tuesday lunch and Monday – **M** 125/160.

XX **La Cigale,** 1 r. Florian ℰ 93 39 65 79 – 🍽, 🆎 🇬🇧
CZ **d**
closed 15 to 30 November, Sunday dinner and Monday – **M** 98/148 ⅃.

X **Côté Jardin,** 12 av. St Louis ℰ 93 38 60 28, 🍽 – 🍽, 🆎 🇬🇧
X **a**
closed February-mid March, Monday (except dinner 1 May-15 September) and Sunday –
M 148.

X **Chez Astoux,** 43 r. F. Faure ℰ 93 39 06 22, Fax 93 99 45 47, 🍽, Seafood – 🆎 ⓞ
🇬🇧 – **M** 92/148.
AZ **s**

X **L'Olivier,** 9 r. Rouguière ℰ 93 39 91 63 – 🆎 ⓞ 🇬🇧
BY **e**
closed 15 December-15 January and Monday – **M** 90/145.

X **Aux Bons Enfants,** 80 r. Meynadier – ⚔
AZ **r**
closed August, 20 December-5 January, Saturday dinner out of season and Sunday
– **M** 84.

Juan-les-Pins 06160 Alpes-Mar. 🎆 ⑨. 🎆 ㉟ ㊴ – alt. 2.

Cannes 8,5.

🏨 ✿✿ **Juana and rest. La Terrasse** 🕭, la Pinède, av. G. Gallice ℰ 93 61 08 70,
Telex 470778, Fax 93 61 76 60, 🍽, ⏚, 🅰 – 🛗 🍽 rm 📺 ☎ ⇔ 🅿
April-October – **M** *(closed Wednesday except 7 to 18 May, 22 to 27 June, July-August and
26 to 30 October)* *(dinner only July-August)* 460/580 and a la carte – ☲ 85 – **45 rm** 650/2300,
5 suites 4000
Spec. Poêlée de supions aux poivrades, Selle d'agneau de Pauillac cuite en terre d'argile, Millefeuille aux fraises des bois à la crème de mascarpone. Wines Côtes de Provence.

Mougins 06250 Alpes-Mar. 🎆 ⑨. 🎆 ㉘ ㊴ – pop. 13 014 alt. 260.

Cannes 7.

XXXX ✿✿✿ **Moulin de Mougins** (Vergé) with rm, at Notre-Dame-de-Vie SE : 2,5 km by D 3
ℰ 93 75 78 24, Telex 970732, Fax 93 90 18 55, 🍽, « Converted 16C oil mill », 🍽 – 🍽 📺
☎ 🅿. 🆎 ⓞ 🇬🇧
closed 31 January-late March – **M** *(closed Monday except dinner 15 July-31 August and Thurs-
day lunch)* 700 and a la carte 600/850 – ☲ 75 – **5 rm** 800/1300
Spec. Poupeton de fleur de courgette aux truffes, Petits artichauts violets à la barigoule d'asperges,
Rougets de roche en croustillants de pommes. Wines Cassis, Côtes de Provence.

La Napoule 06210 Alpes-Mar. 🎆 ⑧. 🎆 ㉞ – alt. 18.

Cannes 8,5.

XXXX ✿✿ **L'Oasis,** ℰ 93 49 95 52, Telex 461389, Fax 93 49 64 13, 🍽, « Shaded and flowered
patio » – 🍽, 🆎 🇬🇧
closed 1 to 17 March, 15 November-7 December, Sunday dinner and Monday – **M** 450/550
and a la carte
Spec. Salade de pâtes fraîches safranées aux palourdes, Risotto de pageot aux fruits de mer,
Caravane de desserts.

LILLE 🅿 59000 Nord 🗺 ⑯ – pop. 172 142 alt. 21 Greater Lille 1 081 479.

See : Old Lille★★ (Vieux Lille) EFY : Old Stock Exchange★★ (Vieille Bourse) FY, Hospice Comtesse★
(keel-shaped ceiling★★) FY B, rue de la Monnaie★ FY 142 – General de Gaulle's Birth place AXW.
🏌 of Flandres (private) ℰ 20 72 20 74 by ② : 4,5 km ; 🏌 of Sart (private) ℰ 20 72 02 51 by ② :
7 km ; 🏌 of Brigode at Villeneuve d'Ascq ℰ 20 91 17 86 by ③ : 9 km ; 🏌 🏌 of Bondues
ℰ 20 23 20 62 by ① : 9,5 km.
✈ of Lille-Lesquin : ℰ 20 49 68 68 by ④ : 8 km. 🚗 ℰ 20 74 50 50.
🛈 Office de Tourisme and Accueil de France (Information and hotel reservations, not more than 5 days
in advance) Palais Rihour ℰ 20 30 81 00, Telex 110213 and at the Railway station ℰ 20 06 40 65 –
A.C. 8 r. Quennette ℰ 20 55 29 44.

Plans on following pages

🏨 **Alliance** 🅼 🕭, quai du Wault ℰ 20 30 62 62, Telex 136210, Fax 20 42 94 25, « Former 17C
convent » – 🛗 ⚔ rm 📺 ☎ 🔥 🅿 – 🔺 150. 🆎 ⓞ 🇬🇧 🇯🇨🇧 ⚔ rest
EY **d**
M 170/225 – ☲ 60 – **80 rm** 580/850, 3 suites 1500.

🏨 **Novotel Lille Centre** 🅼, 116 r. Hôpital Militaire ⌗ 59800 ℰ 20 30 65 26, Telex 160859,
Fax 20 30 04 04 – 🛗 ⚔ rm 🍽 📺 ☎ ♿ – 🔺 30. 🆎 ⓞ 🇬🇧 🇯🇨🇧
EY **s**
M a la carte approx. 140 – ☲ 55 – **102 rm** 580/600.

🏨 **Carlton** without rest, 3 r. Paris ⌗ 59800 ℰ 20 55 24 11, Telex 110400, Fax 20 51 48 17 –
🛗 ⚔ 📺 ☎ 🅿 – 🔺 30 - 100. 🆎 ⓞ 🇬🇧 🇯🇨🇧 – ☲ 65 – **61 rm** 420/740.
FY **n**

🏨 **Gd H. Bellevue** without rest, 5 r. J. Roisin ⌗ 59800 ℰ 20 57 45 64, Telex 120790,
Fax 20 40 07 93 – 🛗 📺 ☎ – 🔺 100. 🆎 ⓞ 🇬🇧 🇯🇨🇧 – ☲ 50 – **80 rm** 390/760.
FY **z**

181

LILLE

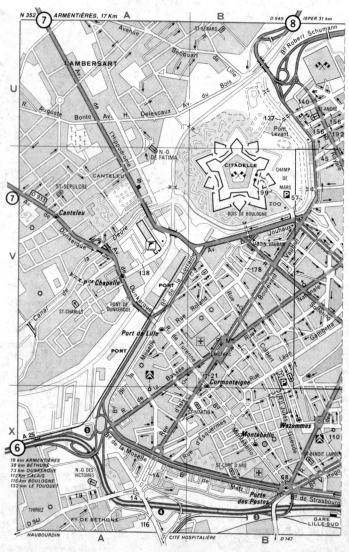

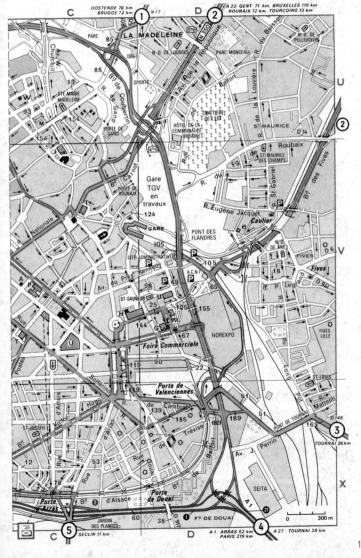

LILLE

🏨 **Mercure Royal Lille Centre** without rest, 2 bd Carnot ⊠ 59800 ℰ 20 51 05 11, Telex 820575, Fax 20 74 01 65 – 🛗 🏃 📺 ☎ – 🔬 30. ⅍ ⓞ ☖ FY **h**
⛲ 55 – **102 rm** 550/620.

🏨 **Treille** Ⓜ without rest, 7 pl. L. de Bettignies ⊠ 59800 ℰ 20 55 45 46, Telex 136761, Fax 20 51 51 69 – 🛗 📺 ☎ ⅄ – 🔬 50. ⅍ ⓞ ☖ FY **d**
⛲ 38 – **40 rm** 300/330.

🏨 **Paix** without rest, 46 bis r. Paris ⊠ 59800 ℰ 20 54 63 93, Fax 20 63 98 97 – 🛗 📺 ☎. ⅍ ⓞ ☖ FY **r**
⛲ 28 – **35 rm** 280/350.

🏨 **Fimotel** Ⓜ, 75 bis r. Gambetta ℰ 20 42 90 90, Fax 20 57 14 24 – 🛗 📺 ☎ ⅄ 🚗 – 🔬 30 - 180. ⅍ ⓞ ☖ EZ **e**
M 98/150 ⅃ – **98 rm** ⛲ 360/380.

🏨 **Ibis** Ⓜ, av. Ch. St-Venant ⊠ 59800 ℰ 20 55 44 44, Telex 136950, Fax 20 31 06 25, 🌳 – 🛗 📺 ☎ ⅄ 🚗 – 🔬 25 - 80. ☖ FY **a**
M 79 – ⛲ 32 – **151 rm** 330/350.

🏨 **Cottage H.** Ⓜ, 1 r. C. Colomb ⊠ 59800 ℰ 20 55 21 55, Fax 20 55 87 49 – 🛗 📺 ☎ ⅄ 🚗 Ⓟ – 🔬 60. ⅍ ⓞ ☖ DV **e**
M 76/98 ⅃ – ⛲ 30 – **61 rm** 270/300.

🏨 **Nord H.**, 46 r. Fg d'Arras ℰ 20 53 53 40, Telex 136589, Fax 20 53 20 95 – 🛗 📺 ☎ 🚗 – 🔬 40. ⅍ ⓞ ☖
M (closed Saturday lunch and Sunday dinner) 77/150 ⅃ – ⛲ 30 – **80 rm** 185/215.

🏨 **Urbis** Ⓜ without rest, 21 r. Lepelletier ⊠ 59800 ℰ 20 06 21 95, Telex 136846, Fax 20 74 91 30 – 🛗 📺 ☎ ⅄. ☖ FY **s**
⛲ 32 – **60 rm** 320/350.

XXXX ✿✿ **Le Flambard** (Bardot), 79 r. Angleterre ⊠ 59800 ℰ 20 51 00 06, Fax 20 55 09 17, « 17C houses in the old part of Lille » – ⅍ ⓞ ☖ EY **r**
closed Sunday dinner – **M** 250/550 and a la carte
Spec. Salade du pêcheur tiède à l'échalote, Meunière de sole Parmentier, Ris de veau rôti à la crème de truffe (20 December-March).

XXXX ✿✿ **Le Restaurant** (Mme Arabian), 1 pl. Sébastopol ℰ 20 57 05 05, Fax 20 54 72 30 – ▤. ⅍ ⓞ ☖ EZ **k**
closed 18 to 27 April, 9 to 24 August, Christmas Holidays, Saturday lunch, Sunday and Bank Holidays – **M** 200 (lunch)/550 and a la carte
Spec. Foie gras d'oie et canard (October-June), Tronçon de turbot rôti à la bière, Poêlée de coquilles Saint-Jacques aux chicons (October-April).

XXX ✿ **A L'Huîtrière**, 3 r. Chats Bossus ⊠ 59800 ℰ 20 55 43 41, Fax 20 55 23 10, « Originaly Decorated with the original fisch shop ceramics » – ⅍ ⓞ ☖ FY **g**
closed 22 July-2 September, dinner on Sunday and Bank Holidays – **M** a la carte 300/450
Spec. Produits de la mer, Turbot aux quatre légumes, Poêlée de homard aux pommes de terre et à l'estragon.

XXX ✿ **Le Paris**, 52 bis r. Esquermoise ⊠ 59800 ℰ 20 55 29 41 – ⅍ ⓞ ☖ EY **f**
closed 8 August-7 September and Sunday except Bank Holidays – **M** 196/300
Spec. Poêlée de Saint-Jacques à la Véronique (October-March), Queues de langoustines au chou et beurre blanc, Gibier (season).

XXX **La Belle Époque** (The Queen Victoria), 10 r. Pas (1st floor) ⊠ 59800 ℰ 20 54 51 28, « 1900 decor » – ▤. ⅍ ⓞ ☖ EY **n**
M 400 b.i./600 b.i.

XXX **La Laiterie**, 138 av. Hippodrome at Lambersart NW : 2 km ⊠ 59130 Lambersart ℰ 20 92 79 73, 🌳, – Ⓟ. ☖ AV **s**
closed Sunday dinner – **M** 230/350.

XXX **Le Varbet**, 2 r. Pas ⊠ 59800 ℰ 20 54 81 40 – ⅍ ⓞ ☖ EFY **t**
closed 17 to 21 April, 14 July-18 August, Sunday, Monday and Bank Holidays – **M** 145/300.

XXX **Le Club**, 16 r. Pas ⊠ 59800 ℰ 20 57 01 10 – ⅍ ⓞ ☖ EY **n**
closed 26 April-4 May, 3 to 31 August, Monday dinner and Sunday – **M** 130/210.

XX **Le Bistrot Tourangeau**, 61 bd Louis XIV ⊠ 59800 ℰ 20 52 74 64 – 🏃 ⅍ ⓞ ☖ DV **t**
closed Sunday – **M** (booking essential) 98/136.

XX **Le Cardinal**, 84 façade Esplanade ℰ 20 06 58 58 – ☖ EY **b**
closed 10 to 16 August and Sunday – **M** 230.

XX **La Fringale**, 141 r. Solférino ℰ 20 42 02 80 – ⅍ ⓞ ☖ EZ **f**
closed 15 July-15 August, 18 to 25 February, Saturday lunch and Sunday – **M** (booking essential) 160/310.

XX **La Salle à Manger**, 91 r. Monnaie ⊠ 59800 ℰ 20 06 44 25 – ☖ EFY **m**
closed Saturday lunch and Sunday – **M** 185/250.

XX **Charlot II**, 26 bd J.-B. Lebas ℰ 20 52 53 38, Seafood – ⅍ ⓞ ☖ FZ **m**
closed Saturday lunch and Sunday – **M** a la carte 210/365.

XX **Lutterbach**, 10 r. Faidherbe ⊠ 59800 ℰ 20 55 13 74 – ⅍ ⓞ ☖ FY **n**
closed 20 July-11 August – **M** 80/130 ⅃.

XX **Le Féguide** (Station Buffet), pl. Gare ⌧ 59800 𝒫 20 06 15 50, Fax 20 06 10 40 – 🆎 ⓞ
ⒼⒷ   FY
closed Sunday dinner and Saturday – **M** 120/180 ⅄ - **Le P'tit Féguide M** 62/80 ⅄.

XX **La Petite Taverne,** 9 r. Plat ⌧ 59800 𝒫 20 54 79 36 – 🆎 ⒼⒷ   FZ **w**
closed August, Tuesday dinner and Monday – **M** 89/199 ⅄.

XX **La Coquille,** 60 r. St-Étienne ⌧ 59800 𝒫 20 54 29 82, 17C house – ⒼⒷ   EY **e**
closed 1 to 25 August, February Holidays, Saturday lunch and Sunday – **M** 130/210.

X **Le Hochepot,** 6 r. Nouveau Siècle 𝒫 20 54 17 59, Fax 20 42 92 43 – ⒼⒷ   EY **a**
closed Saturday lunch and Sunday – **M** 120/170.

at Marcq-en-Baroeul by ② and N 350 : 5 km – pop. 36 601 – ⌧ 59700 :

🏨 **Sofitel** Ⓜ, av. Marne 𝒫 20 72 17 30, Telex 132785, Fax 20 89 92 34 – 📶 ⅏ 🖥 rm 📺 ☎
& Ⓟ – 🕭 200. 🆎 ⓞ ⒼⒷ ⒿⒸⒷ
L'Europe **M** 160 ⅄ – ⌑ 65 – **124 rm** 600.

XXX **Septentrion,** parc du château Vert Bois N : 2 km 𝒫 20 46 26 98, Fax 20 46 38 33, ⌕, « In
a park with lake » – Ⓟ 🆎 ⓞ ⒼⒷ
*closed 4 to 26 August, February Holiday Monday (except Bank Holidays), Thursday dinner and
Sunday dinner* – **M** 145/290.

at Villeneuve-d'Ascq by ②, N 356 and Highway of Roubaix (exit Recueil-La Cousinerie) :
7 km – pop. 65 320 – ⌧ 59650 :

🏨 **Relais d'Hermès** Ⓜ, 13 av. Créativité, Parc des Moulins 𝒫 20 47 46 46, Telex 130060,
Fax 20 91 36 55, ⌕ – 📶 ⅏ rm 📺 ☎ & Ⓟ – 🕭 50 - 180. 🆎 ⓞ ⒼⒷ
M 80/200 – ⌑ 35 – **84 rm** 300.

🏨 **Campanile,** av. Canteleu, La Cousinerie 𝒫 20 91 83 10, Telex 133335, Fax 20 67 21 18 –
📺 ☎ & Ⓟ. 🆎 ⒼⒷ
M 77 b.i./99 b.i. – ⌑ 28 – **50 rm** 258.

XX **Vieille Forge,** 160 r. Lannoy at Le Recueil 𝒫 20 05 50 75, Fax 20 91 28 24, ⌕, ⌖ – Ⓟ.
🆎 ⓞ ⒼⒷ ⒿⒸⒷ
*closed Sunday dinner, Monday dinner 1 June-31 August and dinner (except Saturday) 1 Sep-
tember-31 May* – **M** 110 b.i./250 ⅄.

at Lille-Lesquin Airport by ④ and A 1 : 8 km – ⌧ 59810 Lesquin :

🏨 **Mercure Lille Aéroport** Ⓜ ⌖, 𝒫 20 87 46 46, Telex 132051, Fax 20 87 46 47, 🖾 – 📶
⅏ rm 🖥 📺 ☎ & Ⓟ. 🆎 ⓞ ⒼⒷ ⒿⒸⒷ
Grill La Flamme **M** 95 b.i./170 b.i. – **Snack Angus M** 72/90 ⅄ – ⌑ 55 – **213 rm**
540/680.

🏨 **Novotel Lille Aéroport** Ⓜ, 𝒫 20 97 92 25, Telex 820519, Fax 20 97 36 12, ⌕, ⌦, ⌖ –
📶 ⅏ 🖥 rest 📺 ☎ Ⓟ – 🕭 25 - 200. 🆎 ⓞ ⒼⒷ ⒿⒸⒷ
M a la carte approx. 170 – ⌑ 55 – **92 rm** 490/540.

🏨 **Agena** without rest, ⌧ 59155 Faches-Thumesnil 𝒫 20 60 13 14, Fax 20 97 31 79 – 📺 ☎
& Ⓟ. 🆎 ⒼⒷ
⌑ 42 – **40 rm** 320/350.

🏨 **Climat de France** ⌖, ⌧ 59155 Faches-Thumesnil 𝒫 20 97 00 24, Fax 20 97 00 67 – 📺
☎ & Ⓟ. 🆎 ⓞ ⒼⒷ
M 78/110 ⅄ – ⌑ 30 – **42 rm** 250/280.

at Loos SW : 4 km by D 941 – pop. 20 657 – ⌧ 59120 :

XX ⚬ **L'Enfant Terrible** (Desplanques), 25 r. Mar. Foch 𝒫 20 07 22 11, ⌕ – ⒼⒷ
closed August, Sunday dinner and Monday – **M** (booking essential) 180/400
Spec. Foie gras de canard mariné au vin de pêche, Pigeon à la vapeur d'ail, Millefeuille de crêpes
à la chicorée.

at Englos by ⑥ and A 25 : 10 km (exit Lomme) – ⌧ 59320 :

🏨 **Novotel Lille Lomme** Ⓜ ⌖, 𝒫 20 07 09 99, Telex 132120, Fax 20 44 74 58, ⌕, ⌦, ⌖
– ⅏ rm 📺 ☎ & Ⓟ – 🕭 25 - 300. 🆎 ⓞ ⒼⒷ
M a la carte approx. 120 – ⌑ 52 – **124 rm** 430/480.

🏨 **Mercure Lille Lomme** Ⓜ ⌖, 𝒫 20 92 30 15, Telex 820302, Fax 20 93 75 66, ⌕, 🖾 –
🖥 rest 📺 ☎ ⓞ – 🕭 200. 🆎 ⓞ ⒼⒷ
M 65/145 – ⌑ 50 – **87 rm** 420/530.

See : Site★★★ - Old Lyons★★ (Vieux Lyon) BX : Hôtel Bullioud : loggia★★ **B**, St-Jean★ : Chancel★★, - rue St-Jean★ 92, Hôtel de Gadagne★ **M1**, Basilica of N.-D.-de-Fourvière ✵★★ from the observatory, ← from the esplanade BX - Tête d'Or Park★ rose garden★ (roseraie) – Place des Terreaux : fountain★ CV – Underground passageways (Traboules) – Punch and Judy Show (Théâtre de Guignol) BX **N** – Museums : Textile★★ CZ **M2**, Gallo-Roman Civilization★★ (Claudian table★★★) BX **M3**, Fine Arts★★★ CV **M4**, Decorative Arts★★ CZ **M5**, Printing and Banking★★ CX **M6**, Guimet Natural History★★ – Puppet★ BX **M1**.

Envir. : Rochetaillée : Museum Henri Malartre★★ : 12 km.

🏌 🏌 Villette d'Anthon ✆ 78 31 11 33 to the E : 21 km ; 🏌 Verger-Lyon at St-Symphorien-d'Ozon ✆ 78 02 24 20, to the S : 14 km ; 🏌 Lyon-Chassieu at Chassieu ✆ 78 90 84 77, E : 12 km by D 29 ; 🏌 🏌 Salvagny (private) at the Tour of Salvagny ✆ 78 48 83 60 ; jonction Lyon-Ouest : 8 km.

✈ of Lyon-Satolas ✆ 72 22 76 20 to the E : 27 km.

🚗 ✆ 78 92 50 50.

🛈 Office de Tourisme and Accueil de France (Information, exchange facilities, hotel reservations - not more than 5 days in advance), pl. Bellecour ✆ 78 42 25 75, Telex 330032 and Centre d'Echange de Perrache ✆ 78 42 22 07 – A.C. 7 r. Grolée ✆ 78 42 51 01.

Paris 462 - Genève 151 - Grenoble 105 - Marseilles 313 - St-Étienne 60 - Torino 300.

Plans on following pages

Hotels

Town Centre (Bellecour-Terreaux) :

🏨 **Sofitel** Ⓜ, 20 quai Gailleton ⊠ 69002 ✆ 72 41 20 20, Telex 330225, Fax 72 40 05 50, ← – |≡| ↔ rm ≡ 🔟 ☎ 🚗 – 🔬 250. 🆎 ⓪ 🆚 🇯🇨🇧 CY **k**
Les Trois Dômes (8th floor) **M** a la carte 230/380 – **Sofi Shop** (ground floor) **M** a la carte 130/200 🍷 – �byₑ 75 – **154 rm** 770/995, 21 suites 995/1800.

🏨 **Gd Hôtel Concorde** Ⓜ, 11 r. Grolée ⊠ 69002 ✆ 72 40 45 45, Telex 330244, Fax 78 37 52 55 – |≡| ↔ rm ≡ 🔟 ☎ – 🔬 80. 🆎 ⓪ 🆚 🇯🇨🇧 ✾ DX **e**
Le Fiorelle *(closed Sunday lunch)* **M** 98/180 🍷 – ⊆ 60 – **140 rm** 540/890, 3 suites.

🏨 **Royal,** 20 pl. Bellecour ⊠ 69002 ✆ 78 37 57 31, Telex 310785, Fax 78 37 01 36 – |≡| ↔ rm ≡ rm 🔟 ☎. 🆎 ⓪ 🆚 🇯🇨🇧 CY **d**
M grill 90/130 🍷 – ⊆ 60 – **79 rm** 490/850.

🏨 **Carlton** without rest, 4 r. Jussieu ⊠ 69002 ✆ 78 42 56 51, Telex 310787, Fax 78 42 10 71 – |≡| ≡ 🔟 ☎. 🆎 ⓪ 🆚 🇯🇨🇧 DX **f**
⊆ 50 – **83 rm** 430/700.

🏨 **Gd H. des Beaux-Arts** without rest, 75 r. Prés. E. Herriot ⊠ 69002 ✆ 78 38 09 50, Telex 330442, Fax 78 42 19 19 – |≡| ↔ ≡ 🔟 ☎ – 🔬 30. 🆎 ⓪ 🆚 🇯🇨🇧 CX **t**
⊆ 50 – **79 rm** 330/570.

🏨 **La Résidence** without rest, 18 r. V. Hugo ⊠ 69002 ✆ 78 42 63 28, Telex 900950, Fax 78 42 85 76 – |≡| 🔟 ☎. 🆎 ⓪ 🆚 CY **s**
⊆ 30 – **65 rm** 260/290.

🏨 **Globe et Cécil** without rest, 21 r. Gasparin ⊠ 69002 ✆ 78 42 58 95, Telex 305184, Fax 72 41 99 06 – |≡| 🔟 ☎. 🆎 ⓪ 🆚 🇯🇨🇧 CY **b**
⊆ 42 – **65 rm** 300/440.

🏨 **Bellecordière** without rest, 18 r. Bellecordière ⊠ 69002 ✆ 78 42 27 78, Telex 301633, Fax 72 40 92 27 – |≡| 🔟 ☎ ⅙. 🆎 🆚 CY **a**
⊆ 32 – **45 rm** 240/314.

Perrache :

🏨 **Pullman Perrache,** 12 cours Verdun ⊠ 69002 ✆ 78 37 58 11, Telex 330500, Fax 78 37 06 56, 斎, « Art nouveau decor » – |≡| ↔ rm ≡ 🔟 ☎ ⅙ 🅿 – 🔬 250. 🆎 ⓪ 🆚 BZ **a**
Les Belles Saisons **M** 130 b.i./250 – ⊆ 58 – **124 rm** 450/760.

🏨 **Charlemagne** Ⓜ, 23 cours Charlemagne ⊠ 69002 ✆ 78 92 81 61, Telex 380401, Fax 78 42 94 84, 斎 – |≡| ≡ 🔟 ☎ 🚗 🅿 – 🔬 120. 🆎 ⓪ 🆚
M *(closed Saturday and Sunday)* 120/170 – ⊆ 48 – **116 rm** 383/531.

Vieux-Lyon :

🏨 **Cour des Loges** Ⓜ 🐾, 6 r. Bœuf ⊠ 69005 ✆ 78 42 75 75, Telex 330831, Fax 72 40 93 61, « Contemporary decor in houses of Old Lyons » – |≡| ≡ 🔟 ☎ ⅙ 🚗 – 🔬 45. 🆎 ⓪ 🆚 BX **n**
🇯🇨🇧
Tapas des Loges **M** a la carte approx. 160 – ⊆ 100 – **53 rm** 1150/1600, 10 suites 2000/3000.

🏨 ✿ **Tour Rose** (Chavent) Ⓜ 🐾, 22 r. Bœuf ⊠ 69005 ✆ 78 37 25 90, Fax 78 42 26 02, « 17C house, tasteful decor depicting the story of silk », 斎 – |≡| ≡ 🔟 ☎ 🚗 – 🔬 25. 🆎 ⓪ 🆚 🇯🇨🇧 BX **e**
M *(closed Sunday)* 350/550 – ⊆ 90 – **6 rm** 950/1500, 6 suites 1500/2500, 4 duplex
Spec. Salade de pommes de terre à la crème de caviar, Saumon mi-cuit au fumoir, Foie chaud de canard et filet de rouget aux lentilles. Wines Viognier, Brouilly.

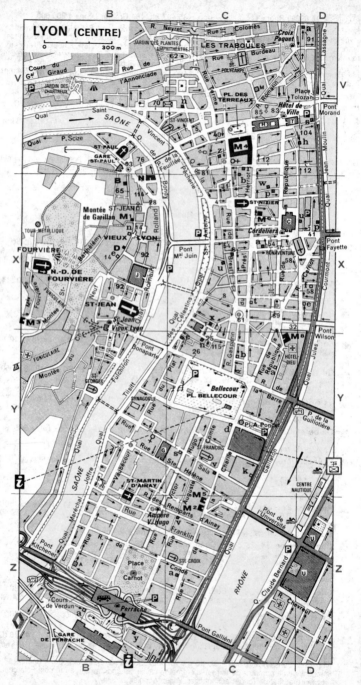

La Croix-Rousse (Bord de Saône) :

🏨🏨 **Lyon Métropole** Ⓜ, 85 quai J. Gillet ⊠ 69004 ☎ 78 29 20 20, Telex 380198, Fax 78 39 99 20, ⇆, 🛁, ⚓ – ⚒ ‰ rm 🗐 📺 ☎ 🅟 – 🔼 350. ఔ ⑩ ⬛
Grill **M** a la carte 100/200 – **Les Eaux Vives** ☎ 78 29 36 36 *(closed 24 December-1 January and Sunday July-August)* **M** 135/200 – 🖵 49 – **119 rm** 455/550.

Les Brotteaux :

🏨🏨 **Roosevelt**, 25 r. Bossuet ⊠ 69006 ☎ 78 52 35 67, Telex 300295, Fax 78 52 39 82 – 🛗 🗐 📺 ☎ ⚓ 🅟 – 🔼 40
87 rm.

🏨 **Olympique** without rest, 62 r. Garibaldi ⊠ 69006 ☎ 78 89 48 04, Fax 78 89 49 97 – 🛗 📺 ☎. ఔ ⬛ ⬛
🖵 28 – **23 rm** 255/265.

La Part-Dieu :

🏨🏨 **Holiday Inn Crowne Plaza** Ⓜ, 29 r. Bonnel ☎ 72 61 90 90, Telex 330703, Fax 72 61 17 54, 🎴 – 🛗 ‰ rm 🗐 📺 ☎ ⚓ – 🔼 200. ఔ ⑩ ⬛ ⬛
M 130/190 🍷 – 🖵 70 – **156 rm** 810/1350.

🏨🏨 ❀ **Pullman Part-Dieu** Ⓜ, 129 r. Servient (32nd floor) ⊠ 69003 ☎ 78 62 94 12, Telex 380088, Fax 78 60 41 77, ⬻ Lyons and Valley of the Rhône – 🛗 ‰ rm 🗐 📺 ☎ ⚓ – 🔼 300. ఔ ⑩ ⬛ ⬛
L'Arc-en-Ciel (closed 20 July-20 August and Sunday dinner) **M** a la carte 240/390 – **La Ripaille** grill (ground floor) **M** a la carte 120/190 🍷 – 🖵 58 – **245 rm** 595/895.
Spéc. Terrine de langoustines au foie gras, Gigotin de lotte braisé au lard fumé, Râble de lapereau au citron et au basilic thai.

🏨🏨 **Mercure** Ⓜ, 47 bd Vivier-Merle ⊠ 69003 ☎ 72 34 18 12, Telex 306469, Fax 78 53 40 69 – 🛗 🗐 📺 ☎ ⚓ 🅟 – 🔼 100. ఔ ⑩ ⬛ ⬛
M 125/145 🍷 – 🖵 50 – **124 rm** 530/610.

🏨 **Créqui** Ⓜ without rest, 158 r. Créqui ⊠ 69003 ☎ 78 60 20 47, Fax 78 62 21 12 – 🛗 📺 ☎. ⬛
🖵 42 – **28 rm** 320/350.

🏨 **Ibis** Ⓜ, pl. Renaudel ⊠ 69003 ☎ 78 95 42 11, Telex 310847, Fax 78 60 42 85, 🍴 – 🛗 ‰ rm 🗐 📺 ☎ ⚓ – 🔼 30. ⬛
M 79/128 🍷 – 🖵 32 – **144 rm** 325/345.

La Guillotière :

🏨 **Gd H. Helder et Institut** without rest, 38 r. Marseille ⊠ 69007 ☎ 78 61 61 61, Telex 306411, Fax 78 61 61 00 – 🛗 📺 ☎. ఔ ⑩ ⬛
98 rm 🖵 340/480.

🏨 **Columbia** without rest, 8 pl. A. Briand ⊠ 69003 ☎ 78 60 54 65, Telex 305551, Fax 78 62 04 88 – 🛗 📺 ☎. ఔ ⬛ ⬛
🖵 31 – **66 rm** 230/270.

🏨 **Urbis Université** Ⓜ without rest, 51 r. Université ⊠ 69007 ☎ 78 72 78 42, Telex 340455, Fax 78 69 24 36 – 🛗 🗐 📺 ☎ ⚓. ఔ ⬛
🖵 34 – **53 rm** 295/345.

Gerland :

🏨 **Mercure** Ⓜ, 70 av. Leclerc ⊠ 69007 ☎ 78 58 68 53, Telex 305484, Fax 78 61 05 54, 🦐, 🔍 – 📳 🔟 🚗 ⅍ ⟷ – 🔥 450. ⒶⒺ ⓪ ⒼⒷ ⒿⒸⒷ
M 125/145 ⅍ – ⚏ 50 – **194 rm** 530/610.

🏨 **Ibis** Ⓜ, 68 av. Leclerc ⊠ 69007 ☎ 78 58 30 70, Telex 305483, Fax 78 72 28 61 – 📳 🔟 ☎ 🚗 ⟷ – 🔥 30. ⒼⒷ
M 79 ⅍ – ⚏ 32 – **129 rm** 310/330.

Montchat-Monplaisir :

🏨 **Mercure Lyon Lumière** Ⓜ, 71 cours Albert Thomas ⊠ 69003 ☎ 78 53 76 76, Fax 72 36 97 65 – 📳 ⅍⅍ rm 🖃 🔟 ☎ ⅍ ⟷ – 🔥 25 - 70. ⒶⒺ ⓪ ⒼⒷ
M 125 ⅍ – ⚏ 49 – **79 rm** 500/550.

🏨 **Altea Park,** 4 r. Prof. Calmette ⊠ 69008 ☎ 78 74 11 20, Telex 380230, Fax 78 01 43 38, 🦐 – 📳 🔟 ☎ 🚗 – 🔥 25. ⒶⒺ ⓪ ⒼⒷ
le Patio *(closed Sunday lunch and Saturday)* M 80/120 ⅍ – ⚏ 46 – **72 rm** 375/410.

🏨 **Lacassagne** without rest, 245 av. Lacassagne ⊠ 69003 ☎ 78 54 09 12, Fax 72 36 99 23 – 📳 🖃 🔟 ☎. ⒶⒺ ⓪ ⒼⒷ
⚏ 25 – **40 rm** 180/260.

at Bron : pop. 39 683 – ⊠ 69500 :

🏨 **Novotel** Ⓜ, av. J. Monnet ☎ 78 26 97 48, Telex 340781, Fax 78 26 45 12, 🦐, 🔍, 🏊 – 📳 🖃 🔟 ☎ ⅍ 🅿 – 🔥 25 - 800. ⒶⒺ ⓪ ⒼⒷ ⒿⒸⒷ
M a la carte approx. 160 ⅍ – ⚏ 47 – **189 rm** 415/430.

Restaurants

❌❌❌❌❌ ❀❀❀ **Paul Bocuse,** bridge of Collonges N : 12 km by the banks of River Saône (D 433, D 51) ⊠ 69660 Collonges-au-Mont-d'Or ☎ 78 22 01 40, Telex 375382, Fax 72 27 85 87, « Tasteful decor » – 🖃 🅿. ⒶⒺ ⓪ ⒼⒷ
M 390 (lunch)/710 and a la carte 470/720
Spec. Soupe aux truffes noires, Rouget barbet en écailles de pommes de terre, Volaille de Bresse en vessie. Wines Saint-Véran, Brouilly.

❌❌❌❌ ❀ **Orsi,** 3 pl. Kléber ⊠ 69006 ☎ 78 89 57 68, Telex 305965, Fax 72 44 93 34, 🦐, « Tasteful decor » – ⅍⅍ 🖃. ⒶⒺ ⒼⒷ
closed Saturday in July-August and Sunday except lunch from September-July – M 260 (lunch)/450
Spec. Raviole de foie gras au jus de Porto, Marinière de rouget et daurade au basilic, Pigeonneau de Bresse rôti aux gousses d'ail.

❌❌❌❌ **Roger Roucou "Mère Guy"** (bedrooms planned), 35 quai J. J. Rousseau ⊠ 69350 La Mulatière ☎ 78 51 65 37, Fax 78 51 99 47 – 🅿. ⒶⒺ ⓪ ⒼⒷ
closed August, Sunday dinner and Monday – M 250/450.

❌❌❌ ❀ **Léon de Lyon** (Lacombe), 1 r. Pleney ⊠ 69001 ☎ 78 28 11 33, Telex 300134, Fax 78 39 89 05, « Lyonnaise atmosphere » – ⅍⅍ 🖃. ⒶⒺ ⒼⒷ ⒿⒸⒷ   CVX **b**
closed 2 to 24 August, Monday lunch and Sunday – M 250/440
Spec. Pâté en croûte à l'ancienne, Pigeonneau "demi-deuil" (April-June and September-November), Six desserts au chocolat amer. Wines Pouilly Fuissé, Moulin à Vent.

❌❌❌ ❀ **Aub. de Fond-Rose** (Brunet), 23 quai Clemenceau ⊠ 69300 Caluire-et-Cuire ☎ 78 29 34 61, Fax 72 00 28 67, 🦐, « Garden » – 🅿. ⒶⒺ ⓪ ⒼⒷ ⒿⒸⒷ
closed Monday from October-April and Sunday dinner – M 190/420
Spec. Volaille de Bresse au vinaigre, Suprême de dorade aux câpres (spring-summer), Salpicon de Saint-Jacques et langoustines (winter-spring).

❌❌❌ ❀ **Bourillot,** 8 pl. Célestins ⊠ 69002 ☎ 78 37 38 64 – 🖃. ⒶⒺ ⓪ ⒼⒷ ⒿⒸⒷ   CY **n**
closed 4 July-3 August, 23 December-2 January, Sunday and Bank Holidays – M 225/425
Spec. Quenelle de brochet au fumet de homard, Volaille de Bresse "Marie" pommes aux truffes, Soufflé glacé au chocolat. Wines Coteaux du Lyonnais, Saint-Véran.

❌❌❌ ❀ **Nandron,** 26 quai J. Moulin ⊠ 69002 ☎ 78 42 10 26, Fax 78 37 69 88 – ⅍⅍ 🖃. ⒶⒺ ⓪ ⒼⒷ ⒿⒸⒷ   DX **p**
closed 25 July-23 August and Saturday – M 310/450
Spec. Terrine tiède de champignons des bois, Quenelle de brochet à la Nantua, Rognon rôti en cocotte au thym. Wines Mâcon, Saint-Joseph.

❌❌❌ ❀ **Mère Brazier,** 12 r. Royale ⊠ 69001 ☎ 78 28 15 49, « Lyonnaise atmosphere » – ⅍⅍. ⒶⒺ ⓪ ⒼⒷ ⒿⒸⒷ   DV **a**
closed August, Saturday (except dinner from 1 August-15 June), Sunday and Bank Holidays – M 300/350
Spec. Fond d'artichaut au foie gras, Quenelle au gratin, Volaille de Bresse "demi-deuil". Wines Chiroubles, Saint-Joseph.

❌❌❌ ❀ **Fédora** (Judéaux), 249 r. M. Merieux ⊠ 69007 ☎ 78 69 46 26, Fax 72 73 38 80, 🦐 – ⒶⒺ ⒼⒷ ⒿⒸⒷ
closed 23 December-4 January, Saturday lunch, Sunday and Bank Holidays – M 160/260 ⅍
Spec. Saint-Jacques en coquille au beurre demi-sel (October-April), Homard en os à moelle, Ragoût d'encornets au poivre. Wines Mâcon.

XXX **Le Saint Alban,** 2 quai J. Moulin ⊠ 69001 *ℰ* 78 30 14 89 – ▤. ⁛ ᵍᵇ   DV **s**
*closed 1 to 23 August, Saturday except dinner September-June, Sunday and Bank Holidays
– M* 140/260.

XXX **Les Fantasques,** 47 r. Bourse ⊠ 69002 *ℰ* 78 37 36 58 – ▤. ⁛ ⓞ ᵍᵇ   DX **u**
closed 8 to 31 August and Sunday – M 250/350.

XXX **Henry,** 27 r. Martinière ⊠ 69001 *ℰ* 78 28 26 08, Fax 78 27 97 15, « Mural paintings » –
▤. ⁛ ⓞ ᵍᵇ – *closed Monday – M* 120/250 ᗐ.   CV **n**

XXX **Junet "Au Petit Col",** 68 r. Charité ⊠ 69002 *ℰ* 78 37 25 18 – ▤. ⁛ ᵍᵇ   CZ **a**
closed Sunday except lunch from September-June and Monday – M 145/355.

XX **La Mère Vittet** (24 hr service), 26 cours Verdun ⊠ 69002 *ℰ* 78 37 20 17, Fax 78 42 40 70
– ⥩ ▤. ⁛ ⓞ ᵍᵇ ᴶᶜᴮ   BZ **y**
M 135/285 ᗐ.

XX **Le Nord,** 18 r. Neuve ⊠ 69002 *ℰ* 78 28 24 54, Fax 72 28 76 58 – ▤. ⁛ ᵍᵇ   CX **p**
closed 8 to 15 August and Saturday – M 90/230 ᗐ.

XX ❀ **Le Passage,** 8 r. Plâtre ⊠ 69001 *ℰ* 78 28 11 16 – ▤. ⁛ ⓞ ᵍᵇ   CV **r**
closed Saturday lunch, Sunday and Bank Holidays – M 245/330
Spec. Homard breton au cumin et lentilles au lard, Matelote de lotte au vin rouge, Pigeonneau
rôti et escalope de foie gras aux épices (except summer). Wines Bourgogne Aligoté, Côtes-du-
Rhône.

XX ❀ **L'Alexandrin** (Alexanian), 83 r. Moncey ⊠ 69003 *ℰ* 72 61 15 69 – ▤. ᵍᵇ. ⥷
closed 9 to 31 August, 24 December-4 January, Sunday and Monday – M 145/185
Spec. Terrine de foie gras de canard aux girolles, Escalope de thon sur purée d'artichaut, Grouse
rôtie à la feuille de vigne (season). Wines Saint-Joseph.

XX ❀ **Tante Alice,** 22 r. Remparts d'Ainay ⊠ 69002 *ℰ* 78 37 49 83 – ▤. ⁛ ᵍᵇ   CZ **v**
closed 31 July-31 August, Friday dinner and Saturday – M 92/194.

XX **La Tassée,** 20 r. Charité ⊠ 69002 *ℰ* 78 37 02 35, Fax 72 40 05 91 – ⁛ ⓞ ᵍᵇ ᴶᶜᴮ   CY **v**
closed 24 December-2 January, Saturday July-August and Sunday – M 120/190.

XX **Gourmet de Sèze,** 129 r. Sèze ⊠ 69006 *ℰ* 78 24 23 42 – ᵍᵇ
closed 15 July-15 August, Saturday lunch, Sunday and Bank Holidays – M 100/220.

XX **Chez Gervais,** 42 r. P. Corneille ⊠ 69006 *ℰ* 78 52 19 13 – ⁛ ⓞ ᵍᵇ
closed July, Saturday except dinner 15 September-1 May, Sunday and Monday –
M 150/185.

XX **La Voûte,** 11 pl. A. Gourju ⊠ 69002 *ℰ* 78 42 01 33, Fax 78 37 36 41 – ▤. ⁛ ⓞ ᵍᵇ
closed 11 to 27 July and Sunday – M 98/160.   CY **e**

X **Chez Jean-François,** 2 pl. Célestins ⊠ 69002 *ℰ* 78 42 08 26 – ᵍᵇ   CX **x**
closed 17 to 26 April, 25 July-24 August, Sunday and Bank Holidays – M 80/150 ᗐ.

X **Le Bistrot de Lyon,** 64 r. Mercière ⊠ 69002 *ℰ* 78 37 00 62, Fax 78 38 32 51, ⥂ – ▤.
ᵍᵇ. ⥷   CX **u**
M a la carte 180/220.

X **La Pinte à Gones,** 59 r. Ney ⊠ 69006 *ℰ* 78 24 81 75 – ᵍᵇ – *closed August, 24 December-
1 January, Saturday lunch, Sunday and Bank Holidays – M* 98/198.

Bouchons : Regional specialities and wine tasting in a typical local atmosphere

X **Le Garet,** 7 r. Garet ⊠ 69001 *ℰ* 78 28 16 94 – ᵍᵇ – *closed 15 July-15 August, 23 Decem-
ber-2 January, Saturday and Sunday – M* (booking essential) a la carte 110/180.   CDV **h**

X **Chez Sylvain,** 4 r. Tupin ⊠ 69002 *ℰ* 78 42 11 98 – *closed 18 July-17 August, February
Holidays, Saturday and Sunday – M* (booking essential) 80/92 a la carte dinner.   CX **s**

X **La Meunière,** 11 r. Neuve ⊠ 69002 *ℰ* 78 28 62 91 – ⁛ ⓞ ᵍᵇ   CX **w**
closed 17 July-18 August, Sunday and Monday – M (booking essential) 80/130.

X **Café du Jura,** 25 r. Tupin ⊠ 69002 *ℰ* 78 42 20 57 – ⁛ ᵍᵇ   CX **a**
*closed 1 to 23 August, 25 December-1 January, Saturday (except dinner 30 September-1 May)
and Sunday – M* (booking essential) a la carte 110/170 ᗐ.

X **Café des Fédérations,** 8 r. Major Martin ⊠ 69001 *ℰ* 78 28 26 00 – ⁛ ᵍᵇ   CV **z**
closed August, Saturday and Sunday – M (booking essential) 135.

Environs

to the NE :

at Rillieux-la-Pape : 7 km by N 83 and N 84 – pop. 30 791 – ⊠ 69140 :

XXX ❀ **Larivoire** (Constantin), chemin des Iles *ℰ* 78 88 50 92, Fax 78 88 35 22, ≤, ⥂ – ℗. ᵍᵇ
closed 24 August-2 September, 1 to 20 February, Monday dinner and Tuesday – M 190/380
Spec. Millefeuille de tourteau, Crépinettes de pieds de veau aux truffes, Volaille de Bresse au
vinaigre. Wines Pouilly, Chénas.

at Neyron (01 Ain) 14 km by N 83 and N 84 – ⊠ 01700 :

XXX ❀ **Le Saint Didier** (Champin), *ℰ* 78 55 28 72, Fax 78 55 01 55, ⥂ – ℗. ⁛ ᵍᵇ
closed 3 to 25 August, 21 December-5 January, Sunday lunch and Monday – M (booking
essential) 175/400
Spec. Profiteroles de foie gras sauce perigourdine (October-May), Salade de rougets et Saint-
Jacques poêlés au safran, Rosace de magrets de canard aux fruits.

to the E :

at the Satolas airport : 27 km by A 43 – ⊠ 69125 Lyon Satolas Airport :

🏨 **Sofitel** Ⓜ without rest, (3rd floor) ℰ 72 23 38 00, Telex 380480, Fax 72 23 98 00, ≼ – 🛗 🖂
🔲 📺 ☎ 🄰🄴 ⑩ 🌫
⌷ 65 – **120 rm** 620.

❌❌❌ **La Gde Corbeille,** (1st floor) ℰ 72 22 71 76, Telex 306723, Fax 72 22 71 72, ≼ – 🔲. 🄰🄴 ⑩ 🌫
closed August, Saturday and Sunday – **M** 135/180.

❌ **Le Bouchon,** (1st floor) ℰ 72 22 71 99, Telex 306723, Fax 72 22 71 72, brasserie – 🔲. 🄰🄴
⑩ 🌫
M 120.

to the NW :

Porte de Lyon - motorway junction A 6, N 6 Exit road signposted Limonest N : 10 km –
⊠ 69570 Dardilly :

🏨 **Novotel Lyon-Nord** Ⓜ, ℰ 78 35 13 41, Telex 330962, Fax 78 35 08 45, 🏡, 🏊, 🎾 – 🛗
🔲 📺 ☎ 🄿 – 🔏 150 ⅄ – ⌷ 47 – **107 rm** 425/445.
M a la carte approx. 150 ⅄ – ⌷ 47 – **107 rm** 425/445.

🏨 **Mercure** Ⓜ, ℰ 78 35 28 05, Telex 330045, Fax 78 47 47 15, 🏡, 🏊, 🎾 – 🛗 🖂 rm 🔲 rest
📺 ☎ 🝁 🄿 – 🔏 30 - 250. 🄰🄴 ⑩ 🌫 🇯🇨🇧
M 150 b.i./190 b.i. – ⌷ 52 – **172 rm** 410/475.

🏨 **Ibis Lyon Nord** Ⓜ, ℰ 78 66 02 20, Telex 305250, Fax 78 47 47 93, 🏡, 🏊 – 📺 ☎ 🝁 🄿
– 🔏 30. 🄰🄴 🌫
M 88/120 – ⌷ 32 – **69 rm** 305/335.

Chagny 71150 Saône-et-Loire. 🔢 ⑨ – pop. 5 346 alt. 216.
Lyon 145.

🏨 ❀❀❀ **Lameloise** Ⓜ, pl. d'Armes ℰ 85 87 08 85, Telex 801086, Fax 85 87 03 57, « Old Bur-
gundian house, tasteful decor » – 🛗 📺 ☎ 🝁. 🄰🄴 🌫
closed 23 December-27 January, Thursday lunch and Wednesday – **M** (booking essential) a
la carte 310/480 – ⌷ 80 – **19 rm** 500/1300
Spec. Ravioli d'escargots de Bourgogne dans leur bouillon d'ail doux, Pigeon de Bresse en vessie
et pâtes fraîches au foie gras, Assiette du chocolatier. **Wines** Chassagne-Montrachet rouge, Rully
blanc.

Mionnay 01390 Ain 🔢 ② – pop. 1 103 alt. 288.
Lyon 23.

❌❌❌❌ ❀❀ **Alain Chapel** with rm, ℰ 78 91 82 02, Telex 305605, Fax 78 91 82 37, 🏡, « Floral
garden » – 📺 ☎ 🝁 🄿. 🄰🄴 ⑩ 🌫
closed January, Tuesday lunch and Monday – **M** 600/720 and a la carte – ⌷ 75 – **13 rm** 700/825
Spec. Bouillon de champignons de printemps, Ragoût de homard breton, Côte de veau (April-
September). **Wines** Mâcon Villages, Vosne-Romanée.

Montrond-les-Bains 42210 Loire 🔢 ⑱ – pop. 3 627 alt. 356.
Lyon 62.

🏨 ❀❀ **Host. La Poularde** (Etéocle), ℰ 77 54 40 06, Telex 307002, Fax 77 54 53 14, 🎾 – 🔲 rest
🔲 ☎ 🝁 – 🔏 40. 🄰🄴 ⑩ 🌫 🇯🇨🇧
closed 2 to 15 January, Tuesday lunch and Monday dinner except Bank Holidays – **M** (Sunday :
booking essential) 180/480 and a la carte – ⌷ 60 – **11 rm** 300/470, 3 duplex 800
Spec. Saumon mariné tiédi aux graines de sésame, Fricassée de poulette aux cèpes, Gibier (season). **Wines** Condrieu, Saint-Joseph.

Roanne ◈ 42300 Loire 🔢 ⑦ – pop. 41 756 alt. 279.
Lyon 87.

🏨 ❀❀❀ **Troisgros** Ⓜ, pl. Gare ℰ 77 71 66 97, Telex 307507, Fax 77 70 39 77, « Tasteful
contemporary decor », 🎾 – 🛗 🔲 📺 ☎ 🝁 🄿. 🄰🄴 ⑩ 🌫
closed February Holidays, Tuesday dinner and Wednesday – **M** (booking essential) 470/600
and a la carte 430/620 – ⌷ 55 – **14 rm** 700/1200, 6 duplex 1400/2000
Spec. Crème de cuisses de grenouilles en champignonade, Halicot de pigeonneau au basilic,
Filet de bœuf poché au bouillon de pot-au-feu et râpé de raifort. **Wines** Pouilly-Fuissé, Côte Roan-
naise.

St-Étienne 🅿 42000 Loire 🔢 ⑲, 🔢 ⑨ – pop. 199 396 alt. 517.
Lyon 60.

❌❌❌ ❀❀ **Pierre Gagnaire,** 3 r. Teissier (moving in May to 7 r. Richelandière) ℰ 77 37 57 93,
Fax 77 32 70 58 – 🖂. 🄰🄴 ⑩ 🌫
closed 9 to 20 August, 2 to 10 January, Monday lunch and Sunday – **M** 270 (lunch)/595 and
a la carte
Spec. Attereaux de crêtes de coq et tourte de volaille aux noix, Pomme Macaire et boudin noir,
Soupe soufflée au chocolat et parfait à la pistache. **Wines** Condrieu, Côtes du Forez.

Valence ℙ 26000 Drôme 📖 ⑫ – pop. 63 437 alt. 123.

Lyon 101.

XXXXX ✿✿✿ **Pic** with rm, 285 av. V. Hugo, Motorway exit sign-posted Valence-Sud ℰ 75 44 15 32, Fax 75 40 96 03, 佘, « Floral garden » – 🍽 🖆 🔟 ☎ 👶 👄 ℗. ⚏ ⓞ ☒ ᴊᴄʙ
closed August, Sunday dinner and Wednesday – **M** (Sunday : booking essential) 250 (lunch)/580 and a la carte 530/560 – 🖙 85 – **3 rm** 650/850
Spec. Galette de truffes et céleri au foie de canard, Filet de loup au caviar, Strate de bœuf au Cornas. Wines Condrieu, Hermitage.

at Pont-de-l'Isère to the N by N 7 : 9 km – 📧 26600 :

XXX ✿✿ **Chabran** 🖩 with rm, N 7 ℰ 75 84 60 09, Telex 346333, Fax 75 84 59 65, 佘 – ✂ rest 🔳 🔟 ☎ 👶 ⚏ ⓞ ☒ ᴊᴄʙ
closed 4 to 18 January, Sunday dinner (except Bank Holidays) September-April and Monday except July-August and Banks – **M** 235/475 and a la carte – 🖙 70 – **12 rm** 350/710
Spec. Salade de homard au museau de porc, Galette de pommes de terre aux champignons des bois, Aile de pintade farcie et tapenade au jus de Crozes-Hermitage. Wines Crozes-Hermitage, Hermitage.

Vienne ☜ 38200 Isère 📖 ⑪ ⑫ – pop. 29 449 alt. 158.

Lyon 32.

🏔 ✿✿ **La Pyramide** 🖩, 14 bd F. Point par ④ ℰ 74 53 01 96, Telex 308058, Fax 74 85 69 73, 佘, 🌳 – 🍽 🖆 🔟 ☎ 👶 👄 ℗ – 🔬 25. ⚏ ⓞ ☒ ᴊᴄʙ
closed 1 February-7 March – **M** (closed Thursday lunch and Wednesday) 260/480 and a la carte – 🖙 80 – **24 rm** 750/800, 4 suites 1250
Spec. Gratin de queues d'écrevisses (15 June-1 October), Pigeonneau de Bresse rôti au jus truffé, Piano praliné aux amandes et chocolat. Wines Saint-Joseph blanc, Côtes du Rhône.

Vonnas 01540 Ain 📖 ② – pop. 2 381 alt. 189.

Lyon 63.

🏔 ✿✿✿ **Georges Blanc** 🖩 👒, ℰ 74 50 00 10, Telex 380776, Fax 74 50 08 80, « Elegant inn on the banks of the Veyle, garden », 🏊, 🎾 – 🍽 ✂ rest 🔳 🔟 ☎ 👶 ℗. ⚏ ⓞ ☒
closed 2 January-8 February – **M** (closed Thursday except dinner from 15 June-15 September and Wednesday except Bank Holidays)* (booking essential) 410/620 and a la carte 450/580 – 🖙 80 – **34 rm** 600/1600, 7 suites 1800/3200
Spec. Crêpe parmentière au saumon et caviar, Saint-Jacques rôties aux cèpes (October-April), Fricassée de poularde de Bresse aux gousses d'ail et foie gras. Wines Mâcon-Azé, Chiroubles.

MARSEILLES ℙ 13000 B.-du-R. 📖 ⑬ – pop. 800 550.

See : N.-D.-de-la-Garde Basilica ✳✳✳ EV – Old Port✳✳ DETU – Corniche Président-J.-F.-Kennedy✳✳ – Modern Port✳✳ – Palais Longchamp✳ GS – St-Victor Basilica✳ : crypt✳✳ DU – Old Major cathedral✳ DS N – Pharo Parc ✳ DU – St-Laurent Belvedere ✳ DT E – Museum : Grobet-Labadié✳✳ GS M7, Cantini✳ FU M5, Fine Arts✳ GS M8, Natural History Museum✳ GS M9 – Mediterranean Archaeology✳ : collection of Egyptian antiquities✳✳ (Old Charity✳) DS M6, Roman Docks DET M2 – Old Marseilles✳ DT M3.

Envir. : Corniche road✳✳ of Callelongue S : 13 km along the sea front.

Exc. : Château d'If✳✳ (✳✳✳) 1 h 30.

🏌 of Marseilles-Aix ℰ 42 24 20 41 to the N : 22 km ; 🏌 of Allauch-Marseilles (private) ℰ 91 05 20 60 ; junction Marseilles-East : 15 km, by D 2 and D 4 A ; 🏌 🏌 Country Club of la Salette ℰ 91 27 12 16 by A 50.

🛫 Marseilles-Marignane : ℰ 42 78 21 00 to the N : 28 km.

🚗 ℰ 91 08 50 50.

🛈 Office de Tourisme 4 Canebière, 13001 ℰ 91 54 91 11, Telex 430402 and St-Charles railway station ℰ 91 50 59 18 – A.C. 149 bd Rabatau, 13010 ℰ 91 78 83 00.

Paris 772 – Lyon 312 – Nice 188 – Torino 407 – Toulon 64 – Toulouse 401.

Plans on following pages

🏨 **Sofitel Vieux Port** 🖩, 36 bd Ch. Livon 📧 13007 ℰ 91 52 90 19, Telex 401270, Fax 91 31 46 52, panoramic restaurant ≤ old port, 🏊 – 🍽 ✂ rm 🔳 🔟 ☎ 👶 – 🔬 180. ⚏ ⓞ ☒
les Trois Forts **M** 180/280 – 🖙 70 – **127 rm** 660/960, 3 suites.   DU **n**

🏨 **Mercure-Centre** 🖩, r. Neuve St-Martin 📧 13001 ℰ 91 39 20 00, Telex 401886, Fax 91 56 24 57 – 🍽 ✂ rm 🔳 🔟 ☎ 👶 – 🔬 150. ⚏ ⓞ ☒   EST **g**
Oursinade *(closed August, Sunday and Bank Holidays)* **M** 198/280 – Oliveraie *(closed Saturday dinner)* **M** 120 – 🖙 50 – **198 rm** 680/750.

🏨 **Pullman Beauvau** without rest, 4 r. Beauvau 📧 13001 ℰ 91 54 91 00, Telex 401778, Fax 91 54 15 76 – 🍽 🖆 🔟 ☎ – 🔬 30. ⚏ ☒   ET **r**
🖙 65 – **71 rm** 600/840.

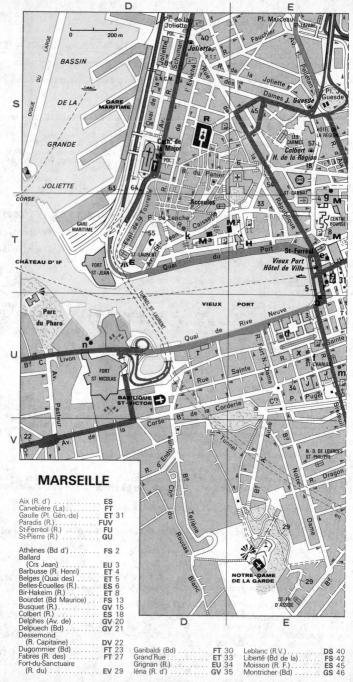

MARSEILLE

Novotel Marseille Centre M, 36 bd Ch. Livon ✉ 13007 ☎ 91 59 22 22, Telex 402937, Fax 91 31 15 48, ←, 🏞, 🏊 - 🛗 ⇸ rm ▤ TV ♿ 🚗 - 🏫 400. AE ⓓ GB JCB DU **n**
M a la carte approx. 150 🍷 - ☕ 47 - **90 rm** 480/540.

Concorde Prado, 11 av. Mazargues ✉ 13008 ☎ 91 76 51 11, Telex 420209, Fax 91 77 95 10 - 🛗 ⇸ rm ▤ TV ☎ - 🏫 100. AE ⓓ GB JCB. ✻ rest
M a la carte 160/250 - ☕ 60 - **100 rm** 545/660.

New H. Bompard 🐎 without rest, 2 r. Flots Bleus ✉ 13007 ☎ 91 52 10 93, Telex 400430, Fax 91 31 02 14, 🏞 - 🛗 TV ☎ Ⓟ - 🏫 40. AE ⓓ GB JCB
☕ 45 - **46 rm** 380/430.

St-Ferréol's M without rest, 19 r. Pisançon ✉ 13001 ☎ 91 33 12 21, Fax 91 54 29 97 - 🛗 ▤ TV ☎. AE GB FU **h**
closed 20 July-10 August - ☕ 35 - **19 rm** 275/410.

New H. Sélect M without rest, 4 allée Gambetta ✉ 13001 ☎ 91 50 65 50, Telex 402175, Fax 91 50 45 56 - 🛗 ▤ TV ☎ - 🏫 25. AE ⓓ GB JCB. ✻ FS **k**
☕ 45 - **60 rm** 310/400.

Alizé M without rest, 7 quai Belges ✉ 13001 ☎ 91 33 66 97, Fax 91 54 80 06, ← - 🛗 ▤ TV ☎. AE ⓓ GB ETU **b**
☕ 30 - **35 rm** 288/358.

New H. Astoria without rest, 10 bd Garibaldi ✉ 13001 ☎ 91 33 33 50, Fax 91 54 80 75 - 🛗 ▤ TV ☎. AE ⓓ GB JCB. ✻ FT **f**
☕ 45 - **58 rm** 310/400.

Castellane M without rest, 31 r. Rouet ✉ 13006 ☎ 91 79 27 54, Telex 402326, Fax 91 25 44 07 - 🛗 ▤ TV ☎. AE GB GV **f**
☕ 39 - **55 rm** 300/400.

Relais Bleus Préfecture M without rest, 13 r. Lafon ✉ 13006 ☎ 91 33 34 34, Fax 91 54 10 59 - 🛗 TV ☎ ♿ 🚗 - 🏫 30. AE GB FU **w**
☕ 32 - **83 rm** 280/350.

Lutétia without rest, 38 allées L. Gambetta ✉ 13001 ☎ 91 50 81 78 - 🛗 TV ☎. ⓓ GB FS **z**
☕ 27 - **29 rm** 218/286.

XXX ✿ **Jambon de Parme,** 67 r. La Palud ✉ 13006 ☎ 91 54 37 98 - ▤. AE ⓓ GB JCB
closed 11 July-25 August, Sunday dinner and Monday - **M** a la carte 190/310 FU **s**
Spec. Rougets du Vallon des Auffes, Tortelloni à la modenese, Saltimbocca à la romaine. Wines Cassis.

XXX **Patalain,** 49 r. Sainte ✉ 13001 ☎ 91 55 02 78, Fax 91 54 15 29, « Elegant decor » - ▤. AE ⓓ GB EU **f**
closed 14 July-3 September, Saturday lunch, Sunday and Bank Holidays - **M** a la carte 185/345.

XXX **La Ferme,** 23 r. Sainte ✉ 13001 ☎ 91 33 21 12 - ▤. AE ⓓ GB JCB EU **m**
closed August, Saturday lunch, Sunday and Bank Holidays - **M** a la carte 230/330.

XXX **Les Échevins,** 44 r. Sainte ✉ 13001 ☎ 91 33 08 08 - ▤. AE ⓓ GB JCB EU **x**
closed 14 July-15 August, Saturday lunch and Sunday - **M** 140/200.

XX **Michel-Brasserie des Catalans,** 6 r. Catalans ✉ 13007 ☎ 91 52 30 63, Seafood - ▤. AE GB JCB
M a la carte 320/440.

XX **Brasserie New-York Vieux Port,** 7 quai Belges ✉ 13001 ☎ 91 33 60 98, Fax 91 33 29 46, 🏞 - ▤. AE ⓓ GB JCB ETU **e**
M a la carte 175/300.

XX **Calypso,** 3 r. Catalans ✉ 13007 ☎ 91 52 64 00, ←, Seafood - AE GB
closed August - **M** 180/250.

X **La Charpenterie,** 22 r. Paix ✉ 13001 ☎ 91 54 22 89 - AE ⓓ GB EU **d**
closed 1 to 21 August, Saturday lunch, Sunday and Bank Holidays - **M** 98/155.

at the Corniche :

Concorde-Palm Beach M 🐎, 2 promenade Plage ✉ 13008 ☎ 91 76 20 00, Telex 401894, Fax 91 77 37 83, ←, 🏞, 🏊, 🏖 - 🛗 ▤ TV ☎ 🚗 Ⓟ - 🏫 450. AE ⓓ GB JCB. ✻ rest
La Réserve M a la carte 200/360 - **Les Voiliers M** a la carte 130/200 🍷 - ☕ 60 - **145 rm** 655/730.

✿✿ **Le Petit Nice** (Passédat) M 🐎, anse de Maldormé (turn off when level with no 160 Corniche Kennedy) ✉ 13007 ☎ 91 59 25 92, Telex 401565, Fax 91 59 28 08, 🏞, « Villas overlooking the sea, elegant decor », 🏊 - 🛗 ▤ TV ☎ Ⓟ. AE GB
M *(closed Sunday from October-March except Bank Holidays)* 550/650 and a la carte - ☕ 100 - **15 rm** 1000/1700
Spec. Loup de palangre, Gâteau de grenouilles aux pieds de porc, Soufflé chaud à la réglisse. Wines Cassis, Palette.

XX **Peron,** 56 corniche Prés. Kennedy ✉ 13007 ☎ 91 52 43 70, ← harbour entrance and château d'If - AE ⓓ GB
closed January, 1 to 9 May, Sunday dinner and Monday - **M** a la carte 200/350.

Les Baux-de-Provence 13520 B.-du-R. 84 ① – pop. 457 alt. 280.
Marseilles 83.

in the Vallon :

🎴🎴🎴 ✿✿ **Oustaù de Baumanière** (Thuilier) 🌿 with rm, ℰ 90 54 33 07, Telex 420203, Fax 90 54 40 46, ≤, « Tastefully decorated period horses, floral terraces 🏡 ⊒ riding club », 🛬 – 🗏 rm 📺 ☎ 🅿. 🖭 ⓞ 🖼
closed 18 January-4 March, Thursday lunch and Wednesday from 31 October-31 March –
M 400/650 and a la carte – 😑 90 – **11 rm** 800/950, 13 suites 1400
Spec. Ravioli de truffes, Filets de rougets au basilic, Gigot d'agneau en croûte. Wines Coteaux des Baux, Gigondas.

🎴🎴🎴 ✿ **La Cabro d'Or** M 🌿 with rm, ℰ 90 54 33 21, Telex 401810, Fax 90 54 45 98, ≤, 🏡, « Shaded terraces, floral garden, lake », ⊒, ℀ – 🗏 rm 📺 ☎ 🅿 – 🔏 80. 🖭 ⓞ 🖼
closed 15 November-19 December, Tuesday lunch and Monday from 31 October-31 March
– **M** 300/370 – 😑 62 – **22 rm** 550/800
Spec. Salade Cabro d'Or, Pageot grillé au pistou, Noisettes d'agneau. Wines Coteaux d'Aix-en-Provence-les-Baux-de-Provence.

Carry-le-Rouet 13620 B.-du-R. 84 ⑩ – pop. 5 224 alt. 4.
Marseilles 27.

🎴🎴🎴 ✿✿ **L'Escale**, ℰ 42 45 00 47, Fax 42 44 72 69, 🏡, « Terraces overlooking the Harbour, pleasant view », 🛬 – 🖼
Early February-early November and closed Monday lunch July-August, Sunday dinner and Monday out of season – **M** (Sunday : booking essential) a la carte 360/500
Spec. Tartare de loup aux huîtres, Suprême de Saint-Pierre et ragoût de tagliatelle aux crustacés, Homard rôti au beurre de corail. Wines Coteaux d'Aix en Provence, Bandol.

MONACO (Principality of) 84 ⑩. 195 ㉗ ㉘ – pop. 29 972 alt. 65 – Casino.

Monaco Capital of the Principality – ✉ 98000.
See : Tropical Garden★★ (Jardin exotique) : ≤★ – Early paintings of the Nice School★★ in Cathedral – Place du Palais★ – Museum : oceanographic★★ (aquarium★★, ≤★★ from the terrace).
Urban racing circuit – A.C.M. 23 bd Albert-1er ℰ 93 15 26 00, Telex 469003.
Paris 956 – ◆ Nice 21 – San Remo 44.

Monte-Carlo Fashionable resort of the Principality – Casinos Grand Casino, Monte-Carlo Sporting Club, Sun Casino.
See : Terrace★★ of the Grand casino – Museum of Dolls and Automata★.
🏌 Monte-Carlo Golf Club ℰ 93 41 09 11 S : 11 km by N 7.
🚹 Direction Tourisme et Congrès, 2A bd Moulins ℰ 93 30 87 01, Telex 469760.

🏨 **Paris**, pl. Casino ℰ 93 50 80 80, Telex 469925, Fax 93 25 59 17, ≤, 🏡, 🔲 – 🛗 🗏 📺 ☎ 🅿 – 🔏 50. 🖭 ⓞ 🖼. ℀ rest
M see **Louis XV** and **Le Grill** below – **Salle Empire** (dinner only) *(26 June-28 September)* **M** a la carte 500/750 – 😑 135 – **206 rm** 2300/2900, 40 suites.

🏨 **Hermitage**, square Beaumarchais ℰ 93 50 67 31, Telex 479432, Fax 93 50 47 12, ≤, 🏡, « Dining room in Baroque style », 🔲 – 🛗 🗏 📺 ☎ 🅿 – 🔏 80. 🖭 ⓞ 🖼. ℀ rest
M 320/450 – 😑 135 – **220 rm** 1800/2700, 22 suites.

🏨 **Métropole Palace** M, 4 av. Madone ℰ 93 15 15 15, Telex 489836, Fax 93 25 24 44, ⊒, 🛬 – 🛗 🗏 📺 ☎ 🕭 🚗 – 🔏 150. 🖭 ⓞ 🖼 🖽
M a la carte 160/260 🍷 – 😑 95 – **54 rm** 1350/1900, 76 suites.

🏨 **Loews** M, 12 av. Spélugues ℰ 93 50 65 00, Telex 479435, Fax 93 30 01 57, ≤, 🏡, Casino and cabaret, 🎰, ⊒ – 🛗 🗏 📺 ☎ 🕭 🚗 – 🔏 30 - 2 000. 🖭 ⓞ 🖼 🖽. ℀ rest
Le Foie Gras (dinner only) *(closed 24 November-23 December)* **M** a la carte 355/570 – **L'Argentin** (dinner only) *(closed 20 October-28 November)* **M** a la carte 260/445 – **Le Pistou** (dinner only) *(closed December-late March)* **M** 240/320 – **Café de la mer M** a la carte 155/300 – 😑 120 – **600 rm** 3350/3800, 35 suites.

🏨 **Beach Plaza** M, av. Princesse Grace, à la Plage du Larvotto ℰ 93 30 98 80, Telex 479617, Fax 93 50 23 14, ≤, 🏡, « Attractive resort with ⊒, 🏖 » – 🛗 🗏 📺 ☎ 🕭 🚗 – 🔏 50 - 300. 🖭 ⓞ 🖼 🖽. ℀ rest
Le Gratin *(closed 26 November-28 December)* **M** a la carte 290/440 – **Le Café-Terrasse M** a la carte 210/370 – 😑 110 – **304 rm** 1600/2050, 9 suites.

🏨 **Mirabeau** M, 1 av. Princesse Grace ℰ 93 25 45 45, Telex 479413, Fax 93 50 84 85, ≤, ⊒ – 🛗 🗏 rm 📺 ☎ 🚗 – 🔏 100. 🖭 ⓞ 🖼. ℀ rest
M see **La Coupole** below – 😑 135 – **99 rm** 1500/2000, 4 suites 2700.

MONACO (Principality of)

🏨 **Balmoral,** 12 av. Costa ☎ 93 50 62 37, Telex 479436, Fax 93 15 08 69, ≤ – 🛗 ⬛ rm 📺 ☎.
ⅢⅢ 🅰 ⓞ ☁ 🅶🅱 ᴊᴄʙ. 🛠
M snack (closed November, Sunday dinner, Monday and Bank Holidays) 80 – ☐ 50 – **77 rm**
400/800.

🏨 **Louvre** without rest, 16 bd Moulins ☎ 93 50 65 25, Telex 479645, Fax 93 30 23 68 – 🛗 ⬛
☎. 🅰 ⓞ 🅶🅱 ᴊᴄʙ. 🛠
75 rm ☐ 900/1200.

🏨 **Alexandra** without rest, 35 bd Princesse Charlotte ☎ 93 50 63 13, Telex 489286,
Fax 92 16 06 48 – 🛗 ⬛ 📺 ☎. 🅰 ⓞ 🅶🅱. 🛠
☐ 47 – **56 rm** 530/730.

🍴🍴🍴🍴🍴 ✿✿✿ **Louis XV** - Hôtel de Paris, pl. Casino ☎ 93 30 23 11, Telex 469925, Fax 93 25 43 46, 🌳
– 🅿 🅰 ⓞ 🅶🅱. 🛠
closed 30 November-30 December, 15 February-4 March, Tuesday and Wednesday except
dinner 30 June-31 August – **M** 630/740 and a la carte 550/810
Spec. Légumes provençaux mijotés à la truffe noire (March-June), Jarret de veau fermier et côtes
de blettes, Pyramide glacée chocolat-nougat-noix. Wines Bellet, Côtes de Provence.

🍴🍴🍴🍴 ✿ **Grill de l'Hôtel de Paris,** pl. Casino ☎ 93 50 80 80, Telex 469925, Fax 93 25 59 17,
« Roof-top restaurant with sliding roof and ≤ the Principality » – 🅿 🅰 ⓞ 🅶🅱.
🛠
closed 30 November-23 December – **M** a la carte 450/660
Spec. Ravioli aux herbes et artichauts violets, Légumes du pays et langoustines "façon rustique",
Pavé de chocolat au croustillant de pralin. Wines Bellet, Côtes de Provence.

🍴🍴🍴 ✿ **La Coupole** - Hôtel Mirabeau, 1 av. Princesse Grace ☎ 93 25 45 45, Telex 479413,
Fax 93 50 84 85, 🌳 – ⬛. 🅰 ⓞ 🅶🅱
closed lunch in July-August – **M** 270/400
Spec. Barigoule d'artichaut en quenelles, Socca de pageot et poêlée d'olivettes noires, Parmentier
de canette en "cuisson de 7 heures".

🍴🍴🍴 **Giacomo,** av. Spélugues (126 galerie Métropole) ☎ 93 25 20 30, Fax 93 15 98 71, Italian
cuisine – ⬛. 🅰 ⓞ 🅶🅱
M (booking essential) a la carte 350/660

🍴🍴 **Le Saint Benoit,** 10 ter av. Costa ☎ 93 25 02 34, Fax 93 30 52 64, ≤ port and Monaco, 🌳
– ⬛. 🅰 ⓞ 🅶🅱 ᴊᴄʙ
closed 13 December-7 January and Monday – **M** 160/225.

🍴 **Polpetta,** 6 av. Roqueville ☎ 93 50 67 84, Italian rest. – 🅶🅱
closed 15 to 31 October, 15 February-8 March, Saturday lunch and Tuesday except July-August
– **M** 150.

at Monte-Carlo-Beach (06 Alpes-Mar.) at 2,5 km – ✉ 06190 Roquebrune-Cap-Martin :

🏨 Monte-Carlo Beach H. Ⓜ 🦢, ☎ 93 78 21 40, Telex 462010, Fax 93 78 14 18, ≤ sea and
Monaco, 🌳 – 🛗 ⬛ rm 📺 ☎ 🅿 – 🔏 30
season – **46 rm.**

NICE 🅿 06000 Alpes-Mar. 🟦 ⑨ ⑩ 🟦🟦 ㉖ ㉗ – pop. 342 439 alt. 5 – Casino Ruhl FZ.

See : Site★★ – Promenade des Anglais★★ EFZ – Old Nice★ : Château ≤★★ JZ, Acropolis★ (Palais
des Arts) HJZ – Misericord chapel★ HZ S, Cimiez : Monastery★ (Masterpieces★★ of the early Nice
School in the church) HV Q, Roman Ruins★ HV – Museums : Marc Chagall★★ GX, Matisse★ HV
M2, Fine Arts Museum★★ DZ M, Masséna★ FZ M1 – International Naive Style Museum★ –
Carnival★★★ (before Shrove Tuesday) – Mount Alban ≤★★ 5 km – Mount Boron ≤★ 3 km –
St-Pons Church★ : 3 km.

Envir. : St-Michel Plateau ≤★★ 9,5 km.

🏌 Biot ☎ 93 65 08 48 : 22 km.

✈ of Nice-Côte d'Azur ☎ 93 21 30 30 : 7 km.

🚗 ☎ 93 87 50 50.

🅱 Office de Tourisme and Accueil de France (hotel reservations - not more than 7 days in advance)
av. Thiers ☎ 93 87 07 07, Telex 460042 ; 5 av. Gustave-V ☎ 93 87 60 60 and Nice-Ferber near the
Airport ☎ 93 83 32 64 – A.C. 9 r. Massenet ☎ 93 87 18 17.

Paris 932 – Cannes 32 – Genova 194 – Lyons 472 – Marseilles 188 – Torino 220.

Plans on following pages

🏨 **Négresco,** 37 promenade des Anglais ☎ 93 88 39 51, Telex 460040, Fax 93 88 35 68, ≤,
🌳, « Empire and Napoléon III fourniture (17C and 18C) » – 🛗 ⬛ 📺 ☎ ⅷ – 🔏 50 - 400.
🅰 ⓞ 🅶🅱 ᴊᴄʙ
FZ **k**
M see **Chantecler** below - **La Rotonde M** a la carte 185/325 ⅙ – ☐ 100 – **150 rm** 1550/2250,
20 suites.

🏨 **Palais Maeterlinck** Ⓜ 🦢, 6 km by Inferior Corniche ✉ 06300 ☎ 93 56 21 12,
Fax 93 26 39 91, ≤ sea, 🌳, 🏊, 🦅ᴏ – 🛗 kitchenette ᵚᵚ rm ⬛ 📺 ☎ ⅷ 🍽 🅿 – 🔏 25.
🅰 ⓞ 🅶🅱. 🛠
closed 6 January-12 February – **M** (closed Saturday dinner and Monday) 250/380 – ☐ 75 –
20 rm 1500/3100, 6 suites.

🏨🏨🏨 **Sofitel** Ⓜ, 2-4 parvis de l'Europe ⌧ 06300 ℰ 92 00 80 00, Telex 461800, Fax 93 26 27 00, 🍽, « Roof-top swimming pool, ⩽ Nice » – 🛗 ⇔ rm 🔲 📺 ☎ ❻ ⚌ 🚗 – 🔬 60. 🖭 ⑩ ⅁
M a la carte 165/305 – ⴵ 152 **rm** 800/1800. JX t

🏨🏨🏨 **Sofitel Splendid**, 50 bd V. Hugo ℰ 93 88 69 54, Telex 460938, Fax 93 87 02 46, 🍽, « Roof-top swimming pool ⩽ Nice » – 🛗 ⇔ rm 🔲 📺 ❻ ❻ – 🔬 30 - 100. 🖭 ⑩ ⅁ ⅉⅭⅮ. ⅏ rest FYZ g
M 135/165 – ⴵ 70 – **116 rm** 720/995, 12 suites 1200/1500.

🏨🏨🏨 **Beach Régency** Ⓜ, 223 promenade des Anglais ℰ 93 37 17 17, Telex 461635, Fax 93 71 21 71, 🍽, « Roof-top swimming pool ⩽ bay », 🏋 – 🛗 🔲 📺 ☎ ⚌ 🚗 – 🔬 400. 🖭 ⑩ ⅁ ⅉⅭⅮ DZ a
Le Régency (closed 15 June-31 August) M 110/175 – **La Piscine** grill (open 15 June-15 September) M a la carte 230/340 – ⴵ 80 – **320 rm** 1050/1400, 12 suites.

🏨🏨🏨 **Élysée Palace** Ⓜ, 59 promenade des Anglais ℰ 93 86 06 06, Telex 970336, Fax 93 44 50 40, « Roof-top swimming pool ⩽ Nice », 🌁 – 🛗 ⇔ rm 🔲 📺 ☎ ❻ ⚌ – 🔬 45. 🖭 ⑩ ⅁. ⅏ rest EZ d
M a la carte 190/390 – ⴵ 95 – **143 rm** 1000/1950, 4 suites 3300.

🏨🏨🏨 **du Louvre** Ⓜ, 20 bd V. Hugo ℰ 93 16 55 00, Telex 461630, Fax 93 16 55 55, 🍽 – 🛗 ⇔ rm 🔲 📺 ☎ ☎ – 🔬 100. 🖭 ⑩ ⅁. ⅏ FY a
M (closed Sunday) 140 – ⴵ 75 – **131 rm** 640/790.

🏨🏨🏨 **Méridien** Ⓜ, 1 promenade des Anglais ℰ 93 82 25 25, Telex 470361, Fax 93 16 08 90, 🍽, « Roof-top swimming pool, ⩽ bay » – 🛗 🔲 📺 ☎ – 🔬 400. 🖭 ⑩ ⅁ ⅉⅭⅮ FZ d
L'Habit Blanc (closed Sunday dinner and Monday July-August) M 240 – **La Terrasse** (late April-September) M a la carte 180/275 – ⴵ 90 – **314 rm** 1100/3150.

🏨🏨🏨 **Plaza Concorde**, 12 av. Verdun ℰ 93 87 80 41, Telex 460979, Fax 93 88 61 11, ⩽, « Roof-top terrace » – 🛗 🔲 📺 ☎ – 🔬 30 - 400. 🖭 ⑩ ⅁ ⅉⅭⅮ GZ f
M 135/195 – ⴵ 60 – **183 rm** 650/1300, 10 suites 1500/2500.

🏨🏨🏨 **Beau Rivage** Ⓜ, 24 r. St-François-de-Paule ⌧ 06300 ℰ 93 80 80 70, Telex 462708, Fax 93 80 55 77, 🏋 – 🛗 ⇔ rm 🔲 📺 ❻ ❻ – 🔬 40. 🖭 ⑩ ⅁ ⅉⅭⅮ. ⅏ rest GZ y
M (closed Sunday dinner) a la carte 205/330 – ⴵ 80 – **106 rm** 800/1000, 12 suites 1500/1700.

🏨🏨🏨 **Westminster Concorde**, 27 promenade des Anglais ℰ 93 88 29 44, Telex 460872, Fax 93 82 45 35, ⩽, 🍽 – 🛗 🔲 📺 ☎ – 🔬 40 - 350. 🖭 ⑩ ⅁ ⅉⅭⅮ. ⅏ FZ m
Le Farniente M a la carte 230/400 – ⴵ 70 – **105 rm** 700/1200.

🏨🏨🏨 **West End**, 31 promenade des Anglais ℰ 93 88 79 91, Telex 460879, Fax 93 88 85 07, ⩽, – 🛗 🔲 📺 ☎ – 🔬 150. 🖭 ⑩ ⅁ ⅉⅭⅮ FZ p
M 150/270 – ⴵ 70 – **130 rm** 475/1365, 5 suites 1260.

🏨🏨 **Pullman Nice** without rest, 28 av. Notre-Dame ℰ 93 13 36 36, Telex 470662, Fax 93 62 61 69, « Hanging garden on 2nd floor, 🏊 on 8th floor, ⩽ » – 🛗 ⇔ 🔲 📺 ☎ – 🔬 25 - 120. 🖭 ⑩ ⅁ FXY q
ⴵ 68 – **200 rm** 590/1100.

🏨🏨 **La Pérouse** 🏡, 11 quai Rauba-Capéu ⌧ 06300 ℰ 93 62 34 63, Telex 461411, Fax 93 62 59 41, 🍽, « ⩽ Nice and Baie des Anges », 🏊 – 🛗 🔲 rm 📺 ☎ – 🔬 25. 🖭 ⑩ ⅁ ⅉⅭⅮ. ⅏ rest HZ k
M grill (15 May-16 September) a la carte 180/230 – ⴵ 70 – **65 rm** 440/1100.

🏨🏨 **Park**, 6 av. de Suède ℰ 93 87 80 25, Telex 970176, Fax 93 82 29 27, ⩽ – 🛗 ⇔ rest 🔲 📺 ☎ ❻ ● – 🔬 100. 🖭 ⑩ ⅁ ⅉⅭⅮ FZ x
Le Passage (closed Sunday) M 115/155 – ⴵ 75 – **130 rm** 700/950, 4 suites 1100.

🏨🏨 **Atlantic**, 12 bd V. Hugo ℰ 93 88 40 15, Telex 460840, Fax 93 88 68 60, 🍽 – 🛗 🔲 📺 ☎ ● – 🔬 30 - 80. 🖭 ⑩ ⅁ ⅉⅭⅮ FY d
M 120/130 – ⴵ 60 – **123 rm** 650/900.

🏨🏨 **Novotel** Ⓜ, 8-10 Parvis de l'Europe ⌧ 06300 ℰ 93 13 30 93, Telex 460243, Fax 93 13 09 04, 🍽, 🏊 – 🛗 ⇔ rm 🔲 📺 ☎ ❻ – 🔬 90. 🖭 ⑩ ⅁ ⅉⅭⅮ JX v
M a la carte approx. 140 ⅃ – ⴵ 48 – **173 rm** 510/780.

🏨🏨 **Altea Masséna** Ⓜ without rest, 58 r. Gioffredo ℰ 93 85 49 25, Telex 470192, Fax 93 62 43 27 – 🛗 🔲 📺 ☎. 🖭 ⑩ ⅁ GZ k
ⴵ 60 – **116 rm** 510/795.

🏨🏨 **Grand H. Aston** Ⓜ, 12 av. F. Faure ℰ 93 80 62 52, Telex 470290, Fax 93 80 40 02, « Roof-top terrace » – 🛗 🔲 📺 ☎ – 🔬 80. 🖭 ⑩ ⅁ HZ u
Le Champagne (closed August and Sunday) M 230/290 – ⴵ 50 – **160 rm** 450/1300.

🏨🏨 **La Malmaison**, 48 bd V. Hugo ℰ 93 87 62 56, Telex 470410, Fax 93 16 17 99 – 🛗 ⇔ rm 🔲 📺 ☎. 🖭 ⑩ ⅁ ⅉⅭⅮ. ⅏ rest FYZ e
M (closed 15 to 30 November, Sunday dinner and Monday) 130/260 – ⴵ 35 – **50 rm** 465/830.

🏨🏨 **Ambassador** without rest, 8 av. Suède ℰ 93 87 90 19, Telex 460025, Fax 93 82 14 90 – 🛗 🔲 📺 ☎ ❻. 🖭 ⑩ ⅁ ⅉⅭⅮ FZ x
closed December and January – ⴵ 50 – **45 rm** 430/750.

🏨🏨 **Frantour Napoléon** without rest, 6 r. Grimaldi ℰ 93 87 70 07, Telex 460949, Fax 93 16 17 80, 🏋 – 🛗 🔲 📺 ☎. 🖭 ⑩ ⅁ FZ r
ⴵ 55 – **83 rm** 500/850.

🏨🏨 **Petit Palais** 🏡 without rest, 10 av. E. Bieckert ℰ 93 62 19 11, Telex 462233, ⩽ Nice and sea – 🛗 📺 ☎. 🖭 ⑩ ⅁ HX p
ⴵ 40 – **25 rm** 480/530.

NICE

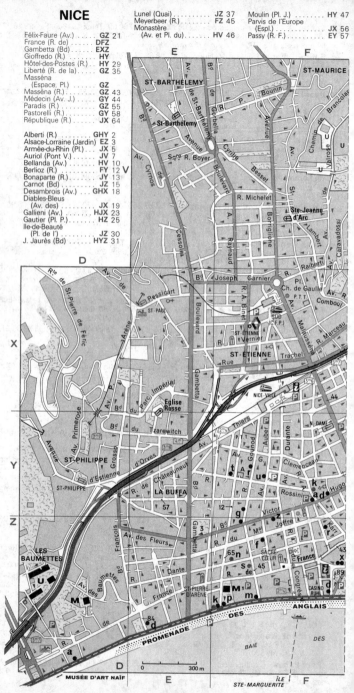

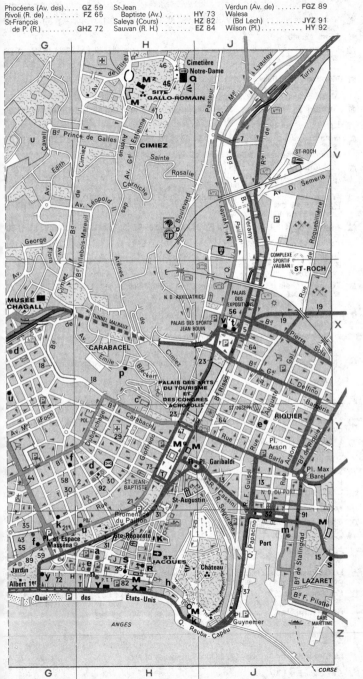

Victoria without rest, 33 bd V. Hugo ✆ 93 88 39 60, Telex 461337, – |‡| TV ☎. AE ⓓ GB JCB FYZ **z**
39 rm ☕ 540/620.

Lausanne without rest, 36 r. Rossini ✆ 93 88 85 94, Telex 461269, Fax 93 88 15 88 – |‡| TV ☎. AE ⓓ GB JCB FY **t**
☕ 52 – **36 rm** 350/650.

Windsor, 11 r. Dalpozzo ✆ 93 88 59 35, Telex 970072, Fax 93 88 94 57, Lб, ∑, – |‡| TV ☎. AE ⓓ GB JCB. ✂ rest FZ **f**
M coffee shop *(closed Sunday)* a la carte 160/190 – ☕ 40 – **60 rm** 390/620.

Apogia M without rest, 26 r. Smolett ✉ 06300 ✆ 93 89 18 88, Telex 461118, Fax 93 89 16 06 – |‡| TV ☎ P. AE ⓓ GB JY **e**
☕ 49 – **101 rm** 495/650.

Gounod without rest, 3 r. Gounod ✆ 93 88 26 20, Telex 461705, Fax 93 88 23 84 – |‡| ▤ TV ☎ P. AE ⓓ GB JCB FYZ **g**
closed 22 November-20 December – **45 rm** ☕ 460/590, 5 suites 780.

Vendôme M without rest, 26 r. Pastorelli ✆ 93 62 00 77, Telex 461762, Fax 93 13 40 78 – |‡| ▤ TV ☎ P. AE ⓓ GB GY **f**
☕ 40 – **51 rm** 510/640, 5 duplex 760.

Alexandra without rest, 41 r. Lamartine ✆ 93 62 14 43, Telex 461802, Fax 93 62 30 34 – |‡| TV ☎. AE ⓓ GB GX **u**
☕ 45 – **53 rm** 404/508.

Agata without rest, 46 bd Carnot ✉ 06300 ✆ 93 55 97 13, Telex 462426, Fax 93 55 67 38, ≤ – |‡| ▤ TV ☎ ⇔. AE GB JZ **s**
☕ 35 – **45 rm** 400/520.

Oasis ⓢ without rest, 23 r. Gounod ✆ 93 88 12 29, Telex 462705, Fax 93 16 14 40, – |‡| TV ☎ P. AE ⓓ GB FY **r**
☕ 35 – **38 rm** 320/400.

Trianon without rest, 15 av. Auber ✆ 93 88 30 69, Telex 970984, Fax 93 88 11 35 – |‡| TV ☎. AE ⓓ GB FY **u**
☕ 25 – **32 rm** 250/310.

Marbella without rest, 120 bd Carnot ✉ 06300 ✆ 93 89 39 35, ≤ – TV ☎. AE GB. ✂
☕ 28 – **17 rm** 230/430.

XXXXX ✿ **Chantecler** - Hôtel Négresco, 37 promenade des Anglais ✆ 93 88 39 51, Telex 460040, Fax 93 88 35 68 – ▤. AE ⓓ GB JCB FZ **k**
closed mid November-mid December – **M** 390/550
Spec. Ravioli ouvert aux artichauts, asperges et langoustines, St-Pierre au jus de ratatouille safrané, Filets de rougets en salade d'artichauts.

XXX ✿ **Florian** (Gillon), 22 r. A. Karr ✆ 93 88 86 60, Fax 93 87 31 98 – ▤. GB FY **k**
closed 1 July-31 August, Saturday lunch and Sunday – **M** 235/335
Spec. Filets de rougets "niçoise", Pastilla de pied de porc aux truffes, Noisettes de faon en poivrade (15 September-15 January). Wines Bellet, Côtes de Provence.

XXX **L'Ane Rouge,** 7 quai Deux-Emmanuel ✉ 06300 ✆ 93 89 49 63 – AE ⓓ GB JCB JZ **m**
closed 20 July-1 September, Saturday and Sunday – **M** a la carte 340/500.

XXX **L'Eridan,** 6 pl. Wilson ✆ 93 92 43 75, – ▤. AE ⓓ GB HY **d**
closed 10 to 23 August, 21 December-3 January, Saturday lunch, Sunday and Bank Holidays – **M** a la carte 250/370.

XXX **La Toque Blanche,** 40 r. Buffa ✆ 93 88 38 18 – ▤. GB JCB FZ **n**
closed Sunday dinner and Monday – **M** (booking essential) 130/160.

XX **Les Dents de la Mer,** 2 r. St-François-de-Paule ✉ 06300 ✆ 93 80 99 16, , Seafood, « Unusual decor representing a submerged galleon » – ▤. AE ⓓ GB HZ **n**
M 135/255.

XX **Boccaccio,** 7 r. Masséna ✆ 93 87 71 76, Fax 93 82 09 06, Seafood, « Resembling Spanish sailing ship » – ▤. AE ⓓ GB GZ **f**
M a la carte 220/360.

XX **Flo,** 4 r. S. Guitry ✆ 93 80 70 10, Fax 93 62 37 79, Brasserie – ▤. AE ⓓ GB GYZ **m**
M a la carte 145/210 ♂.

XX **Le Gd Pavois "Chez Michel",** 11 r. Meyerbeer ✆ 93 88 77 42, Seafood – ⇔ ▤. GB JCB FZ **s**
closed Monday except season and Bank Holidays – **M** 195/250.

XX **Los Caracolès,** 5 r. St-François-de-Paule ✉ 06300 ✆ 93 80 98 23 – ▤. GB JCB HZ **e**
closed 8 July-13 August, February Holidays, Saturday lunch and Wednesday – **M** 185/225.

XX **Don Camillo,** 5 r. Ponchettes ✉ 06300 ✆ 93 85 67 95 – ▤. GB HZ **h**
closed Sunday and Monday – **M** 180.

X **Mireille,** 19 bd Raimbaldi ✆ 93 85 27 23, One dish only : paella – ▤. GB GX **d**
closed 8 June-10 July, Monday and Tuesday except Bank Holidays – **M** a la carte approx. 135.

X **La Merenda,** 4 r. Terrasse ✉ 06300, Specialities of Nice HZ **a**
closed August, Christmas-New Year, February, Saturday, Sunday, Monday and Bank Holidays – **M** a la carte 130/170.

at the airport : 7 km – ⊠ 06200 Nice :

🏨 **Holiday Inn** Ⓜ, 179 bd R. Cassin ℘ 93 83 91 92, Telex 970202, Fax 93 21 69 57, 舘, ⛴ – 🛗 🍴 🖭 ☎ 🅿 ♿, 🍸 – 🔬 150. 🖭 ⓪ 🇬🇧 🇯🇨🇧
M 95/160 🍷 – 🖵 80 – **150 rm** 850/950.

🏨 **Nice Arenas** Ⓜ, 455 promenade des Anglais ℘ 93 21 22 50, Telex 461660, Fax 93 21 63 50 – 🛗 🍴 🖭 ☎ ♿ 🅿 – 🔬 200. 🖭 ⓪ 🇬🇧
M a la carte approx. 170 🍷 – 🖵 45 – **130 rm** 500/600.

🏨 **Campanile** Ⓜ, 459 promenade des Anglais ℘ 93 21 20 20, Telex 461640, Fax 93 83 83 96 – 🛗 🍴 🖭 ☎ ♿ 🚗 – 🔬 25 - 80. 🖭 🇬🇧
M 85 b.i./113 b.i. – 🖵 29 – **170 rm** 360.

Nice 26.

XXXX ✿✿ **Jean-François Issautier,** S : 3 km by N 202 ℘ 93 08 10 65, Fax 93 29 19 73 – 🅿. 🖭 ⓪ 🇬🇧
closed 2 to 12 November, mid February-mid March, Sunday except lunch 28 June-6 September and Monday – **M** (booking essential)(lunch except Saturday) 250/400 and a la carte
Spec. Courgette de Gattières et sa fleur farcie, Marinière de poissons de roche aux aromates, Rognon de veau rôti entier au vin de Bandol. Wines Bellet blanc, Bandol.

See : Cathedral★★★ : Astronomical clock★, ←★ of rue Mercière CX 53 – Old City★★★ BCX : la Petite France★★ BX, Rue du Bain-aux-Plantes★★ BX 7, Château des Rohan★ CX, – Ponts couverts★ BX B, Place Kléber★ CV 53 – Barrage Vauban ✳★★ BX D – Mausoleum of Maréchal de Saxe★★ in St-Thomas Church CX E – Hôtel de Ville★ CV H – Boat trips on the river Ill and the canals★ CX – Museums : Œuvre N.-Dame★★★ CX M1, Château des Rohan (Museums★★) CX, Alsatian★ CX M2 – Palais de l'Europe★.

🅱 🅱 🅱 at Illkirch-Graffenstaden (private) ℘ 88 66 17 22 ; 🅱 of the Wantzenau at Wantzenau ℘ 88 96 37 73 ; N : 12 km by D 468.

✈ of Strasbourg International : Air France ℘ 88 68 86 21 SW : 12 km by D 392 FR.
🚄 ℘ 88 22 50 50.

🅱 Office de Tourisme and Accueil de France (Information and hotel reservations, not more than 5 days in advance), Palais des Congrès av. Schutzenberger ℘ 88 37 67 68, Telex 870860 ; 10 pl. Gutenberg ℘ 88 32 57 07 and pl. Gare ℘ 88 32 51 49 - Welcome Office, Pont Europe (exchange facilities) ℘ 88 61 39 23 – A.C. 5 av. Paix ℘ 88 36 04 34.

Paris 490 – Basel 145 – Bonn 360 – Bordeaux 915 – Frankfurt 218 – Karlsruhe 81 – Lille 525 – Luxembourg 223 – Lyons 485 – Stuttgart 157.

Plan on next page

🏨 **Hilton** Ⓜ, av. Herrenschmidt ℘ 88 37 10 10, Telex 890363, Fax 88 36 83 27, 舘 – 🛗 kitchenette 辷★ rm 🍴 🖭 ☎ ♿ 🅿 – 🔬 30 - 350. 🖭 ⓪ 🇬🇧. 🎜 rest
La Maison du Boeuf *(closed 18 July-16 August, 20 February-7 March, Saturday and Sunday)* **M** a la carte 270/420 – **Le Jardin M** a la carte 150/260 🍷 – 🖵 80 – **241 rm** 870/970, 5 suites.

🏨 **Sofitel** Ⓜ, pl. St-Pierre-le-Jeune ℘ 88 32 99 30, Telex 870894, Fax 88 32 60 67, 舘, patio – 🛗 辷★ rm 🍴 🖭 ☎ 🚗 – 🔬 120. 🖭 ⓪ 🇬🇧 🇯🇨🇧   CV s
L'Alsace Gourmande ℘ 88 75 11 10 **M** 139/150 🍷 – 🖵 75 – **158 rm** 725/835, 5 suites.

🏨 **Holiday Inn** Ⓜ, 20 pl. Bordeaux ℘ 88 37 80 00, Telex 890515, Fax 88 37 07 04, 🗘, 🖀 – 🛗 辷★ rm 🖭 ☎ ♿ 🅿 – 🔬 50 - 600. 🖭 ⓪ 🇬🇧 🇯🇨🇧
La Louisiane M a la carte 170/365 🍷 – 🖵 70 – **170 rm** 780/950.

🏨 **Régent Contades** Ⓜ without rest, 8 av. Liberté ℘ 88 36 26 26, Telex 890641, Fax 88 37 13 70, 🗘 – 🛗 🍴 🖭 ☎ ♿. 🖭 ⓪ 🇬🇧 🇯🇨🇧   CV f
closed 23 December-2 January – 🖵 70 – **36 rm** 700/1200, 8 suites 1350/1800.

🏨 **Nouvel H. Maison Rouge** without rest, 4 r. Francs-Bourgeois ℘ 88 32 08 60, Telex 880130, Fax 88 22 43 73, « Tasteful decor with antique furniture » – 🛗 🖭 ☎ – 🔬 40. 🖭 🇬🇧
🖵 52 – **140 rm** 365/520.   CX g

🏨 **Terminus-Plaza,** 10 pl. Gare ℘ 88 32 87 00, Telex 870998, Fax 88 32 16 46 – 🛗 🖭 ☎ – 🔬 60. 🖭 ⓪ 🇬🇧 🇯🇨🇧   BV m
M *(closed 24 December-10 January)* 160 🍷 – **La Brasserie M** 90 🍷 – 🖵 50 – **66 rm** 260/570, 12 suites 640/700.

🏨 **Monopole-Métropole** without rest, 16 r. Kuhn ℘ 88 32 11 94, Telex 890366, Fax 88 32 82 55, « Alsatian and contemporary decor » – 🛗 🖭 ☎ 🚗. 🖭 🇬🇧 🇯🇨🇧 BV p
closed Christmas-New Year – 🖵 35 – **94 rm** 340/540.

🏨 **Europe** without rest, 38 r. Fossé des Tanneurs ℘ 88 32 17 88, Telex 890220, Fax 88 75 65 45, « Half timbered Alsatian house » – 🛗 辷★ rm 🖭 ☎ 🅿 🇯🇨🇧   BX g
🖵 32 – **60 rm** 290/445.

🏨 **Novotel** Ⓜ, quai Kléber ℘ 88 22 10 99, Telex 880700, Fax 88 22 20 92, 舘 – 🛗 🍴 🖭 ☎ ♿ 🅿 – 🔬 30 - 200. 🖭 ⓪ 🇬🇧   BV k
M a la carte approx. 150 🍷 – 🖵 49 – **97 rm** 500/560.

Attention : restriction de circulation prévue en 1992

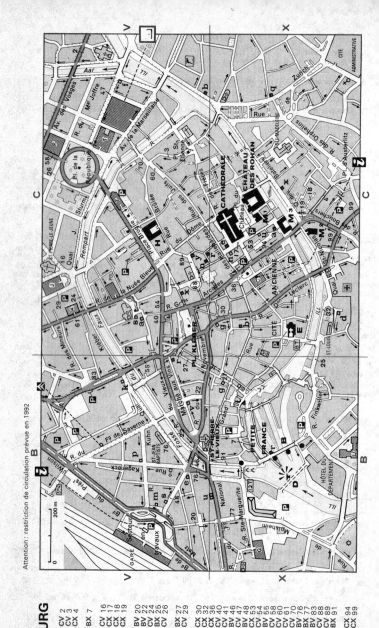

STRASBOURG

🏨 **Mercure** M without rest, 25 r. Thomann ℘ 88 75 77 88, Telex 880955, Fax 88 32 08 66 –
|≢| ⇆ ≡ TV ⚑ 🕭.   CV **a**
⬢ 52 – **80 rm** 515/650.

🏨 **Gd Hôtel** without rest, 12 pl. Gare ℘ 88 32 46 90, Telex 870011, Fax 88 32 16 50 – |≢| TV
🕿 – 🔏 25. AE ① GB   BV **m**
⬢ 65 – **80 rm** 360/660.

🏨 **France** M without rest, 20 r. Jeu des Enfants ℘ 88 32 37 12, Telex 890084, Fax 88 22 48 08
– |≢| TV 🕿 ⟵ – 🔏 30. AE GB   BV **v**
⬢ 47 – **66 rm** 360/580.

🏨 **des Rohan** without rest, 17 r. Maroquin ℘ 88 32 85 11, Telex 870047, Fax 88 75 65 37 –
|≢| ≡ TV 🕿. AE GB   CX **u**
⬢ 50 – **36 rm** 300/555.

🏨 **Cathédrale** M without rest, 12 pl. Cathédrale ℘ 88 22 12 12, Telex 871054, Fax 88 23 28 00
– |≢| TV 🕿 – 🔏 25. AE ① GB JCB   CX **n**
⬢ 45 – **32 rm** 420/700, 3 duplex 700.

🏨 **Royal** M without rest, 3 r. Maire Kuss ℘ 88 32 28 71, Telex 871067, Fax 88 23 05 39, ♨
– |≢| TV 🕿 🕭 – 🔏 40. AE GB JCB. ⌖   BV **e**
⬢ 49 – **52 rm** 295/455.

🏨 **Dragon** M without rest, 2 r. Ecarlate ℘ 88 35 79 80, Telex 871102, Fax 88 25 78 95 – |≢| TV
🕿 🕭. GB. ⌖   CX **d**
⬢ 48 – **30 rm** 400/560.

🏨 **La Dauphine** without rest, 30 r. 1ᵉ Armée ℘ 88 36 26 61, Telex 880766, Fax 88 35 50 07 –
|≢| TV 🕿 ⟵. ① GB
closed 23 December-2 January – ⬢ 38 – **45 rm** 395/460.

🏨 **Pax,** 24 r. Fg National ℘ 88 32 14 54, Telex 880506, Fax 88 32 01 16, ☞ – |≢| TV 🕿 – 🔏 25
– 100. AE GB JCB   BVX **u**
closed 25 December-1 January – **M** (closed Sunday from November-March) 85/175 ⅛ – ⬢
32 – **119 rm** 285/305.

🏨 **Continental** without rest, 14 r. Maire Kuss ℘ 88 22 28 07, Telex 880881, Fax 88 32 22 25
– |≢| TV 🕿. AE ① GB JCB   BV **s**
⬢ 35 – **48 rm** 287/330.

XXXXX ❀❀❀ **Le Crocodile** (Jung), 10 r. Outre ℘ 88 32 13 02, Fax 88 75 72 01 – ≡. AE ① GB JCB
closed 7 July-3 August, 24 December-4 January, Sunday and Monday – **M** 380/580 and a la
carte 370/550   CV **x**
Spec. Foie d'oie poêlé à la brunoise et zestes de citron, Homard aux vermicelles blonds, Lièvre
à la royale (October-January). Wines Riesling, Tokay-Pinot gris.

XXXX ❀❀ **Buerehiesel** (Westermann), set in the Orangery Park ℘ 88 61 62 24, Fax 88 61 32 00,
« Attractive Alsatian mansion in a park » – ≡ ℗. AE ① GB JCB
closed 12 to 26 August, 22 December-5 January, 16 February-1 March, Tuesday except lunch
1 April-31 October and Wednesday – **M** 320/510 and a la carte ⅛
Spec. Schniedespaetle et cuisses de grenouilles poêlées au cerfeuil, Matelote de poissons d'eau
douce en raviole au Riesling, Cuisses et dos de lapereau rôtis. Wines Chasselas, Riesling.

XXX **Maison Kammerzell and H. Baumann** M with rm, 16 pl. Cathédrale ℘ 88 32 42 14,
Telex 891012, Fax 88 23 03 92, « Attractive 16C Alsatian house » – |≢| ≡ rm TV 🕿 – 🔏 120.
AE ① GB   CX **e**
M 190/260 ⅛ – ⬢ 50 – **9 rm** 420/630.

XXX **Valentin Sorg,** 6 pl. Homme de Fer (14th floor) ℘ 88 32 12 16, Fax 88 32 40 62, ≼ Strasbourg – ≡. AE ① GB   BV **r**
closed 10 to 31 August, February Holidays, Monday lunch and Sunday – **M** 200/400.

XXX **Maison des Tanneurs dite "Gerwerstub",** 42 r. Bain aux Plantes ℘ 88 32 79 70, « Old
Alsatian house on the banks of the River III » – 🕭. AE ① GB   BX **t**
closed 12 to 28 July, 21 December-25 January, Sunday and Monday – **M** a la carte 170/280.

XXX **Zimmer,** 8 r. Temple Neuf ℘ 88 32 35 01, Fax 88 32 42 28, ☞ – AE ① GB   CV **y**
closed 3 to 23 August, Saturday lunch and Sunday – **M** 130/380.

XXX **Estaminet Schloegel,** 19 r. Krutenau ℘ 88 36 21 98 – ≡.   CX **q**
closed 14 to 23 July, 23 December-6 January, Sunday and Monday – **M** 180/270.

XX ❀ **Julien,** 22 quai Bateliers ℘ 88 36 01 54, Fax 88 35 40 14 – AE ① GB   CX **x**
closed 1 to 23 August, 24 December-4 January, Saturday and Sunday – **M** a la carte 270/
340 ⅛
Spec. Duo croustillant de saumon en millefeuille, Tian d'agneau au romarin à l'ail confit, Feuilleté
de pommes tièdes. Wines Riesling, Tokay-Pinot gris.

XX **Au Gourmet Sans Chiqué,** 15 r. Ste Barbe ℘ 88 32 04 07, Fax 88 22 42 40 – ≡. AE ①
GB   CX **b**
closed 2 to 25 August, 2 to 11 February, Monday lunch and Sunday – **M** 240/320.

XX **Buffet Gare,** pl. Gare ℘ 88 32 68 28, Fax 88 32 88 34 – AE ① GB   BV
L'Argentoratum M 90/140 ⅛ – **L'Assiette M** 66 ⅛.

XX **Bec Doré,** 8 quai Pêcheurs ℘ 88 35 39 57 – ≡. AE ① GB   CV **b**
closed Monday and Tuesday – **M** 150 ⅛.

X **Ami Schutz,** 1 r. Ponts Couverts ℘ 88 32 76 98, Fax 88 32 38 40, ☞ – ⇆. AE GB   BX **r**
closed 24 to 31 December – **M** 155/179 b.i. ⅛.

Winstubs : Regional specialities and wine tasting in a typical Alsatian atmosphere :

X **Zum Strissel,** 5 pl. Gde Boucherie ✆ 88 32 14 73, Fax 88 32 70 24, rustic decor – ▤. GB
closed 5 to 29 July, 27 February-9 March, Sunday and Monday – **M** 54/106 ♁. CX **a**

X **S'Burjerstuewel (Chez Yvonne),** 10 r. Sanglier ✆ 88 32 84 15 – GB CVX **r**
closed 12 July-13 August, 22 December-2 January, Monday lunch and Sunday – **M** (booking essential) a la carte 125/215 ♁.

X **Le Clou,** 3 r. Chaudron ✆ 88 32 11 67 – ▤. GB CV **n**
closed 15 to 31 August, 1 December-7 January and Sunday – **M** (dinner only) a la carte 150/270 ♁.

at La Wantzenau : NE : 12 km by D 468 - pop. 4 394 - ✉ 67610 :

Hôtel Le Moulin M without rest, S : 1,5 km by D 468 ✆ 88 96 27 83, Fax 88 96 68 32, ←, « Ancient watermill on a branch of the River Ill », – |‡| TV ☎ P. AE GB
closed 24 December-2 January – **M** see **Au Moulin** below – 40 – **19 rm** 275/375.

A la Gare without rest, 32 r. Gare ✆ 88 96 63 44 – TV ☎ P. GB
closed 27 July-9 August – 25 – **18 rm** 180/250.

XXX **Relais de la Poste** M with rm, 21 r. Gén. de Gaulle ✆ 88 96 20 64, Fax 88 96 36 84, – |‡| ▤ TV ☎ ♿ P. AE ⓓ GB
closed 23 December-15 January – **M** *(closed Saturday lunch)* 250/380 ♁ – 50 – **17 rm** 300/500.

XXX **A la Barrière,** 3 rte Strasbourg ✆ 88 96 20 23, Fax 88 96 25 59, – P. AE ⓓ GB JCB
closed 6 to 27 August, February Holidays, Tuesday dinner and Wednesday – **M** (Sunday : booking essential) 195/250 ♁.

XXX **Zimmer,** 23 r. Héros ✆ 88 96 62 08 – AE ⓓ GB
closed 12 July-4 August, 24 January-8 February, Sunday dinner and Monday – **M** 130/320.

XX **Rest. Au Moulin** - Hôtel Au Moulin, S : 1,5 km by D 468 ✆ 88 96 20 01, Fax 88 96 68 32, , « Floral garden » – ▤ P. AE ⓓ GB
closed 29 June-23 July, 4 to 18 January, Wednesday, Sunday and Bank Holiday dinner – **M** 140/340.

XX **Schaeffer,** 1 quai Bateliers ✆ 88 96 20 29, – P. AE ⓓ GB
closed 13 to 31 July, 21 December-8 January, Sunday dinner and Monday – **M** 135/240 ♁.

Colmar P 68000 H.-Rhin 62 ⑲ – pop. 63 498 alt. 193.
Strasbourg 70.

XXXX ✿✿ **Schillinger,** 16 r. Stanislas ✆ 89 41 43 17, Fax 89 24 28 87, « Fine decor » – ▤. AE ⓓ GB
closed 5 July-3 August, Sunday dinner and Monday except Bank Holidays – **M** 270/480 and a la carte ♁
Spec. Foie gras truffé, Filet de Saint-Pierre et brochette de langoustines, Caneton au citron. Wines Pinot blanc, Riesling.

Colroy-la-Roche 67420 B.-Rhin 62 ⑧ – pop. 435 alt. 424.
Strasbourg 62.

✿✿ **Host. La Cheneaudière** M , ✆ 88 97 61 64, Telex 870438, Fax 88 47 21 73, ←, , « Elegant country inn, garden », , , – ▤ rest TV ☎ P. AE ⓓ GB JCB
closed January and February – **M** 360/510 and a la carte – 100 – **25 rm** 520/990, 7 suites 1250/1850
Spec. Foie gras fumé maison, Ravioles de Munster frais au persil frit, Filet de chevreuil en strudel de chou vert (May-December). Wines Pinot noir, Riesling.

Illhaeusern 68 H.-Rhin 62 ⑲ – pop. 578 alt. 176 – ✉ 68150 Ribeauvillé.
Strasbourg 60.

La Clairière M without rest, rte Guémar ✆ 89 71 80 80, Fax 89 71 86 22, – |‡| TV ☎ P. GB
closed January and February – 55 – **27 rm** 420/1100.

XXXXX ✿✿✿ **Aub. de l'Ill** (Haeberlin), ✆ 89 71 83 23, Telex 871289, Fax 89 71 82 83, « Tasteful decor, set on the banks of the River Ill, ← floral gardens » – ▤. AE ⓓ GB
closed 3 February-6 March, 1 to 10 July, Monday (except lunch in summer) and Tuesday – **M** (booking essential) 450 (lunch)/620 and a la carte 450/600
Spec. Salade de tripes panées au foie gras et fèves, Esturgeon poêlé sur lit de chou et choucroute, Colvert laqué aux épices (August-late January). Wines Riesling, Pinot blanc.

Lembach 67510 B.-Rhin 57 ⑲ – pop. 1 710 alt. 190.
Strasbourg 55.

XXXX ✿✿ **Aub. Cheval Blanc,** ✆ 88 94 41 86, Fax 88 94 20 74, « Old coaching inn », – P. AE GB.
closed 6 to 24 July, 8 to 26 February, Monday and Tuesday – **M** 160/370 and a la carte
Spec. Foie de canard aux épices, Suprême de sandre au fumet de truffes, Médaillons de chevreuil à la moutarde aux fruits rouges (June-15 February). Wines Pinot Auxerrois, Tokay-Pinot gris.

Marlenheim 67520 B.-Rhin 📗 ⑨ – pop. 2 956 alt. 184.

Strasbourg 20.

XXX ✿✿ **Host. du Cerf** (Husser) with rm, ℰ 88 87 73 73, Fax 88 87 68 08, 🍽, 🌿 – 📺 ☎ 🅿
– 🏛 25. ᴁᴇ ☷
closed February Holidays, Tuesday and Wednesday – **M** 350/500 and a la carte ♨ – ⬜ 60 –
15 rm 510/650
Spec. Presskopf de tête de veau poêlé sauce gribiche, Choucroute au cochon de lait et foie gras
fumé, Aumônières aux griottes et glace au fromage blanc. **Wines** Muscat, Riesling.

VALLEY OF THE LOIRE

Tours 🅿 37000 I.-et-L. 🔟 ⑮ – pop. 129 509 alt. 48.

See : Cathedral quarter★★ : Cathedral★★ CY, Fine Arts Museum★★ CY **M2** – Historial de
Touraine★ (château) CY – Old Tours★★ : Place Plumereau★ AY Craft Guilds Museum★★
(Musée du Compagnonnage) BY **M5** – St-Cosme Priory★ W : 3 km – Meslay Tithe Barn★
(Grange de Meslay) NE : 10 km.

Envir. : Chenonceau Château★★★ E : 35 km – Azay-le-Rideau Château★★★ SW : 28 km –
Gardens★★★ of Villandry Château W : 20 km.

🏊 of Touraine ℰ 47 53 20 28 ; domaine de la Touche at Ballan-Miré : 14 km ; 🏊 of Ardrée
ℰ 47 56 77 38 : 14 km.

✈ of Tours-St-Symphorien : T.A.T ℰ 47 51 94 22 NE : 7 km.

🗗 Office de Tourisme and Accueil de France (Information, exchange facilities and hotel reservations - not more than 5 days in advance) bd Heurteloup ℰ 47 05 58 08, Telex 750008 –
Automobile Club de l'Ouest 4 pl. J. Jaurès ℰ 47 05 50 19.

Paris 237 – Angers 109 – Bordeaux 346 – Chartres 140 – Clermont-Ferrand 335 – Limoges 220 – Le Mans 80
– Orléans 115 – Rennes 219 – St-Étienne 474.

Plan on following pages

🏨 ✿✿ **Jean Bardet** M ⌂, 57 r. Groison ⌧ 37100 ℰ 47 41 41 11, Telex 752463,
Fax 47 51 68 72, ≼, « Park », ⬛, – 🗏 rest 📺 ☎ 🅿. ᴁᴇ ☷ ☷
closed 21 February-9 March – **M** *(closed Monday except lunch April-October and Sunday dinner
November-March except Bank Holidays)* 300/750 and a la carte – ⬜ 110 – **16 rm** 650/1300,
5 suites 1800
Spec. Saumon mi-fumé en harmonie de jeunes poireaux, Gésier de canard et homard rôti au four,
Pintadeau fermier truffé. **Wines** Vouvray, Bourgueil.

🏨 **Alliance** M, 292 av. Grammont ⌧ 37200 ℰ 47 28 00 80, Telex 750922, Fax 47 27 77 61,
≼, 🍽, 🌿 – 🗏 ⬚ rm 🗏 📺 ☎ 🅿 – 🏛 200. ᴁᴇ ☷ ☷
M a la carte 200/310 – ⬜ 55 – **119 rm** 440/515, 6 suites.

🏨 **H. de Groison and rest. Jardin du Castel** M ⌂, 16 r. Groison ⌧ 37100 ℰ 47 41 94 40,
Fax 47 51 50 28, 🍽, « Former 18C mansion », 🌿 – 📺 ☎ ⬚. ᴁᴇ ☷ ☷
closed 15 January-15 February – **M** *(closed Saturday lunch and Wednesday)* 220/430 – ⬜
78 – **10 rm** 490/750.

🏨 **Harmonie** M, 15 r. F. Joliot-Curie ℰ 47 66 01 48, Telex 752587, Fax 47 61 66 38, ✂ – 🗏
⬚ rm 📺 ☎ ♿ ⬚. ᴁᴇ ☷ ☷   CZ **b**
*hotel : closed 20 December-5 January ; rest. : closed 31 october-1 March, Saturday and Sunday
in season* – **M** *(dinner only)* 99 – ⬜ 48 – **48 rm** 360/750, 6 suites 550/885.

🏨 **Royal** M without rest, 65 av. Grammont ℰ 47 64 71 78, Telex 752006, Fax 47 05 84 62 –
🗏 📺 ☎ ♿ – 🏛 40. ᴁᴇ ☷ ☷
⬜ 36 – **50 rm** 306/362.

🏨 **Univers and rest. La Touraine,** 5 bd Heurteloup ℰ 47 05 37 12, Telex 751460,
Fax 47 61 51 80 – 🗏 📺 ☎ ♿ – 🏛 30. ᴁᴇ ☷ ☷   BZ **u**
M *(closed Saturday)* 180/200 – ⬜ 54 – **89 rm** 400/630.

🏨 **Bordeaux,** 3 pl. Mar. Leclerc ℰ 47 05 40 32, Telex 750414, Fax 47 64 05 72 – 🗏 📺 ☎. ᴁᴇ
☷ ☷   BZ **t**
closed 6 to 20 January – **M** 137 ♨ – ⬜ 38 – **56 rm** 295/460.

🏨 **Le Francillon** M, 9 r. Bons Enfants ℰ 47 66 44 66, Fax 47 66 17 18, 🍽 – 📺 ☎. ᴁᴇ ☷
M *(closed lunch Saturday and Sunday)* 290/400 – ⬜ 40 – **10 rm** 320/380.   AY **s**

🏨 **Altéa** M, 4 pl. Thiers ℰ 47 05 50 05, Telex 752740, Fax 47 20 22 07 – 🗏 🗏 rest 📺 ☎ ♿
♿ 🅿 – 🏛 70. ᴁᴇ ☷ ☷
M 160 – ⬜ 48 – **120 rm** 420/590.

🏨 **Central H.** without rest, 21 r. Berthelot ℰ 47 05 46 44, Telex 751173, Fax 47 66 10 26 – 🗏
📺 ☎ ♿ ⬚. ᴁᴇ ☷ ☷   BY **k**
⬜ 40 – **41 rm** 280/380.

🏨 **Criden** M without rest, 65 bd Heurteloup ℰ 47 20 81 14 – 🗏 📺 ☎ ♿. ᴁᴇ ☷ ☷ ☷
⬜ 34 – **32 rm** 273/337.   CZ **g**

🏨 **Mirabeau** without rest, 89 bis bd Heurteloup ℰ 47 05 24 60, Fax 47 05 31 09 – 🗏 📺 ☎.
ᴁᴇ ☷ ☷
⬜ 28 – **25 rm** 250/310.   CZ **e**

TOURS

Bordeaux (R. de) . . . . . . **BZ**
Commerce (R. du) . . . . **AY** 8
Grammont (Av. de) . . . . **BZ**
Halles (Pl. et R.) . . . . . . **AY**
Marceau (R.) . . . . **ABYZ**
National (R.) . . . . **BYZ**
Scellerie (R. de la) . . . . . **BY**

Bretonneau (R.) . . . . **AY** 2
Briçonnet (R.) . . . . **AY** 3
Carmes (Pl. des) . . . . . . **AY** 4
Châteauneuf (R. de) . . . **AY** 7
Constantine (R.) . . . . . . **AY** 9
Courrier (R. L.) . . . . **AY** 10
Courteline (R. G.) . . . . . . **AY** 12
Cygne (R. du) . . . . **BY** 13
Descartes (R.) . . . . **AY** 15
Foire-le-Roi (Pl.) . . . . . . **BY** 16
Grand-Marché (Pl. du) . . **AY** 18
Grand-Marché (R. du) . . **AY** 19
Grégoire-de-Tours (Pl.) . . **CY** 20
Grosse-Tour (R. de la) . . **AY** 22
Lavoisier (R.) . . . . **BY** 23
Manceau (R.) . . . . **CY** 24
Merville (R. du Prés.) . . **AY** 25
Meunier (R. Gén.) . . . . . **CY** 26
Monnaie (R. de la) . . . . **AY** 28
Paix (R. de la) . . . . **AY** 30
Picou (Pl. R.) . . . . **AY** 32
Racine (R.) . . . . **CY** 33
Tanneurs (R. des) . . . . . **AY** 34
Victoire (Pl. de la) . . . . . **AY** 36

The names of main shopping streets are indicated in red at the beginning of the list of streets.

Do not lose your way in Europe, use the Michelin Main Road *maps. scale: 1 inch: 16 miles.*

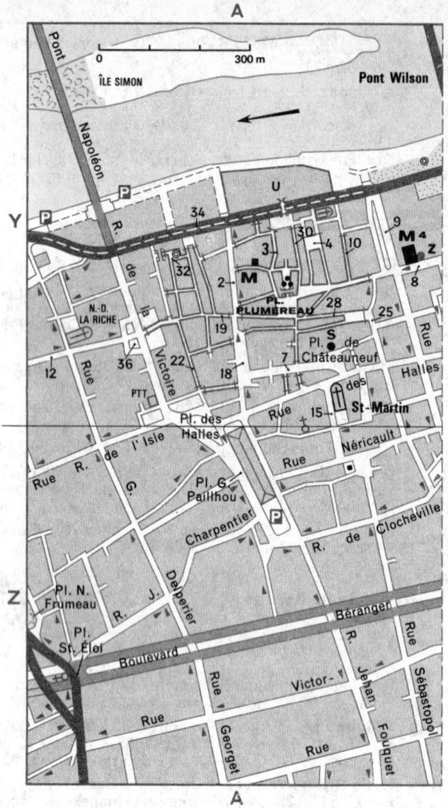

🏨 **Fimotel** M, 247 r. Giraudeau ✆ 47 37 00 36, Fax 47 38 50 91 – |⇕| TV ☎ ♿ Ⓟ – 🎤 40. AE ⓓ GB
M 75/95 🍷 – ☕ 34 – **48 rm** 270/350.

XXXX ❀❀ **Barrier,** 101 av. Tranchée ✉ 37100 ✆ 47 54 20 39, Fax 47 41 80 95 – ▤ Ⓟ. GB
closed Sunday dinner – **M** 230/420 and a la carte
Spec. Matelote d'anguille au Chinon et pruneaux, Sandre en peau au beurre blanc, Pied de cochon farci aux ris d'agneau et truffes. Wines Vouvray, Bourgueil.

XXX ❀ **La Roche Le Roy** (Couturier), 55 rte St Avertin ✉ 37200 ✆ 47 27 22 00, Fax 47 28 08 39, 🍽 – Ⓟ. AE GB
closed 1 to 24 August, Saturday lunch and Sunday – **M** 198/275
Spec. Brandade de sandre au beurre de pamplemousse, Aiguillettes de pigeonneau à l'échalote confite, Soufflé chaud aux fruits. Wines Chinon, St Nicolas de Bourgueil.

XX **Les Tuffeaux,** 19 r. Lavoisier ✆ 47 47 19 89 – ▤. GB BY **r**
closed 13 to 27 July, Monday lunch and Sunday – **M** 150/200.

X **La Ruche,** 105 r. Colbert ✆ 47 66 69 83 – GB JCB BY **a**
closed 27 July-4 August, 21 December-13 January, Monday lunch, Saturday lunch and Sunday – **M** 78/120.

at Rochecorbon NE : by N 152 – ✉ 37210 :

🏨 ❀ **Les Hautes Roches** M 🐎, 86 quai Loire ✆ 47 52 88 88, Telex 300121, Fax 47 52 81 30, ←, 🍽, « Former troglodyte dwellings, elegant decor » – |⇕| TV ☎ Ⓟ. AE GB
closed 15 January-15 March – **M** *(closed Sunday dinner and Monday except Bank Holidays)* 220/300 – ☕ 65 – **8 rm** 580/995, 3 suites 1300
Spec. Dos de rouget à la lie de vin, Turbot aux ravioles de Sainte-Maure, Tarte fine aux pommes caramélisées. Wines Vouvray, Chinon.

If you find you cannot take up a hotel booking you have made, please let the hotel know immediately.

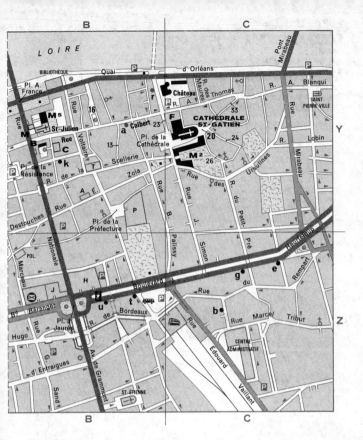

Bracieux 41250 L.-et-Ch. 🔢 ⑱ – pop. 1 157 alt. 81.

Tours 82.

XXXX ✿✿ **Bernard Robin,** 𝒫 54 46 41 22, Fax 54 46 03 69, 🎐 – **GB**
closed 22 December-late January, Tuesday dinner and Wednesday – **M** (booking essential) 290/510 and a la carte
Spec. Salade de pigeon et homard, Caille farcie rôtie au four, Gibier (October-January). Wines Vouvray, Chinon.

Montbazon 37250 I.-et-L. 🔢 ⑮ – pop. 3 354 alt. 71 – Tours 15.

🏨 ✿ **Château d'Artigny** ⤵, SW : 2 km by D 17 𝒫 47 26 24 24, Telex 750900, Fax 47 65 92 79, « Park, ≤ River Indre, 8 bedroom lodge beside the river », ⊥, ※ – 📶 📺 ☎ 🅿 – 🔏 80. **GB**
closed 29 November-9 January – **M** 270/420 – ☑ 80 – **51 rm** 600/1500
Spec. Sandre aux truffes, Pièce de veau "d'ici", Macarons tendres aux fruits rouges (March-October). Wines Vouvray, Chinon.

XXXX ✿✿ **La Chancelière,** 1 pl. Marronniers 𝒫 47 26 00 67, Fax 47 73 14 82, « Tasteful decor » – 🍽. **GB**
closed 1 to 7 September, February Holidays, Sunday (except lunch Sept.-June) and Monday except Bank Holidays – **M** 280 (except Saturday dinner)/460 and a la carte
Spec. Ravioles d'huîtres au Champagne, Sauté de homard au lard, Colvert aux figues fraîches (late August-October). Wines Montlouis, Chinon.

to the W : 5 km by N 10, D 287 and D 87 – ✉ 37250 Montbazon :

XX **Moulin Fleuri** ⤵ with rm, 𝒫 47 26 01 12, ≤, « Terrace overlooking the River Indre », 🎐 – 📺 ☎ 🅿. 🅰🅴 **GB**
closed 1 to 7 March, February and Monday except Bank Holidays – **M** 130 – ☑ 38 – **12 rm** 160/300.

Romorantin-Lanthenay ⊛ **41200** L.-et-Ch. 🔢 ⑱ – pop. 17 865 alt. 88.

Tours 91.

🏰 ✿✿ **Gd H. Lion d'Or** M, 69 r. Clemenceau ☏ 54 76 00 28, Telex 750990, Fax 54 88 24 87, « Tastefully decorated, flowered patio » – 🛗 📺 ☎ ⚒ 🅿 – 🔔 50. ⚿ ⚿ ⚿ ⚿ *closed early January-mid-February* – **M** (booking essential) 350 (lunch)/600 and a la carte – 🍽 100 – **13 rm** 600/1700, 3 suites 2000

Spec. Cuisses de grenouilles à la rocambole, Langoustines rôties à la poudre d'épices douces, Fraises confites au vin rouge (April-September). **Wines** Bourgueil, Vouvray.

Germany

Deutschland

BERLIN - COLOGNE - DRESDEN
DÜSSELDORF - FRANKFURT AM MAIN
HAMBURG - HANOVER - LEIPZIG
MUNICH - STUTTGART

PRACTICAL INFORMATION

Deutsche Mark: 100 DM = 65.96 US $ (Jan. 92)

TOURIST INFORMATION

Deutsche Zentrale für Tourismus (DZT) :
Beethovenstr. 69, 6000 Frankfurt 1, ✆ 069/7 57 20, Fax 069/75 19 03
Hotel booking service :
Allgemeine Deutsche Zimmerreservierung (ADZ)
Corneliusstr. 34, 6000 Frankfurt 1, ✆ 069/74 07 67
Telex 416666, Fax 069/75 10 56

AIRLINES

DEUTSCHE LUFTHANSA AG: Von-Gablenz-Str. 2, 5000 Köln 21,
✆ 0221/82 61
AIR CANADA: 6000 Frankfurt, Friedensstr. 7, ✆ 069/23 40 32
AIR FRANCE: 6000 Frankfurt, Friedensstr. 11, ✆ 069/2 56 63 20
AMERICAN AIRLINES: 6000 Frankfurt, Wiesenhüttenplatz 26,
✆ 069/2 56 01 72
BRITISH AIRWAYS: 1000 Berlin 15, Kurfürstendamm 178,
✆ 030/8 800 01 10
JAPAN AIRLINES: 6000 Frankfurt, Roßmarkt 15, ✆ 069/1 36 00
SABENA: 6000 Frankfurt, Roßmarkt 10, ✆ 069/29 90 06 94
SAS: 6000 Frankfurt, Saonestr. 3, ✆ 069/66 44 61 50
TWA: 6000 Frankfurt 90, Hamburger Allee 2, ✆ 069/77 06 01

FOREIGN EXCHANGE

Is possible in banks, savings banks and at exchange offices.
Hours of opening from Monday to Friday 8.30am to 12.30pm and 2.30pm
to 4pm except Thursday 2.30pm to 6pm.

SHOPPING

In the index of street names, those printed in red are where the principal
shops are found.

BREAKDOWN SERVICE

ADAC: for the addresses see text of the towns mentioned
AvD: Lyoner Str. 16, 6000 Frankfurt 71-Niederrad, ✆ 069/6 60 60, Telex
41 12 37, Fax 069/660 62 10
In Germany the ADAC (emergency number 01308/19211), and the AvD
(emergency number 0130/99 09), make a special point of assisting foreign
motorists. They have motor patrols covering main roads.

TIPPING

In Germany, prices include service and taxes. You may choose to leave
a tip if you wish but there is no obligation to do so.

SPEED LIMITS

The speed limit, generally, in built up areas is 50 km/h - 31 mph and on
all other roads it is 100 km/h - 62mph. On motorways and dual
carriageways, the recommanded speed limit is 130 km/h - 80 mph.

SEAT BELTS

The wearing of seat belts is compulsory for drivers and passengers.

Berlin

1 000. Berlin 987 ⑰ ⑱, 984 ⑮ ⑯ – Pop. 3 210 000 – alt. 40 m. –
✪ 030 (00372 fur den Ostteil).

MUSEUMS, GALLERYS

Pergamon Museum★★★ PY – Old National Gallery★ (Alte Nationalgalerie) PY **M 1**
– Bode-Museum★★ PY **M 2** – Altes Museum PY **M3** – Museum of Decorativ Arts★
(Kunstgewerbemuseum) NZ **M 4** – New National Gallery★ (Neue Nationalgalerie)
NZ **M 5** – Schoß Charlottenburg★★ (Equestrian Statue of the Great Elector★★,
Historical Rooms★, Porcelain Room★★) – National Gallery★★ White Hall★
(Nationalgalerie, Weißer Saal) – Golden Gallery★★ (Goldene Galerie) EY – Antique
Museum★ (Antikenmuseum) (Ancient Treasure★★★) EY **M 6** – Egyptian Museum★
(Ägyptisches Museum) (Bust of Queen Nefrititi★★) EY **M 6** – Dahlem Museums★★★
(Museum Dahlem) (Painting Gallery★★, Sculpture Department★★, Drawing and
Prints Department★, Ethnographic Museum★★) by Rheinbabenallee EZ – Museum
of Transport and Technology★ (Museum für Verkehr und Technik) GZ **M 8** –
Käthe-Kollwitz-Museum★ LXY **M 9** – Berlin Museum★ GY – Museum of Decorative
Arts★ (at Schloß Köpenick) (Kunstgewerbemuseum) by Stralauer Allee HY.

HISTORIC BUILDINGS AND MONUMENTS, STREETS, SQUARES

Brandenburg Gate★★ (Brandenburger Tor) NZ – Unter den Linden★ NPZ – Platz der
Akademie★ PZ – State Opera House★ (Deutsche Staatsoper) PZ – Neue Wache★ PY
– Arsenal★★ (Zeughaus) PY – Nikolaiviertel★ RZ – Victory Column ≼★ (Siegessäule)
MX – Philharmonie★★★ NZ – Kurfürstendamm★ JLY – Martin-Gropius-Building★ NZ
– Soviet Memorial★ (Sowjetisches Ehrenmal) by Köpenicker Straße HYZ – Radio
Tower ≼★ (Funkturm) EY – Olympic Stadium★ (Olympia Stadion) by Kaiserdamm
EY – Nikolai Church★ (Nikolaikirche) RZ **B** – Memorial Church (Kaiser-Wilhelm-
Gedächtniskirche) (Ceilling-and Wallmosaic★ of the former Entrancehall) MX.

PARKS, GARDENS, LAKES

Zoological Park★★ (Zoologischer Garten) MX – Castle Park of Charlottenburg★
(Schloßpark Charlottenburg) (at Belvedere Historical Porcelain Exhibition★) EY –
Botanical Gardens★ (Botanischer Garten) by Rheinbabenallee EZ – Grunewald
Forest★ (at Grunewald Lake : Hunting Lodge) by Rheinbabenallee EZ – Havel★
and Peacock Island★ by Clay-Allee EZ – Wannsee★★ by Clay-Allee EZ.

🏕 Berlin-Wannsee, Am Stölpchenweg, ℰ 8 05 50 75.

✈ Tegel, ℰ 4 11 01 – ✈ Schönefeld (S : 25 km), ℰ (00372) 6 78 70.

🚢 Berlin – Wannsee, ℰ 31 04 33.

Exhibition Grounds (Messegelände) AV, ℰ 3 03 81, Telex 182908.

🛈 Berlin Tourist-Information, Europa-Center (Budapester Straße), ℰ 2 62 60 31, Telex
183356, Fax 21 23 25 20.

🛈 Berlin Information, at Television Tower (Fernsehturm) 1020 Berlin ℰ 2 12 46 75.

🛈 Verkehrsamt at Airport Tegel ℰ 41 01 31 45

ADAC, Berlin-Wilmersdorf, Bundesallee 29 (B 31), ℰ 8 68 61, Telex 183513.

Frankfurt/Oder 105 – Hamburg 289 – Hannover 288 – Leipzig 183 – Rostock 222.

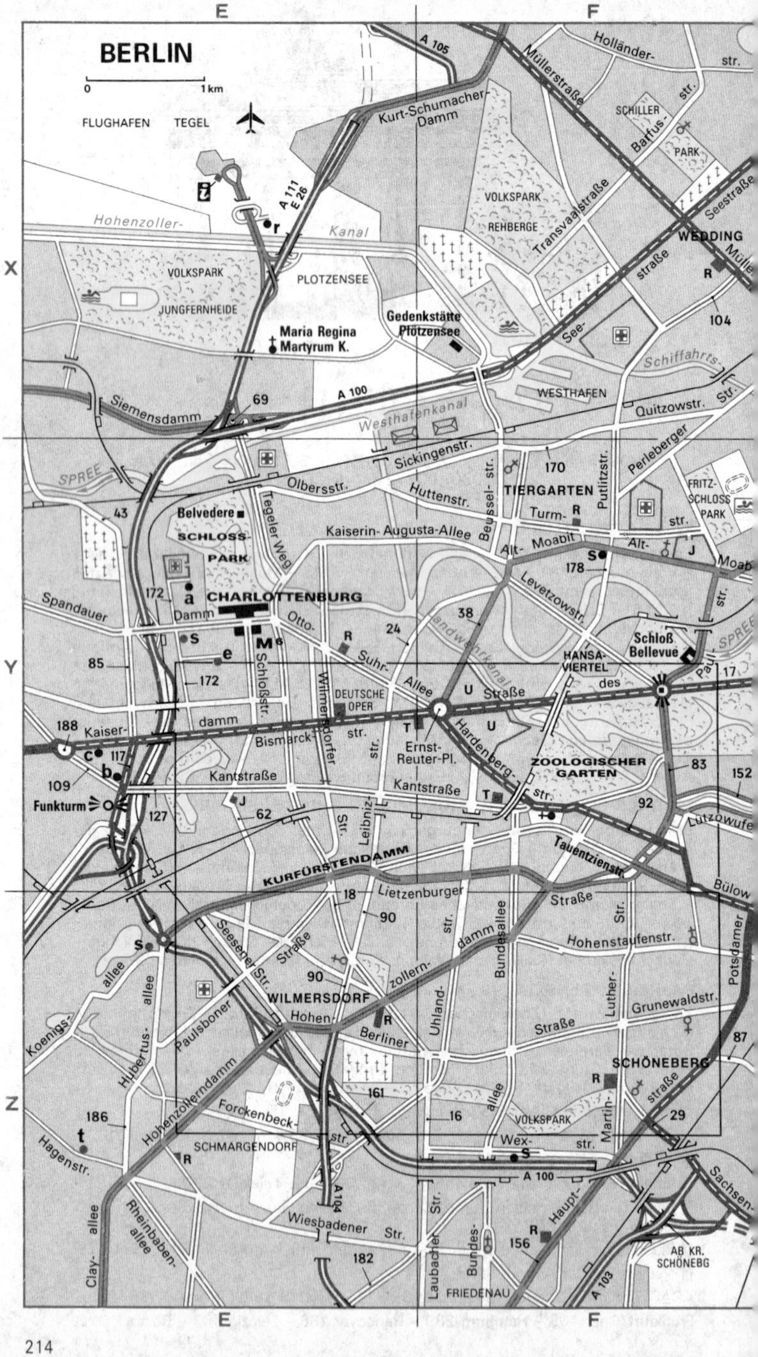

BERLIN

0   1 km

FLUGHAFEN TEGEL

A 111
E 26

Hohenzoller-   Kanal

r

PLOTZENSEE

VOLKSPARK
JUNGFERNHEIDE

Maria Regina
Martyrum K.

Gedenkstätte
Plötzensee

A 105

Kurt-Schumacher-
Damm

Müllerstraße

Hollander-
str.

SCHILLER
Bartus- PARK str.

Seestraße

VOLKSPARK
REHBERGE

Transvaalstraße

See-

straße

WEDDING

R   Müller

104

Schiffahrts-

WESTHAFEN

Siemensdamm

A 100

69

Westhafenkanal

Quitzowstr.

Perleberger

Sickingenstr.

170

FRITZ-
SCHLOSS
PARK

SPREE

43

Belvedere

SCHLOSS-
PARK

172

Olbersstr.

Huttenstr.

Kaiserin- Augusta-Allee

Beussel- str.

TIERGARTEN

Turm- R

Putlitzstr.

Alt- Moabit

J

Alt-   Moab

a   CHARLOTTENBURG
Damm

Otto-

R

24

178

S

Levetzowstr.

38

SPRE

Schloß
Bellevue

17

Spandauer

85

172

damm

S

e

M

Schloßstr.

Suhr-

Allee

Wilmersdorfer

DEUTSCHE
OPER

str.

U   Straße

U

HANSA-
VIERTEL

des

188   Kaiser-

C   117

b

109

Funkturm

127

Bismarck-

Kantstraße

str.

Ernst-
Reuter-Pl.

T

Hardenberg-

Kantstraße

T

str.

ZOOLOGISCHER
GARTEN

83   152

92

Lützowufe

J

62

Leibniz-

Str.

KURFÜRSTENDAMM

Tauentzienstr.

Bülow-

18

Lietzenburger

90

str.

Straße

Str.

Potsdamer

Hohenstaufenstr.

Bundesallee

S

allee

Hippertus-

Paulsborner

90

WILMERSDORF

Hohen-

Seesener Str.

Straße

zollern-

dammallee

Uhland-

Berliner

Straße

Luther-

Grunewaldstr.

SCHÖNEBERG

R

87

str.

Koenigs-

allee

186

t

Hagenstr.

Hohenzollerndamm

Forckenbeck-

SCHMARGENDORF

R

161

str.

16

VOLKSPARK

Wex-

S
str.

Martin-

straße

29

A 100

Clay-

allee

Rheinbaben-
allee

Wiesbadener   Str.

A 104

182

FRIEDENAU

Laubacher

Str.

Bundes-

R

156

Haupt-

str.

A 103

Sachsen-

AB KR.
SCHÖNEBG

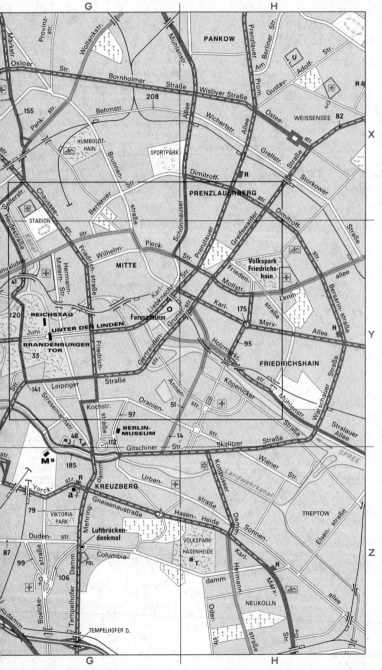

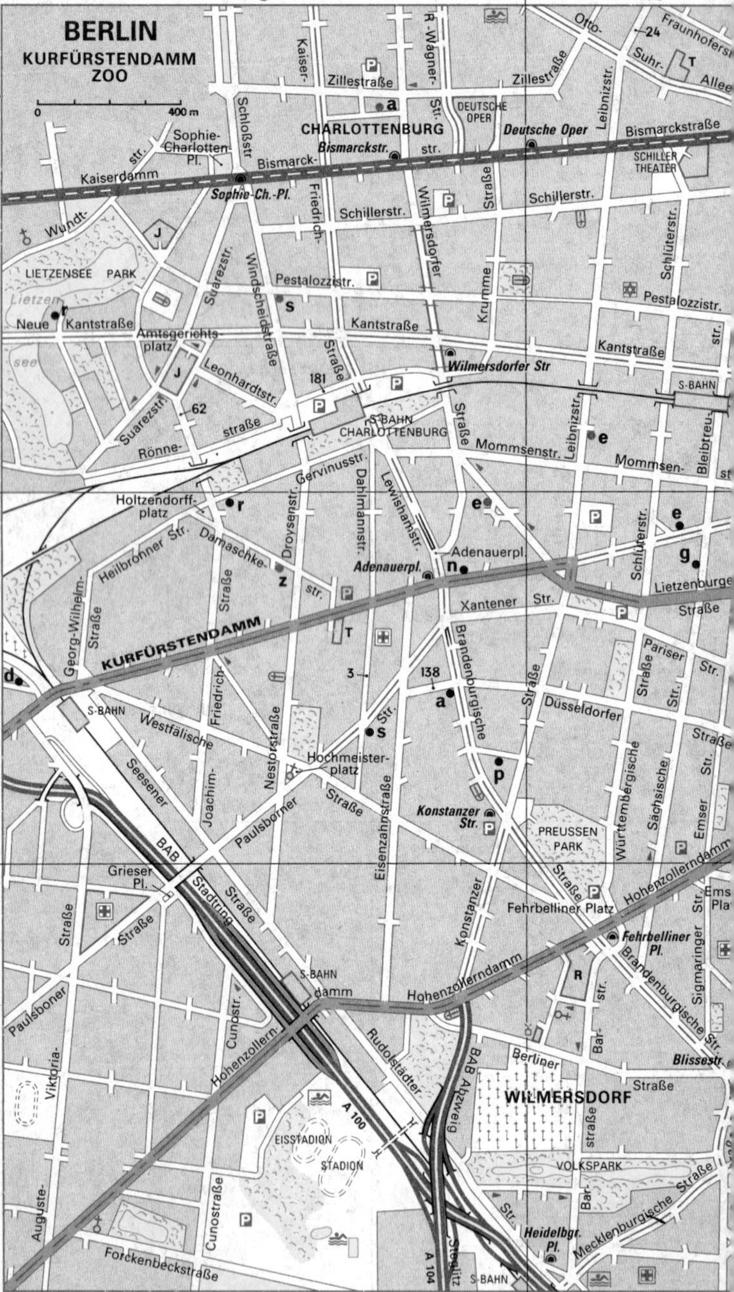

BERLIN
KURFÜRSTENDAMM
ZOO

0   400 m

CHARLOTTENBURG

Zillestraße

DEUTSCHE OPER

Deutsche Oper

Bismarckstraße

SCHILLER THEATER

Kaiser-

R.-Wagner-

Str.

Otto-

Fraunhofer-

Suhr-

24

T

Leibnizstr.

Schloßstr.

Sophie-Charlotten-Pl.

Bismarck-

str.

Sophie-Ch.-Pl.

Bismarckstr.

Kaiserdamm

Wundt-

Friedrich-

Schillerstr.

Schillerstr.

Wilmersdorfer

Straße

Schillerstr.

X

LIETZENSEE PARK

Lietzen

see

Neue Kantstraße

Suarezstraße

Windscheidstraße

Amtsgerichts-platz

Leonhardtstr.

Kantstraße

Krumme

Kantstraße

Pestalozzistr.

Pestalozzistr.

Schlüterstr.

Kantstraße

str.

Suarezstr.

Rönne-

straße

62

181

S-BAHN
CHARLOTTENBURG

Straße

Wilmersdorfer Str

S-BAHN

Mommsenstr.

Leibnizstr.

Mommsen-

Bleibtreu-

st

e

Holtzendorff-platz

Gervinusstr.

Dahlmannstr.

Lewishanstr.

e

r

Heilbronner Str.

Darmaschke-

Droysenstr.

str.

z

Adenauerpl.

Adenauerpl.

n

e

Schlüterstr.

e

g

Lietzenburge

Straße

Georg-Wilhelm-Straße

Straße

KURFÜRSTENDAMM

Xantener Str.

Brandenburgische

T

3

138

a

Düsseldorfer

Pariser

Str.

Straße

Y

d

S-BAHN

Westfälische

Friedrich-

Nestorstraße

Straße

Hochmeister-platz

s

Brandenburgische

Straße

Würtembergische

Sächsische

Emser

Straße

Seesener

Joachim-

Paulsborner

Straße

Eisenzahnstraße

p

Konstanzer Str.

PREUSSEN PARK

Straße

Hohenzollerndamm

BAB

Grieser Pl.

Stadtring

Cunostr.

Konstanzer

Straße

Fehrbelliner

Fehrbelliner Platz

Fehrbelliner Pl.

Brandenburgische Str.

Sigmaringer Str.

Ems Pla

Straße

Paulsborner

Straße

Viktoria-

Hohenzollern

damm

Hohenzollerndamm

R

str.

Bar-

Blissestr.

Z

Auguste-

Cunostraße

S-BAHN

Rudolstädter-

Berliner

Straße

WILMERSDORF

VOLKSPARK

BAB Abzweig

Steglitz

str.

Bar-

Mecklenburgische Straße

A 100

EISSTADION

STADION

Forckenbeckstraße

A 104

S-BAHN

Heidelbgr. Pl.

Mecklenburgische

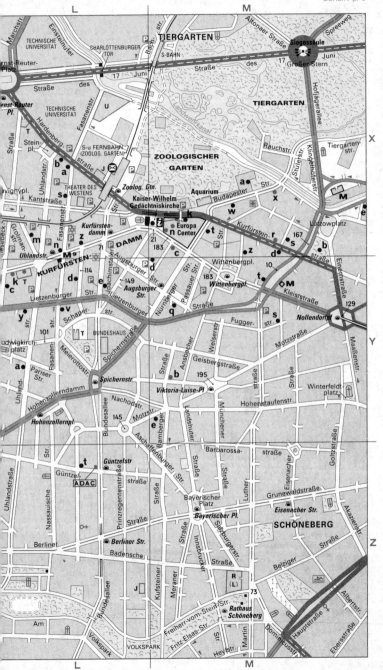

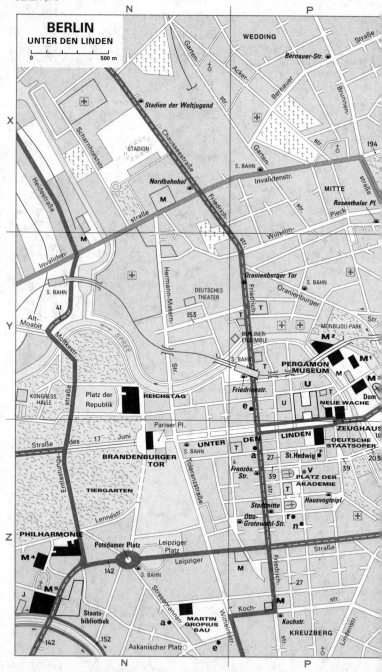

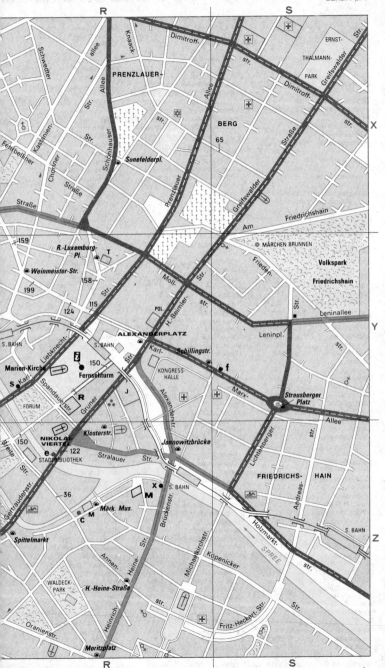

STREET INDEX TO BERLIN TOWN PLANS

Continued p. 9

Town Centre (Berlin - City. - Schöneberg and - Tiergarten) :

Bristol-Hotel Kempinski ⅏, Kurfürstendamm 27 (B 15), ℰ 88 43 40, Telex 185651, Fax 8836075, ☜, Massage, ⇌, ☒ – 🛗 ✳ rm 📧 📺 ⚎ – 🕍 25/300. 🖭 ⑩ ℇ 𝘝𝘐𝘚𝘈.
LX n
Restaurants : **Kempinski-Grill M** a la carte 69/105 – **Kempinski-Restaurant M** a la carte 60/95 – **Kempinski-Eck M** a la carte 48/64 – **315 rm** 447/654 Bb – 32 suites 850/1854.

Grand Hotel, Friedrichstr. 158, ⊠ O-1080, ℰ 2 32 70, Telex 115189, Fax 2294095, ☜, Massage, ⇌ – 🛗 📺 ⚒ ⚎ – 🕍 25/100. 🖭 ⑩ ℇ 𝘝𝘐𝘚𝘈
PZ z
Restaurants : **Coelln** *(remarkable wine list)* **M** a la carte 47/88 – **Le Grand Silhouette** *(dinner only) (closed Sunday and 20 July - 20 August)* **M** a la carte 79/98 – **Goldene Gans M** a la carte 41/59 – **350 rm** 325/680 Bb – 35 suites 1000/3450.

Inter-Continental, Budapester Str. 2 (B 30), ℰ 2 60 20, Telex 184380, Fax 260280760, Massage, ⇌, – 🛗 ✳ rm 📧 📺 ⚒ ⚎ 🄿 – 🕍 25/800. 🖭 ⑩ ℇ 𝘝𝘐𝘚𝘈. ⅏ rest   MX a
Restaurants : **Zum Hugenotten** *(remarkable wine list)* **M** a la carte 77/98 – **Buffet-Restaurant Brasserie M** a la carte 49/68 – **507 rm** 390/560 Bb – 70 suites 810/2600.

Grand Hotel Esplanade (modern hotel featuring contemporary art), Lützowufer 15 (B 30), ℰ 26 10 11, Telex 185986, Fax 2629121, Massage, ⇌, ☒ – 🛗 ✳ rm 📧 📺 ⚎ – 🕍 25/450. 🖭 ⑩ ℇ 𝘝𝘐𝘚𝘈. ⅏ rest   MX e
M *(closed Sunday)* a la carte 62/86 – **402 rm** 365/495 Bb – 17 suites 720/1850.

Metropol, Friedrichstr. 150, ⊠ O-1086, ℰ 20 30 70, Telex 114141, Fax (030) 3919108, ☜, Massage, 🛁, ⇌, ☒ – 🛗 ✳ rm 📺 ⚒ ⚎ – 🕍 25/150. 🖭 ⑩ ℇ 𝘝𝘐𝘚𝘈. ⅏ rest PY e
Restaurants : **Friedrichstadt – International – Grill – 340 rm** – 34 suites.

Schweizerhof, Budapester Str. 21 (B 30), ℰ 2 69 60, Telex 185501, Fax 2696900, Massage, 🛁, ⇌, ☒ – 🛗 ✳ rm 📧 📺 ⚎ 🄿 – 🕍 25/400. 🖭 ⑩ ℇ 𝘝𝘐𝘚𝘈. ⅏ rest   MX w
M *(also vegetarian dishes)* a la carte 47/88 – **430 rm** 390/560 Bb – 7 suites 660/2060.

Palace, Budapester Str. 42 (Europa-Centre) (B 30), ℰ 25 49 70, Telex 184825, Fax 2626577, free entrance to the thermal recreation centre – 🛗 ✳ rm 📺 – 🕍 25/260. 🖭 ⑩ ℇ 𝘝𝘐𝘚𝘈. ⅏ rest   MX k
M *(lunch only)* a la carte 32/77 – **La Réserve** *(dinner only)* **M** a la carte 60/90 – **252 rm** 364/548 Bb – 7 suites 548/748.

🏨🏨🏨 **Domhotel** ⑤, Mohrenstr. 30, ⊠ O-1080, ℰ 2 09 80, Telex 113401, Fax 20988269, Massage, ⌨, ⇌, 🖵 – ⌷ 💱 rm ⊟ ⇋ ⇦ – 🕍 25/400
Restaurants : **Mark Brandenburg** – **La Coupole** – **Beletage** *(dinner only)* – **357 rm** – 12 suites.
PZ **r**

🏨🏨🏨 **Berlin**, Lützowplatz 17 (B 30), ℰ 2 60 50, Telex 184332, Fax 26052716, ⌬, Massage, ⇌ – ⌷ 💱 rm ⊟ rest 📺 ⇦ ⑫ – 🕍 25/500. 🆎 ⓞ ⒠ 🆅🆂🅰
M 27 buffet (lunch) and a la carte 41/88 – **490 rm** 294/598 Bb – 6 suites 698/1548.
MX **b**

🏨🏨🏨 **Steigenberger Berlin**, Los-Angeles-Platz 1 (B 30), ℰ 2 10 80, Telex 181444, Fax 2108117, ⌬, Massage, ⇌, 🖵 – ⌷ 💱 rm ⊟ 📺 ⇋ ⇦ – 🕍 25/600. 🆎 ⓞ ⒠ 🆅🆂🅰
Restaurants : **Park-Restaurant** *(dinner only)* *(closed Sunday and Monday)* **M** a la carte 62/105 – **Berliner Stube M** a la carte 33/59 – **397 rm** 356/572 Bb – 11 suites 902/2452.
MY **d**

🏨🏨 **Savoy**, Fasanenstr. 9 (B 12), ℰ 31 10 30, Telex 184292, Fax 31103333, ⇌ – ⌷ 📺 – 🕍 30. 🆎 ⓞ ⒠ 🆅🆂🅰. 💱 rest
M a la carte 46/67 – **130 rm** 340/530 Bb – 6 suites 570/950.
LX **s**

🏨🏨 **Mondial** ⑤, Kurfürstendamm 47 (B 15), ℰ 88 41 10, Telex 182839, Fax 88411150, ⌬, 🖵 – ⌷ 💱 rm ⇋ ⇦ – 🕍 25/65. 🆎 ⓞ ⒠ 🆅🆂🅰. 💱 rest
M a la carte 52/77 – **75 rm** 190/400 Bb.
KY **e**

🏨🏨 **Palasthotel**, Karl-Liebknecht-Str. 5, ⊠ O-1020, ℰ 24 10, Telex 115050, Fax 2127273, ⌬, Massage, ⌨, ⇌, 🖵 – ⌷ 📺 ⇋ ⑫ – 🕍 25/420. 🆎 ⓞ ⒠ 🆅🆂🅰
Restaurants : **Märkisches Restaurant M** a la carte 32/61 – **Rôti d'or M** a la carte 33/82 – **Domklause M** a la carte 21/42 – **600 rm** 250/450 Bb – 40 suites 490/1050.
RY **s**

🏨🏨 **Berlin Penta Hotel** ⑤, Nürnberger Str. 65 (B 30), ℰ 21 00 70, Telex 182877, Fax 2132009, Massage, ⇌, 🖵 – ⌷ 💱 rm ⊟ ⇋ ⇦ ⑫ – 🕍 25/120. 🆎 ⓞ ⒠ 🆅🆂🅰. 💱 rest
M a la carte 59/75 – **425 rm** 318/436 Bb – 20 suites.
MX **t**

🏨🏨 **Ambassador**, Bayreuther Str. 42 (B 30), ℰ 21 90 20, Telex 184259, Fax 21902380, Massage, ⇌, 🖵 – ⌷ 💱 rm ⊟ rest 📺 ⇋ ⇦ – 🕍 25/80. 🆎 ⓞ ⒠ 🆅🆂🅰. 💱 rest
Restaurants : **Conti** *(closed Sunday, Monday, 1 to 15 January and 2 weeks July)* **M** a la carte 69/81 – **Schöneberger Krug M** 25 (lunch), dinner a la carte 32/60 – **199 rm** 280/440 Bb.
MX **z**

🏨🏨 **Alsterhof**, Augsburger Str. 5 (B 30), ℰ 21 99 60, Telex 183484, Fax 243949, Massage, ⇌, 🖵 – ⌷ 📺 ⇋ ⑫. 🆎 ⓞ ⒠ 🆅🆂🅰. 💱 rest
M a la carte 47/68 – **144 rm** 185/330 Bb.
MY **q**

🏨🏨 **President**, An der Urania 16 (B 30), ℰ 21 90 30, Telex 184018, Fax 2141200, ⇌ – ⌷ ⊟ 📺 ⑫ – 🕍 40. 🆎 ⓞ ⒠ 🆅🆂🅰. 💱 rest
M *(closed Saturday dinner)* a la carte 43/68 – **132 rm** 275/355 Bb – 6 suites 450/465.
MY **t**

🏨 **Art-Hotel Sorat** without rest (modern hotel with exhibition of contemporary art), Joachimstalerstr. 28 (B 15), ℰ 88 44 70, Fax 88447700 – ⌷ 📺 ☎ ⇋ ⇦. 🆎 ⓞ ⒠ 🆅🆂🅰. 💱
75 rm 216/297 Bb.
LY **e**

🏨 **Am Zoo** without rest, Kurfürstendamm 25 (B 15), ℰ 88 43 70, Telex 183835, Fax 88437714 – ⌷ 📺 ☎ ⑫ – 🕍 30. 🆎 ⓞ ⒠ 🆅🆂🅰
136 rm 160/420 Bb.
LX **z**

🏨 **Berliner-Congress-Center**, Märkisches Ufer 54, ⊠ O-1026, ℰ 2 70 05 31, Telex 114810, Fax (0161) 3610740, ⌬, ⇌ – ⌷ 📺 ☎ – 🕍 25/350
110 rm – 12 suites.
RZ **x**

🏨 **Berlin Excelsior Hotel**, Hardenbergstr. 14 (B 12), ℰ 3 19 90, Telex 184781, Fax 31992849 – ⌷ ⊟ rest 📺 ⇋ ⑫ – 🕍 25/120. 🆎 ⓞ ⒠ 🆅🆂🅰
Restaurants : **Peacock M** a la carte 46/80 – **Store House Grill M** a la carte 33/60 – **320 rm** 268/398 Bb.
LX **b**

🏨 **Residenz-Restaurant Grand Cru**, Meinekestr. 9 (B 15), ℰ 88 44 30, Telex 18 30 82, Fax 8824726 – ⌷ 📺 ☎ ⇋ ⇦. 🆎 ⓞ ⒠ 🆅🆂🅰. 💱 rest
M a la carte 60/88 – **92 rm** 220/380 Bb – 10 suites 560.
LY **d**

🏨 **Hecker's Deele**, Grolmanstr. 35 (B 12), ℰ 8 89 00, Telex 184954, Fax 8890260 – ⌷ 💱 rm ⊟ rest 📺 ☎ ⇋ ⇦. 🆎 ⓞ ⒠ 🆅🆂🅰
M a la carte 32/63 – **52 rm** 275/360 Bb.
LX **e**

🏨 **Sylter Hof**, Kurfürstenstr. 116 (B 30), ℰ 2 12 00, Telex 183317, Fax 2142826 – ⌷ 📺 ☎ ⑫ – 🕍 25/120. 🆎 ⓞ ⒠ 🆅🆂🅰. 💱 rest
M a la carte 42/73 – **154 rm** 225/404 Bb – 16 suites 550.
MX **d**

🏨 **Bremen** without rest, Bleibtreustr. 25 (B 15), ℰ 8 81 40 76, Telex 184892, Fax 8824685 – ⌷ 📺 ☎. 🆎 ⓞ ⒠ 🆅🆂🅰
53 rm 250/330 Bb.
KY **g**

🏨 **Curator** without rest, Grolmanstr. 41 (B 12), ℰ 88 42 60, Telex 183389, Fax 88426500, ⇌ – ⌷ 📺 ☎ ⇋. 🆎 ⓞ ⒠ 🆅🆂🅰
100 rm 220/350 – 3 suites 500.
LX **m**

🏨 **Kronprinz** without rest (restored 1894 house), Kronprinzendamm 1 (B 31), ℰ 89 60 30, Telex 181459, Fax 8931215 – ⌷ 📺 ☎ – 🕍 30. 🆎 ⓞ ⒠ 🆅🆂🅰
53 rm 180/285 Bb.
JY **d**

🏨 **Park Consul** without rest, Alt-Moabit 86a, ℰ 39 07 80, Fax 39078900 – ⌷ 💱 rm 📺 ⇋. 🆎 ⓞ ⒠ 🆅🆂🅰
52 rm 235/315 Bb.
FY **N**

Domus without rest, Uhlandstr. 49 (B 15), ℰ 88 20 41, Telex 185975, Fax 8820410 – |≢| ⇔
☎. AE ⓪ E VISA
LY **a**
closed 24 December - 2 January – **73 rm** 125/230 Bb.

Hamburg, Landgrafenstr. 4 (B 30), ℰ 26 91 61, Telex 184974, Fax 2629394 – |≢| ⇔ rm TV
☎ ⇔ ℗ – ⚑ 25/100. AE ⓪ E VISA. ⁒ rest
MX **s**
M a la carte 40/63 – **240 rm** 211/290 Bb.

Berlin-Plaza, Knesebeckstr. 63 (B 15), ℰ 88 41 30, Telex 184181, Fax 88413754, ☆ – |≢|
TV ☎ ⇔ ℗ – ⚑ 30. AE ⓪ E VISA
LY **c**
M a la carte 35/60 – **131 rm** 210/300 Bb.

Krone without rest, Kronenstr. 48, ⊠ O-1080, ℰ 20 98 82 55, Fax 20988269 – ⇔ TV ☎
148 rm.
PZ **n**

Arosa Parkschloß - Hotel, Lietzenburger Str. 79 (B 15), ℰ 88 00 50, Telex 183397,
Fax 8824579, ☆, ⅃ – |≢| TV ☎ ⇔ – ⚑ 40. AE ⓪ E VISA
LY **y**
M *(closed Sunday)* a la carte 45/76 – **90 rm** 173/314 Bb.

Castor, Fuggerstr. 8 (B 30), ℰ 21 30 30, Fax 21303160 – |≢| TV ☎. AE ⓪ E VISA MY **s**
M *(dinner only) (closed Saturday, Sunday and July)* a la carte 34/54 – **78 rm** 180/260 Bb.

Astoria without rest, Fasanenstr. 2 (B 12), ℰ 3 12 40 67, Telex 181745, Fax 3125027 – |≢|
TV ☎. AE ⓪ E VISA
LX **a**
32 rm 189/360 Bb.

Kurfürstendamm without rest, Kurfürstendamm 68 (B 15), ℰ 88 28 41, Telex 184630,
Fax 8825528 – |≢| TV ☎ ℗ – ⚑ 25/45. AE ⓪ E VISA
JY **n**
34 rm 145/228 Bb – 4 suites 250/295.

Atrium-Hotel without rest, Motzstr. 87 (B 30), ℰ 2 18 40 57, Fax 2117563 – |≢| TV ☎. E
22 rm 90/140.
MY **e**

Berolina, Karl-Marx-Allee 31, ⊠ O-1026, ℰ 2 10 95 41, Telex 114331, Fax 2123409 – |≢| TV
☎ ℗ – ⚑ 25/60. AE ⓪ E VISA
SY **f**
M a la carte 26/42 – **344 rm** 130/220 – 11 suites 330/390.

XXX **Ristorante Anselmo**, Damaschkestr. 17 (B 31), ℰ 3 23 30 94, Fax 3246228, « Modern
Italian rest. » – AE. ⁒
JY **z**
closed Monday – **M** a la carte 51/78.

XX ✿ **Bamberger Reiter**, Regensburger Str. 7 (B 30), ℰ 24 42 82/ 2 18 42 82, Fax 2142348,
☆ AE ⓪ E VISA. ⁒
MY **b**
dinner only, closed Saturday, Sunday, 1 to 13 January and 2 to 24 August – **M** (booking
essential) 115/155 and a la carte 87/105 - **Bistro** (lunch and dinner) **M** a la carte 45/60
Spec. Marinierte Gänsestopfleber in Trüffelgelee, Bretonischer Hummer in Sauternes, Lammrücken im Kartoffelmantel.

XX **Mövenpick**, Europa-Centre (1st floor) (B 30), ℰ 2 62 70 77, Fax 2629486, ≤ – AE ⓪ E VISA
M a la carte 55/64.
MX **n**

XX **Ephraim - Palais**, Poststr. 16, ⊠ O-1020, ℰ 21 71 31 64
RZ **e**

XX **Französischer Hof**, Otto-Nuschke-Str. 56, ⊠ O-1086, ℰ 2 29 39 69, Fax 2293152 – ⅙ PZ **v**

XX **Du Pont**, Budapester Str. 1 (B 30), ℰ 2 61 88 11, ☆ – AE ⓪ E VISA
MX **x**
closed Saturday lunch, Sunday, Bank Holidays and 24 December - 2 January – **M** a la carte
52/79.

XX **Ermeler Haus** (reconstructed 18 C Patrician house), Märkisches Ufer 10 (1st floor), ⊠ O-
1026, ℰ 2 79 40 28 – ⁒
RZ **c**
M a la carte 38/80.

XX **Daitokai** (Japanese rest.), Tauentzienstr. 9 (Europa Centre, 1st floor) (B 30), ℰ 2 61 80 99,
Fax 2616036 – ⁒
MX **n**

XX **Ming's Garden** (Chinese rest.), Tauentzienstr. 16 (entrance Marburger Str.) (B 30),
ℰ 2 11 87 28, Fax 2118914 – AE ⓪ E VISA. ⁒
MX **c**
M 15 (lunch) and a la carte 38/60.

XX **Ristorante Il Sorriso** (Italian rest.), Kurfürstenstr. 76 (B 30), ℰ 2 62 13 13, Fax 2650277, ☆
– AE E VISA. ⁒
MX **r**
closed Sunday – **M** *(booking essential for dinner)* a la carte 49/71.

XX **Peppino** (Italian rest.), Fasanenstr. 65 (B 15), ℰ 8 83 67 22
LY **v**
closed Monday and 4 weeks July - August – **M** a la carte 47/68.

X **Stachel** (Rest. Bistro style), Giesebrechtstr. 3 (B 12), ℰ 8 82 36 29, ☆ – AE E VISA JY **e**
(dinner only), closed Bank Holidays – **M** a la carte 48/75.

X **Kopenhagen** (Danish Smørrebröd), Kurfürstendamm 203 (B 15), ℰ 8 81 62 19 – ▤. AE E
VISA
LY **k**
M a la carte 35/60.

X **Hongkong** (Chinese rest.), Kurfürstendamm 210 (2nd floor), |≢|) (B 15), ℰ 8 81 57 56 – AE
⓪ E VISA
LY **T**
M a la carte 26/70.

at Berlin-Charlottenburg :

🏨 **Seehof** ⑤, Lietzensee-Ufer 11 (B 19), ℰ 32 00 20, Telex 182943, Fax 32002251, ≤,
« Garden terrace », ⇔, ⅃ – |≢| ▤ rest TV ⇔ – ⚑ 25/50. AE ⓪ E VISA. ⁒ rest JX **r**
M 41/65 (lunch) and a la carte 60/80 – **77 rm** 195/450 Bb.

🏨 **Kanthotel** without rest, Kantstr. 111 (B 12), ℘ 32 30 26, Telex 183330, Fax 3240952 – 🛗
📺 ☎ 🅿 🝅 ⚙ 🝔 *VISA*. 🛠
55 rm 199/239 Bb.   JX **e**

🏨 **Schloßparkhotel** ⏚, Heubnerweg 2a (B 19), ℘ 3 22 40 61, Telex 183462, Fax 3258861,
🗟, 🝲 – 🛗 📺 ☎ 🅿 – 🔬 50. 🝅 ⚙ 🝔 *VISA*
M a la carte 32/58 – **39 rm** 149/275 Bb.   EY **a**

🏨 **Kardell**, Gervinusstr. 24 (B 12), ℘ 3 24 10 66, Fax 3249710 – 🛗 📺 ☎ 🝳 🅿. 🝅 ⚙ 🝔
VISA   JY **r**
M *(closed Saturday lunch)* a la carte 45/65 – **33 rm** 115/200 Bb.

🏨 **Am Studio** without rest, Kaiserdamm 80 (B 19), ℘ 30 20 81, Telex 182825, Fax 3019578
– 🛗 📺 ☎ 🝳. 🝅 ⚙ 🝔 *VISA*   EY **c**
80 rm 135/210 Bb.

🏨 Ibis without rest, Messedamm 10 (B 19), ℘ 30 39 30, Telex 182882, Fax 3019536 – 🛗 📺
☎ – 🔬 40   EY **b**
191 rm

✕✕ ⁂ **Ponte Vecchio** (Tuscan rest.), Spielhagenstr. 3 (B 10), ℘ 3 42 19 99 – ⚙   JX **a**
closed Tuesday and 4 weeks July - August – **M** (dinner only, booking essential) a la carte 55/80
Spec. Insalata di coniglio alle noci, Tagliolini al nero con cappe sante, Filetti di branzino ai carciofini.

✕✕ ⁂ **Alt Luxemburg**, Windscheidtstr. 31 (B 12), ℘ 3 23 87 30 – ⚙   JX **s**
closed Sunday, Monday, 3 weeks January and 3 weeks June - July – **M** (dinner only, booking
essential) 98/130 and a la carte 71/90.

✕✕ **Ugo** (Italian rest.), Sophie-Charlotten-Str. 101 (B 19), ℘ 3 25 71 10 – 🝅   EY **s**
closed Sunday, Monday and 3 weeks June - July – **M** (dinner only) a la carte 57/75.

✕✕ **Trio**, Klausenerplatz 14 (B 19), ℘ 3 21 77 82   EY **e**
closed Wednesday and Thursday – **M** (dinner only, booking essential) a la carte 47/65.

✕✕ **Funkturm - Restaurant** (🛗, DM 3), Messedamm 22 (B 19), ℘ 30 38 29 96, Fax 30383915,
≤ Berlin – 🅿. 🝅 ⚙ 🝔 *VISA*. 🛠   EY
M a la carte 53/81.

at Berlin-Dahlem by Clayallee EZ :

🏨 **Forsthaus Paulsborn** ⏚, Am Grunewaldsee (B 33), ℘ 8 14 11 56, 🝞 – 📺 ☎ 🅿. 🝅 ⚙
🝔 *VISA*
M *(closed Monday)* 28/35 (lunch) and a la carte 47/72 – **11 rm** 105/190.

✕✕ **Alter Krug**, Königin-Luise-Str. 52 (B 33), ℘ 8 32 77 49, « Terrace » – 🅿. ⚙ 🝔 *VISA*
closed Thursday – **M** a la carte 38/77.

at Berlin-Grunewald :

✕✕✕ **Hemingway's**, Hagenstr. 18 (B 33), ℘ 8 25 45 71 – 🝅 ⚙ 🝔 *VISA*   EZ **t**
closed Saturday lunch – **M** (booking essential for dinner) a la carte 65/83.

✕✕ **Chalet Corniche**, Königsallee 5b (B 33), ℘ 8 92 85 97, Fax 4328094, « Terrace on the bank
of lake Halensee » – 🅿. 🝅 ⚙ 🝔 *VISA*   EZ **s**
M (Monday - Saturday dinner only, remarkable wine list) a la carte 60/90.

at Berlin-Kreuzberg :

🏨 **Stuttgarter Hof**, Anhalter Str. 9 (B 61), ℘ 26 48 30, Telex 183966, Fax 26483900, ≦s –
🛠 rm 📺 ☎ 🝳 – 🔬 30. 🝅 ⚙ 🝔 *VISA*   NZ **e**
M a la carte 46/70 – **110 rm** 245/410 Bb.

🏨 **Riehmers Hofgarten** without rest, Yorckstr. 83 (B 61), ℘ 78 10 11, Fax 7866059 – 🛗 📺
☎. 🝅 ⚙ 🝔 *VISA*   GZ **a**
21 rm 186/246.

🏨 **Hervis** without rest, Stresemannstr. 97 (B 61), ℘ 2 61 14 44, Telex 184063, Fax 2615027 –
🛗 📺 ☎ 🅿 – 🔬 30. 🝅 ⚙ 🝔 *VISA*   NZ **a**
73 rm 110/240 Bb.

at Berlin-Reinickendorf by Sellerstr. GX :

🏨 **Rheinsberg am See**, Finsterwalder Str. 64 (B 26), ℘ 4 02 10 02, Telex 185972,
Fax 4035057, « Lakeside garden terrace », ≦s, ⛁, 🗟, 🝲 – 🛗 📺 ☎ 🅿. 🝔 *VISA*
M a la carte 40/71 – **80 rm** 155/295 Bb.

at Berlin-Siemensstadt by Siemensdamm EX :

🏨 **Novotel**, Ohmstr. 4 (B 13), ℘ 38 10 61, Telex 181415, Fax 3819403, ⛁ – 🛗 🝟 rest 📺 ☎
🖰 🅿 – 🔬 25/200. 🝅 ⚙ 🝔 *VISA*
M a la carte 48/65 – **119 rm** 189/236 Bb – 5 suites 279.

at Berlin-Steglitz by Hauptstr. FZ :

🏨 **Steglitz International**, Albrechtstr. 2 (B 41), ℘ 79 00 50, Telex 183545, Fax 79005550,
Massage, ≦s – 🛗 📺 🖰 🝳 – 🔬 25/400. 🝅 ⚙ 🝔 *VISA*
M a la carte 43/65 – **212 rm** 190/350 Bb – 3 suites 560.

🏨 **Ravenna Hotel** without rest, Grunewaldstr. 8 (B 41), ℘ 7 92 80 31, Telex 184310,
Fax 7924412 – 🛗 📺 ☎ 🝳 🅿. 🝅 ⚙ 🝔 *VISA*
48 rm 125/190 Bb – 3 suites 280.

at Berlin-Tegel :

🏨 **Novotel Berlin Airport**, Kurt-Schumacher-Damm 202 (by airport approach) (B 51), ℰ 4 10 60, Telex 181605, Fax 4106700, 斎, ≘s, ⌇ (heated) – 劇 ▤ ⎘ ☎ & ⓟ – 🛣 25/250. 〔AE〕 ⓞ Ɛ 〔VISA〕
EX **r**
M a la carte 36/57 – **185 rm** 199/260 Bb.

at Berlin-Waidmannslust by Sellerstr. GX :

✗✗✗ ⊛⊛ **Rockendorf's Restaurant**, Düsterhauptstr. 1 (B 28), ℰ 4 02 30 99, Fax 4022742, « Elegant installation » – ⓟ. 〔AE〕 ⓞ Ɛ 〔VISA〕
closed Sunday, Monday, 28 June - 21 July and 22 December - 6 January – **M** (booking essential) 95/160 (lunch), 160/200 (dinner)
Spec. Gelee von Berliner Krebsen, Irish Stew mit Lammrücken, Schokoladensoufflé auf Gewürz-kaffeesauce.

at Berlin-Wilmersdorf :

🏨 **Queens Hotel** without rest, Güntzelstr. 14 (B 31), ℰ 87 02 41, Telex 182948, Fax 8619326 – 劇 ▥ ☎ ⓟ
LZ **t**
110 rm 189/360 Bb.

🏨 **Pension Wittelsbach** without rest, Wittelsbacher Str. 22 (B 31), ℰ 87 63 45, Fax 8621532, « Tasteful decor » – 劇 ▥ ☎ ⊹. Ɛ 〔VISA〕
JY **p**
37 rm 115/280 Bb.

🏨 **Prinzregent** without rest, Prinzregentenstr. 47 (B 31), ℰ 8 53 80 51, Telex 185217, Fax 8547637 – 劇 ▥ ☎. 〔AE〕 Ɛ 〔VISA〕
FZ **s**
35 rm 110/160.

🏨 **Franke**, Albrecht-Achilles-Str. 57 (B 31), ℰ 8 92 10 97, Telex 184857, Fax 8911639 – 劇 ▥ ☎ ⇌ ⓟ. 〔AE〕 ⓞ Ɛ 〔VISA〕
JY **s**
M a la carte 28/45 – **69 rm** 150/220.

🏨 **Lichtburg**, Paderborner Str. 10 (B 15), ℰ 8 91 80 41, Telex 184208, Fax 8926106 – 劇 ▥ ☎. 〔AE〕 ⓞ Ɛ
JY **a**
M a la carte 27/45 – **66 rm** 130/250.

at Großer Müggelsee SE : 15 km by Holzmarktstr. SZ :

🏨 **Müggelsee** ⊰, Am Müggelsee (southern bank), ⊠ O-1170 Berlin-Köpenick, ℰ (00372) 6 60 20, Fax 6602263, 斎, Massage, ≘s, ✗ – 劇 ▥ ☎ ⓟ – 🛣 25/200. 〔AE〕 ⓞ Ɛ 〔VISA〕
M a la carte 34/54 – **175 rm** 200/280 Bb – 7 suites 440/600.

🏨 **Seehotel Belvedere**, Müggelseedamm 288 (northern bank), ⊠ O-1162 Berlin-Köpenick-Friedrichshagen, ℰ (00372) 6 45 56 82, ≤, « Lakeside terrace », ≘s – ▥ ☎ ⓟ – 🛣 25/100. ⊰⊰
M a la carte 36/59 – **32 rm** 175/215 Bb – 8 suites 220/240.

at Peetzsee SE : 31 km by Köpenicker Landstraße SZ :

🏨 **Seegarten Grünheide** ⊰, Am Schlangenbuch 12, ⊠ O-1252 Grünheide, ℰ (0037357) 61 29, 斎, ≘s, 斎 – ▥ ☎ & ⓟ – 🛣 40. 〔AE〕 Ɛ 〔VISA〕. ⊰⊰
M a la carte 27/44 – **22 rm** 80/205 – 14 suites.

☞ *Inclusion in the Michelin Guide cannot be achieved by pulling strings or by offering favours.*

COLOGNE (KÖLN) 5000. Nordrhein-Westfalen 〖987〗 ㉓ ㉔, 〖412〗 D 14 – pop. 992 000 – alt. 65 m – 🕿 0221.

See : Cathedral (Dom)✶✶ (Magi's Shrine✶✶✶, gothic stained glass windows✶, Cross of Gero (Gerokreuz)✶, south chapel (Marienkapelle) : altarpiece✶✶✶, stalls✶, treasury✶) GY – Roman-Germanic Museum (Römisch-Germanisches Museum)✶✶✶ (Dionysos Mosaic) GY M1 – Wallraf-Richartz-Museum and Museum Ludwig✶✶✶ (Photo-Historama Agfa✶) GY M2 – Diocesan Museum (Diözesan-Museum)✶ GY M3 – Schnütgen-Museum✶✶ GZ M4 – Museum of East-Asian Art (Museum für Ostasiatische Kunst)✶✶ S M5 – Museum for Applied Art (Museum für Angewandte Kunst)✶ GYZ M6 – St. Maria Lyskirchen (frescoes✶✶) FX – St. Severin (inside✶) FX – St. Pantaleon (rood screen✶) EX – St. Aposteln (apse✶) EV – St. Ursula : treasure (Goldene Kammer) FU – St. Kunibert (chancel : stained glass windows✶) FU – St. Mary the Queen (St. Maria Königin) : wall of glass✶ – Old Town Hall (Altes Rathaus)✶ GZ – Botanical garden Flora✶.

🏌 Köln-Marienburg, Schillingsrotter Weg, ℰ 38 40 53 ; 🏌 Bergisch Gladbach-Refrath (E : 17 km), ℰ (02204) 6 31 14.

✈ Köln-Bonn at Wahn (SE : 17 km), ℰ (02203) 4 01.

🚗 ℰ 1 41 56 66.

Exhibition Centre (Messegelände) by Dentzer Brücke, FV ℰ 82 11, Telex 8873426.

🛈 Tourist office (Verkehrsamt), Am Dom, ℰ 2 21 33 40, Telex 8883421, Fax 2213320.

ADAC, Luxemburger Str. 169, ℰ 47 27 47.

Düsseldorf 40 – Aachen 69 – Bonn 28 – Essen 68.

The reference (K 15) at the end of the address is the postal district : Köln 15

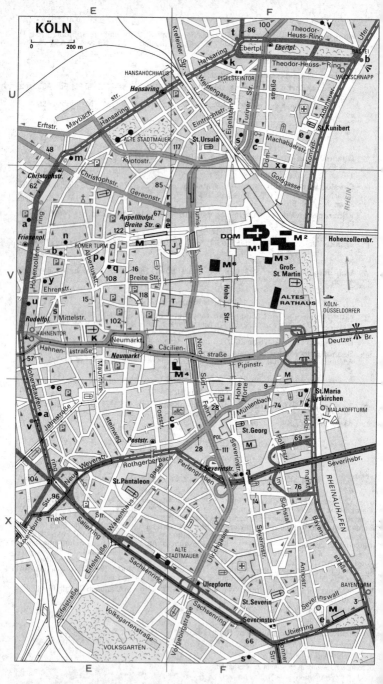

KÖLN

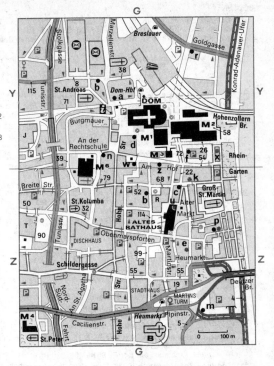

🏨🏨🏨🏨 Excelsior Hotel Ernst - Restaurant Hanse Stube, Trankgasse 1 (K 1), ℰ 27 01, Telex 8882645, Fax 135150 – ⫯ 🖿 TV – 🔏 25/100. AE ⓪ E VISA. ⅍ rest GY **a**
M a la carte 62/102 – **160 rm** 325/580 Bb – 20 suites 950/1200.

🏨🏨🏨 Maritim, Heumarkt 20 (K 1), ℰ 2 02 70, Telex 8886667, Fax 2027826, Massage, ⛭s, 🔲
– ⫯ 🖙 rm 🖿 TV – 🔏 25/1300. AE ⓪ E VISA GZ **m**
Restaurants : **La Galérie** ⅍ (dinner only, closed Sunday, Monday, July and August) M a la carte
64/98 – **Bellevue** ⅍ « Terrace with < Cologne » M a la carte 63/118
– **Rôtisserie** M 39/45 (buffet lunch) and a la carte 44/71 – **450 rm** 219/464 Bb – 28 suites
550/800.

🏨🏨🏨 Hotel im Wasserturm ⅏ (former 19 C water tower, elegant modern installation), Kaygasse
2 (K 1), ℰ 2 00 80, Telex 8881109, Fax 2008888, roof garden terrace with < Cologne, ⛭s
– ⫯ 🖙 rm 🖿 rest TV 🚘 – 🔏 20. AE ⓪ E VISA. ⅍ rest FX **c**
M a la carte 66/91 – **90 rm** 376/502 Bb – 42 suites 582/852.

🏨🏨🏨 Dom-Hotel ⅏, Domkloster 2a (K 1), ℰ 2 02 40, Telex 8882919, Fax 2024260,
« Terrace with < » – ⫯ TV – 🔏 25/70. AE ⓪ E VISA. ⅍ rest GY **d**
M a la carte 49/94 – **126 rm** 332/694 Bb.

🏨🏨🏨 Ramada Renaissance Hotel, Magnusstr. 20 (K 1), ℰ 2 03 40, Telex 8882221,
Fax 2034777, ⇖, Massage, ⛭s, 🔲 – ⫯ 🖙 rm 🖿 TV 🔥 🚘 – 🔏 25/220. AE ⓪ E VISA.
⅍ rest EV **b**
M 43 buffet (lunch) and a la carte 47/86 – **240 rm** 265/775 Bb.

🏨🏨🏨 Inter-Continental, Helenenstr. 14 (K 1), ℰ 22 80, Telex 8882162, Fax 2281301, Massage,
⛭s, 🔲 – ⫯ 🖿 TV 🚘 – 🔏 25/800. AE ⓪ E VISA. ⅍ rest EV **p**
M 45 buffet (lunch) and a la carte 56/92 – **290 rm** 279/498 Bb – 13 suites 828/1648.

🏨🏨 Holiday Inn Crowne Plaza, Habsburger Ring 9 (K 1), ℰ 2 09 50, Telex 8886618,
Fax 251206, Massage, ⛭s, 🔲 – ⫯ 🖙 rm 🖿 TV 🔥 🚘 – 🔏 25/300. AE ⓪ E VISA.
Restaurants : **La Cave** (dinner only, closed Sunday and Bank Holidays) M a la carte 65/100 –
Le Bouquet M a la carte 54/85 – **300 rm** 286/592 Bb – 3 suites 1225/1652.
by Hahnenstraße EV

🏨 **Consul**, Belfortstr. 9 (K 1), ℰ 7 72 10, Telex 8885242, Fax 7721259, Massage, 😒, 🖼 –
|🎿| 💤 rm 🗐 🕭 🖚 – 🔔 25/200. 🖭 ⑩ Ε 𝘝𝘐𝘚𝘈
Restaurants : **Quirinal** 💥 **M** a la carte 55/70 – **Consülchen Pub M** a la carte 38/48 – **120 rm** FU **v**
186/502 Bb.

🏛 **Senats Hotel**, Unter Goldschmied 9 (K 1), 🕿 2 06 20, Telex 8881765, Fax 247863 – |🎿| 🗐 **b**
🕿 🕭 – 🔔 25/200. 🖭 ⑩ Ε 𝘝𝘐𝘚𝘈. 💥 rest GZ **b**
closed 21 to 31 December – **M** *(closed Sunday dinner)* 29/38 (lunch) and a la carte 44/72
– **60 rm** 198/335 Bb.

🏛 **Pullman-Hotel Mondial**, Kurt-Hackenberg-Platz 1 (K 1), 🕿 2 06 30, Telex 8881932,
Fax 2063522, ☕ – |🎿| 💤 rm 🗐 🕿 🖚 – 🔔 25/250. 🖭 ⑩ Ε 𝘝𝘐𝘚𝘈. 💥 rest GY **f**
M 28/38 (lunch) and a la carte 47/80 – **204 rm** 195/350 Bb.

🏛 **Dorint Hotel**, Friesenstr. 44 (K 1), 🕿 1 61 40, Telex 8881483, Fax 1614100 – |🎿| 💤 rm 🗐
🕿 🕭 – 🔔 25/100. 🖭 ⑩ Ε 𝘝𝘐𝘚𝘈. 💥 rest EV **n**
M a la carte 46/78 – **103 rm** 240/520 Bb.

🏛 **Haus Lyskirchen**, Filzengraben 28 (K 1), 🕿 2 09 70, Telex 8885449, Fax 2097718, 😒, 🖼
– |🎿| 🗐 rest 🗐 🕿 🖚 – 🔔 25/90. 🖭 ⑩ Ε 𝘝𝘐𝘚𝘈 FX **u**
closed 23 December - 2 January – **M** *(closed Saturday lunch, Sunday and Bank Holidays)* a
la carte 48/70 – **94 rm** 150/320 Bb.

🏛 **Altea Hotel Severinshof**, Severinstr. 199 (K 1), 🕿 2 01 30, Telex 8881852, Fax 2013666,
☕, 😒 – |🎿| 🗐 🕿 🖚 – 🔔 25/140. 🖭 ⑩ Ε 𝘝𝘐𝘚𝘈 FX **a**
M a la carte 44/71 – **253 rm** 180/300 Bb – 15 suites 310/420.

🏛 **Viktoria** without rest, Worringer Str. 23 (K 1), 🕿 72 04 76, Telex 8881979, Fax 727067 – |🎿|
🗐 🕿 🅿. 🖭 ⑩ Ε 𝘝𝘐𝘚𝘈 by Konrad-Adenauer-Ufer FU
closed 24 December - 1 January – **47 rm** 145/420 Bb.

🏛 **Bristol** without rest (antique furniture), Kaiser-Wilhelm-Ring 48 (K 1), 🕿 12 01 95,
Telex 8881146, Fax 131495 – |🎿| 🗐 🕿. 🖭 ⑩ Ε 𝘝𝘐𝘚𝘈 EU **m**
closed 22 December - 2 January – **44 rm** 145/350 Bb.

🏛 **Savoy** without rest, Turiner Str. 9 (K 1), 🕿 1 62 30, Telex 8886360, Fax 1623200, 😒 – |🎿|
💤 rm 🗐 🕿 🅿. 🖭 ⑩ Ε 𝘝𝘐𝘚𝘈 FU **s**
closed 24 to 31 December – **112 rm** 160/450 Bb.

🏛 **Ascot-Hotel** without rest, Hohenzollernring 95 (K 1), 🕿 52 10 76, Telex 8883018,
Fax 521070, 🗗, 😒 – |🎿| 💤 🗐 🕿. 🖭 ⑩ Ε 𝘝𝘐𝘚𝘈. 💥 EV **a**
closed 23 December - 4 January – **46 rm** 159/389 Bb.

🏛 **Europa Hotel am Dom**, Am Hof 38 (K 1), 🕿 2 05 80, Telex 8881728, Fax 211021 – |🎿| 🗐
🕿 – 🔔 25. 🖭 ⑩ Ε 𝘝𝘐𝘚𝘈 GYZ **z**
M see rest. **Ambiance am Dom** – **90 rm** 165/320 Bb.

🏛 **Coellner Hof**, Hansaring 100 (K 1), 🕿 12 20 75, Telex 8885264, Fax 135235 – |🎿| 🗐 🕿 🖚
– 🔔 30. 🖭 ⑩ Ε 𝘝𝘐𝘚𝘈 FU **k**
M *(closed Friday dinner and Saturday)* a la carte 38/67 – **70 rm** 125/280 Bb.

🏛 **Königshof** without rest, Richartzstr. 14 (K 1), 🕿 23 45 83, Telex 8881318, Fax 238642 – |🎿|
🕿. 🖭 ⑩ Ε 𝘝𝘐𝘚𝘈 GY **n**
85 rm 115/395 Bb.

🏛 **Kommerzhotel** without rest, Breslauer Platz (K 1), 🕿 1 61 00, Fax 1610122, 😒 – |🎿| 🗐
🕿. 🖭 ⑩ Ε 𝘝𝘐𝘚𝘈 GY **r**
77 rm 155/255 Bb.

🏛 **Lasthaus am Ring - Restaurant Charrue d'or**, Hohenzollernring 20 (K 1),
🕿 2 57 00 85 (hotel) 25 46 10 (rest.), Telex 8882856, Fax 253714 – |🎿| 🗐 🕿 🅿. 🖭 Ε
M *(closed Monday and 30 June - 20 July)* a la carte 47/80 – **52 rm** 120/285 Bb. EV **u**

🏛 **Residence** without rest, Alter Markt 55 (K 1), 🕿 23 57 81, Telex 8885344, Fax 234140 – |🎿|
💤 rm 🗐 🕿. 🖭 ⑩ Ε 𝘝𝘐𝘚𝘈 GZ **c**
60 rm 165/420 Bb.

🏛 **Central Hotel** without rest, An den Dominikanern 3 (K 1), 🕿 13 50 88, Telex 8881807,
Fax 135080 – |🎿| 🗐 🕿. 🖭 ⑩ Ε 𝘝𝘐𝘚𝘈 GY **b**
closed 20 December - 6 January – **62 rm** 105/310.

🏛 **Esplanade** without rest, Hohenstaufenring 56 (K 1), 🕿 21 03 11, Telex 8881029, Fax 216822
– |🎿| 🗐 🕿 🖚. 🖭 ⑩ Ε 𝘝𝘐𝘚𝘈 EX **a**
closed 24 December - 2 January – **33 rm** 145/385 Bb.

🏛 **Eden-Hotel** without rest, Am Hof 18 (K 1), 🕿 23 61 23, Telex 8882889, Fax 246604 – |🎿| 🗐
🕿. 🖭 ⑩ Ε 𝘝𝘐𝘚𝘈 GY **w**
closed 24 December - 3 January – **33 rm** 176/299 Bb.

🏛 **Astor und Aparthotel** without rest, Friesenwall 68 (K 1), 🕿 25 31 01, Telex 8886367,
Fax 253106 – |🎿| 💤 🗐 🕿 🅿. 🖭 ⑩ Ε 𝘝𝘐𝘚𝘈 EV **y**
52 rm 144/284 Bb.

🏛 **Merian-Hotel** without rest, Allerheiligenstr. 1 (K 1), 🕿 1 66 50, Telex 8883305, Fax 1665200
– |🎿| 🗐 🕿 🖚. FU **c**
closed 22 December - 4 January – **32 rm** 95/350 Bb.

🏛 **Leonet** without rest, Rubensstr. 33 (K 1), 🕿 23 60 16, Telex 8883506, Fax 210893, 😒,
🖼 – |🎿| 🗐 🕿 🅿. 🖭 ⑩ Ε 𝘝𝘐𝘚𝘈 EX **e**
closed 20 December - 5 January – **78 rm** 120/270 Bb.

🏛 **Kolpinghaus International**, St.-Apern-Str. 32 (K 1), ℰ 2 09 30, Fax 246518 – ☎ ℗ –
🔥 25/200. ◪ ◉ �E 𝘝𝘐𝘚𝘈 EV **q**
M a la carte 28/62 – **48 rm** 95/155 Bb.

🏛 **Conti** without rest, Brüsseler Str. 40 (K 1), ℰ 25 20 62, Telex 8881644, Fax 252107 – 🛗 ☎
🚗, ◪ �E 𝘝𝘐𝘚𝘈 by Rudolfplatz EV
closed 13 December - 1 January – **43 rm** 98/235 Bb.

🏛 **Ludwig** without rest, Brandenburger Str. 24 (K 1), ℰ 16 05 40, Telex 8885326, Fax 16054444
– 🛗 📺 ☎ 🚗, ◪ ◉ �E 𝘝𝘐𝘚𝘈 FU **x**
closed 18 December - 3 January – **61 rm** 110/275 Bb.

𝗫𝗫𝗫𝗫 ✤ **Chez Alex**, Mühlengasse 1 (K 1), ℰ 23 05 60 – ◪ ◉ �E 𝘝𝘐𝘚𝘈 GZ **k**
closed Saturday lunch and except exhibitions Sunday and Bank Holidays – **M** *(booking essential)*
40/60 (lunch) and a la carte 83/113
Spec. Mille-feuille von Gänseleber und Trüffel, Lammrücken mit Artischockenconfit, Tarte Tatin
mit weißem Kaffee-Eis.

𝗫𝗫𝗫𝗫 ✤ **Rino Casati**, Ebertplatz 3 (K 1), ℰ 72 11 08, Fax 728097 – ◪ ◉ �E 𝘝𝘐𝘚𝘈. 🍽 FU **t**
closed 4 weeks July - August and Sunday except exhibitions – **M** (dinner only, booking essential)
a la carte 75/107
Spec. Hausgemachte Nudelgerichte, Salm mit Sesam in Barolo, Barbarie-Ente mit Honigsauce.

𝗫𝗫𝗫 **Ambiance am Dom** (at Europa Hotel am Dom), Am Hof 38 (K 1), ℰ 24 91 27 – ◪ ◉ �E 𝘝𝘐𝘚𝘈. 🍽
closed Saturday lunch, Sunday, Monday, Bank Holidays and 3 weeks August – **M** 50 (lunch)
and a la carte 65/100. GYZ **z**

𝗫𝗫𝗫 **Börsen-Restaurant Maître**, Unter Sachsenhausen 10 (K 1), ℰ 13 30 21, Fax 133040 – 🍴.
◪ ◉ �E 𝘝𝘐𝘚𝘈. 🍽 EV **r**
closed Sunday, Bank Holidays and 4 weeks July - August – **M** a la carte 69/95 – **Börsenstube**
M a la carte 42/74.

𝗫𝗫𝗫 **Die Bastei**, Konrad-Adenauer-Ufer 80 (K 1), ℰ 12 28 25, Fax 138047, ← Rhein – ◪ ◉ �E
𝘝𝘐𝘚𝘈. 🍽 FU **b**
closed Saturday lunch – **M** a la carte 68/115.

𝗫𝗫 **Em Krützche**, Am Frankenturm 1 (K 1), ℰ 21 14 32, Fax 253417 – ◉ �E 𝘝𝘐𝘚𝘈 GY **x**
closed Monday – **M** *(booking essential)* a la carte 45/70.

𝗫𝗫 **Weinhaus im Walfisch** (17C timber framed house), Salzgasse 13 (K 1), ℰ 21 95 75,
Fax 235681 – ◪ ◉ �E 𝘝𝘐𝘚𝘈 GZ **p**
closed Saturday lunch, Sunday, Bank Holidays and 22 December - 6 January – **M** a la carte
60/96.

𝗫𝗫 **Soufflé**, Hohenstaufenring 53 (K 1), ℰ 21 20 22, 😋 – ◪ ◉ �E 𝘝𝘐𝘚𝘈 EX **v**
closed 1 to 6 January, Saturday lunch, Sunday and Bank Holidays except exhibitions – **M** a
la carte 62/75.

𝗫𝗫 **Ratskeller**, Rathausplatz 1 (entrance Alter Markt) (K 1), ℰ 21 83 01, Fax 246942,
« Courtyard » – 🍴 🔥 – 🔥 25/80. ◪ ◉ �E 𝘝𝘐𝘚𝘈 GZ **u**
M a la carte 38/68.

𝗫𝗫 **Restaurant Wack**, Benesisstr. 57 (K 1), ℰ 24 36 46, Fax 241551 – ◪ �E 𝘝𝘐𝘚𝘈. 🍽 EV **s**
closed Saturday lunch, Sunday and 20 May - 20 August – **M** *(booking essential)* a la carte 61/81
– **Wackes** *(dinner only)* **M** a la carte 34/50.

𝗫𝗫 Daitokai (Japanese rest.), Kattenbug 2 (K 1), ℰ 12 00 48, Fax 137503 – 🍴. 🍽 EV **e**

𝗫 **Ballarin** (Bistro), Ubierring 35 (K 1), ℰ 32 61 33 – ◉ FX **e**
dinner only, closed Sunday and Bank Holidays – **M** a la carte 62/79.

𝗫 **Ristorante Pan e vin**, Heumarkt 75 (K 1), ℰ 24 84 10 – ◪ �E. 🍽 GZ **e**
closed Monday except exhibitions – **M** a la carte 48/78.

at Cologne 41-Braunsfeld by Rudolfplatz EV :

🏨 **Regent**, Melatengürtel 15, ℰ 5 49 90, Telex 8881824, Fax 5499998, 🛎 – 🛗 ⇆ rm 📺 ℗
– 🔥 25/80. ◪ ◉ �E 𝘝𝘐𝘚𝘈
M *(closed 24 December - 7 January)* a la carte 35/67 – **168 rm** 203/436 Bb – 3 suites 573/926.

at Cologne 21-Deutz by Deutzer Brücke FV :

🏨 **Hyatt Regency**, Kennedy-Ufer 2a, ℰ 8 28 12 34, Telex 887525, Fax 8281370, ←, beer-
garden, massage, 🐟, 🛎, 🔲 – 🛗 ⇆ rm 🍴 📺 🔥 🚗 ℗ – 🔥 25/400. ◪ ◉ �E 𝘝𝘐𝘚𝘈. 🍽 rest
Restaurants : **Graugans** *(closed Saturday lunch and Sunday)* **M** 45 (lunch) and a la carte 72/87
– **Glashaus M** a la carte 55/65 – **307 rm** 320/641 Bb – 15 suites.

🏛 **Ilbertz** without rest, Mindener Str. 6, ℰ 88 20 49, Fax 883484, 🛎 – 🛗 📺 ☎ 🚗. ◪ �E 𝘝𝘐𝘚𝘈
30 rm 85/200 Bb.

𝗫𝗫 **Der Messeturm**, Kennedy-Ufer (18th floor, 🛗), ℰ 88 10 08, Fax 811941, ← Cologne – 🍴
– 🔥 25. ◪ ◉ �E 𝘝𝘐𝘚𝘈. 🍽
closed Saturday lunch and mid July - mid August – **M** a la carte 55/86.

at Cologne 30-Ehrenfeld by Rudolfplatz EV :

🏨 **Imperial**, Barthelstr. 93, ℰ 51 70 57, Telex 8883452, Fax 520993, 🛎 – 🛗 📺 ☎ 🔥 🚗.
◉ �E 𝘝𝘐𝘚𝘈 – **M** *(dinner only)* a la carte 34/62 – **35 rm** 160/320 Bb.

𝗫𝗫𝗫 **Zum offenen Kamin**, Eichendorffstr. 25, ℰ 55 68 78 – ◪ ◉ �E 𝘝𝘐𝘚𝘈 by Erftstraße EU
closed Saturday lunch and Sunday except exhibitions – **M** *(also vegetarian menu)* 50 (lunch)
and a la carte 68/91.

at Cologne 80-Holweide by Konrad-Adenauer-Ufer FU :

XXX **Isenburg**, Johann-Bensberg-Str. 49, 🅟 69 59 09, Fax 698703, « Garden terrace » – 🅟. ⓞ
E VISA
closed Saturday lunch, Sunday, Monday, carnival, mid July - mid August and Christmas –
M *(booking essential)* a la carte 51/85.

at Cologne 50-Immendorf by Bonner Str. FX :

XX **Bitzerhof** with rm (1821 farmyard), Immendorfer Hauptstr. 21, 🅟 (02236) 6 19 21, « Country house atmosphere, courtyard terrace » – 📺 ☎ ⇦ E. ⅏ rm
M a la carte 56/79 – **3 rm** 115/155.

at Cologne 41-Lindenthal by Rudolfplatz EV and B 264 :

🏨 **Queens Hotel**, Dürener Str. 287, 🅟 4 67 60, Telex 8882516, Fax 433765, « Garden with
🍴 » – 📳 ⅏ rm 🔲 rest 📺 ☎ ⇦ 🅟 – 🔏 25/600. 🖭 E VISA. ⅏ rest
M a la carte 52/88 – **147 rm** 238/451 Bb.

at Cologne 51-Marienburg by Bonner Straße FX :

🏨 **Marienburger Bonotel**, Bonner Str. 478, 🅟 3 70 20, Telex 8881515, Fax 3702132, ♨, ⇐s
– 📳 📺 ☎ ⇦ 🅟 – 🔏 25/100. 🖭 ⓞ E VISA. ⅏ rest
M a la carte 46/68 – **93 rm** 180/345 Bb – 4 suites 350/650.

XX **Marienburger Eule**, Bonner Str. 471, 🅟 38 15 78, Fax 343420 – 🖭 ⓞ E VISA
closed lunch Saturday and Sunday – **M** a la carte 61/91.

at Cologne 40-Marsdorf by Rudolfplatz EV and B 264 :

🏨 **Novotel Köln-West**, Horbeller Str. 1, 🅟 (02234) 51 40, Telex 8886355, Fax 514106, ♨,
⇐s, ⏉ (heated), 📳 📺 rest 📺 ☎ ⅋ 🅟 – 🔏 25/300. 🖭 ⓞ E VISA
M a la carte 36/62 – **199 rm** 175/220 Bb.

at Cologne 91-Merheim by Deutzer Brücke FV :

XXXX ✿✿ **Goldener Pflug**, Olpener Str. 421 (B 55), 🅟 89 55 09 – 🅟
closed Sunday and Bank Holidays – **M** a la carte 64/116
Spec. Rouget und Langostinos mit Ratatouille, Steinbutt mit Meerrettichkruste, Crépinette vom
Täubchen.

at Cologne 41-Müngersdorf by Rudolfplatz EV and B 55 :

XXX **Landhaus Kuckuck**, Olympiaweg 2, 🅟 49 23 23, Fax 4972847, ♨ – 🔏 25/120. 🖭 ⓞ
E VISA
closed Monday and 24 February - 3 March – **M** 45 (lunch) and a la carte 62/85.

XX **Remise**, Wendelinstr. 48, 🅟 49 18 81, « Historic farmhouse » – 🅟. ⓞ E VISA
closed Saturday lunch and Sunday – **M** *(booking essential)* a la carte 56/90.

at Cologne 90- Porz-Wahnheide SE : 17 km by A 59 :

🏨 **Holiday Inn**, Waldstr. 255, 🅟 (02203) 56 10, Telex 8874665, Fax 5619, ⇐s, ⏉ , 🍴 – 📳
⅏ rm 📳 📺 ☎ 🅟 – 🔏 25/90. 🖭 ⓞ E VISA
M a la carte 42/75 – **113 rm** 252/404 Bb.

🏨 **Quelle** without rest, Heidestr. 246, 🅟 (02203) 60 81, Fax 608317 – 📳 📺 ☎ ⇦ 🅟 – 🔏 30
95 rm 80/160.

Wittlich 5560. Rheinland - Pfalz 987 ㉓ ㉔, 412 D 17 – pop. 17 000 – alt. 155 m –
✆ 06571.
Köln 130.

at Dreis 5561 SW : 8 km :

🏨 ✿✿ **Waldhotel Sonnora** ⅏, Auf dem Eichelfeld, 🅟 (06578) 4 06, Fax 1402, ≤, « Garden »
– 📺 ☎ 🅟. E. ⅏
closed 6 January - 6 February – **M** *(closed Monday and Tuesday)* (booking essential) 105/128
and a la carte 74/92 – **20 rm** 60/120
Spec. Ravioli von Langustinen in Krustentiersauce, Gegrillter Steinbutt mit warmer Nußöl-
Vinaigrette, Taube mit Gänseleber im Kohlblatt gedämpft.

Michelin Green Guides in English

		New York City
Austria	Greece	Portugal
Canada	Italy	Rome
England : The West Country	London	Scotland
France	Mexico	Spain
Germany	Netherlands	Switzerland
Great Britain	New England	Washington

DRESDEN O-8010. Sachsen 984 ㉔, 987 ⑱ – pop. 500 000 – alt. 105 m – ✿ 003751.

See : Zwinger★★★ (Wall Pavilion★★, Nymphs' Bath★★, Porcelain Collection★★, National Mathematical-Physical Salon★★) AY – Semper Opera★★ AY – Former court church★★ (Hofkirche) BY – Palace (Schloß) : royal houses★ (Fürstenzug-Mosaik), Long Passage★ (Langer Gang) BY – Albertinum : Picture Gallery Old Masters★★★ (Gemäldegalerie Alte Meister), Picture Gallery New Masters★★★ (Gemäldegalerie Neue Meister), Green Vault★★★ (Grünes Gewölbe) BY – Prager Straße★ ABZ – Museum of History of the town Dresden★ (Museum für Geschichte der Stadt Dresden) BY L – Church of the Cross★ (Kreuzkirche) BY – Japanese Palace★ (Japanisches Palais) ABX – Museum of Folk Art★ (Museum für Volkskunst) BX **M2** – Great Garden★ (Großer Garten) CDZ – Russian-Orthodox Church★ (Russisch-orthodoxe Kirche) (by Leningrader Str. BZ) – Brühl's Terrace ⩵★ (Brühlsche Terrasse) BY **6** – Equestrian statue of Augustus the Strong★ (Reiterstandbild Augusts des Starken) BX **E**.

Envir. : Schloß (palace) Moritzburg★ (NW : 14 km by Hansastr. BX) – Schloß (palace) Pillnitz★ (SE : 15 km by Bautzener Str. CX) – Saxon Swiss★★★ (Sächsische Schweiz) : Bastei★★★, Festung (fortress) Königstein★★ ⩵★★, Großsedlitz : Baroque Garden★.

✈ Dresden-Klotzsche (N : 13 km), ℰ 58 31 41. City Office, Rampische Str. 2, ℰ 4 95 60 13.

🛈 Dresden-Information, Prager Str. 10, ℰ 4 95 50 25, Telex 26198, Fax 4951276.

Berlin 198 – Chemnitz 70 – Görlitz 98 – Leipzig 111 – Praha 152.

Plans on following pages

🏨 **Bellevue**, Köpckestr. 15, ☒ O-8060, ℰ 5 66 20, Telex 26162, Fax 55997, ⩵, 🏠, « Courtyard terraces », Massage, ♨, ⇔, 🔲 – 📶 ⇔ rm 🍽 🔲 📺 🕭 ⟨⟩ ⇔ – BX **a** ﹩ 25/320
Restaurants : Canaletto – Palais – Buri-Buri – **328 rm** – 16 suites.

🏨 **Dresdner Hof**, An der Frauenkirche 5, ℰ 4 84 10, Telex 2488, Fax 4841700, ⇔, 🔲 (charge) – 📶 ⇔ rm 🍽 🔲 📺 🕭 ⟨⟩ 🅴 ① 🅴 – ﹩ 30/300. 🆎 ① 🅴 ﹩ BY **e**
Restaurants : **Gourmet** *(dinner only)* a la carte 70/110 – **Grüner Baum M** a la carte 38/68 – **Rossini** (Italian rest.) **M** a la carte 47/68 – **333 rm** 260/390 Bb – 12 suites 460/575.

🏨 **Newa**, Prager Straße, ℰ 4 96 71 12, Telex 26067, Fax 4955137, 🏠, ⇔ – 📶 📺 ☎ BZ **n**
310 rm.

🏨 **Martha Hospiz** without rest., Nieritzstr. 11, ℰ 5 24 25, Fax 53218 – 📶 📺 ☎ 🕭 🅴 BX **s** 𝑽𝑰𝑺𝑨
36 rm 110/230 Bb.

🏨 **Königstein**, Prager Str. 9, ℰ 4 85 66 69, Telex 26165, Fax 4856499, ⇔ – 📶 BZ **d**
295 rm Bb – 8 suites.

🏨 **Bastei**, Prager Straße, ℰ 4 85 63 85, Fax 4955499 – 📶 📺 ☎ BZ **e**
300 rm Bb – 9 suites.

🏨 **Lilienstein**, Prager Str. 15, ℰ 4 85 63 72, Telex 26165, Fax 4856499 – 📶 📺 ☎. 🆎 ① 🅴 BZ **b** 𝑽𝑰𝑺𝑨
303 rm Bb – 12 suites.

🏨 **Motel Dresden** ⟨⟩, Münzmeisterstr. 10, ☒ 8020, ℰ 47 58 51, Fax 479486, 🏠, ⇔ – 📺 ☎ 🅿 by Leningrader Str. BZ
87 rm Bb.

🏨 **Hotelships Florentina and St. Caspar**, Terrassenufer, ℰ 4 59 01 69, Fax 4595036 – 📺 ☎. 🆎 ① 🅴 𝑽𝑰𝑺𝑨 CY **a**
M a la carte 40/60 – **66 rm** 195/240 Bb.

🏨 **Astoria**, Ernst-Thälmann-Platz 1, ℰ 47 51 71, Telex 2442, Fax 478872 – 📶 📺 ☎ 🅿 by Parkstr. BZ
68 rm Bb.

XX **Opernrestaurant**, Theaterplatz 2 (1st floor), ℰ 4 84 25 00, 🏠 – 🆎 ① 🅴 𝑽𝑰𝑺𝑨 AY **r**
closed 4 weeks July - August – **M** a la carte 31/56.

XX **Blockhaus**, Neustädter Markt 19 (2nd floor, 📶), ☒ O-8060, ℰ 54 41, ⩵ – ﹩ 25/110. BX **f** ⟨⟩

X **Ratskeller**, Dr.-Külz-Ring 19, ℰ 4 88 29 50 – 🆎 🅴 BZ **R**
M a la carte 26/40.

XX **Kügelgenhaus** (18C historic building, early Romanticism Museum), Straße der Befreiung 13, ☒ O-8060, ℰ 5 45 18, 🏠 BX **h**

at Dresden-Reick O-8036 by Parkstraße BZ :

XX **Coventry**, Hülßestr. 1, ℰ 2 74 30 14 – 🆎 🅴 𝑽𝑰𝑺𝑨
M a la carte 32/68.

If you would like a more complete selection of hotels and restaurants,
*consult the **MICHELIN Red Guides** for the following countries :*
Benelux, Deutschland, España Portugal, France,
Great Britain and Ireland, and Italia,
all in annual editions.

231

DRESDEN

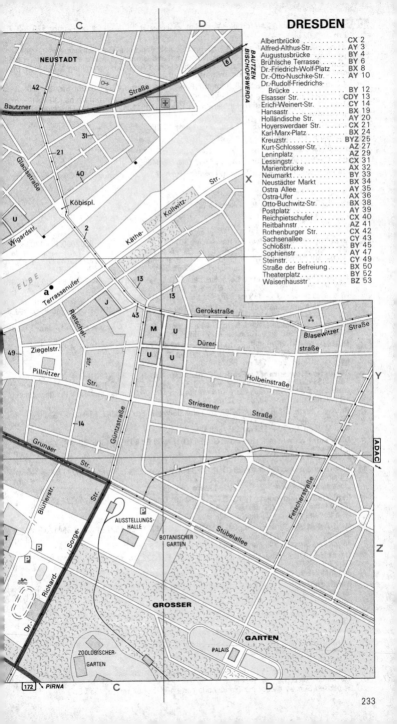

DÜSSELDORF **4000.** Nordrhein-Westfalen 411 412 D 13, 987 ㉓ ㉔ – pop. 570 000 – alt. 40 m – ☎ 0211.

See : Königsallee★ EZ – Hofgarten★ DEY und Schloß Jägerhof (Goethemuseum★ EY **M1**) – Hetjensmuseum★ DZ **M4** – Land Economic Museum (Landesmuseum Volk u. Wirtschaft)★ DY **M5** – Museum of Art (Kunstmuseum)★ DY **M2** – Collection of Art (Kunstsammlung NRW)★ DY **M3** – Löbbecke-Museum und Aquazoo★ by Kaiserswerther Str. AU.

Envir. : Chateau of Benrath (Schloß Benrath) (Park★) S : 10 km by Siegburger Str. CX.

18 Ratingen-Hösel, NE : 16 km, ☎ (02102) 6 86 29 ; 18 Gut Rommeljans, NE : 12 km, ☎ (02102) 8 10 92 ; 18 Düsseldorf-Hubbelrath, E : 12 km, ☎ (02104) 7 21 78 ; 9 Düsseldorf-Hafen, Auf der Lausward, ☎ (0211) 39 65 98

18 Düsseldorf-Schmidtberg, NE : 12 km, ☎ (02104) 7 70 60.

Düsseldorf-Lohausen (N : 8 km), ☎ 42 10.

☎ 3 68 04 68.

Exhibition Centre (Messegelände), ☎ 4 56 01, Telex 8584853.

Tourist office, Konrad-Adenauer-Platz and Heinrich-Heine-Allee 24, ☎ 35 05 05, Telex 8587785, Fax 161071.

ADAC, Himmelgeister Str. 63, ☎ 3 10 93 33.

Amsterdam 225 – Essen 31 – Köln 40 – Rotterdam 237.

The reference (D 15) at the end of the address is the postal district : Düsseldorf 15

Plans on following pages

Breidenbacher Hof, Heinrich-Heine-Allee 36 (D 1), ☎ 1 30 30, Telex 8582630, Fax 1303830, – rm – 25/90. AE E VISA. rest EY **a**
Restaurants : **Grill Royal M** a la carte 79/101 – **Breidenbacher Eck M** a la carte 48/76 – **Trader Vic's** *(dinner only)* **M** a la carte 56/97 – **132 rm** 290/590 – 30 suites 750/2700.

Steigenberger Parkhotel, Corneliusplatz 1 (D 1), ☎ 1 38 10, Telex 8582331, Fax 131679 – rm – 25/250. AE E VISA. rest EY **p**
M a la carte 67/101 – **160 rm** 335/520 Bb – 12 suites 950/1650.

Nikko, Immermannstr. 41 (D 1), ☎ 83 40, Telex 8582080, Fax 161216, , Massage, , – rm – 25/500. AE E VISA. rest BV **g**
Restaurants : **Benkay** (Japanese rest.) **M** a la carte 85/135 – **Traveller's M** a la carte 53/88 – **301 rm** 321/502 Bb – 18 suites 752/1552.

Holiday Inn, Graf-Adolf-Platz 10 (D 1), ☎ 3 87 30, Telex 8586359, Fax 3873390, , – rm – 25/80. AE E VISA EZ **t**
M a la carte 55/86 – **177 rm** 420/490 Bb.

Majestic - Restaurant La Grappa, Cantadorstr. 4 (D 1), ☎ 36 70 30 (hotel) 35 72 92 (rest.), Telex 8584649, Fax 3670399, – – 40. AE E VISA BV **a**
closed 24 December - 4 January – **M** *(Italian rest.)* (closed Sunday and Bank Holidays except exhibitions) a la carte 43/82 – **52 rm** 198/410 Bb.

Savoy, Oststr. 128 (D 1), ☎ 36 03 36, Telex 8584215, Fax 356642, Massage, , – – 25/100. AE E VISA EZ **w**
M a la carte 42/70 – **123 rm** 195/368 Bb.

Madison I without rest, Graf-Adolf-Str. 94 (D 1), ☎ 1 68 50, Fax 1685328, , , – – 25/60. AE E VISA BV **n**
95 rm 150/260 Bb.

Eden without rest, Adersstr. 29 (D 1), ☎ 3 89 70, Telex 8582530, Fax 3897777 – rm – 25/130. AE E VISA EZ **m**
closed 22 December - 2 January – **130 rm** 193/393 Bb.

Esplanade, Fürstenplatz 17 (D 1), ☎ 37 50 10, Telex 8582970, Fax 374032, , – – 25/60. AE E VISA BX **s**
M a la carte 48/75 – **80 rm** 159/428 Bb.

Graf Adolf , Stresemannplatz 1 (D 1), ☎ 3 55 40, Telex 8587844, Fax 354120 – – 25/70. AE E VISA. rest EZ **j**
M *(closed Sunday)* a la carte 52/66 – **151 rm** 175/375 Bb.

Carat Hotel, Benrather Str. 7a (D 1), ☎ 1 30 50, Fax 322214, – rm – 30. AE E VISA DZ **r**
M (dinner only residents only) – **73 rm** 195/395.

Madison II without rest, Graf-Adolf-Str. 47 (D 1), ☎ 37 02 96, Fax 1685328 – . AE E VISA EZ **e**
closed August and 20 December - 8 January – **24 rm** 130/240 Bb.

Astoria without rest, Jahnstr. 72 (D 1), ☎ 38 20 88, Fax 372089 – . AE E VISA. BX **b**
closed 22 December - 7 January – **27 rm** 130/290 Bb – 3 suites 310.

Concorde without rest, Graf-Adolf-Str. 60 (D 1), ☎ 35 46 04, Telex 8588008, Fax 354606 – . AE E VISA EZ **f**
83 rm 165/320 Bb.

Uebachs, Leopoldstr. 5 (D 1), ☎ 36 05 66, Telex 8587620, Fax 358064 – – 30. AE E VISA. rest BV **r**
M *(closed Sunday except exhibitions)* a la carte 46/75 – **82 rm** 167/350 Bb.

DÜSSELDORF

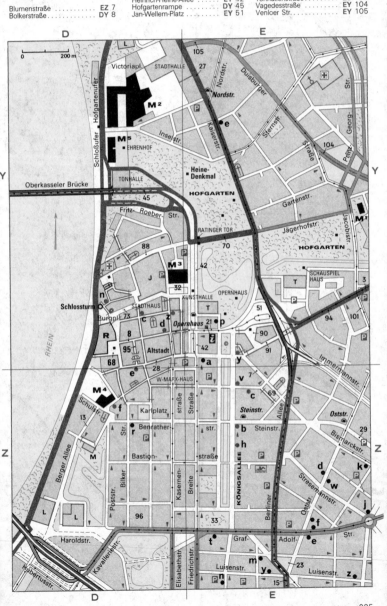

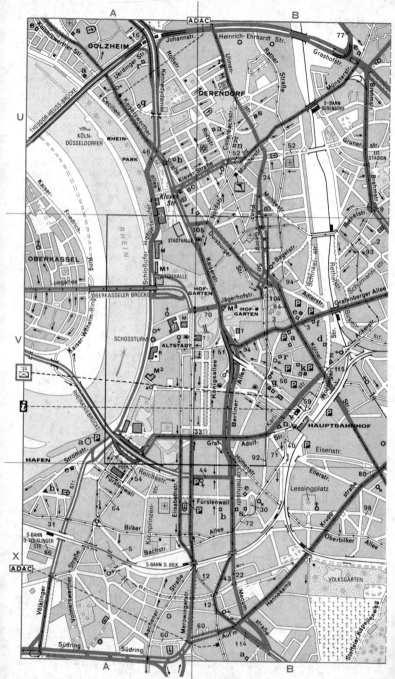

DÜSSELDORF

🏨 **Hotel An der Kö** without rest, Talstr. 9 (D 1), ℰ 37 10 48, Fax 370835 – 🛗 📺 ☎ 🅿️, 🖭 ⓪ 🗲 *VISA*
44 rm 148/320 Bb.   EZ **n**

🏨 **Monopol** without rest, Oststr. 135 (D 1), ℰ 8 42 08, Telex 8587770, Fax 328843 – 🛗 ↔
📺 ☎ 🖭 ⓪ 🗲 *VISA*
50 rm 195/320 Bb.   EZ **d**

🏨 **Central** without rest, Luisenstr. 42 (D 1), ℰ 37 90 01, Telex 8582145, Fax 379094 – 🛗 📺
☎ 🖭 ⓪ 🗲 *VISA*
closed 20 December - 1 January – **72 rm** 175/450 Bb.   EZ **y**

🏨 **Bellevue** without rest, Luisenstr. 98 (D 1), ℰ 37 70 71, Fax 377076 – 🛗 📺 ☎ 🚗, 🖭 ⓪ 🗲 *VISA*
closed 23 December - 4 January – **52 rm** 195/265 Bb.   EZ **z**

🏨 **Terminus** without rest, Am Wehrhahn 81 (D 1), ℰ 35 05 91, Telex 8586576, Fax 358350,
⇌s, 🔲 – 🛗 📺 ☎ 🖭 *VISA*
closed 23 December - 4 January – **44 rm** 150/370 Bb.   BV **f**

🏨 **Fürstenhof** without rest, Fürstenplatz 3 (D 1), ℰ 37 05 45, Telex 8586540, Fax 379062, ⇌s
– 🛗 ↔ 📺 ☎ 🖭 ⓪ 🗲 *VISA*
closed 24 December - 2 January – **43 rm** 210/285 Bb.   BX **e**

🏨 **City** without rest, Bismarckstr. 73 (D 1), ℰ 36 50 23, Telex 8587362, Fax 365343 – 🛗 📺 ☎.
🖭 ⓪ 🗲 *VISA*
closed 23 December - 2 January – **54 rm** 130/300.   EZ **k**

🏨 **Cornelius** without rest, Corneliusstr. 82 (D 1), ℰ 38 20 55, Telex 8587385, Fax 382050, ⇌s
– 🛗 📺 ☎ 🅿️ – 🕭 25. 🖭 ⓪ 🗲 *VISA*
closed 20 December - 7 January – **48 rm** 130/230 Bb.   BX **s**

🏨 **Prinz Anton** without rest, Karl-Anton-Str. 11 (D 1), ℰ 35 20 00, Fax 362010 – 🛗 📺 ☎. 🖭
⓪ 🗲 *VISA*
closed 23 December - 2 January – **40 rm** 110/285 Bb.   BV **k**

🏨 **Residenz** without rest, Worringer Str. 88 (D 1), ℰ 36 08 54, Telex 8587897, Fax 364676 –
🛗 📺 ☎ 🖭 ⓪ 🗲 *VISA*
34 rm 130/295 Bb.   BV **z**

🏨 **Schumacher** without rest, Worringer Str. 55 (D 1), ℰ 36 78 50, Fax 3678570, ⇌s – 🛗 📺
☎ 🚗, 🖭 ⓪ 🗲 *VISA*
30 rm 130/350 Bb.   BV **d**

🏨 **Lancaster** without rest, Oststr. 166 (D 1), ℰ 35 10 66, Fax 162884 – 🛗 📺 ☎. 🖭 ⓪ 🗲 *VISA*, 🛠
40 rm 145/205 Bb.   EZ **f**

🏨 **Minerva** without rest, Cantadorstr. 13a (D 1), ℰ 35 09 61, Fax 356398 – 🛗 📺 ☎. 🖭 ⓪
🗲 *VISA*
15 rm 92/225 Bb.   BV **a**

🏨 **Astor** without rest, Kurfürstenstr. 23 (D 1), ℰ 36 06 61, Telex 8586201, Fax 162597, ⇌s –
📺 ☎. 🖭 🗲
closed 22 December - 5 January – **16 rm** 95/210.   BV **k**

🏨 **Großer Kurfürst** without rest, Kurfürstenstr. 18 (D 1), ℰ 35 76 47, Telex 8586201,
Fax 162597 – 🛗 📺 ☎. 🖭 🗲
22 rm 95/210.   BV **k**

XXX ✿ **Victorian**, Königstr. 3a (1st floor) (D 1), ℰ 32 02 22, Fax 131013 – 🍽. 🖭 ⓪ 🗲 *VISA*. 🛠
closed Sunday and Bank Holidays – **M** (booking essential) a la carte 70/105 – **Lounge** *(closed
Sunday and Bank Holidays mid July - August)* **M** a la carte 38/82   EZ **c**
Spec. Gänseleberterrine, Kaisergranat mit Paprikasauce und Safrannudeln, Rehfilet in Wirsing
gebraten (September - November).

XXX **La Scala** (Italian rest.), Königsallee 14 (1st floor 🛗) (D 1), ℰ 32 68 32 – 🖭 ⓪ 🗲 *VISA*
closed Sunday, during exhibitions Sunday dinner only – **M** a la carte 53/89.   EY **y**

XX **La Terrazza** (Italian rest.), Königsallee 30 (Kö-Centre, 2nd floor, 🛗) (D 1), ℰ 32 75 40,
Fax 320975 – 🖭
closed Saturday, Sunday and Bank Holidays except exhibitions – **M** (booking essential) a la carte
62/88.   EZ **v**

XX **Mövenpick - Café des Artistes**, Königsallee 60 (Kö-Galerie) (D 1), ℰ 32 03 14, Fax 328058
– 🍽. 🖭 ⓪ 🗲 *VISA*
closed 9 to 30 August and Sunday in July **M** a la carte 54/90 – **Locanda Ticinese M** a la carte
35/61.   EZ **h**

XX **Tse Yang** (Chinese rest.), Immermannstr. 65 (Immermannhof, entrance Konrad-Adenauer-
Platz) (D 1), ℰ 36 90 20 – 🖭 ⓪ 🗲 *VISA*
M a la carte 42/65.   BV **v**

XX **Weinhaus Tante Anna** (1593 former private chapel), Andreasstr. 2 (D 1), ℰ 13 11 63,
Fax 132974, remarkable winelist, « Antique paintings and furniture » – 🖭 ⓪ 🗲 *VISA*,
🛠
dinner only, closed Sunday except exhibitions – **M** (booking essential) a la carte 50/84.   DY **c**

XX **Nippon Kan** (Japanese rest.), Immermannstr. 35 (D 1), ℰ 35 31 35, Fax 3613625 – 🖭 ⓪
🗲 *VISA*. 🛠
M (booking essential) a la carte 34/76.   BV **g**

XX **Daitokai** (Japanese rest.), Mutter-Ey-Str. 1 (D 1), ℰ 32 50 54, Fax 325056 – 🍽. 🖭 ⓪ 🗲 *VISA*. 🛠
closed Sunday except exhibitions – **M** (booking essential) a la carte 52/87.   DY **z**

Brewery-inns :

✗ **Zum Schiffchen**, Hafenstr. 5 (D 1), ✆ 13 24 22, Fax 134596 – AE ◑ ⴹ VISA   DZ **f**
closed Christmas - New Year, Sunday and Bank Holidays – **M** a la carte 31/62.

✗ Frankenheim, Wielandstr. 14 (D 1), ✆ 35 14 47, beer garden   BV **e**

✗ Im Goldenen Ring, Burgplatz 21 (D 1), ✆ 13 31 61, Fax 324780, beer garden   DY **n**

✗ **Benrather Hof**, Steinstr. 1 (D 1), ✆ 32 52 18, Fax 132957, ⯅   EZ **b**
closed Christmas and New Year – **M** a la carte 27/56.

✗ **Im Goldenen Kessel**, Bolker Str. 44 (D 1), ✆ 32 60 07   DY **d**
M a la carte 29/51.

at Düsseldorf 13-Benrath by Siegburger Str. CX :

🏨 **Rheinterrasse**, Benrather Schloßufer 39, ✆ 71 10 70, Telex 8582459, Fax 7110770,
« Terrace with � » – TV ☎ ⨎ – 🛐 25. AE ◑ ⴹ VISA
M a la carte 22/69 – **42 rm** 135/245 Bb.

✗✗ **Lignano** (Italian rest.), Hildener Str. 43, ✆ 71 19 36 – AE ◑ ⴹ VISA. ⬦
closed Saturday lunch, Sunday and 3 weeks July - August – **M** a la carte 55/80.

✗✗ **Giuseppe Verdi** (Italian rest.), Paulistr. 5, ✆ 7 18 49 44 – AE ◑ ⴹ VISA
closed Monday, 1 to 13 January and 8 to 24 June – **M** a la carte 50/80.

at Düsseldorf 1-Bilk :

🏨 **Grand Hotel** without rest, Varnhagenstr. 37 (D 1), ✆ 31 08 00, Telex 8584072, Fax 316667,
⯅ – ▮❙ ⨎ TV ⬦ ⬦ ⬌ – 🛐 30. AE ◑ ⴹ VISA   BX **a**
70 rm 215/395 Bb.

🏨 **Aida** without rest, Ubierstr. 36, ✆ 1 59 90, Fax 1599103, ⯅ – ▮❙ TV ☎ ⬦ ⨎ – 🛐 30. AE
◑ ⴹ VISA – **93 rm** 138/268 Bb.   *by Aachener Str.* AX

at Düsseldorf 30-Derendorf by Prinz-Georg-Str. BU :

🏨 **Lindner Hotel Rhein Residence**, Kaiserswerther Str. 20, ✆ 4 99 90, Fax 4999499, Massage, ⯅ – ▮❙ ⨎ rm TV – 🛐 30. AE ◑ ⴹ VISA. ⬦ rest   ABU **f**
closed 23 December - 1 January – **M** *(closed Saturday)* a la carte 37/62 – **126 rm** 223/396 Bb.

🏨 **Saga Excelsior** without rest, Kapellstr. 1, ✆ 48 60 06, Telex 8584737, Fax 490242 – ▮❙ TV. ⬦
65 rm.   EY **e**

🏨 **Michelangelo** without rest, Roßstr. 61, ✆ 48 01 01, Telex 8588649, Fax 467742 – ▮❙ TV ☎
⬌, AE ◑ ⴹ VISA   BU **a**
closed 21 December - 1 January – **70 rm** 130/260 Bb.

🏨 **Consul** without rest, Kaiserswerther Str. 59, ✆ 4 92 00 78, Telex 8584624, Fax 4982577 –
▮❙ TV ☎ ⬌. AE ◑ ⴹ VISA   AU **c**
29 rm 137/240 Bb.

🏨 Gildors Hotel without rest (with guest house), Collenbachstr. 51, ✆ 48 80 05, Telex 8584418,
Fax 446329 – ▮❙ TV ☎ ⬌ – **50 rm** Bb.   BU **n**

✗✗ **Amalfi** (Italian rest.), Ulmenstr. 122, ✆ 43 38 09 – AE ◑ ⴹ   BU **r**
closed Sunday and 3 weeks August – **M** a la carte 43/75.

✗✗ **Gatto Verde** (Italian rest.), Rheinbabenstr. 5, ✆ 46 18 17, ⯅ – AE ◑ ⴹ VISA   BU **s**
closed Saturday lunch, Sunday, Monday and 4 weeks July - August – **M** a la carte 46/65.

at Düsseldorf 13-Eller by Karl-Geusen-Str. CX :

🏨 **Novotel Düsseldorf Süd**, Am Schönenkamp 9, ✆ 74 10 92, Telex 8584374, Fax 745512,
⯅, ⬙ (heated), ⬌ – ▮❙ ⨎ rm ▤ TV ☎ ⬦ ⨎ – 🛐 25/300. AE ⴹ VISA
M a la carte 36/66 – **120 rm** 173/205 Bb.

at Düsseldorf 30-Golzheim by Fischerstr. BV :

🏨 **Inter-Continental**, Karl-Arnold-Platz 5, ✆ 4 55 30, Telex 8584601, Fax 4553110, Massage,
⯅, ⬙, ⬕ ▤ TV ⬦ ⬌ ⨎ – 🛐 25/400. AE ◑ ⴹ VISA. ⬦ rest   AU **q**
Restaurants : **Les Continents** *(closed Saturday lunch, Sunday and 4 weeks July - August)*
M a la carte 72/94 – **Café de la Paix M** a la carte 47/71 – **310 rm** 284/613 Bb – 20 suites
1032/1514.

🏨 **Düsseldorf Hilton**, Georg-Glock-Str. 20, ✆ 4 37 70, Telex 8584376, Fax 4377791, ⯅, Massage, ⬒, ⯅, ⬕, ⬖ – ▮❙ ⨎ rm ▤ TV ☎ ⬦ ⬌ – 🛐 25/1000. AE ◑ ⴹ VISA. ⬦ rest
Restaurants : **San Francisco** *(dinner only, closed Monday and July)* **M** a la carte 67/98 – Hofgarten **M** a la carte 48/70 – **374 rm** 287/564 Bb – 9 suites 850/1700.   AU **r**

🏨 **Golzheimer Krug** ⬠, Karl-Kleppe-Str. 20, ✆ 43 44 53, Telex 8588919, Fax 453299, ⯅ –
TV ☎ ⬦ – 🛐 40. AE ◑ ⴹ VISA   AU **e**
M *(closed Monday)* a la carte 45/71 – **33 rm** 170/320 Bb.

🏨 **Rheinpark** without rest, Bankstr. 13, ✆ 49 91 86 – ⬌. ⬦   AU **b**
29 rm 60/130 Bb.

✗✗ **Fischer-Stuben-Mulfinger**, Rotterdamer Str. 15, ✆ 43 26 12, « Garden terrace » – AE ⴹ   AU **a**
closed Saturday – **M** (booking essential) a la carte 47/77.

✗✗ **Rosati** (Italian rest.), Felix-Klein-Str. 1, ✆ 4 36 05 03, Fax 452963, ⯅ – ⬦. AE ◑ ⴹ VISA
closed Saturday lunch and Sunday – **M** (booking essential) a la carte 62/79 – **Rosati due**
M a la carte 47/65.   AU **s**

DÜSSELDORF

at Düsseldorf 12-Grafenberg by Grafenberger Allee CU :

🏨 **Rolandsburg** 🦢, Rennbahnstr. 2, 🍴 61 00 90, Fax 6100943, 🌧, 🔄, 🔲 – 🕴 📺 🕿 🅿 – 🔬 25/50. 🆎 ⓪ 🔳 𝗩𝗜𝗦𝗔
   M a la carte 61/91 – **59 rm** 210/490 Bb.

at Düsseldorf 31-Kaiserswerth by Kaiserswerther Str. AU :

🍴🍴🍴🍴 ✿✿✿ **Im Schiffchen** (French rest.), Kaiserswerther Markt 9 (1st floor), 🍴 40 10 50, Fax 403667 – 🆎 ⓪ 🔳 𝗩𝗜𝗦𝗔. ✂
   closed Sunday and Bank Holidays – **M** (dinner only, booking essential) 154/186 and a la carte 112/152
   Spec. Bretonischer Hummer in Kamillenblüten gedämpft, Kalbsbries-Canelloni in Trüffelbutter-sauce, Plinsen mit Quarkschaum.

🍴🍴 ✿ **Aalschokker** (German rest.), Kaiserswerther Markt 9, 🍴 40 39 48, Fax 403667 – 🆎 ⓪ 🔳 𝗩𝗜𝗦𝗔
   closed Sunday and Bank Holidays – **M** (dinner only, booking essential) 135 and a la carte 64/100
   Spec. Sülze von Schweinebacke mit grünen Linsen, Himmel und Erde mit Gänseleber, Schwarzwälder Kirschtorte "eigene Art".

at Düsseldorf 11-Lörick by Luegallee AV :

🏨 **Fischerhaus** 🦢, Bonifatiusstr. 35, 🍴 59 20 07, Telex 8584449, Fax 593989 – 📺 🕿 🅿. 🆎 ⓪ 🔳 𝗩𝗜𝗦𝗔
   M (see **Hummerstübchen** below) – **35 rm** 189/298 Bb.

🍴🍴 ✿✿ **Hummerstübchen**, Bonifatiusstr. 35 (at Fischerhaus H.), 🍴 59 44 02 – 🅿. 🆎 ⓪ 🔳 𝗩𝗜𝗦𝗔
   closed Sunday, Monday and 3 weeks July - August – **M** (booking essential) a la carte 81/105
   Spec. Hummersuppe, Gratin von Hummer mit Gemüseravioli, Lammrücken in der Kartoffelkruste.

at Düsseldorf 30-Lohausen by Danziger Str. AU :

🏨 **Arabella Airport Hotel** 🦢, am Flughafen, 🍴 4 17 30, Telex 8584612, Fax 4173707 – 🕴 ✸✸ rm 🍴 📺 🕭 – 🔬 25/190. 🆎 ⓪ 🔳 𝗩𝗜𝗦𝗔
   M a la carte 42/67 – **200 rm** 187/388 Bb.

at Düsseldorf 30-Mörsenbroich by Rethelstr. DV :

🏨 **Ramada-Renaissance-Hotel**, Nördlicher Zubringer 6, 🍴 6 21 60, Telex 172114001, Fax 6216666, Massage, 🔄, 🔲 – 🕴 ✸✸ rm 🍴 📺 🕭 🚗 – 🔬 25/400. 🆎 ⓪ 🔳 𝗩𝗜𝗦𝗔. ✂ rest   BU **e**
   Restaurants : **Summertime M** a la carte 52/84 – **Café Orchidee M** a la carte 35/58 – **245 rm** 271/512 Bb – 8 suites 802/1402.

🏨 **Merkur** without rest, Mörsenbroicher Weg 49, 🍴 63 40 31, Fax 622525 – 📺 🕿 🅿. 🆎 ⓪ 🔳 𝗩𝗜𝗦𝗔   CU **a**
   closed 1 to 5 January – **28 rm** 95/290 Bb.

at Düsseldorf 11-Oberkassel by Luegallee AV :

🏨 **Ramada**, Am Seestern 16, 🍴 59 10 47, Telex 8585575, Fax 593569, 🔄, 🔲 – 🕴 ✸✸ rm 🍴 📺 🅿 – 🔬 25/150. 🆎 🔳 𝗩𝗜𝗦𝗔. ✂ rest
   M a la carte 49/76 – **222 rm** 223/543 Bb – 6 suites 800/1300.

🏨 **Hanseat** without rest, Belsenstr. 6, 🍴 57 50 69, Telex 8581997, Fax 589662, « Elegant furnishings » – 📺 🕿. 🆎 ⓪ 🔳 𝗩𝗜𝗦𝗔
   37 rm 150/280 Bb.

🍴🍴🍴 **De' Medici** (Italian rest.), Amboßstr. 3, 🍴 59 41 51 – 🆎 ⓪ 🔳 𝗩𝗜𝗦𝗔
   closed Saturday lunch, Sunday and Bank Holidays except exhibitions – **M** (booking essential for dinner) a la carte 50/77.

🍴🍴 **Edo** (Japanese restaurants : Teppan, Robata and Tatami), Am Seestern 3, 🍴 59 10 82, Fax 591394, « Japanese garden » – 🍴 🅿. 🆎 ⓪ 🔳 𝗩𝗜𝗦𝗔. ✂
   closed Saturday lunch, Sunday, Easter and 25 December - 1 January – **M** a la carte 50/90.

at Düsseldorf 12-Unterbach SE : 11 km by Grafenberger Allee BV :

🏨 **Landhotel Am Zault - Residenz**, Gerresheimer Landstr. 40, 🍴 25 10 81, Telex 8581872, Fax 254718, 🔄 – 📺 🕿 🅿 – 🔬 120. 🆎 ⓪ 🔳 𝗩𝗜𝗦𝗔
   M *(closed Saturday lunch)* 28/59 (lunch) and a la carte 58/89 – **61 rm** 170/480 Bb.

at Düsseldorf 1-Unterbilk :

🍴🍴🍴 **Savini**, Stromstr. 47, 🍴 39 39 31, Fax 391719 – ⓪ 🔳   AX **e**
   closed Sunday, Monday and 2 weeks both Easter and July - August – **M** (booking essential) a la carte 67/103.

🍴🍴 **Rheinturm Top 180** (revolving restaurant at 172 m), Stromstr. 20, 🍴 84 85 80, Fax 325619, ☀ Düsseldorf and Rhein (🕴, DM 5,00) – 🍴 🕭 – 🔬 60. 🆎 ⓪ 🔳 𝗩𝗜𝗦𝗔. ✂   AV **a**
   M a la carte 48/78.

🍴🍴 **Breuer's Restaurant**, Hammer Str. 38, 🍴 39 31 13, Fax 307979 – 🆎 ⓪ 🔳 𝗩𝗜𝗦𝗔. ✂   AX **b**
   closed Sunday – **M** a la carte 40/72.

240

at Meerbusch 1-Büderich **4005** by Luegallee AV – ❸ 02132 :

XXX **Landhaus Mönchenwerth**, Niederlöricker Str. 56 (at the boat landing stage), ℘ 7 79 31, Fax 71899, ≤, « Garden terrace » – ℗. 𝐀𝐄 ⓞ 𝐄 𝘝𝘐𝘚𝘈. ⅏
closed Saturday – **M** a la carte 56/96.

XXX **Landsknecht** with rm, Poststr. 70, ℘ 59 47, Fax 10978 – 📺 ☎ ℗. 𝐀𝐄 ⓞ 𝐄. ⅏
M *(closed Saturday lunch September and June, Saturday July - August)* a la carte 50/95 – **8 rm** 120/260.

X **Lindenhof**, Dorfstr. 48, ℘ 26 64
closed Monday, 10 - 31 July and Christmas - New Year – **M** (dinner only, booking essential) a la carte 39/70.

Essen **4300**. Nordrhein-Westfalen 𝟺𝟷𝟷 𝟺𝟷𝟸 E 12. 𝟿𝟾𝟽 ⑭ – pop. 620 000 – alt. 120 m –
❸ 0201.
Düsseldorf 31.

at Essen 18-Kettwig S : 11 km :

XXXX ❀❀ **Romantik-Hotel Résidence** ⑩ with rm, Auf der Forst 1, ℘ (02054) 89 11, Fax 82501
– ⅏ rest 📺 ☎ ℗. 𝐀𝐄 ⓞ 𝐄 𝘝𝘐𝘚𝘈
closed 1 to 9 January and 6 to 31 July – **M** *(closed Sunday and Monday)* (dinner only, booking essential, remarkable winelist) 120/180 and a la carte 95/116 – **18 rm** 175/450 Bb
Spec. Sülze von Gänsestopfleber und Ochsenschwanz mit Trüffelremoulade, Hummer auf Dicken Bohnen in Thymianrahm, Quarkauflauf mit Sherryeis.

Grevenbroich **4048**. Nordrhein-Westfalen 𝟺𝟷𝟸 C 13, 𝟿𝟾𝟽 ㉓ – pop. 57 000 – alt. 60 m
– ❸ 02181.
Düsseldorf 28.

XXXX ❀❀ **Zur Traube** with rm, Bahnstr. 47, ℘ 6 87 67, Telex 8517193, Fax 61122 – 📺 ☎ ℗.
𝐀𝐄 ⓞ 𝐄 𝘝𝘐𝘚𝘈. ⅏
closed 12 - 20 April, 19 July - 3 August and 20 December - 19 January – **M** *(closed Sunday and Monday)* (booking essential) (remarkable winelist) 138/178 and a la carte 83/120 – **6 rm** 190/490
Spec. Meerwolf auf Stielmus mit Trüffelbutter (spring), Variation von der Ente, Tannenhonigparfait mit Mus von Waldbeeren.

When in a hurry use the Michelin Main Road Maps :

𝟿𝟽𝟶 *Europe,* 𝟿𝟾𝟶 *Greece,* 𝟿𝟾𝟺 *Germany,* 𝟿𝟾𝟻 *Scandinavia-Finland,*
𝟿𝟾𝟼 *Great Britain and Ireland,* 𝟿𝟾𝟽 *Germany-Austria-Benelux,* 𝟿𝟾𝟾 *Italy,*
𝟿𝟾𝟿 *France,* 𝟿𝟿𝟶 *Spain-Portugal and* 𝟿𝟿𝟷 *Yugoslavia.*

FRANCFORT ON MAIN **(FRANKFURT AM MAIN)** 6000. Hessen 𝟺𝟷𝟸 𝟺𝟷𝟹 IJ 16. 𝟿𝟾𝟽 ㉕ –
pop. 627 500 – alt. 91 m – ❸ 069.

See : Zoo★★★ FX – Goethe's House (Goethehaus)★ GZ M2 – Cathedral (Dom)★ (Gothic Tower★★, Choir-stalls★, Museum★) HZ – Tropical Garden (Palmengarten)★ CV – Senckenberg-Museum★ (Palaeontology department★★) CV M9 – Städel Museum (Städelsches Museum und Städtische Galerie)★★ GZ – Museum of Applied Arts (Museum für Kunsthandwerk)★ HZ – German Cinema Museum★ GZ M7 – Henninger Turm ⅏★ FX.

🖪 Frankfurt-Niederrad, by Kennedy-Allee CDX, ℘ 6 66 23 17.

✈ Rhein-Main (SW : 12 km), ℘ 6 90 25 95.

🚗 at Neu-Isenburg (S : 7 km) ℘ (06102) 85 75.

Exhibition Centre (Messegelände) (CX), ℘ 7 57 50, Telex 411558.

🖪 Tourist Information, Main Station (Hauptbahnhof), ℘ 21 23 88 49.

🖪 Tourist Information, im Römer, ℘ 21 23 87 08.

Wiesbaden 41 – Bonn 178 – Nürnberg 226 – Stuttgart 204.

The reference (F 15) at the end of the address is the postal district : Frankfurt 15

Plans on following pages

🏨 **Steigenberger Frankfurter Hof**, Bethmannstr. 33 (F 1), ℘ 2 15 02, Telex 411806, Fax 215900, ☲ – ⑂ ⅏ rm ■ 📺 – ⚙ 25/300. 𝐀𝐄 ⓞ 𝐄 𝘝𝘐𝘚𝘈. ⅏ rest GZ **e**
Restaurants (see **Restaurant Français** and **Frankfurter Stubb** below) : – Hofgarten *(closed Saturday)* **M** a la carte 58/85 – **Kaiserbrunnen M** a la carte 33/50 – **350 rm** 332/684 Bb – 30 suites 1154/1754.

🏨 **Hessischer Hof**, Friedrich-Ebert-Anlage 40 (F 1), ℘ 7 54 00, Telex 411776, Fax 7540924, « Rest. with collection of Sèvres porcelain » – ⑂ ⅏ rm ■ 📺 ⬛ ℗ – ⚙ 25/300. 𝐀𝐄 ⓞ 𝐄 𝘝𝘐𝘚𝘈. ⅏ rest CX **p**
M 40 lunch and a la carte 65/100 – **114 rm** 301/617 – 11 suites 862/1679.

241

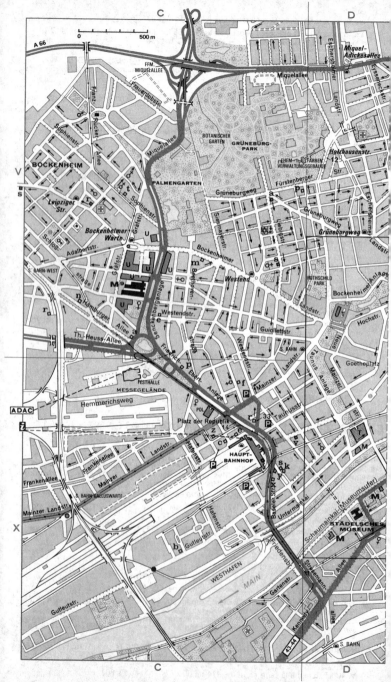

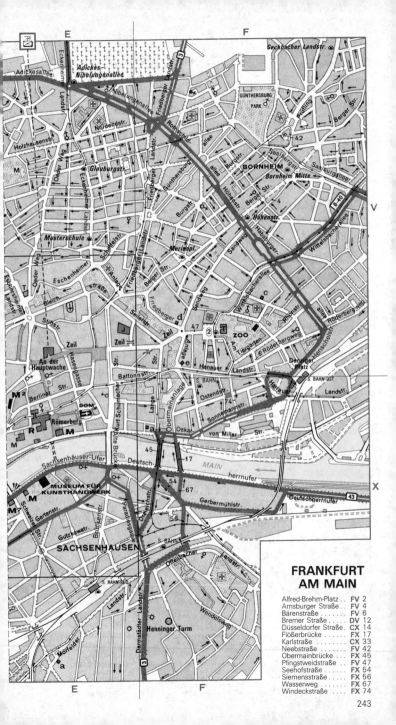

FRANKFURT
AM MAIN

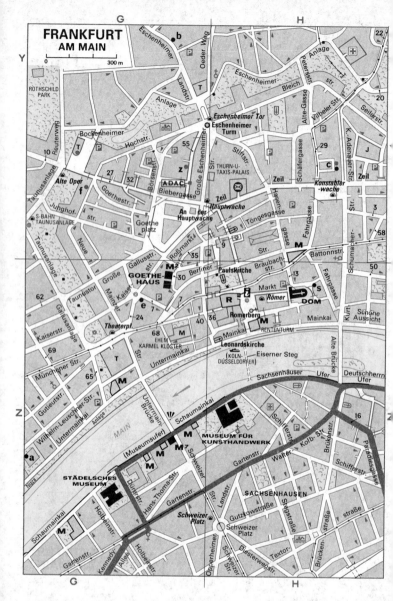

FRANKFURT AM MAIN

0   300 m

Arabella Grand Hotel, Konrad-Adenauer-Str. 7 (F 1), ℰ 2 98 10, Telex 4175926, Fax 2981810, Massage, ⇌, 🔲 – ⃒🕴 ⇝ rm 🍴 🔲 🗗 ⇐ ⟺ – 🔏 25/500. 🆎 ⓞ 🇪 𝘝𝘐𝘚𝘈, ⋇ rest
Restaurants (see also **Dynasty** below) **Premiere** *(dinner only, closed Sunday, Monday, Bank Holidays and 5 July - 2 August)* **M** a la carte 65/95 – **Brasserie M** a la carte 42/66 – **378 rm** 399/547 Bb – 11 suites 951/2000.
HY **c**

Frankfurt Intercontinental, Wilhelm-Leuschner-Str. 43 (F 1), ℰ 2 60 50, Telex 413639, Fax 252467, Massage, 🇮🇨, ⇌, 🔲 – ⃒🕴 ⇝ rm 🍴 🔲 🗗 – 🔏 25/800. 🆎 ⓞ 🇪 𝘝𝘐𝘚𝘈, ⋇ rest
M a la carte 48/99 – **800 rm** 422/579 Bb – 45 suites 1200/4000.
GZ **a**

Mövenpick Parkhotel Frankfurt, Wiesenhüttenplatz 28 (F 1), ℰ 2 69 70, Telex 412808, Fax 26978849, ⇌ – ⃒🕴 ⇝ rm 🍴 🔲 🗗 ⇐ ⟺ 🅿 – 🔏 25/160. 🆎 ⓞ 🇪 𝘝𝘐𝘚𝘈
CX **k**
Restaurants: **La Truffe** *(closed Saturday, Sunday, Bank Holidays and 4 weeks June - July)* **M** a la carte 70/100 – **Mövenpick-Restaurants M** a la carte 35/68 – **300 rm** 321/574 Bb – 4 suites 634/2446.

Frankfurt Marriott Hotel, Hamburger Allee 2 (F 90), ℰ 7 95 50, Telex 412573, Fax 79552432, ⩤ Frankfurt – ⃒🕴 ⇝ rm 🍴 🔲 – 🔏 25/600. 🆎 ⓞ 🇪 𝘝𝘐𝘚𝘈, ⋇ rest CV **a**
M a la carte 46/80 – **585 rm** 366/577 Bb – 17 suites 652/1252.

Altea Hotel, Voltastr. 29 (F 90), ℰ 7 92 60, Telex 413791, Fax 79261606, ⇌ – ⃒🕴 ⇝ rm 🔲 ⇐ 🆎 ⓞ 🇪 𝘝𝘐𝘚𝘈
by Th.-Heuss-Allee CV
M a la carte 43/80 – **426 rm** 180/340 Bb – 12 suites 390/490.

Scandic Crown Hotel, Wiesenhüttenstr. 42 (F 16), ℰ 27 39 60, Telex 416394, Fax 27396795, ⇌, 🔲 – ⃒🕴 ⇝ rm 🔲 ⇐ – 🔏 25/100. 🆎 ⓞ 🇪 𝘝𝘐𝘚𝘈 CX **s**
M *(closed Sunday lunch)* a la carte 50/80 – **144 rm** 225/410 Bb.

Palmenhof - Restaurant Bastei, Bockenheimer Landstr. 89 (F 1), ℰ 7 53 00 60, Fax 75300666 – ⃒🕴 🔲 ⇐. 🆎 ⓞ 🇪 𝘝𝘐𝘚𝘈 CV **m**
closed 20 December - 6 January – **M** *(closed Saturday, Sunday and Bank Holidays)* a la carte 55/85 – **47 rm** 150/280 Bb.

Pullman Hotel Savigny, Savignystr. 14 (F 1), ℰ 7 53 30, Telex 412061, Fax 7533175 – ⃒🕴
🔲 – 🔏 25/80. 🆎 ⓞ 🇪 𝘝𝘐𝘚𝘈 CX **f**
M a la carte 43/75 – **124 rm** 215/390 Bb.

National, Baseler Str. 50 (F 1), ℰ 27 39 40, Telex 412570, Fax 234460 – ⃒🕴 🔲 – 🔏 25/60.
🆎 ⓞ 🇪 𝘝𝘐𝘚𝘈 CX **x**
M *(also vegetarian dishes)* a la carte 40/72 – **70 rm** 167/366 Bb.

An der Messe without rest, Westendstr. 104 (F 1), ℰ 74 79 79, Telex 4189009, Fax 748349 – ⃒🕴 🔲 ⇐. 🆎 ⓞ 🇪 𝘝𝘐𝘚𝘈 CV **e**
46 rm 200/430 Bb.

Imperial, Sophienstr. 40 (F 90), ℰ 7 93 00 30, Telex 4189636, Fax 79300388 – ⃒🕴 🍴 🔲 ☎ ⇐. 🆎 ⓞ 🇪 𝘝𝘐𝘚𝘈 CV **t**
M *(dinner only)* a la carte 40/71 – **60 rm** 290/390 Bb.

Novotel Frankfurt-Messe, Voltastr. 1 b (F 90), ℰ 79 30 30, Telex 412054, Fax 79303930, 🏖, ⇌ – ⃒🕴 ⇝ rm 🔲 🗗 🏊 ⇐ 🅿 – 🔏 25/250. 🆎 ⓞ 🇪 𝘝𝘐𝘚𝘈 CV **r**
M a la carte 36/68 – **235 rm** 194/233 Bb.

Rhein-Main without rest, Heidelberger Str. 3 (F 1), ℰ 25 00 35, Telex 413434, Fax 252518 – ⃒🕴 🔲 ☎ 🅿. 🆎 ⓞ 🇪 𝘝𝘐𝘚𝘈, ⋇ CX **b**
50 rm 180/350 Bb.

Mozart without rest, Parkstr. 17 (F 1), ℰ 55 08 31 – ⃒🕴 🔲 ☎. 🆎 ⓞ 🇪 𝘝𝘐𝘚𝘈 CV **p**
closed 23 December - 2 January – **35 rm** 139/199 Bb.

Turm - Hotel without rest, Eschersheimer Landstr. 20 (F 1), ℰ 15 40 50, Fax 553578 – ⃒🕴 🔲 ☎ 🅿. 🆎 ⓞ 🇪 𝘝𝘐𝘚𝘈 GY **b**
closed 21 December - 6 January – **75 rm** 120/175 Bb.

Continental, Baseler Str. 56 (F 1), ℰ 23 03 41, Telex 412502, Fax 232914 – ⃒🕴 🔲 ☎ – 🔏 30.
🆎 ⓞ 🇪 𝘝𝘐𝘚𝘈, ⋇ CX **y**
M *(closed Sunday and Bank Holidays)* a la carte 34/61 – **80 rm** 155/325.

Intercity, Poststr. 8 (F 1), ℰ 27 39 10, Telex 414709, Fax 27391999 – ⃒🕴 ⇝ rm 🔲 ☎ – 🔏 35. 🆎 ⓞ 🇪 𝘝𝘐𝘚𝘈 CX **e**
M a la carte 38/57 – **227 rm** 182/286 Bb.

Concorde without rest, Karlstr. 9 (F 1), ℰ 23 32 30, Fax 237828 – ⃒🕴 ⇝ 🔲 ☎. 🆎 ⓞ 🇪 𝘝𝘐𝘚𝘈, ⋇ CX **r**
closed 20 December - 2 January – **45 rm** 140/260.

Topas without rest, Niddastr. 88 (F 1), ℰ 23 08 52, Fax 237228 – ⃒🕴 🔲 ☎. 🆎 ⓞ 🇪 𝘝𝘐𝘚𝘈 CX **z**
31 rm 110/295 Bb.

Cristall without rest, Ottostr. 3 (F 1), ℰ 23 03 51, Telex 4170654, Fax 253368 – ⃒🕴 🔲 ☎. 🆎 ⓞ 🇪 𝘝𝘐𝘚𝘈, ⋇ CX **c**
38 rm 110/295 Bb.

Am Dom without rest, Kannengießergasse 3 (F 1), ℰ 28 21 41, Telex 414955, Fax 283237 – ⃒🕴 🔲 ☎. 🇪 𝘝𝘐𝘚𝘈 HZ **s**
30 rm 125/300 Bb.

Falk without rest, Falkstr. 38a (F 90), ℰ 70 80 94, Fax 708017 – ⃒🕴 🔲 ☎ 🅿 CV **n**
closed 2 weeks July - August and Christmas - early January – **32 rm** 120/205.

XXXX ✿ **Restaurant Français** (at Steigenberger Frankfurter Hof H.), Bethmannstr. 33 (F 1), ☎ 2 15 02 – ▤. AE ⓓ E VISA. ✈ GZ **e**
closed Sunday, Monday and 4 weeks June - July – **M** *(booking essential)* a la carte 86/120
Spec. Salat von Hummer und Zwergorangen, Pochierter Wolfsbarsch mit Gemüse-Ingwer-Fond, Dessert vom Wagen.

XXXX **Zauberflöte**, Opernplatz 1 (F 1), ☎ 1 34 03 86, Fax 1340391, ☂ – AE ⓓ E VISA. ✈
closed Sunday, Monday, Bank Holidays and 6 July - 16 August – **M** (dinner only, booking essential) a la carte 65/93 – **Bistro** *(lunch also)* **M** a la carte 30/45. GY **T**

XXXX ✿ **Weinhaus Brückenkeller**, Schützenstr. 6 (F 1), ☎ 28 42 38, « Old vaulted cellar with precious antiques » – ▤ Ⓟ. AE ⓓ E VISA. ✈ FX **a**
closed Sunday and Bank Holidays except exhibitions and Christmas - 7 January – **M** *(booking essential)* 135/160 and a la carte 80/115
Spec. Gebackene Sellerie-Tascherl mit Kalbsbries, Zander mit Linsen, Auflauf und Eis von Kürbiskernen.

XXX ✿ **Humperdinck**, Grüneburgweg 95 (F 1), ☎ 72 21 22 – AE ⓓ E VISA. ✈ CV **b**
closed Saturday lunch, Sunday, 3 weeks June - July and Christmas - early January – **M** a la carte 82/120
Spec. Variation von der Gänsestopfleber, Lammrücken mit Olivenkruste, Variation von Schokolade.

XXX **Mövenpick - Baron de la Mouette**, Opernplatz 2 (F 1), ☎ 2 06 80, Fax 296135, ☂ – ▤. AE ⓓ E VISA GY **f**
M a la carte 50/82 – **Orangerie M** a la carte 32/61.

XXX **Tse-Yang** (Chinese rest.), Kaiserstr. 67 (F 1), ☎ 23 25 41, Fax 237825 – AE ⓓ E VISA. ✈ CX **v**
M a la carte 40/75.

XXX **Dynasty** (Chinese rest.), Konrad-Adenauer-Str. 7 (at Arabella Grand Hotel) (F 1), ☎ 29 30 41, Fax 283866 – AE ⓓ E VISA. ✈ HY **c**
M 20 (lunch) and a la carte 45/80.

XX **La Femme**, Am Weingarten 5 (F 90), ☎ 7 07 16 06 – AE ⓓ E VISA. ✈ CV **c**
closed Sunday and Bank Holidays – **M** (dinner only) 73/108.

XX Kikkoman (Japanese rest.), Friedberger Anlage 1 (Zoo-Passage) (F 1), ☎ 4 99 00 21, Fax 447032 – ▤. ✈ FV **e**

XX **Casa Toscana** (Italian rest.), Friedberger Anlage 14 (F 1), ☎ 44 98 44, « Courtyard-terrace » – AE ⓓ E VISA FV **d**
closed Monday – **M** a la carte 52/75.

XX **Frankfurter Stubb** (In the vaulted cellar of Steigenberger Frankfurter Hof Hotel), Bethmannstr. 33 (F 1), ☎ 2 15 02 – ▤. AE ⓓ E VISA. ✈ GZ **e**
closed Sunday and Bank Holidays except exhibitions and 4 weeks June - July – **M** *(booking essential)* a la carte 42/65.

XX **Börsenkeller**, Schillerstr. 11 (F 1), ☎ 28 11 15, Fax 294551 – ▤. AE ⓓ E VISA GY **z**
closed Sunday and Bank Holidays except exhibitions – **M** a la carte 32/75.

XX **Intercity-Restaurant**, im Hauptbahnhof (1 st floor |♦|) (F 1), ☎ 27 39 50, Fax 27395168 – ▤ – 🏛 25/80. E CX
M a la carte 27/60.

X **Gasthof im Elsass**, Waldschmidtstr. 59 (F 1), ☎ 44 38 39 FV **c**
dinner only, closed 22 December - 4 January – **M** a la carte 35/76.

X **Ernos Bistro** (French rest.), Liebigstr. 15 (F 1), ☎ 72 19 97, ☂ – AE ⓓ E VISA CV **k**
closed Saturday and Sunday except exhibitions and mid June - mid July – **M** *(booking essential)* a la carte 70/92.

X **Gargantua** (Bistro), Friesengasse 3 (F 90), ☎ 77 64 42 – AE ⓓ E VISA. ✈ CV **s**
closed Saturday lunch, Sunday and Christmas - early January – **M** *(booking essential)* a la carte 70/92.

at Francfort 80-Griesheim by Th.-Heuss-Allee CV :

🏨 **Ramada**, Oeserstr. 180, ☎ 3 90 50, Telex 416812, Fax 3808218, ≘s, 🏊 – |♦| ⇔ rm ▤ rest 📺 Ⓟ – 🏛 25/350. AE ⓓ E VISA
M a la carte 60/85 – **238 rm** 283/473 Bb.

at Francfort 71-Niederrad by Kennedy-Allee CDX :

🏨 **Queens Hotel International**, Isenburger Schneise 40, ☎ 6 78 40, Telex 416717, Fax 6702634, ☂ – |♦| ⇔ rm ▤ 📺 Ⓟ – 🏛 25/400. AE ⓓ E VISA. ✈ rest
Restaurants : **La Fleur** *(closed Sunday and Monday except exhibitions)* **M** a la carte 60/85 – **Brasserie Brentano M** a la carte 32/70 – **279 rm** 267/429 Bb – 3 suites 596/814.

🏨 **Arabella Congress Hotel**, Lyoner Str. 44, ☎ 6 63 30, Telex 416760, Fax 6633666, ≘s, 🏊 – |♦| ⇔ rm ▤ 📺 🚗 Ⓟ – 🏛 25/500. AE ⓓ E VISA
M a la carte 30/70 – **400 rm** 225/380 Bb – 8 suites 550/660.

🏨 **Dorint**, Hahnstr. 9, ☎ 66 30 60, Telex 4032180, Fax 66306600, ≘s, 🏊 – |♦| ⇔ rm ▤ 📺 ☎ ♿ Ⓟ – 🏛 25/200. AE ⓓ E VISA
M a la carte 45/75 – **191 rm** 250/670 Bb.

XX **Weidemann**, Kelsterbacher Str. 66, ☎ 67 59 96, ☂ – Ⓟ. AE ⓓ E VISA
closed Saturday lunch, Sunday and Bank Holidays – **M** *(booking essential)* a la carte 62/87.

at Francfort 70 - Sachsenhausen :

🏨 **Holiday Inn - Conference Center**, Mailänder Str. 1, 🏦 6 80 20, Telex 411805, Fax 6802333, 🆘 – 📶 ⅙⅙ rm 🔳 📺 ⅙ 🕾 🅟 – 🔬 25/400. 🎤 rest
M a la carte 45/77 – **404 rm** 300/610 Bb.　　　by Darmstädter Landstr. (B 3) FX

XX ✿ **Bistrot 77**, Ziegelhüttenweg 1, 🏦 61 40 40, 🍴 – 🔳 ⓞ 🇪 𝐕𝐈𝐒𝐀　　　　　　EX **a**
closed Saturday lunch, Sunday, 15 June - 8 July and 23 December - 6 January – **M** a la carte 78/110
Spec. Perigord-Trüffel im Blätterteig (November-March), Zanderfilet auf Linsen, Challans-Ente "en trois facons".

at Eschborn **6236** NW : 12 km :

🏨 **Novotel**, Philipp-Helfmann-Str. 10, 🏦 (06196) 90 10, Telex 4072842, Fax 482114, 🍴, ☄ (heated), ☄ – 📶 ⅙⅙ rm 🔳 📺 ⅙ 🅟 – 🔬 25/350. 🎤 ⓞ 🇪 𝐕𝐈𝐒𝐀 by A 66　CV
M a la carte 34/65 – **227 rm** 200/240 Bb.

at Neu-Isenburg 2-Gravenbruch **6078** SE : 11 km by Darmstädter Landstr. FX and B 459 :

🏨 **Gravenbruch-Kempinski-Frankfurt**, 🏦 (06102) 50 50, Telex 417673, Fax 505445, 🍴, « Park », 🆘, ☄ (heated), 🔳, ☄, ✠ – 📶 ⅙⅙ rm 🔳 📺 🕾 🅟 – 🔬 25/450. 🎤 ⓞ 🇪 𝐕𝐈𝐒𝐀. 🎤 rest
Restaurants : a la carte 52/92 – **Gourmet-Restaurant** (dinner only) *(closed Saturday, Sunday, Bank Holidays and 5 weeks June - July)* **M** a la carte 82/135 – **Forsthaus M** a la carte 59/105 – **298 rm** 341/572 Bb – 30 suites 782/2152.

near Rhein-Main airport SW : 12 km by Kennedy-Allee CX – 🖂 **6000** Francfort 75 – ✿ 069 :

🏨 **Sheraton**, at the airport (Central Terminal), 🏦 6 97 70, Telex 4189294, Fax 69772209, 🆘, 🔳 – 📶 ⅙⅙ rm 🔳 📺 ⅙ 🅟 – 🔬 25/900. 🎤 ⓞ 🇪 𝐕𝐈𝐒𝐀. 🎤 rest
Restaurants : **Papillon** (remarkable wine-list) *(closed Saturday lunch, Sunday and Bank Holidays)* **M** a la carte 78/135 – **Kachelofen M** a la carte 54/94 – **Maxwell's Bistro and Taverne** *(closed Saturday and Sunday)* **M** a la carte 41/75 – **1050 rm** 343/626 Bb – 30 suites 1006/3056.

🏨 **Steigenberger Hotel Frankfurt Airport**, Unterschweinstiege 16, 🏦 6 97 50, Telex 413112, Fax 69752505, Massage, 🆘, 🔳 – 📶 ⅙⅙ rm 🔳 📺 🕾 – 🔬 25/550. 🎤 ⓞ 🇪 𝐕𝐈𝐒𝐀
M 39 (buffet) and a la carte 53/72 *(Italian rest.)* – **430 rm** 352/544 Bb – 9 suites 650/2800.

XXX **Rôtisserie 5 Continents**, in the Airport, Ankunft Ausland B (Besucherhalle, Ebene 3), 🏦 6 90 34 44, Fax 694730, ≼ – 🔳 – 🔬 30. 🎤 ⓞ 🇪 𝐕𝐈𝐒𝐀. 🎤
M a la carte 57/95.

XX **Waldrestaurant Unterschweinstiege**, Unterschweinstiege 16, 🏦 69 75 25 00, « Country house atmosphere, terrace » – 🔳 🅟. 🎤 ⓞ 🇪 𝐕𝐈𝐒𝐀
M *(booking essential)* 39 buffet and a la carte 43/78.

on the road from Neu-Isenburg to Götzenhain S : 13 km by Darmstädter Landstr. FX :

XXX **Gutsschänke Neuhof**, 🖂 6072 Dreieich-Götzenhain, 🏦 (06102) 32 00 14, Fax 31710, « Country house atmosphere, terrace » – 🅟. 🎤 ⓞ 🇪 𝐕𝐈𝐒𝐀
M a la carte 48/91.

at Maintal-Dörnigheim **6457** E : 13 km :

XXX ✿ **Hessler**, Am Bootshafen 4 (Dörnigheim), 🏦 (06181) 49 29 51, remarkable wine list – 🅟. 🇪. 🎤
closed Sunday - Monday and 3 weeks July – **M** *(booking essential)* 60/73 (lunch) and a la carte 88/117
Spec. Lasagne von Meeresfrüchten in Ingwersauce, Galantine von Kaninchenrücken in Trüffelsauce, Taube in Piroggenteig.

Guldental 6531. Rheinland-Pfalz 𝟜𝟙𝟚 G 17 – pop. 2 600 – alt. 150 m – ✿ 06707.
Frankfurt am Main 75.

XXX ✿✿ **Le Val d'Or**, Hauptstr. 3, 🏦 17 07, Fax 8489, 🍴 – ⓞ 🇪
Tuesday to Friday dinner only, closed Monday, 3 weeks January and 2 weeks August – **M** *(remarkable wine list)* (booking essential) 121/151 and a la carte 92/123
Spec. Kalbsbriesparfait, Gefüllte Bresse-Taube in Blätterteig, Dessert-Impressionen.

Mannheim 6800 Baden-Württemberg 𝟡𝟠𝟟 ㉕. 𝟜𝟙𝟚 𝟜𝟙𝟛 I 18 – pop. 310 000 – alt. 95 m – ✿ 0621.
Frankfurt am Main 79.

XXX ✿✿ **Da Gianni** (elegant italian rest.), R 7, 34 (Friedrichsring), 🏦 2 03 26 – 🎤 🇪
closed Monday, Bank Holidays and 3 weeks July – **M** *(booking essential)* a la carte 84/102
Spec. Variation von Vorspeisen, Risotto mit Taube und Bohnen, Steinbutt und Muscheln in Tomatensud.

247

Wertheim **6980.** Baden-Württemberg 987 ㉕, 412 413 L 17 – pop. 21 700 – alt. 142 m – ☉ 09342.

Frankfurt am Main 87.

🏯 ✿✿ **Schweizer Stuben** ⬍, at Wertheim-Bettingen (E : 10 km), Geiselbrunnweg 11, 🖉 30 70, Telex 689190, Fax 307155, ☜, « Hotel in a park », ☎s, ⤡ (heated), ☞, ⚒ (indoor) – 🕸 🄿 – ▲ 30, 🄰🄴 ⨀ ⋿ 𝚅𝙸𝚂𝙰
  M *(closed Monday and 1 to 23 January)* (booking essential) 158/198 and a la carte 95/145 – **33 rm** 210/395 – 11 suites 440/990
  Spec. Suprême vom Steinbutt, Zicklein mit Olivenölsauce, Lamm in zwei Gängen.

HAMBURG **2000.** 🄻 Stadtstaat Hamburg 411 N 6, 987 ⑤ – pop. 1 650 000 – alt. 10 m – ☉ 040.

See : Jungfernstieg★ GY – Außenalster★★★ (trip by boat★★★) GHXY – Hagenbeck Zoo (Tierpark Hagenbeck)★★ by Schröderstiftstr. EX – Television Tower (Fernsehturm)★ (⚒★★) EX – Fine Arts Museum (Kunsthalle)★★ HY **M1** – St. Michael's church (St. Michaelis)★ (tower ⚒★)EFZ – Stintfang (≼★) EZ – Port (Hafen)★★ EZ – Decorative Arts and Crafts Museum (Museum für Kunst und Gewerbe)★ HY **M2** – Historical Museum (Museum für Hamburgische Geschichte)★ EYZ **M3** – Post-Museum★ FY **M4** – Planten un Blomen Park★ EFX – Museum of Ethnography (Hamburgisches Museum für Völkerkunde)★ by Rothenbaumchaussee FX.

Envir. : Altona and Northern Germany Museum (Norddeutsches Landesmuseum)★★ by Reeperbahn EZ – Altona Balcony (Altonaer Balkon) ≼★ by Reeperbahn EZ – Elbchaussee★ by Reeperbahn EZ.

🛢 Hamburg-Blankenese, In de Bargen 59 (W : 17 km), 🖉 81 21 77 ; 🛢 Ammersbek (NE : 15 km), 🖉 (040) 6 05 13 37 ; 🛢 Hamburg-Wendlohe (N : 14 km), 🖉 5 50 50 14 ; 🛢 Wentorf, Golfstr. 2 (SE : 21 km), 🖉 (040) 7 20 26 10.

✈ Hamburg-Fuhlsbüttel (N : 15 km), 🖉 50 80.

🚗 🖉 39 18 45 56.

Exhibition Centre (Messegelände) (EFX), 🖉 3 56 91, Telex 212609.

🖪 Tourismus-Zentrale Hamburg, Burchardstr. 14, 🖉 30 05 10, Telex 2163036, Fax 30051253.

🖪 Tourist-Information im Bieberhaus, Hachmannplatz, 🖉 30 05 12 45.

🖪 Tourist-Information im Hauptbahnhof (main station), 🖉 30 05 12 30.

🖪 Tourist-Information im Flughafen (airport, terminal 3 - arrivals), 🖉 30 05 12 40.

ADAC, Amsinckstr. 39 (H 1), 🖉 2 39 90.

Berlin 289 – Bremen 120 – Hannover 151.

    The reference (H 15) at the end of the address is the postal district : Hamburg 15

Plan on following pages

near Hauptbahnhof, at St. Georg, east of the Außenalster :

🏯🏯 **Atlantic-Hotel Kempinski** ⬍, An der Alster 72 (H 1), 🖉 2 88 80, Telex 2163297, Fax 247129, ≼ Außenalster, Massage, ☎s, ⤡ – 🕸 🕸 ⟷ – ▲ 25/400. 🄰🄴 ⨀ ⋿ 𝚅𝙸𝚂𝙰, ⚒ rest   HY **a**
  M a la carte 76/106 – **256 rm** 315/460 Bb – 13 suites 650/1250.

🏯 **Maritim Hotel Reichshof**, Kirchenallee 34 (H 1), 🖉 24 83 30, Telex 2163396, Fax 24833588, ☎s, ⤡ – 🕸 🕸 ⟷ – ▲ 25/250. 🄰🄴 ⨀ ⋿ 𝚅𝙸𝚂𝙰. ⚒ rest   HY **d**
  M a la carte 68/92 – **303 rm** 219/424 Bb – 6 suites 650.

🏯 **Holiday Inn Crowne Plaza**, Graumannsweg 10 (H 76), 🖉 22 80 60, Telex 2165287, Fax 2208704, Massage, ☎s, ⤡ – 🕸 ⚒ rm 🖩 🕸 ⟷ 🍴 ⟷ – ▲ 25/120. 🄰🄴 ⨀ ⋿ 𝚅𝙸𝚂𝙰   by Lange Reihe HX
  M a la carte 68/92 – **290 rm** 316/482 Bb.

🏯 **Europäischer Hof**, Kirchenallee 45 (H 1), 🖉 24 82 48, Telex 2162493, Fax 24824799, Massage, ☎s, ⤡ – 🖩 ⚒ rest 🕸 ⟷ – ▲ 25/120. 🄰🄴 ⨀ ⋿ 𝚅𝙸𝚂𝙰   HY **e**
  M a la carte 38/71 – **320 rm** 194/386 Bb.

🏯 **Prem-Restaurant La mer**, An der Alster 9 (H 1), 🖉 24 17 26, Telex 2163115, Fax 2803851, « Antique furnishing, garden », ☎s – 🖩 🕸 🄿 🄰🄴 ⨀ ⋿ 𝚅𝙸𝚂𝙰. ⚒ rest   HX **c**
  M *(Saturday and Sunday dinner only)* (remarkable wine-list) a la carte 83/136 – **59 rm** 188/451 Bb – 3 suites 636.

🏨 **Berlin**, Borgfelder Str. 1 (H 26), 🖉 25 16 40, Telex 213939, Fax 25164413 – 🖩 🖩 rest 🕸 ☎ ⟷ 🄿 – ▲ 30. 🄰🄴 ⨀ ⋿ 𝚅𝙸𝚂𝙰. ⚒ rest   by Kurt-Schumacher-Allee HY
  M a la carte 53/70 – **93 rm** 138/210 Bb.

🏨 **St. Raphael**, Adenauerallee 41 (H 1), 🖉 24 82 00, Telex 2174733, Fax 24820333, ☎s – 🖩 ⚒ rm 🕸 ☎ ☎ – ▲ 25/70. 🄰🄴 ⨀ ⋿ 𝚅𝙸𝚂𝙰. ⚒ rest   by Adenauerallee HY
  M *(closed Saturday, Sunday and Bank Holidays)* a la carte 37/66 – **135 rm** 180/270 Bb – 3 suites 600.

🏨 **Senator** without rest, Lange Reihe 18 (H 1), 🖉 24 12 03, Telex 2174002, Fax 2803717 – 🖩 ⚒ 🕸 ☎ ⟷. 🄰🄴 ⨀ ⋿ 𝚅𝙸𝚂𝙰   HY **u**
  56 rm 158/210 Bb.

🏨 **Aussen-Alster-Hotel**, Schmilingskystr. 11 (H 1), ℰ 24 15 57, Telex 211278, Fax 2803231,
⇌ – 🛗 📺 ☎ 🖭 ⤶ 📧 🗺 — 💳 _VISA_   HX **e**
closed 24 - 27 December – **M** _(closed Saturday lunch and Sunday)_ a la carte 42/78 – **27 rm**
180/310 Bb.

🏨 **Ambassador**, Heidenkampsweg 34 (H 1), ℰ 23 00 02, Telex 2166100, Fax 230009, ⇌, 🗲
– 🛗 📺 ☎ 👈 – 🔏 25/120. 🖭 ⤶ 📧 _VISA_. 🗶 rest   by Amsinckstr.   HZ
M a la carte 41/75 – **124 rm** 155/240 Bb.

🏨 **Eden** without rest, Ellmenreichstr. 20 (H 1), ℰ 24 84 80, Telex 2174350, Fax 241521 – 🛗 📺
☎. 🖭 ⤶ 📧 _VISA_   HY **r**
63 rm 120/190.

🏨 **Alte Wache** without rest, Adenauerallee 25 (H 1), ℰ 24 12 91, Telex 2162254, Fax 2801754
– 🛗 📺 ☎ 🖭 – 🔏 40. 🖭 ⤶ 📧 _VISA_   HY **s**
85 rm 125/195.

🏨 **Fürst Bismarck** without rest, Kirchenallee 49 (H 1), ℰ 2 80 10 91, Telex 2162980,
Fax 2801096 – 🛗 📺 ☎. 🖭 ⤶ 📧 _VISA_   HY **x**
59 rm 95/165.

🏨 **Kronprinz - Restaurant Schiffer Börse**, Kirchenallee 46 (H 1), ℰ 24 32 58 (hotel) 24 52
40 (rest.), Telex 2161005, Fax 2801097 – 🛗 📺 ☎. 🖭 ⤶ 📧 _VISA_   HY **c**
M a la carte 35/70 – **73 rm** 120/170 Bb.

🍴🍴 **Peter Lembcke**, Holzdamm 49 (H 1), ℰ 24 32 90 – 🖭 ⤶ 📧 _VISA_   HY **t**
closed Saturday lunch, Sunday and Bank Holidays – **M** (booking essential) a la carte 55/102.

at Binnenalster, Altstadt, Neustadt :

🏛️ **Vier Jahreszeiten**, Neuer Jungfernstieg 9 (H 36), ℰ 3 49 40, Telex 211629, Fax 3494602,
≼ Binnenalster – 🛗 📺 ⇆ rm 📺 ⇆ – 🔏 25/70. 🖭 ⤶ 📧 _VISA_. 🗶   GY **v**
M a la carte 77/118 – **172 rm** 355/767 – 11 suites 909/1209.

🏛️ **Ramada Renaissance Hotel**, Große Bleichen (H 36), ℰ 34 91 80, Fax 34918431, Massage,
⇌ – 🛗 ⇆ rm 🏢 📺 📶 – 🔏 25/150. 🖭 ⤶ 📧 _VISA_. 🗶 rest   FY **e**
M a la carte 54/92 – **211 rm** 337/580 Bb – 4 suites 950/2000.

🏛️ **Marriott Hotel**, ABC-Str. 52 (H 36), ℰ 3 50 50, Telex 2165871, Fax 35051777, Massage,
🎣, ⇌ – 🛗 ⇆ rm 🏢 📺 📶 👈 – 🔏 25/300. 🖭 ⤶ 📧 _VISA_. 🗶 rest   FY **b**
M _(mainly Seafood)_ 35 buffet (lunch) and a la carte 60/95 – **278 rm** 319/456 Bb – 6 suites
610/1258.

🏛️ **SAS Plaza Hotel**, Marseiller Str. 2 (H 36), ℰ 3 50 20, Telex 214400, Fax 35023333,
≼ Hamburg, ⇌, 🗲 – 🛗 ⇆ rm 🏢 📺 📶 👈 – 🔏 25/600. 🖭 ⤶ 📧 _VISA_.
🗶 rest   FX **a**
M a la carte 56/82 – **562 rm** 275/460 Bb – 7 suites 700/1500.

🏨 **Hafen Hamburg**, Seewartenstr. 9 (H 11), ℰ 31 11 30, Telex 2161319, Fax 3192736, ≼ –
🛗 📺 ☎ 👈 📶 – 🔏 25/80. 🖭 ⤶ 📧 _VISA_   EZ **y**
M a la carte 47/87 – **250 rm** 148/200 Bb.

🏨 **Alster-Hof** without rest, Esplanade 12 (H 36), ℰ 35 00 70, Fax 35007514 – 🛗 📺 ☎. 🖭 ⤶
📧 _VISA_   GY **x**
closed 23 December - 1 January – **117 rm** 130/275 Bb.

🏨 **Baseler Hof**, Esplanade 11 (H 36), ℰ 35 90 60, Telex 2163707, Fax 35906918 – 🛗 📺 ☎
– 🔏 25/40. 🖭 ⤶ 📧 _VISA_. 🗶   GY **x**
M a la carte 32/60 – **160 rm** 120/330.

🍴🍴🍴 **Zum alten Rathaus** (with Fleetenkieker entertainment-rest.), Börsenbrücke 10 (H 11),
ℰ 36 75 70, Fax 365617 – 🖭 ⤶ 📧 _VISA_   GZ **n**
closed Sunday and Bank Holidays – **M** (booking essential) a la carte 52/90.

🍴🍴🍴 ✿ **Cölln's Austernstuben**, Brodschrangen 1 (H 11), ℰ 32 60 59 – 🖭 ⤶ 📧 _VISA_ GZ **v**
closed Saturday lunch, Sunday and Bank Holidays – **M** _(mainly seafood)_ (booking essential) a
la carte 80/114
Spec. Krusten- und Schalentiere, "Feines vom Fischmarkt", Karamelisierter Apfelpfannkuchen.

🍴🍴 **Ratsweinkeller**, Gr. Johannisstr. 2 (H 11), ℰ 36 41 53, Fax 372201, « 1896 Hanseatic
rest. » – 🔏 25/400. 🖭 ⤶ 📧 _VISA_   GZ **R**
closed Sunday and Bank Holidays – **M** a la carte 36/76.

🍴🍴 **Deichgraf**, Deichstr. 23 (H 11), ℰ 36 42 08, Fax 373055 – 🖭 ⤶ 📧 _VISA_   FZ **a**
closed Saturday lunch, Sunday and Bank Holidays – **M** (booking essential) a la carte 48/92.

🍴🍴 **il Ristorante** (Italian rest.), Große Bleichen 16 (1st floor) (H 36), ℰ 34 33 35, Fax 481719 –
🖭 ⤶ 📧   FY **c**
M a la carte 66/88.

🍴🍴 **Mövenpick - Café des Artistes**, Große Bleichen 36 (ground-floor), 🛗 (H 36), ℰ 34 10 00,
Fax 3410042 – 🖭 ⤶ 📧   FY **r**
closed Sunday – **M** a la carte 48/77 – **Mövenpick-Restaurant M** a la carte 32/63.

🍴🍴 **al Pincio** (Italian rest.), Schauenburger Str. 59 (1st floor, 🛗) (H 1), ℰ 36 52 55 – 🖭 ⤶ 📧.
🗶   GZ **a**
closed Saturday, Sunday and Bank Holidays – **M** (booking essential) a la carte 40/69.

🍴 **Dominique**, Karl-Muck-Platz 11 (H 36), ℰ 34 45 11 – ⤶   FY **a**
closed Saturday lunch, Sunday and 2 weeks June - July – **M** a la carte 60/74.

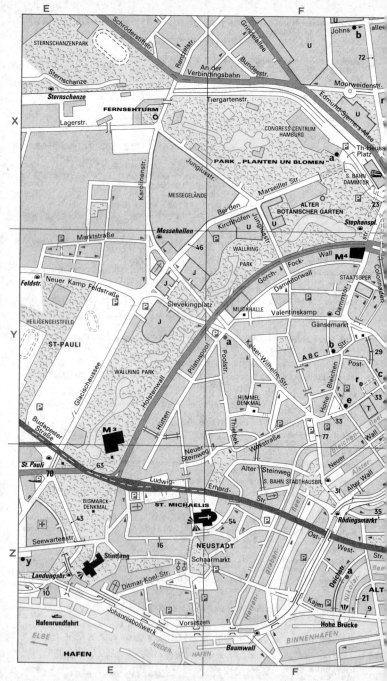

HAMBURG

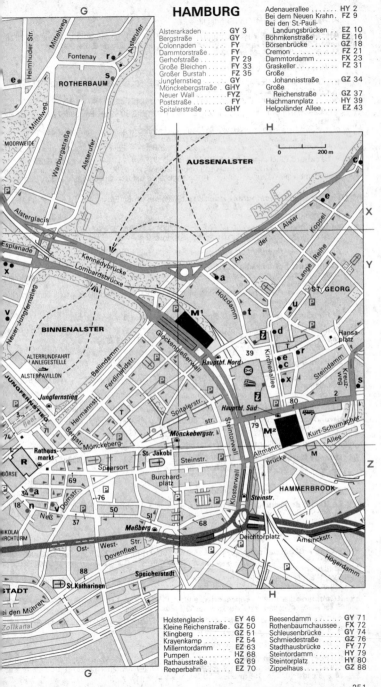

at Hamburg-Alsterdorf by Grindelallee FX :

🏨 **Alsterkrug-Hotel**, Alsterkrugchaussee 277 (H 60), ℘ 51 30 30, Telex 2173828, Fax 51303403, 🕿 – 🛁 🖭 rm 🖭 ⟳ 🅿 – 🔬 25/60. 🖭 ⓪ 🗲 🎴. 🛠 rest
M a la carte 50/71 – **80 rm** 172/271 Bb.

at Hamburg-Altona by Reeperbahn EZ :

🏨 **Raphael Hotel Altona**, Präsident-Krahn-Str. 13 (H 50), ℘ 38 02 40, Fax 38024444, 🕿 –
🛁 🖭 🕿 🅿. 🖭 ⓪ 🗲 🎴
closed 23 December - 2 January – (dinner only, residents only) – **45 rm** 125/250 Bb.

🏵🏵 **Landhaus Scherrer**, Elbchaussee 130 (H 50), ℘ 8 80 13 25, Fax 8806260 – 🅿. 🖭 ⓪
🗲 🎴
closed Sunday and Bank Holidays – **M** (booking essential, remarkable wine-list) a la carte 75/125
– **Bistro-Restaurant** *(lunch only)* **M** a la carte 60/85
Spec. Tempura von Nordseefischen, Kalbskopf mit Bohnen, Ente mit Wirsinggemüse (2 pers.).

🏵 **Le canard**, Elbchaussee 139 (H 50), ℘ 8 80 50 57, Fax 472413, ≤, 🌤 – 🅿. ⓪ 🗲 🎴. 🛠
closed Sunday – **M** (booking essential) (remarkable wine-list) 60 (lunch) and a la carte 71/120
Spec. Hamburger Aalsuppe "Andere Art", Langostinos mit Bohnenpurée und Algen, Lachs mit Currysauce.

🏵 **Fischereihafen-Restaurant Hamburg** (Seafood), Große Elbstr. 143 (H 50), ℘ 38 18 16, Fax 3893021, ≤ – 🅿. 🖭 ⓪ 🗲 🎴
M (booking essential) a la carte 62/111.

🏵 **La Mouette**, Neumühlen 50 (H 50), ℘ 39 65 04 – 🖭 ⓪ 🗲 🎴
closed Monday lunch and Sunday – **M** (booking essential for dinner) a la carte 50/72.

at Hamburg-Bahrenfeld by Budapester Str. EY :

🏵 **Tafelhaus**, Holstenkamp 71 (H 54), ℘ 89 27 60, Fax 8993324, 🌤 – 🅿
closed Saturday lunch, Sunday, Monday and 22 December - 19 January – **M** (booking essential)
45 (lunch) and a la carte 66/81
Spec. Ragout von Seezunge und Jakobsmuscheln, Ochsenschwanz mit Morcheln, Topfensoufflé mit Schokoladeneis.

at Hamburg-Billstedt by Kurt Schumacher-Allee and B 5 HY :

🏨 **Panorama** without rest, Billstedter Hauptstr. 44 (H 74), ℘ 73 35 90, Telex 212162, Fax 73359950, 🔲 – 🛁 🖭 🕿 ⟳ 🅿 – 🔬 25/200. 🖭 ⓪ 🗲 🎴
closed 24 December - 2 January – **111 rm** 195/275 Bb – 7 suites 325.

at Hamburg-Blankenese W : 16 km by Reeperbahn EZ :

🏨 **Strandhotel** 🦐, Strandweg 13 (H 55), ℘ 86 13 44, Fax 864936, ≤, 🌤, « Villa with elegant installation », 🕿 – 🖭 🕿 🅿. 🖭 ⓪ 🗲 🎴
M *(closed Sunday dinner and Monday)* a la carte 49/75 – **16 rm** 148/420 Bb.

🏵 Sagebiels Fährhaus, Blankeneser Hauptstr. 107 (H 55), ℘ 86 15 14, « Terrace with ≤ » – 🅿.

🏵 **Strandhof**, Strandweg 27 (H 55), ℘ 86 52 36, Fax 863353, ≤, 🌤 – 🅿. 🖭 ⓪ 🗲 🎴
closed Monday and Tuesday – **M** a la carte 45/81.

at Hamburg-City Nord by Grindelallee FX :

🏨 **Queens Hotel**, Mexicoring 1 (H 60), ℘ 63 29 40, Telex 2174155, Fax 6322472 – 🛁 🗝 rm
🖭 🅿 – 🔬 25/200. 🖭 ⓪ 🗲 🎴. 🛠 rest
M a la carte 52/76 – **183 rm** 237/327 Bb – 4 Suites 332.

at Hamburg-Duvenstedt by Grindelallee FX :

🏵 **Le Relais de France**, Poppenbütteler Chaussee 3 (H 65), ℘ 6 07 07 50 – 🅿
closed Sunday - Monday – **M** (dinner only, booking essential) a la carte 74/98 – **Bistro** *(also lunch)* **M** a la carte 39/50.

at Hamburg-Eppendorf by Grindelallee FX :

🏵 **Anna e Sebastiano** (Italian rest.), Lehmweg 30 (H 20), ℘ 4 22 25 95, Fax 4208008 – ⓪
🗲 🎴. 🛠 – *closed Sunday, Monday, 22 December - 2 January and 3 weeks June - July* –
M (dinner only, booking essential) 95/105 and a la carte 74/85
Spec. Warmer Salat von Hummer und weißen Bohnen, Milchlamm mit Artischocken und Balsamessig, Feige in Barolo mit Mandelmousse.

🏵 **Il Gabbiano** (Italian rest.), Eppendorfer Landstr. 145 (H 20), ℘ 4 80 21 59, Fax 4807921 – 🖭 ⓪
🗲 🎴 – *closed Sunday and 3 weeks July* – **M** (booking essential) a la carte 56/79.

🏵 **Sellmer** (mainly Seafood), Ludolfstr. 50 (H 20), ℘ 47 30 57, Fax 4601569 – 🅿. 🖭 ⓪ 🗲 🎴
M a la carte 48/94.

at Hamburg-Fuhlsbüttel by Grindelallee FX :

🏨 **Airport Hotel Hamburg**, Flughafenstr. 47 (H 62), ℘ 53 10 20, Telex 2166399, Fax 53102222, Massage, 🕿, 🔲 – 🛁 🗝 rm 🍽 rest 🖭 ⟳ 🅿 – 🔬 25/300. 🖭 ⓪ 🗲 🎴
M a la carte 40/67 – **158 rm** 229/359 Bb – 12 suites 423.

at Hamburg-Hamm by Kurt-Schumacher-Allee HY :

🏛 **Hamburg International**, Hammer Landstr. 200 (H 26), 🕿 21 14 01, Telex 2164349, Fax 211409 – |‡| 🖺 🕿 ⟵⟶ 🅟 – 🔥 25/40. 🆎 🖃 𝖵𝖨𝖲𝖠
M *(closed Sunday)* a la carte 45/80 – **112 rm** 115/275 Bb.

at Hamburg-Harburg 2100 S : 15 km by Amsinckstr. HZ :

🏛 **Panorama**, Harburger Ring 8 (H 90), 🕿 76 69 50, Telex 2164824, Fax 76695183 – |‡| 🖺
⟵⟶ – 🔥 25/120. 🆎 🕦 🖃 𝖵𝖨𝖲𝖠
M a la carte 35/73 – **98 rm** 195/340 Bb.

at Hamburg-Harvestehude :

🏛 **Inter-Continental**, Fontenay 10 (H 36), 🕿 41 41 50, Telex 211099, Fax 41415186, ≼ Hamburg and Alster, 🍴, Massage, 🚅, 🖎 – |‡| 🌤 rm 🗐 🖺 ⟵⟶ 🅟 – 🔥 25/240. 🆎
🕦 🖃 𝖵𝖨𝖲𝖠 ⟵⟶   GX **r**
Restaurants : **Fontenay-Grill** *(dinner only)* **M** a la carte 74/109 – **Orangerie M** a la carte 51/75
– **300 rm** 286/597 Bb – 16 suites 852/1452.

🏛 **Garden Hotels Pöseldorf** 🌤 without rest, Magdalenenstr. 60 (H 13), 🕿 41 40 40, Telex 212621, Fax 4140420, « Elegant modern installation », 🍴 – |‡| 🖺 🕿. 🆎 🕦 🖃 𝖵𝖨𝖲𝖠
61 rm 220/590.   by Mittelweg GX

🏛 **Smolka**, Isestr. 98 (H 13), 🕿 47 50 57, Telex 215275, Fax 473008 – |‡| 🖺 🕿 ⟵⟶. 🆎 🕦
🖃 𝖵𝖨𝖲𝖠, 🍴 rest   by Rothenbaumchaussee FX
M *(closed Saturday dinner, Sunday and Bank Holidays)* a la carte 39/64 – **38 rm** 143/296 Bb.

🏛 **Abtei** 🌤, Abteistr. 14 (H 13), 🕿 45 75 65, Fax 449820, 🍴 – 🖺 🕿. 🕦 🖃 𝖵𝖨𝖲𝖠. 🍴
M *(residents only)* – **12 rm** 210/450.   by Rothenbaumchaussee FX

✕✕✕ ✿ **Die Insel - Restaurant Amadeus**, Alsterufer 35 (1st floor) (H 36), 🕿 4 10 69 55, Fax 4103713 – 🆎 🕦 🖃 𝖵𝖨𝖲𝖠   GX **s**
closed Monday January - October – **M** *(dinner only, booking essential)* a la carte 95/125
Spec. Seezunge in Blätterteig, Sylter Lammrücken mit Kräutern überbacken, Pfirsichtarte mit Mohneis.

✕✕ **La vite** (Italian rest.), Heimhuder Str. 5 (H 13), 🕿 45 84 01   GX **e**

✕✕ **Daitokai** (Japanese rest.), Milchstr. 1 (H 13), 🕿 4 10 10 61, Fax 4102296 – 🗐. 🆎 🕦 🖃 𝖵𝖨𝖲𝖠.
🍴   by Mittelweg GX
closed Sunday – **M** *(booking essential)* a la carte 48/73.

at Hamburg-Langenhorn N : 8 km by B 433 :

🏛 **Dorint-Hotel-Airport**, Langenhorner Chaussee 183 (H 62), 🕿 53 20 90, Fax 53209600, 🚅,
🖎 – |‡| 🌤 rm 🗐 🖺 🖕 ⟵⟶ – 🔥 25/100. 🆎 🕦 🖃 𝖵𝖨𝖲𝖠. 🍴 rest
M a la carte 42/76 – **147 rm** 200/420 Bb.

at Hamburg-Rotherbaum :

🏛 **Elysee** 🌤, Rothenbaumchaussee 10 (H 13), 🕿 41 41 20, Telex 212455, Fax 41412733, Massage, 🚅, 🖎 – |‡| 🌤 rm 🗐 🖺 🖕 ⟵⟶ – 🔥 25/500. 🆎 🕦 🖃 𝖵𝖨𝖲𝖠   FX **m**
Restaurants : **Piazza Romana M** a la carte 50/63 – **Brasserie M** a la carte 40/55 – **299 rm**
249/368 Bb.

🏛 **Vorbach** without rest, Johnsallee 63 (H 13), 🕿 44 18 20, Telex 213054, Fax 44182888 – |‡|
🖺 🕿 ⟵⟶. 🆎 🕦 🖃   FX **b**
106 rm 135/260.

✕✕ **Ventana** (European-Asiatic cooking), Grindelhof 77 (H 13), 🕿 45 65 88 – 🆎 🕦 🖃
closed Saturday lunch and Sunday – **M** *(booking essential for dinner)* a la carte 73/87.
                                                                          by Grindelallee FX

✕✕ ✿ **L'auberge française** (French rest.), Rutschbahn 34 (H 13), 🕿 4 10 25 32, Fax 4105857 –
🆎 🕦 🖃. 🍴   by Grindelallee FX
closed Saturday lunch, Sunday, 4 weeks June - July and 21 December - 7 January – **M** *(booking essential)* a la carte 56/85
Spec. Gebratene Gänsestopfleber in Trüffelsauce, Gegrillte Seezunge mit Schnittlauchcremesauce, Gratinierte Früchte mit Kirschwassercreme.

at Hamburg-St. Pauli :

✕✕ **Bavaria-Blick**, Bernhard-Nocht-Str. 99 (7th floor, |‡|) (H 36), 🕿 31 16 31 16, Fax 31163199,
≼ harbour – 🗐. 🆎 🕦 🖃 𝖵𝖨𝖲𝖠   by Seewartenstr.   EZ
M *(booking essential)* a la carte 45/86.

at Hamburg-Schnelsen by Grindelallee FX :

🏛 **Novotel-Nord**, Oldesloer Str. 166 (H 61), 🕿 5 50 20 73, Telex 212923, Fax 5592020, 🍴,
🏊 (heated) – |‡| 🖺 🕿 🖕 🅟 – 🔥 25/250. 🆎 🕦 🖃 𝖵𝖨𝖲𝖠. 🍴 rest
M a la carte 34/60 – **122 rm** 178/216 Bb.

at Hamburg-Stellingen by Grindelallee FX :

🏛 **Helgoland** without rest, Kieler Str. 177 (H 54), 🕿 85 70 01, Fax 8511445 – |‡| 🖺 🕿 ⟵⟶
🅟 – 🔥 25. 🆎 🕦 🖃 𝖵𝖨𝖲𝖠
110 rm 150/240 Bb.

at Hamburg-Stillhorn by Amsinckstr. HZ :

🏫 **Forte Hotel**, Stillhorner Weg 40 (H 93), ℰ 7 52 50, Telex 217940, Fax 7525444, 🖘, 🔲 – ▮❙ 🍴 rest 📺 ᎭᏏ 🅿 – 🔏 25/200. ፚፓ ⑩ ⴹ 𝘝𝘐𝘚𝘈, 🏶 rest
M a la carte 41/72 – **148 rm** 208/476 Bb.

at Hamburg-Uhlenhorst by An der Alster HX :

🏨 **Parkhotel Alster-Ruh** 🕙 without rest, Am Langenzug 6 (H 76), ℰ 22 45 77, Fax 2278966 – 📺 🕿 🚗. ፚፓ ⴹ
24 rm 130/325 Bb.

🏨 **Nippon** (Japanese installation and rest.), Hofweg 75 (H 76), ℰ 2 27 11 40, Telex 211081, Fax 22711490 – ▮❙ 📺 🕿 🚗. ፚፓ ⑩ ⴹ 𝘝𝘐𝘚𝘈. 🏶
M *(closed Monday)* (dinner only) a la carte 46/73 – **42 rm** 165/340 Bb.

XX **Ristorante Roma** (Italian rest.), Hofweg 7 (H 76), ℰ 2 20 25, 🏤 – ፚፓ ⑩ 𝘝𝘐𝘚𝘈
closed Saturday lunch and Monday **M** a la carte 55/73.

at Hamburg-Veddel by Amsinckstr. HZ :

🏨 **Carat-Hotel**, Sieldeich 9 (H 26), ℰ 78 96 60, Telex 2163354, Fax 786196, 🖘 – ▮❙ 🏶 rm 📺 🕿 🅿 – 🔏 25/40. ፚፓ ⑩ ⴹ 𝘝𝘐𝘚𝘈
M a la carte 38/63 – **91 rm** 160/230 Bb.

HANOVER (HANNOVER) 3000. 🔟 Niedersachsen 𝟦𝟢𝟣 𝟦𝟣𝟤 LM 9, 𝟫𝟪𝟩 ⑮ – pop. 510 000 – alt. 55 m – ✆ 0511.

See : Herrenhausen Gardens (Herrenhäuser Gärten)★★ (Großer Garten★★, Berggarten★) CV – Kestner-Museum★ DY **M1** – Market Church (Marktkirche) (Altarpiece★★) DY – Museum of Lower Saxony (Niedersächsisches Landesmuseum) (Prehistorical department★) EZ **M2** – Museum of Arts (Kunstmuseum) (Collection Sprengel★) EZ.

🏐 Garbsen, Am Blauen See (⑥ : 14 km), ℰ (05137) 7 30 68 ; 🏐 Isernhagen FB, Gut Lohne, ℰ (05139) 29 98.

🛬 Hanover-Langenhagen (① : 11 km), ℰ 7 30 51.

🚗 ℰ 1 28 54 52.

Exhibition Center (Messegelände) (by ② and B 6), ℰ 8 90, Telex 922728.

🛈 Tourist office, Ernst-August-Platz 8, ℰ 1 68 23 19, Fax 1685072.

ADAC, Hindenburgstr. 37, ℰ 8 50 00.

Berlin 288 ② (über Helmstedt) – Bremen 123 ① – Hamburg 151 ①.

Plan on following pages

🏩 **Kastens Hotel Luisenhof**, Luisenstr. 1, ℰ 3 04 40, Fax 3044807 – ▮❙ 🍴 rest 📺 🍴 🚗 🅿 – 🔏 25/160. ፚፓ ⑩ ⴹ 𝘝𝘐𝘚𝘈. 🏶 rest
EX **b**
M *(closed Sunday July - August)* a la carte 48/87 – **160 rm** 195/538 Bb – 5 suites 490/850.

🏩 **Inter-Continental**, Friedrichswall 11, ℰ 3 67 70, Telex 923656, Fax 325195 – ▮❙ 🏶 rm 🍴 rest 🍴 🚗 🅿. ፚፓ ⑩ ⴹ 𝘝𝘐𝘚𝘈
DY **a**
Restaurants : **L'Adresse** *(closed 15 July - 11 August)* **M** a la carte 62/92 – **Wilhelm-Busch-Stube**
M a la carte 26/42 – **285 rm** 280/600 Bb – 14 suites 910/1660.

🏩 **Maritim**, Hildesheimer Str. 34, ℰ 1 65 31, Telex 9230268, Fax 884846, 🖘, 🔲 – ▮❙ 🏶 rm 📺 🍴 🚗 🅿 – 🔏 25/400. ፚፓ ⑩ ⴹ 𝘝𝘐𝘚𝘈. 🏶 rest
EZ **b**
M a la carte 50/81 – **293 rm** 219/524 Bb.

🏩 ❀ **Schweizerhof Hannover - Schu's Restaurant**, Hinüberstr. 6, ℰ 3 49 50 (hotel) 3 49 52 52 (rest.), Telex 923359, Fax 3495123 – ▮❙ 🍴 rest 📺 🚗 – 🔏 25/250. ፚፓ ⑩ ⴹ 𝘝𝘐𝘚𝘈
EX **d**
M *(closed Saturday lunch and Sunday)* (remarkable wine list) a la carte 77/120 – **200 rm** 248/398 Bb – 3 suites 650
Spec. Terrine von Büsumer Krabben, Pot au feu vom Hummer, Geschmorte Heidschnucke (Saison).

🏫 **Grand Hotel Mussmann** without rest, Ernst-August-Platz 7, ℰ 32 79 71, Telex 922859, Fax 324325 – ▮❙ 📺 – 🔏 25/50. ፚፓ ⑩ ⴹ 𝘝𝘐𝘚𝘈
EX **v**
100 rm 168/498 Bb.

🏫 **Congress-Hotel am Stadtpark**, Clausewitzstr. 6, ℰ 2 80 50, Telex 921263, Fax 814652, 🏤, Massage, 🖘, 🔲 – ▮❙ 🏶 rm 📺 🅿 – 🔏 25/3000. ፚፓ ⑩ ⴹ 𝘝𝘐𝘚𝘈
by ②
M *(also diet menu)* a la carte 42/79 – **252 rm** 154/448 Bb – 4 suites 650/1200.

🏨 **Königshof** without rest, Königstr. 12, ℰ 31 20 71, Telex 922306, Fax 312079 – ▮❙ 📺 🕿 🚗 – 🔏 30. ፚፓ ⑩ ⴹ 𝘝𝘐𝘚𝘈
EX **c**
84 rm 178/470 Bb.

🏨 **Plaza**, Fernroder Str. 9, ℰ 3 38 80, Telex 921513, Fax 3388488, 🏤 – ▮❙ 🏶 rm 🍴 📺 🕿 – 🔏 25/200. ፚፓ ⑩ ⴹ 𝘝𝘐𝘚𝘈
EX **e**
M a la carte 39/65 – **102 rm** 168/396 Bb.

🏨 **Mercure**, Am Maschpark 3, ℰ 8 00 80, Telex 921575, Fax 8093704, 🖘 – ▮❙ 🏶 rm 🍴 rest 📺 🕿 🍴 🚗 – 🔏 25/230. ፚፓ ⑩ ⴹ 𝘝𝘐𝘚𝘈
EZ **n**
M a la carte 37/60 – **144 rm** 195/413 Bb.

🏨 **Central-Hotel Kaiserhof**, Ernst-August-Platz 4, ℘ 3 68 30, Telex 922810, Fax 3683114 – 🛗
📺 ☎ – 🛎 25/100   EX **a**
81 rm.

🏨 **Am Funkturm - Ristorante Milano**, Hallerstr. 34, ℘ 3 39 80 (hotel) 33 23 09 (rest.),
Telex 922263, Fax 3398111 – 🛗 📺 ☎ 🅟   EV **s**
accommodation closed mid July - mid August – **M** a la carte 31/58 – **45 rm** 98/296 Bb.

🏨 **Intercity-Hotel**, Ernst-August-Platz 1, ℘ 32 74 61, Telex 921171, Fax 324119 – 🛗 ▤ rest
📺 ☎ – 🛎 25/100. 🆎 ⓞ 🗲 𝘷𝘪𝘴𝘢   EX **r**
M a la carte 23/54 – **57 rm** 105/290 Bb.

🏨 **Am Leineschloß** without rest, Am Markte 12, ℘ 32 71 45, Telex 922010, Fax 325502 – 🛗
↝ 📺 ☎ ⇦. 🆎 ⓞ 🗲 𝘷𝘪𝘴𝘢   DY **z**
81 rm 177/349 Bb.

🏨 **Loccumer Hof**, Kurt-Schumacher-Str. 16, ℘ 1 26 40, Fax 131192 – 🛗 📺 ☎ ⇦
🛎 25/50. 🆎 ⓞ 🗲 𝘷𝘪𝘴𝘢   DX **s**
M a la carte 36/68 – **75 rm** 125/200 Bb.

🏨 **Körner**, Körnerstr. 24, ℘ 1 63 60, Telex 921313, Fax 18048, �഻, 🔲 – 🛗 📺 ☎ ⇦
🛎 25/60. 🆎 ⓞ 🗲 𝘷𝘪𝘴𝘢   DX **e**
M (closed Christmas - New Year) a la carte 42/57 – **81 rm** 138/196 Bb.

🏨 **Am Rathaus**, Friedrichswall 21, ℘ 32 62 68, Fax 328868, ⇌ – 🛗 📺 ☎. ⓞ 🗲
𝘷𝘪𝘴𝘢   EY **y**
M (closed Saturday and Sunday) a la carte 33/61 – **47 rm** 125/340 Bb.

🏨 **Vahrenwalder Hotel 181** without rest, Vahrenwalder Str. 181, ℘ 35 80 60, Fax 3505250,
⇌ – 🛗 📺 ☎ 🅟. ⓞ 🗲 𝘷𝘪𝘴𝘢   by ①
34 rm 110/180 Bb.

🏨 **Vahrenwald**, Vahrenwalder Str. 205, ℘ 63 30 77, Telex 923713, Fax 673163 – 🛗 📺 ☎
🅟   by ①
26 rm Bb.

🏨 **Thüringer Hof** without rest, Osterstr. 37, ℘ 32 64 37, Telex 923994, Fax 3681793 – 🛗 📺
☎. ⓞ 🗲 𝘷𝘪𝘴𝘢   EY **e**
closed 23 December - 2 January – **52 rm** 98/250 Bb.

🏨 **Atlanta** without rest, Hinüberstr. 1, ℘ 34 29 39, Telex 924603, Fax 345928 – 🛗 📺 ☎ ⇦.
🗲 𝘷𝘪𝘴𝘢   EX **t**
closed 20 December - 3 January – **38 rm** 120/260 Bb.

🏨 **Alpha - Tirol** without rest, Lange Laube 20, ℘ 13 10 66, Fax 341535 – 📺 ☎ ⇦ DX **f**
15 rm 118/170.

XXXX ⊛ **Landhaus Ammann** with rm, Hildesheimer Str. 185, ℘ 83 08 18, Fax 8437749, « Elegant
installation, patio with terrace », �഻ – 🛗 📺 ✄ ⇦ 🅟 – 🛎 25/100. 🆎 ⓞ 🗲 𝘷𝘪𝘴𝘢.
⇻ rest   by ③
M (remarkable wine-list) 110/160 and a la carte 75/115 – **14 rm** 235/530 Bb.
Spec. Kohlrabiflan mit gebackenem Kalbsbries, Langustinen und Hummer mit Tomatenschaum,
Reh- und Wildschweingerichte.

XXX **Lila Kranz**, Kirchwender Str. 23, ℘ 85 89 21, Fax 854383, �഻ – ⓞ 🗲 𝘷𝘪𝘴𝘢   FX **b**
closed Saturday and Sunday lunch – **M** a la carte 68/93.

XXX ⊛ **Romantik Hotel Georgenhof - Stern's Restaurant** 🍃 with rm, Herrenhäuser
Kirchweg 20, ℘ 70 22 44, Fax 708559, « Lower Saxony country house in a park, terrace »
– 📺 ☎ 🅟. 🆎 ⓞ 🗲 𝘷𝘪𝘴𝘢   by Engelbosteler Damm CV
M (also vegetarian Menu) (remarkable wine list) a la carte 75/120 – **14 rm** 140/360 Bb.
Spec. Hausgemachte Nudeln mit Pilzen, Steinbutt in Champagner, Heidschnucken-Rücken (Sai-
son).

XXX **Bakkarat im Casino am Maschsee**, Arthur-Menge-Ufer 3 (1st floor), ℘ 88 40 57,
Fax 885733, ◁, – 🆎 ⓞ 🗲 𝘷𝘪𝘴𝘢   DZ **a**
closed Sunday and 15 February - 1 March – **M** (dinner only) a la carte 68/90.

XXX **Mövenpick - Baron de la Mouette**, Georgenstr. 35 (1st floor), ℘ 32 62 85, Fax 323160 –
▤   EX **x**

XX **Gattopardo** (Italian rest.), Hainhölzer Str. 1 (Am Klagesmarkt), ℘ 1 43 75, Fax 318283 –
🆎   DV **f**
M (dinner only) a la carte 39/56.

XX **Clichy**, Weißekreuzstr. 31, ℘ 31 24 47, Fax 318283 – 🆎   EV **d**
closed Saturday lunch, Sunday and 3 weeks June - July – **M** a la carte 68/96.

XX **Das Körbchen**, Körnerstr. 3, ℘ 1 31 82 96 – 🗲. ⇻   DX **a**
closed Saturday lunch, Sunday and Bank Holidays – **M** 68/105.

XX **Ratskeller**, Köbelinger Str. 60 (entrance Schmiedestraße), ℘ 36 36 44   DY **n**

X **Rôtisserie Helvetia**, Georgsplatz 11, ℘ 30 10 00, Fax 3010046, 🌻 – ⓞ 🗲
𝘷𝘪𝘴𝘢   EY **k**
M a la carte 26/55.

X **Mandarin-Pavillon** (Chinese rest.), Marktstr. 45 (Passage), ℘ 30 66 30 – 🆎 ⓞ 🗲
𝘷𝘪𝘴𝘢   DY **x**
M (also vegetarian dishes) a la carte 30/58.

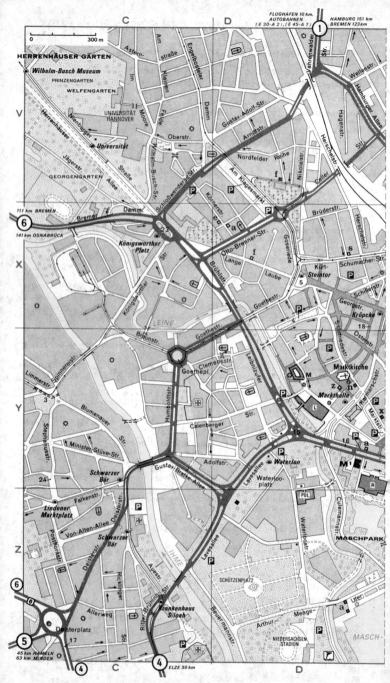

HERRENHÄUSER GÄRTEN

Wilhelm-Busch Museum
PRINZENGARTEN
WELFENGARTEN

UNIVERSITÄT
HANNOVER

Universität

GEORGENGARTEN

FLUGHAFEN 10 km.
AUTOBAHNEN
(E 30-A 2), (E 45-A 7)

HAMBURG 151 km
BREMEN 123 km

111 km BREMEN
141 km OSNABRÜCK

Königsworther Platz

LEINE

Schwarzer Bär

Lindener Marktplatz

Schwarzer Bär

45 km HAMELN
63 km MINDEN

ELZE 30 km

Deisterplatz

Krankenhaus Siloah

SCHÜTZENPLATZ

NIEDERSACHSEN STADION

IHME

Kröpcke

Marktkirche

Markthalle

Waterloo

Waterlooplatz

MASCHPARK

MASCH-

256

HANNOVER

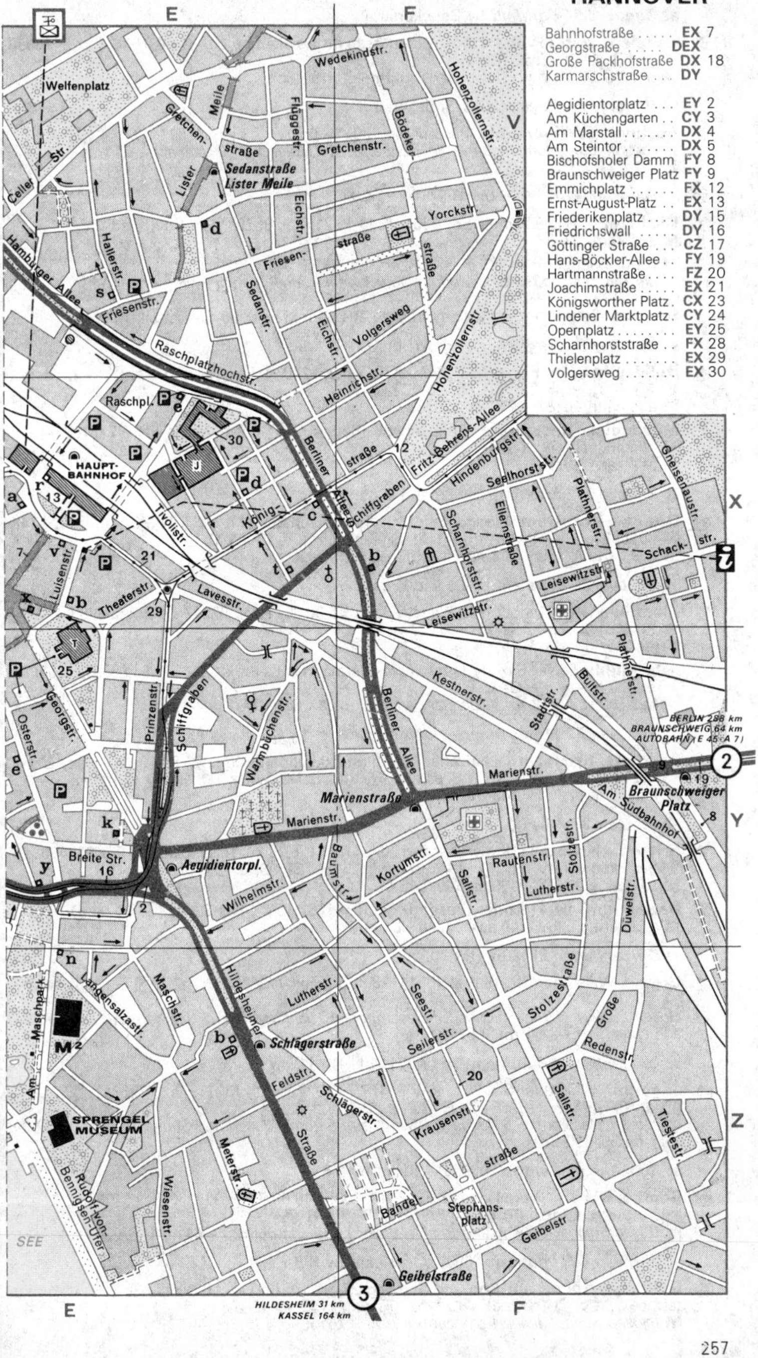

E
F
V
X
Y
Z
Welfenplatz
Celler Str.
Hamburger Allee
Gretchenstraße
Meile
Wedekindstr.
Flüggestr.
Gretchenstr.
Bödekerstraße
Hohenzollernstr.
Sedanstraße Lister Meile
Lister Meile
Eichstr.
Yorckstr.
Friesenstraße
Hallerstr.
Friesenstr.
Sedanstr.
Volgersweg
Raschplatzhochstr.
Heinrichstr.
Raschpl.
HAUPT-BAHNHOF
Berliner Allee
Fritz-Behrens-Allee
Hindenburgstr.
Seelhorststr.
Gneisenaustr.
Schiffgraben
Scharnhorststr.
Ellernstraße
Plathnerstr.
Schackstr.
Tivolistr.
Königstr.
Luisenstr.
Theaterstr.
Lavesstr.
Leisewitzstr.
Kestnerstr.
Bultstr.
Stadtstr.
Georgstr.
Osterstr.
Prinzenstr.
Warmbüchenstr.
BERLIN 288 km
BRAUNSCHWEIG 64 km
AUTOBAHN (E 45-A 7)
Marienstr.
Braunschweiger Platz
Am Südbahnhof
Marienstraße
Breite Str.
Aegidientorpl.
Baumstr.
Kortumstr.
Rautenstr.
Stolzestr.
Sallstr.
Lutherstr.
Düwelstr.
Wilhelmstr.
Langensalzastr.
Maschpark
Maschstr.
Hildesheimer Straße
Lutherstr.
Seestr.
Stolzestraße
Große Redenstr.
Schlägerstraße
Seilerstr.
Am Maschpark
SPRENGEL MUSEUM
Feldstr.
Schlägerstr.
Krausenstr.
Sallstr.
Tiestestr.
Meterstr.
Wiesenstr.
Rudolf-von-Bennigsen-Ufer
Bandelstraße
Stephansplatz
Geibelstr.
SEE
Geibelstraße
HILDESHEIM 31 km
KASSEL 164 km

at Hanover 51-Bothfeld by Bödekerstr. FV :

🏠 **Residenz Hotel Halberstadt** without rest, Im Heidkampe 80, ℰ 64 01 18, Fax 6478988, ☞ – 📺 🅿. ⅋Ⅎ 𝖵𝖨𝖲𝖠
closed 20 December - 3 January – **40 rm** 100/190 Bb.

at Hanover 51-Buchholz by Bödekerstr. FV :

XX **Buchholzer Windmühle**, Pasteurallee 30, ℰ 64 91 38, Fax 6478930, ☞ – 🅿. ⅋
closed Sunday, Monday, Bank Holidays and 22 December - 5 January – **M** a la carte 42/75.

at Hanover 81-Döhren by ③ :

XXX **Wichmann**, Hildesheimer Str. 230, ℰ 83 16 71, Fax 8379811, « Courtyard » – **M** a la carte 63/97.

XX ⚙ **Etoile**, Wiehbergstr. 98, ℰ 83 55 24 – ⅋Ⅎ ⓞ Ⅎ 𝖵𝖨𝖲𝖠
dinner only, closed Sunday, Monday and 3 weeks July - August – **M** *(booking essential)* a la carte 57/93
Spec. Rote Bete-Apfel-Suppe, Lammrücken aus dem Kräutersud, Dessertteller.

at Hanover 42-Flughafen (Airport) by ① : 11 km :

🏨 **Holiday Inn**, Am Flughafen, ℰ 7 70 70, Telex 924030, Fax 737781, ⇌s, 🔲 – 📳 ⇔ rm 📺 ⴞ 🅿 – 🍽 25/180. ⅋Ⅎ ⓞ Ⅎ 𝖵𝖨𝖲𝖠
M a la carte 46/87 – **210 rm** 320/500 Bb.

X **Mövenpick- Restaurant**, Abflugebene (departure), ℰ 9 77 25 09, Fax 9772709 – ▤ – 🍽 25/400. ⅋Ⅎ ⓞ Ⅎ 𝖵𝖨𝖲𝖠
M a la carte 30/56.

at Hanover 71-Kirchrode by ② and B 65 :

🏨 **Queens Hotel am Tiergarten** 🌲, Tiergartenstr. 117, ℰ 5 10 30, Telex 922748, Fax 526924, ☞ – 📳 ⇔ rm 📺 ⴞ 🅿 – 🍽 25/200. ⅋Ⅎ ⓞ Ⅎ 𝖵𝖨𝖲𝖠
M a la carte 42/65 – **108 rm** 230/450 Bb – 3 suites.

at Hanover 61-Kleefeld by ② and B 65 :

🏨 **Kleefelder Hof** without rest, Kleestr. 3a, ℰ 5 30 80, Telex 922474, Fax 5308333 – 📳 📺 ⴞ ⴞ ⇦ 🅿. ⅋Ⅎ ⓞ Ⅎ 𝖵𝖨𝖲𝖠
90 rm 165/450 Bb.

XX **Alte Mühle** (lower Saxony farmhouse), Hermann-Löns-Park 3, ℰ 55 94 80, Fax 552680, « Terrace » – ⴞ 🅿. ⅋Ⅎ Ⅎ
closed Thursday, 12 to 30 January and 13 to 30 July – **M** a la carte 50/79.

at Hanover 72-Messe (near exhibition Centre) by ② :

🏨 **Parkhotel Kronsberg**, Laatzner Str. 18 (at Exhibition Centre), ℰ 86 10 86, Telex 923448, Fax 867112, ☞, ⇌s, 🔲 – 📳 ▤ rest 📺 ⇦ 🅿 – 🍽 25/200. ⅋Ⅎ ⓞ Ⅎ 𝖵𝖨𝖲𝖠
M a la carte 38/70 – **145 rm** 140/330 Bb.

at Laatzen 3014 by ③ : 9 km :

🏨 **Britannia Hannover**, Karlsruher Str. 26, ℰ (0511) 8 78 20, Telex 9230392, Fax 863466, ⇌s ⅋ (covered court) – 📳 📺 ⴞ ⴞ 🅿 – 🍽 25/80. ⅋Ⅎ ⓞ Ⅎ 𝖵𝖨𝖲𝖠
M a la carte 41/75 – **100 rm** 145/545 Bb.

🏠 **Haase**, Am Thie 4 (district Grasdorf), ℰ (0511) 82 10 41, Fax 828079 – 📺 ⴞ 🅿
M a la carte 33/50 – **40 rm** 95/240 Bb.

at Langenhagen 3012 by ① : 10 km :

🏨 **Grethe**, Walsroder Str. 151, ℰ (0511) 73 80 11, Fax 772418, ☞, ⇌s, 🔲 – 📳 📺 ⴞ 🅿 – 🍽 25/40. ⅋Ⅎ Ⅎ
closed 28 July - 18 August and 22 December - 10 January – **M** *(closed Saturday and Sunday)* a la carte 33/57 – **51 rm** 105/170 Bb.

at Langenhagen 6-Krähenwinkel 3012 by ① : 11 km :

🏨 **Jägerhof**, Walsroder Str. 251, ℰ (0511) 7 79 60, Telex 9218211, Fax 7796111, ☞, ⇌s – 📺 ⴞ 🅿 – 🍽 25/70. ⅋Ⅎ ⓞ Ⅎ 𝖵𝖨𝖲𝖠
closed 21 December - 4 January – **M** *(closed Saturday lunch and Sunday)* a la carte 42/69 – **77 rm** 90/200 Bb.

at Ronnenberg-Benthe 3003 ⑤ : 10 km by B 65 :

🏨 **Benther Berg** 🌲, Vogelsangstr. 18, ℰ (05108) 6 40 60, Telex 922253, Fax 640650, ☞, ⇌s, 🔲, ☞ – 📳 ▤ rest 📺 🅿 – 🍽 25/60. ⅋Ⅎ ⓞ Ⅎ 𝖵𝖨𝖲𝖠. ⅋
M *(Closed dinner Sunday and Bank Holidays)* a la carte 65/95 – **64 rm** 116/220 Bb.

at Garbsen 4-Berenbostel 3008 ⑥ : 13 km by B 6 :

🏨 **Landhaus Köhne am See** 🌲, Seeweg 27, ℰ (05131) 9 10 85, Fax 8367, ≤, « Garden terrace », ⇌s, 🔲 (heated), ☞, ⅋ – 📺 ⴞ 🅿. ⅋Ⅎ ⓞ Ⅎ 𝖵𝖨𝖲𝖠
M *(closed Sunday dinner)* a la carte 41/65 – **26 rm** 95/195 Bb.

See : Old Town Hall★ (Altes Rathaus) BY – Old Stock Exchange★ (Naschmarkt) BY – Museum of Fine Arts★ (Museum der Bildenden Künste) BZ.

✈ Leipzig-Schkeuditz (NW : 15 km), ✆ 39 13 65, Sachsenplatz 1, ✆ 28 62 46, BY.

Exhibition Grounds (Messegelände), Universitätsstr. 5 (Information Centre), ✆ 29 53 36. Messeamt (Fair Office), Markt 11, ✆ 7 18 10, Telex 512294, Fax 7181575.

🛈 Leipzig-Information, Sachsenplatz 1, ✆ 7 95 90, Fax 281854.

ADAC, Georg-Schumann-Str. 134, ✉ O-7022, ✆ 41 58 42 81.

Berlin 165 – Dresden 109 – Erfurt 126.

Plan on following pages

🏨🏨 **Merkur**, Gerberstr. 15, ✆ 79 90, Telex 512609, Fax 7991229, 🍴, Massage, ⇔, 🖥 – 🛗 🖬 📺 ⇔ ❷ – 🔬 30/350. 🖭 ① Ε 💳   BY **a**
M a la carte 38/82 – **440 rm** 265/420 Bb – 16 suites 600/900.

🏨 **Astoria**, Am Hauptbahnhof 2, ✆ 7 22 20, Telex 51535, Fax 7224747, Massage, ⇔ – 🛗 🖩 rest 📺 – 🔬 30/100. 🖭 ① Ε 💳   CY **b**
M a la carte 43/76 – **314 rm** 195/395 Bb – 5 suites 490.

🏨 **Gästehaus am Park**, Schwägrichstr. 14, ✆ 3 93 90, Telex 512301, Fax 326098, 🍴, « Park » – 🛗 📺 🕭 ⇔ ❷ – 🔬 30/120. 🖭 Ε 💳   by Wächterstraße AZ
M (closed Sunday) a la carte 25/59 – **35 rm** 250/350 Bb – 5 suites 550.

🏨 **Deutschland**, Augustusplatz 5, ✆ 7 95 20, Telex 51559, Fax 289165 – 🛗 📺 ☎ – 🔬 40. 🎇 rest   CZ **f**
275 rm – 10 suites.

🏨 **Stadt Leipzig**, Richard-Wagner-Str. 1, ✆ 28 88 14, Telex 51426, Fax 284037, ⇔ – 🛗 📺 ☎ ❷ – 🔬 25/120   CY **d**
348 rm Bb.

🏨 **Zum Löwen**, Rudolf-Breitscheid-Str. 1, ✆ 7 22 30 – 🛗 🖩 rest 📺 ☎   CY **g**
(dinner only) – **110 rm** Bb.

🏨 **Continental**, Georgiring 13, ✆ 75 66 – 🛗 ☎   CY **e**
52 rm Bb.

XX **Auerbachs Keller** (16 C. wine tavern), Grimmaische Str. 2, ✆ 20 91 31, Fax 281990 – 🖭 Ε 💳   BYZ
M a la carte 29/60.

XX **Falstaff**, Georgiring 9, ✆ 28 64 03   CY **m**
closed Sunday dinner – **M** a la carte 26/42.

XX **Plovdiv** (Bulgarian rest.), Katharinenstr. 17, ✆ 20 92 27, Fax 291767 – 🖭 Ε   BY **p**
M (also vegetarian dishes) a la carte 41/65.

XX **Apels Garten** Kolonnadenstr. 2, ✆ 28 50 93, 🍴 – 🖭 Ε 💳   AZ **q**
closed Saturday lunch, Sunday dinner and 23 July - 5 August – **M** a la carte 24/43.

X Ratskeller, Lotter Str. 1 (Neues Rathaus), ✆ 7 91 35 91   BZ **n**

X **Thüringer Hof**, Burgstr. 19, ✆ 20 98 84   BZ **r**
closed Friday – **M** a la carte 19/44.

X Kaffeebaum (15 C. citizen house), Kleine Fleischergasse 4, ✆ 20 04 52   BY **s**

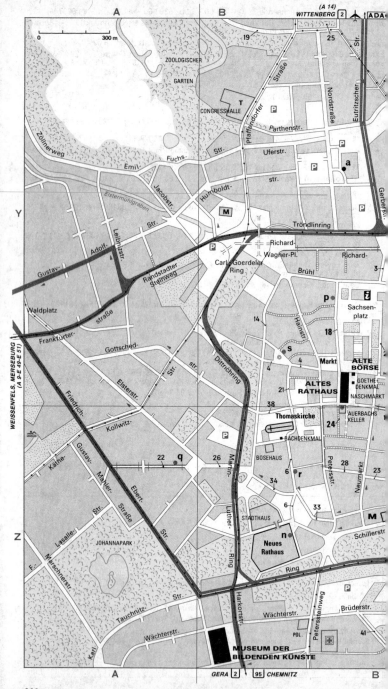

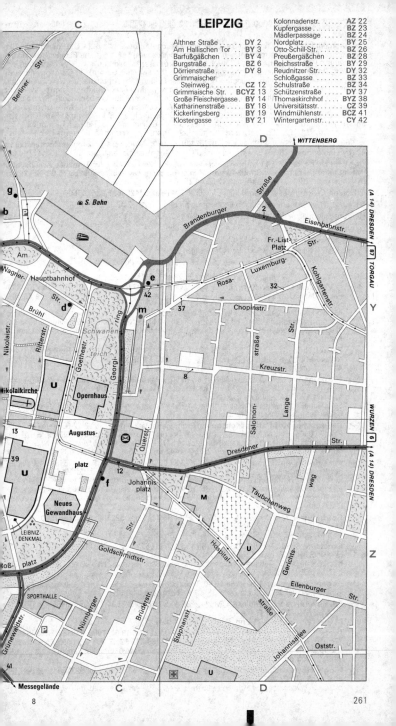

LEIPZIG

C

D

WITTENBERG

Berliner Str.

g

b

P

S. Bahn

Am

Wagner-

Hauptbahnhof

Str.

Brühl

d

Nikolaistr.

Ritterstr.

Goethestr.

Georgi-

ring

Schwanen teich

Brandenburger

Straße

2

Eisenbahnstr.

Fr.-List-Platz

Str.

(A 14) DRESDEN | 87 | TORGAU

Luxemburg-

Rosa-

42

e

m

37

Chopinstr.

32

Kohlgartenstr.

Str.

Y

Nikolaikirche

U

Opernhaus

straße

Kreuzstr.

Lange

WURZEN | 6 | (A 14) DRESDEN

13

39

U

Augustus-

platz

f

8

Salomon-

Dresdener

Str.

12

Johannis-platz

Neues Gewandhaus

Str.

M

Täubchenweg

weg

LEIBNIZ-DENKMAL

oß- platz

Goldschmidtstr.

Hospital-

U

Gerichts-

Z

SPORTHALLE

P

Grünewaldstr.

Nürnberger

Brüderstr.

Stephanstr.

Straße

Eilenburger

Str.

Oststr.

Johannisallee

41

Messegelände

U

C

D

8

261

Querstr.

MUNICH (MÜNCHEN) 8000. ⓘ Bayern ⁤⁤⁤ R 22, ⁤⁤⁤ ㊲, ⁤⁤⁤ G 4 – pop. 1 300 000 – alt. 520 m – ✪ 089.

See : Marienplatz★ KZ – Church of Our Lady (Frauenkirche)★ (tower ✳★) KZ – Old Pinakothek (Alte Pinakothek)★★★ KY – German Museum (Deutsches Museum)★★★ LZ – The Palace (Residenz)★ (Treasury★★ Palace Theatre★) KY – Church of Asam Brothers (Asamkirche)★ KZ – Nymphenburg★★ (Castle★, Park★, Amalienburg★★, Botanical Garden (Botanischer Garten)★★, Carriage Museum (Marstallmuseum) and China-Collection (Porzellansammlung★) by Arnulfstr. EV – New Pinakothek (Neue Pinakothek)★ KY – City Historical Museum (Münchener Stadtmuseum)★ (Moorish Dancers★★) KZ M7 – Villa Lenbach Collections (Städt. Galerie im Lenbachhaus) (Portraits by Lenbach★) JY M4 – Antique Collections (Staatliche Antikensammlungen)★ JY M3 – Glyptothek★ JY M2 – German Hunting Museum (Deutsches Jagdmuseum)★ KZ M1 – Olympic Park (Olympia-Park) (Olympic Tower ✳ ★★★) by Schleißheimer Str. FU – Hellabrunn Zoo (Tierpark Hellabrunn)★ by Lindwurmstr. (B 11) EX – English garden (Englischer Garten)★ (view from Monopteros Temple ★) LY.

🏌 Straßlach, Tölzer Straße (S : 17 km), ℰ (08170) 4 50 ; 🏌 München-Thalkirchen, Zentralländstr. 40 (by Lindwurmstr. (B 11) EX ; 🏌 Eichenried (NE : 24 km), Münchener Str. 55, ℰ (08123) 10 05.

✈ München-Riem (E : 11 km) by Einsteinstr. HX, ℰ 92 11 21, City Air Terminal, Arnulfstraße (Main Station) - Franz-Josef-Strauß-Airport Munich opening May 1992 ℰ (089) 9 75 00, NE 29 km by Ungererstr. (B 11) HU. – 🚗 ℰ 12 88 44 25.

Exhibition Centre (Messegelände) (EX), ℰ 5 10 70, Telex 5212086, Fax 5107506.

🛈 Tourist office in the Main Station, (opposite plattform 11), ℰ 2 39 12 56.

🛈 Tourist-Information, Pettenbeckstr. 3, ℰ 2 39 12 72, Fax 2391313.

🛈 Tourist-office, airport München-Riem, ℰ 2 39 12 66.

ADAC, Sendlinger-Tor-Platz 9, ℰ 59 39 79.

Innsbruck 162 – Nürnberg 165 – Salzburg 140 – Stuttgart 222.

The reference (M 15) at the end of the address is the postal district : Munich 15

Plans on following pages

🏨🏨🏨 ❀ **Vier Jahreszeiten Kempinski** 🦢, Maximilianstr. 17 (M 22), ℰ 23 03 90, Telex 523859, Fax 23039693, Massage, ⇌s, 🔲 – 🛗 ⇅ rm 🖿 🔟 🚗 – 🔬 25/350. 🖭 ⓞ 🗈 🖾. ✻ rest   LZ **a**
M *(Monday and Saturday dinner only, closed August)* 95/135 and a la carte 66/105 – **Bistro Eck** (also vegetarian dishes) **M** a la carte 46/74 – **344 rm** 362/684 Bb – 9 suites 1279/2806
Spec. Salat von Meeresfrüchten und Krustentieren, Entenbrust in der Salzkruste, Lammsattel im Kräutersud.

🏨🏨🏨 **Rafael**, Neuturmstr. 1 (M 2), ℰ 29 09 80, Telex 5213666, Fax 222539, « Roof garden with terrace and 🔳 » – 🛗 🔟 🚗 – 🔬 25/60. 🖭 ⓞ 🗈 🖾. ✻ rest   KZ **s**
M 45 (lunch) and a la carte 67/107 – **74 rm** 380/680 – 7 suites 1400/2000.

🏨🏨🏨 ❀ **Königshof**, Karlsplatz 25 (M 2), ℰ 55 13 60, Telex 523616, Fax 55136113 – 🛗 🗐 🔟 🚗 – 🔬 30/90. 🖭 ⓞ 🗈 🖾. ✻ rest – **M** (booking essential, remarkable wine list) 108/138 and a la carte 73/112 – **106 rm** 275/415 Bb. – 9 suites 540/1000   JY **s**
Spec. Gänseleberterrine mit Rosinenbrioche, Petersfisch gebraten mit Orangen-Basilikumsauce, Rinderfilet in schwarzer Trüffelsauce.

🏨🏨🏨 **Bayerischer Hof-Palais Montgelas**, Promenadeplatz 6 (M 2), ℰ 2 12 00, Telex 523409, Fax 2120906, 🔐, Massage, ⇌s, 🔲 – 🛗 ⇅ rm 🔟 🚗 – 🔬 25/800. 🖭 ⓞ 🗈 🖾
Restaurants : **Garden-Restaurant M** a la carte 54/84 – **Trader Vic's** *(dinner only)* **M** a la carte 46/77 – **Palais Keller M** a la carte 28/50 – **442 rm** 265/519 – 40 suites 699/1549.   KY **y**

🏨🏨🏨 **Park Hilton**, Am Tucherpark 7 (M 22), ℰ 3 84 50, Telex 5215740, Fax 38451845, 🔐, beer-garden, Massage, ⇌s, 🔲 – 🛗 ⇅ rm 🖿 🔟 🖢 🚗 – 🔬 25/250. 🖭 ⓞ 🗈 🖾 HU **n**
Restaurants : **Hilton-Grill** (also vegetarian dishes) *(closed Saturday lunch, 1 week January and 3 weeks July - August)* **M** a la carte 66/103 – **Tse Yang** (Chinese rest.) **M** a la carte 45/76 – **Isar-Terrassen** (also vegetarian dishes) **M** a la carte 36/58 – **477 rm** 309/553 – 21 suites 858/1658.

🏨🏨🏨 **Continental**, Max-Joseph-Str. 5 (M 2), ℰ 55 15 70, Telex 522603, Fax 55157500, 🔐 – 🛗 ⇅ rm 🔟 🚗 – 🔬 25/160. 🖭 ⓞ 🗈 🖾. ✻ rest   KY **f**
M a la carte 62/94 – **149 rm** 282/564 Bb – 12 suites 710/1270.

🏨🏨🏨 **Excelsior**, Schützenstr. 11 (M 2), ℰ 55 13 70, Telex 522419, Fax 55137121 – 🛗 🔟 – 🔬 30. 🖭 ⓞ 🗈 🖾. ✻ rest   JY **z**
M a la carte 51/90 – **Vinothek** *(closed Sunday and Bank Holidays)* **M** a la carte 36/77 – **114 rm** 223/341 Bb – 4 suites 396/426.

🏨🏨 **Regent**, Seidlstr. 2 (M 2), ℰ 55 15 90, Telex 523787, Fax 55159154, ⇌s – 🛗 🗐 rest 🔟 🚗 – 🔬 25/70. 🖭 🗈 – **M** a la carte 38/69 – **183 rm** 205/400 Bb.   JY **d**

🏨🏨 **Eden-Hotel-Wolff**, Arnulfstr. 4 (M 2), ℰ 55 11 50, Telex 523564, Fax 55115555 – 🛗 🔟 🚗 – 🔬 25/250. 🖭 ⓞ 🗈 🖾   JY **p**
M a la carte 33/66 – **214 rm** 165/370 Bb – 4 suites 550.

🏨🏨 **Arabella-Westpark-Hotel**, Garmischer Str. 2 (M 2), ℰ 5 19 60, Telex 523680, Fax 5196649, ⇌s, 🔲 – 🛗 ⇅ rm 🗐 rest 🔟 🖢 🚗 – 🔬 25/80. 🖭 ⓞ 🗈 🖾 by Leopoldstr. GU
closed 21 December - 5 January – **M** *(also vegetarian dishes)* 35 buffet (lunch) and a la carte 44/67 – **258 rm** 215/380 Bb – 5 suites 380/440.

🏨🏨 **King's Hotel** without rest, Dachauer Str. 13 (M 2), ℰ 55 18 70, Fax 5232667 – 🛗 ⇅ 🔟 🚗 – 🔬 30. 🖭 ⓞ 🗈 🖾   JY **f**
closed 20 December - 4 January – **85 rm** 180/220 Bb – 8 suites 320/540.

🏨🏨 **Drei Löwen**, Schillerstr. 8 (M 2), ℰ 55 10 40, Telex 523867, Fax 55104905 – 🛗 ✻ rm 📺
⇔ 🅿 – 🔏 35. 🅰🅴 ① 🅴 𝑽𝑰𝑺𝑨 – **M** a la carte 39/67 – **130 rm** 165/238 Bb. JZ **m**

🏨🏨 **Trustee Parkhotel**, Parkstr. 31 (approach Gollierstraße) (M 2), ℰ 51 99 50, Telex 5218296,
Fax 51995420 – 🛗 📺 ⇔ – 🔏 25. 🅰🅴 ① 🅴 𝑽𝑰𝑺𝑨 EX **r**
closed 24 December - 2 January – (dinner only, residents only) – **36 rm** 211/372 Bb – 7 suites.

🏨🏨 **Exquisit** without rest, Pettenkoferstr. 3 (M 2), ℰ 5 51 99 00, Telex 529863, Fax 55199499,
⇔ – 🛗 📺 ⅃ ⇔ – 🔏 25. 🅰🅴 ① 🅴 𝑽𝑰𝑺𝑨 – **50 rm** 180/260 Bb – 5 suites 340. JZ **s**

🏨 **Krone** ☎. 🅰🅴 ① 🅴 𝑽𝑰𝑺𝑨 **Theresienhöhe 8 (M 2), ℰ 50 40 52, Telex 5213870, Fax 506706 – 🛗
☎. 🅰🅴 ① 🅴 𝑽𝑰𝑺𝑨 – **30 rm** 170/280 Bb. EX **a**

🏨 **Platzl-Restaurant Pfistermühle**, Platzl 1 (Entrance Sparkassenstraße) (M 2), ℰ 23 70 30,
Telex 522910, Fax 23703800, ⇔ – 🛗 ✻ rm 📺 ☎ ⅃ ⇔ – 🔏 25/120. 🅰🅴 ① 🅴 𝑽𝑰𝑺𝑨 ❀ rest
M (closed Sunday and mid July - mid August) 35 (lunch) and a la carte 46/68 – **167 rm**
188/375 Bb. KZ **z**

🏨 **Arabella-Central-Hotel** without rest, Schwanthalerstr. 111 (M 2), ℰ 51 08 30,
Telex 5216031, Fax 51083249, ⇔ – 🛗 📺 ⇔ – 🔏 30. 🅰🅴 ① 🅴 𝑽𝑰𝑺𝑨 EX **x**
closed 21 December - 7 January - **103 rm** 170/375 Bb.

🏨 **Erzgießerei-Europe**, Erzgießereistr. 15 (M 2), ℰ 1 26 82, Telex 5214977, Fax 1236198 –
🛗 📺 ☎ ⇔ – 🔏 70. 🅰🅴 📺 ☎ 🅴 𝑽𝑰𝑺𝑨 JY **a**
M a la carte 39/61 – **106 rm** 160/260 Bb.

🏨 **Mercure** without rest, Senefelder Str. 9 (M 2), ℰ 55 13 20, Telex 5218428, Fax 596444 – 🛗
📺 ☎ ⅃ ⇔ – 🔏 25/80 – **167 rm** JZ **r**

🏨 **Hungar-Hotel**, Paul-Heyse-Str. 24 (M 2), ℰ 51 49 00, Telex 522395, Fax 51490701, ⇌
🛗 📺 ☎ ⅃ ⇔ – 🔏 25/90. 🅰🅴 ① 🅴 𝑽𝑰𝑺𝑨 JZ **c**
M a la carte 44/55 – **182 rm** 170/395 Bb.

🏨 **Budapest**, Schwanthalerstr. 36 (M 2), ℰ 55 11 10, Telex 529213, Fax 55111992 – 🛗 ▤ rest
📺 ☎ ⇔ – 🔏 25/150. 🅰🅴 ① 🅴 𝑽𝑰𝑺𝑨 JZ **h**
M (closed Sunday, July and August) a la carte 35/55 – **100 rm** 170/395 Bb.

🏨 **Germania**, Schwanthalerstr. 28 (M 2), ℰ 5 16 80, Telex 523790, Fax 598491, ⇔ – 🛗 ✻ rm
📺 ☎ – 🔏 40. 🅰🅴 ① 🅴 𝑽𝑰𝑺𝑨 JZ **z**
M (closed Sunday) a la carte 34/65 – **100 rm** 205/355 Bb.

🏨 **Metropol**, Bayerstr. 43, (Entrance Goethestr.) (M 2), ℰ 53 07 64, Telex 522816,
Fax 5328134 – 🛗 📺 ☎ – 🔏 25/60. 🅰🅴 ① 🅴 𝑽𝑰𝑺𝑨 JZ **k**
M a la carte 29/65 – **275 rm** 115/210.

🏨 **Concorde** without rest, Herrnstr. 38 (M 22), ℰ 22 45 15, Telex 522002, Fax 2283282 – 🛗
📺 ☎. 🅰🅴 ① 🅴 𝑽𝑰𝑺𝑨 – closed 23 December - 1 January – **73 rm** 170/360 Bb. LZ **q**

🏨 **Domus** without rest, St.-Anna-Str. 31 (M 22), ℰ 22 17 04, Telex 529835, Fax 2285359 – 🛗
📺 ☎. 🅰🅴 ① 🅴 𝑽𝑰𝑺𝑨 LY **b**
closed 23 December - 2 January - **45 rm** 180/280 Bb.

🏨 **Austrotel - Deutscher Kaiser**, Arnulfstr. 2 (M 2), ℰ 5 38 60, Telex 522650, Fax 53862255,
15th floor rest. with ≤ Munich – 🛗 📺 ☎ – 🔏 25/300. 🅰🅴 ① 🅴 𝑽𝑰𝑺𝑨 JY **r**
M a la carte 39/77 – **174 rm** 195/360 Bb.

🏨 **Intercity-Hotel**, Bayerstr. 10 (M 2), ℰ 55 85 71, Telex 523174, Fax 596229 – 🛗 📺 ☎ –
🔏 25/150. ① 🅴 𝑽𝑰𝑺𝑨 – **M** a la carte 37/62 – **209 rm** 150/265 Bb – 4 suites 295. JY **u**

🏨 **Admiral** without rest, Kohlstr. 9 (M 5), ℰ 22 66 41, Telex 529111, Fax 293674 – 🛗 📺 ☎
⇔. 🅰🅴 ① 🅴 𝑽𝑰𝑺𝑨 – **33 rm** 180/270 Bb. LZ **r**

🏨 **Torbräu** without rest, Tal 37 (M 2), ℰ 22 50 16, Telex 522212, Fax 225019 – 🛗 📺 ☎ ⇔
🅿. 🅰🅴 ① 🅴 𝑽𝑰𝑺𝑨 – closed 22 December - 11 January – **88 rm** 160/290 – 3 suites. LZ **g**

🏨 **Atrium** without rest, Landwehrstr. 59 (M 2), ℰ 51 41 90, Telex 5212162, Fax 598491, ⇔
– 🛗 ✻ 📺 ☎ ⇔ – 🔏 50. 🅰🅴 ① 🅴 𝑽𝑰𝑺𝑨 – **163 rm** 195/245 Bb. JZ **d**

🏨 **Apollo** without rest, Mittererstr. 7 (M 2), ℰ 53 95 31, Telex 5212981, Fax 534033 – 🛗 📺
☎ ⇔. 🅰🅴 ① 🅴 𝑽𝑰𝑺𝑨 – closed 20 to 30 December – **74 rm** 130/245 Bb. JZ **x**

🏨 **Europäischer Hof** without rest, Bayerstr. 31 (M 2), ℰ 55 15 10, Telex 522642, Fax 55151222
– 🛗 📺 ☎ ⇔ 🅿. 🅰🅴 ① 🅴 𝑽𝑰𝑺𝑨 – **160 rm** 100/280 Bb. JZ **b**

🏨 **Schlicker** without rest, Tal 74 (M 2), ℰ 22 79 41, Fax 296059 – 🛗 📺 ☎ 🅿. 🅰🅴 ① 🅴
closed 20 December - 7 January - **70 rm** 115/250 Bb. KZ **a**

🏨 **Brack** without rest, Lindwurmstr. 153 (M 2), ℰ 77 10 52, Telex 524416, Fax 7250615 – 🛗
📺 ☎ ⇔. 🅰🅴 ① 🅴 𝑽𝑰𝑺𝑨 – **50 rm** 125/195 Bb. EX **b**

🏨 **Mark** without rest, Senefelderstr. 12 (M 2), ℰ 55 98 20, Telex 522721, Fax 55982333 – 🛗
📺 ☎ ⇔ 🅿. 🅰🅴 ① 🅴 𝑽𝑰𝑺𝑨 – **91 rm** 120/190. JZ **v**

🏨 **Daniel** without rest, Sonnenstr. 5 (M 2), ℰ 55 49 45, Telex 523863, Fax 553420 – 🛗 📺 ☎.
🅰🅴 ① 🅴 𝑽𝑰𝑺𝑨 – **76 rm** 110/280 Bb. JZ **q**

🏨 **Adria** without rest, Liebigstr. 8a (M 22), ℰ 29 30 81, Telex 5214111, Fax 227015 – 🛗 📺 ☎.
🅰🅴 ① 🅴 𝑽𝑰𝑺𝑨 – closed 22 to 25 December – **47 rm** 98/200. LY **a**

🏨 **Andi** without rest, Landwehrstr. 33 (M 2), ℰ 59 60 67, Fax 553427 – 🛗 📺 ☎. 🅰🅴 ① 🅴
𝑽𝑰𝑺𝑨 – closed 21 December - 7 January – **30 rm** 98/140 Bb. JZ **x**

🏨 **Müller** without rest, Fliegenstr. 4 (M 2), ℰ 26 60 63, Fax 268624 – 🛗 📺 ☎ 🅿. ① 🅴
𝑽𝑰𝑺𝑨 JZ **p**
closed 23 December - 6 January - **44 rm** 105/195.

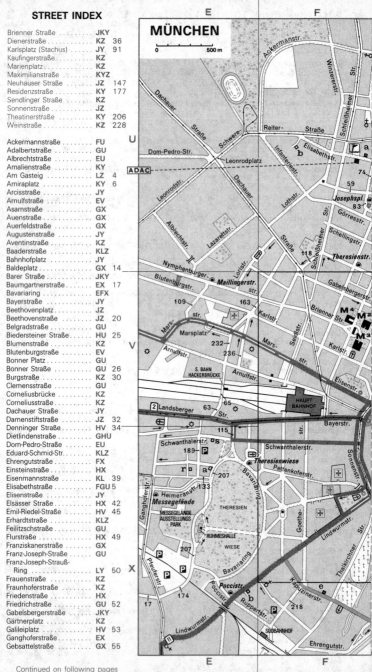

MÜNCHEN

0   500 m

Continued on following pages

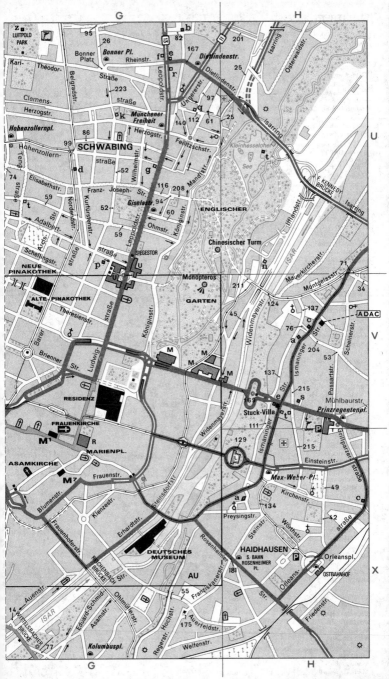

STREET INDEX

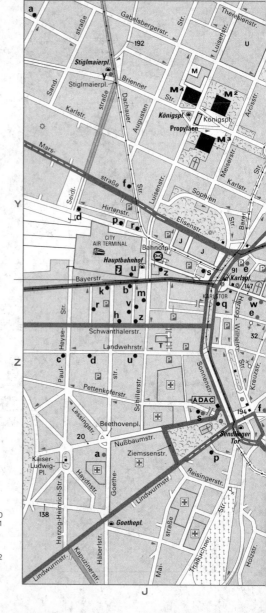

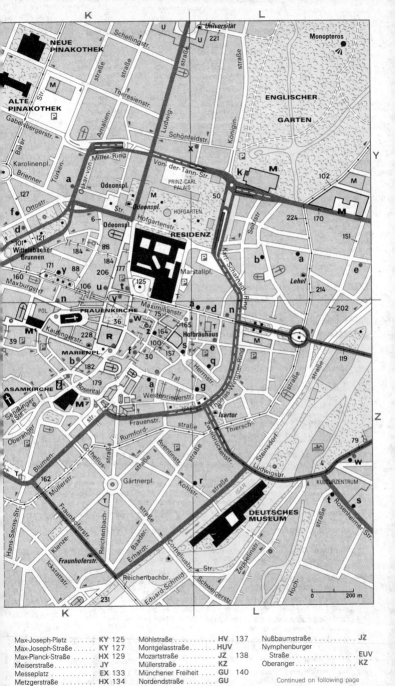

Continued on following page

STREET INDEX TO MÜNCHEN TOWN PLANS (Concluded)

XXXX ❀❀❀ **Aubergine**, Maximiliansplatz 5 (M 2), ✆ 59 81 71, Fax 5236753 – ⓸ ☰ 𝑉𝐼𝑆𝐴 KY **d**
closed Sunday, Monday, Bank Holidays, first 2 weeks of August and 23 December - 7 January – **M** (booking essential) 165/225 and a la carte 105/146
Spec. Sauté vom Hummer mit Tomaten und Oliven, Bresse-Taube mit Linsen, Feigen mit geeistem Schokoladenschaum und Ingwer.

XXXX ❀ **Le Gourmet Schwarzwälder**, Hartmannstr. 8 (1st floor) (M 2), ✆ 2 12 09 58, Fax 2023172 – 𝐀𝐄 ⓸ ☰ 𝑉𝐼𝑆𝐴 KYZ **n**
closed Sunday, Monday and 23 December - 7 January – **M** (booking essential) (remarkable wine list) 150/180 and a la carte 88/116
Spec. Salat mit glacierten Schweinsschwänzchen, Soufflierte Wachtelbrüstchen mit Trüffelsauce, Champagnercreme mit Vanille-Sabayon.

XXX ❀ **Sabitzer**, Reitmorstr. 21 (M 22), ✆ 29 85 84, Fax 3003304 – 𝐀𝐄 ☰ 𝑉𝐼𝑆𝐴 LY **e**
closed Sunday, 7 to 24 January and 10 to 22 August – **M** (dinner only, booking essential) a la carte 89/119
Spec. Lasagne von Lachs und Steinbutt in Schnittlauchsauce, Lamm- und Wildgerichte, Topfenmousse auf Himbeermark.

XXX **Weinhaus Schwarzwälder** (Old Munich wine restaurant), Hartmannstr. 8 (M 2), ✆ 2 12 09 79, Fax 2120172 – 𝐀𝐄 ☰ – **M** a la carte 49/83. KYZ **n**

XXX **El Toula**, Sparkassenstr. 5 (M 2), ✆ 29 28 69 – ☰. 𝐀𝐄 ⓸ ☰ 𝑉𝐼𝑆𝐴 KZ **f**
closed Sunday, Monday, and 3 weeks July - August – **M** (booking essential for dinner) a la carte 68/95.

XX ❀ **Boettner** (small Old Munich rest.), Theatinerstr. 8 (M 2), ✆ 22 12 10 – 𝐀𝐄 ⓸ ☰ 𝑉𝐼𝑆𝐴 KY **u**
closed Saturday dinner, Sunday and Bank Holidays – **M** (booking essential) a la carte 67/130
Spec. Hechtsoufflé mit Sauce Nantua, Hummereintopf "Hartung", Rote Grütze.

XX **Zum Bürgerhaus**, Pettenkoferstr. 1 (M 2), ✆ 59 79 09, « Bavarian farmhouse furniture, court terrace » JZ **s**
closed Saturday lunch, Sunday and Bank Holidays – **M** (booking essential) 30 (lunch) and a la carte 55/76.

XX **Gasthaus Glockenbach** (former old Bavarian pub), Kapuzinerstr. 29 (M 2), ✆ 53 40 43 – ☰ FX **e**
closed Sunday, Monday, Bank Holidays and 24 December - 2 January – **M** (booking essential) a la carte 69/89.

XX **Weinhaus Neuner** (19C wine restaurant), Herzogspitalstr. 8 (M 2), ✆ 2 60 39 54 – ☰ JZ **e**
closed Sunday, Bank Holidays and August – **M** a la carte 43/65.

XX **Halali**, Schönfeldstr. 22 (M 22), ✆ 28 59 09 – ☰ LY **x**
closed Sunday and Bank Holidays – **M** (booking essential) a la carte 48/76.

XX **La Belle Epoque**, Maximilianstr. 29 (M 22), ✆ 29 33 11, 🍴 LZ **n**
(booking essential for dinner).

XX **Goethe-Keller**, Goethestr. 68 (M 2), ✆ 5 30 93 21, Fax 5309321, 🍴 – 𝐀𝐄 ⓸ ☰ 𝑉𝐼𝑆𝐴 JZ **a**
closed 21 December - 12 January – **M** a la carte 37/73.

XX **Chesa Rüegg**, Wurzerstr. 18 (M 22), ✆ 29 71 14 – ☰ – (booking essential). LZ **d**

XX **Austernkeller**, Stollbergstr. 11 (M 22), ✆ 29 87 87 – 𝐀𝐄 ⓸ ☰ 𝑉𝐼𝑆𝐴, ✀ LZ **e**
closed Monday and 23 to 26 December – **M** (dinner only, booking essential) a la carte 47/83.

XX **La Piazzetta**, Oskar-v.-Miller-Ring 3 (M 2), ℰ 28 29 90, Fax 2809324, 🌤, beer-garden – ⒶⒺ
 ⓄⒺ 𝗩𝗜𝗦𝗔   KY **a**
M (booking essential) a la carte 55/78.

XX **Mövenpick**, Lenbachplatz 8 (M 2), ℰ 55 78 65, Fax 5236538, 🌤 – 🏋 25/280   JY **e**

XX **Csarda Piroschka** (Hungarian rest. with gipsy music), Prinzregentenstr. 1 (M 22),
 ℰ 29 54 25, Fax 293850 – ℗. ⒶⒺ ⓄⒺ 𝗩𝗜𝗦𝗔   LY **k**
closed Sunday – **M** (dinner only, booking essential) a la carte 38/65.

XX **Dallmayr**, Dienerstr. 14 (1st floor)(M 2), ℰ 2 13 51 00, Fax 2135167 – ⒶⒺ ⓄⒺ 𝗩𝗜𝗦𝗔   KZ **w**
closed Saturday dinner and Sunday, August lunch only – **M** a la carte 43/83.

X **Goldene Stadt** (Bohemian specialities), Oberanger 44 (M 2), ℰ 26 43 82 – ⒶⒺ ⓄⒺ
M (booking essential for dinner) a la carte 26/57.   JZ **f**

X **Ratskeller**, Marienplatz 8 (M 2), ℰ 22 03 13, Fax 229195 – ⒶⒺ Ⓔ 𝗩𝗜𝗦𝗔   LY **R**
M a la carte 29/55.

Brewery - inns :

X **Spatenhaus-Bräustuben**, Residenzstr. 12 (M 2), ℰ 22 78 43, Fax 294076, 🌤, « Furnished
in traditional alpine style » – ⓄⒺ 𝗩𝗜𝗦𝗔 – **M** a la carte 38/74.   KY **t**

X **Augustiner - Gaststätten**, Neuhauser Str. 16 (M 2), ℰ 55 19 92 57, Fax 2605379, « Beer
garden » – ⒶⒺ ⓄⒺ 𝗩𝗜𝗦𝗔 – **M** a la carte 26/56.   JZ **w**

X **Franziskaner Fuchs'n Stuben**, Perusastr. 5 (M 2), ℰ 2 31 81 20, Fax 23181244, 🌤 – ⒶⒺ
 ⓄⒺ 𝗩𝗜𝗦𝗔 – **M** a la carte 31/58.   KY **v**

X **Zum Spöckmeier**, Rosenstr. 9 (M 2), ℰ 26 80 88, Fax 2022909, 🌤 – ⒶⒺ ⓄⒺ 𝗩𝗜𝗦𝗔   KZ **b**
closed Sunday June - August – **M** a la carte 31/56.

X **Spatenhofkeller**, Neuhauser Str. 26 (M 2), ℰ 26 40 10, Fax 685586, 🌤 – ⒶⒺ Ⓔ 𝗩𝗜𝗦𝗔   JZ **w**
M a la carte 23/47.

X **Löwenbräukeller**, Nymphenburger Str. 2 (M 2), ℰ 52 60 21, Fax 528933, beer garden – Ⓔ
M a la carte 30/65.   JY **y**

at Munich-Bogenhausen :

🏨 **Sheraton**, Arabellastr. 6 (M 81), ℰ 9 26 40, Telex 522391, Fax 916877, ≤ Munich, beer
garden, Massage, ☒, ▧ – 🛗 ⠧ rm 🖬 ⇔ – 🏋 25/1200. ⒶⒺ ⓄⒺ 𝗩𝗜𝗦𝗔. ⁘ rest
Restaurants : **Atrium M** a la carte 56/85 – **Alt Bayern Stuben** *(dinner only)* **M** a la carte 53/74
– **650 rm** 258/536 Bb – 16 suites 906/2000.   by Isarring HU

🏨 **Palace** without rest, Trogerstr. 21 (M 80), ℰ 4 70 50 91, Telex 528256, Fax 4705090, « Elegant
installation with period furniture », ☎, 🌤 – 🛗 ⠧ 🖬 ⇔ – 🏋 50. ⒶⒺ ⓄⒺ 𝗩𝗜𝗦𝗔   HV **t**
73 rm 249/468 Bb – 9 suites 488/898.

🏨 **Arabella-Hotel**, Arabellastr. 5 (M 81), ℰ 9 23 20, Telex 529987, Fax 92324449, ≤ Munich,
Massage, ☎, ▧ – 🛗 ⠧ rm 🖬 rest 🖬 ᴧ ⇔ – 🏋 25/320. ⒶⒺ ⓄⒺ 𝗩𝗜𝗦𝗔
M a la carte 38/69 – **478 rm** 243/432 Bb – 32 suites 500/1450.   by Isarring HU

🏨 **Rothof** without rest, Denninger Str. 114 (M 81), ℰ 91 50 61, Fax 915066, 🌤 – 🛗 🖬 ⇔.
ⒶⒺ ⓄⒺ Ⓔ. ⁘   by Einsteinstr. HX
closed 24 December - 6 January – **37 rm** 198/460 Bb.

🏨 **Prinzregent** without rest, Ismaninger Str. 42 (M 80), ℰ 41 60 50, Telex 524403,
Fax 41605466, ☎ – 🛗 🖬 ⇔ – 🏋 40. ⒶⒺ ⓄⒺ Ⓔ 𝗩𝗜𝗦𝗔   HV **t**
closed 23 December - 7 January – **68 rm** 230/410 Bb.

🏨 **Queens Hotel München**, Effnerstr. 99 (M 81), ℰ 92 79 80, Telex 524757, Fax 983813 –
🛗 ⠧ rm 🖬 ☎ ℗ – 🏋 25/220. ⒶⒺ ⓄⒺ Ⓔ 𝗩𝗜𝗦𝗔   by Ismaninger Str. HV
M a la carte 49/62 – **155 rm** 249/408 Bb.

XXX **da Pippo** (Italian rest.), Mühlbaurstr. 36 (M 80), ℰ 4 70 48 48, Fax 476464, 🌤 – Ⓔ.
⁘   by Mühlbaurstr. HV
closed Saturday lunch, Sunday and Bank Holidays – **M** a la carte 51/86.

XX **Käfer-Schänke**, Schumannstr. 1 (M 80), ℰ 4 16 82 47, Fax 4703658, 🌤, « Elegant rustic
installation » – ⒶⒺ ⓄⒺ 𝗩𝗜𝗦𝗔. ⁘   HV **s**
closed Sunday and Bank Holidays – **M** (booking essential) a la carte 54/105.

XX **Bogenhauser Hof** (1825 former hunting lodge), Ismaninger Str. 85 (M 80), ℰ 98 55 86,
Fax 9810221, « Terrace » – ⓄⒺ 𝗩𝗜𝗦𝗔   HV **c**
closed Sunday, Bank Holidays and Christmas - 6 January – **M** (booking essential) a la carte 61/99.

XX **Louis XIII**, Ismaninger Str. 71a (M 80), ℰ 98 92 00, 🌤 – ⒶⒺ Ⓔ   HV **a**
closed Sunday and Bank Holidays – **M** a la carte 64/86.

XX **Prielhof**, Oberföhringer Str. 44 (M 81), ℰ 98 53 53, 🌤 – ⓄⒺ Ⓔ
closed Saturday lunch, Sunday, Bank Holidays and 23 December - 6 January – **M** (booking
essential) a la carte 63/84.   by Ismaninger Str. HV

XX **Tai Tung** (Chinese rest.), Prinzregentenstr. 60 (Villa Stuck) (M 80), ℰ 47 11 00, Fax 4707413
– ⒶⒺ ⓄⒺ Ⓔ 𝗩𝗜𝗦𝗔 – **M** (also vegetarian dishes) a la carte 32/61.   HV **e**

at Munich 80-Haidhausen :

🏨 **City Hilton**, Rosenheimer Str. 15, ℰ 4 80 40, Telex 529437, Fax 48044804, 🌤 – 🛗 ⠧ rm
🖬 🖬 ᴧ ⇔ – 🏋 25/180. ⒶⒺ ⓄⒺ Ⓔ 𝗩𝗜𝗦𝗔   LZ **s**
Restaurants : **Zum Gasteig M** a la carte 49/73 – **Löwenschänke M** a la carte 44/59 – **483 rm**
277/514 – 10 suites.

🏨 **Preysing**, Preysingstr. 1, ℘ 48 10 11, Telex 529044, Fax 4470998, ≦s, ⊠ – ⧖ ☰ 📺 ⇔
closed 23 December - 6 January – **M** (see **Preysing-Keller** below) – **76 rm** 155/284 – 5 suites
357/515.   LZ **w**

🏨 **München Penta Hotel**, Hochstr. 3, ℘ 4 80 30, Telex 529046, Fax 4488277, Massage, ≦s,
⊠ – ⧖ ✻⇔ rm 📺 ⇔ 🅰 – 🔬 25/400. 🆎 ⓪ 🗲 𝚅𝙸𝚂𝙰   LZ **t**
M a la carte 51/83 – **583 rm** 264/392 Bb – 12 suites 602.

🍴🍴🍴 ❀ **Preysing-Keller**, Innere-Wiener-Str. 6, ℘ 48 10 15, « Vaulted cellar, country house
furniture » – 🗲   LZ **w**
closed Sunday, Bank Holidays and 23 December - 6 January – **M** (dinner only, booking essential,
remarkable wine list) 109 and a la carte 61/82
Spec. Sautierte Garnelen auf Chicoree mit Limonenbutter, Hasenrücken im Crêpeteig, Rotwein-
parfait mit Briochekrapfen.

🍴🍴 **Balance**, Grillparzerstr. 1, ℘ 4 70 54 72, 🍽 – 🆎 ⓪ 🗲   HX **c**
closed Saturday lunch, Sunday and Bank Holidays – **M** a la carte 50/68.

🍴 **Rue des Halles** (Bistro), Steinstr. 18, ℘ 48 56 75 – 🗲   HX **a**
M (dinner only, booking essential) a la carte 54/71.

at Munich 45-Harthof by Schleißheimer Str. FU :

🍴🍴 **Zur Gärtnerei**, Schleißheimer Str. 456, ℘ 3 13 13 73, 🍽 – 🄿
closed Wednesday – **M** 36 and a la carte 40/60.

at Munich 21-Laim by Landsberger Str. (B 2) EV :

🏨 **Transmar-Park-Hotel** without rest, Zschokkestr. 55, ℘ 57 93 60, Telex 5218609,
Fax 57936100, ≦s – ⧖ 📺 ☎ ⇔ – 🔬 30. 🆎 ⓪ 🗲 𝚅𝙸𝚂𝙰 – **71 rm** 175/295 Bb.

at Munich 60 - Langwied NW : 13 km by Arnulfstr. EV :

🍴🍴 ❀ **Das kleine Restaurant im Gasthof Böswirth** ⌂ with rm, Waidachanger 9,
℘ 8 64 41 63, Fax 8643857 – ⇔ 🄿 🆎 🗲
closed 3 weeks January and 2 weeks June – **M** (closed Sunday, Monday and Bank Holidays)
(remarkable wine list) 70/120 and a la carte 67/92 – **12 rm** 70/115
Spec. Sülze von geräucherter Lachsforelle, Bayrisches Lamm in Rosmarin, Karamelisierte Tarte.

at Munich 83-Neu Perlach by Rosenheimer Str. HX :

🏨 Orbis Hotel, Karl-Marx-Ring 87, ℘ 6 32 70, Telex 5213357, Fax 6327407, beer garden, ≦s,
⊠ – ⧖ ✻⇔ rm ☰ rest 📺 ⇔ 🄿 – 🔬 25/130
Restaurants : **Perlacher Bürgerstuben** – **Hubertuskeller** (dinner only) – **Sakura** (dinner only) –
185 rm – 4 suites.

at Munich 40-Schwabing :

🏨 **Ramada Parkhotel**, Theodor-Dombart-Str. 4, ℘ 36 09 90, Telex 5218720, Fax 36099684,
🍽, ≦s – ⧖ ✻⇔ rm 📺 ⇔ – 🔬 25/60. 🆎 ⓪ 🗲 𝚅𝙸𝚂𝙰   by Ungererstr. (B 11) HU
M a la carte 36/70 – **260 rm** 241/422 Bb – 80 suites 500/632.

🏨 **Marriott-Hotel**, Berliner Str. 93, ℘ 36 00 20, Telex 5216641, Fax 36002200, 𝕱𝕤, ≦s, ⊠
– ⧖ ✻⇔ rm 📺 🗲 & ⇔ – 🔬 25/350. 🆎 ⓪ 🗲 𝚅𝙸𝚂𝙰. ✻ rest
M a la carte 48/81 – **350 rm** 329/497 Bb – 18 suites 542/1352.   by Ungererstr. (B 11) HU

🏨 **Holiday Inn**, Leopoldstr. 194, ℘ 38 17 90, Fax 38179888, 🍽, Massage, ≦s, ⊠ – ⧖ ✻⇔ rm
📺 ⇔ – 🔬 25/320. 🆎 ⓪ 🗲 𝚅𝙸𝚂𝙰   by Leopoldstr. GU
M a la carte 42/74 – **363 rm** 275/480 Bb – 3 suites 1050.

🏨 **Residence**, Artur-Kutscher-Platz 4, ℘ 38 17 80, Telex 529788, Fax 38178951, 🍽, ⊠ – ⧖
✻⇔ rm ☰ rest 📺 ☎ ⇔ – 🔬 25/100. 🆎 ⓪ 🗲 𝚅𝙸𝚂𝙰. ✻ rest   GU **q**
M a la carte 49/68 – **165 rm** 193/350.

🏨 **König Ludwig** without rest, Hohenzollernstr. 3, ℘ 33 59 95, Telex 5216607, Fax 394658 –
⧖ 📺 ☎ ⇔. 🆎 ⓪ 🗲 𝚅𝙸𝚂𝙰 – **46 rm** 180/280 Bb.   GU **g**

🏨 **Mercure** without rest, Leopoldstr. 120, ℘ 39 05 50, Fax 349344 – ⧖ 📺 ☎ ⇔. 🆎 ⓪ 🗲 𝚅𝙸𝚂𝙰
67 rm 148/290 Bb.   GU **r**

🏨 **Vitalis**, Kathi-Kobus-Str. 24, ℘ 12 00 80, Telex 5215161, Fax 1298382 – ⧖ 📺 ☎ ⇔ 🄿
– 🔬 25/100. 🆎 ⓪ 🗲 𝚅𝙸𝚂𝙰   FU **u**
M (closed Saturday, Sunday and Bank Holidays) (dinner only) a la carte 37/65 – **100 rm**
150/235 Bb.

🏨 **Arabella - Olympiapark-Hotel**, Helene-Mayer-Ring 12, ℘ 3 51 60 71, Telex 5215231,
Fax 3543730, 🍽 – ⧖ 📺 ☎ 🄿 – 🔬 30. 🆎 ⓪ 🗲 𝚅𝙸𝚂𝙰   by Schleißheimer Str. FU
closed 18 December - 6 January – **M** a la carte 31/55 – **105 rm** 194/288 Bb.

🏨 **Weinfurtners Garden-Hotel** without rest, Leopoldstr. 132, ℘ 36 80 04, Telex 5214315,
Fax 362089 – ⧖ 📺 ☎ ⇔ – 🔬 30. 🆎 🗲 – **174 rm** 170/230 Bb.   GU **e**

🏨 **Consul** without rest, Viktoriastr. 10, ℘ 33 40 35, Fax 399266 – ⧖ 📺 ☎ ⇔ 🄿   GU **k**
31 rm 70/180 Bb.

🏨 **Leopold**, Leopoldstr. 119, ℘ 36 70 61, Telex 5215160, Fax 367061, 🍽 – ⧖ 📺 ☎ ⇔ 🄿.
🆎 ⓪ 🗲 𝚅𝙸𝚂𝙰 – *closed 23 December - 3 January* – **M** (closed Saturday and 4 to 10 January)
a la carte 36/65 – **78 rm** 120/195 Bb.   GU **f**

🍴🍴🍴🍴 ❀❀ **Tantris**, Johann-Fichte-Str. 7, ℘ 36 20 61, Fax 3618469, 🍽 – ☰ 🄿. 🆎 ⓪ 🗲 𝚅𝙸𝚂𝙰.
Monday and Saturday dinner only, closed Sunday, Bank Holidays, 1 week January and 7 to 28
June – **M** (booking essential) a la carte 93/145.   GU **b**

XX **Romagna Antica** (Italian rest.), Elisabethstr. 52, ℰ 2 71 63 55, Fax 2711364, 佘 – ⅍. 🖭
🛈 E 𝑉𝐼𝑆𝐴. ⅍   FU a
closed Sunday and Bank Holidays – **M** (booking essential) a la carte 47/65.

XX **Seehaus**, Kleinhesselohe 3, ℰ 3 81 61 30, Fax 341803, ≤, « Lake side setting, terrace »
– 佘 🖭 𝑉𝐼𝑆𝐴 – **M** a la carte 44/74.   HU t

XX **Bistro Terrine**, Amalienstr. 89 (Amalien-Passage), ℰ 28 17 80, 佘 – 🖭 E.   GU q
closed Monday lunch, Sunday, Bank Holidays, 1 to 10 January and 3 weeks July - August –
M (booking essential for dinner) a la carte 65/90.

XX **Daitokai** (Japanese rest.), Nordendstr. 64 (entrance Kurfürstenstr.), ℰ 2 71 14 21,
Fax 2718392 – ▤. 🖭 🛈 E 𝑉𝐼𝑆𝐴. ⅍   GU d
closed Sunday – **M** (booking essential) a la carte 51/78.

XX **Savoy** (Italian rest.), Tengstr. 20, ℰ 2 71 14 45   GU t

X **Bamberger Haus**, Brunnenstr. 2 (at Luitpoldpark), ℰ 3 08 89 66, Fax 3003304, « 18C
palace with brewery and terrace » – 🅿. 🖭 E 𝑉𝐼𝑆𝐴 – **M** a la carte 34/68.   GU z

X **Ristorante Grazia** (Italian rest.), Ungererstr. 161, ℰ 36 69 31 – E by Ungererstr.   HU
closed Saturday and Sunday – **M** (booking essential) a la carte 48/62.

at Munich 70 - Sendling by Lindwurmstr. (B 11) EX :

🏨 **Holiday Inn München - Süd**, Kistlerhofstr. 142, ℰ 78 00 20, Telex 5218645, Fax 78002672,
beer garden, Massage, 佘, 🖫, – ﹩ ⅍ rm ▤ 🖵 ₺ ⇔ – 🕍 25/100. 🖭 🛈 E 𝑉𝐼𝑆𝐴
M a la carte 53/75 – **320 rm** 253/406 Bb - 8 suites 596.

🏨 **Ambassador Parkhotel**, Plinganserstr. 102, ℰ 72 48 90, Telex 524444, Fax 7248100, beer
garden – ﹩ ⅍ rm 🖵 ☎ ⇔ – 🕍 30. 🖭 🛈 E 𝑉𝐼𝑆𝐴
closed 20 December - 6 January – **M** a la carte 40/63 – **42 rm** 160/230 Bb.

🏨 **K u. K Hotel am Harras**, Albert-Rosshaupter-Str. 4, ℰ 77 00 51, Telex 5213167,
Fax 7212820 – ﹩ 🖵 ☎ ⇔ – 🕍 40. 🖭 🛈 E 𝑉𝐼𝑆𝐴
M (residents only) – **129 rm** 180/330 Bb.

at Munich 50-Untermenzing by Arnulfstr. EV :

🏨 **Romantik-Hotel Insel Mühle**, von-Kahr-Str. 87, ℰ 8 10 10, Telex 5218292, Fax 8120571,
佘, beer garden, « Converted 16C riverside mill » – 🖵 ⇔ 🅿 🖭 🛈 E 𝑉𝐼𝑆𝐴
M *(closed Sunday and Bank Holidays)* 28 (lunch) and a la carte 51/77 – **37 rm** 150/370.

at Aschheim 8011 NE : 13 km by Riem :

🏨 **Schreiberhof**, Erdinger Str. 2, ℰ (089) 90 00 60, Fax 90006459, 佘 – ﹩ ⅍ rm 🖵 ₺ ⇔
🅿 – 🕍 25/100. 🖭 🛈 E 𝑉𝐼𝑆𝐴
M a la carte 49/77 – **86 rm** 180/265 Bb.

🏨 **Zur Post**, Ismaninger Str. 11 (B 471), ℰ (089) 9 03 20 27, Fax 9044669, 佘 – ﹩ 🖵 ☎ ⇔
🅿 – 🕍 30. 🖭 E – **M** a la carte 24/50 – **55 rm** 75/155 Bb.

at Grünwald 8022 S : 13 km by Wittelsbacher Brücke GX – 🕿 089 :

🏨 **Tannenhof** without rest, Marktplatz 3, ℰ 6 41 70 74, Fax 6415608, « Period house with Art
Nouveau interior » – 🖵 ☎ 🅿 🖭 🛈 E 𝑉𝐼𝑆𝐴
closed 20 December - 6 January – **21 rm** 130/200 Bb.

🏨 **Alter Wirt**, Marktplatz 1, ℰ 6 41 78 55, Fax 6414266, 佘, « Bavarian inn with intimate
atmosphere » – ﹩ 🖵 ☎ ⇔ 🅿 – 🕍 25/70. 🖭 E
M a la carte 37/70 – **49 rm** 110/190 Bb.

🏨 **Schloß-Hotel Grünwald** ⑤, Zeillerstr.1, ℰ 6 41 79 35, Fax 6414771, ≤, « Terrace » – 🖵
☎ 🅿. 🖭 🛈 E 𝑉𝐼𝑆𝐴
closed 27 December - 15 January – **M** a la carte 35/71 – **16 rm** 120/270 Bb.

STUTTGART 7000. 🄻 Baden-Württemberg 🄐🄑🄓 KL 20, 🄐🄑🄒 ㉟ – pop. 559 000 – alt. 245 m –
🕿 0711.

See : Linden Museum ✱✱ KY **M1** – Park Wilhelma✱ HT and Killesberg-Park✱ GT – Television Tower
(Fernsehturm) ☀✱✱ HX – Stuttgart Gallery (Otto-Dix-Collection✱) LY **M4** – Swabian Brewerymu-
seum (Schwäb. Brauereimuseum)✱ by Böblinger Straße FX – Old Castle (Altes Schloß) (Renaissance
courtyard✱) – Württemberg Regional Museum✱ (Sacred Statuary✱✱) LY **M3** – State Gallery✱ (Old
Masters Collection✱✱) LY **M2** – Collegiate church (Stiftskirche) (Commemorative monuments of
dukes✱) KY A – State Musem of Natural History (Staatl. Museum für Naturkunde)✱ HT **M5** – Daimler-
Benz Museum✱ JV **M6** – Porsche Museum✱ by Heilbronner Straße GT – Schloß Solitude✱ by
Rotenwaldstraße FX.

Envir. : Bad Cannstatt Spa Park (Kurpark)✱ E : 4 km JT.

🏌 Kornwestheim, Aldinger Str. (N : 11 km), ℰ (07141) 87 13 19 ; 🏌 Mönsheim (NW : 30 km by
A 8), ℰ (07044) 69 09.

✈ Stuttgart-Echterdingen, by Obere Weinsteige (B 27) GX, ℰ 7 90 11, City Air Terminal, Stuttgart,
Lautenschlagerstr. 14, ℰ 20 12 68.

Exhibition Centre (Messegelände Killesberg) (GT), ℰ 2 58 91, Telex 722584.

🛈 Amt für Touristik - Tourist-Info, Königstr. 1a, ℰ 2 22 82 40, Fax 2228251.

ADAC, Am Neckartor 2, ℰ 2 80 00.

Frankfurt am Main 204 – Karlsruhe 88 – München 222 – Strasbourg 156.

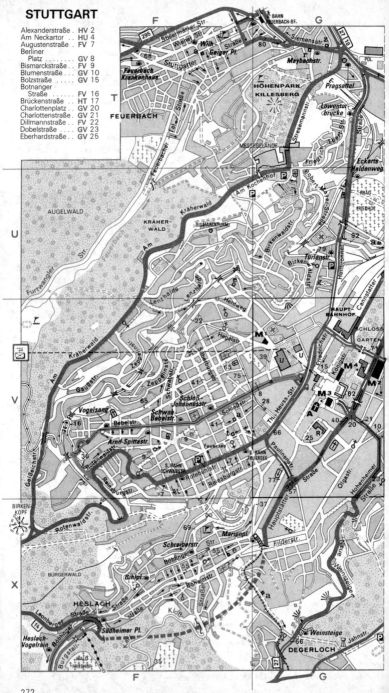

STUTTGART

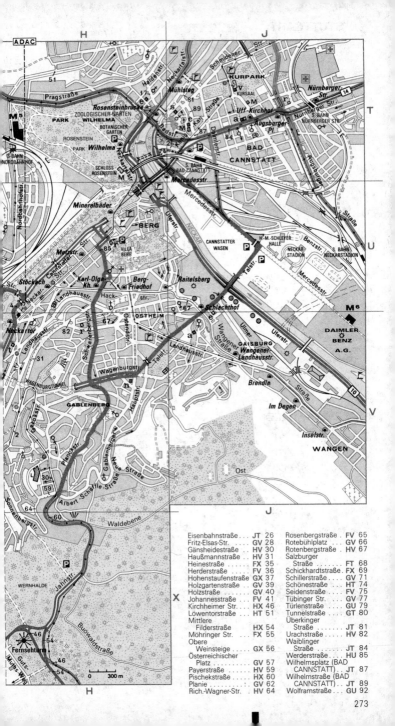

STUTTGART

🏨🏨🏨 ✿ **Steigenberger-Hotel Graf Zeppelin** ⟫, Arnulf-Klett-Platz 7, 𝒫 29 98 81, Telex 722418, Fax 292141, Massage, ⟨s, 🖂 – |⫘| ✻ rm 🔳 📺 ⟨ – 🛦 25/300. 🕮 ⓞ 🗉 ₘₛₐ, ✻ rest
M *(closed Saturday, Sunday, Bank Holidays and 6 July - 9 August)* (dinner only, booking essential) a la carte 74/108 – **Bistro Zepp 7 M** a la carte 33/53 – **280 rm** 295/480 Bb – 20 suites 650/1780
LY **s**
Spec. Hummer auf Sesamkruste, Stern von Lachs, Seezunge und Jacobsmuscheln, Rehrücken im Wirsingmantel.

🏨🏨 **Inter-Continental**, Neckarstr. 60, 𝒫 2 02 00, Telex 721996, Fax 202012, ₤₅, ⟨s, 🖂 – |⫘|
✻ rm 🔳 📺 ⟨ ⟨⟩ – 🛦 25/500. 🕮 ⓞ 🗉 ₘₛₐ
HV **t**
Restaurants : **Les Continents** *(closed Saturday lunch)* **M** a la carte 70/100 – **Neckarstube** *(closed Sunday)* **M** a la carte 38/60 – **277 rm** 273/505 Bb – 24 suites 865/3555.

🏨🏨 **Am Schloßgarten**, Schillerstr. 23, 𝒫 2 02 60, Telex 722936, Fax 2026888, « Terrace with
⟨≶⟩ » – |⫘| ✻ rm 📺 ⟨⟩ – 🛦 25/120. 🕮 ⓞ 🗉 ₘₛₐ, ✻ rest
LY **u**
M a la carte 59/92 – **125 rm** 245/450 Bb – 2 suites 700.

🏨🏨 **Royal**, Sophienstr. 35, 𝒫 62 50 50, Telex 722449, Fax 628809 – |⫘| 🗐 rest 📺 ⟨⟩ 🄿 –
🛦 25/70. 🕮 ⓞ 🗉 ₘₛₐ
KZ **b**
M a la carte 41/72 – **100 rm** 208/420 Bb – 2 suites 605.

🏨🏨 **Park-Hotel**, Villastr. 21, 𝒫 2 80 10, Telex 723405, Fax 284353, 🈸 – |⫘| 📺 ⟨⟩ 🄿 –
🛦 25/80. 🕮 ⓞ 🗉 ₘₛₐ
HU **r**
M a la carte 47/85 – **75 rm** 180/300 Bb.

🏨 **Ruff**, Friedhofstr. 21, 𝒫 2 58 70, Telex 721645, Fax 2587404, ⟨s, 🖂 – |⫘| 📺 ☎ ⟨⟩ 🄿.
🕮 ⓞ 🗉 ₘₛₐ
GU **a**
closed 20 December - 4 January, 16 to 20 April and 18 July - 2 August – **M** *(closed Sunday lunch and Saturday)* a la carte 32/57 – **85 rm** 123/186 Bb.

🏨 **Rega-Hotel**, Ludwigstr. 18, 𝒫 61 93 40, Telex 722701, Fax 6193477 – |⫘| 📺 ☎ ⟨⟩ – 🛦 30.
🕮 ⓞ 🗉 ₘₛₐ
FV **k**
M a la carte 31/59 – **60 rm** 160/210 Bb.

🏨 **Intercity-Hotel** without rest, Arnulf-Klett-Platz 2, 𝒫 29 98 01, Telex 723543, Fax 2261899
– |⫘| 📺 ☎ – 🛦 25/60. 🕮 ⓞ 🗉 ₘₛₐ
LY **p**
112 rm 160/240 Bb.

🏨 **Unger** without rest, Kronenstr. 17, 𝒫 2 09 90, Telex 723995, Fax 2099100 – |⫘| 📺 ☎ ⟨⟩.
🕮 ⓞ 🗉 ₘₛₐ
LY **a**
closed 21 December - 6 January – **80 rm** 149/239 Bb.

🏨 **Bergmeister** without rest, Rotenbergstr. 16, 𝒫 28 33 63, Fax 283719, ⟨s – |⫘| 📺 ☎ 🄿.
🕮 ⓞ 🗉 ₘₛₐ – **45 rm** 148/330 Bb.
HV **r**

🏨 **Kronen-Hotel** without rest, Kronenstr. 48, 𝒫 29 96 61, Telex 723632, Fax 296940, ⟨s – |⫘|
📺 ☎ ⟨⟩. 🕮 ⓞ 🗉 ₘₛₐ
KY **m**
closed 22 December - 7 January – **85 rm** 110/280 Bb.

🏨 **Wörtz zur Weinsteige** ⟫, Hohenheimer Str. 30, 𝒫 24 06 81, Telex 723821, Fax 6407279,
« Terrace » – 📺 ☎. 🕮 ⓞ 🗉 ₘₛₐ
LZ **p**
closed 15 December - 15 January – **M** *(closed Saturday, Sunday and Bank Holidays)* a la carte 37/69 – **25 rm** 80/260 Bb.

🏨 **Stadthotel am Wasen** without rest, Schlachthofstr. 19, 𝒫 48 30 61, Fax 4800509 – |⫘| 📺
☎ ⟨⟩ 🄿. 🕮 ⓞ 🗉 ₘₛₐ. ✻ – **31 rm** 125/170 Bb.
JUV **e**

🏨 **Azenberg** ⟫, Seestr. 114, 𝒫 22 10 51, Fax 297426, ⟨s, 🖂 – |⫘| 📺 ☎ ⟨⟩ 🄿. 🕮 ⓞ
🗉 ₘₛₐ
FU **e**
(residents only) (dinner only) – **55 rm** 140/250 Bb.

🏨 **Wartburg**, Lange Str. 49, 𝒫 2 04 50, Telex 721587, Fax 2045450 – |⫘| 🗐 rest 📺 ☎ 🄿 –
🛦 45
KY **g**
closed Easter and 21 December - 2 January – **M** *(closed Sunday)* a la carte 26/51 – **81 rm** 132/250 Bb.

🏨 **Ketterer**, Marienstr. 3, 𝒫 2 03 90, Telex 722340, Fax 2039600 – |⫘| 📺 ☎ ⟨⟩. 🕮 ⓞ 🗉
ₘₛₐ
KZ **y**
closed 21 December - 7 January – **M** *(closed Friday, Saturday and 24 July - 17 August)* a la carte 36/60 – **107 rm** 132/255 Bb.

🏨 **Rieker** without rest, Friedrichstr. 3, 𝒫 22 13 11, Fax 293894 – |⫘| 📺 ☎. 🕮 🗉 ₘₛₐ LY **d**
63 rm 145/210.

🏨 **Am Feuersee**, Johannesstr. 2, 𝒫 62 61 03 – |⫘| 📺 ☎. 🕮 ⓞ 🗉 ₘₛₐ
FV **t**
closed 30 - 31 December – **M** *(dinner only, closed Saturday, Sunday and Bank Holidays)* a la carte 25/50 – **38 rm** 135/180 Bb.

🏨 **Astoria** without rest, Hospitalstr. 29, 𝒫 29 93 01, Telex 722783, Fax 299307 – |⫘| 📺 ☎ 🄿.
🕮 ⓞ 🗉 ₘₛₐ
KY **r**
closed 22 December - 2 January – **55 rm** 165/320 Bb.

XXX **Alte Post**, Friedrichstr. 43, 𝒫 29 30 79 – ⓞ 🗉 ₘₛₐ
KY **e**
Monday and Saturday dinner only, closed Sunday, Bank Holidays and 27 July - 8 August –
M *(booking essential)* 46 (lunch) and a la carte 69/100.

XX **Da Franco** (modern Italian rest.), Calwer Str. 23, 𝒫 29 15 81, Fax 294549 – 🗐. 🕮 ⓞ 🗉 ₘₛₐ
closed Monday – **M** a la carte 37/71.
KYZ **c**

XX **La nuova Trattoria da Franco**, Calwer Str. 32 (1st floor), 𝒫 29 47 44, Fax 294945 KYZ **c**

XX **Mövenpick-La Pêcherie** (mainly Seafood), Kleiner Schloßplatz 11 (entrance Theodor-Heuss-Str.), ℰ 2 26 89 34, Fax 2268728, ☜ – ▤. ⚏ ⓘ ⋤ 𝗩𝗜𝗦𝗔   KY **a**
M a la carte 45/75.

XX **Intercity-Restaurant**, Arnulf-Klett-Platz 2, ℰ 29 49 46, Fax 2268256 – ⚏ ⓘ ⋤ 𝗩𝗜𝗦𝗔
M a la carte 34/65.   LY **v**

XX **Der Goldene Adler**, Böheimstr. 38, ℰ 6 40 17 62 – ℗. ⚏ ⓘ ⋤ 𝗩𝗜𝗦𝗔   FX **e**
closed Monday and August – **M** a la carte 38/72.

XX **Gaisburger Pastetchen**, Hornbergstr. 24, ℰ 48 48 55, Fax 487565   JV **a**
closed Saturday lunch, Sunday and Bank Holidays – **M** a la carte 65/84.

XX **Zeppelin - Stüble**, Lautenschlagerstr. 2 (at Graf Zeppelin Hotel), ℰ 2 26 40 13, ☜ – ▤.
⚏ ⓘ ⋤ 𝗩𝗜𝗦𝗔   LY **s**
M (Swabian cooking) (booking essential) a la carte 31/59.

XX **Krämer's Bürgerstuben**, Gablenberger Hauptstr. 4, ℰ 46 54 81 – ⚏ ⓘ ⋤ 𝗩𝗜𝗦𝗔   HV **n**
closed Monday and 3 weeks July - August – **M** (booking essential) a la carte 53/88.

X **Brauereigasthof Ketterer**, Marienstr. 3b, ℰ 29 75 51, Fax 297065 – ⚏ ⋤   KZ **y**
closed Sunday – **M** a la carte 26/54.

Swabian wine taverns (Weinstuben) (light meals only) :

X **Kachelofen**, Eberhardstr. 10 (entrance Töpferstraße), ℰ 24 23 78   KZ **x**
closed Sunday, Bank Holidays and 22 December - 2 January – **M** (dinner only) a la carte 35/47.

X **Weinstube am Stadtgraben**, Am Stadtgraben 6 (S 50-Bad Cannstatt), ℰ 56 70 06   JT **e**
closed Saturday, Sunday, Bank Holidays and 2 weeks September - October – **M** a la carte 25/37.

X **Weinstube Schreinerei**, Zaisgasse 4 (S 50-Bad Cannstatt), ℰ 56 74 28, ☜ – ℗   JT **s**
closed Saturday dinner, Sunday and Bank Holidays – **M** a la carte 34/65.

X **Bäcka-Metzger**, Aachener Str. 20 (S 50-Bad Cannstatt), ℰ 54 41 08   HT **e**
closed Sunday, Monday, Bank Holidays, 23 August - 14 September and 23 December - 10 January – **M** (dinner only) a la carte 28/42.

X **Weinhaus Stetter**, Rosenstr. 32, ℰ 24 01 63, remarkable wine list   LZ **e**
closed Monday to Friday until 3 p.m., Saturday dinner, Sunday, Bank Holidays, 13 July - 15 August and 24 December - 8 January – **M** (mainly cold dishes) a la carte 12/17 ♨.

at Stuttgart 80-Büsnau by Rotenwaldstraße FX :

▟▙ **Relexa Hotel Stuttgart**, Am Solitudering, ℰ 6 86 70, Telex 7255557, Fax 6867999, ☜,
☎ – ▐▌ ✲ rm �📺 ♿ ⇔ – ⚿ 25/120. ⚏ ⓘ ⋤ 𝗩𝗜𝗦𝗔. ✀ rest
Restaurants : **La Fenêtre** (dinner only, closed Sunday, Monday and 4 weeks July - August)
M a la carte 70/95 – **Kaminrestaurant M** a la carte 40/70 – **144 rm** 175/330 Bb – 9 suites 510.

at Stuttgart 50 - Bad Cannstatt :

🏨 **Spahr** without rest, Waiblinger Str. 63 (B 14), ℰ 55 39 30, Telex 7254608, Fax 5539333 –
▐▌ �📺 ☎ ⇔ ℗. ⚏ ⓘ ⋤ 𝗩𝗜𝗦𝗔   JT **a**
62 rm 145/235.

🏨 **Krehl's Linde**, Obere Waiblinger Str. 113, ℰ 52 75 67, Fax 548370, ☜ – ▤ ☎ ⇔. ⚏
⋤   JT **r**
M (closed Sunday, Monday and 3 weeks July - August) a la carte 35/79 – **25 rm** 85/200 Bb.

XX **Weinstube Pfund**, Waiblinger Str. 61a, ℰ 56 63 63, ☜, beer-garden – ℗. ⚏ ⓘ ⋤ 𝗩𝗜𝗦𝗔
closed Saturday lunch, Sunday, Bank Holidays, 3 weeks August and 23 December - 6 January
– **M** a la carte 39/70.   JT **a**

X **Alt Cannstatt**, Königsplatz 1 (Kursaal), ℰ 56 11 15, Fax 560080, ☜, beer-garden –
⚿ 25/300. ⚏ ⓘ ⋤ 𝗩𝗜𝗦𝗔   JT **v**
M a la carte 29/61.

at Stuttgart 70 - Degerloch :

🏨 **Waldhotel Degerloch** ♨, Guts-Muths-Weg 18, ℰ 76 50 17, Telex 7255728, Fax 7653762,
☜, ⇔s, ✵ – ▐▌ �📺 ☎ ♿ ℗ – ⚿ 25/100. ⚏ ⓘ ⋤ 𝗩𝗜𝗦𝗔   by Guts-Muths-Weg HX
M a la carte 35/68 – **50 rm** 120/250 Bb.

XXX **Wielandshöhe**, Alte Weinsteige 71, ℰ 6 40 88 48, Fax 6409408 – ⚏ ⓘ ⋤ 𝗩𝗜𝗦𝗔   GX **v**
closed Monday lunch, Sunday and Bank Holidays – **M** a la carte 68/90.

at Stuttgart 30 - Feuerbach :

🏨 **Messehotel Europe**, Siemensstr. 33, ℰ 81 48 30, Telex 7252132, Fax 8148348 – ▐▌ ✲ rm
▤ �📺 ⇔. ⚏ ⓘ ⋤ 𝗩𝗜𝗦𝗔   GT **r**
M (closed Sunday and Bank Holidays) a la carte 41/78 – **120 rm** 230/500 Bb.

🏨 **Kongresshotel Europe**, Siemensstr. 26, ℰ 81 50 91, Telex 723650, Fax 854082, ⇔s – ▐▌
✲ rm ▤ �📺 ⇔ – ⚿ 25/130. ⚏ ⓘ ⋤ 𝗩𝗜𝗦𝗔   GT **z**
M a la carte 48/81 – **150 rm** 150/500 Bb.

X **Anker**, Grazer Str. 42, ℰ 85 44 19 – ⚏ ⓘ ⋤ 𝗩𝗜𝗦𝗔   FT **a**
closed Sunday dinner, Saturday, Bank Holidays 3 to 26 July and 2 August and 23 December - 6 January – **M** (also vegetarian dishes) a la carte 38/69.

at Stuttgart 23 - Flughafen (Airport) S : 15 km by Obere Weinsteige (B 27) GX :

🏨 **Airport Mövenpick-Hotel**, Randstraße, ℰ 7 90 70, Telex 7245677, Fax 793585, ㄲ, ⇌ – 🛗 ⇆ rm ▤ rest 📺 ৬ 🅿 – 🔬 25/70. ㄸ ⧁ 🖪 ₥₥
M a la carte 34/66 – **230 rm** 234/438 Bb.

XX **top air**, Randstraße (in the airport), ℰ 79 01 21 37, Fax 7979210 – ▤ – 🔬 25/220. ㄸ ⧁
🖪 ₥₥ – **M** a la carte 63/85.

at Stuttgart 80 - Möhringen SW : 7 km by Obere Weinsteige GX :

🏨 **Gloria - Restaurant Möhringer Hexle**, Sigmaringer Str. 59, ℰ 7 18 50, Fax 7185121, ⇌ – 🛗 📺 ☎ ⇌ 🅿 – 🔬 25/50. ㄸ
M a la carte 25/47 – **79 rm** 129/194 Bb.

🏨 **Möhringen** without rest, Filderbahnstr. 43, ℰ 71 60 80, Fax 7160850 – 🛗 📺 ☎ ⇌. ㄸ ₥₥
39 rm 165/310 Bb.

🏨 **Neotel** without rest, Vaihinger Str. 151, ℰ 7 80 06 35, Telex 7255179, Fax 7804314 – 🛗 📺
☎ 🅿. ㄸ ⧁ 🖪 ₥₥
71 rm 152/214 Bb.

XXX ❀ **Hirsch-Weinstuben**, Maierstr. 3, ℰ 71 13 75, remarkable wine-list – 🅿. ㄸ ⧁ 🖪
₥₥
closed lunch Monday and Saturday, Sunday, Bank Holidays and Easter – **M** (booking essential)
59/155 and a la carte 50/85
Spec. Gänseleber in Ochsenschwanzgelee, Lachs mit Kartoffelschuppen und Ingwersauce, Kalbsbries mit Basilikumsauce.

at Stuttgart 61 - Obertürkheim by Augsburger Straße JU :

🏨 **Brita Hotel - Restaurant Post**, Augsburger Str. 671, ℰ 32 02 30, Fax 32023400 – 🛗 ⇆ rm
▤ rest 📺 ☎ ⇌ – 🔬 30/100. ㄸ ⧁ 🖪 ₥₥. ⅍ rest
closed 24 December - 6 January – **M** (closed Sunday and Bank Holidays) a la carte 37/66 –
70 rm 112/354 Bb.

X **Weinstube Paule**, Augsburger Str. 643, ℰ 32 14 71 – 🅿. ㄸ ⧁ 🖪 ₥₥
*closed Wednesday dinner, Thursday, last Sunday of the month, 7 to 20 February, 1 to 25 August
and 24 to 30 December* – **M** a la carte 36/63.

at Stuttgart 70 - Plieningen S : 14 km by Mittlere Filderstraße HX :

🏨 **Fissler-Post**, Filderhauptstr. 2, ℰ 4 58 40, Fax 4584333 – 🛗 📺 ☎ ⇌ 🅿 – 🔬 25/80. ㄸ
⧁ 🖪 ₥₥
M (also vegetarian menu) (booking essential) 35/40 and a la carte 51/74 – **61 rm** 90/190 Bb.

🏨 **Traube**, Brabandtgasse 2, ℰ 45 48 33, Fax 4569567, ㄲ – ☎ 🅿
closed 23 December - 6 January and 3 weeks August – **M** (booking essential) (closed Saturday
and Sunday) a la carte 51/96 – **22 rm** 135/280.

🏨 **Apartment Hotel** without rest, Scharnhauser Str. 4, ℰ 4 50 10, Fax 4501100 – 🛗 📺 ☎
⇌. ㄸ ⧁ 🖪 ₥₥
56 rm 152/329 Bb.

XX Recknagel's Nagelschmiede, Brabandtgasse 1, ℰ 45 74 54 – 🅿
Monday - Saturday dinner only.

at Stuttgart 40 - Stammheim by Heilbronner Straße GT :

🏨 **Novotel**, Korntaler Str. 207, ℰ 80 10 65, Telex 7252137, Fax 803673, ⇌, ⅃ – 🛗 ▤ 📺
☎ ৬ 🅿 – 🔬 25/200. ㄸ ⧁ 🖪 ₥₥
M a la carte 35/58 – **117 rm** 164/209 Bb.

at Stuttgart 80-Vaihingen by Böblinger Str. FX :

🏨 **Fontana**, Vollmöllerstr. 5, ℰ 73 00, Telex 7255763, Fax 7302525, Massage, ₣₆, ⇌, 🖾,
ㄲ – 🛗 ⇆ rm ▤ 📺 ৬ ⇌ 🅿 – 🔬 25/380. ㄸ ⧁ 🖪 ₥₥. ⅍ rest
Restaurants : **Fontana M** a la carte 55/89 – **Bräustube M** a la carte 35/70 – **250 rm** 220/355 Bb
– 5 suites 500/1100.

near Schloß Solitude by Rotenwaldstr. FX :

XXX ❀ **Herzog Carl Eugen**, ⊠ 7000 Stuttgart, ℰ (0711) 6 99 07 24, Fax 6990771, ㄲ – 🅿. ㄸ
🖪 ₥₥
closed Sunday, Monday, Bank Holidays and 21 July - 1 August – **M** a la carte 75/88 – **Schloß
- Restaurant** (also vegetarian dishes) (closed Monday) **M** a la carte 43/65
Spec. Gebratene Garnelen auf Artischocken-Tomatengemüse, Lammrücken in Wirsing, Nougat-
terrine mit marinierten Himbeeren.

at Stuttgart 40-Zuffenhausen by Heilbronner Straße GT :

🏨 **Residence**, Schützenbühlstr. 16, ℰ 8 20 01 00, Fax 8200101, ㄲ – 🛗 ⇆ rm ▤ rest 📺
☎ ৬ ⇌ – 🔬 25/60. ㄸ ⧁ 🖪 ₥₥
M a la carte 39/63 – **120 rm** 195/220 Bb.

at Fellbach 7012 NE : 8 km by Nürnberger Straße (B 14) JT – ✆ 0711 :

🏨 **Classic Congress Hotel**, Tainer Str. 7, ℰ 5 85 90, Telex 7254900, Fax 5859304, ⇌ – 🛗
📺 ⇌ 🅿 – 🔬 30. ㄸ ⧁ 🖪 ₥₥
closed 24 to 30 December – **M** (rest. see **Alt Württemberg** below) – **148 rm** 195/280 Bb.

🏠 **City-Hotel** without rest, Bruckstr. 3, ✆ 58 80 14, Fax 582627 – 📺 ☎ 🅿. 🅰🅴 ① 🅴 *VISA*. ⚡
closed 3 to 19 July – **26 rm** 70/125 Bb.

🏠 **Alte Kelter**, Kelterweg 7, ✆ 58 90 74 – 📺 ☎ ⇔ 🅿. 🅰🅴 🅴 *VISA*
(restaurant for residents only) – **20 rm** 90/140.

XX **Alt Württemberg**, Tainer Str. 7 (Schwabenlandhalle), ✆ 58 00 88 – 🔳 🅿. 🅰🅴 ① 🅴 *VISA*
M a la carte 47/74.

X **Weinstube Germania** with rm, Schmerstr. 6, ✆ 58 20 37 – 📺 ☎. ⚡
closed mid July - mid August and 24 December - 9 January – **M** *(closed Sunday, Monday and Bank Holidays)* a la carte 34/58 – **8 rm** 75/140.

X **Weinkeller Häussermann** (18 C. vaulted cellar), Kappelbergstr. 1, ✆ 58 77 75 – 🔳. 🅴
dinner only, closed Sunday, Bank Holidays and 2 weeks July - August – **M** a la carte 35/57.

at Fellbach-Schmiden 7012 NE : 8,5 km by Nürnberger Straße (B 14) JT :

🏨 **Hirsch**, Fellbacher Str. 2, ✆ (0711) 51 40 60, Fax 5181065, ⬥s, 🔲 – 🛗 📺 ☎ ⇔ 🅿 – 🔏 25.
🅰🅴 ① 🅴 *VISA* – **M** *(closed Friday and Sunday)* a la carte 30/59 – **114 rm** 85/180 Bb.

at Gerlingen 7016 W : 10 km by Rotenwaldstraße FX :

🏨 **Krone**, Hauptstr. 28, ✆ (07156) 2 10 04, Fax 21009 – 🛗 📺 ☎ ⇔ 🅿 – 🔏 25/80. 🅰🅴 🅴 *VISA*
M *(closed Monday, Sunday, Bank Holidays, Easter, Christmas and 2 weeks July - August)* (booking essential) a la carte 43/80 – **50 rm** 118/230 Bb.

at Korntal-Münchingen 2 7015 NW : 9 km, by Heilbronner Str. GT :

🏨 **Mercure**, Siemensstr. 50, ✆ (07150) 1 30, Telex 723589, Fax 13266, beer garden, ⬥s, 🔲
– 🛗 🔳 📺 ⬥ 🅿 – 🔏 25/170. 🅰🅴 ① 🅴 *VISA*
M a la carte 45/70 – **209 rm** 205/271 Bb – 6 suites.

at Leinfelden-Echterdingen 1 7022 S : 10 km by Obere Weinsteige GX :

🏠 **Drei Morgen** without rest, Bahnhofstr. 39, ✆ (0711) 75 10 85 – 🛗 📺 ☎ ⇔ 🅿. 🅰🅴 🅴 *VISA*
25 rm 95/150 Bb.

🏠 **Stadt Leinfelden** without rest, Lessingstr. 4, ✆ (0711) 75 25 10, Fax 755649 – ☎ 🅿
20 rm 85/130.

at Leinfelden-Echterdingen 2 7022 S : 11 km by Obere Weinsteige (B 27) GX :

🏨 **Filderland** without rest, Tübinger Str. 16, ✆ (0711) 7 97 89 13, Telex 7255972, Fax 7977576
– 🛗 📺 ☎ ⇔ 🅿 – 🔏 25. 🅰🅴 ① 🅴 *VISA*
closed 24 December - 2 January – **48 rm** 135/220 Bb.

🏨 **Lamm**, Hauptstr. 98, ✆ (0711) 79 90 65, Fax 795275 – 📺 ☎ 🅿. 🅰🅴 ① 🅴 *VISA*
M a la carte 23/49 – **26 rm** 95/130 Bb.

🏠 **Adler**, Obergasse 16, ✆ (0711) 79 35 90, ⬥s, 🔲 – 🛗 📺 ☎ 🅿 – 🔏 30
closed 24 December - 6 January – **M** *(closed Saturday, Sunday and 3 weeks July - August)*
a la carte 27/59 – **18 rm** 105/170.

Baiersbronn 7292. Baden-Württemberg 🔠🔡🔢 HI 21, 🔢🔢🔢 ㉟ – pop. 14 000 – alt. 550 m
– 🕽 07442.
Stuttgart 100.

XXXX ✿✿ **Restaurant Bareiss**, Gärtenbühlweg 14 (at Kurhotel Mitteltal), ✆ 4 70, Fax 47320, ≼,
remarkable wine list – 🔳 🅿. 🅰🅴 ① 🅴 *VISA*
closed Monday, Tuesday, 9 June - 10 July and 23 November - 24 December – **M** *(booking essential)* 140/180 and a la carte 94/127
Spec. Salat von Hummer mit Olivenvinaigrette, Milchlammrücken mit Artischocken, Mohntarte mit Rumsahne.

XXXX ✿✿ **Schwarzwaldstube** (French rest.), Tonbachstr. 237 (at Kur- and Sporthotel Traube Tonbach), ✆ 49 26 65, ≼ – 🅿. 🅰🅴 ① 🅴 *VISA*. ⚡
closed Monday, Tuesday, 7 to 30 January and 6 to 30 July – **M** *(booking essential)* 135/170
and a la carte 85/125
Spec. Muschelgelee mit Caviar (September February), Chartreuse von Gänseleber, Trüffel und Wirsing, Karamelparfait mit marinierten Früchten.

Öhringen 7110. Baden-Württemberg 🔠🔡🔢 L 19, 🔢🔢🔢 ㉕ – pop. 18 000 – alt. 230 m –
🕽 07941.
See : Former Collegiate Church (ehem. Stiftskirche)★ with St. Margaret's altar★.
🏌 Friedrichsruhe (N : 6 km), ✆ (07941) 6 28 01.
Stuttgart 68.

at Friedrichsruhe 7111 N : 6 km :

🏨 ✿✿ **Waldhotel und Schloß Friedrichsruhe** ♨, ✆ (07941) 6 08 70, Telex 74498,
Fax 61468, ☂, « Garden, park », ⬥s, 🔲, 🔲, ✼, 🏌 – 🛗 📺 ☎ ⇔ 🅿 – 🔏 25/80. 🅰🅴 ① 🅴
VISA – **M** *(closed Monday und Tuesday)* (remarkable wine list) 115/185 and a la carte 85/120
– **49 rm** 165/405 – 11 suites 427/573
Spec. Bretonischer Hummer auf marinierten Kartoffelscheiben, Jacobsmuscheln mit Lauchvariationen, Lammcoteletts im Kartoffelrösti.

Greece

Hellás

ATHENS

PRACTICAL INFORMATION

LOCAL CURRENCY

Greek Drachma: 100 Drs = 0.57 US $ (Jan. 92)

TOURIST INFORMATION

National Tourist Organisation (EOT): 2 Kar. Servias, ✆ 322 25 45 (information) and 1 Ermou, 325 22 67. Hotel reservation: Hellenic Chamber of Hotels, 24 Stadiou, ✆ 323 69 62, Telex: 214 269. Also at East Airport ✆ 970 23 95 - Tourist Police: 7 Singrou ✆ 171.

FOREIGN EXCHANGE

Banks are usually open on weekdays from 8am to 2pm. A branch of the National Bank of Greece is open daily from 8am to 2pm (from 9am to 1pm at weekends) at 2 Karageorgi Servias (Sindagma).

AIRLINES

OLYMPIC AIRWAYS: 96 Leoforos Singrou 117 41 Athens, ✆ 929 22 51 and 6 Othonos (Sindagma) 105 57 Athens, ✆ 961 61 61.
All following Companies are located near Sindagma Square:
AIR FRANCE: 4 Karageorgi Servias 105 62 Athens, ✆ 323 85 07.
BRITISH AIRWAYS: 10 Othonos 105 57 Athens, ✆ 325 06 01.
JAPAN AIRLINES: 4 Amalias 105 57 Athens, ✆ 324 82 11.
LUFTHANSA: 11 El. Venizelou 106 71 Athens, ✆ 771 60 02.
SABENA: 8 Othonos 105 57 Athens, ✆ 323 68 21.
SWISSAIR: 4 Othonos 105 57 Athens, ✆ 323 75 81.
TWA: 8 Xenofondos 105 57 Athens, ✆ 322 64 51.

TRANSPORT IN ATHENS

Taxis: may be hailed in the street even when already engaged: it is advised to always pay by the meter.
Bus: good for sightseeing and practical for short distances: 75 Drs.
Metro: one single line crossing the city from North (Kifissia) to South (Pireas) : 100 Drs.

POSTAL SERVICES

General Post Office: 100 Eolou (Omonia) with poste restante, and also at Sindagma.
Telephone (OTE): 15 Stadiou, and 85 Patission (all services), 65 Stadiou and 50 Athinas (only for telephone calls).

SHOPPING IN ATHENS

In summer, shops are usually open from 8am to 1.30pm, and 5.30 to 8.30pm. They close on Sunday, and at 2.30pm on Monday, Wednesday and Saturday. In winter they open from 9am to 5pm on Monday and Wednesday, from 10am to 7pm on Tuesday, Thursday and Friday, from 8.30am to 3.30pm on Saturday. Department Stores in Patission and Eolou are open fron 8.30 am to 8 pm on weekdays and 3 pm on Saturdays. The main shopping streets are to be found in Sindagma, Kolonaki, Monastiraki and Omonia areas. Flea Market (generally open on Sunday) and Greek Handicraft in Plaka and Monastiraki.

TIPPING

Service is generally included in the bills but it is usual to tip employees.

SPEED LIMITS

The speed limit in built up areas is 50 km/h (31 mph); on motorways the maximum permitted speed is 100 km/h (62 mph) and 80 km/h (50 mph) on others roads.

SEAT BELTS

The wearing of seat belts is compulsory for drivers and front seat passengers.

BREAKDOWN SERVICE

The ELPA (Automobile and Touring Club of Greece) operate a 24 hour breakdown service: phone 104.

Athens

(ATHÍNA) Atikí 980 ③ – Pop. 3 076 786 (Athens and Piraeus area) – ✪ 01.

SIGHTS :

Views of Athens : Lycabettos (Likavitós) 🌲★★★ DX – Philopappos Hill (Lófos Filopápou) ≼★★★ AY.

ANCIENT ATHENS

Acropolis★★★ (Akrópoli) ABY – Theseion★★ (Thissío) AY and Agora★ (Arhéa Agorá) AY – Theatre of Dionysos★★ (Théatro Dioníssou) BY and Odeon of Herod Atticus★ (Odío Iródou Atikóu) AY – Olympieion★★ (Naós Olimbíou Diós) BY and Hadrian's Arch★ (Píli Adrianóu) BY – Tower of the Winds★ BY **G** in the Roman Forum (Romaïkí Agorá).

OLD ATHENS AND THE TURKISH PERIOD

Pláka★★ : Old Metropolitan★★ BY **A2** – Monastiráki★ (Old Bazaar) : Kapnikaréa (Church) BY **A6**, Odós Pandróssou★ BY **29**, Monastiráki Square★ BY.

MODERN ATHENS

Sindagma Square★ CY : Greek guard on sentry duty – Academy, University and Library Buildings★ (Akadimía CX, Panepistímio CX, Ethnikí Vivliothíki BX) – National Garden★ (Ethnikós Kípos) CY.

MUSEUMS

National Archaelogical Museum★★★ (Ethnikó Arheologikó Moussío) BX – Acropolis Museum★★★ BY **M** – Museum of Cycladic and Ancient Greek Art★★ DY **M15** – Byzantine Museum★★ (Vizandinó Moussío) DY – Benaki Museum★★ (private collection of antiquities and traditional art) CDY – Museum of Traditional Greek Art★ BY **M2** – National Historical Museum★ BY **M7** – Jewish Museum of Greece★ BY **M16** – National Gallery and Soutzos Museum★ (painting and sculpture) DY **M8**.

EXCURSIONS

Cape Sounion★★★ (Soúnio) SE : 71 km BY – Kessariani Monastery★★, E : 9 km DY – Daphne Monastery★★ (Dafní) NW : 10 km AX – Aigina Island★ (Égina) : Temple of Aphaia★★, 3 hours Return.

🏌 Glifáda (near airport) 𝒫 894 68 20.

✈ S : 15 km, East Airport 𝒫 969 91 11 (International Airport – All companies except Olympic Airways), West Airport 𝒫 929 21 11 (Eliniko Airport – Olympic Airways only) – East Airport Terminal : 4 Amalias 𝒫 324 20 24, West Airport Terminal : 96 Singrou 𝒫 981 12 01.

🚂 1 Karolou 𝒫 524 06 46.

🛈 Tourist Information (EOT), 26 Amerikis 𝒫 322 31 11 and East Airport 𝒫 970 23 95.
ELPA (Automobile and Touring Club of Greece), 2 Messogion 𝒫 779 16 15.

Igoumenítsa 581 – Pátra 215 – Thessaloníki 479.

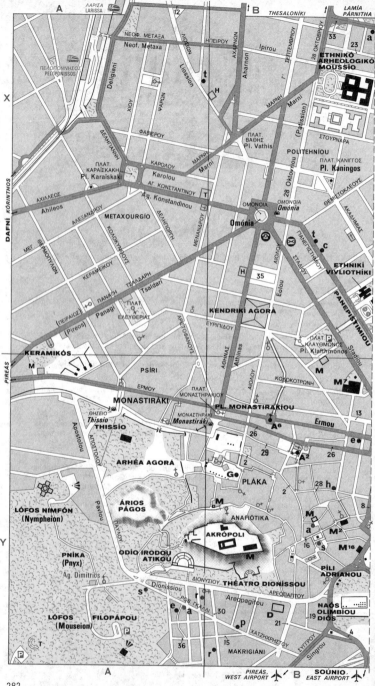

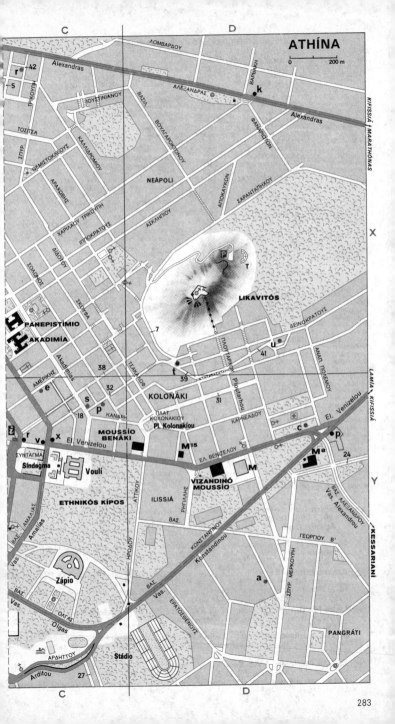

STREET INDEX TO ATHÍNA TOWN PLAN

Athenaeum Inter-Continental, 89-93 Singrou, 117 45, SW : 2 ¾ km ⌀ 9023 666, Telex 221554, Fax 9217 653, « Première rooftop restaurant with ≤ Athens », ⅊, ⇆, ⅃ – ᵇ ᵇ rm ▥ ☎ & ⇌ – ⩜ 2 000. 🅐🅔 ◑ 🅔 𝑽𝑰𝑺𝑨 ⚜
by Singrou BY
M (see also **La Rotisserie** below) – **Kublai Khan** *(dinner only)* 7500 and a la carte 6900/12050 – **Première** (dinner only) a la carte 5500/10600 – ☷ 3750 – **511 rm** 35800/47900, **40 suites** 55000/90000.

Athens Hilton, 46 El Venizelou, 115 28, ⌀ 7220 201, Telex 215808, Fax 7213 110, ≤, ⇆, ⅃ heated – ᵇ ᵇ rm ▥ ☎ & – ⩜ 1 700. 🅐🅔 ◑ 🅔 𝑽𝑰𝑺𝑨
DY **p**
M Ta Nissia *(closed July and August)* (dinner only) 5500 and a la carte – **Kellari** – Byzantine 8258 and a la carte – ☷ 3670 – **434 rm** 61720/72492, **19 suites** 85333/292039.

Ledra Marriott, 115 Singrou, 117 45, SW : 3 km ⌀ 934 7711, Telex 221833, Fax 935 9153, « Rooftop terrace with pool and ⚘ Athens » – ᵇ ᵇ rm ▥ ☎ ⇌ – ⩜ 500. 🅐🅔 ◑ 🅔 𝑽𝑰𝑺𝑨 ⚜
by Singrou BY
M (see also **Kona Kai** below) – **Ledra Grill** *(closed Tuesday and June-September)* (dinner only) 6500/8000 and a la carte – ☷ 2000 – **242 rm** 32000/39500, **16 suites** 80000/270000.

Le NJV Meridien, 2 Vas. Georgiou A , Sindagma, 105 64, ⌀ 3255 301, Telex 210568, Fax 3235 856 – ᵇ ᵇ rm ▥ ☎ & – ⩜ 100. 🅐🅔 ◑ 🅔 𝑽𝑰𝑺𝑨 ⚜
CY **r**
M La Brasserie des Arts a la carte 10900 – ☷ 3100 – **162 rm** 30280/49550, **15 suites** 56891/82584.

Grande Bretagne, Vas. Georgiou A , Sindagma, 105 63, ✆ 3230 251, Telex 219615, Fax 3228 034 – 🛗 ▤ TV ☎ – 🏛 400. AE ⓓ E VISA CY **v**
M G B Corner a la carte 6200/10500 – ☕ 2200 – **330 rm** 34987/55300, **22 suites** 63340/148840.

Astir Palace, Panepistimiou and El Venizelou, 106 71, ✆ 3643 112, Telex 222380, Fax 3642 825 – 🛗 ▤ TV ☎ – 🏛 150. AE ⓓ E VISA. ✻ CY **x**
M 5500 and a la carte 4300/7650 – ☕ 2800 – **59 rm** 29000/37000, **18 suites** 55000/77000.

Divani Palace Acropolis, 19-25 Parthenonos, 117 42, ✆ 9222 945, Telex 218306, Fax 9214 993, « Ancient ruins of Themistoccles wall in basement », 🏊 – 🛗 ▤ TV ☎ – 🏛 500. AE ⓓ E VISA. ✻ BY **r**
M Aspassia 4300 and a la carte – **Roof Garden** *(summer only)* – **247 rm**, **6 suites.**

Holiday Inn, 50 Mihalakopoulou, 115 28, ✆ 7248 322, Telex 218870, Fax 7248 187, 🏊 – 🛗 ▤ TV ☎ 🚗 – 🏛 700. AE ⓓ E VISA. ✻ by Mihalakopoulou DY
M 3700 and a la carte – ☕ 2300 – **185 rm** 24000/32000, **4 suites** 54000/75000.

Novotel Mirayia, 4-6 Mihail Voda, 104 39, ✆ 8627 053, Telex 226264, Fax 8837 816, « Roof garden with 🏊 and ✻ Athens » – 🛗 ▤ TV ☎ 🚗 – 🏛 520. AE ⓓ E VISA AX **t**
M 2700/3000 and a la carte – ☕ 1600 – **190 rm** 14000/16500, **5 suites** 26000/30000.

Chandris, 385 Singrou, 175 64, SW : 7 km ✆ 9414 824, Telex 218112, Fax 9425 082, « Summer rooftop restaurant with 🏊 and ✻ Athens » – 🛗 ▤ TV ☎ – 🏛 500. AE ⓓ E VISA. ✻ by Singrou BY
M Four Seasons *(October-May) (closed Sunday)* a la carte 3200/5200 – **Flamingo** 3000 and a la carte – **364 rm** ☕ 17000/20500, **6 suites** 30000/60000.

St. George Lycabettus, 2 Kleomenous, 106 75, ✆ 7290 711, Telex 214253, Fax 7290 439, ≤, « ≤ Athens from Grand Balcon rooftop restaurant », 🏊 – 🛗 ▤ TV ☎ – 🏛 120. AE ⓓ E VISA DX **t**
M 3000 (lunch) and a la carte approx. 6000 – **141 rm** ☕ 16500/29720, **5 suites** 42000/59000.

Park, 10 Alexandras, 106 82, ✆ 8832 712, Telex 214748, Fax 8238 420, « Roof garden with 🏊 and ✻ Athens » – 🛗 ▤ TV ☎ 🚗 – 🏛 700. AE ⓓ E VISA. ✻ BX **a**
M 3400 and a la carte – **126 rm** ☕ 16500/21900, **19 suites** 33000.

Zafolia, 87-89 Alexandras, 114 74, ✆ 6449 002, Telex 214468, Fax 6442 042, « Rooftop terrace with 🏊 and ≤ Athens » – 🛗 ▤ TV ☎ 🚗 – 🏛 200. AE ⓓ E VISA. ✻ DX **k**
M 2450/3000 and a la carte – **183 rm** ☕ 7500/13800, **8 suites** 13800/19250.

Herodion, 4 Rov. Gali, 117 42, ✆ 9236 832, Telex 219423, Fax 9235 851, « Roof garden with ≤ Acropolis » – 🛗 ▤ TV ☎ – 🏛 50. AE ⓓ E VISA. ✻ BY **p**
M 2500/2800 and a la carte – **86 rm** ☕ 15600/19800, **4 suites** 26000.

Titania, 52 Panepistimiou, 106 78, ✆ 3609 611, Telex 214673, Fax 3630 497, « Roof garden with ≤ Athens » – 🛗 ▤ ☎ 🚗 – 🏛 700. AE ⓓ E VISA. ✻ BX **t**
M 3000/3250 and a la carte – **380 rm** ☕ 10820/18120, **20 suites** 24030/35980.

Electra Palace, 18 Nikodimou, 105 57, ✆ 3241 401, Group Telex 216896, Fax 3241 875, 🏊 – 🛗 ▤ TV ☎ 🚗 – 🏛 50. AE ⓓ E VISA. ✻ BY **h**
M 3400 and a la carte – **106 rm** ☕ 15600/19600, **5 suites** 26600.

Electra, 5 Ermou, 105 63, ✆ 3223 222, Group Telex 216896, Fax 3220 310 – 🛗 ▤ TV ☎. AE ⓓ E VISA. ✻ BY **e**
M 3400 and a la carte – **110 rm** ☕ 15600/19600.

Acropolis View without rest., 10 Wemster, off Rov. Gali, 117 42, ✆ 9217 303, Telex 219936, Fax 9230 705, ≤ – 🛗 ▤ ☎. AE E VISA AY **e**
32 rm ☕ 8200/10900.

XXXX **Mare Nostrum,** 292 Kifissias (3rd floor), N. Psihiko, 154 51, NE : 7 ½ km on Kifissia Rd ✆ 6722 891, Fax 6479 422, 🏕, French rest. – 🛗 ▤. AE ⓓ E VISA
closed Sunday – **M** 12000/16000 and a la carte 15000/12000.

XXXX **La Rotisserie** (at Athenaeum Inter-Continental H.), 89-93 Singrou, 117 45, ✆ 9023 666, Telex 221554, Fax 9217 653 – ▤ 🚗. AE ⓓ E VISA by Singrou BY
closed Sunday, Monday and mid June-1 October – **M** (dinner only) a la carte 7950/12900.

XXX **Precieux, Gastronomie,** 14 Akadimias (1st floor), 106 71, ✆ 3608 616, Fax 3608 619, French rest., « Skyscape mural by Italian artist » – 🛗 ▤ – 🏛 50. AE ⓓ E VISA CY **s**
closed Sunday, Easter, 25 December and 1 January – **M** a la carte 10000/15000.

XXX **Athenaeum,** 8 Amerikis, International Cultural Centre, 106 71, ✆ 3631 125 – ▤. AE ⓓ E VISA CY **e**
closed Sunday, July-August and Bank Holidays – **M** a la carte 8000/18000.

XXX **Boschetto,** Evangelismos Park, off El Venizelou, 106 75, ✆ 7210 893, Fax 7223 598, 🏕, Italian rest., « Summerhouse in small park » – ▤. AE ⓓ VISA DY **c**
closed lunch November-March, Sunday and 2 weeks August – **M** a la carte 8000/10000.

XXX **Kona Kai** (at Ledra Marriott H.), 115 Singrou, 117 45, ✆ 9347 711, Telex 223465, Fax 9358 603, Polynesian and Japanese (Teppan-Yaki) rest., « Pacific islands style decor » – ▤ 🚗. AE ⓓ E VISA by Singrou BY
closed Sunday – **M** (dinner only) a la carte 6500/11500.

XX **Symbosium,** 46 Erehthiou, 117 42, ✆ 9225 321, « Conservatory in winter, 🌣 in summer »
– 🏧 ⓘ 🅴 𝗩𝗜𝗦𝗔　　　　　　　　　　　　　　　　　　　　　　　　AY　r
　　closed Sunday – **M** (dinner only) 5000/8500 and a la carte.

XX **Ideal,** 46 Panepistimiou, 106 78, ✆ 3614 604, Fax 3631 000 – 🏧 ⓘ 🅴 𝗩𝗜𝗦𝗔　　　BX　c
　　closed Sunday – **M** a la carte 3000/5000.

XX **La Brasserie,** 292 Kifissias (3rd floor), N. Psihiko, 154 51, NE : 7 ½ km on Kifissia Rd
　　✆ 6716 572, Fax 6417 940, 🌣 – |🕏| 🍴, 🏧 ⓘ 🅴 𝗩𝗜𝗦𝗔
　　closed Sunday – **M** 2900/3900 (lunch) and a la carte 6150/8050.

XX **Dioscuri,** 16 Dimitriou Vassiliou, N. Psihiko, 154 51, NE : 7 km by Kifissia Rd turning at A.B.
　　supermarket ✆ 6713 997, 🌣 – 🍴, 🏧 ⓘ 🅴 𝗩𝗜𝗦𝗔　　　　7 km by El Venizelou　DY
　　closed lunch July and August, Sunday and Bank Holidays – **M** (booking essential) a la carte
　　4000/8000.

XX **L'Abreuvoir,** 51 Xenokratous, Kolonaki, 106 76, ✆ 7229 106, 🌣, French rest. – 🍴, 🏧 ⓘ
　　🅴 𝗩𝗜𝗦𝗔　　　　　　　　　　　　　　　　　　　　　　　　　　　　　　DX　u
　　M a la carte 7000/9000.

XX **Spiros Vasilis,** 5 Lahitos, 115 21, off El Venizelou, turn left at second set of traffic lights
　　after Hilton H. ✆ 7237 575, Steak rest. – 🏧 ⓘ　　　　　　　　by El Venizelou　DY
　　closed Sunday, 3 days Easter and June-September – **M** (booking essential) (dinner only) a la
　　carte 4500/8000.

XX **Gerofinikas,** 10 Pindarou, 106 71, ✆ 3636 710 – 🍴, 🏧 ⓘ 🅴 𝗩𝗜𝗦𝗔　　　　　CY　p
　　closed Easter and 25 December – **M** a la carte 6000/9000.

XX **Dionysos,** 43 Rov. Gali, 117 42, ✆ 9233 182, Fax 9221 998, ≤ Acropolis, 🌣 – 🅿, 🏧 ⓘ
　　🅴 𝗩𝗜𝗦𝗔　　　　　　　　　　　　　　　　　　　　　　　　　　　　　　AY　s
　　M 4500/6600 and a la carte.

X **Strofi,** 25 Rov. Gali, 117 42, ✆ 9214 130, 🌣, « ≤ Acropolis from rooftop terrace » – 🏧
　　ⓘ 🅴 𝗩𝗜𝗦𝗔　　　　　　　　　　　　　　　　　　　　　　　　　　　　　AY　a
　　closed Sunday, Easter and Christmas – **M** (dinner only) a la carte 1800/2950.

"The Tavernas"

Typical little Greek restaurants, generally very modest, where it is pleasant to spend
the evening, surrounded with noisy but friendly locals, sometimes with guitar
or bouzouki entertainment. These particular restaurants are usually open for dinner
only.

XX **Myrtia,** 32-34 Trivonianou, 116 36, ✆ 7012 276 – 🍴, 🏧 ⓘ 🅴 𝗩𝗜𝗦𝗔　　　　CY　a
　　closed Sunday – **M** (music) (booking essential) (dinner only) 6500/9000.

X **Kostoyanis,** 37 Zaïmi, 106 82, ✆ 8220 624　　　　　　　　　　　　　　　　CX　r
　　closed Sunday and 15 July-15 August – **M** (dinner only) a la carte 3000/4100.

X **O Anthropos,** 13 Arhelaou, ✆ 7235 914, Seafood – 🅴　　　　　　　　　　　DY　a
　　closed Sunday and June-early October – **M** (dinner only) a la carte 3200/7500.

X **Kidathineon,** 3 Filomoussou Eterias Sq., 105 58, ✆ 3234 281, 🌣 – 🏧 ⓘ 🅴 𝗩𝗜𝗦𝗔 BY　s
　　M (dinner only) 2600/3800 and a la carte.

X **Xinos,** 4 Geronda, ✆ 3221 065　　　　　　　　　　　　　　　　　　　　　　BY　a
　　closed Saturday, Sunday and July – **M** (music) (booking essential) (dinner only) a la carte approx.
　　3000.

At Kifissia NE : 15 km by El Venizelou DY :

🏨 **Penteliko,** 66 Diligiani, 145 62 (Kifissia), off Harilaou Trikoupi follow signs to Politia
　　✆ 8080 311, Telex 224649, Fax 8010 314, 🌣, 🏊, 🎾 – |🕏| 🏧 rm 🍴 📺 ☎ – 🔒 350. 🏧
　　ⓘ 🅴 𝗩𝗜𝗦𝗔. 🛇
　　M 2000/6000 and a la carte 6000/9000 **Vardis** (dinner only) 6000/9000 and a la carte
　　7000/11500 – **Belle Epoque** *(closed mid June-September)* (dinner only) 5000/8500 and a la
　　carte 6000/10000 – 🍽 3200 – **31 rm** 42000/48100, 11 suites 66500/115000.

at Pireas SW : 10 km by Singrou BY :

🏨 **Mistral,** 105 Vas. Pavlou, Kastella, 185 33, ✆ 4117 150, Telex 212811, Fax 4122 096 – |🕏|
　　🍴 ☎ 🚗 – 🔒 200. 🏧 ⓘ 🅴 𝗩𝗜𝗦𝗔. 🛇
　　M 2400 and a la carte – **71 rm** 🍽 10800/14100, **3 suites** 25500.

XX **Aglamer,** 54-56 Akti Koumoundourou, Mikrolimano, 185 33, ✆ 4115 511, ≤, 🌣, Seafood
　　– 🍴, 🏧 ⓘ 🅴 𝗩𝗜𝗦𝗔
　　closed 25 December – **M** a la carte approx. 6000.

X **Durambeis,** 29 Athinas Dilaveri, 185 33, ✆ 4122 092, 🌣, Seafood
　　closed 4 days Easter, August and 25 December – **M** a la carte 3000/9000.

X **Psaropoula,** 22 Akti Koumoundourou, Mikrolimano, 185 33, ✆ 4112 479, ≤, 🌣, Seafood
　　– 🏧 ⓘ 🅴 𝗩𝗜𝗦𝗔
　　M a la carte 3500/8000.

Hungary

Magyarország

PRACTICAL INFORMATION

LOCAL CURRENCY

Forint : 100 Forints = 1.37 US $ (Jan. 92)

PRICES

Prices may change if goods and service costs in Hungary are revised and it is therefore always advisable to confirm rates with the hotelier when making a reservation.

FOREIGN EXCHANGE

It is strongly advised against changing money other than in banks, exchange offices or authorised offices such as large hotels, tourist offices, etc... Banks are usually open on weekdays from 8.30 to 11.30 am.

HOTEL RESERVATIONS

In case of difficulties in finding a room through our hotel selection, it is always possible to apply to IBUSZ Hotel Service, Petőfi tér 3, Budapest 5th ℰ (1) 18 68 88. This office offer a 24 hour assistance to the visitor.

POSTAL SERVICES

Post offices are open from 8am to 6pm on weekdays and 2pm on Saturdays.
General Post Office : Varoshaz u. 19, Budapest 5th, ℰ (1) 17 01 11.

SHOPPING IN BUDAPEST

In the index of street names, those printed in red are where the principal shops are found. Typical goods to be bought include embroidery, lace, china, leather goods, paprika, salami, Tokay, palinka, foie-gras... Shops are generally open from 10am to 6pm on weekdays (8pm on Thursday) and 9am to 1pm on Saturday.

TIPPING

Hotel, restaurant and café bills include service in the total charge but it is usual to leave the staff a gratuity which will vary depending upon the service given.

CAR HIRE

The international car hire companies have branches in Budapest. Your hotel porter should be able to give details and help you with your arrangements.

BREAKDOWN SERVICE

A breakdown service is operated by SARGA ANGYAL (Yellow Angel), ℰ (1) 69 18 31.

SPEED LIMIT

On motorways, the maximum permitted speed is 110 km/h – 68 mph, 80 km/h – 50 mph on other roads and 60 km/h – 37 mph in built up areas.

SEAT BELTS

In Hungary, the wearing of seat belts is compulsory for drivers and all passengers.

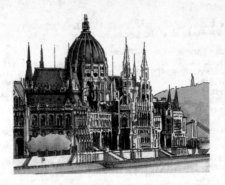

Budapest

Hungary 970 N 6 – Pop. 2 172 000 – ✪ 1.

Views of Budapest

St. Gellert Monument and Citadel (Szt. Gellért-szobor, Citadella) ≼*** EX – Fishermen's Bastion (Halászbástya) ≼** DU.

BUDA

Matthias Church** (Mátyás-templom) DU – Attractive Streets** (Tancsics Mihaly utca – Fortuna utca – Uri utca) CDU – Royal Palace** (Budavári palota) DV – Hungarian National Gallery** (Magyar Nemzeti Galéria) DV **M1** – Budapest Historical Museum* (Budapesti Történeti Múzeum) DV **M1** – Vienna Gate* (Bécsi kapu) CU **D** – War History Museum* (Hadtörténety Múzeum) CU **M2**.

PEST

Parliament Building*** (Országház) EU – Museum of Fine Arts*** (Szepmüveszeti Múzeum) BY **M3** – Hungarian National Museum** (Magyar Nemzeti Múzeum) FVX **M4** – Museum of Applied Arts** (Iparmüvészeti Múzeum) BZ **M5** – Szechenyi Thermal Baths** (Széchényi Gyógyés Strandfürdö) BY **D** – Hungarian State Opera House* (Magyar Állami Operaház) FU **B** – Liszt Conservatory : foyer* (Liszt Ferenc Zeneművészeti Föiskola) FU **D** – Chinese Art Museum* (Kína Muzéum) BYZ **M6** – St. Stephen's Basilica* (Szt. István-bazilika) EU **E** – City Parish Church* (Belvárosi plébániatemplom) EV **K** – University Church* (Egyetemi Templom) FX **R** – Franciscan Church* (Ferences templom) FV **L** – Municipal Concert Hall* (Vigadó) EV **F** – Town Hall* (Fövárosi Tanács) EFV **H** – Paris Arcade* (Parisi udvar) EV – Vaci Street* (Vaci utca) EV – Hungaria Restaurant* (Hungaria Ettermek) BZ **N** – Budapest West Station* (Nyugati pályaudvar) AY – Millenary Monument* (Millenniumi emlékmu) BY **F** – City Park* (Városliget) BYZ – Vajdahunyad Castle* (Vajdahunyad vára) BY **B** – Hungarian Transport Museum* (Magyar Közlekedesi Múzeum) BY **M7**.

ADDITIONAL SIGHTS

Chain Bridge** (Széchényi Lanchíd) DEV – Margaret Island* (Margitsziget) AY – Aquincum Museum* (Aquincumi Muzéum) N : 12 km by Szentendrei út AY – Gellert Thermal Baths* (Géllert gyógyfürdö) EX – St. Ann's Church* (Szent Anna templom) DU.

Envir.

Szentendre* N : 20 km – Visegrad N : 42 km : Citadel, view**

⚓ Ferihegy SE : 16 km by Üllol FX, 𝒫 57 22 24 (information) and 57 00 86 (passenger service), Bus to airport : Volán, from International Bus station, Engels tér, Station 6 Budapest 5th and Express Bus Airport, Erzsebet Place – MALEV, Roosevelt tér 2, Budapest 5th 𝒫 18 90 33

𝔹 Tourinform, Sütö u. 2, ✉ H 1052 𝒫 17 98 00 – IBUSZ Head Office, Felszabadulas tér 5, Budapest 5th 𝒫 18 68 88 – Documentation : IPV, Angol u. 22 ✉ H 1149.

München 678 – Praha 533 – Venezia 740 – Wien 243 – Zagreb 350

🏨 **Hilton**, Hess András tér 1/3, 1044, ✆ 1751000, Telex 225984, Fax 1751000, ≤ Danube and Buda, « Remains of a 13C Dominican church » – 🛗 ⇔ rm 🖭 📺 ☎ 㐂 ⇔ – 🏛 600
DU **a**
M Dominican – Kolocsa – **295 rm, 28 suites.**

🏨 **Forum**, Apáczai Csere J. utca 12, 1368, ✆ 117 80 88, Telex 224178, Fax 117 98 08, ≤ Danube and Buda, ♨, ⇌, 🔄 – 🛗 ⇔ rm 🖭 📺 ☎ 㐂 ⇔ – 🏛 300
EV **n**
M Silhouette a la carte 1005/2400 – **392 rm** ⌫ 13950/19530 **16 suites.**

🏨 **Atrium Hyatt**, Roosevelt tér 2, 1366, ✆ 138 30 00, Telex 225485, Fax 118 86 59, ≤, ♨, ⇌, 🔄 – 🛗 ⇔ 🖭 📺 ☎ 㐂 ⇔ – 🏛 350. 🆎 ⑩ 🖂 𝘝𝘐𝘚𝘈
EV **k**
M – Old Timer 3060/4208 and a la carte – Tokaj – **331 rm** ⌫ 15300/20655, **22 suites** 22567/35955.

🏨 **Beke Radisson**, Teréz Krt. 43, 1067, ✆ 132 33 00, Telex 22 57 48, Fax 153 33 80, ⇌, 🔄 – 🛗 ⇔ rm 🖭 📺 ☎ 㐂 ⇔ – 🏛 200. 🆎 ⑩ 🖂 𝘝𝘐𝘚𝘈
FU **a**
M 1627/2325 and a la carte – **238 rm** ⌫ 12555/14880, **8 suites** 23250.

🏨 **Thermal Helia**, Kárpát utca 62-64, 1133, ✆ 129 86 50, Telex 202539, Fax 120 14 29, ≤, Therapy centre, ♨, ⇌, 🔄 – 🛗 ⇔ rm 🖂 rest 📺 ☎ 㐂 ⓟ – 🏛 400. 🆎 ⑩ 🖂 𝘝𝘐𝘚𝘈
AY **c**
M 1162/1627 and a la carte – **254 rm** ⌫ 9300/13950, **8 suites** 21855/35805.

🏨 **Gellert**, Gellert tér 1, 1111, ✆ 185 22 00, Telex 224363, Fax 166 66 31, Direct entrance to the Therapic bath, ♨, ⇌, 🔄 heated, 🔄 – 🛗 🖂 📺 ☎ 㐂 ⓟ – 🏛 500
EX **n**
M A la carte 1150/3300 – **221 rm** ⌫ 9140/14230, **14 suites.**

🏨 **Korona**, Kecskeméti utca 14, 1053, ✆ 117 91 17, Telex 223622, Fax 118 38 67, ♨, ⇌, 🔄 – 🛗 ⇔ rm 🖭 📺 ☎ 㐂 ⇔ – 🏛 80
FX **s**
M A la carte 890/1780 – **422 rm** ⌫ 12790/15110, **11 suites.**

🏨 **Ramada Grand Hotel** ⅀, Margitsziget, 1138, ✆ 132 11 00, Telex 226682, Fax 153 30 29, ⛲ – 🛗 ⇔ rm 📺 ☎ 㐂 ⓟ – 🏛 85
AY **b**
M A la carte 670/1570 – **152 rm** ⌫ 8695/14320, **10 suites.**

🏨 **Astoria**, Kossuth Lajos utca 19, 1053, ✆ 117 34 11, Telex 224205, Fax 118 67 98 – 📺 ☎ – 🏛 30. 🆎 ⑩ 🖂 𝘝𝘐𝘚𝘈
FV **q**
M 744/1162 and a la carte – **123 rm** ⌫ 6882/10090, **6 suites** 11625/13485.

🏨 **Grand Hotel Hungaria**, Rákóczi utca 90, 1074, ✆ 122 90 50, Fax 122 80 29, ♨, ✂ – 🛗 📺 ☎ ⇔ – 🏛 500
BZ **f**
M A la carte 695/1245 – **520 rm** ⌫ 8185/10250, **8 suites.**

🏨 **Flamenco**, Tas Vezér utca 7, 1113, ✆ 161 22 50, Telex 224647, Fax 165 80 07, ⇌, 🔄 – 🛗 🖂 📺 ☎ ⇔ – 🏛 200. 🆎 ⑩ 🖂 𝘝𝘐𝘚𝘈
AZ **p**
M 765/1530 and a la carte – **336 rm** ⌫ 8950/11016, **12 suites** 18666.

🏨 **Buda Penta**, Krisztina Krt. 41-43, 1013, ✆ 156 63 33, Fax 155 69 64, ♨, ⇌, 🔄 – 🛗 ⇔ rm 🖂 📺 ☎ ⇔ ⓟ – 🏛 100
CV **f**
M A la carte 560/1645 – **389 rm** ⌫ 9625/12650, **6 suites.**

🏨 **Alba** without rest., Apor Péter utca 3, 1011, ✆ 175 86 58, Telex 225671, Fax 175 98 99 – 🛗 ⇔ rm 📺 ☎ ⇔ ⓟ – 🏛 25. 🆎 ⑩ 🖂 𝘝𝘐𝘚𝘈
DV **e**
95 rm ⌫ 10230/12555

🏨 **Novotel**, Alkotás utca 63-67, 1123, ✆ 186 95 88, Telex 225496, Fax 166 56 36, ≤, ⇌ – 🛗 ⇔ rm 🖂 📺 ☎ ⓟ – 🏛 2 000. 🆎 ⑩ 🖂 𝘝𝘐𝘚𝘈
CX **h**
M 1860 and a la carte – **318 rm** ⌫ 9253/11485, **6 suites** 12555/14880.

🏨 **Taverna**, Váci utca 20, ✆ 138 49 99, Telex 227707, Fax 118 71 88, ⇌ – 🛗 🖂 rest 📺 ☎ ⇔ – 🏛 100
EV **h**
M (residents only) – **196 rm** ⌫ 7675/9765, **28 suites.**

🏨 **Victoria**, without rest., Bem Rakpart 11, 1011, ✆ 201 86 44, Telex 202650, Fax 201 58 16, ≤, ⇌ – 🛗 🖂 📺 ☎ ⓟ
DU **d**
23 rm ⌫ 9765/10230, **1 suite.**

🏨 **Liget** without rest., Dozsa György utca 106, 1068, ✆ 111 32 00, Telex 223648, Fax 131 71 53, ⇌ – 🛗 🖂 📺 ☎ ⇔ ⓟ
BY **e**
140 rm ⌫ 7675/8695.

🏨 **Nemzeti**, József krt. 4, 1088, ✆ 133 91 60, Telex 227710, Fax 114 00 19 – 🛗 📺 ☎ – 🏛 30. 🆎 ⑩ 🖂 𝘝𝘐𝘚𝘈
BZ **k**
M 604 and a la carte – **75 rm** ⌫ 6649/9160, **1 suite** 10788.

🍴🍴🍴 **Alabardos**, Orszaghaz utca 2, 1014, ✆ 156 02 51, ⛲, Vaulted, « Gothic interior, covered courtyard » ⛲
CU **c**
M (booking essential) (dinner only) a la carte 2200/3000.

🍴🍴🍴 **Gundel**, Állatkertí utca 2, ✆ 122 10 02, Fax 142 29 17, ⛲ – ⓟ – 🏛 200
BY **d**
M (booking essential) a la carte 2800/3800.

🍴🍴🍴 **Legradí Testverek**, Magyar utca 3, 1053, ✆ 118 68 04, Vaulted cellar
FX **r**
closed 6 weeks end June-mid August – **M** *(closed Saturday and Sunday)* (booking essential) dinner only a la carte 1950/3550.

🍴🍴🍴 **Barokk**, Mozsar utca 12, 1066, ✆ 131 89 42, cellar – 🆎
FU **c**
M (booking essential) 3200/5000 and a la carte.

🍴🍴 **Szindbád**, Bajcsy-Zsilinszky utca 74, 1055, ✆ 132 27 49, Fax 112 38 36, Vaulted cellar
EU **d**
M (booking essential) a la carte 2200/3500.

BUDAPEST

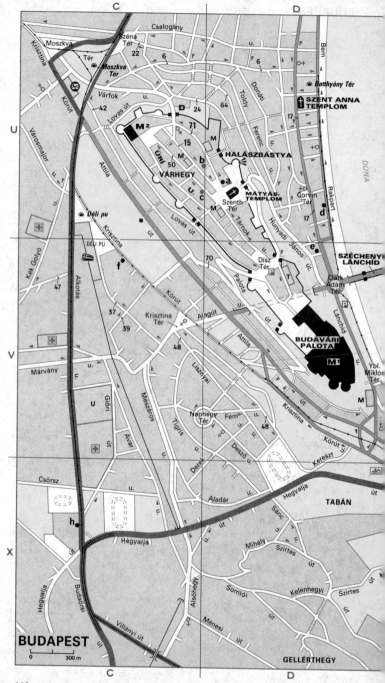

BUDAPEST

0   300 m

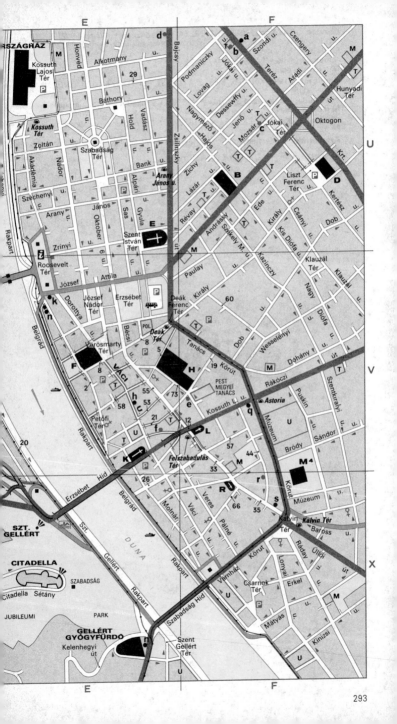

XX **Garvics,** Urömí Köz 2, 1025, ☎ 168 32 54, Vaulted converted chapel – AE E — AY **a**
closed Sunday and Bank Holidays – **M** (booking essential) (dinner only) 2500/4800 and a la
carte.

XX **Pilvax,** Pitvax Köz 1, 1052, ☎ 117 63 96 — FV **e**
M a la carte approx 1500.

XX **Gambrinus,** Teréz Körut 46, 1066, ☎ 112 76 31, Fax 112 32 51 – AE ① E VISA — FU **b**
M 3000/4000 and a la carte.

X **Pest-Buda,** Fortuna utca 3, 1014, ☎ 156 98 49, Vaulted restaurant, antiques — CU **b**
M (booking essential) a la carte 1500/2500.

X **Apostolok,** Kigyo utca 4, 1052, ☎ 118 37 04, « Old chapel decor, wood carving » EV **f**
M a la carte 495/1750.

X **Aranymókus,** Istenhegyi utca 25, 1126, ☎ 155 67 28, Fax 155 95 94, 🏫 – AE ① E
VISA — by CV
M 300/700 (buffet lunch) and a la carte 500/1050.

Republic of
Ireland

DUBLIN

PRACTICAL INFORMATION

LOCAL CURRENCY

Punt (Irish Pound): 1 punt = 1.75 US $ (Jan. 92)

TOURIST INFORMATION

The telephone number and address of the Tourist Information office is given in the text under 🄱.

FOREIGN EXCHANGE

Banks are open 10am to 12.30pm and 1.30pm to 3pm on weekdays only. Banks in Dublin stay open to 5pm on Thursdays and banks at Dublin and Shannon airports are open on Saturdays and Sundays.

SHOPPING IN DUBLIN

In the index of street names those printed in red are where the principal shops are found.

CAR HIRE

The international car hire companies have branches in each major city. Your hotel porter should be able to give details and help you with your arrangements.

TIPPING

Many hotels and restaurants include a service charge but where this is not the case an amount equivalent to between 10 and 15 per cent of the bill is customary. Additionally doormen, baggage porters and cloakroom attendants are generally give a gratuity.
Taxi drivers are customarily tipped between 10 and 15 per cent of the amount shown on the meter in addition to the fare.

SPEED LIMITS

The maximum permitted speed in the Republic is 55 mph (88 km/h) except where a lower speed limit is signposted.

SEAT BELTS

The wearing of seat belts is compulsory if fitted for drivers and front seat passengers. Additionally, children under 12 are not allowed in front seats unless in a suitable safety restraint.

ANIMALS

It is forbildden to bring domestic animals (dogs, cats...) into the Republic of Ireland.

Dublin

(BAILE ÁTHA CLIATH) Dublin 405 N 7 – pop. 528 882 – ✪ 01.

See : Trinity College★★★ EY – Chester Beatty Library★★★ – Phoenix Park★★★ – Dublin Castle★★ DY – Christ Church Cathedral★★ DY – St. Patrick's Cathedral★★ DZ – March's Library★★ DZ – National Museum★★ FZ – National Gallery★★ FZ – Merrion Square★★ FZ – Rotunda Hospital Chapel★★ EX – Kilmainham Hospital★★ – Kilmainham Gad Museum★★ – National Botanic Gardens★★ – N° 29★ FZ D – Liffey Bridge★ EY – Tailors' Hall★ DY – City Hall★ DY H – Viking Adventure★ DY K – St. Audoen's Gate★ DY B – St. Stephen's Green★ EZ – Grafton Street★ EYZ – Powerscourt Centre★ EY – Civic Museum★ EY M1 – Bank of Ireland★ EY – O'Connel Street★ EX – St. Michan's Church★ DY E – Hugh Lane Municipal Gallery of Modern Art★ EX M4 – Pro-Cathedral★ EX – Garden of remembrance★ EX – Custom House★ FX – Bluecoat school★ F – Guiness Museum★ – Marino Casino★ – Zoological Gardens★.

Envir. : St. Doolagh's Church★ (13C) 5open Saturday and Sunday, afternoon only NE : 7 m. by L 87.

🏌 Edmondstown, Rathfarnham 🖉 932461, S : 3 m by N 81 – 🏌 Elm Park, Nutley House, Donnybrook 🖉 693438, S : 3 m. – 🏌 Lower Churchtown Rd, Milltown 🖉 977060, S : by T 43 – 🏌 Royal Dublin, Bull Island 🖉 336346.

✈ 🖉 379900, Telex 31266, N : 5 ½ m. by N 1 – Terminal : Busaras (Central Bus Station) Store St.

⛴ to Holyhead (B & I Line) 2-3 daily (3 h 30 mn – 4 h 45 mn) – to the Isle of Man : Douglas (Isle of Man Steam Packet Co.) June to September 1-6 weekly (4 h 30 mn).

🅱 14 Upper O'Connell St. 🖉 747733 – Dublin Airport 🖉 376387 – Baggot St., 🖉 747733 (weekdays only in summer).

Belfast 103 – Cork 154 – Londonderry 146.

DUBLIN
CENTRE

*Town plans:
roads most used by traffic
and those on which guide-
listed hotels and restaurants
stand are fully drawn;
the beginning only
of lesser roads is indicated.*

298

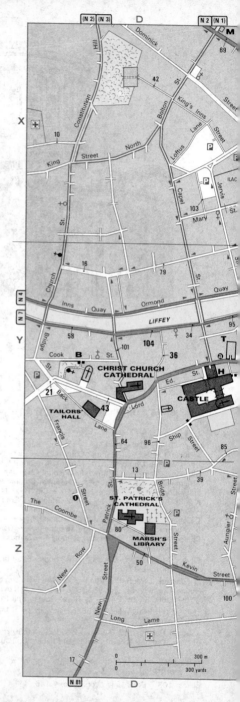

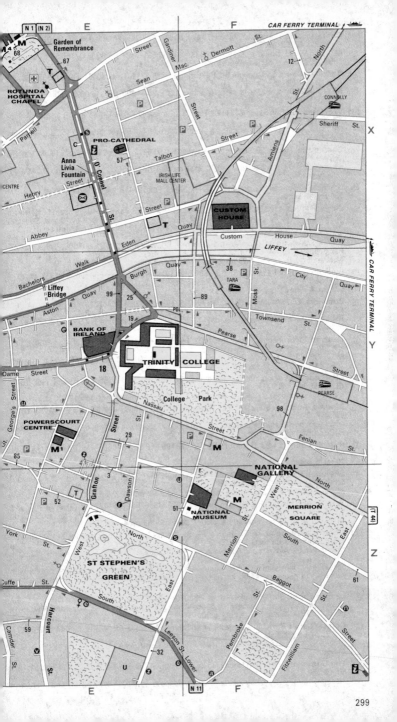

🏨🏨 **Conrad,** Earlsfort Terr., ℰ 765555, Telex 91872, Fax 765424 – 🛗 🍽 rm 🗏 ﺩﺩ 🕿 & 🅿
– 🔬 300. 🛐 🗚 🗚 🗚
M 15.50/21.95 **t.** and a la carte ᐕ 6.00 – ☲ 9.50 – **181 rm** 125.00/150.00 **t.**, **9 suites**
285.00/525.00 **t.** - SB (weekends only) 210.00/240.00 **st.**

🏨🏨 **Berkeley Court,** Lansdowne Rd, Ballsbridge, ℰ 601711, Telex 30554, Fax 617238, 🚗, 🛐
– 🛗 🗏 rest 🗏 ﺩﺩ 🕿 🚗 🅿 – 🔬 250. 🛐 🗚 🗚 🗚 🗚 SE 1 m by Nassau St. North
M 19.50/24.00 **t.** and a la carte ᐕ 5.25 – ☲ 8.25 – **200 rm** 115.00/135.00 **t.**, **9 suites**
185.00/1300.00 **t.**

🏨🏨 **Westbury,** Grafton St., ℰ 6791122, Telex 91091, Fax 6797078 – 🛗 🗏 rest 🗏 ﺩﺩ 🕿 🅿 – 🔬 200.
🛐 🗚 🗚 🗚 🗚
M 13.75/18.25 **t.** and a la carte ᐕ 4.25 – ☲ 6.50 – **195 rm** 115.00/145.00 **t.**, **8 suites**
175.00/475.00 **t.**

🏨🏨 **Shelbourne** (Forte), 27 St. Stephen's Green, ℰ 766471, Telex 93653, Fax 616006 – 🛗 🗏
🕿 🚗 – 🔬 350. 🛐 🗚 🗚 🗚
M 12.75/20.00 **t.** and a la carte ᐕ 6.00 – **159 rm** ☲ 101.00/165.00 **t.**, **5 suites** 198.00/500.00 **t.**
- SB (weekends only) 94.00 **st.**

🏨🏨 Gresham, O'Connell St., ℰ 746881, Telex 32473, Fax 787175 – 🛗 🗏 rest 🗏 ﺩﺩ 🕿 🅿 – 🔬 300
180 rm, 10 suites.

🏨🏨 **Jurys,** Pembroke Rd, Ballsbridge, ℰ 605000, Telex 93723, Fax 605540, 🛐 heated – 🛗 🍽 rm
🗏 rest 🗏 ﺩﺩ 🕿 & 🅿 – 🔬 400. 🛐 🗚 🗚 🗚 SE 1 m by Nassau St. North
M 17.00/21.00 **t.** and a la carte – **294 rm** 99.00/115.00 **t.**, **4 suites** 350.00/
450.00 **t.**
Annex : 🏨🏨 **Jurys (Towers),** Pembroke Rd, Ballsbridge, ℰ 605000, Telex 93723,
Fax 605540 – 🛗 🍽 rm 🗏 ﺩﺩ 🕿 & 🅿. 🛐 🗚 🗚 🗚
M (see Jurys H. above) – **98 rm** 145.00/175.00 **t.**, **2 suites.**

🏨🏨 Burlington, Upper Leeson St., ℰ 605222, Telex 93815, Fax 608496 – 🛗 🗏 🕿 🅿 –
🔬 1 000 S 1 m by Leeson St. Lower
478 rm, 4 suites.

🏨 **Buswells,** 25-26 Molesworth St., ℰ 764013, Telex 90622, Fax 762090 – 🛗 🗏 🕿 – 🔬 100.
🛐 🗚 🗚 🗚
M (closed Sunday lunch and Saturday) 11.95/14.50 **t.** and a la carte ᐕ 4.50 – ☲ 6.50 – **67 rm**
55.00/86.00 **t.**

🏨 **Central,** 1-5 Exchequer St., ℰ 6797302, Fax 6797303 – 🛗 🍽 rm 🗏 🕿 – 🔬 100. 🛐 🗚
🗚 🗚
M 12.00/20.00 **t.** and a la carte ᐕ 4.50 – ☲ 7.50 – **69 rm** 70.00/95.00 **t.**, **1 suite**
150.00 **t.**

🏨 **Stephens Hall** without rest., 14-17 Lower Leeson St., ℰ 610585, Fax 610606 – 🛗 🗏 🕿
🅿. 🛐 🗚 🗚 🗚
☲ 6.00 – **3 rm** 85.00/130.00 **t.**, **34 suites** 130.00 **t.** - SB (weekends only)190.00 **st.**

🏨 **Blooms,** Anglesea St., ℰ 715622, Telex 31688, Fax 715997 – 🛗 🗏 🕿 🅿 – 🔬 30. 🛐 🗚
🗚 🗚
M (closed lunch Saturday and Sunday) 20.00/40.00 **t.** and a la carte ᐕ 6.00 – ☲ 6.90 – **86 rm**
80.00/200.00 **t.**

🏨 Russell Court, 21-23 Harcourt St., ℰ 784991, Fax 784066 – 🛗 🗏 🕿 – 🔬 100.
🗚
20 rm, 1 suite.

🏨 **Skylon,** Upper Drumcondra Rd, N : 2 ½ m. on N 1 ℰ 379121, Fax 372778 – 🛗 🗏 rest 🗏
🕿 🅿 – 🔬 35. 🛐 🗚 🗚 🗚 🗚 N 2 m by Bolton St.
M 9.30/11.30 **t.** and a la carte ᐕ 3.60 – ☲ 5.00 – **92 rm** 44.00/75.00 **t.**

🏨 **Tara Tower,** Merrion Rd, SE : 4 m. on T 44 ℰ 2694666, Fax 2691027 – 🛗 🗏 🕿 🅿 – 🔬 180.
🛐 🗚 🗚 🗚 🗚 SE 2 m by Nassau St. North
M 10.00/13.00 **t.** and a la carte ᐕ 3.60 – ☲ 5.10 – **82 rm** 48.00/75.00 **t.**

XXX ❀ **Patrick Guilbaud,** 46 St. James' Pl., St. James' St., off Lower Baggot St., ℰ 764192,
Fax 601546, French rest. – 🗏. 🛐 🗚 🗚 🗚
closed Sunday, Monday and Bank Holidays – **M** 15.50/25.00 **t.** and a la carte 21.50/32.50 ᐕ
ᐕ 7.00
Spec. Fresh Irish Salmon baked under a potato blinis with caviar, Breast of pigeon with
spinach and pears marinated in saffron, Fillet of new season lamb with fresh herbs (spring
only).

XXX **Le Coq Hardi,** 35 Pembroke Rd, ℰ 689070 – 🅿. 🛐 🗚 🗚 🗚
closed Saturday lunch, Sunday, 2 weeks August, 1 week Christmas and Bank Holidays –
M 16.00/28.00 **t.** and a la carte ᐕ 8.00. SE ½ m by Baggot St.

XXX **Colin O'Daly's Park,** 40 The Mews, Main Street, Blackrock, SE : 4 ½ m. by T 44 ℰ 2886177,
Fax 2834365 – 🛐 🗚 🗚 🗚
closed Saturday lunch, Sunday, 1 week Christmas and Bank Holidays - **M** 12.00/26.50 **t.**
ᐕ 7.50.

XXX **The Commons,** Newman House, 85-86 St. Stephen's Green, ℰ 752608, Fax 780551 – 🛐
🗚 🗚 🗚
closed Saturday lunch, Sunday and Bank Holidays - **M** 15.00/22.50 **st.** and a la carte
ᐕ 6.00.

XXX **Ernie's,** Mulberry Gdns, off Morehampton Rd, Donnybrook, ✆ 2693300, « Contemporary
Irish Art collection » – 🔼 AE ① VISA   SE 1 ½ m by Nassau St. North
closed Saturday lunch, Sunday, Monday and 1 week Christmas – **M** 13.50/22.50 **t.** and a la
carte ▯ 6.25.

XXX **Shannons,** Portobello Harbour, ✆ 782933, Fax 783212 – ▤. 🔼 AE ① VISA
closed Saturday lunch, Sunday and Bank Holidays – **M** 14.50/21.00 **t.** and a la carte
▯ 6.00.   S ½ m by Harcourt St.

XX **Locks,** 1 Windsor Terr., Portobello, ✆ 543391 – 🔼 AE ① VISA
closed Saturday lunch, Sunday, 1 week Christmas and Bank Holidays – **M** 12.95/18.95 **t.** and
a la carte ▯ 5.15.   S ½ m by Clanbrassil St.

XX **Thorntons,** 147 Upper Rathmines Rd, ✆ 962348 – 🔼 VISA   S 1 ½ m by Harcourt St.
closed Sunday and Monday – **M** 25.00/35.00 ▯ 7.95.

XX **Old Dublin,** 90-91 Francis St., ✆ 542028, Fax 541406, Russian-Scandinavian rest. – 🔼 AE
① VISA   DZ **i**
closed Saturday lunch, Sunday and Bank Holidays – **M** 11.50/23.00 **t.** ▯ 5.00.

XX **Grey Door** with rm, 22/23 Upper Pembroke St., ✆ 763286, Fax 763287 – 📺 ☎. 🔼 AE ①
VISA   FZ **a**
M *(closed Saturday lunch, Sunday and Bank Holidays)* 15.00/25.00 **t.** and a la carte ▯ 5.50 –
⊒ 6.95 – **7 rm** 55.00/95.00 **t.** – **SB** 120.00/150.00 **st.**

XX **Les Frères Jacques,** 74 Dame St., ✆ 6794555, Fax 6794725, French rest. – 🔼 AE VISA
closed Saturday lunch, Sunday, Christmas-New year and Bank Holidays – **M** 13.00/20.00 **t.** and
a la carte ▯ 5.10.   DY **a**

XX **Chandni,** 174 Pembroke Rd, Ballsbridge, ✆ 681458, Indian rest. – ▤. 🔼 AE ① VISA.
🍴   SE 1 m by Nassau St. North
closed 17 April and 25-26 December – **M** 7.95/15.95 **t.** and a la carte ▯ 4.50.

XX **Kapriol,** 45 Lower Camden St., ✆ 751235, Italian rest. – **M** *(dinner only)* a la carte 22.50/36.80 **t.**
▯ 5.00.   S by Harcourt St.

XX **Zen,** 89 Upper Rathmines Rd, ✆ 979428, Chinese (Szechuan) rest. – 🔼 AE ① VISA
closed lunch Saturday, Sunday and Bank Holidays – **M** 8.00/16.50 **t.** and a la carte
▯ 6.50.   S 1 ½ m by Harcourt St.

XX **Puerto Bella,** 1 Portobello Rd, ✆ 720851 – 🔼 AE ① VISA   S 1 m by Clanbrassil St.
closed Saturday lunch, Sunday and Bank Holidays – **M** 12.95 **t.** and a la carte ▯ 5.95.

XX La Stampa, 35 Dawson St., ✆ 778611.   EZ **r**

at Dublin Airport N : 6 ½ m. by N 1 – ✉ ❀ 01 Dublin :

🏨 **Forte Crest, ,** ✆ 379211, Telex 32849, Fax 425874 – 📺 ☎ & 🅿 – 🔬 120. 🔼 AE ①
VISA
M 8.75/30.00 **t.** ▯ 5.00 – ⊒ 6.50 – **192 rm** 68.00/91.00 **t.** – SB (weekends only) 104.00 **st.**

Italy
Italia

ROME - FLORENCE - MILAN - NAPLES
PALERME - TAORMINA - TURIN - VENICE

PRACTICAL INFORMATION

LOCAL CURRENCY

Italian Lire: 1000 lire = 0.87 US $ (Jan. 92)

TOURIST INFORMATION

Welcome Office (Ente Provinciale per il Turismo), closed Saturday and Sunday:
– Via Parigi 5 - 00185 ROMA, ✆ 06/4883748, Fax 481 93 16
– Via Marconi 1 - 20123 MILANO, ✆ 02/809662, Fax 720 22 432
See also telephone number and address of other Tourist Information offices in the text of the towns under 🛈.
American Express:
– Piazza di Spagna 38 - 00187 ROMA, ✆ 06/67641, Fax 678 24 56
– Via Brera 3 - 20121 MILANO, ✆ 02/85571, Fax 86 46 34 78

AIRLINES

ALITALIA: Via Bissolati 13 - 00187 ROMA, ✆ 06/46881
Piazzale Pastore (EUR) - 00144 ROMA, ✆ 06/54441
Via Albricci 5 - 20122 MILANO, ✆ 02/62817
AIR FRANCE: Via Vittorio Veneto 93 - 00187 ROMA, ✆ 06/4818741
Piazza Cavour 2 - 20121 MILANO, ✆ 02/77381
DELTA AIRLINES: Via Bissolati 46 - 00187 ROMA, ✆ 06/47001
Via Melchiorre Jioia - 20125 MILANO, ✆ 02/66 80 35 00
TWA: Via Barberini 59 - 00187 ROMA, ✆ 06/47241
Corso Europa 9/11 - 20122 MILANO, ✆ 02/77961

FOREIGN EXCHANGE

Money can be changed at the Banca d'Italia, other banks and authorised exchange offices (Banks close at 1.15pm and at weekends).

POSTAL SERVICES

Local post offices: open Monday to Saturday 8.00am to 2.00pm
General Post Office (open 24 hours only for telegrams):
– Piazza San Silvestro 00187 ROMA – Piazza Cordusio 20123 MILANO

SHOPPING

In the index of street names those printed in red are where the principal shops are found. In Rome, the main shopping streets are: Via del Babuino, Via Condotti, Via Frattina, Via Vittorio Veneto; in Milan: Via Dante, Via Manzoni, Via Monte Napoleone, Corso Vittorio Emanuele.

BREAKDOWN SERVICE

Certain garages in the centre and outskirts of towns operate a 24 hour breakdown service. If you break down the police are usually able to help by indicating the nearest one.
A free car breakdown service (a tax is levied) is operated by the A.C.I. for foreign motorists carrying the fuel card (Carta Carburante). The A.C.I. also offerts telephone information in English (8am to 5pm) for road and weather conditions and tourist events: 06/4212.

TIPPING

As well as the service charge, it is the custom to tip employees. The amount can vary with the region and the service given.

SPEED LIMITS

On motorways, the maximum permitted speed is 130 km/h - 80 mph for vehicles over 1000 cc, 110 km/h - 68 mph for all other vehicles. On other roads, the speed limit is 90 km/h - 56 mph.

Rome

(ROMA) 00100 🔲🔲🔲 ⊘ 🔲🔲🔲 Q 19 – Pop. 2 791 351 – alt. 20 – ✪ 06.

🔲 🔲 Parco de' Medici (closed Tuesday) ⊠ 00148 Roma SW : 4,5 km
𝒫 655 34 77 – Fax 655 33 44.

🔲 (closed Monday) at Acquasanta ⊠ 00178 Roma SE : 12 km. 𝒫 78 34 07.

🔲 Fioranello (closed Wednesday) at Santa Maria delle Mole ⊠ 00040 Roma
SE : 19 km 𝒫 713 82 91 – Fax 713 82 12.

🔲 and 🔲 (closed Monday) at Olgiata ⊠ 00123 Roma NW : 19 km 𝒫 3789141.

✈ Ciampino SE : 15 km 𝒫 794941, Telex 611168 and Leonardo da Vinci
di Fiumicino 𝒫 60121, Telex 620511 – Alitalia, via Bissolati 13 ⊠ 00187
𝒫 46881 and piazzale Pastore (EUR) ⊠ 00144 𝒫 65643.

🚆 Termini 𝒫 464923 – Tiburtina 𝒫 4956626.

🄵 via Parigi 5 ⊠ 00185 𝒫 4883748 ; at Termini station 𝒫 4871270 ; at Fiumicino
Airport 𝒫 6011255.

A.C.I. via Cristoforo Colombo 261 ⊠ 00147 𝒫 5106 and via Marsala 8 ⊠ 00185
𝒫 49981, Telex 610686.
Distances from Rome are indicated in the text of the other towns listed in this Guide.

SIGHTS

Rome's most famous sights are indicated on the town plans pp. 2 to 5.
For a more complete visit see the Green Guide to Italy.

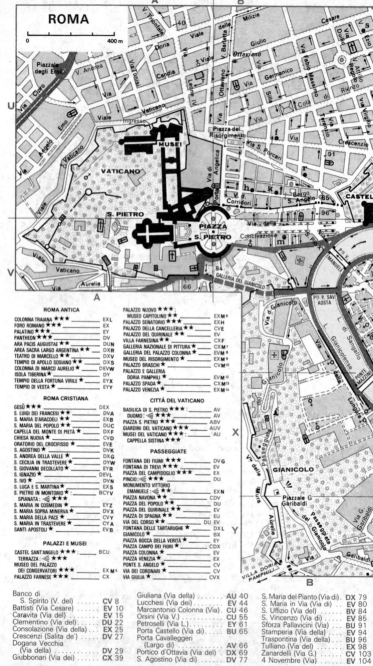

ROMA

0 — 400 m

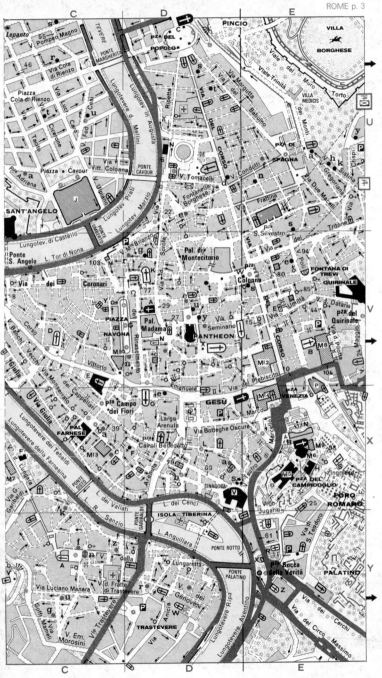

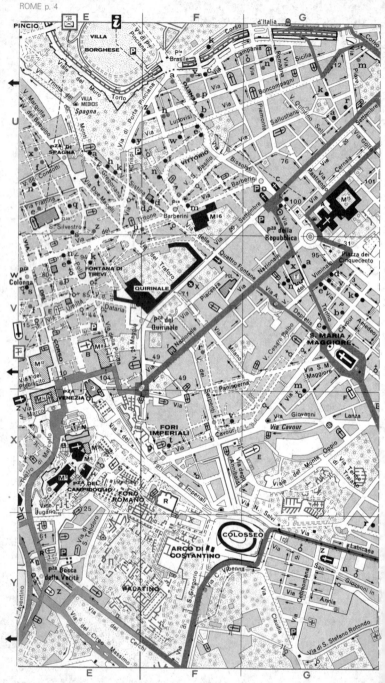

ROMA

ROMA ANTICA

ARCO DI COSTANTINO ★★★	
BASILICA DI MASSENZIO ★★★	R
COLONNA TRAIANA ★★★	L
COLOSSEO ★★★	
FORI IMPERIALI ★★★	
FORO ROMANO ★★★	
PALATINO ★★★	
TEATRO DI MARCELLO ★★★	V
COLONNA DI MARCO AURELIO ★	W
TEMPIO DELLA FORTUNA VIRILE ★	X
TEMPIO DI VESTA ★	Y

ROMA CRISTIANA

GESÙ ★★★	Z
S. GIOVANNI IN LATERANO ★★★	
S. MARIA MAGGIORE ★★★	
S. ANDREA AL QUIRINALE ★★★	X
S. CARLO	
ALLE QUATTRO FONTANE ★★	Y
S. CLEMENTE ★★	Z
S. MARIA DEGLI ANGELI ★★	A
S. MARIA D'ARACOELI ★★	B
S. MARIA DELLA VITTORIA ★★	C
S. SUSANNA ★★	D
ORATORIO DEL CROCIFISSO ★	E
S. IGNAZIO ★	L
S. GIOVANNI DECOLLATO ★	R
S. LUCA E S. MARTINA ★	S
S. MARIA IN COSMEDIN ★	Z
S. PIETRO IN VINCOLI ★	E
S. PRASSEDE ★	F
SANTI APOSTOLI ★	B

PALAZZI E MUSEI

MUSEO NAZIONALE ROMANO ★★★	M15
MUSEO DEL PALAZZO	
DEI CONSERVATORI ★★★	M5
PALAZZO NUOVO ★★★ :	
MUSEO CAPITOLINO ★★	M6
PALAZZO SENATORIO ★★★	H
PALAZZO BARBERINI ★★	M16
PALAZZO DEL QUIRINALE ★	
GALLERIA DEL PALAZZO COLONNA ★	M8
MUSEO DEL RISORGIMENTO ★	M9
PALAZZO E GALLERIA	
DORIA PAMPHILI ★	M12
PALAZZO VENEZIA ★	M14

PASSEGGIATE

FONTANA DI TREVI ★★★	
PIAZZA DEL CAMPIDOGLIO ★★★	
MONUMENTO VITTORIO	
EMANUELE : ≤ ★★	N
PIAZZA DEL QUIRINALE ★★	
PIAZZA DI SPAGNA ★★	
VIA VITTORIO VENETO ★★	
PIAZZA BOCCA DELLA VERITÀ ★	
PIAZZA COLONNA ★	
PIAZZA DI PORTA MAGGIORE ★	
PIAZZA VENEZIA ★	
PORTA PIA ★	

North area Monte Mario, Stadio Olimpico, via Flaminia-Parioli, Villa Borghese, via Salaria, via Nomentana (Plans : Rome pp. 2 to 5).

🏨🏨🏨 **Cavalieri Hilton** ⚡, via Cadlolo 101 ✉ 00136 ☎ 31511, Telex 625337, Fax 31512241, ≤ town, ☞, « Terraces and park », ⅃, ⚒ – 🛗 ▤ 🆃🆅 ☎ ⅊ 🖭 ☎ 🅿 – 🏛 25-2500
374 rm.
by via Trionfale AU

🏨🏨 **Lord Byron** ⚡, via De Notaris 5 ✉ 00197 ☎ 3220404, Telex 611217, Fax 3220405, ☞
– 🛗 ▤ 🆃🆅 ☎. 🆎 🅂 🅾 🄴 🆅🅸🆂🅰
by lungotevere in Augusta DU
M (see rest. **Relais le Jardin** below) – ☋ 25000 – **50 rm** 350/500000 suites 600/1200000.

🏨🏨 **Aldrovandi Palace Hotel,** via Aldrovandi 15 ✉ 00197 ☎ 3223993, Telex 616141, Fax 3221435, ⅃, ☞ – 🛗 ⇵ ▤ 🆃🆅 ☎ ⅊ – 🏛 50-350. 🆎 🅂 🅾 🄴 🆅🅸🆂🅰 ⚘
M Grill Le Relais Rest. a la carte 75/115000 – **143 rm** ☋ 380/400000 suites 550/2000000.
by viale Trinità EU

🏨🏨 **Polo** without rest., piazza Gastaldi 4 ✉ 00197 ☎ 3221041, Telex 623107, Fax 3221359 –
🛗 ▤ 🆃🆅 ☎ – 🏛 80. 🆎 🅂 🅾 🄴 🆅🅸🆂🅰 ⚘
by lungotevere in Augusta DU
66 rm ☋ 300/360000.

🏨🏨 **Rivoli,** via Torquato Taramelli 7 ✉ 00197 ☎ 3224042, Telex 614615, Fax 870143 – 🛗 ▤
🆃🆅 ☎ – 🏛 40
by lungotevere in Augusta DU
55 rm.

🏨🏨 **Albani** without rest., via Adda 45 ✉ 00198 ☎ 84991, Telex 625594, Fax 8499399 – 🛗 ▤
🆃🆅 ☎ ⇔ – 🏛 80. 🆎 🅂 🅾 🄴 🆅🅸🆂🅰 ⚘
by via Piave GU
157 rm ☋ 270/375000 suites 450000.

🏨🏨 **Borromini** without rest., via Lisbona 7 ✉ 00198 ☎ 8841321, Telex 621625, Fax 8417550
– 🛗 ▤ 🆃🆅 ☎ ⅊ ⇔ – 🏛 50-100. 🆎 🅂 🅾 🄴 🆅🅸🆂🅰 ⚘
☋ 20000 – **75 rm** 288/320000 suites 470/550000.
by viale Regina Margherita JU

🏨 **Degli Aranci,** via Oriani 11 ✉ 00197 ☎ 870202, Telex 805250, ☞ – 🛗 ▤ 🆃🆅 ☎ – 🏛 50.
🆎 🅂 🄴 🆅🅸🆂🅰 ⚘
by lungotevere in Augusta DU
M 32000 (10 %) – **40 rm** ☋ 188/260000.

🏨 **Clodio** without rest., via di Santa Lucia 10 ✉ 00195 ☎ 317541, Telex 625050, Fax 3250745
by via Ottaviano Barletta BU
114 rm ☋ 160/220000.

🏨 **Panama** without rest., via Salaria 336 ✉ 00199 ☎ 8552558, Telex 620189, Fax 8413929,
☞ – 🛗 🆃🆅 ☎. 🆎 🅂 🅾 🄴 🆅🅸🆂🅰 ⚘
by via Piave GU
43 rm ☋ 130/190000.

XXXXX 🕸🕸 **Relais le Jardin,** via De Notaris 5 ✉ 00197 ☎ 3220404, Fax 3220405, Elegant rest.
– ▤. 🆎 🅂 🅾 🄴 🆅🅸🆂🅰 ⚘
by lungotevere in Augusta DU
closed Sunday – **M** (booking essential) a la carte 115/174000
Spec. Zuppa di arzilla e cicorietta piccante, Spaghetti con "pajatina" al nero di seppia, Oratina alle erbe olive e frutti di mare. Wines Frascati, Cesanese del Piglio.

XXX **Relais la Piscine,** via Mangili 6 ✉ 00197 ☎ 3216126, ☞, ⅃, ☞ – ▤ 🅿. 🆎 🅂 🅾 🄴
🆅🅸🆂🅰 ⚘
by lungotevere in Augusta DU
closed Sunday dinner – **M** a la carte 75/110000.

XXX **Il Peristilio,** via Monte Zebio 10/d ✉ 00195 ☎ 3223623, Fax 3223639 – ▤. 🆎 🅾 🄴 🆅🅸🆂🅰.
⚘
by via Marcantonio Colonna CU
closed Monday and 10 to 31 August – **M** a la carte 40/83000 (12 %).

XX **Al Fogher,** via Tevere 13/b ✉ 00198 ☎ 8417032, Typical Venetian rest. – ▤
by via Piave GU

XX **Al Ceppo,** via Panama 2 ✉ 00198 ☎ 8419696 – 🆎 🅂 🅾 🄴 🆅🅸🆂🅰
by viale Regina Margherita JU
closed Monday and 8 to 30 August – **M** a la carte 44/64000.

XX **Il Caminetto,** viale dei Parioli 89 ✉ 00197 ☎ 8083946, ☞ – ▤. 🆎 🅂 🅾 🄴 🆅🅸🆂🅰.
⚘
by lungotevere in Augusta DU
closed Thursday and 12 to 18 August – **M** a la carte 37/57000.

X **Delle Vittorie,** via Monte Santo 62/64 ✉ 00195 ☎ 386847 – 🆎 🅂 🅾 🄴 🆅🅸🆂🅰.
by via Marcantonio Colonna CU
closed Sunday, 1 to 20 August and 23 December-3 January – **M** a la carte 39/59000.

Middle-western area San Pietro (Vatican City), Gianicolo, corso Vittorio Emanuele, piazza Venezia, Pantheon and Quirinale, Pincio and Villa Medici, piazza di Spagna, Palatino and Fori (Plans : Rome pp. 2 and 3).

🏨🏨🏨 **Hassler,** piazza Trinità dei Monti 6 ✉ 00187 ☎ 6792651, Telex 610208, Fax 6789991, ≤
town from roof-garden rest. – 🛗 ▤ 🆃🆅 ☎. 🆎 🅂 🆅🅸🆂🅰. ⚘
EU **a**
M (closed Sunday dinner) a la carte 95/150000 – ☋ 24000 – **100 rm** 420/650000 suites 1200/2700000.

🏨🏨🏨 **Eden,** via Ludovisi 49 ✉ 00187 ☎ 4743551, Telex 610567, Fax 4821584, « Roof-garden rest. with ≤ town » – 🛗 ▤ 🆃🆅 ☎ – 🏛 50-100. 🆎 🅂 🅾 🄴 🆅🅸🆂🅰. ⚘
EU **y**
M a la carte 100/160000 – ☋ 38000 – **119 rm** 360/510000.

🏨🏨🏨 **D'Inghilterra,** via Bocca di Leone 14 ✉ 00187 ☎ 672161, Telex 614552, Fax 6840828 –
🛗 ▤ 🆃🆅 ☎ ⅊. 🆎 🅂 🅾 🄴 🆅🅸🆂🅰 ⚘
EU **n**
M (residents only) a la carte 56/91000 – ☋ 22000 – **97 rm** 285/425000 suites 490/580000.

Jolly Leonardo da Vinci, via dei Gracchi 324 ✉ 00192 ℘ 32499, Telex 611182, Fax 3610138 – 🛗 ▤ 📺 ☎ 🚗 – 🎤 30-220. AE ⑤ ⓓ E VISA. ✗ rest CU **r**
M 50000 – **256 rm** ☕ 250/360000.

De la Ville Inter-Continental, via Sistina 69 ✉ 00187 ℘ 67331, Telex 620836, Fax 6784213 – 🛗 ▤ 📺 ☎ – 🎤 40-120. AE ⑤ ⓓ E VISA. ✗ EU **h**
M a la carte 71/120000 – **189 rm** ☕ 416/528000 suites 660/1200000.

Visconti Palace without rest., via Cesi 37 ✉ 00193 ℘ 3684, Telex 622489, Fax 3200551 – 🛗 ▤ 📺 ☎ ♿ 🚗 – 🎤 25-150. AE ⑤ ⓓ E VISA. ✗ CU **u**
247 rm ☕ 250/350000 suites 450000.

Plaza, via del Corso 126 ✉ 00186 ℘ 672101, Telex 624669 – 🛗 ▤ ☎ – 🎤 50. AE ⑤ ⓓ E VISA. ✗ DU **d**
M a la carte 54/89000 – ☕ 18000 – **230 rm** 239/310000 suites 580000, ▤ 15000.

Dei Borgognoni without rest., via del Bufalo 126 ✉ 00187 ℘ 6780041, Telex 623074, Fax 6841501 – 🛗 ▤ 📺 ☎ 🚗 – 🎤 25-60. AE ⑤ ⓓ E VISA. ✗ EUV **s**
50 rm ☕ 330/390000 suite 550000.

Cicerone and Rest. Robià, via Cicerone 55/c ✉ 00193 ℘ 3576, Telex 622498, Fax 3244786 – 🛗 ▤ 📺 ☎ 🚗 – 🎤 160. AE ⑤ ⓓ E VISA. ✗ CU **t**
M a la carte 42/64000 – **237 rm** ☕ 250/350000 suites 460/720000.

Atlante Star, via Vitelleschi 34 ✉ 00193 ℘ 6879558, Telex 622355, Fax 6872300, « Roof-garden rest. with ≤ St. Peter's Basilica » – 🛗 ⇔ ▤ 📺 ☎ – 🎤 70. AE ⑤ ⓓ E VISA. ✗ rest BU **r**
M Les Etoiles Rest. a la carte 90/120000 – **61 rm** ☕ 400/425000 suites 520/2250000.

Delle Nazioni without rest., via Poli 7 ✉ 00187 ℘ 6792441, Telex 614193 – 🛗 ▤ 📺 ☎. AE ⑤ ⓓ E VISA. ✗ EV **e**
74 rm ☕ 283/376000.

Colonna Palace without rest., piazza Montecitorio 12 ✉ 00186 ℘ 6781341, Telex 621467, Fax 6794496 – 🛗 ▤ 📺 ☎. AE ⑤ ⓓ E VISA. ✗ EV **s**
105 rm ☕ 325/440000 suites 590000.

Valadier, via della Fontanella 15 00187 ℘ 3611998, Telex 620873, Fax 3201558 – ▤ 📺 ☎ – 🎤 35. AE ⑤ ⓓ E VISA. ✗ rest DU **s**
M a la carte 50/75000 – **38 rm** ☕ 270/390000 suite 510000.

Giulio Cesare without rest., via degli Scipioni 287 ✉ 00192 ℘ 3210751, Telex 613010, Fax 3211736, 🌳 – 🛗 ▤ 📺 ☎ 🅿 – 🎤 60. AE ⑤ ⓓ E VISA. ✗ CU **s**
86 rm ☕ 280/380000.

Nazionale, piazza Montecitorio 131 ✉ 00186 ℘ 6789251, Telex 621427, Fax 6786677, 📡 – 🛗 ▤ 📺 ☎. AE ⑤ ⓓ E VISA. ✗ DV **t**
M *(closed Sunday)* a la carte 50/60000 – **86 rm** ☕ 250/380000 suites 450/600000.

Del Sole al Pantheon without rest., piazza della Rotonda 63 ✉ 00186 ℘ 6780441, Fax 6840689 – 🛗 ▤ 📺 ☎. AE ⑤ ⓓ E VISA. ✗ DV **u**
26 rm ☕ 250/380000.

Columbus, via della Conciliazione 33 ✉ 00193 ℘ 6865435, Telex 620096, Fax 6864874, « 15 C building, period decor », 🌳 – 🛗 ▤ 📺 ☎ 🅿 – 🎤 30-200. AE ⑤ ⓓ E VISA. ✗ rest BV **m**
M a la carte 52/73000 – **105 rm** ☕ 170/220000 suites 250/400000.

Atlante Garden without rest., via Crescenzio 78/a ✉ 00193 ℘ 6872361, Telex 623172, Fax 6872315 – 🛗 ⇔ ▤ 📺 ☎ – 🎤 30. AE ⑤ ⓓ E VISA BU **f**
43 rm ☕ 252/297000.

Internazionale without rest., via Sistina 79 ✉ 00187 ℘ 6793047, Telex 614333, Fax 6784764 – 🛗 ▤ 📺 ☎. AE ⑤ E VISA. ✗ EU **k**
37 rm ☕ 160/220000 suites 600000.

Gerber without rest., via degli Scipioni 241 ✉ 00192 ℘ 3216485, Fax 3217048 – 🛗 ☎. AE ⑤ ⓓ E VISA. ✗ BU **s**
27 rm ☕ 118/168000.

Della Torre Argentina without rest., corso Vittorio Emanuele 102 ✉ 00186 ℘ 6833886, Telex 623281, Fax 6541641 – 🛗 ▤ ☎. AE ⑤ ⓓ E VISA. ✗ DX **e**
☕ 22000 – **32 rm** 108/146000, ▤ 20000.

Sant'Anna without rest., borgo Pio 134 ✉ 00193 ℘ 6547152, Fax 6548717 – ▤ 📺 ☎. AE ⑤ ⓓ E VISA BU **h**
18 rm ☕ 154/213000.

Della Conciliazione without rest., borgo Pio 165 ✉ 00193 ℘ 6875400, Fax 6541164 – 🛗 ☎ ♿. AE ⑤ ⓓ E VISA BU **k**
☕ 12000 – **55 rm** 90/145000.

Senato without rest., piazza della Rotonda 73 ✉ 00186 ℘ 6793231, Fax 6840297, ≤ Pantheon – 🛗 ▤ 📺 ☎. AE ⑤ VISA. ✗ DV **y**
☕ 18000 – **51 rm** 114/146000, ▤ 22000.

Margutta without rest., via Laurina 34 ✉ 00187 ℘ 3223674 – 🛗 ☎. AE ⑤ ⓓ E VISA. ✗ DU **t**
21 rm ☕ 113000.

Portoghesi without rest., via dei Portoghesi 1 ✉ 00186 ℘ 6864231, Fax 6876976 – 🛗 ▤ ☎. ⑤ E VISA DV **g**
27 rm ☕ 90/150000.

XXX **El Toulà,** via della Lupa 29/b ⊠ 00186 𝒞 6873498, Fax 6871115, Elegant rest. – 🗐. 🖭 🖽 ⓘ **E** 𝒱𝒮𝒜. 🛇 – *closed Saturday lunch, Sunday, August and 24 to 26 December* – **M** (booking essential) a la carte 64/98000 (15 %).   DU **e**

XXX ❀ **Patrizia e Roberto del Pianeta Terra,** via dell'Arco del Monte 95 (via dei Pettinari) ⊠ 00186 𝒞 6869893, Elegant rest. – 🗐. 🖭 🖽 ⓘ 𝒱𝒮𝒜   CX **c** *closed Monday and August* **M** (dinner only) (booking essential) a la carte 110/150000 (15 %) **Spec.** Cipolline rosse in agrodolce con foie gras, Agnello in salsa di aceto balsamico, Pasticceria della Casa. **Wines** Vallocaia.

XXX **Ranieri,** via Mario de' Fiori 26 ⊠ 00187 𝒞 6791592 – 🗐. 🖭 🖽 ⓘ **E** 𝒱𝒮𝒜. 🛇   EU **f** *closed Sunday* – **M** (booking essential) a la carte 50/83000.

XXX **4 Colonne,** via della Posta 4 ⊠ 00186 𝒞 6545261 – 🗐. 🛇   DV **n** *closed Sunday and 5 to 31 August* – **M** (booking essential) a la carte 50/100000.

XX ❀ **Quinzi Gabrieli,** via delle Coppelle 6 ⊠ 00186 𝒞 6879389 – 🖭 ⓘ. 🛇   DV **c** *closed lunch, Sunday and August* – **M** (booking essential) (fish only) a la carte 80/150000 **Spec.** Carpaccio di pesce, Spaghetti con crostacei, Pesce al sale. **Wines** Riesling.

XX **Camponeschi,** piazza Farnese 50 ⊠ 00186 𝒞 6874927, Fax 6865244, « Summer service with ⪉ Farnese palace » – 🗐. 🖭 ⓘ 𝒱𝒮𝒜. 🛇   CX **a** *closed lunch and Sunday* – **M** (booking essential) a la carte 63/102000 (13 %).

XX ❀ **La Rosetta,** via della Rosetta 9 ⊠ 00187 𝒞 6861002, Fax 6872852, Seafood trattoria – 🗐. ⓘ 𝒱𝒮𝒜 – *closed Sunday and August* – **M** (booking essential) a la carte 72/107000 (15 %)   DV **e** **Spec.** Marinati di pesce e crostacei, Linguine alle triglie e olive, Scorfano alla cipolla rossa. **Wines** Regaleali.

XX **Vecchia Roma,** piazza Campitelli 18 ⊠ 00186 𝒞 6864604, Typical roman rest with local and seafood specialities – 🗐. 🖭 ⓘ – *closed Wednesday and 1 to 15 August* – **M** a la carte 47/77000 (12 %).   DX **a**

XX **Eau Vive,** via Monterone 85 ⊠ 00186 𝒞 6541095, Catholic missionaries ; international cuisine, « 16C building » – 🗐. 🖭 🖽 𝒱𝒮𝒜. 🛇   DV **f** *closed Sunday and August* – **M** (booking essential for dinner) a la carte 39/69000.

X **Hostaria da Cesare,** via Crescenzio 13 ⊠ 00193 𝒞 6861227, Trattoria-pizzeria, seafood – 🛇 🗐. 🖭 🖽 ⓘ **E** 𝒱𝒮𝒜. 🛇   CU **a** *closed Sunday dinner, Monday, August, Christmas and Easter* – **M** a la carte 49/74000.

X **L'Orso 80,** via dell'Orso 33 ⊠ 00186 𝒞 6864904 – 🗐. 🖭 🖽 ⓘ **E** 𝒱𝒮𝒜. 🛇   CDV **r** *closed Monday and 2 to 28 August* – **M** a la carte 42/62000.

Central eastern area via Vittorio Veneto, via Nazionale, Viminale, Santa Maria Maggiore, Colosseum, Porta Pia, via Nomentana, Stazione Termini, Porta San Giovanni (Plans : Rome pp. 4 and 5) :

🏨 **Le Grand Hotel,** via Vittorio Emanuele Orlando 3 ⊠ 00185 𝒞 4709, Telex 610210, Fax 4747307 – 🛗 🗐 📺 ☎ ﴾. – 🎩 25-500 – **168 rm.**   GU **t**

🏨 **Excelsior,** via Vittorio Veneto 125 ⊠ 00187 𝒞 4708, Telex 610232, Fax 4826205 – 🛗 🗐 📺 ☎ – 🎩 25-450. 🖭 🖽 ⓘ **E** 𝒱𝒮𝒜. 🛇   FU **b** **M** a la carte 85/124000 – ⲍ 29000 – **359 rm** 381/584000 suites 893/1606000.

🏨 **Ambasciatori Palace,** via Vittorio Veneto 70 ⊠ 00187 𝒞 47493, Telex 610241, Fax 4743601, ⪉ – 🛗 🗐 📺 ☎ 🎩 50-200. 🖭 🖽 ⓘ **E** 𝒱𝒮𝒜. 🛇 rest   FU **e** **M** Grill Bar ABC Rest. a la carte 73/115000 – **149 rm** ⲍ 305/410000 suites 550/750000.

🏨 **Bernini Bristol,** piazza Barberini 23 ⊠ 00187 𝒞 4883051, Telex 610554, Fax 4824266 – 🛗 ⪆ rm 🗐 📺 ☎ – 🎩 40-120. 🖭 🖽 ⓘ **E** 𝒱𝒮𝒜. 🛇 rest   FU **m** **M** a la carte 66/110000 – ⲍ 22000 – **124 rm** 340/470000 suites 595/1190000.

🏨 **Majestic,** via Vittorio Veneto 50 ⊠ 00187 𝒞 486841, Telex 622262, Fax 4880984 – 🛗 🗐 📺 ☎ ﴾. – 🎩 150. 🖭 🖽 ⓘ **E** 𝒱𝒮𝒜. 🛇   FU **f** **M** a la carte 80/150000 – **95 rm** ⲍ 400/540000 suites 800/2500000.

🏨 **Holiday Inn Minerva,** piazza della Minerva 69 ⊠ 00186 𝒞 6841888, Telex 620091, Fax 6794165 – 🛗 ⪆ rm 🗐 📺 ☎ ﴾. – 🎩 80. 🖭 🖽 ⓘ **E** 𝒱𝒮𝒜. 🛇 rest   DV **d** **M** a la carte 70/117000 – ⲍ 30000 – **133 rm** 345/492000 suites 492/1300000.

🏨 **Jolly Vittorio Veneto,** corso d'Italia 1 ⊠ 00198 𝒞 8495, Telex 612293, Fax 8841104 – 🛗 🗐 📺 ☎ ﴾ – 🎩 35-450. 🖭 🖽 ⓘ **E** 𝒱𝒮𝒜. 🛇 rest   FU **k** **M** 55000 – **200 rm** ⲍ 275/400000.

🏨 **Quirinale,** via Nazionale 7 ⊠ 00184 𝒞 4707, Telex 610332, Fax 4820099, « Summer rest., service in garden » – 🛗 🗐 📺 ☎ ﴾. – 🎩 250. 🖭 🖽 ⓘ **E** 𝒱𝒮𝒜. 🛇 rest   GV **x** **M** 50000 – **186 rm** ⲍ 265/350000 suites 500/800000.

🏨 **Regina Baglioni,** via Vittorio Veneto 72 ⊠ 00187 𝒞 476851, Telex 620863, Fax 485483 – 🛗 ⪆ rm 🗐 📺 ☎. 🖭 🖽 ⓘ **E** 𝒱𝒮𝒜. 🛇   FU **e** **M** a la carte 65/103000 – **130 rm** ⲍ 350/480000 suites 700/950000.

🏨 **Metropole,** via Principe Amedeo 3 ⊠ 00185 𝒞 4774, Telex 611061, Fax 4740413 – 🛗 🗐 📺 ☎ ﴾ ⟷ – 🎩 90. 🖭 🖽 ⓘ **E** 𝒱𝒮𝒜. 🛇   GV **e** **M** a la carte 46/74000 – **268 rm** ⲍ 250/310000.

🏨 **Victoria,** via Campania 41 ⊠ 00187 𝒞 473931, Telex 610212, Fax 4941330 – 🛗 🗐 📺 ☎. 🖭 🖽 ⓘ **E** 𝒱𝒮𝒜. 🛇 rest   FU **c** **M** 30000 – **110 rm** ⲍ 170/280000.

Mediterraneo, via Cavour 15 ⊠ 00184 *&* 4884051, Fax 4744105 - |≋| ▤ 🖵 ☎ - 🔬 25-90.
AE 🕄 ⓪ E VISA. ⋇
GV **k**
M *(closed Saturday)* 45000 - **272 rm** ⊇ 247/343000 suites 450/900000.

Genova without rest., via Cavour 33 ⊠ 00184 *&* 476951, Telex 621599, Fax 4827580 - |≋|
▤ 🖵 🕉 🕄. AE 🕄 ⓪ E VISA. ⋇
GV **b**
91 rm ⊇ 217/314000.

Londra e Cargill, piazza Sallustio 18 ⊠ 00187 *&* 473871, Telex 622227, Fax 4746674 - |≋|
▤ 🖵 ☎ ⟷ - 🔬 25-200 - **105 rm.**
GU **k**

Forum, via Tor de' Conti 25 ⊠ 00184 *&* 6792446, Telex 622549, Fax 6786478,
« Roof-garden rest. with ≤ Imperial Forums » - |≋| ▤ 🖵 ☎ ⟷ - 🔬 100. AE 🕄 ⓪ E
VISA. ⋇
FX **t**
M *(closed Sunday)* a la carte 73/118000 - ⊇ 25000 - **81 rm** 280/400000 suites 600/700000.

Massimo D'Azeglio, via Cavour 18 ⊠ 00184 *&* 4870270, Telex 610556, Fax 4827386 -
|≋| ▤ 🖵 ☎ - 🔬 200. AE 🕄 ⓪ E VISA. ⋇
GV **s**
M *(closed Sunday)* 45000 - **210 rm** ⊇ 215/298000.

Pullman Boston, via Lombardia 47 ⊠ 00187 *&* 473951, Telex 622247, Fax 4821019 - |≋|
▤ 🖵 ☎ - 🔬 25-90 - **125 rm.**
FU **z**

Imperiale, via Vittorio Veneto 24 ⊠ 00187 *&* 4826351, Telex 4826352 - |≋| ▤ 🖵 ☎. AE
🕄 ⓪ E VISA. ⋇
FU **n**
M a la carte 43/58000 - **85 rm** ⊇ 280/380000.

Mondial without rest., via Torino 127 ⊠ 00184 *&* 472861, Telex 612219, Fax 4824822 -
|≋| ▤ 🖵 ☎ ⟷ - 🔬 25. AE 🕄 ⓪ E VISA. ⋇
GV **a**
77 rm ⊇ 202/286000.

Napoleon, piazza Vittorio Emanuele 105 ⊠ 00185 *&* 4467337, Telex 611069, Fax 4467282
- |≋| ▤ 🖵 ☎ - 🔬 25-60. AE 🕄 ⓪ E VISA. ⋇
HX **a**
M (dinner only) (residents only) a la carte 33/50000 - **80 rm** ⊇ 170/275000.

La Residenza without rest., via Emilia 22 ⊠ 00187 *&* 4880789, Fax 485721 - |≋| ▤ 🖵 ☎
Ɒ. ⋇ - **27 rm** ⊇ 120/215000.
FU **w**

Universo, via Principe Amedeo 5 ⊠ 00185 *&* 476811, Telex 610342 - |≋| ▤ 🖵 ☎ 🕉 -
🔬 25-300 - **207 rm.**
GV **e**

Britannia without rest., via Napoli 64 ⊠ 00184 *&* 4883153, Telex 611292, Fax 4882343 -
|≋| ▤ 🖵 ☎ Ɒ. AE 🕄 ⓪ E VISA
GV **t**
32 rm ⊇ 160/240000.

Commodore without rest., via Torino 1 ⊠ 00184 *&* 485656, Telex 612170, Fax 4747562
- |≋| ▤ 🖵 ☎. AE 🕄 ⓪ E VISA
GV **c**
⊇ 25000 - **60 rm** 200/300000.

Marcella without rest., via Flavia 106 ⊠ 00187 *&* 4746451, Telex 621351, Fax 4815832 -
|≋| ▤ 🖵 ☎. AE 🕄 ⓪ E VISA. ⋇
GU **r**
68 rm ⊇ 155/225000.

Regency without rest., via Romagna 42 ⊠ 00187 *&* 4819281, Telex 622321, Fax 4746850
- |≋| ▤ 🖵 ☎ 🕢. AE 🕄 ⓪ E VISA. ⋇
GU **n**
51 rm ⊇ 220/330000.

Sitea, without rest., via Vittorio Emanuele Orlando 90 ⊠ 00185 *&* 4827560, Telex 614163,
Fax 4817637 - |≋| ▤ 🖵 ☎ - **37 rm.**
GU **t**

Edera ⌂ without rest., via Poliziano 75 ⊠ 00184 *&* 7316341, Telex 623651, Fax 899371,
🌿 - |≋| 🖵 ☎ Ɒ. AE 🕄 ⓪ E VISA. ⋇
GY **r**
53 rm ⊇ 130/190000.

Milani without rest., via Magenta 12 ⊠ 00185 *&* 4457051, Telex 614356, Fax 4462317 -
|≋| 🖵 ☎. ⋇ - **77 rm** ⊇ 121/182000.
HU **z**

Colosseum without rest., via Sforza 10 ⊠ 00184 *&* 4827228, Fax 4827285 - |≋| ☎. AE 🕄
⓪ E VISA - **49 rm** ⊇ 125/175000.
GVX **m**

Diana, via Principe Amedeo 4 ⊠ 00185 *&* 4827541, Telex 611198, Fax 486998 - |≋| ▤ 🖵
☎ - 🔬 25. AE 🕄 E VISA. ⋇
GV **e**
M (residents only) 35000 - **187 rm** ⊇ 120/180000.

Canada without rest., via Vicenza 58 ⊠ 00185 *&* 4457770, Telex 613037, Fax 4450749 -
|≋| ▤ 🖵 ☎. AE 🕄 E VISA. ⋇
HU **e**
74 rm ⊇ 120/172000.

King without rest., via Sistina 131 ⊠ 00187 *&* 4743487, Telex 626246, Fax 4871813 - |≋|
▤ 🖵 ☎. AE 🕄 ⓪ E VISA
FU **d**
72 rm ⊇ 155/205000.

Nord-Nuova Roma without rest., via Amendola 3 ⊠ 00185 *&* 4885441, Fax 4817163 -
|≋| ▤ 🖵 ☎. AE 🕄 ⓪ E VISA. ⋇
GV **d**
156 rm ⊇ 151/210000.

Medici without rest., via Flavia 96 ⊠ 00187 *&* 4827319, Fax 4740767 - |≋| 🖵 ☎. AE 🕄
⓪ E VISA. ⋇ - **68 rm** ⊇ 120/180000.
GU **a**

Centro without rest., via Firenze 12 ⊠ 00184 *&* 4828002, Telex 612125, Fax 4871902 - |≋|
▤ 🖵 ☎. AE 🕄 ⓪ E VISA. ⋇ - **38 rm** ⊇ 150/200000.
GV **n**

Duca d'Alba without rest., via Leonina 12 ⊠ 00184 *&* 484471, Telex 620401, Fax 4884840
- |≋| ▤ 🕢. AE 🕄 ⓪ E VISA - **26 rm** ⊇ 90/140000, ▤ 20000.
FX **v**

XXXX ✿ **Sans Souci,** via Sicilia 20/24 ✉ 00187 ℘ 4821814, Fax 4821771, Elegant tavern-late night dinners – ▤. AE ⑤ ⓓ E VISA. ✻ FU **p**
closed lunch and 13 August-4 September – **M** (booking essential) a la carte 78/135000 (15 %)
Spec. Blinis di scampi alla crema acidula e caviale, Tagliolini all'astice, Costata di Bue in crosta di sale. Wines Sauvignon, Rubesco.

XXX **Harry's Bar,** via Vittorio Veneto 150 ✉ 00187 ℘ 4745832, Fax 4884643 – ▤. AE ⑤ ⓓ VISA. ✻ FU **a**
closed Sunday and 10 to 25 August – **M** (booking essential) a la carte 64/90000.

XX **Piccolo Mondo,** via Aurora 39/d ✉ 00187 ℘ 4814595, Elegant tavern – ▤ FU **h**
closed Sunday and 7 August-5 September – **M** a la carte 35/60000.

XX **Coriolano,** via Ancona 14 ✉ 00198 ℘ 8551122 – ▤. AE ⑤ ⓓ E VISA HU **g**
closed Sunday and 9 to 24 August – **M** (booking essential) a la carte 66/106000 (15 %).

XX **Cesarina,** via Piemonte 109 ✉ 00187 ℘ 4880828, Bolognese rest. – ▤. AE ⑤ ⓓ E VISA. ✻ GU **n**
closed Sunday – **M** a la carte 42/68000.

XX **Loreto,** via Valenziani 19 ✉ 00187 ℘ 4742454, Seafood – ▤. AE VISA. ✻ GU **m**
closed Sunday and 10 to 28 August – **M** a la carte 51/79000.

XX **Andrea,** via Sardegna 28 ✉ 00187 ℘ 4821891, Fax 4828151 – ▤. AE ⑤ ⓓ E VISA. ✻ FU **v**
closed Sunday, Monday lunch, August and Christmas – **M** (booking essential) a la carte 56/99000.

XX **Girarrosto Toscano,** via Campania 29 ✉ 00187 ℘ 4821899, Fax 4821899 – ▤. AE ⑤ ⓓ E VISA. ✻ FU **v**
closed Wednesday – **M** a la carte 44/73000 (15 %).

X **La Taverna,** via Massimo d'Azeglio 3/f ✉ 00184 ℘ 4744305 – ▤. AE ⑤ ⓓ E VISA
closed Saturday and 1 to 26 August – **M** a la carte 27/53000. GV **v**

X **Hostaria Costa Balena,** via Messina 5/7 ✉ 00198 ℘ 8417686, Seafood trattoria – ▤. AE ⑤ ⓓ E VISA. ✻ HU **b**
closed Saturday lunch, Sunday and 10 to 29 August – **M** a la carte 30/58000.

X **Crisciotti-al Boschetto,** via del Boschetto 30 ✉ 00184 ℘ 4744770, ⛱, Rustic trattoria – ⑤ VISA FV **r**
closed Saturday and August – **M** a la carte 24/39000 (10 %).

X **Tempio di Bacco,** via Lombardia 36/38 ✉ 00187 ℘ 4814625, « Fresco mural in small hall » – ▤. AE ⑤ ⓓ E VISA. ✻ FU **h**
closed Saturday and August holiday – **M** a la carte 37/54000 (16 %).

Southern area Aventino, Porta San Paolo, Terme di Caracalla, via Appia Nuova (Plans : Rome pp. 2 to 5) :

⌂ **Sant'Anselmo** without rest., piazza Sant'Anselmo 2 ✉ 00153 ℘ 5743547, Telex 622812, Fax 5783604, ⛱ – ✈ ☎. ⑤ VISA. ✻ by lungotevere Aventino DY
45 rm ▭ 120/170000.

⌂ **Villa San Pio** without rest., via di Sant'Anselmo 19 ✉ 00153 ℘ 5755231, Fax 5783604, ⛱ – |♣| ✈ ☎. ⑤ VISA. ✻ by lungotevere Aventino DY
59 rm ▭ 120/170000.

XX ✿ **Checchino dal 1887,** via Monte Testaccio 30 ✉ 00153 ℘ 5746318, ⛱, Period building typical roman food – AE ⑤ ⓓ VISA. ✻ by lungotevere Aventino DY
closed August, 21 to 27 December, Sunday dinner, Monday and Sunday lunch June-September – **M** (booking essential) a la carte 44/74000 (15 %)
Spec. Bucatini alla gricia, Coda alla vaccinara, Coratella con carciofi. Wines Marino, Le Vignole.

XX **Da Severino,** piazza Zama 5/c ✉ 00183 ℘ 7000872 – ▤. AE ⑤ ⓓ VISA. ✻
closed Sunday dinner, Monday and 1 to 28 August – **M** a la carte 47/73000.
by via dell'Amba Aradam HY

XX **Apuleius,** via Tempio di Diana 15 ✉ 00153 ℘ 5742160, « Tavern in ancient roman style »
closed Sunday – **M** a la carte 47/77000. by lungotevere Aventino DY

Trastevere area (typical district) (Plan : Rome p. 3) :

XXX **Alberto Ciarla,** piazza San Cosimato 40 ✉ 00153 ℘ 5818668, Fax 5884377, ⛱ – AE ⑤ ⓓ E VISA. ✻ CY **u**
closed lunch, Sunday, 12 to 28 August and 23 December-6 January – **M** (booking essential) a la carte 76/114000.

XXX **Cul de Sac 2,** vicolo dell'Atleta 21 ✉ 00153 ℘ 5813324 – ▤. AE ⑤ ⓓ DY **a**
closed Sunday dinner, Monday and August – **M** (booking essential) a la carte 63/72000.

XX **Corsetti-il Galeone,** piazza San Cosimato 27 ✉ 00153 ℘ 5816311, Fax 5896255, Seafood, « Typical atmosphere » – ▤. AE ⑤ ⓓ E VISA. ✻ CY **g**
closed Wednesday and 18 to 26 July – **M** a la carte 37/70000.

XX **Carlo Menta,** via della Lungaretta 101 ✉ 00153 ℘ 5884450, ⛱, Seafood – ▤. AE ⑤ ⓓ E VISA. ✻ CY **z**
closed Monday, July and January – **M** (dinner only) (booking essential) a la carte 67/82000 (15 %).

XX **Sabatini a Santa Maria in Trastevere,** piazza di Santa Maria in Trastevere 13 ⊠ 00153
✉ 5812026, 🍽️, Roman and Seafood rest. – 🅰️🅴 🕒 ⓞ 🅴 𝗩𝗜𝗦𝗔 CY **n**
M a la carte 60/90000.

XX **Galeassi,** piazza di Santa Maria in Trastevere 3 ⊠ 00153 ✉ 5803775, 🍽️, Roman and
Seafood rest. – 🔲. 🍴 CY **f**
closed Monday and 20 December-20 January – **M** a la carte 45/64000.

XX **Sabatini,** vicolo Santa Maria in Trastevere 18 ⊠ 00153 ✉ 5818307, 🍽️, Roman and Seafood rest. – 🅰️🅴 🕒 ⓞ 🅴 𝗩𝗜𝗦𝗔 CY **n**
closed Wednesday – **M** a la carte 60/90000.

XX **Checco er Carettiere,** via Benedetta 10 ⊠ 00153 ✉ 5817018, 🍽️, Typical Roman and
Seafood rest. – 🔲. 🅰️🅴 ⓞ 𝗩𝗜𝗦𝗔 CX **k**
closed Sunday dinner, Monday and 10 August-10 September – **M** a la carte 43/72000.

XX **Pastarellaro,** via di San Crisogono 33 ⊠ 00153 ✉ 5810871, Roman and Seafood rest. –
🔲. 🅰️🅴 🕒 ⓞ 🅴 𝗩𝗜𝗦𝗔 DY **r**
closed Tuesday and August – **M** a la carte 34/53000 (10 %).

Outskirts of Rome

on national road 1 - Aurelia :

🏨 **Jolly Hotel Midas,** via Aurelia al 8 km ⊠ 00165 ✉ 6506, Telex 622821, Fax 6808457, 🏊,
🌳, 🎾 – 🛗 🔲 📺 ☎ 🅿️ – 🔬 800. 🅰️🅴 🕒 ⓞ 🅴 𝗩𝗜𝗦𝗔. 🍴 rest by via Aurelia AV
M 45000 – **357 rm** ⊑ 220/315000.

🏨 **Villa Pamphili,** via della Nocetta 105 ⊠ 00164 ✉ 5862, Telex 626539, Fax 6257747, 🕭,
🛁, 🏊 (covered in winter), 🌳, 🎾 – 🛗 🔲 📺 ☎ 🅿️ – 🔬 25-500. 🅰️🅴 🕒 ⓞ 🅴 𝗩𝗜𝗦𝗔.
🍴 rest by via Garibaldi BY
M a la carte 46/78000 – **254 rm** ⊑ 216/286000.

🏨 **Holiday Inn St. Peter's,** via Aurelia Antica 415 ⊠ 00165 ✉ 6642, Telex 625434,
Fax 6637190, 🕭, 🏊, 🌳, 🎾 – 🛗 ⇆ rm 🔲 📺 ☎ 🅿️ – 🔬 25-300. 🅰️🅴 🕒 ⓞ 🅴 𝗩𝗜𝗦𝗔.
🍴 by via Garibaldi BY
M a la carte 56/85000 – ⊑ 17000 – **321 rm** 367000.

🏨 **AgipHotel,** via Aurelia al 8 km ⊠ 00165 ✉ 6379001, Telex 613699, Fax 6804437, 🏊 – 🛗
🔲 📺 ☎ 🅿️ – 🔬 25-160. 🅰️🅴 🕒 ⓞ 🅴 𝗩𝗜𝗦𝗔. 🍴 rest by via Aurelia AV
M 30000 – **213 rm** ⊑ 165/215000.

XX **La Maielletta,** via Aurelia Antica 270 ⊠ 00165 ✉ 6374957, Fax 6374957, Typical Abruzzi
rest. – 🅿️ by via Aurelia AV

on national road 4 - Salaria :

🏨 Motel la Giocca and Rest. L'Elite, via Salaria 1223 ⊠ 00138 ✉ 8804365 and rest ✉ 8804503,
Fax 8804495, 🏊 – 🛗 🔲 ☎ 🚗 🅿️ – 🔬 30 by via Piave AV
50 rm.

🏨 **Eurogarden** without rest., raccordo anulare Salaria Flaminia ⊠ 00138 ✉ 8804507, 🏊, 🌳
– 🔲 📺 ☎ 🅿️. 🅰️🅴 🕒 ⓞ 𝗩𝗜𝗦𝗔. 🍴 by via Piave AV
⊑ 20000 – **40 rm** 150000, 🔲 10000.

on the Ancient Appian way :

XX **Cecilia Metella,** via Appia Antica 125/127 ⊠ 00179 ✉ 5136743, 🍽️, « Shaded garden »
– 🅿️. 🅰️🅴 𝗩𝗜𝗦𝗔 by via Claudia GY
closed Monday and 12 to 30 August – **M** a la carte 40/60000.

to E.U.R. Garden City :

🏨 **Sheraton,** viale del Pattinaggio ⊠ 00144 ✉ 5453, Telex 626073, Fax 5423281, 🕭, 🏊, 🎾
– 🛗 🔲 📺 ☎ 🅿️ – 🔬 25-1800. 🅰️🅴 🕒 ⓞ 🅴 𝗩𝗜𝗦𝗔. 🍴
M a la carte 60/120000 – **615 rm** ⊑ 440000 suites 780/2000000.
by via di San Gregorio FY

🏨 **Shangri Là-Corsetti,** viale Algeria 141 ⊠ 00144 ✉ 5916441, Telex 614664, Fax 5413813,
🏊 heated, 🌳 – 🔲 📺 ☎ 🅿️ – 🔬 25-80. 🅰️🅴 🕒 ⓞ 🅴 𝗩𝗜𝗦𝗔. 🍴
M *(closed 5 to 25 August)* a la carte 37/70000 – **52 rm** ⊑ 195/260000 suites 265/
360000. by via di San Gregorio FY

🏨 **Dei Congressi** without rest., viale Shakespeare 29 ⊠ 00144 ✉ 5926021, Telex 614140,
Fax 5911903 – 🛗 🔲 ☎ – 🔬 25-300. 🅰️🅴 🕒 ⓞ 🅴 𝗩𝗜𝗦𝗔. 🍴 by via di San Gregorio FY
96 rm ⊑ 120/220000.

XX **Vecchia America-Corsetti,** piazza Marconi 32 ⊠ 00144 ✉ 5926601, Typical rest. and
ale house – 🔲. 🅰️🅴 🕒 ⓞ 🅴 𝗩𝗜𝗦𝗔 by via di San Gregorio FY
closed Tuesday – **M** a la carte 48/74000.

on the motorway to Fiumicino close to the ring-road :

🏨 **Holiday Inn-Eur Parco dei Medici,** viale Castello della Magliana 65 ⊠ 00148 ✉ 65581,
Telex 613302, Fax 6557005, 🏊, 🌳, 🎾 – 🛗 🔲 📺 ☎ 🅿️ – 🔬 160-800. 🅰️🅴 🕒 ⓞ 🅴 𝗩𝗜𝗦𝗔.
🍴 by viale Trastevere CY
M 60000 – ⊑ 17000 – **316 rm** 330/420000.

FLORENCE **(FIRENZE) 50100** P 988 ⑮, 429 430 K 15 – pop. 408 403 alt. 49 – ☎ 055.

See : Cathedral★★ : east end★★★, dome★★★ (※★★) Campanile★★ : ※★★ Baptistry★★★ : doors★★★, mosaics★★★ Cathedral Museum★★ – Piazza della Signoria★★ Loggia della Signoria★★ : Perseus★★★ by B. Cellini Palazzo Vecchio★★★ Uffizi Gallery★★★ – Bargello Palace and Museum★★★ San Lorenzo★★★ : Church★★, Laurentian Library★★, Medici tombs★★★ in Medici Chapels★★ – Medici-Riccardi★★ : Chapel★★★, Luca Giordano Gallery★★ – Church of Santa Maria Novella★★ : frescoes by Ghirlandaio★★★ – Ponte Vecchio★ Pitti Palace★★ : Palatine Gallery★★★, Silver Museum★★, Works by the Macchiaioli★★ in Modern Art Gallery★ – Boboli Garden★ ABZ : ※★★ from the Citadel Belvedere Monastery and Museum of St. Mark★★ : works by Fra Angelico★★★ – Academy Gallery★★ : main gallery★★★ Piazza della Santissima Annunziata★ CX : frescoes★ in the church **E**, portico★ with corners decorated with terracotta medallions★★ in the Foundling Hospital – Church of Santa Croce★★ – Pazzi Chapel★★ Excursion to the hills★★ : ≤★★ from Michelangelo Square, Church of San Miniato al Monte★★ Strozzi Palace★★ BY **F** – Palazzo Rucellai★ BYZ Frescoes by Masaccio★★ in the Church of Santa Maria del Carmine AY **G** – Last Supper of San Salvi★★ – Orsanmichele★ : tabernacle by Orcagna★★ BCY **L** – La Badia CY **S** : campanile★, delicate relief sculpture in marble★★, tombs★, Virgin appearing to St. Bernard★ by Filippino Lippi – Sassetti Chapel★★ and the Chapel of the Annunciation★ in the Holy Trinity Church BY **N** – Church of the Holy Spirit★ ABY **R** – Last Supper of Sant'Apollonia★ CVX **V** – Last Supper by Ghirlandaio★ AX **X** – Palazzo Davanzanti★ BY **M5** New Market Loggia★ BY **Y** – Museums : Archaeological★ (Chimera from Arezzo★★) CX **M4**, Science★ CY **M6**, Semi-precious Stone Workshop★ CX **M7**.

Envir. : Medici Villas★★ : garden★ of the Villa della Pretaia, Villa di Poggio a Caiano★ by via P. Toselli AV : 17 km – Cloister★ in the Galluzzo Carthusian Monastery S : 6 km.

18 Dell'Ugolino (closed Monday), to Grassina ✉ 50015 ☎ 2301009, S : 12 km.

✈ of Peretola NW : 4 km ☎ 373498 – Alitalia, lungarno Acciaiuoli 10/12 r, ✉ 50123 ☎ 27888.

i via Manzoni 16 ✉ 50121 ☎ 2478141 – via de' Tornabuoni 15 ✉ 50123 ☎ 216544, Telex 572263.

A.C.I. viale Amendola 36 ✉ 50121 ☎ 24861.

Roma 277 – Bologna 105 – Milano 298.

Plans on following pages

Excelsior, piazza Ognissanti 3 ✉ 50123 ☎ 264201, Telex 570022, Fax 210278, « Rest. with summer service on terrace with ≤ » – |‡| ▤ TV ☎ ♿ – 🏛 50-350. AE 🅂 ⦿ E VISA. ✻ rest AY **g**
M a la carte 82/120000 – ☕ 24000 – **203 rm** 369/536000 suites 893/1428000.

Savoy, piazza della Repubblica 7 ✉ 50123 ☎ 283313, Telex 570220, Fax 284840 – |‡| ▤ TV ☎ ♿ – 🏛 150. AE 🅂 ⦿ E VISA. ✻ rest BY **e**
M (dinner only) a la carte 64/104000 – **101 rm** ☕ 330/530000 suites 850/1050000.

Villa Medici and Rest. Lorenzo de' Medici, via Il Prato 42 ✉ 50123 ☎ 238331, Telex 570179, Fax 238336, 🌴, 🏊, 🌳 – |‡| ▤ TV ☎ – 🏛 30-90. AE 🅂 ⦿ E VISA AX **g**
M a la carte 40/80000 – ☕ 22000 – **103 rm** 321/500000 suites 607/893000.

Regency and Rest. Relais le Jardin, piazza Massimo D'Azeglio 3 ✉ 50121 ☎ 245247, Telex 571058, Fax 2342938, 🌳 – |‡| ▤ TV ☎ 🚗. AE 🅂 ⦿ E VISA. ✻ rest DX **c**
M *(closed Sunday)* (booking essential) a la carte 70/110000 – ☕ 25000 – **38 rm** 350/500000 suites 600/900000.

Helvetia e Bristol, via dei Pescioni 2 ✉ 50123 ☎ 287814, Telex 572696, Fax 288353 – |‡| ▤ TV ☎. AE 🅂 ⦿ E VISA. ✻ BY **f**
M a la carte 56/88000 – ☕ 26500 – **52 rm** 340/500000 suites 619/1167000.

Brunelleschi, piazza Santa Elisabetta 3 ✉ 50122 ☎ 562068, Telex 575805, Fax 219653 – |‡| ⇔ rm ▤ TV ☎ – 🏛 100. AE 🅂 ⦿ E VISA. ✻ rest CY **p**
M a la carte 48/75000 – **94 rm** ☕ 260/360000 suites 420/560000.

Plaza Hotel Lucchesi, lungarno della Zecca Vecchia 38 ✉ 50122 ☎ 264141, Telex 570302, Fax 2480921, ≤ – |‡| ▤ TV ☎ ♿ – 🏛 50-100. AE 🅂 ⦿ E VISA. ✻ rest DY **f**
M (residents only) *(closed Sunday)* a la carte 54/86000 – **97 rm** ☕ 255/365000 suites 485000.

Grand Hotel Baglioni, piazza Unità Italiana 6 ✉ 50123 ☎ 218441, Telex 570225, Fax 215695, « Roof-garden rest. with ≤ » – |‡| ▤ TV ☎ ♿ – 🏛 25-200. AE 🅂 ⦿ E VISA. ✻ rest BX **e**
M a la carte 48/63000 – **195 rm** ☕ 245/345000 suites 500/1000000.

Grand Hotel Ciga, piazza Ognissanti 1 ✉ 50123 ☎ 288781, Telex 570055, Fax 217400 – |‡| ▤ TV ☎ ♿ 🚗 – 🏛 30-200. AE 🅂 ⦿ E VISA. ✻ rest AXY **a**
M a la carte 66/108000 – ☕ 28000 – **107 rm** 440/630000 suites 952/1666000.

Jolly, piazza Vittorio Veneto 4/a ✉ 50123 ☎ 2770, Telex 570191, Fax 294794, « 🏊 on terrace with panorama » – |‡| ⇔ rm ▤ TV ☎ – 🏛 30-100. AE 🅂 ⦿ E VISA. ✻ rest AX **u**
M 55000 – **167 rm** ☕ 220/330000.

Majestic, via del Melarancio 1 ✉ 50123 ☎ 264021, Telex 570628, Fax 268428 – |‡| ▤ TV ☎ ♿ 🚗 – 🏛 80. AE 🅂 ⦿ E VISA. ✻ rest BX **u**
M a la carte 43/63000 – ☕ 25000 – **103 rm** 220/295000 suite 495000.

De la Ville, piazza Antinori 1 ✉ 50123 ☎ 2381805, Telex 570518, Fax 2381809 – |‡| ▤ TV ☎ – 🏛 60. AE 🅂 ⦿ E VISA. ✻ BX **n**
M a la carte 45/55000 – **75 rm** ☕ 254/361000 suites 620/720000.

🏨🏨 **Berchielli** without rest., piazza del Limbo 6 r ⊠ 50123 *𝒫* 264061, Telex 575582, Fax 218636,
≤ – |𝄞| ▤ ▥ ☎ – 🔏 80. 🖭 🗗 ⓞ ▐ *VISA*. 🛇   BY **b**
74 rm ⊑ 320/350000 suites 480/570000.

🏨🏨 **Bernini Palace** without rest., piazza San Firenze 29 ⊠ 50122 *𝒫* 288621, Telex 573616,
Fax 268272 – |𝄞| ▤ ▥ ☎ – 🔏 40. 🖭 🗗 ⓞ ▐ *VISA*   CY **x**
86 rm ⊑ 250/360000 suites 440/470000.

🏨🏨 **Montebello Splendid,** via Montebello 60 ⊠ 50123 *𝒫* 2398051, Telex 574009, Fax 211867,
🌣 – |𝄞| ▤ ▥ ☎ – 🔏 100. 🖭 🗗 ⓞ ▐ *VISA*. 🛇 rest   AX **e**
M *(closed Sunday)* a la carte 47/91000 – **53 rm** ⊑ 240/340000 suite 680000.

🏨🏨 **Michelangelo,** via Fratelli Rosselli 2 ⊠ 50123 *𝒫* 2784, Telex 571113, Fax 2382232 – |𝄞|
▤ ▥ ☎ ⇆ – 🔏 50-250. 🖭 🗗 ⓞ ▐ *VISA*. 🛇 rest   AX **w**
M a la carte 49/81000 – **138 rm** ⊑ 255/360000.

🏨🏨 **Anglo American,** via Garibaldi 9 ⊠ 50123 *𝒫* 282114, Telex 570289, Fax 268513 – |𝄞| ▤
▥ ☎ – 🔏 50-150. 🖭 🗗 ⓞ ▐ *VISA*. 🛇 rest   AX **d**
M *(closed Sunday)* a la carte 60/85000 – **107 rm** ⊑ 240/330000 suites 400/450000.

🏨🏨 **Gd H. Minerva,** piazza Santa Maria Novella 16 ⊠ 50123 *𝒫* 284555, Telex 570414,
Fax 268281, ⅃ – |𝄞| ▤ ▥ ☎ 🖑 – 🔏 30-90. 🖭 🗗 ⓞ ▐ *VISA*. 🛇 rest   BX **s**
M a la carte 42/69000 – ⅃ 20000 – **96 rm** 220/295000 suites 395000.

🏨🏨 **Augustus** without rest., piazzetta dell'Oro 5 ⊠ 50123 *𝒫* 283054, Telex 570110, Fax 268557
– |𝄞| ▤ ▥ ☎. 🖭 🗗 ⓞ ▐ *VISA*   BY **a**
⊑ 20000 – **62 rm** 200/270000.

🏨🏨 **Kraft,** via Solferino 2 ⊠ 50123 *𝒫* 284273, Telex 571523, Fax 298267, « Roof-garden rest.
with ≤ », ⅃ – |𝄞| ▤ ▥ ☎ – 🔏 50   AX **c**
68 rm.

🏨🏨 **Londra,** via Jacopo da Diacceto 18 ⊠ 50123 *𝒫* 262791, Telex 571152, Fax 210682, 🌣
– |𝄞| ▤ ▥ ☎ 🖑 ⇆ – 🔏 200. 🖭 🗗 ⓞ ▐ *VISA*. 🛇 rest   AX **n**
M a la carte 50/77000 – **107 rm** ⊑ 240/335000.

🏨🏨 **Lungarno** without rest., borgo Sant'Jacopo 14 ⊠ 50125 *𝒫* 264211, Telex 570129,
Fax 268437, ≤, « Collection of modern pictures » – |𝄞| ▤ ▥ ☎ – 🔏 30. 🖭 🗗 ⓞ ▐
VISA   BY **d**
⊑ 20000 – **66 rm** 200/280000 suites 380/420000.

🏨🏨 **Alexander,** viale Guidoni 101 ⊠ 50127 *𝒫* 4378951, Telex 574026, Fax 416818 – |𝄞| ▤ ▥
☎ 🖑 🅿 – 🔏 50-400. 🖭 🗗 ⓞ ▐ *VISA*. 🛇 rest   by viale F. Redi AV
M a la carte 35/68000 – **88 rm** ⊑ 228/298000.

🏨🏨 **Pullman Astoria Palazzo Gaddi,** via del Giglio 9 ⊠ 50123 *𝒫* 2398022, Telex 571070,
Fax 214632 – |𝄞| ▤ ▥ ☎ 🖑 – 🔏 50-130. 🖭 🗗 ⓞ ▐ *VISA*. 🛇 rest   BX **f**
M *(closed Sunday)* a la carte 42/72000 – **88 rm** ⊑ 240/340000 suite 600000.

🏨🏨 **Holiday Inn and Rest. la Tegolaia,** viale Europa 205 ⊠ 50126 *𝒫* 6531841, Telex 570376,
Fax 6531806, 🌣, ⅃ – |𝄞| ⇆ rm ▤ ▥ ☎ 🖑 🅿 – 🔏 50-120. 🖭 🗗 ⓞ ▐ *VISA*.
🛇 rest   by G. Orsini DZ
M a la carte 45/70000 – **92 rm** ⊑ 210000.

🏨🏨 **Pierre** without rest., via de' Lamberti 5 ⊠ 50123 *𝒫* 217512, Telex 573175, Fax 2396573 –
|𝄞| ▤ ▥ ☎. 🖭 🗗 ⓞ ▐ *VISA*   BY **k**
⊑ 22500 – **39 rm** 273000.

🏨🏨 **Raffaello,** viale Morgagni 19 ⊠ 50134 *𝒫* 439871, Telex 580035, Fax 434374 – |𝄞| ▤ ▥
☎ ⇆ – 🔏 110. 🖭 🗗 ⓞ ▐ *VISA*. 🛇 rest   by via del Romito AV
M a la carte 35/62000 – **141 rm** ⊑ 270/294000 suites 444/494000.

🏨 **Principe** without rest., lungarno Vespucci 34 ⊠ 50123 *𝒫* 284848, Telex 571400,
Fax 283458, ≤, 🌣 – |𝄞| ▤ ▥ ☎. 🖭 🗗 ⓞ ▐ *VISA*. 🛇   AX **b**
⊑ 20000 – **21 rm** 240/290000.

🏨 **J and J,** via di Mezzo 20 ⊠ 50121 *𝒫* 240951, Telex 570554, Fax 240282 –
▤ ▥ ☎. 🖭 🗗 ⓞ ▐ *VISA*   DY **c**
19 rm ⊑ 320000 suites 320/400000.

🏨 **Continental** without rest., lungarno Acciaiuoli 2 ⊠ 50123 *𝒫* 282392, Telex 580525,
Fax 283139, « Floral terrace with ≤ » – |𝄞| ▤ ▥ ☎. 🖭 🗗 ⓞ ▐ *VISA*   BY **a**
⊑ 20000 – **61 rm** 190/260000 suites 350/400000.

🏨 **Loggiato dei Serviti** without rest., piazza SS. Annunziata 3 ⊠ 50122 *𝒫* 289592,
Telex 575808, Fax 289595 – |𝄞| ▤ ▥ ☎. 🖭 🗗 ⓞ ▐ *VISA*   CX **d**
⊑ 18000 – **29 rm** 106/166000 suites 200/450000.

🏨 **Fleming** without rest., viale Guidoni 87 ⊠ 50127 *𝒫* 4376773, Fax 574027 – |𝄞| ▤ ▥ ☎
– 🔏 35-60. 🖭 🗗 ⓞ ▐ *VISA*. 🛇   by via P. Toselli AV
119 rm ⊑ 116/188000.

🏨 **Villa Azalee** without rest., viale Fratelli Rosselli 44 ⊠ 50123 *𝒫* 214242, Fax 268264, 🌣
– ▤ ▥ ☎. 🖭 🗗 ⓞ ▐ *VISA*   AVX **y**
24 rm ⊑ 112/174000.

🏨 **Privilege** without rest., lungarno della Zecca Vecchia 26 ⊠ 50122 *𝒫* 2341221, Fax 243287
– ▤ ▥ ☎. 🖭 🗗 ⓞ ▐ *VISA*   DY **e**
15 rm ⊑ 120/190000.

FIRENZE

0   300 m

★★ S. LORENZO
★★ STA MA NOVELLA

MICHELIN

★ PONTE VECCHIO ★
★★ PALAZZO PITTI ★★

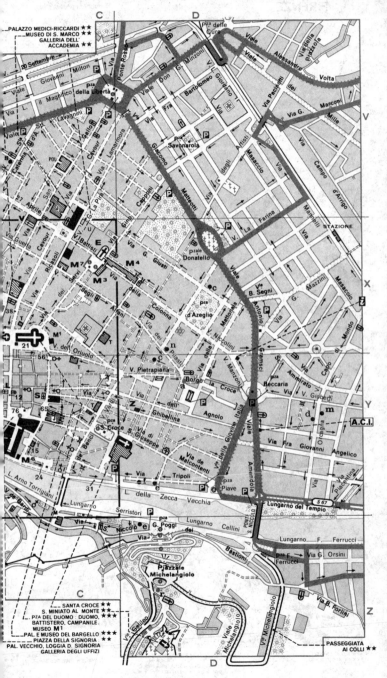

PALAZZO MEDICI-RICCARDI ★★
MUSEO DI S. MARCO ★★
GALLERIA DELL'
ACCADEMIA ★★

SANTA CROCE ★★
S. MINIATO AL MONTE ★★
PZA DEL DUOMO : DUOMO, ★★★
BATTISTERO, CAMPANILE,
MUSEO M1
PAL. E MUSEO DEL BARGELLO ★★★
PIAZZA DELLA SIGNORIA ★★
PAL. VECCHIO, LOGGIA D. SIGNORIA
GALLERIA DEGLI UFFIZI

PASSEGGIATA
AI COLLI ★★

319

FIRENZE

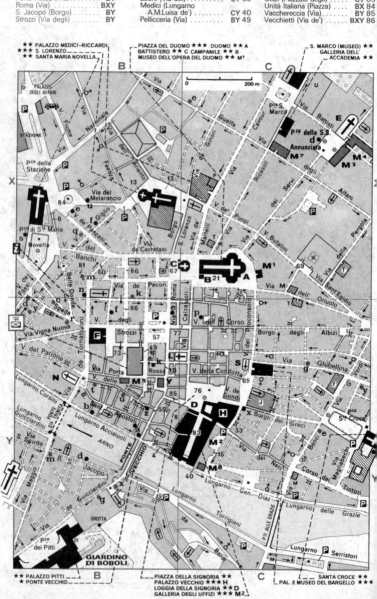

Rapallo, via di Santa Caterina d'Alessandria 7 ✉ 50129 ✆ 472412, Telex 574251, Fax 470385 – |‡| ▤ ☎ ⇐. AE ⓢ ⓞ E VISA. ✂ CV **s**
M (residents only) 32000 – ☕ 13000 – **30 rm** 87/130000.

Franchi without rest., via Sgambati 28 ✉ 50127 ✆ 315425, Telex 580425, Fax 315563 – |‡| ☎ ⓟ. AE ⓢ ⓞ E VISA by via P. Toselli AV
☕ 12000 – **35 rm** 75/113000.

Arizona without rest., via Farini 2 ✉ 50121 ✆ 245321, Telex 575572 – |‡| TV ☎. AE ⓢ ⓞ E VISA. ✂ DX **n**
21 rm ☕ 98/152000.

Fiorino without rest., via Osteria del Guanto 6 ✉ 50122 ✆ 210579 – ▤ ☎ CY **b**
☕ 10000 – **21 rm** 65/95000, ▤ 8000.

Jane without rest., via Orcagna 56 ✉ 50121 ✆ 677382, Fax 677383 – |‡| ▤ ☎. ✂ DY **m**
☕ 10000 – **24 rm** 70/95000, ▤ 7000.

Orcagna without rest., via Orcagna 57 ✉ 50121 ✆ 669959 – |‡| ☎. ⓢ ⓞ E VISA. ✂ DY **d**
☕ 10000 – **18 rm** 54/79000.

San Remo without rest., lungarno Serristori 13 ✉ 50125 ✆ 2342823, Fax 2342269 – |‡| ▤ TV ☎. AE ⓢ ⓞ E VISA DZ **e**
☕ 8500 – **20 rm** 82/120000.

XXXX ✿✿ **Enoteca Pinchiorri,** via Ghibellina 87 ✉ 50122 ✆ 242777, Fax 244983, « Summer service in a cool court yard » – ▤. AE ⓢ VISA CY **y**
closed Sunday, Monday lunch, August, 24 to 28 December and February – **M** (booking essential) a la carte 115/185000
Spec. Scaloppa di branzino ai frutti di mare gratinati, Ravioli di astice e porri con olive nere e timo, Petto di piccione ai frutti di bosco e spezie. Wines Vergena, Cannaio di Montevertine.

XXXX **Sabatini,** via de' Panzani 9/a ✉ 50123 ✆ 211559, Fax 210293, Elegant traditional decor – ▤. AE ⓢ ⓞ E VISA. ✂ BX **q**
closed Monday – **M** a la carte 59/99000 (13 %).

XXX **Al Lume di Candela,** via delle Terme 23 r ✉ 50123 ✆ 294566 – ▤. AE ⓢ ⓞ E VISA. ✂ BY **u**
closed Sunday, Monday lunch and 10 to 25 August – **M** (booking essential) a la carte 54/85000 (12 %).

XXX **Harry's Bar,** lungarno Vespucci 22 r ✉ 50123 ✆ 2396700 – ▤. AE VISA AY **x**
closed Sunday and 15 December-5 January – **M** (booking essential) a la carte 46/71000 (16 %).

XXX **Don Chisciotte,** via Ridolfi 4 r ✉ 50129 ✆ 475430 – ▤ BV **u**
closed Sunday, Monday lunch and August – **M** (booking essential) a la carte 47/80000.

XXX **Toulà-Oliviero,** via delle Terme 51 r ✉ 50123 ✆ 287643, Fax 2302407 – AE ⓢ ⓞ E VISA BY **t**
closed Sunday, Monday lunch, 4 to 26 August and Christmas – **M** (booking essential) a la carte 54/80000.

XX **La Loggia,** piazzale Michelangiolo 1 ✉ 50125 ✆ 2342832, Fax 2345288, « Outdoor service in summer with ≤ » – ▤ ⓟ – 🏛 50. AE ⓢ ⓞ E VISA. ✂ DZ **r**
closed Wednesday – **M** a la carte 44/61000 (13 %).

XX **Al Campidoglio,** via del Campidoglio 8 r ✉ 50123 ✆ 287770, Fax 287770 – ▤. AE ⓢ ⓞ E VISA. ✂ BXY **k**
closed Tuesday – **M** a la carte 45/60000 (12 %).

XX ✿ **I 4 Amici,** via degli Orti Oricellari 29 ✉ 50123 ✆ 215413 – ▤. AE ⓢ ⓞ E VISA. ✂ AX **h**
closed Wednesday and 7 to 25 August – **M** (fish only) a la carte 45/63000 (12 %)
Spec. Antipasti di mare, Spaghetti alle vongole veraci, Dentice alla paesana. Wines Vermentino.

XX **La Posta,** via de' Lamberti 20 r ✉ 50123 ✆ 212701 – ▤. AE ⓢ E VISA BY **s**
closed Tuesday – **M** a la carte 38/65000 (13 %).

XX **i' Toscano,** via Guelfa 70/r ✉ 50129 ✆ 215475 – ▤. AE ⓢ ⓞ E VISA CX **e**
closed Tuesday and August – **M** a la carte 30/50000.

XX **13 Gobbi,** via del Porcellana 9 r ✉ 50123 ✆ 2398769, Tuscan rest. – ▤. ⓢ ⓞ E VISA. ✂ AX **v**
closed Sunday, Monday and 31 July-30 August – **M** a la carte 35/61000 (12 %).

XX **La Sagrestia,** via Gucciardini 27/r ✉ 50125 ✆ 210003 – ▤. AE ⓢ ⓞ E VISA. ✂ BY **g**
closed Monday – **M** a la carte 30/47000.

XX **Buca Mario,** piazza Ottaviani 16 r ✉ 50123 ✆ 214179, Typical trattoria – ▤. AE ⓢ ⓞ E VISA. ✂ BXY **d**
closed Wednesday, Thursday lunch and August – **M** a la carte 38/60000 (12 %).

XX **Acquerello,** via Ghibellina 156 r ✉ 50122 ✆ 2340554 – ▤. AE ⓢ ⓞ E VISA CY **g**
closed Thursday – **M** a la carte 35/53000 (12 %).

✗ **La Capannina di Sante,** piazza Ravenna ang. Ponte da Verrazzano ⊠ 50126 ℰ 688345, ≤, 🍴 – 🗐, ⒶⒺ 🚼 ⑩ Ⓔ 𝘝𝘐𝘚𝘈, 🍽   by Lungarno F. Ferrucci   DZ
closed Sunday, Monday lunch, 10 to 20 August and 24 to 31 December – **M** (fish only) a la carte 75/90000.

✗ **Il Giardino di Barbano,** piazza Indipendenza 3 r ⊠ 50129 ℰ 486752, « Summer service in garden » – ⒶⒺ 🚼 ⑩ Ⓔ 𝘝𝘐𝘚𝘈   BV **w**
closed Wednesday – **M** a la carte 29/47000 (12 %).

✗ **Cibreo,** via dei Macci 118 ⊠ 50122 ℰ 2341100, Fax 244966 – ⒶⒺ 🚼 ⑩ Ⓔ 𝘝𝘐𝘚𝘈   DY **a**
closed Sunday, Monday and 26 July-6 September – **M** (booking essential) a la carte 40/49000 (15 %).

✗ **Buca Lapi,** via del Trebbio 1 r ⊠ 50123 ℰ 213768, Typical tavern – 🗐, ⒶⒺ ⑩ 𝘝𝘐𝘚𝘈
closed Sunday and Monday lunch – **M** a la carte 38/57000 (12 %).   BX **m**

✗ **Celestino,** piazza Santa Felicita 4 r ⊠ 50125 ℰ 296574 – 🗐, ⒶⒺ 🚼 ⑩ Ⓔ 𝘝𝘐𝘚𝘈   BY **x**
closed Sunday and 5 to 20 August – **M** a la carte 34/48000 (12 %).

on the hills S : 3 km :

🏨 **Gd H. Villa Cora and Rest. Taverna Machiavelli** ⑤, viale Machiavelli 18 ⊠ 50125 ℰ 2298451, Telex 570604, Fax 229086, 🍴, « Floral park with ⌿ » – 🛗 🗐 📺 ☎ 🅟 – 🔬 50-150. ⒶⒺ 🚼 ⑩ 𝘝𝘐𝘚𝘈, 🍽 rest   by viale Machiavelli ABZ
M a la carte 52/76000 (15 %) – � 24000 – **48 rm** 464/539000 suites 817/1024000.

🏨 **Torre di Bellosguardo** ⑤ without rest., via Roti Michelozzi 2 ⊠ 50124 ℰ 2298145, 🌿 town and hills, « Park and terrace with ⌿ » – 🛗 ☎ 🅟. ⒶⒺ 🚼 ⑩ Ⓔ 𝘝𝘐𝘚𝘈
⊠ 20000 – **13 rm** 230/300000 suites 400/530000.   by via Senese AZ

🏨 **Villa Carlotta** ⑤, via Michele di Lando 3 ⊠ 50125 ℰ 2336134, Telex 573485, Fax 2336147, 🌿 – 🛗 🗐 📺 ☎ 🅟. ⒶⒺ 🚼 ⑩ Ⓔ 𝘝𝘐𝘚𝘈, 🍽 rest   AZ **a**
M a la carte 44/70000 – **27 rm** ⊠ 240/340000.

🏨 **Villa Belvedere** ⑤ without rest., via Benedetto Castelli 3 ⊠ 50124 ℰ 222501, Telex 575648, Fax 223163, ≤ town and hills, « Garden-Park with ⌿ », ✗ – 🛗 🗐 📺 ☎ 🕭 🅟. ⒶⒺ 🚼 ⑩ Ⓔ 🍽   by ④
March-November – **27 rm** ⊠ 165/250000.

✗✗ **Antico Crespino,** largo Enrico Fermi 15 ⊠ 50125 ℰ 221155, ≤ – ⒶⒺ 🚼 ⑩ Ⓔ 𝘝𝘐𝘚𝘈
closed Wednesday – **M** a la carte 46/77000 (13 %).   by via Senese AZ

at Arcetri S : 5 km – ⊠ **50125** Firenze :

✗ **Omero,** via Pian de' Giullari 11 r ℰ 220053, Country trattoria with ≤, « Summer service on terrace » – ⒶⒺ 🚼 ⑩ Ⓔ 𝘝𝘐𝘚𝘈, 🍽   by viale Galileo DZ
closed Tuesday and August – **M** a la carte 33/47000 (13 %).

at Galluzzo S : 6,5 km – ⊠ **50124** Firenze :

🏨 **Relais Certosa,** via Colle Ramole 2 ℰ 2047171, Telex 574332, Fax 268575, ≤, « Garden-Park », ⌿, ✗ – 🛗 ⋈ 🗐 📺 ☎ 🅟 – 🔬 30-60. ⒶⒺ 🚼 ⑩ Ⓔ 𝘝𝘐𝘚𝘈, 🍽 rest
M a la carte 45/77000 – **69 rm** ⊠ 258/296000 suites 430000.   by via Senese AZ

at Candeli E : 7 km – ⊠ **50010** :

🏨 **Villa La Massa and Rest. Il Verrocchio** ⑤, via La Massa 6 ℰ 666141, Telex 573555, Fax 632579, ≤, 🍴, « 18C house and furnishings », ⌿, 🌿, ✗ – 🛗 🗐 📺 ☎ 🕭 🅟 – 🔬 100. ⒶⒺ 🚼 ⑩ Ⓔ 𝘝𝘐𝘚𝘈, 🍽 rest
M *(closed Monday and Tuesday lunch November-March)* a la carte 55/70000 – ⊠ 25000 – **38 rm** 290/490000 suites 700000.

towards Trespiano N : 7 km :

🏨 **Villa le Rondini** ⑤, via Bolognese Vecchia 224 ⊠ 50139 Firenze ℰ 400081, Telex 575679, Fax 268212, ≤ town, « Among the olive trees », ⌿, 🌿, ✗ – ⋈ rest ☎ 🅟 – 🔬 80-200. ⒶⒺ 🚼 ⑩ Ⓔ 𝘝𝘐𝘚𝘈, 🍽 rest
M a la carte 45/130000 – **33 rm** ⊠ 145/230000 suites 331000.

on the motorway at ring-road A1-A11 NW : 10 km

🏨 **AgipHotel,** ⊠ 50013 Campi Bisenzio ℰ 4211881, Telex 570263, Fax 4219015 – 🛗 🗐 📺 ☎ 🕭 🅟 – 🔬 40-200. ⒶⒺ 🚼 ⑩ Ⓔ 𝘝𝘐𝘚𝘈, 🍽
M *(closed Sunday and August)* 50000 – **163 rm** ⊠ 165/240000.

close to motorway station A1 Florence South SE : 6 km :

🏨 **Sheraton Firenze Hotel,** ⊠ 50126 ℰ 64901, Telex 575860, Fax 680747, ⌿, ✗ – 🛗 🗐 📺 ☎ 🚐 🅟 – 🔬 30-1500. ⒶⒺ 🚼 ⑩ Ⓔ 𝘝𝘐𝘚𝘈, 🍽
M a la carte 47/87000 – **321 rm** ⊠ 320000 suites 460/1080000.

In addition to establishments indicated by

✗✗✗✗✗ ... ✗,

many hotels possess

good class restaurants.

MILAN (MILANO) 20100 ᴾ ❾❽❽ ③. ❹❷❽ F 9 – pop. 1 423 184 alt. 122 – ✿ 02.

See : Cathedral★★★ (Duomo) – Cathedral Museum★ CV **M1** – Via and Piazza Mercanti★ CV – La Scala Opera House★ CU – Brera Art Gallery★★★ CU – Castle of the Sforzas★★★ BU : Municipal Art Collection★★★ – Sempione Park★ ABTU– Ambrosian Library★★ BV : portraits★★★ of Gaffurio and Isabella d'Este, Raphael's cartoons★★★ – Poldi-Pezzoli Museum★★ CU : portrait of a woman★★★ (in profile) by Pollaiolo – Leonardo da Vinci Museum of Science and Technology★ AV **M2** : Leonardo da Vinci Gallery★★ – Church of St. Mary of Grace★ AV **A** : Leonardo da Vinci's Last Supper★★★ – Basilica of St. Ambrose★ AV **B** : altar front★★ – Church of St. Eustorgius★ BY **C** : Portinari Chapel★★ General Hospital★ DX **U** – Church of St. Maurice★ BV **E** – Church of St. Lawrence Major★ BX **F** – Dome★ of the Church of St. Satiro CV **K**.

Envir. : Chiaravalle Abbey★ SE : 7 km.

▮₈, ▮₉ (closed Monday) at Monza Park ⊠ 20052 Monza ℘ (039) 303081, Fax (039) 304427 by ② : 20 km;

▮₆ Molinetto (closed Monday) at Cernusco sul Naviglio ⊠ 20063 ℘ (02) 9238500, Fax (02) 9233460 by ⑤ : 14 km;

▮₆ Barlassina (closed Monday) at Birago di Camnago ⊠ 20030 ℘ (0362) 560621, Fax (0362) 560934 by ① : 26 km;

▮₆ (closed Monday) at Zoate di Tribiano ⊠ 20067 ℘ (02) 90632183, SE : 20 km by Strada Paullese;

▮₉ Le Rovedine at Noverasco di Opera ⊠ 20090 Opera ℘ (02) 57602730, Fax (02) 57606405 S : 8 km by via Ripamonti.

Motor-Racing circuit at Monza Park by ② : 20 km, ℘ (039) 22366.

✈ Forlanini di Linate E : 8 km ℘ 74852200 and Malpensa by ⑫ : 45 km ℘ 74852200 – Alitalia, corso Como 15 ⊠ 20154 ℘ 62818 and via Albricci 5 ⊠ 20122 ℘ 62817.

🚗 ℘ 6690734.

🛈 via Marconi 1 ⊠ 20123 ℘ 809662 – Central Station ⊠ 20124 ℘ 6690532.

A.C.I. corso Venezia 43 ⊠ 20121 ℘ 77451.

Roma 572 ⑦ – Genève 323 ⑫ – Genova 142 ⑨ – Torino 140 ⑫.

Plans on following pages

Northern area Piazza della Repubblica, Central Station, viale Zara, Porta Garibaldi Station, Porta Volta, corso Sempione (Plans : Milan pp. 2 and 3) :

🏨 **Principe di Savoia**, piazza della Repubblica 17 ⊠ 20124 ℘ 6230, Telex 310052, Fax 6595838, ◨ – ▮ ▤ TV ☎ ᵭ ℗ – 🔏 700. ﾷ ⓢ ⓞ ⒠ 𝘝𝘐𝘚𝘈. ⋙ DS **x**
M a la carte 89/137000 – ⊇ 43000 – **287 rm** 429/631000 suites 833/1904000.

🏨 **Palace and Rest. Casanova Grill,** piazza della Repubblica 20 ⊠ 20124 ℘ 6336 and rest ℘ 29000803, Telex 311026, Fax 654485 – ▮ ▤ TV ☎ ᵭ ℗ – 🔏 25-250. ﾷ ⓢ ⓞ ⒠ 𝘝𝘐𝘚𝘈. ⋙ rest DS **t**
M (booking essential) a la carte 95/120000 – ⊇ 27500 – **212 rm** 417/595000 suites 833/1785000.

🏨 **Excelsior Gallia,** piazza Duca d'Aosta 9 ⊠ 20124 ℘ 6785, Telex 311160, Fax 66713239, ₤₆, ⓢ – ▮ ▤ TV ☎ – 🔏 60-400. ﾷ ⓢ ⓞ ⒠ 𝘝𝘐𝘚𝘈. ⋙ DR **a**
M 90/150000 – ⊇ 28000 – **260 rm** 441/590000 suites 893/1428000.

🏨 **Milano Hilton,** via Galvani 12 ⊠ 20124 ℘ 69831, Telex 330433, Fax 6071904 – ▮ ▤ TV ☎ ᵭ ⇌ – 🔏 40-250. ﾷ ⓢ ⓞ ⒠ 𝘝𝘐𝘚𝘈. ⋙ rest DR **t**
M a la carte 43/90000 – ⊇ 32500 – **332 rm** 460/560000 suites 1150/1750000.

🏨 Duca di Milano, piazza della Repubblica 13 ⊠ 20124 ℘ 6284, Telex 325026, Fax 655966 – ▮ ▤ TV ☎ – 🔏 60 – **99 rm**. DS **v**

🏨 **Michelangelo,** via Scarlatti 33 ⊠ 20124 ℘ 6755, Telex 340330, Fax 6694232 – ▮ ⋙ rm ▤ TV ☎ ᵭ ⇌ – 🔏 250. ﾷ ⓢ ⓞ ⒠ 𝘝𝘐𝘚𝘈. ⋙ rest DR **c**
M a la carte 85/115000 – **303 rm** ⊇ 360/500000 suites 750/1000000.

🏨 **Executive,** viale Luigi Sturzo 45 ⊠ 20154 ℘ 6294, Telex 310191, Fax 29010238 – ▮ ▤ TV ☎ ᵭ ⇌ – 🔏 25-800. ﾷ ⓢ ⓞ ⒠ 𝘝𝘐𝘚𝘈. ⋙ rest CRS **v**
M (closed Friday) a la carte 66/101000 – **420 rm** ⊇ 400000 suites 600000.

🏨 **Anderson** without rest., piazza Luigi di Savoia 20 ⊠ 20124 ℘ 6690141, Telex 321018, Fax 6690331 – ▮ ▤ TV ☎ ᵭ ⇌ ﾷ ⓢ ⓞ ⒠ 𝘝𝘐𝘚𝘈 DR **v**
closed August – ⊇ 18000 – **106 rm** 210/265000 suites 265/310000.

🏨 **Jolly Hotel Touring and Rest. Amadeus,** via Tarchetti 2 ⊠ 20121 ℘ 6335, Telex 320118, Fax 6592209 – ▮ ▤ TV ☎ – 🔏 40-100. ﾷ ⓢ ⓞ ⒠ 𝘝𝘐𝘚𝘈. ⋙ rest DT **v**
M 65000 – **270 rm** ⊇ 410000.

🏨 **Century Tower Hotel** without rest., via Fabio Filzi 25/b ⊠ 20124 ℘ 67504, Telex 330557, Fax 66980602 – ▮ ⋙ rm ▤ TV ☎ ᵭ ⇌ – 🔏 40-60. ﾷ ⓢ ⓞ ⒠ 𝘝𝘐𝘚𝘈. ⋙ DR **w**
146 rm ⊇ 450000.

🏨 **Splendido,** viale Andrea Doria 4 ⊠ 20124 ℘ 6789, Telex 321413, Fax 66713369 – ▮ ▤ TV ☎ – 🔏 25-100. ﾷ ⓢ ⓞ ⒠ 𝘝𝘐𝘚𝘈. ⋙ DR **x**
M a la carte 50/70000 – **156 rm** ⊇ 300/380000.

🏨 **Royal** without rest., via Cardano 1 ⊠ 20124 ℘ 6709151, Telex 333167, Fax 6703024 – ▮ ⋙ rm ▤ TV ☎ ᵭ ⇌ – 🔏 60-200. ﾷ ⓢ ⓞ ⒠ 𝘝𝘐𝘚𝘈 DR **b**
closed August – ⊇ 20000 – **205 rm** 228/292000 suites 348/450000.

MILANO

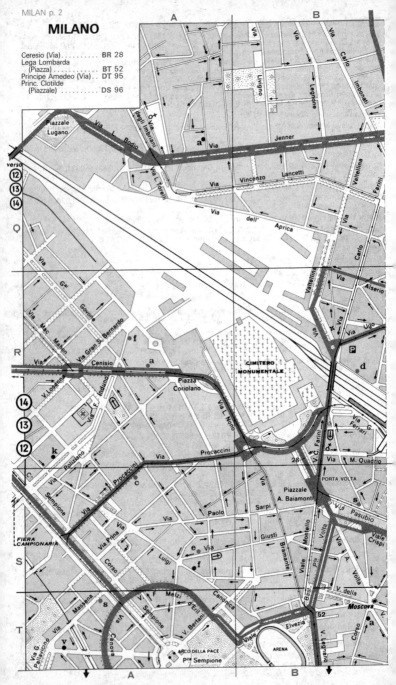

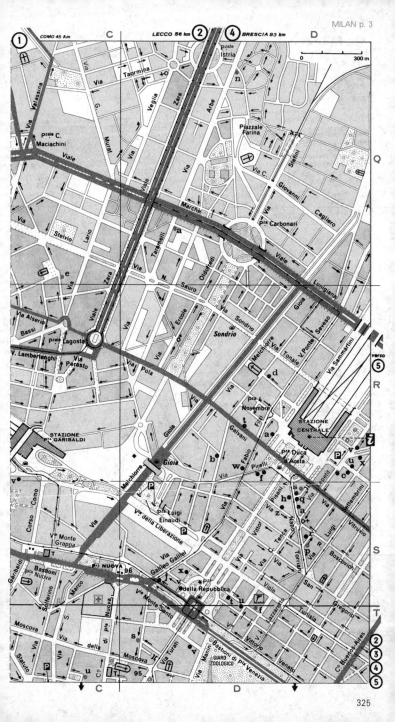

MILANO

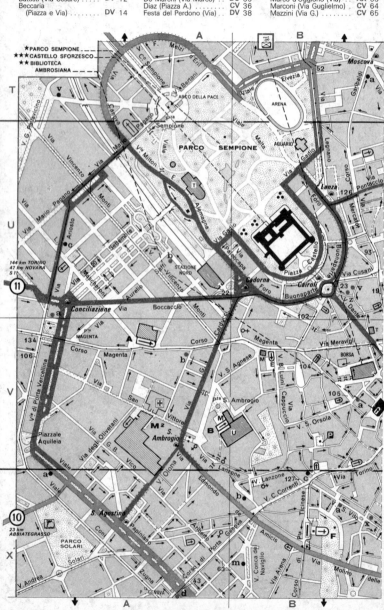

★★★ DUOMO
★★ MUSEO POLDI-PEZZOLI
★ VIA E P.ZA MERCANTI
★ TEATRO ALLA SCALA
★★★ PINACOTECA DI BRERA

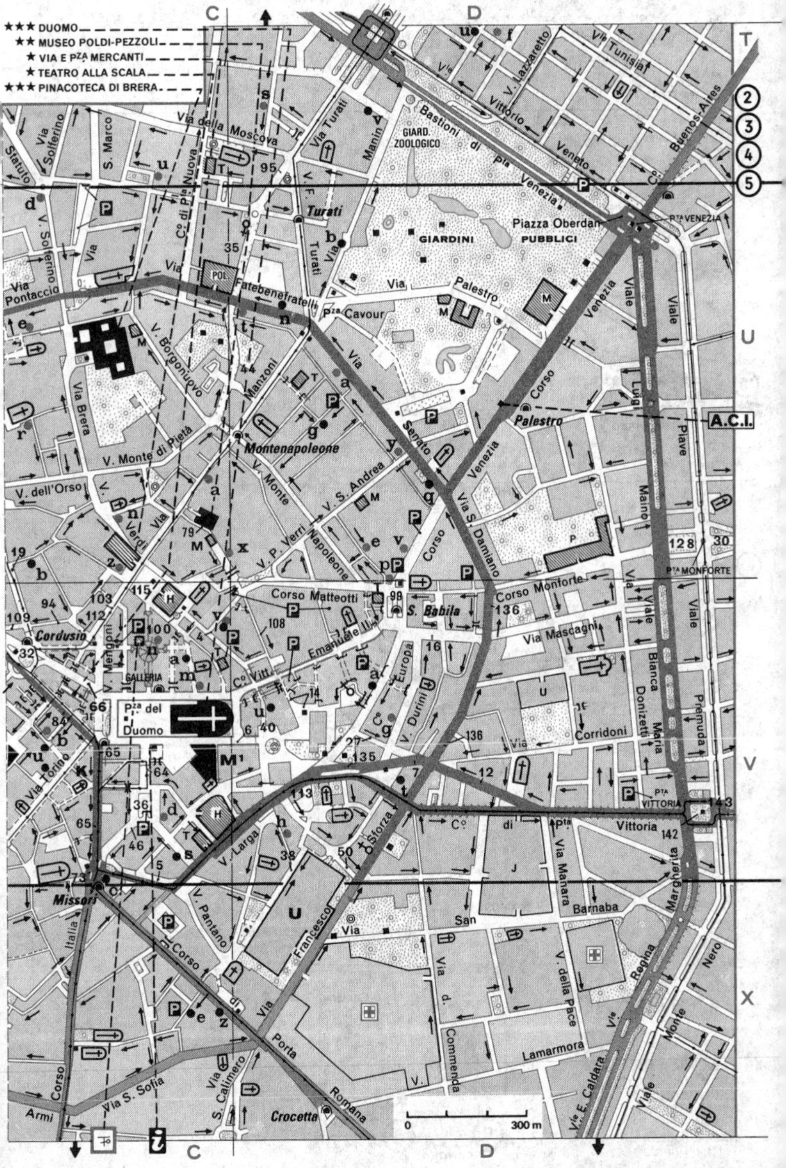

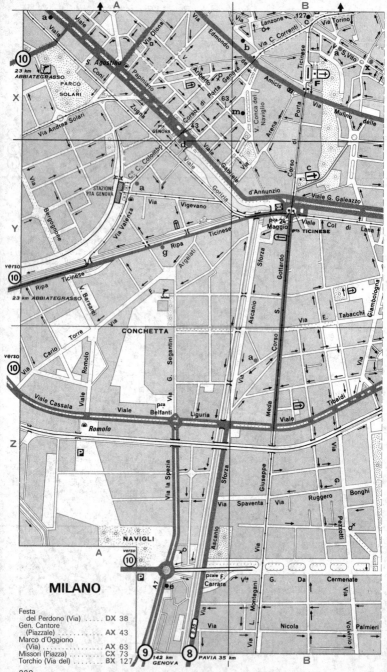

MILANO

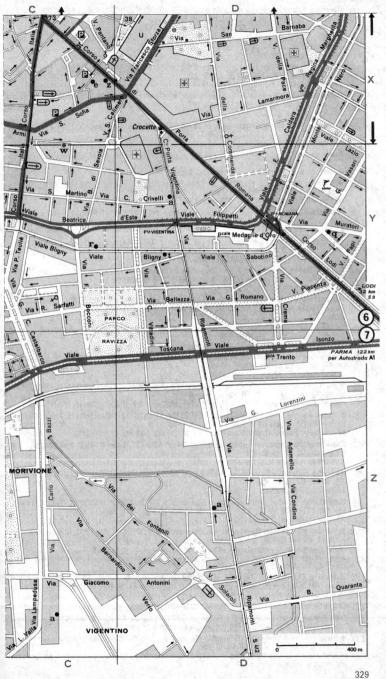

Blaise e Francis without rest., via Butti 9 ⊠ 20158 ℰ 66802366, Fax 66802909 – |‡| ⇔
▤ 🏧 🖭 ☎ 🕭 ⇔ – 🛁 40-200. 🖭 🕄 ⑩ 🗲 𝘝𝘐𝘚𝘈
AQ a
closed 2 to 23 August – ⌷ 15000 – **110 rm** 250000.

Atlantic without rest., via Napo Torriani 24 ⊠ 20124 ℰ 6691941, Telex 321451, Fax 6706533
– |‡| ▤ 🖭 ☎ ⇔ – 🛁 25. 🖭 🕄 🗲 𝘝𝘐𝘚𝘈
DS q
62 rm ⌷ 210/310000.

Madison without rest., via Gasparotto 8 ⊠ 20124 ℰ 6085991, Telex 326543, Fax 6887821
– |‡| ▤ 🖭 ☎ – 🛁 100. 🖭 🕄 🗲 𝘝𝘐𝘚𝘈
DR d
92 rm ⌷ 205/310000 suites 400000.

Poliziano without rest., via Poliziano 11 ⊠ 20154 ℰ 33602494, Fax 33106410 – |‡| ▤ 🖭
☎ ⇔ – 🛁 80. 🖭 🕄 ⑩ 🗲 𝘝𝘐𝘚𝘈
AR k
100 rm ⌷ 230/270000.

Berna without rest., via Napo Torriani 18 ⊠ 20124 ℰ 6691441, Telex 334695, Fax 6693892
– |‡| ▤ 🖭 ☎ – 🛁 30-60. 🖭 🕄 ⑩ 🗲 𝘝𝘐𝘚𝘈. ⇌
DS a
115 rm ⌷ 200/275000.

Auriga without rest., via Pirelli 7 ⊠ 20124 ℰ 66985851, Fax 66980698 – |‡| ▤ 🖭 ☎ – 🛁 25.
🖭 🕄 ⑩ 🗲 𝘝𝘐𝘚𝘈. ⇌
DR f
closed August – ⌷ 18000 – **65 rm** 190/235000.

Windsor, via Galilei 2 ⊠ 20124 ℰ 6346, Telex 330562, Fax 6590663 – |‡| ▤ 🖭 ☎ ⇔
– 🛁 40. 🖭 🕄 ⑩ 🗲 𝘝𝘐𝘚𝘈. ⇌ rest
DS j
M *(closed Saturday)* 35000 – **118 rm** ⌷ 205/260000 suites 310000.

Mediolanum without rest., via Mauro Macchi 1 ⊠ 20124 ℰ 6705312, Telex 310448,
Fax 66981921 – |‡| ▤ 🖭 ☎ ♿. 🖭 🕄 🗲 𝘝𝘐𝘚𝘈
DS r
52 rm ⌷ 182/276000.

Bristol without rest., via Scarlatti 32 ⊠ 20124 ℰ 6694141, Fax 6702942 – |‡| ▤ 🖭 ☎ –
🛁 50. 🖭 🕄 ⑩ 🗲 𝘝𝘐𝘚𝘈
DR u
closed August – **71 rm** ⌷ 223/297000.

Carlyle Brera Hotel without rest., corso Garibaldi 84 ⊠ 20121 ℰ 29003888, Telex 323357,
Fax 29003993 – |‡| ⇔ ▤ 🖭 ☎ ♿ ⇔. 🖭 🕄 ⑩ 🗲 𝘝𝘐𝘚𝘈. ⇌
BT a
98 rm ⌷ 310/360000.

Augustus without rest., via Napo Torriani 29 ⊠ 20124 ℰ 66988271, Telex 333112,
Fax 6703096 – |‡| ▤ 🖭 ☎. 🖭 🕄 ⑩ 🗲 𝘝𝘐𝘚𝘈
DS h
closed 25 July-25 August and 23 December-5 January – **56 rm** ⌷ 130/195000.

Europeo without rest., via Canonica 38 ⊠ 20154 ℰ 3314751, Fax 33105410, ⌆ – |‡| ▤
🖭 ☎ ⇔ – 🛁 25. 🖭 🕄 🗲 𝘝𝘐𝘚𝘈. ⇌
AS f
closed August – **45 rm** ⌷ 150/240000.

Lancaster without rest., via Abbondio Sangiorgio 16 ⊠ 20145 ℰ 315602, Fax 344649 – |‡|
▤ 🖭 ☎. 🖭 🕄 🗲 𝘝𝘐𝘚𝘈. ⇌
AT v
closed August – **30 rm** ⌷ 150/240000.

New York without rest., via Pirelli 5 ⊠ 20124 ℰ 66985551, Telex 325057, Fax 6697267 –
|‡| ▤ 🖭 ☎ – 🛁 40. 🖭 🕄 ⑩ 🗲 𝘝𝘐𝘚𝘈. ⇌
DR f
closed 1 to 28 August and 24 December-5 January – ⌷ 15000 – **70 rm** 109/154000.

Sempione, via Finocchiaro Aprile 11 ⊠ 20124 ℰ 6570323, Telex 340498, Fax 6575379 –
|‡| ⇔ ▤ 🖭 ☎. 🖭 🕄 🗲 𝘝𝘐𝘚𝘈
DST u
M (see rest. **Piazza Repubblica** below) – ⌷ 20000 – **39 rm** 110/150000.

Florida without rest., via Lepetit 33 ⊠ 20124 ℰ 6705921, Telex 314102, Fax 6692867 – |‡|
▤ 🖭 ☎. 🖭 🕄 ⑩ 🗲 𝘝𝘐𝘚𝘈
DR c
⌷ 20000 – **52 rm** 103/147000.

Bolzano without rest., via Boscovich 21 ⊠ 20124 ℰ 6691451, Fax 6691455, ⌆ – |‡| ▤
🖭 ☎. 🖭 🕄 ⑩ 🗲 𝘝𝘐𝘚𝘈. ⇌
DS z
35 rm ⌷ 120/180000.

San Carlo without rest., via Napo Torriani 28 ⊠ 20124 ℰ 6693236, Telex 314324,
Fax 6703116 – |‡| ▤ 🖭 ☎ – 🛁 30. 🖭 🕄 ⑩ 🗲 𝘝𝘐𝘚𝘈
DS s
⌷ 16000 – **75 rm** 109/154000.

XXX ❀ **Alfredo-Gran San Bernardo,** via Borgese 14 ⊠ 20154 ℰ 3319000, Milanese cuisine
– ▤. 🖭 🕄 ⑩ 🗲 𝘝𝘐𝘚𝘈
AR f
closed Sunday and August – **M** (booking essential) a la carte 60/85000
Spec. Risotto alla milanese ed al salto, Ossobuco in cremolata, Costoletta alla milanese. Wines
Lugana, Franciacorta rosso.

XXX **Gianni e Dorina,** via Pepe 38 ⊠ 20159 ℰ 606340, 🌣 – ▤. 🖭 🕄 🗲 𝘝𝘐𝘚𝘈. ⇌
closed Saturday lunch, Sunday and 25 July-15 September – **M** (booking essential) a la carte
BR d
56/85000.

XXX China Club, via Giusti 34 ⊠ 20154 ℰ 33104309, (booking essential) – ▤
AS e

XXX **Dall'Antonio,** via Cenisio 8 ⊠ 20154 ℰ 33101511 – ▤. 🖭 🕄 ⑩ 𝘝𝘐𝘚𝘈. ⇌
AR a
closed Sunday and August – **M** (booking essential) a la carte 60/85000.

XXX **3 Pini,** via Tullo Morgagni 19 angolo via Arbe ⊠ 20125 ℰ 6898464, « Summer service
under the pergola » – 🖭 🕄 🗲 𝘝𝘐𝘚𝘈
DQ n
closed Saturday, Sunday dinner, 5 to 31 August and 25 December-4 January – **M** (booking
essential) a la carte 42/63000.

XX ✿ **A Riccione,** via Taramelli 70 ⊠ 20124 ℰ 6686807, Seafood – ▤. 🆎 🛐 ⓞ ⴹ 𝗩𝗜𝗦𝗔   **a**
    closed Monday – **M** (booking essential) a la carte 83/116000   DQ
    Spec. Pasta fresca con sugo di pesce, Paella valenciana o di solo pesce, Grigliata mista alla brace.
    Wines del Collio.

XX **Joia,** via Panfilo Castaldi 18 ⊠ 20124 ℰ 29522124, Vegetarian cuisine – ✎ ▤. 🆎 🛐 ⓞ
    ⴹ 𝗩𝗜𝗦𝗔   DT   **z**
    closed Saturday lunch, Sunday and 1 to 21 August – **M** a la carte 46/69000.

XX **Cavallini,** via Mauro Macchi 2 ⊠ 20124 ℰ 6693174, 🌤 – ▤. 🆎 🛐 ⓞ ⴹ 𝗩𝗜𝗦𝗔 DS   **p**
    closed Saturday, Sunday, 3 to 23 August and 22 December-4 January – **M** a la carte 36/75000
    (12 %).

XX **La Buca,** via Antonio da Recanate ang. via Napo Torriani ⊠ 20124 ℰ 6693774 – ▤. 🆎
    🛐 ⓞ ⴹ 𝗩𝗜𝗦𝗔   DS   **s**
    closed Friday dinner, Saturday, August and 25 December-6 January – **M** a la carte 47/80000.

XX **Al Tronco-da Vitaliano,** via Thaan di Revel 10 ⊠ 20159 ℰ 606072 – ▤. 🆎 🛐 ⓞ ⴹ 𝗩𝗜𝗦𝗔
    closed Saturday lunch, Sunday and August – **M** a la carte 29/55000.   CQ   **e**

XX **La Torre del Mangia,** via Procaccini 37 ⊠ 20154 ℰ 314871 – ▤. 🆎 🛐 ⴹ 𝗩𝗜𝗦𝗔. ✿
    closed Sunday dinner and Monday – **M** (booking essential) a la carte 40/69000.   AS   **c**

XX **Le 5 Terre,** via Appiani 9 ⊠ 20121 ℰ 653034, Seafood – ▤. 🆎 🛐 ⓞ ⴹ 𝗩𝗜𝗦𝗔   DT   **s**
    closed Sunday and 8 to 22 August – **M** a la carte 56/81000.

XX **Piazza Repubblica,** via Manunzio 11 ⊠ 20124 ℰ 6552715 – ▤. 🆎 🛐 ⴹ 𝗩𝗜𝗦𝗔   DT   **f**
    closed Saturday lunch, Sunday and 8 to 31 August – **M** a la carte 36/57000.

XX **Il Verdi,** piazza Mirabello 5 ⊠ 20121 ℰ 6590797 – ▤   CT   **u**
    closed Saturday lunch, Sunday, 11 to 31 August and 23 December-1 January – **M** a la carte
    35/55000 (13 %).

X **Trattoria della Pesa,** viale Pasubio 10 ⊠ 20154 ℰ 6555741, Typical old Milan trattoria
    with Lombardy specialities – ▤   BS   **s**
    closed Sunday and August – **M** a la carte 40/63000.

Central area Duomo, Scala, Sempione Park, Sforza Castle, Public gardens, corso Venezia, via
Manzoni, North Station, corso Magenta, Porta Vittoria (Plans : Milan pp. 4 and 5) :

🏨 **Jolly Hotel President,** largo Augusto 10 ⊠ 20122 ℰ 7746, Telex 312054, Fax 783449
    – 📶 ✎ rm ▤ 📺 ☎ 🔥 – 🔬 30-100. 🆎 🛐 ⓞ ⴹ 𝗩𝗜𝗦𝗔. ✿ rest   DV   **t**
    M 65000 – **220 rm** ⚏ 370/450000.

🏨 **Gd H. Duomo,** via San Raffaele 1 ⊠ 20121 ℰ 8833, Telex 312086, Fax 86462027 – 📶 ▤
    📺 ☎. 🛐 ⴹ 𝗩𝗜𝗦𝗔. ✿ rest   CV   **m**
    M 65000 – ⚏ 23000 – **160 rm** 310/440000 suites 640000.

🏨 **Brunelleschi** without rest., via Baracchini 12 ⊠ 20123 ℰ 8843, Telex 312256, Fax 870144
    – 📶 ▤ 📺 ☎. 🆎 🛐 ⓞ ⴹ 𝗩𝗜𝗦𝗔   CV   **s**
    120 rm ⚏ 340/470000 suites 860000.

🏨 **Dei Cavalieri,** piazza Missori 1 ⊠ 20123 ℰ 8857, Telex 312040, Fax 72021683 – 📶 ▤ 📺
    ☎ – 🔬 40-60. 🆎 🛐 ⓞ ⴹ 𝗩𝗜𝗦𝗔. ✿ rest   CVX   **c**
    M 70/136000 – **177 rm** ⚏ 265/313000 suites 700000.

🏨 **Galileo** without rest., corso Europa 9 ⊠ 20122 ℰ 7743, Telex 322095, Fax 76020584 – 📶
    ▤ 📺 ☎. 🆎 🛐 ⓞ ⴹ 𝗩𝗜𝗦𝗔. ✿   DV   **a**
    76 rm ⚏ 330/440000 suites 500000.

🏨 **Carlton Hotel Senato,** via Senato 5 ⊠ 20121 ℰ 76015535, Telex 331306, Fax 783300
    – 📶 ▤ 📺 ☎ 🛋. 🆎 🛐 ⴹ 𝗩𝗜𝗦𝗔. ✿ rest   DU   **q**
    closed August – **M** *(closed Saturday, Sunday and 20 December-7 January)* a la carte 47/70000
    – ⚏ 18000 – **79 rm** 210/270000.

🏨 **Manin,** via Manin 7 ⊠ 20121 ℰ 6596511, Telex 320385, Fax 6552160, 🌳 – 📶 ▤ 📺 ☎
    – 🔬 30-120. 🆎 🛐 ⓞ ⴹ 𝗩𝗜𝗦𝗔. ✿ rest – *closed 7 to 23 August* – **M** *(closed Sunday)* a la carte
    66/95000 – ⚏ 20000 – **118 rm** 205/270000 suites 400/500000.   DU   **b**

🏨 **Cavour,** via Fatebenefratelli 21 ⊠ 20121 ℰ 6572051, Telex 320498, Fax 6592263 – 📶 ▤
    📺 ☎ 🔥. 🆎 🛐 ⓞ ⴹ 𝗩𝗜𝗦𝗔. ✿ rest   DU   **n**
    M *(closed Friday dinner, Saturday and Sunday lunch)* 55000 – ⚏ 18000 – **113 rm** 205/230000
    suites 280000.

🏨 **Rosa** without rest., via Pattari 5 ⊠ 20122 ℰ 8831, Telex 316067, Fax 8057964 – 📶 ▤ 📺
    ☎ – 🔬 30-120. 🆎 🛐 ⓞ ⴹ 𝗩𝗜𝗦𝗔   DV   **u**
    165 rm ⚏ 340/450000.

🏨 **De la Ville** without rest., via Hoepli 6 ⊠ 20121 ℰ 867651, Telex 312642, Fax 866609 – 📶
    ▤ 📺 ☎ – 🔬 60. 🆎 🛐 ⓞ ⴹ 𝗩𝗜𝗦𝗔   CV   **v**
    104 rm ⚏ 330/400000 suites 550/600000.

🏨 **Ariosto** without rest., via Ariosto 22 ⊠ 20145 ℰ 4817844, Fax 4980516 – 📶 ▤ 📺 ☎ 🔥
    – 🔬 40. 🆎 🛐 ⓞ ⴹ 𝗩𝗜𝗦𝗔   AU   **c**
    ⚏ 12000 – **53 rm** 109/154000.

🏨 **Manzoni** without rest., via Santo Spirito 20 ⊠ 20121 ℰ 76005700, Fax 784212 – 📶 ☎ 🛋. ✿
    ⚏ 16000 – **52 rm** 120/165000 suites 230000.   DU   **g**

🏨 **Spadari al Duomo,** via Spadari 11 ⊠ 20123 ℰ 72002371, Fax 861184 – 📶 ▤ 📺 ☎. 🆎
    🛐 ⓞ ⴹ 𝗩𝗜𝗦𝗔. ✿   CV   **u**
    closed August – **M** (booking essential) a la carte 42/66000 – **40 rm** ⚏ 330/400000.

🏠 **Casa Svizzera** without rest., via San Raffaele 3 ⌧ 20121 ℰ 8692246, Telex 316064, Fax 3498190 – 🛗 🖿 📺 🕿. ⌸ 🛐 **E** 𝘝𝘐𝘚𝘈   CV **a**
closed 28 July-24 August – **45 rm** ⌇ 124/181000.

🏠 **Gritti** without rest., piazza Santa Maria Beltrade 4 ⌧ 20123 ℰ 801056, Telex 350597, Fax 89010999 – 🛗 🖿 📺 🕿. ⌸ 🛐 ⓪ **E** 𝘝𝘐𝘚𝘈   CV **u**
48 rm ⌇ 125/183000.

🏠 **Star** without rest., via dei Bossi 5 ⌧ 20121 ℰ 801501, Fax 861787 – 🛗 🖿 📺 🕿. ⌸ 🛐 **E** 𝘝𝘐𝘚𝘈. 🅵   CU **b**
closed August – ⌇ 18000 – **30 rm** 100/145000.

XXXXX **Savini**, galleria Vittorio Emanuele II ⌧ 20121 ℰ 72003433, Fax 86461060, Elegant traditional decor, « Winter garden » – 🖿. ⌸ 🛐 ⓪ **E** 𝘝𝘐𝘚𝘈   CV **n**
closed Sunday, 10 to 19 August and 23 December-3 January – **M** (booking essential) a la carte 102/161000 (15 %).

XXXX **St. Andrews**, via Sant'Andrea 23 ⌧ 20121 ℰ 76023132, Elegant installation, late night dinners – 🖿. ⌸ 🛐 ⓪ **E** 𝘝𝘐𝘚𝘈. 🅵   DU **y**
closed Sunday and August – **M** (booking essential) a la carte 76/114000 (15 %).

XXX **Biffi Scala**, piazza della Scala ⌧ 20121 ℰ 866651, Fax 86461060, Late night dinners – 🖿. ⌸ 🛐 ⓪ **E** 𝘝𝘐𝘚𝘈   CU **z**
closed Sunday, 10 to 20 August and 25 December-6 January – **M** a la carte 75/118000 (15 %).

XXX ❀ **Peck**, via Victor Hugo 4 ⌧ 20123 ℰ 876774, Fax 860408 – 🖿. ⌸ 🛐 ⓪ **E** 𝘝𝘐𝘚𝘈. 🅵
closed 2 to 23 July – **M** a la carte 59/97000   CV **b**
Spec. Insalata di pescatrice alle erbe aromatiche, Risotto con rognoncino di vitello prezzemolo e prosciutto, Ratatouille all'aglio dolce. Wines Chardonnay, Pinot nero.

XXX **Tino Fontana**, piazza Diaz 5 ⌧ 20123 ℰ 860598 – 🖿. ⌸ 🛐 ⓪ **E** 𝘝𝘐𝘚𝘈. 🅵   CV **d**
closed Sunday and 6 to 20 August – **M** a la carte 52/81000.

XXX **Santini**, corso Venezia 3 ⌧ 20121 ℰ 782010, Fax 76014691, 🏫 – 🖿. ⌸ 🛐 ⓪ 𝘝𝘐𝘚𝘈. 🅵   DU **v**
closed Sunday and 12 to 26 August – **M** a la carte 67/116000.

XXX **Don Lisander**, via Manzoni 12/a ⌧ 20121 ℰ 76020130, Fax 784573, « Outdoor summer service » – 🖿. ⌸ 🛐 ⓪ **E** 𝘝𝘐𝘚𝘈   CU **a**
closed Saturday dinner and Sunday – **M** (booking essential) a la carte 67/105000.

XXX **Orti di Leonardo**, via Aristide de' Togni 6/8 ⌧ 20123 ℰ 4983197, Fax 4983476 – 🖿 🅿. ⌸ 🛐 ⓪ **E** 𝘝𝘐𝘚𝘈. 🅵   AV **b**
closed Sunday and 5 to 26 August – **M** a la carte 58/92000.

XXX ❀ **Canoviano**, via Hoepli 6 ⌧ 20121 ℰ 86460147 – 🖿. ⌸ 🛐 ⓪ **E** 𝘝𝘐𝘚𝘈. 🅵   CV **v**
closed Saturday lunch, Sunday and August – **M** (booking essential) a la carte 63/108000
Spec. Sfogliatina di carciofi e scampi (winter), Ravioli di pesce, Branzino con funghi e asparagi (autumn-winter). Wines Pigato, Schiopettino.

XXX **Suntory**, via Verdi 6 ⌧ 20121 ℰ 8693022, Fax 72023282, Japanese rest. – 🖿. ⌸ 🛐 ⓪ **E** 𝘝𝘐𝘚𝘈   CU **n**
closed Sunday, 9 to 16 August and Christmas – **M** a la carte 70/110000.

XXX **Alfio**, via Senato 31 ⌧ 20121 ℰ 780731, Fax 783446 – 🖿. ⌸ 🛐 ⓪ **E** 𝘝𝘐𝘚𝘈. 🅵   DU **a**
closed Saturday, Sunday lunch, August and 23 December-3 January – **M** a la carte 58/114000.

XXX **Boeucc**, piazza Belgioioso 2 ⌧ 20121 ℰ 76020224, Fax 76005861, 🏫 – 🖿. ⌸ **E** CDU **x**
closed Saturday, Sunday lunch, August and 24 December-2 January – **M** (booking essential) a la carte 61/93000.

XXX **Peppino**, via Durini 7 ⌧ 20122 ℰ 781729 – 🖿. ⌸ 🛐 ⓪ **E** 𝘝𝘐𝘚𝘈. 🅵   DV **g**
closed Friday dinner, Saturday and July – **M** a la carte 46/69000.

XXX **Royal Dynasty**, via Bocchetto 15/a ⌧ 20123 ℰ 86450905, Chinese rest. – 🖿. ⌸ 🛐 ⓪ **E** 𝘝𝘐𝘚𝘈. 🅵   BV **a**
closed Sunday and 14 to 21 August – **M** a la carte 33/58000 (12 %).

XX **Bistrot di Gualtiero Marchesi**, via San Raffaele ⌧ 20121 ℰ 877120, ≤ Rest. and piano-bar, ≤ Duomo – 🖿. ⌸ 🛐 ⓪ **E** 𝘝𝘐𝘚𝘈   CV **m**
closed Sunday, Monday lunch and August – **M** a la carte 55/102000.

XX **Odeon**, via Bergamini 11 ⌧ 20122 ℰ 58307418 – 🖿. 🛐 ⓪ 𝘝𝘐𝘚𝘈   DV **h**
closed Saturday lunch, Sunday and August – **M** a la carte 29/42000 (10 %).

XX **Le Api**, via Bagutta 2 ⌧ 20121 ℰ 76005780, 🏫 – 🖿. ⌸ 🛐 ⓪ **E** 𝘝𝘐𝘚𝘈. 🅵   DUV **p**
closed Saturday lunch and Sunday – **M** a la carte 50/60000.

XX **La Bitta**, via del Carmine 3 ⌧ 20121 ℰ 879159 – 🖿. ⌸ 🛐 ⓪ **E** 𝘝𝘐𝘚𝘈   CU **r**
closed Saturday lunch, Sunday, August and Christmas – **M** (fish only) a la carte 58/87000.

XX **Bagutta**, via Bagutta 14 ⌧ 20121 ℰ 76002767, Fax 799613, 🏫, Artists' meeting place, « Typical paintings and caricatures » – ⌸ 🛐 ⓪ **E** 𝘝𝘐𝘚𝘈. 🅵   DU **e**
closed Sunday, 7 to 31 August and 23 December-5 January – **M** a la carte 67/101000.

XX **Franco il Contadino**, via Fiori Chiari 20 ⌧ 20121 ℰ 808153, Typical rest. and artists' meeting place – 🖿. ⌸ 🛐 ⓪ **E** 𝘝𝘐𝘚𝘈   CU **e**
closed Tuesday and July – **M** a la carte 45/62000 (10 %).

XX **Rovello**, via Rovello 18 ⌧ 20121 ℰ 864396 – 🖿. ⌸ 🛐 ⓪ **E** 𝘝𝘐𝘚𝘈   BU **z**
closed Saturday lunch, Sunday, 10 to 20 August and Christmas – **M** a la carte 45/65000.

XX **L'Infinito**, via Leopardi 25 ⌧ 20123 ℰ 4692276 – 🖿. ⌸ 🛐 ⓪ **E** 𝘝𝘐𝘚𝘈. 🅵   AU **b**
closed Saturday lunch and Sunday – **M** a la carte 40/60000.

XX **Opera Prima,** via Rovello 3 ✉ 20121 ✆ 865235 – ▤. AE SI ⓞ E VISA. ✻ BU **v**
closed Saturday lunch and Sunday – **M** a la carte 51/82000.

XX **Rigolo,** via Solferino 11 angolo largo Treves ✉ 20121 ✆ 8646322, Locals rest. – ▤. AE SI ⓞ E VISA. ✻ CU **d**
closed Monday and August – **M** a la carte 38/58000.

XX **Kota Radja,** piazzale Baracca 6 ✉ 20123 ✆ 468850, Chinese rest. – ▤. AE SI ⓞ E VISA AU **a**
closed Monday – **M** a la carte 23/55000 (12 %).

X **La Tavernetta-da Elio,** via Fatebenefratelli 30 ✉ 20121 ✆ 653441 – ▤. AE VISA DU **t**
closed Sunday and August – **M** a la carte 45/65000.

Southern area Porta Ticinese, Porta Romana, Genova Station, Navigli, Ravizza Park, Vigentino (Plans : Milan pp. 6 and 7) :

Pierre Milano, via Edmondo de Amicis 32 ✉ 20123 ✆ 72000581, Telex 333303, Fax 8052157 – |‡| ⇆ rm ▤ TV ☎. AE SI ⓞ E VISA. ✻ BX **b**
M *(closed August)* a la carte 65/113000 – **47 rm** ☕ 430/640000 suites 800/950000.

Quark, via Lampedusa 11/a ✉ 20141 ✆ 84431, Telex 353448, Fax 8464190 – |‡| ▤ TV ☎ ♿ 🚗 Ⓟ – 🎤 25-1000. AE SI ⓞ E VISA. ✻ rest CZ **a**
M *(closed 31 July-22 August)* a la carte 64/106000 – **285 rm** ☕ 330000.

Liberty without rest., viale Bligny 56 ✉ 20136 ✆ 55182698, Fax 55191059 – |‡| ▤ 🚗. AE SI E VISA. ✻ DY **t**
closed 10 to 25 August – ☕ 15000 – **52 rm** 160/230000.

Ascot without rest., via Lentasio 3/5 ✉ 20122 ✆ 58303300, Telex 311303, Fax 58303203 – |‡| ▤ TV ☎ 🚗. AE SI ⓞ E VISA. ✻ CX **e**
closed August – **63 rm** ☕ 210/300000.

Lloyd without rest., corso di Porta Romana 48 ✉ 20122 ✆ 58303332, Telex 335028, Fax 58303365 – |‡| ▤ TV ☎ – 🎤 40-80. AE SI ⓞ E VISA CX **z**
☕ 22000 – **52 rm** 210/275000.

D'Este without rest., viale Bligny 23 ✉ 20136 ✆ 5461041, Telex 324216, Fax 5454330 – |‡| ▤ TV ☎ – 🎤 40-80. AE SI ⓞ E VISA. ✻ CY **r**
☕ 20000 – **54 rm** 180/260000.

Crivi's without rest., corso Porta Vigentina 46 ✉ 20122 ✆ 58302000, Telex 313255, Fax 5400637 – |‡| ▤ TV ☎ 🚗 – 🎤 60. AE SI ⓞ E VISA. ✻ DY **a**
closed August – **86 rm** ☕ 190/260000.

Carrobbio without rest., via Medici 3 ✉ 20123 ✆ 89010740, Fax 8053334 – |‡| ▤ TV ☎. AE SI ⓞ E VISA BX **c**
closed August and 22 December-6 January – **35 rm** ☕ 210/290000 suite 350000.

Sant'Ambroeus without rest., viale Papiniano 14 ✉ 20123 ✆ 48008989, Telex 313373, Fax 48008687 – |‡| ▤ TV ☎ – 🎤 50. AE SI ⓞ E VISA AX **a**
closed August and Christmas – ☕ 18000 – **52 rm** 109/154000.

Mediterraneo without rest., via Muratori 14 ✉ 20135 ✆ 55019151, Telex 335812, Fax 55019155 – |‡| TV ☎ – 🎤 120. AE SI ⓞ E VISA DY **q**
closed 1 to 21 August – ☕ 16000 – **93 rm** 109/153000.

Adriatico without rest., via Conca del Naviglio 20 ✉ 20123 ✆ 58104141, Fax 58104145 – |‡| ▤ TV ☎. AE SI ⓞ E VISA BX **m**
closed 1 to 21 August – ☕ 16000 – **105 rm** 103/145000.

Dei Fiori without rest., raccordo autostrada A7 ✉ 20142 ✆ 8436441, Fax 89501096 – |‡| ▤ TV ☎ Ⓟ. AE SI ⓞ E VISA AZ **e**
55 rm ☕ 82/128000, ▤ 9500.

Garden without rest., via Rutilia 6 ✉ 20141 ✆ 537368, Fax 57300678 – ☎ Ⓟ DZ **a**
closed August – no ☕ – **23 rm** 61/84000.

XXX **L'Ulmet,** via Disciplini ang. via Olmetto ✉ 20123 ✆ 86452718 – ▤. AE SI E VISA BX **x**
closed Sunday and Monday lunch – **M** (booking essential) a la carte 70/85000.

XXX **San Vito da Nino,** via San Vito 5 ✉ 20123 ✆ 8377029 – ▤. VISA. ✻ BX **a**
closed Monday and August – **M** (booking essential) a la carte 60/75000 (13 %).

XXX ✿ **Scaletta,** piazzale Stazione Genova 3 ✉ 20144 ✆ 58100290 – ▤. ✻ AY **a**
closed Sunday, Monday, Easter, August and 24 December-6 January – **M** (booking essential) a la carte 100/110000
Spec. Terrina di trippa in gelatina, Tagliatelle vongole e broccoli, Rognone con porcini. Wines Villa Bucci, I Sodi di S. Niccolò.

XX ✿ **Al Genovese,** via Pavia 9/14 ang. via Conchetta ✉ 20136 ✆ 8373180, 🌂, Ligurian rest. – ▤. AE SI ⓞ E VISA. ✻ BZ **a**
closed Sunday, Monday lunch, 10 to 25 August and 1 to 7 January – **M** (booking essential) a la carte 57/93000
Spec. Piccagge (pasta) con pinoli e maggiorana, Filetti di triglia in salsa alle olive, Sfogliatina di mele con gelato alla cannella. Wines Vermentino.

XX **Yar,** via Mercalli 22 ✉ 20122 ✆ 58305234, Typical Russian cuisine – ▤. AE SI ⓞ E VISA. ✻ CXY **w**
closed Sunday, Monday and August – **M** (booking essential) a la carte 56/80000.

XX ❀ **Al Porto,** piazzale Generale Cantore ✉ 20123 ✆ 8321481, Seafood – 🍽. 🝏 🗊 ⓪ 🝏
VISA   AXY **d**
closed Sunday, Monday lunch, August and 24 December-3 January – **M** (booking essential)
a la carte 55/78000
Spec. Zuppa di fagioli e scampi, Branzino al Pigato e olive nere, Frutti di mare gratinati. **Wines**
Ribolla gialla, Grignolino.

XX ❀ **Sadler-Osteria di Porta Cicca,** ripa di Porta Ticinese 51 ✉ 20143 ✆ 58104451 – 🍽.
🗊 ⓪ 🝏 *VISA*   AY **g**
closed lunch, Sunday, 5 to 30 August and 1 to 10 January – **M** (booking essential) a la carte
62/90000
Spec. Ravioli di melanzane con mozzarella e pomodoro, Astice con fagioli borlotti, Orata alle olive
nere. **Wines** Chardonnay.

Districts : Bruzzano, Niguarda, Bicocca, viale Fulvio Testi N : by : Monza, Lecco, Erba, Venezia :

🏨 **Novotel Milano Nord,** viale Suzzani 13 ✉ 20162 ✆ 66101861, Telex 331292,
Fax 66101961, 🏊 – 🛗 🍽 📺 🛁 🏧 ⇔ 🅿 – 🔬 25-300. 🝏 🗊 ⓪ 🝏 *VISA*
M 36000 – **172 rm** ⊡ 200/230000.   by corso Buenos Aires   DT

🏨 **Leonardo da Vinci** ⤜, via Senigallia 6 ✉ 20161 ✆ 64031, Telex 331552, Fax 64074839,
🏊, – 🛗 ⇅ rm 🍽 📺 ☎ ⇔ 🅿 – 🔬 1200. 🝏 🗊 ⓪ 🝏 *VISA*. ❀   by ⓘ
M 70000 – **290 rm** ⊡ 380000 suites 719/925000.

🏨 **Starhotel Tourist,** viale Fulvio Testi 300 ✉ 20126 ✆ 6437777, Telex 326852, Fax 6472516
– 🛗 🍽 📺 ☎ 🛁 ⇔ – 🔬 30-70. 🝏 🗊 ⓪ 🝏 *VISA* ❀ rest   by viale Zara   DQ
closed August – **M** *(closed Saturday)* a la carte 45/60000 – **139 rm** ⊡ 200/240000.

Districts : corso Buenos Aires, Loreto, Lambrate NE : by : Bergamo, Brescia :

🏨 **Nasco,** via Spallanzani 40 ✉ 20129 ✆ 2055, Telex 333116, Fax 29518679 – 🛗 🍽 📺 ☎
⇔ – 🔬 50. 🝏 🗊 ⓪ 🝏 *VISA* ❀   by corso Buenos Aires   DT
M a la carte 48/64000 – **154 rm** ⊡ 300/380000.

🏨 **Concorde** without rest., via Petrocchi 1 ang. viale Monza ✉ 20125 ✆ 26112020,
Telex 315805, Fax 26147879 – 🛗 🍽 📺 ☎ ⇔. 🝏 🗊 ⓪ 🝏 *VISA*. ❀
closed 1 to 24 August – ⊡ 25000 – **120 rm** 210/290000.   by corso Buenos Aires   DT

🏨 **Galles** without rest., via Ozanam 1 ✉ 20129 ✆ 29404250, Telex 322091, Fax 29404872 –
🛗 🍽 📺 ☎ – 🔬 25-120. 🝏 🗊 ⓪ 🝏 *VISA* ❀   by corso Buenos Aires   DT
104 rm ⊡ 175/275000.

XX ❀ **Calajunco,** via Stoppani 5 ✉ 20129 ✆ 2046003, Aeolian rest. – 🍽. 🗊 ⓪ 🝏 *VISA*
❀   by corso Buenos Aires   DT
closed Saturday lunch, Sunday, 10 to 31 August and 23 December-4 January – **M** a la carte
74/128000
Spec. Tortino di riso al ragù di scorfano, Involtino di triglia, Crostata di fichi d'India. **Wines** Terre
di Ginestra, Pinot nero.

XX **Montecatini Alto,** viale Monza 7 ✉ 20125 ✆ 2846773 – 🍽. 🝏
closed Saturday lunch, Sunday and August – **M** a la carte 34/58000 (10 %).
                                                                                       by Corso Buenos Aires   DT

Districts : Città Studi, Monforte, corso 22 Marzo, viale Corsica E : by : Linate Airport, Idroscalo,
strada Rivoltana :

🏨 **Novotel Milano Est,** via Mecenate 121 ✉ 20138 ✆ 58011085, Telex 331237,
Fax 58011086, 🏊 – 🛗 🍽 📺 ☎ 🛁 🅿 – 🔬 25-350. 🝏 🗊 ⓪ 🝏 *VISA* ❀ rest
M a la carte 36/67000 – **205 rm** ⊡ 286000.   by corso Porta Vittoria   DV

🏨 **Zefiro** without rest., via Gallina 12 ✉ 20129 ✆ 7384253, Fax 713811 – 🛗 🍽 📺 ☎ – 🔬 30.
🗊 🝏 *VISA* ❀   by corso Concordia   DU
closed August and 23 December-3 January – **55 rm** ⊡ 124/184000.

🏨 **Vittoria** without rest., via Pietro Calvi 32 ✉ 20129 ✆ 55190196, Fax 55190246 – 🛗 🍽 📺
☎. 🝏 🗊 ⓪ 🝏 *VISA*   by corso 22 Marzo   DV
⊡ 30000 – **18 rm** 109/154000.

🏨 **Città Studi** without rest., via Saldini 24 ✉ 20133 ✆ 744666, Fax 713122 – 🛗 ☎. 🝏 🗊 🝏
VISA   by corso Concordia   DU
⊡ 12000 – **45 rm** 65/95000.

XXXX ❀❀❀ **Gualtiero Marchesi,** via Bonvesin de la Riva 9 ✉ 20129 ✆ 741246, Fax 7384079,
Elegant installation – 🍽. 🝏 🗊 ⓪ 🝏 *VISA*. ❀   by corso 22 Marzo   DV
closed holidays, Sunday, Monday lunch, July, August and 23 December-7 January – **M** (booking
essential) a la carte 93/135000
Spec. Raviolo aperto, Filetti di sogliola fritti in salsa agrodolce, Costoletta di vitello alla milanese.
Wines Selezione di Gualtiero Marchesi.

XXXX **Giannino,** via Amatore Sciesa 8 ✉ 20135 ✆ 5452948, Traditional style, « Original decor,
winter garden » – 🅿. 🝏 🗊 ⓪ 🝏 *VISA*. ❀   by corso 22 Marzo   DV
closed Sunday and August – **M** a la carte 90/138000.

XXXX **Soti's,** via Pietro Calvi 2 ✉ 20129 ✆ 796838, Fax 796838, Elegant installation – 🍽. 🝏 🗊
⓪ 🝏 *VISA*. ❀   by corso 22 Marzo   DV
closed Saturday lunch, Sunday and 10 to 24 August – **M** (booking essential) 80000 bi (lunch
only) and a la carte 90/120000 (dinner only).

XXX ❀ **L'Ami Berton,** via Nullo 14 angolo via Goldoni ✉ 20129 ℰ 713669 – ▣. 🆎 🆂 🅴 𝘝𝘐𝘚𝘈
✼   by corso 22 Marzo   DV
closed Saturday lunch, Sunday, August and Christmas – **M** (booking essential) a la carte
87/127000
Spec. Aspic di sogliola e caviale, Linguine al filetto di triglia e fiori di zucca, Filetto di cernia con
finferli e zafferano. **Wines** Sauvignon.

XXX **La Zelata,** via Anfossi 10 ✉ 20135 ℰ 5484115 – ▣. 🆎 🆂 🅾 🅴 𝘝𝘐𝘚𝘈. ✼
closed Saturday lunch, Sunday and August – **M** (booking essential) a la carte 54/91000.
                                                                              by corso 22 Marzo   DV

XXX **Nino Arnaldo,** via Poerio 3 ✉ 20129 ℰ 76005981 – ▣   by corso 22 Marzo   DV
closed Saturday lunch, Sunday, August and 23 December-7 January – **M** (booking essential)
a la carte 82/114000.

Districts : Fiera Campionaria, San Siro, Porta Magenta NW : by ⑩ and ⑪ : Novara, Torino :

🏨 **Gd H. Brun and Rest. Ascot** ⑤, via Caldera 21 ✉ 20153 ℰ 45271 and rest. ℰ 4526279,
Telex 315370, Fax 48204746 – 🛗 ▤ ▣ 🆃🆅 ☎ ♿ ⇔ 🅿 – 🔥 500. 🆎 🆂 🅾 🅴 𝘝𝘐𝘚𝘈. ✼
closed August – **M** *(closed Sunday)* a la carte 69/87000 – **306 rm** ⇆ 420000 suites 650000.
                                                                              by corso Sempione   AT

🏨 **Gd H. Fieramilano,** viale Boezio 20 ✉ 20145 ℰ 336221, Telex 331426, Fax 314119, ⤢
– 🛗 ▤ ☎ ♿ – 🔥 60. 🆎 🆂 🅾 🅴 𝘝𝘐𝘚𝘈. ✼ rest   by via Vincenzo Monti   AT
M a la carte 38/62000 – **238 rm** ⇆ 335/390000.

🏨 **Rubens** without rest., via Rubens 21 ✉ 20148 ℰ 40302, Telex 353617, Fax 48193114 – 🛗
▤ 🆃🆅 ☎ ♿. 🆎 🆂 🅾 🅴 𝘝𝘐𝘚𝘈. ✼   by corso Vercelli   AV
closed 1 to 21 August – **87 rm** ⇆ 210/290000.

🏨 **Washington,** without rest., via Washington 23 ✉ 20146 ℰ 4813216, Fax 4814761 – 🛗 ▤
🆃🆅 ☎   by corso Vercelli   AV
34 rm.

🏨 **Capitol,** via Cimarosa 6 ✉ 20144 ℰ 4988851, Telex 316150, Fax 4694724 – 🛗 ▤ 🆃🆅 ☎
– 🔥 500. 🆎 🆂 🅾 🅴 𝘝𝘐𝘚𝘈 ✼ rest   by corso Vercelli   AV
M *(closed lunch and August)* a la carte 41/60000 – **96 rm** ⇆ 215/290000.

🏨 **Domenichino** without rest., via Domenichino 41 ✉ 20149 ℰ 48009692, Fax 48003953 –
🛗 ▤ 🆃🆅 ⇔ 🅿 – 🔥 50. 🆎 🆂 🅾 🅴 𝘝𝘐𝘚𝘈. ✼   by ⑪
⇆ 15000 – **71 rm** 126/186000 suites 320000.

🏨 **Green House** without rest., viale Famagosta 50 ✉ 20142 ℰ 8132451, Telex 353428,
Fax 816624 – 🛗 ▤ 🆃🆅 ☎ ⇔. 🆎 🆂 🅾 🅴 𝘝𝘐𝘚𝘈. ✼   by ⑩
⇆ 14000 – **45 rm** 110/149000.

🏨 **Mini Hotel Tiziano** without rest., via Tiziano 6 ✉ 20145 ℰ 4988921, Telex 325420,
Fax 4812153, « Small park » – 🛗 ▤ ☎ 🅿 – 🔥 30. 🆎 🆂 🅾 🅴 𝘝𝘐𝘚𝘈   by ⑪
54 rm ⇆ 120/180000.

XXX ❀❀ **Aimo e Nadia,** via Montecuccoli 6 ✉ 20147 ℰ 416886 – ▣. 🆎 🆂 🅾 🅴. ✼
closed Saturday lunch, Sunday and August – **M** (booking essential) a la carte 78/120000
Spec. Farfalle di ortica pomodoro crudo e caprino, Fiori di zucca farciti con rossetti e ricotta,
Fagottino di cinghiale con cavolo nero al finocchio. **Wines** Riesling renano, Dolcetto.   by ⑩

XXX **Trattoria del Ruzante,** via Massena 1 ✉ 20145 ℰ 316102 – ▣. 🆎   AT s
closed Sunday – **M** (booking essential) a la carte 54/69000.

XXX **Raffaello,** via Monte Amiata 4 ✉ 20149 ℰ 4814227 – ▣. 🆎 🆂 🅴 𝘝𝘐𝘚𝘈   by ⑪
closed Wednesday and 1 to 24 August – **M** a la carte 41/68000.

XX **La Corba,** via dei Gigli 14 ✉ 20147 ℰ 4158977, « Summer service in garden » – 🆎 🆂
🅾 𝘝𝘐𝘚𝘈   by ⑩
closed Sunday dinner, Monday and 7 to 30 August – **M** a la carte 50/75000.

XX **Furio,** via Montebianco 2/A ✉ 20152 ℰ 4814677 – ▣. 🆎 🆂 🅾 🅴 𝘝𝘐𝘚𝘈   by ⑪
closed Sunday and August – **M** a la carte 48/83000.

XX **Ribot,** via Cremosano 41 ✉ 20148 ℰ 33001646, « Summer service in garden » – 🅿. 🆎
🆂 𝘝𝘐𝘚𝘈. ✼   by ⑪
closed Monday and 10 to 25 August – **M** a la carte 45/60000.

Districts : Sempione-Bullona, viale Certosa NW : by ⑫ ⑬ and ⑭ : Varese, Como, Torino,
Malpensa Airport :

🏨 **Accademia** without rest., viale Certosa 68 ✉ 20155 ℰ 39211122, Telex 315550,
Fax 33103878, « Rooms with fresco murals » – 🛗 ▤ 🆃🆅 ☎ 🅿. 🆎 🆂 🅾 🅴 𝘝𝘐𝘚𝘈
67 rm ⇆ 235/340000.   by via Cenisio   AR

🏨 **Raffaello** without rest., viale Certosa 108 ✉ 20156 ℰ 3270146, Telex 315499, Fax 3270440
– 🛗 ▤ 🆃🆅 ☎ – 🔥 180. 🆎 🆂 🅾 🅴 𝘝𝘐𝘚𝘈   by via Cenisio   AR
149 rm ⇆ 180/250000.

🏨 **Mirage** without rest., via Casella 61 angolo viale Certosa ✉ 20156 ℰ 39210471,
Fax 39210589 – 🛗 ▤ 🆃🆅 ☎ ♿ – 🔥 60. 🆎 🆂   by via Cenisio   AR
⇆ 15000 – **50 rm** 190/250000.

🏨 **Berlino** without rest., via Plana 33 ✉ 20155 ℰ 324141, Telex 312609, Fax 324145 – 🛗 ▤
🆃🆅 ☎. 🆎 🆂 🅾 🅴 𝘝𝘐𝘚𝘈   by via Cenisio   AR
closed August and 23 December-3 January – ⇆ 17000 – **47 rm** 108/150000.

XX **La Pobbia,** via Gallarate 92 ⊠ 20151 𝒫 38006641, Modern rustic rest., « Outdoor service in summer » – 🕼 40. ⫴ 🕄 𝖵𝖨𝖲𝖠. ⫸   by via Cenisio   AR
closed Sunday and August – **M** a la carte 44/61000 (12 %).

XX **Da Stefano il Marchigiano,** via Arimondi 1 angolo via Plana ⊠ 20155 𝒫 33001863 –
🔲 ⫴ 🕄 ⊙ ⫴ 𝖵𝖨𝖲𝖠   by via Cenisio   AR
closed Friday dinner, Saturday and August – **M** a la carte 41/68000.

XX **Al Bimbo,** via Marcantonio dal Re 38 ⊠ 20156 𝒫 3272290, Fax 39216365 – 🔲. ⫴ 🕄 ⊙
⫴ 𝖵𝖨𝖲𝖠   by via Cenisio   AR
closed Saturday lunch, Sunday and August – **M** a la carte 37/58000.

X **Al Vöttantott,** corso Sempione 88 ⊠ 20154 𝒫 33603114 – 🔲. ⫴
closed Sunday and August – **M** a la carte 32/48000.   by corso Sempione   AS

Outskirts of Milan

on national road 35-Milanofiori by ⑧ : 10 km

🏨 **Jolly Hotel Milanofiori,** Strada 2 ⊠ 20090 Assago 𝒫 82221, Telex 325314, Fax 89200946,
⫸ – 🕼 🔲 📺 ☎ 🕾 🄿 – 🕼 120. ⫴ 🕄 ⊙ ⫴ 𝖵𝖨𝖲𝖠. ⫸ rest
M 60000 – **255 rm** ⊑ 360000.

on road New Vigevanese-Zingonia by ⑩ : 11 km

🏨 **Eur** without rest., ⊠ 20090 Zingone di Trezzano 𝒫 4451951, Fax 4451075 – 🕼 🔲 📺 ☎
🄿 – 🕼 80. ⫴ 🕄 ⊙ ⫴ 𝖵𝖨𝖲𝖠 – *closed 4 to 25 August* – **41 rm** ⊑ 162/210000.

on national road West-Assago by ⑩ : 14 km

🏨 **AgipHotel,** ⊠ 20094 Assago 𝒫 4880441, Telex 325191, Fax 48843958, 🌊 – 🕼 🔲 📺 ☎
🕾 🄿 – 🕼 300. ⫴ 🕄 ⊙ ⫴ 𝖵𝖨𝖲𝖠. ⫸ rest
M 43000 – **222 rm** ⊑ 250/270000.

Abbiategrasso 20081 Milano 𝟵𝟴𝟴 ③, 𝟰𝟮𝟴 F 8 – pop. 27 787 alt. 120 – ✆ 02.
Roma 590 – Alessandria 74 – Milano 23 – Novara 29 – Pavia 33.

at Cassinetta di Lugagnano N : 3 km – ⊠ 20080 :

XXXX ❀❀❀ **Antica Osteria del Ponte,** 𝒫 9420034, Fax 9420610 – 🔲 🄿. ⫴ 🕄 ⊙ 𝖵𝖨𝖲𝖠. ⫸
closed Sunday, Monday, August and 25 December-12 January – **M** (booking essential) a la carte 90/142000
Spec. Lasagnetta ai cipollotti e tartufi neri (January-April), Fagottino di pasta fresca ai frutti di mare (October-April), Buridda di rombo branzino e scampi. Wines Franciacorta bianco, Barbaresco.

Malgrate 22040 Como 𝟰𝟮𝟴 E 10, 𝟮𝟭𝟵 ⑨ ⑩ – pop. 4 203 alt. 224 – ✆ 0341.
Roma 623 – Bellagio 20 – Como 27 – Lecco 2 – Milano 54.

🏨 ❀❀ **Il Griso,** 𝒫 202040, Fax 202248, ≤ lake and mountains, 🍴, « park », 🏋, 🈴, 🔲 –
🕼 🔲 📺 ☎ 🄿 – 🕼 30. ⫴ 🕄 ⊙ ⫴ 𝖵𝖨𝖲𝖠
closed 20 December-6 January – **M** a la carte 66/134000 – ⊑ 18000 – **41 rm** 140/170000,
🔲 10000
Spec. Ravioli di lumache di Borgogna nel loro brodo d'aglio, Suprema di luccio perca al forno con salsa al dragoncello, Spiedini di pollo alla cantonese. Wines Franciacorta bianco, Sassella superiore.

Ranco 21020 Varese 𝟰𝟮𝟴 E 7, 𝟮𝟭𝟵 ⑦ – pop. 996 alt. 214 – ✆ 0331.
Roma 644 – Laveno Mombello 21 – Milano 67 – Novara 51 – Sesto Calende 12 – Varese 27.

XXX ❀❀ **Del Sole** ⫸ with rm, 𝒫 976507, Fax 976620, ≤, « Summer service under pergola »,
🈴, 🍴 – 📺 🄿. ⫴ 🕄 ⊙ ⫴ 𝖵𝖨𝖲𝖠. ⫸
closed January-14 February – **M** (booking essential) (closed Monday dinner and Tuesday) a la carte 72/119000 (10 %) – 7 suites ⊑ 230/240000
Spec. Uova di quaglia in brioche ai quattro caviali, Pasta farcita con astice e basilico, Ossobuco di storione in gremolata. Wines Ribolla, Barbaresco.

Soriso 28018 Novara 𝟰𝟮𝟴 E 7, 𝟮𝟭𝟵 ⑯ – pop. 769 alt. 452 – ✆ 0322.
Roma 654 – Arona 20 – Milano 78 – Novara 40 – Torino 114 – Varese 46.

XXXX ❀❀❀ **Al Sorriso** with rm, 𝒫 983228, Fax 983328 – 📺 ☎. 🕄 𝖵𝖨𝖲𝖠. ⫸
closed 7 to 21 August and 10 to 31 January – **M** (booking essential) (closed Monday and Tuesday lunch) a la carte 100/140000 – **8 rm** ⊑ 130/190000
Spec. Sfogliatine di patate con crostacei, Medaglione di sanato al midollo, Zuppa di ciliegie con gelato di cannella e pepe rosso. Wines Sauvignon, Boca.

Do not mix up :

Comfort of hotels	: 🏨🏨🏨 ... 🏠, 🏡
Comfort of restaurants	: XXXXX ... X
Quality of the cuisine	: ❀❀❀, ❀❀, ❀

See : National Archaeological Museum★★★ KY – New Castle★★ KZ – Port of Santa Lucia★★ : ≼★★ of Vesuvius and bay – ≼★★★ at night from via Partenope of the Vomero and Posillipo FX – San Carlo Theatre★ KZ T – Piazza del Plebiscito★ JKZ – Royal Palace★ KZ – Carthusian Monastery of St. Martin★★ JZ : ≼★★★ of the Bay of Naples from gallery 25.

Spacca-Napoli quarter★★ : Tomb★★ of King Robert the wise in Church of Santa Chiara★ KY C – Caryatids★ by Tino da Camaino in Church of St. Dominic Major KY L – Sculptures★ in Chapel of San Severo KY V – Arch★, Tomb★ of Catherine of Austria, apse★ in Church of St. Lawrence Major LY K – Capodimonte Palace and National Gallery★★.

Mergellina★ : ≼★★ of the bay – Villa Floridiana★ EVX : ≼★ – Catacombs of San Gennaro★ FU X – Church of Santa Maria Donnaregina★ LY B – Church of San Giovanni Carbonara★ LY G – Capuan Gate★ LMY D – Cuomo Palace★ LY Q – Sculptures★ in the Church of St. Anne of the Lombards KYZ R – Posillipo★ – Marechiaro★ – ≼★★ of the Bay from Virgiliano Park (or Rimembranza Park).

Exc. : Bay of Naples★★★ by the coast road to Campi Flegrei★★ by ⑧, to Sorrento Peninsula by ⑦ Island of Capri★★★ Island of Ischia★★★.

🛦 (closed Monday) in Arco Felice ⊠ 80072 𝒫 8674296, by ⑧ : 19 km.

✈ Ugo Niutta of Capodichino NE : 6 km (except Saturday and Sunday) 𝒫 5425333 – Alitalia, via Medina 41 ⊠ 80133 𝒫 5425222.

🛥 to Capri daily (1 h 15 mn) – Navigazione Libera del Golfo, molo Beverello ⊠ 80133 𝒫 5520763, Telex 722661; to Capri (1 h 15 mn), Ischia (1 h 15 mn) and Procida (1 h), daily – Caremar-De Luca Agency, molo Beverello ⊠ 80133 𝒫 5513882; to Cagliari June-September, Tuesday, Friday and Sunday, Friday and Sunday in other months (15 h 45 mn) and Palermo daily (10 h 30 mn) – Tirrenia Navigazione, Stazione Marittima, molo Angioino ⊠ 80133 𝒫 5512181, Telex 710030, Fax 7201441 ; to Ischia daily (1 h 15 mn) – Libera Navigazione Lauro, via Caracciolo 11 ⊠ 80122 𝒫 991889, Telex 720354.

🛥 to Capri (45 mn), Ischia (45 mn) and Procida (35 mn) daily – Caremar De Luca Agency, molo Beverello ⊠ 80133 𝒫 5513882; to Ischia daily (1 h) – Alilauro, via Caracciolo 11 ⊠ 80122 𝒫 7611004, Telex 720354; to Capri daily (45 mn) and Aeolian Island May-15 September daily (5 h) and Procida-Ischia daily (45 mn) – SNAV, via Caracciolo 10 ⊠ 80122 𝒫 7612348, Telex 720446, Fax 7612141.

🛈 via Partenope 10/a ⊠ 80121 𝒫 7644871 – piazza del Plebiscito (Royal Palace) ⊠ 80132 𝒫 418744 – Central Station ⊠ 80142 𝒫 268779 - Capodichino Airport ⊠ 80133 𝒫 7805761 – piazza del Gesù Nuovo 7 ⊠ 80135 𝒫 5523328 - Passaggio Castel dell'Ovo ⊠ 80132 𝒫 411461.

A.C.I. piazzale Tecchio 49/d ⊠ 80125 𝒫 614511.

Roma 219 ③ – Bari 261 ⑤

Plans on following pages

🏨🏨🏨🏨 **Excelsior,** via Partenope 48 ⊠ 80121 𝒫 417111, Telex 710043, Fax 411743, ≼ gulf, Vesuvius and Castel dell'Ovo – 📳 🔟 ☎ – 🔬 30-200. 🖭 🚹 ⓞ 🖻 𝗩𝗜𝗦𝗔. GX **w**
M a la carte 80/120000 – ☲ 27000 – **114 rm** 286/429000 suites 655/1131000.

🏨🏨🏨 **Gd H. Parker's,** corso Vittorio Emanuele 135 ⊠ 80121 𝒫 761247, Telex 710578, Fax 663527, « Roof-garden rest. with ≼ town and gulf » – 📳 🔲 🔟 ☎ 🚗 – 🔬 50-250. 🖭 🚹 ⓞ 🖻 𝗩𝗜𝗦𝗔. ❄ rest EX
M a la carte 54/84000 – **89 rm** ☲ 260/310000 suites 750/1500000.

🏨🏨🏨 **Vesuvio and Rest. Caruso,** via Partenope 45 ⊠ 80121 𝒫 417044 and rest. 𝒫 407520, Telex 710127, Fax 417044, « Roof-garden rest. with ≼ gulf and Castel dell'Ovo » – 📳📳 🔲 🔟 ☎ – 🔬 25-250. 🖭 🚹 ⓞ 🖻 𝗩𝗜𝗦𝗔. ❄ FX **n**
M a la carte 45/73000 – **171 rm** ☲ 220/330000 suites 500/1200000.

🏨🏨 **Britannique,** corso Vittorio Emanuele 133 ⊠ 80121 𝒫 7614145, Telex 722281, Fax 669760, ≼, « Garden » – 📳 🔲 🔟 ☎ 🚗 – 🔬 25-100. 🖭 🚹 ⓞ 🖻 𝗩𝗜𝗦𝗔. ❄ rest EX **r**
M 40000 – ☲ 11000 – **80 rm** 180/240000 suites 260000.

🏨🏨 **Jolly,** via Medina 70 ⊠ 80133 𝒫 416000, Telex 720335, Fax 5518010, « Roof-garden rest. with ≼ town, gulf and Vesuvius » – 📳 🔲 🔟 ☎ – 🔬 250. 🖭 🚹 ⓞ 🖻 𝗩𝗜𝗦𝗔. ❄ rest
M a la carte 67/101000 – **278 rm** ☲ 200/260000, 🗐 33000. KZ **s**

🏨🏨 **Paradiso,** via Catullo 11 ⊠ 80122 𝒫 7614161, Telex 722049, Fax 7613449, ≼ gulf, town and Vesuvius, 🌳 – 📳 🔲 🔟 ☎ – 🔬 40-50. 🖭 🚹 ⓞ 🖻 𝗩𝗜𝗦𝗔. ❄
M *(closed 6 to 26 August)* a la carte 45/67000 – **71 rm** ☲ 158/250000.
by via Caracciolo EX

🏨🏨 **Santa Lucia** without rest., via Partenope 46 ⊠ 80121 𝒫 416566, Telex 710595, Fax 415566, ≼ gulf and Castel dell'Ovo – 🗐 ☎ – 🔬 50-180. 🖭 🚹 ⓞ 🖻 𝗩𝗜𝗦𝗔. ❄ GX **w**
107 rm ☲ 194/286000 suites 500000, 🗐 24000.

🏨🏨 **San Germano,** via Beccadelli 41 ⊠ 80125 𝒫 5705422, Telex 720080, Fax 5701546, « Attractive garden-park », 🛋 – 📳 🔲 🔟 ☎ 🚗 🅿 – 🔬 220. 🖭 🚹 ⓞ 🖻 𝗩𝗜𝗦𝗔. ❄ rest
M *(closed Sunday and 3 to 31 August)* 42000 – **101 rm** ☲ 126/200000. by ⑧

🏨🏨 **Royal,** via Partenope 38 ⊠ 80121 𝒫 7644800, Telex 710167, Fax 7645707, ≼ gulf, Posillipo and Castel dell'Ovo, 🛋 – 📳 🔲 🔟 ☎ 🚗 – 🔬 25-200. 🖭 🚹 ⓞ 🖻 𝗩𝗜𝗦𝗔. ❄ rest FX **n**
M a la carte 65/108000 – **273 rm** ☲ 200/300000 suites 600000, 🗐 48000.

🏨🏨 **Continental** without rest., via Partenope 44 ⊠ 80121 𝒫 7644636, Fax 7644661, ≼ gulf and Castel dell'Ovo – 📳 rm 🗐 ☎ – 🔬 600. 🖭 🚹 ⓞ 🖻 𝗩𝗜𝗦𝗔. ❄ FX **n**
166 rm ☲ 233/340000 suites 420/640000.

NAPOLI

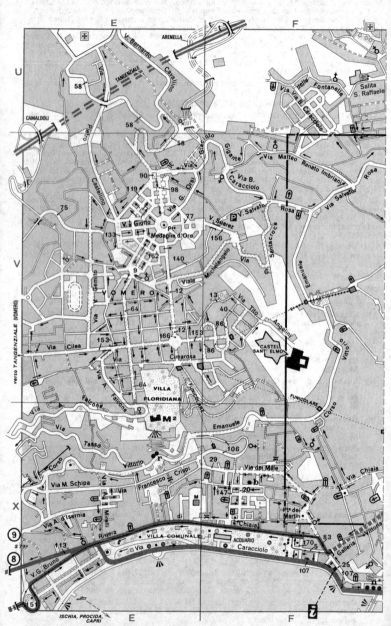

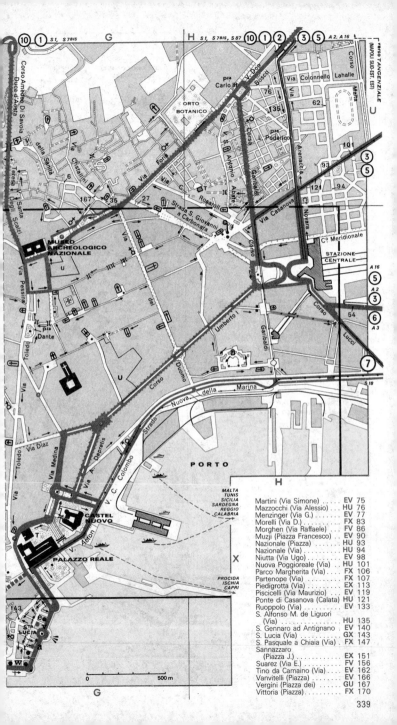

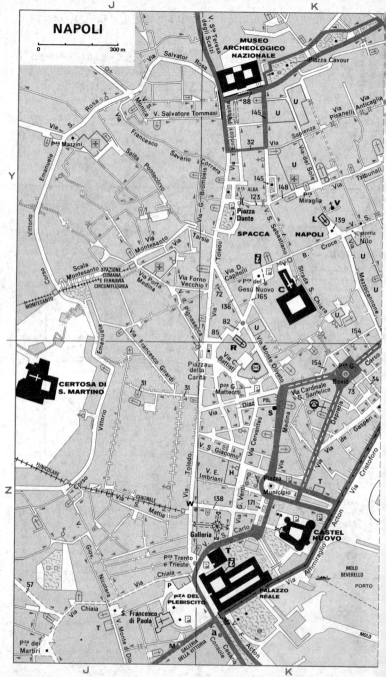

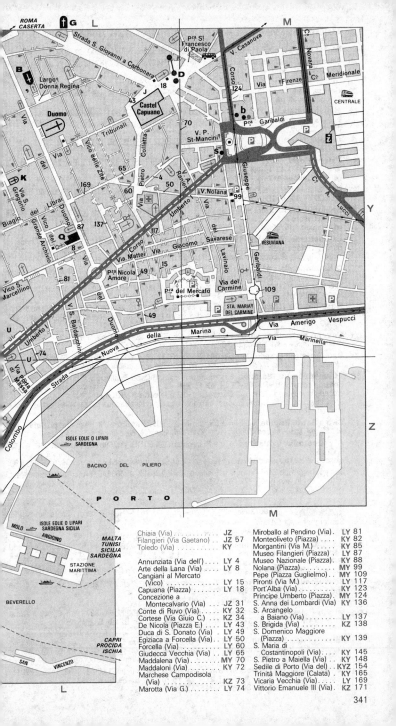

341

🏨 **Majestic,** largo Vasto a Chiaia 68 ⊠ 80121 ℰ 416500, Telex 720408, Fax 416500 – 🛗 🖃
📺 ☎ 🚗 – 🛆 25-100. ⁂ 🛐 ⓞ 🗲 *VISA*. ⁒
FX **b**
M a la carte 35/50000 – **132 rm** ⊇ 150/240000 suites 330/400000, 🗏 10000.

🏨 **Miramare,** via Nazario Sauro 24 ⊠ 80132 ℰ 427388, Fax 416775, ≼ – 🛗 🖃 📺 ☎. ⁂
🛐 ⓞ 🗲 *VISA*. ⁒
GX **e**
M *(closed 16 to 31 August)* a la carte 30/45000 – **30 rm** ⊇ 185/300000.

🏨 **Serius,** viale Augusto 74 ⊠ 80125 ℰ 614844 – 🛗 🖃 📺 ☎ 🚗. ⁂. ⁒ by ⑧
M 36000 – **69 rm** ⊇ 100/150000, 🗏 10000.

🏨 **Nuovo Rebecchino** without rest., corso Garibaldi 356 ⊠ 80142 ℰ 5535327, Fax 268026
– 🛗 🖃 📺 ☎. ⁂ 🛐 ⓞ 🗲 *VISA*. ⁒
MY **b**
58 rm ⊇ 105/145000.

🏨 **Cavour,** piazza Garibaldi 32 ⊠ 80142 ℰ 283122 – 📺 ☎. ⁂ 🛐 ⓞ 🗲 *VISA*. MY **b**
M (see **Cavour** below) – **94 rm** ⊇ 104/148000.

🏨 **Palace Hotel,** piazza Garibaldi 9 ⊠ 80142 ℰ 5535978, Telex 720262, Fax 264306 – 🛗 📺
☎ – 🛆 30-80. ⁂ 🛐 ⓞ 🗲 *VISA*. ⁒
MY **s**
M (see **Cavour** below) – **102 rm** ⊇ 104/148000.

🏨 **Rex** without rest., via Palepoli 12 ⊠ 80132 ℰ 416388, Fax 416919 – 🖃 📺 ☎. ⁂ ⓞ *VISA*
⊇ 9000 – **40 rm** 105/155000, 🗏 20000.
GX **r**

🏨 **Splendid,** via Manzoni 96 ⊠ 80123 ℰ 7141955, Fax 659991 – 🛗 📺 ☎ 🅿. ⁂ 🛐 ⓞ 🗲
VISA. ⁒ rest
by via G. Bruno EX
M a la carte 35/50000 – ⊇ 15000 – **55 rm** 100/150000.

XXX **La Sacrestia,** via Orazio 116 ⊠ 80122 ℰ 7611051, Elegant rest., « Summer service in
garden-terrace with ≼ » – 🖃. ⁂ ⓞ *VISA*. ⁒
by via Caracciolo EX
closed August, Sunday in July and Monday in other months – **M** a la carte 80/100000 (14 %).

XXX ⊛ **La Cantinella,** via Cuma 42 ⊠ 80132 ℰ 405375, Fax 415523 – 🖃. ⁂ 🛐 ⓞ 🗲 *VISA*. ⁒ GX **v**
closed Sunday, August, Christmas and New Year's Day – **M** a la carte 46/86000 (12 %)
Spec. Canestrini "Nettuno", Linguine con scampi e frutti di mare, Pesce "all'acqua pazza". Wines
Fiano, Taurasi.

XXX **Rosolino,** via Nazario Sauro 577 ⊠ 80132 ℰ 415873, Fax 405457, Rest. piano bar –
🖃 – 🛆 70. ⁂ 🛐 ⓞ 🗲 *VISA* – *closed Sunday and 11 to 31 August* – **M** a la carte 42/
71000.
GX **a**

XX **Cavour,** piazza Garibaldi 34 ⊠ 80142 ℰ 264730 – 🖃. ⁂ 🛐 ⓞ 🗲 *VISA*. ⁒ MY **b**
closed Sunday – **M** a la carte 36/60000 (15 %).

XX **San Carlo,** via Cesario Console 18/19 ⊠ 80132 ℰ 426057 – ⁂ 🛐 ⓞ 🗲 *VISA*. ⁒ KZ **a**
closed Sunday and 10 to 20 August – **M** (booking essential) a la carte 32/69000.

XX ⊛ **Giuseppone a Mare,** via Ferdinando Russo 13-Capo Posillipo ⊠ 80123 ℰ 7696002,
Seaside rest. with ≼ – 🅿. ⁂ 🛐 ⓞ 🗲 *VISA*. ⁒
by via Caracciolo EX
closed Sunday and 23 to 31 December – **M** a la carte 37/62000 (12 %)
Spec. Linguine con scampi, Polipetti al pignatiello, Spigola all'acqua pazza. Wines Ischia bianco
e rosso.

XX **Ciro a Santa Brigida,** via Santa Brigida 73 ⊠ 80132 ℰ 5524072, Rest. and pizzeria – ⁒
🖃. ⁂ ⓞ *VISA* – *closed Sunday and 10 to 25 August* – **M** a la carte 40/64000. JZ **w**

XX **A' Fenestrella,** calata Ponticello a Marechiaro ⊠ 80123 ℰ 7690020, Fax 7690020, ≼, ⁒
– 🅿. *VISA*
by via Caracciolo FX
closed 12 to 18 August, Wednesday and lunch July-August – **M** a la carte 36/59000 (15 %).

X **Sbrescia,** rampe Sant'Antonio a Posillipo 109 ⊠ 80122 ℰ 669140, Typical Neapolitan rest.
with ≼ town and gulf – ⁂ *VISA*. ⁒
by via Caracciolo EX
closed Monday and 15 to 28 August – **M** a la carte 28/53000.

Island of Capri 80073 Napoli 988 ㉗ – pop. 12 761 – High Season : Easter and June-
September – ⊕ 081.
The limitation of motor-vehicles' access is regulated by legislative rules.

🏨 **Gd H. Quisisana,** via Camerelle 2 ℰ 8370788, Telex 710520, Fax 8376080, ≼ sea and
Certosa, ⁒, « Garden with ⊼ », 🏋, ⊜, 🏊, ⁒ – 🛗 🖃 📺 ☎ – 🛆 25-400. ⁂ 🛐 ⓞ
🗲 *VISA*. ⁒
Easter-October – **M** a la carte 65/120000 – **150 rm** ⊇ 340/550000 suites 750/1250000.

🏨 **Scalinatella** ⁒ without rest., via Tragara 8 ℰ 8370633, Telex 721204, Fax 8378291, ≼ sea
and Certosa, ⊼ heated – 🛗 🖃 📺 ☎. ⁂
15 March-5 November – **28 rm** ⊇ 220/450000.

🏨 **Europa Palace,** via Capodimonte 2 ℰ 8370955, Telex 710397, Fax 8373191, ≼, ⁒, « Floral
terraces with ⊼ », 🏋, ⊜, 🏊 – 🛗 🖃 📺 ☎ – 🛆 400. ⁂ 🛐 ⓞ 🗲 *VISA*. ⁒
April-October – **M** a la carte 60/94000 – **92 rm** ⊇ 215/400000 suites 570/650000.

🏨 **Luna** ⁒, viale Matteotti 3 ℰ 8370433, Telex 721247, Fax 8377459, ≼ sea, Faraglioni and
Certosa, ⁒, « Terraces and garden with ⊼ » – 🛗 🖃 📺 ☎. ⁂ 🛐 ⓞ 🗲 *VISA*. ⁒ rest
April-October – **M** a la carte 55/73000 – ⊇ 25000 – **44 rm** 195/330000, 🗏 10000.

🏨 **La Palma and Rest. Relais la Palma,** via Vittorio Emanuele 39 ℰ 8370133, Telex 722015,
Fax 8376966, ⁒, ⊜ – 🛗 🖃 📺 ☎ – 🛆 25-200. ⁂ 🛐 ⓞ 🗲 *VISA*. ⁒
M a la carte 59/89000 – **80 rm** ⊇ 245/350000.

🏨 **La Pazziella** 🛇 without rest., via Fuorlovado 36 ✆ 8370044, Fax 8370085, « Floral garden » – 🗏 📺 ☎. 🖭 🗓 ⓪ Ε 𝗩𝗜𝗦𝗔. ⛝
19 rm ⊂⊃ 200/300000 suites 350/500000.

🏨 **Punta Tragara** 🛇, via Tragara 57 ✆ 8370844, Telex 710261, Fax 8377790, ≤ Faraglioni and coast, 🍽, « Panoramic terrace with ⤢ heated » – 📶 🗏 📺 ☎. 🖭 🗓 ⓪ Ε 𝗩𝗜𝗦𝗔. ⛝
22 March-22 October – **M** a la carte 57/94000 – 33 suites ⊂⊃ 280/650000.

🏨 **La Pineta** 🛇, via Tragara 6 ✆ 8370644, Telex 710011, Fax 8376445, ≤ sea and Certosa, « Pine terraces, flowers », 🕭, 🌊, ⤢ – 🗏 📺 ☎ – ⚙ 30. 🖭 🗓 ⓪ Ε 𝗩𝗜𝗦𝗔. ⛝
M a la carte 34/61000 – **52 rm** ⊂⊃ 250/280000 suites 380/430000.

🏨 **Villa delle Sirene,** via Camerelle 51 ✆ 8370102, Fax 8370957, ≤, 🍽, « Lemon-grove with ⤢ » – 📶 🗏 🗏. 🖭 🗓 ⓪ Ε 𝗩𝗜𝗦𝗔
April-October – **M** *(closed Tuesday)* a la carte 33/46000 – **35 rm** ⊂⊃ 240/300000, 🗏 20000.

🏨 **La Brunella** 🛇, via Tragara 24 ✆ 8370122, Telex 721451, Fax 8370430, ≤ sea and coast, 🍽, « Floral terraces », ⤢ heated – 🗏 rm ☎. 🖭 🗓 Ε 𝗩𝗜𝗦𝗔. ⛝
19 March-5 November – **M** a la carte 33/56000 (12 %) – **18 rm** ⊂⊃ 260000.

🏨 **Flora** 🛇, via Serena 26 ✆ 8370211, Fax 8378949, ≤ sea and Certosa, « Floral terrace » – 🗏 📺 ☎. 🖭 🗓 ⓪ Ε 𝗩𝗜𝗦𝗔. ⛝
closed 9 January-14 March – **M** a la carte 58/88000 – ⊂⊃ 20000 – **24 rm** 230/400000, 🗏 20000.

🏨 **Gatto Bianco,** via Vittorio Emanuele 32 ✆ 8370446, Fax 8378060, « Summer rest. service under pergola » – 📶 🗏 rm 📺 ☎. 🖭 🗓 ⓪ Ε 𝗩𝗜𝗦𝗔. ⛝
March-October and 27 December-6 January – **M** 40/50000 – **37 rm** ⊂⊃ 120/230000, 🗏 20000.

🏨 **Villa Sarah** 🛇 without rest., via Tiberio 3/a ✆ 8377817, ≤, « Shaded garden » – 📺 ☎. 🖭. ⛝
Easter-October – **20 rm** ⊂⊃ 95/170000.

🏨 San Felice, without rest., via li Campi 13 ✆ 8376122, Fax 8378264, 🍽, ⤢ – 🗏 rm ☎
season – **30 rm**.

🏨 **Florida** without rest., via Fuorlovado 34 ✆ 8370710, Fax 8370497, 🍽 – ☎. 🖭 🗓 ⓪ Ε 𝗩𝗜𝗦𝗔
March-11 November – ⊂⊃ 14000 – **19 rm** 62/100000.

🍴🍴🍴 **La Certosella,** via Tragara 15 ✆ 8370713, Fax 8370541, ≤, « Summer service on terrace with ⤢ heated » – 🖭 🗓 ⓪ 𝗩𝗜𝗦𝗔. ⛝
May-October ; closed Tuesday (except July-September) – **M** a la carte 57/94000.

🍴🍴 **La Capannina,** via Le Botteghe 14 ✆ 8370732, Fax 8376990 – 🗏. 🖭 🗓 Ε 𝗩𝗜𝗦𝗔
15 March-6 November ; closed Wednesday (except August) – **M** (booking essential for dinner) a la carte 43/63000 (15 %).

🍴🍴 **La Pigna,** via Roma 30 ✆ 8370280, Fax 8370280, ≤ gulf of Naples, « Summer service in lemon-grove » – 🖭 🗓 ⓪ Ε 𝗩𝗜𝗦𝗔
Easter-October ; closed Tuesday (except July-September) – **M** a la carte 38/60000 (15 %).

🍴🍴 **Casanova,** via Le Botteghe 46 ✆ 8377642 – 🖭 🗓 ⓪ Ε 𝗩𝗜𝗦𝗔
April-October ; closed Thursday (except July-September) – **M** a la carte 39/62000.

🍴🍴 **La Tavernetta,** via Lo Palazzo 23/a ✆ 8376864 – 🖭 🗓 ⓪ Ε 𝗩𝗜𝗦𝗔
closed 15 January-15 February, Monday and lunch October to May (except week end) – **M** a la carte 32/66000 (15 %).

🍴 **Al Grottino,** via Longano 27 ✆ 8370584 – 🗏. 🖭 Ε 𝗩𝗜𝗦𝗔
closed Tuesday, 26 January-9 March and 11 November-28 December – **M** a la carte 26/39000 (15 %).

Sant'Agata sui due Golfi 80064 Napoli – alt. 391 – High Season : April-September – 🕿 081.
Roma 266 – Castellammare di Stabia 28 – ✦Napoli 57 – Salerno 56 – Sorrento 9.

🍴🍴🍴 🟊🟊 **Don Alfonso 1890** with rm, ✆ 8780026, Fax 5330226, 🍽 – 🄿. 🖭 ⓪ Ε 𝗩𝗜𝗦𝗔. ⛝
closed 7 January-27 February – **M** *(closed Sunday and Monday except Easter, 15 July-15 September, Christmas and New Year's Day)* (booking essential) a la carte 59/87000 (15 %) 2 suites 180/200000
Spec. Insalata di aragosta o astice agli agrumi, Linguine alle vongole e zucchine, Filetti di triglie alle lenticchie in salsa di Aglianico. **Wines** Biancolella, Aglianico.

Michelin Green Guides in English		
		New York City
Austria	Greece	Portugal
Canada	Italy	Rome
England : The West Country	London	Scotland
France	Mexico	Spain
Germany	Netherlands	Switzerland
Great Britain	New England	Washington

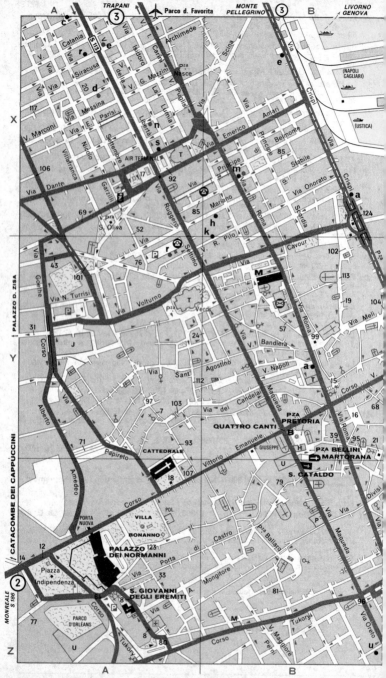

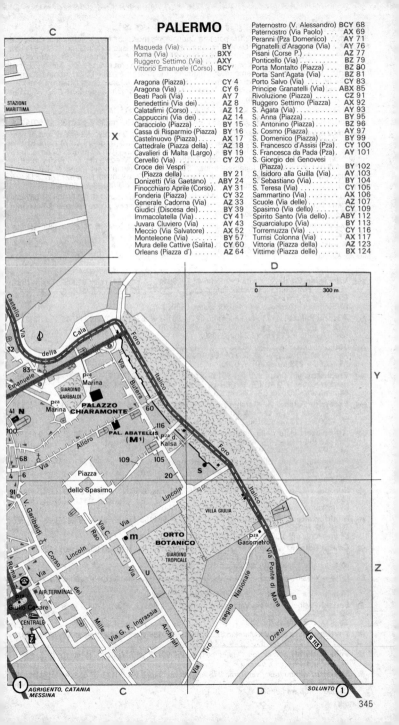

PALERMO

See : Palace of the Normans★★ : the palatine Chapel★★★, mosaics★★★ AZ – Regional Gallery of Sicily★★ in Abbatellis Palace★ : Death Triumphant★★★ by Antonello da Messina CY **M1** – Piazza Bellini★★ BY : Martorana Church★★, Church of St. Cataldo★★ – Church of St. John of the Hermits★★ AZ – Capuchin Catacombs★★ – Piazza Pretoria★ BY : fountain★★ B – Archaeological Museum★ : metopes from the temples at Selinus★★, the Ram★★ BY **M** – Chiaramonte Palace★ : magnolia fig trees★★ in Garibaldi Gardens CY – St. Lawrence Oratory★ CY **N** Quattro Canti★ BY – Cathedral★ AYZ Villa Bonanno★ AZ – Palazzo della Zisa★ – Botanical garden★ CDZ – Sicilian carts★ in Ethnographic Museum.

Envir. : Monreale★★★ by ② : 8 km – Monte Pellegrino★★ by ③ : 14 km.

✈ Punta Raisi by ③ : 30 km 𝒫 6019333 – Alitalia, via della Libertà 29 ✉ 90139 𝒫 6019111.

🚢 to Genova June-December, Tuesday, Friday and Sunday, Tuesday and Friday rest of year (22 h) and to Livorno Monday, Wednesday and Friday (19 h) – Grandi Traghetti, via Mariano Stabile 53 ✉ 90141 𝒫 587939, Telex 910098, Fax 689629; to Napoli daily (10 h 30 mn), to Genova June-September, Monday, Wednesday, Friday and Saturday, Monday, Wednesday and Friday in other months (23 h) and to Cagliari June-September, Sunday and Friday in other months (12 h 30 mn) – Tirrenia Navigazione, via Roma 385 ✉ 90133 𝒫 333300, Telex 910020, Fax 6021221; to Ustica daily (2 h 20 mn) – Siremar Prestifilippo Agency, via Crispi 118 ✉ 90133 𝒫 582403.

🚢 to Ustica daily (1 h 15 mn) – Siremar Prestifilippo Agency, via Crispi 118 ✉ 90133 𝒫 582403; to Aeolian Island June-September daily (4 h) – SNAV Barbaro Agency, piazza Principe di Belmonte 51/55 ✉ 90139 𝒫 586533, Telex 910093.

🛈 piazza Castelnuovo 34 ✉ 90141 𝒫 583847, Telex 910179 – Punta Raisi Airport 𝒫 591698 – Central Station ✉ 90127 𝒫 6165914, Fax 331854.

A.C.I. via delle Alpi 6 ✉ 90144 𝒫 300471.

Messina 235 ①.

Plan on preceding pages

🏨 **Villa Igiea Gd H.** ॐ, salita Belmonte 43 ✉ 90142 𝒫 543744, Telex 910092, Fax 547654, ≼, 🍴, « Floral terraces overlooking the sea », 🏊, 🎾, ✵ – 🛗 🖭 📺 ☎ 🖕 🅿 – 🛗 50-500.
🖭 🖸 ⓞ **E** 𝓥𝓘𝓢𝓐. ✵ rest   by ③
M 80000 – **117 rm** ☲ 290/450000 suites 680000.

🏨 **Astoria Palace**, via Monte Pellegrino 62 ✉ 90142 𝒫 6371820, Telex 911045, Fax 6372178 – 🛗 📺 ☎ 🅿 – 🛗 30-1000. 🖭 🖸 ⓞ 𝓥𝓘𝓢𝓐. ✵   by via Crispi BX
M 50/66000 – **325 rm** ☲ 140/193000.

🏨 **Jolly**, Foro Italico 22 ✉ 90133 𝒫 6165090, Telex 910076, Fax 6161441, 🍴, 🏊, ✵ – 🛗 ✵ rm 🖭 📺 ☎ 🅿 – 🛗 50-2000. 🖭 🖸 ⓞ **E** 𝓥𝓘𝓢𝓐. ✵ rest   DY **s**
M 40000 – **273 rm** ☲ 155/200000.

🏨 **President,** via Crispi 230 ✉ 90139 𝒫 580733, Telex 910359, Fax 6111588, ≼, « Roof garden rest. » – 🛗 🖭 📺 ☎ 🅿 – 🛗 30-150. 🖭 🖸 ⓞ **E** 𝓥𝓘𝓢𝓐. ✵   BX **e**
M a la carte 36/52000 – **129 rm** ☲ 120/170000.

🏨 **Excelsior Palace**, via Marchese Ugo 3 ✉ 90141 𝒫 6256176, Telex 911149, Fax 342139 – 🛗 ✵ rest 🖭 📺 ☎ – 🛗 50-100. 🖭 🖸 ⓞ **E** 𝓥𝓘𝓢𝓐. ✵ rest   AX **c**
M 40000 – **128 rm** ☲ 150/200000 suites 185/240000.

🏨 **AgipHotel,** viale della Regione Siciliana 2620 ✉ 90145 𝒫 552033, Telex 911196, Fax 408198 – 🛗 🖭 📺 ☎ 🅿 – 🛗 90. 🖭 🖸 ⓞ **E** 𝓥𝓘𝓢𝓐. ✵ rest   by ③
M 32000 – **105 rm** ☲ 110/162000.

🏨 **Politeama Palace,** piazza Ruggero Settimo 15 ✉ 90139 𝒫 322777, Telex 911053, Fax 6111589 – 🛗 🖭 📺 ☎ – 🛗 50-130   AX **s**
102 rm.

🏨 **Europa,** via Agrigento 3 ✉ 90141 𝒫 6256323, Fax 6256323 – 🛗 🖭 📺 ☎. 🖭 🖸 ⓞ **E** 𝓥𝓘𝓢𝓐. ✵   AX **r**
M (residents only) – ☲ 15000 – **73 rm** 80/115000.

🏨 **Mediterraneo,** via Rosolino Pilo 43 ✉ 90139 𝒫 581133, Fax 586974 – 🛗 🖭 📺 ☎ – 🛗 50. 🖭 🖸 ⓞ **E** 𝓥𝓘𝓢𝓐. ✵   BX **k**
M (residents only) 30000 – ☲ 15000 – **105 rm** 80/115000.

🏨 **Cristal Palace,** via Roma 477/d ✉ 90139 𝒫 6112580, Telex 911205, Fax 6112589 – 🛗 🖭 📺 ☎ – 🛗 80. 🖭 🖸 ⓞ **E** 𝓥𝓘𝓢𝓐. ✵   BX **m**
M a la carte 53/89000 – **90 rm** ☲ 105/150000.

🏨 **Ponte,** via Crispi 99 ✉ 90139 𝒫 583744, Telex 910492, Fax 581845 – 🛗 🖭 📺 ☎. 🖭 🖸 ⓞ **E** 𝓥𝓘𝓢𝓐. ✵   BX **a**
M a la carte 35/40000 – ☲ 8000 – **137 rm** 80/115000.

🏨 **Sausele** without rest., via Vincenzo Errante 12 ✉ 90127 𝒫 6161308 – 🛗 ☜ 🚗. 🖭 🖸 ⓞ **E** 𝓥𝓘𝓢𝓐   BZ **u**
☲ 9000 – **37 rm** 45/65000.

🏨 **Touring** without rest., via Mariano Stabile 136 ✉ 90139 𝒫 584444 – 🛗 🖭 ☎. 🖭 ⓞ 𝓥𝓘𝓢𝓐. ✵
☲ 15000 – **22 rm** 60/85000, 🗄 20000.   BX **h**

🏨 **Villa Archirafi** without rest., via Lincoln 30 ✉ 90133 𝒫 6168827 – 🛗 ☎ 🅿. 🖸 **E** 𝓥𝓘𝓢𝓐
☲ 10000 – **30 rm** 45/65000.   CZ **m**

🏨 **Moderno** without rest., via Roma 276 angolo via Napoli ✉ 90133 𝒫 588683 – 📺 ☜. 🖭 🖸 ⓞ **E** 𝓥𝓘𝓢𝓐   BY **a**
☲ 3000 – **38 rm** 38/60000.

XXXX ✿ **Charleston,** piazzale Ungheria 30 ⊠ 90141 ℘ 321366, Fax 321347 – 🗐. 🖭 🕄 ⑩ **E**
~~VISA~~. ✑ AY **r**
closed Sunday and June-25 September – **M** a la carte 60/90000
Spec. Cornetti di Spada "Nettuno", Fusilli caserecci, Involtini alla siciliana. Wines Feudo dei Fio.
Terre di Ginestra.

XXX ✿ **L'Approdo da Renato,** via Messina Marine 224 ⊠ 90123 ℘ 6302881, 🍴 – 🖭 ⑩.
✑ by ① DZ
closed Wednesday and 10 to 25 August – **M** (booking essential) a la carte 46/73000
(10 %)
Spec. Crespella ai frutti di mare, Trancio di cernia al pane aceto e mentuccia, Semifreddo alla
mandorla. Wines Donnafugata.

XXX **Gourmand's,** via della Libertà 37/e ⊠ 90139 ℘ 323431, Fax 323431 – 🗐. 🖭 🕄 ⑩ **E**
~~VISA~~. ✑ AX **e**
closed Sunday and 5 to 25 August – **M** a la carte 45/71000.

XXX **Friend's Bar,** via Brunelleschi 138 ⊠ 90145 ℘ 201401, 🍴 – 🗐. 🖭 ⑩ by ③
closed Monday and 16 to 31 August – **M** (booking essential) a la carte 34/49000.

XXX **La Scuderia,** viale del Fante 9 ⊠ 90146 ℘ 520467 – 🗐 ⑫. 🖭 🕄 ⑩ **E**
~~VISA~~ by via C.A. Dalla Chiesa AX
closed Sunday and 15 to 31 August – **M** a la carte 49/80000.

XX **Savoya,** via Torrearsa 22 ⊠ 90139 ℘ 582173 – 🗐. 🖭 🕄 ⑩ **E** ~~VISA~~ AX **n**
closed Monday and August – **M** a la carte 40/50000.

XX **Regine,** via Trapani 4/a ⊠ 90141 ℘ 586566 – 🗐. 🖭 🕄 ⑩ **E** ~~VISA~~. ✑ AX **d**
closed Sunday and August – **M** a la carte 40/50000.

XX **A Cuccagna,** via Principe Granatelli 21/a ⊠ 90139 ℘ 587267 – 🗐. 🖭 🕄 ⑩ **E** ~~VISA~~
✑ BX **m**
closed Friday and 7 to 24 August – **M** a la carte 32/52000.

TAORMINE (TAORMINA) 98039 Messina 🔢 ㉝ – pop. 10 905 alt. 250 – ✆ 0942.

See : Site✶✶✶ – Greek Theatre✶✶ : ≤✶✶✶ B – Public garden✶✶ B – ✳✶✶ from the Square 9 Aprile
A 12 – Corso Umberto✶ A – Belvedere✶ B – Castle✶ : ≤✶ A.

Exc. : Etna✶✶✶, SW : for Linguaglossa.

🛈 (June-September) largo Santa Caterina (Corvaja palace) ℘ 23243, Telex 981167, Fax 24941.

Catania 52 ② – Enna 135 ② – Messina 52 ① – Palermo 255 ② – Siracusa 111 ② – Trapani 359 ②.

TAORMINA	Cappuccini (Via)	A 2	Rotabile Castelmola	A 8
	Crocifisso (Via)	A 3	S. Antonio (Piazza)	A 9
	Dionisio (Via)	A 5	Vittorio Emanuele (Pza)	B 10
Umberto (Corso)	A	Duomo (Piazza)	A 6	9 Aprile (Piazza)	A 13

🏛 **San Domenico Palace** ✑, piazza San Domenico 5 ℘ 23701, Telex 980013, Fax 625506,
🍴, « 15C Monastery with floral garden, ≤ sea, coast and Etna », 🌊 heated – 🛗 🗐 📺
🕿 – 🔬 400. 🖭 🕄 ⑩ **E** ~~VISA~~. ✑ rest A m
M 120000 – **101 rm** 🖙 350/610000 suites 1000/2000000.

Excelsior Palace , via Toselli 8 23975, Telex 980185, Fax 23978, ≤ sea, coast and Etna, « Small park, heated on terrace with panoramic view » - rest A **v**
M 65000 - **89 rm** 160/230000.

Jolly Diodoro, via Bagnoli Croci 75 23312, Telex 980028, Fax 23391, ≤ sea, coast and Etna, « on terrace with panoramic view », - 250. rest B **q**
M 56000 - **102 rm** 160/230000.

Bristol Park Hotel, via Bagnoli Croci 92 23006, Telex 980005, Fax 24519, ≤ sea, coast and Etna, - . rest B **r**
closed 1 to 20 December and 10 January to February - **M** 50/60000 - **50 rm** 155/240000 suites 213/270000.

Monte Tauro , via Madonna delle Grazie 3 24402, Telex 980048, Fax 24403, ≤ sea and coast, - - 100. rest AB **u**
M 40000 - **70 rm** 248000.

Villa Paradiso, via Roma 2 23922, Fax 625800, ≤ sea, coast and Etna - . rest B **h**
closed November-18 December - **M** *(closed lunch June-September)* 30/40000 - **33 rm** 135/220000.

Villa Fiorita without rest., via Pirandello 39 24122, Fax 625967, ≤ sea and coast, , - . B **s**
24 rm 110000.

Vello d'Oro, via Fazzello 2 23788, Telex 980186, Fax 626117, « Sun bathing terrace with ≤ sea and coast » - . A **r**
15 March-October - **M** *(dinner only)* 25/30000 - 15000 - **57 rm** 70/120000.

Villa Belvedere without rest., via Bagnoli Croci 79 23791, Fax 625830, ≤ gardens, sea and Etna, « on terrace with panoramic view », - . B **b**
16 March-October - **43 rm** 86/157000.

Villa Sirina, contrada Sirina 51776, Fax 51671, , - . 2 km by via Crocifisso A
closed November-20 December - **M** *(dinner only)* 30/38000 - **15 rm** 135000.

Villa Riis , via Rizzo 13 24874, Fax 626254, ≤ sea, coast and Etna, , , - . rest A **b**
April-October - **M** (dinner only) (resident only) 50000 - **30 rm** 120/210000.

Continental, via Dionisio I nº 2/a 23805, Telex 981144, , « Panoramic terrace with ≤ sea and coast », - . rest A **s**
M *(closed lunch May-September)* 30/40000 - 15000 - **43 rm** 80/125000.

Andromaco without rest., via Fontana Vecchia 23436, Fax 24985, ≤, - . by via Cappuccini A
16 rm 66/115000.

La Campanella without rest., via Circonvallazione 3 23381, ≤ - A **g**
12 rm 55/95000.

Villa Carlotta without rest., via Pirandello 81 23732, Fax 23732, ≤ sea and coast, - B **a**
15 March-October - 15000 - **21 rm** 50/94000.

Condor without rest., via Cappuccini 25 23124, Fax 24559, ≤ - A **a**
12 rm 80000.

Belsoggiorno, via Pirandello 60 23342, ≤ sea and coast, - . rest B **u**
M *(dinner only)* 25/30000 - 7000 - **19 rm** 60/96000.

XXXX **La Giara,** vico La Floresta 1 23360, Fax 23233, - . A **f**
closed lunch - **M** a la carte 48/79000.

XXX **Granduca,** corso Umberto 172 24420, Fax 625446 - A **n**
closed Monday and lunch in August - **M** a la carte 46/82000.

XX Al Castello da Ciccio, via Madonna della Rocca 28158, « Outdoor service summer with ≤ Giardini Naxos, sea and Etna » A **e**

XX **La Griglia,** corso Umberto 54 23980, Fax 626047 - . A **c**

closed Tuesday - **M** a la carte 35/58000.

XX **Quattropini,** contrada Sant'Antonio 24832, ≤, - . 1 km by ①
closed Monday and 26 November-26 December - **M** a la carte 28/46000.

X **A' Zammara,** via Fratelli Bandiera 15 24408, - A **z**
closed Wednesday and 5 to 20 January - **M** a la carte 31/44000.

X **La Chioccia d'Oro,** rotabile Castelmola 28066, ≤ A **d**
closed Wednesday and 30 May-June - **M** a la carte 24/35000.

at Capo Taormina by ② : 3 km - ✉ **98030** Mazzarò :

Grande Alb. Capotaormina, 24000, Telex 980147, Fax 625467, ≤ sea and coast, , , - - 150-350.
20 March-October - **M** 88000 - **207 rm** 212/323000.

at Castelmola NO : 5 km A – alt. 550 – ⊠ 98030 :

✕ **Il Faro,** contrada Petralia ℰ 28193, ≤ sea and coast, 🏠 – **℗**
closed Wednesday – **M** a la carte 26/41000.

at Mazzarò by ② : 5,5 km – ⊠ 98030 :

🏨🏨 **Mazzarò Sea Palace,** ℰ 24004, Telex 980041, Fax 626237, ≤ small bay, 🏠, ⤱ heated,
🏊 – 🛗 🗏 TV ☎ ⟺. AE 🖪 ⓪ E VISA. ✻ rest
April-October – **M** 80000 – � 25000 – **87 rm** 215/430000 suites 510/680000.

🏨🏨 **Villa Sant'Andrea,** ℰ 23125, Telex 980077, Fax 24838, ≤ small bay, 🏠, « Shaded
terraces », 🏊, 🌴 – 🗏 ☎ **℗**
M (dinner only) (booking essential) Oliviero Rest. – **67 rm**.

✕ **Il Pescatore,** ℰ 23460, ≤ sea, cliffs and Isolabella – **℗**. VISA.
3 March-October ; closed Monday – **M** a la carte 34/54000.

✕ **Il Delfino-da Angelo,** ℰ 23004, ≤ small bay, 🏠 – AE 🖪 ⓪ E VISA
15 March-October – **M** a la carte 28/49000.

✕ **Da Giovanni,** ℰ 23531, ≤ sea and Isolabella – AE ⓪ VISA. ✻
closed Monday and 7 January-7 February – **M** a la carte 38/70000.

TURIN (TORINO) 10100 **P** 988 ⑫, 428 G 5 – pop. 991 870 alt. 239 – ✪ 011.

See : Piazza San Carlo★★ CXY – Egyptian Museum★★, Sabauda Gallery★★ in Academy of Science
CX **M** – Cathedral★ CX : relic of the Holy Shroud★★★ – Mole Antonelliana★ : ☀★★ DX – Palazzo
Madama★ : museum of Ancient Art★ CX **A** – Royal Palace★ : Royal Armoury★ CDVX – Risor-
gimento Museum★ in Palazzo Carignano CX **M2** – Carlo Biscaretti di Ruffia Motor Museum★ –
Model medieval village★ in the Valentino Park CDZ.

Envir. : Basilica of Superga★ : ≤★★★, royal tombs★ – Tour to the pass, Colle della Maddalena★ :
≤★★ of the city from the route Superga-Pino Torinese, ≤★ of the city from the route Colle della
Maddalena-Cavoretto.

🏌 🏌 I Roveri (March-November ; closed Monday) at La Mandria ⊠ 10070 Fiano ℰ 9235719, Fax
9235669, by ① : 18 km;

🏌 🏌 (closed January, February and Monday), at Fiano ⊠ 10070 ℰ 9235440, Fax 9235886, by
① : 20 km.

🏌 Le Fronde (closed Monday and January) at Avigliana ⊠ 10051 ℰ 938053, Fax 938053, W : 24 km;

🏌 (closed Monday and August), at Stupinigi ⊠ 10135 ℰ 343975;

🏌 (closed Monday and 24 December-7 January) at Vinovo ⊠ 10048 ℰ 9653880.

✈ Turin Airport of Caselle by ① : 15 km ℰ 5778361, Fax 5778420 – Alitalia, via Lagrange 35
⊠ 10123 ℰ 57697.

🚗 ℰ 537766.

🛈 via Roma 222 (piazza C.L.N.) ⊠ 10121 ℰ 535901, Fax 532450 – Porta Nuova Railway station ⊠
10125 ℰ 531327.

A.C.I. via Giovanni Giolitti 15 ⊠ 10123 ℰ 57791.

Roma 669 ⑦ – Briançon 108 ⑪ – Chambéry 209 ⑪ – Genève 252 ③ – Genova 170 ⑦ – Grenoble 224 ⑪ – Milano
140 ③ – Nice 220 ⑨.

Plans on following pages

🏨🏨 **Turin Palace Hotel,** via Sacchi 8 ⊠ 10128 ℰ 5625511, Telex 221411, Fax 5612187 – 🛗
🗏 TV ☎ 🔌 ⟺ – 🔏 30-200. AE 🖪 ⓪ E VISA. ✻ rest   CY **u**
M *(closed 3 to 23 August)* a la carte 57/105000 – ⊠ 28000 – **125 rm** 280/330000 suites
500/550000.

🏨 **Jolly Principi di Piemonte,** via Gobetti 15 ⊠ 10123 ℰ 519693, Telex 221120, Fax 510270
– 🛗 🗏 TV ☎ – 🔏 100. AE 🖪 ⓪ E VISA. ✻ rest   CY **z**
M 65000 – **107 rm** ⊠ 300/380000.

🏨 **Gd H. Sitea,** via Carlo Alberto 35 ⊠ 10123 ℰ 5570171, Telex 220229, Fax 548090 – 🛗
🗏 TV ☎ – 🔏 30-100. AE 🖪 ⓪ E VISA. ✻ rest   CY **t**
M a la carte 58/90000 – **116 rm** ⊠ 240/320000.

🏨 **Jolly Ambasciatori,** corso Vittorio Emanuele 104 ⊠ 10121 ℰ 5752, Telex 221296,
Fax 544978 – 🛗 🗏 TV ☎ ⟺ – 🔏 25-400. AE 🖪 ⓪ E VISA. ✻ rest   BX **a**
M 45000 – **199 rm** ⊠ 235/300000.

🏨 **Jolly Hotel Ligure,** piazza Carlo Felice 85 ⊠ 10123 ℰ 55641, Telex 220167, Fax 535438
– 🛗 🗏 TV ☎ 🔌 – 🔏 30-250. AE 🖪 ⓪ E VISA. ✻ rest   CY **b**
M 45000 – **156 rm** ⊠ 255/322000.

🏨 **Diplomatic,** via Cernaia 42 ⊠ 10122 ℰ 5612444, Telex 225445, Fax 540472 – 🛗 🗏 TV
☎ ⟺ – 🔏 50-200. AE 🖪 ⓪ E VISA. ✻ rest   BX **g**
M (residents only) *(closed Saturday and Sunday)* 40/60000 – **129 rm** ⊠ 220/295000.

🏨 **City** without rest., via Juvarra 25 ⊠ 10122 ℰ 540546, Telex 216228, Fax 548188 – 🛗 🗏
TV ☎ – 🔏 25. AE 🖪 ⓪ E VISA. ✻   BV **e**
closed August, Christmas and New Year's Day – **44 rm** ⊠ 280/375000 suites 320/350000.

🏨 **Concord,** via Lagrange 47 ⊠ 10123 ℰ 5576756, Telex 221323, Fax 5576305 – 🛗 🗏 TV
☎ 🔌 ⟺ – 🔏 180. AE 🖪 ⓪ E VISA. ✻ rest   CY **s**
M 55000 – **139 rm** ⊠ 233/295000 suites 395000.

TORINO

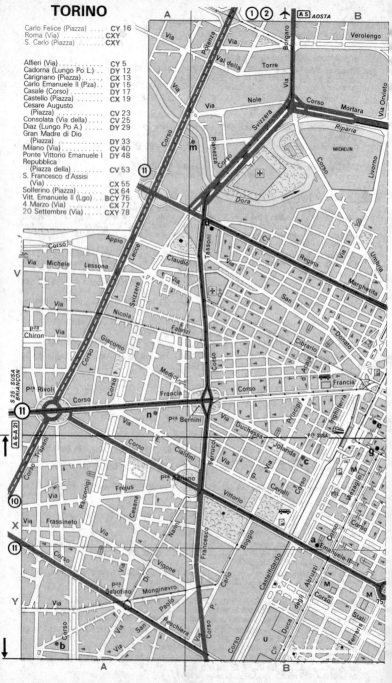

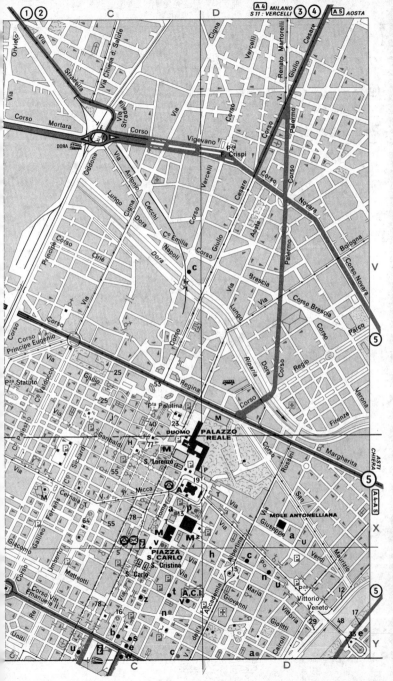

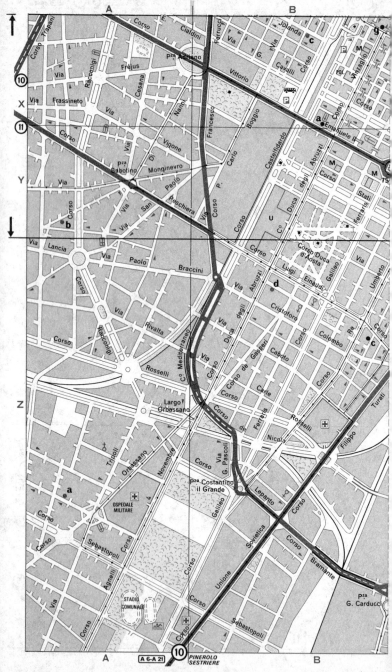

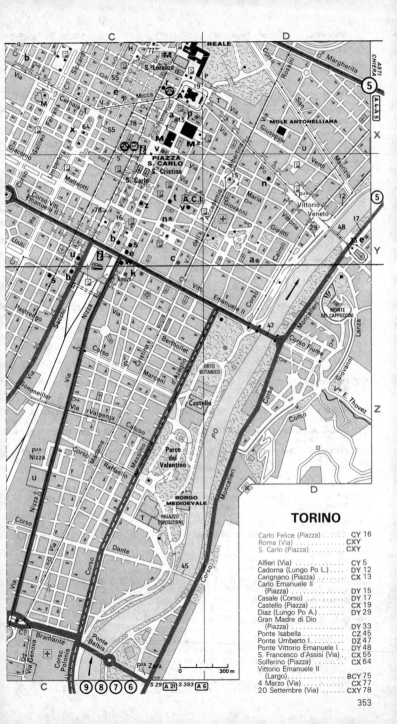

TORINO

🏨🏨 **Majestic,** corso Vittorio Emanuele II 54 ⊠ 10123 ☎ 539153, Telex 216260, Fax 534963
– 🛗 ▤ ▥ ☎ 🕭 – ⛴ – ⚿ 30-150. ㏂ 🚫 ⓞ ㉿ ⅥⅤ𝐀. 🍽
M (residents only) 40/45000 – **159 rm** ⌧ 230/290000.   CY **e**

🏨🏨 **Genio** without rest., corso Vittorio Emanuele II 47 ⊠ 10125 ☎ 6505771, Telex 220308,
Fax 6508264 – 🛗 ▤ ▥ ☎ 🕭 – ⚿ 35. ㏂ 🚫 ⓞ ㉿ ⅥⅤ𝐀
75 rm ⌧ 115/165000, ▤ 12000.   CYZ **w**

🏨🏨 **Royal** without rest., corso Regina Margherita 249 ⊠ 10144 ☎ 748444, Telex 220259,
Fax 748393, 🍽 – 🛗 ▤ ▥ ☎ 🚗 – ⚿ 25-600. ㏂ 🚫 ⓞ ㉿ ⅥⅤ𝐀. 🍽
closed 1 to 28 August – ⌧ 17000 – **72 rm** 170/230000.   BV **u**

🏨 **Victoria** without rest., via Nino Costa 4 ⊠ 10123 ☎ 5611909, Telex 212580, Fax 5611806
– 🛗 ▥ ☎. ㏂ 🚫 ⓞ ⅥⅤ𝐀. 🍽 – ⌧ 15000 – **65 rm** 100/130000.   CY **v**

🏨 **Stazione e Genova** without rest., via Sacchi 14 ⊠ 10128 ☎ 545323, Telex 224242,
Fax 519896 – 🛗 ▥ ☎ – ⚿ 50. ㏂ 🚫 ⓞ ㉿ ⅥⅤ𝐀. 🍽 – **40 rm** ⌧ 115/165000.   CZ **b**

🏨 **Alexandra** without rest., lungo Dora Napoli 14 ⊠ 10152 ☎ 858327, Telex 221562,
Fax 2483805 – 🛗 ▤ ▥ ☎ 🕭 – ㏂ 🚫 ⓞ ㉿ – **55 rm** ⌧ 155/200000.   CV **c**

🏨 **Boston** without rest., via Massena 70 ⊠ 10128 ☎ 500359, Fax 599358 – ▤ ▥ ☎ 🚗.
㏂ 🚫 ⓞ ㉿ ⅥⅤ𝐀 – **40 rm** ⌧ 115/165000, ▤ 12000.   BZ **c**

🏨 **Luxor** without rest., corso Stati Uniti 7 ⊠ 10128 ☎ 5620777, Telex 225549 – 🛗 ▤ ▥ ☎.
㏂ 🚫 ⓞ ㉿ ⅥⅤ𝐀   CZ **s**
closed August – **70 rm** ⌧ 115/165000, ▤ 12000.

🏨 **Goya** without rest., via Principe Amedeo 41 bis ⊠ 10123 ☎ 874951, Fax 874953 – 🛗 ▤
▥ ▥ ㏂ 🚫 ⓞ ㉿   DY **n**
closed 1 to 26 August – ⌧ 15000 – **30 rm** 90/110000, ▤ 15000.

🏨 **Cristallo** 🐾 without rest., corso Traiano 28/9 ⊠ 10135 ☎ 618383, Fax 3171565 – ▥ ☎.
㏂ 🚫 ⓞ ㉿ ⅥⅤ𝐀 – ⌧ 20000 – **20 rm** 120/150000.   by ⑩

🗙🗙🗙🗙 **Villa Sassi-El Toulà** 🐾 with rm, strada al Traforo del Pino 47 ⊠ 10132 ☎ 890556,
Telex 225437, Fax 890095, 🍴, « 18C country house in extensive park land » – 🛗 ▤ rest
▥ ☎ 🅿 – ⚿ 200. ㏂ 🚫 ⓞ ㉿ ⅥⅤ𝐀. 🍽   by ⑤
closed August – **M** (closed Sunday) a la carte 84/118000 – ⌧ 20000 – **15 rm** 250/380000,
suite 480000.

🗙🗙🗙🗙 ❀❀ **Vecchia Lanterna,** corso Re Umberto 21 ⊠ 10128 ☎ 537047, Elegant installation –
▤. ㏂ 🚫 ⓞ ㉿   CY **x**
closed Saturday lunch, Sunday and 10 to 20 August – **M** (booking essential) a la carte
78/116000
Spec. Savarin di Gries con tartufi alla Medici, Risotto mantecato al fegato d'oca, Amoretti di
piccione in crosta con salsa chasseur. Wines Gewürztraminer, Nebbiolo.

🗙🗙🗙🗙 **Del Cambio,** piazza Carignano 2 ⊠ 10123 ☎ 546690, Elegant traditional decor, « 19C
decor » – ▤. ㏂ 🚫 ⓞ ㉿ ⅥⅤ𝐀. 🍽   CX **a**
closed Sunday and 27 July-27 August – **M** (booking essential) a la carte 62/100000 (15 %).

🗙🗙🗙 **Al Saffi,** via Aurelio Saffi 2 ⊠ 10138 ☎ 442213, Elegant installation – 🍴 ▤. ㏂ ⓞ ⅥⅤ𝐀
closed Sunday and August – **M** (booking essential) a la carte 55/70000.   AV **n**

🗙🗙🗙 **Balbo,** via Andrea Doria 11 ⊠ 10123 ☎ 832274 – ▤. ㏂ 🚫 ⓞ ㉿ ⅥⅤ𝐀. 🍽   CY **n**
closed Monday and 18 July-18 August – **M** (booking essential) a la carte 70/95000.

🗙🗙🗙 ❀ **Due Lampioni da Carlo,** via Carlo Alberto 45 ⊠ 10123 ☎ 8397409, Fax 831970 – 🍴
▤. ㏂ ⅥⅤ𝐀. 🍽   CY **n**
closed Sunday and August – **M** a la carte 64/88000
Spec. Terrina di scampi in salsa agrodolce, Risotto alla trota e Champenoise, Filetto di vitello con
funghi fonduta e tartufo bianco (October-January). Wines Chardonnay, Barbaresco.

🗙🗙🗙 ❀ **Neuv Caval'd Brôns,** piazza San Carlo 157 ⊠ 10123 ☎ 553491 – 🍴 ▤. ㏂ 🚫 ⓞ ㉿ ⅥⅤ𝐀
closed Sunday – **M** (booking essential) a la carte 65/115000   CXY **v**
Spec. Pescatrice affumicata con verdure marinate, Maltagliati con ragúdi calamaretti, Nocetta di
capriolo al Barbera. Wines Favorita, Brachetto secco.

🗙🗙🗙 ❀ **La Smarrita,** corso Unione Sovietica 244 ⊠ 10134 ☎ 390657 – ▤. ㏂ 🚫 ⓞ ㉿ ⅥⅤ𝐀.
🍽   by ⑩
closed Monday and 3 to 27 August – **M** (booking essential) a la carte 50/80000
Spec. Moscardini pomodoro e basilico, Tortelli di mozzarella e pomodorini (autumn), Capretto
allo spiedo con salsa di menta (spring). Wines Gavi, Nebbiolo.

🗙🗙 **Adriano,** via Pollenzo 39 ⊠ 10141 ☎ 3358311, 🍴 – ㏂ 🚫 ㉿ ⅥⅤ𝐀. 🍽   AY **b**
closed Saturday and August – **M** a la carte 38/54000.

🗙🗙 **Al Bue Rosso,** corso Casale 10 ⊠ 10131 ☎ 830753 – ▤. ㏂ ⓞ ⅥⅤ𝐀   DY **e**
closed Monday, Saturday lunch and August – **M** a la carte 50/75000 (10 %).

🗙🗙 **Della Rocca,** via della Rocca 22/b ⊠ 10123 ☎ 831814 – ▤. ㏂ 🚫 ⓞ ㉿ ⅥⅤ𝐀. 🍽 DY **a**
closed Sunday – **M** (booking essential) a la carte 40/64000.

🗙🗙 **Due Mondi-da Ilio,** via San Pio V 3 ang. via Saluzzo ⊠ 10125 ☎ 6692056 – ㏂ 🚫 ⅥⅤ𝐀
closed Sunday and 1 to 15 August – **M** a la carte 39/72000.   CZ **k**

🗙🗙 **Il Porticciolo,** via Barletta 58 ⊠ 10136 ☎ 321601, Seafood – 🍴 ▤. ㏂ ⓞ ㉿ ⅥⅤ𝐀. 🍽
closed Monday, Saturday lunch and August – **M** a la carte 44/77000.   AZ **a**

🗙🗙 **Duchesse,** via Duchessa Jolanda 7 ang. via Beaumont ⊠ 10138 ☎ 4346494 – ㏂ 🚫 ⓞ ㉿ ⅥⅤ𝐀
closed Sunday dinner and Monday – **M** a la carte 40/79000.   BX **c**

X **Crocetta,** via Marco Polo 21 ⊠ 10129 𝒫 597789, 🛪 – 🗏. AE 🗗 ⊙ E VISA. ℁ BZ **d**
closed Sunday and August – **M** a la carte 34/55000.

X **Ostu Bacu,** corso Vercelli 226 ⊠ 10155 𝒫 264579, Modern Piedmontese trattoria – 🗏.
🗗 ⊙ E VISA   by corso Vercelli DV
closed Sunday and 25 July-25 August – **M** a la carte 28/63000.

X **Alberoni,** corso Moncalieri 288 ⊠ 10133 𝒫 6963255, 🛪, 🝅 – 🄿. VISA. ℁
closed Sunday dinner, Tuesday and January – **M** a la carte 35/50000.
          by corso Moncalieri CZ

X **C'era una volta,** corso Vittorio Emanuele II n° 41 ⊠ 10125 𝒫 655498, Typical Piedmontese
rest. – 🗏. AE 🗗 ⊙ E VISA   CZ **k**
closed lunch, Sunday and August – **M** (booking essential) 45000.

X **Anaconda,** via Angiolino 16 (corso Potenza) ⊠ 10143 𝒫 752903, Rustic trattoria,
« Outdoor service in Summer » – 🄿. AE 🗗 ⊙ E VISA   BV **m**
closed Friday dinner, Saturday and August – **M** 45000 bc.

X **Da Giudice,** strada Valsalice 78 ⊠ 10131 𝒫 6602020, Fax 6602020, « Summer service
under pergola » – 🛬 🄿. AE ⊙ VISA. ℁   by ⑤
closed Tuesday, Wednesday lunch and August – **M** a la carte 41/58000.

X **Trattoria della Posta,** strada Mongreno 16 ⊠ 10132 𝒫 890193, locals trattoria Piedmontese cheese specialities – 🗏. ℁   by ⑤
closed Sunday dinner, Monday and 10 July-20 August – **M** a la carte 30/50000.

Costigliole d'Asti 14055 Asti 988 ⑫. 428 H 6 – pop. 5 960 alt. 242 – ✪ 0141.
Roma 629 – Acqui Terme 34 – Alessandria 51 – Asti 15 – Genova 98 – Milano 141 – Torino 70.

XXX ✿✿ **Guido,** piazza Umberto I n° 27 𝒫 966012, Fax 966012 – 🗗 E VISA. ℁
closed lunch, Sunday, Bank Holidays, 1 to 20 August and 23 December-10 January – **M** (booking essential) 100/130000
Spec. Agnolotti di Costigliole, Zuppa di funghi, Cardo gobbo con fonduta e tartufi, Coniglio disos-
sato ripieno. Wines Arneis, Barbaresco.

VENICE **(VENEZIA)** 30100 🄿 988 ⑤. 429 F 19 – pop. 317 837 – High Season : 15 March-
October and Christmas – ✪ 041.

See : St. Marks Square★★★ FGZ :
St. Mark's Basilica★★★ GZ – Doges Palace★★★ GZ – Campanile★★ : ☀★★ FGZ **F** – Procuratie★★
FZ – Libreria Vecchia★ GZ – Correr Museum★ FZ **M** – Clock Tower★ FZ **K** – Bridge of Sighs★ GZ.
Grand Canal★★★ :
Rialto Bridge★ FY – Right bank : Cà d'Oro★★★ : Franchetti Gallery★★ EX – Palazzo
Vendramin-Calergi★★ BT **R** – Cà Loredan★★ EY **H** – Palazzo Grimani★★ EY **Q** Palazzo
Corner-Spinelli★★ BTU **D** Palazzo Grassi★★ BU **M5** – Left bank : Academy of Fine Arts★★★ BV Palazzo
Dario★★ BV **S** – Peggy Guggenheim Collection★★ in Palazzo Venier dei Leoni BV **M2** – Palazzo
Rezzonico★★ AU **M3** : masterpieces by Guardi★★, frescoes★★ by Tiepolo in Venice in the 18C★ –
Palazzo Giustinian★★ AU **X** – Cà Foscari★★ AU **Y** Palazzo Bernardo★★ BT **Z** – Palazzo dei
Camerlenghi★★ FX **A** – Palazzo Pesaro★★ : Museum of Modern Art★ EX.
Churches :
Santa Maria della Salute★★ : Marriage at Cana★★★ by Tintoretto BV – San Giorgio Maggiore★★ :
☀★★★ from campanile★★ CV – San Zanipolo★★ : polyptych★★★ of San Vincenzo Ferrari,
ceiling★★★ of the Rosary Chapel GX – Santa Maria Gloriosa dei Frari★★ : works by Titian★★★ AT – San
Zaccaria★ : altarpiece★★★ by Bellini, altarpieces★★ by Vivarini and by Ludovico da Forlì DT – Interior
decoration★★ by Veronese in the Church of San Sebastiano AU – Paintings★ by Guardi in the Church
of Angelo Raffaele AU – Ceiling★ of the Church of San Pantaleone AT – Santa Maria dei Miracoli★ GX
– Madonna and Child★ in the Church of San Francesco della Vigna DT – Madonna and Child★ in the
Church of Redentore (Giudecca Island) AV.
Scuola di San Rocco★★★ AT – Scuola di San Giorgio degli Schiavoni★ : paintings★★ by Carpaccio DT –
Scuola dei Carmini★ : paintings★★ by Tiepolo AU – Palazzo Querini-Stampalia★ GY – Rio dei Men-
dicanti★ GX – Facade★ of the Scuola di San Marco★ GX – Frescoes★ by Tiepolo in Palazzo Labia LX.
The Lido – Murano★★ : Glass Museum★★★, Church of Santi Maria e Donato★★ – Burano★★ – Tor-
cello★★ : mosaics★★★ in the Cathedral of Santa Maria Assunta★★, peristyle★★ and columns★
inside the Church of Santa Fosca★.

🄘 (closed Monday) at Lido Alberoni ⊠ 30011 𝒫 731333, Fax 731339, 15 mn by boat and 9 km;
🄘, 🄘 Cà della Nave (closed Tuesday), at Martellago ⊠ 30030 𝒫 5401555, Fax 5401926, NW :
12 km.

🛫 Marco Polo di Tessera, NE : 13 km 𝒫 661262 – Alitalia, San Marco-Bacino Orseolo 1166
⊠ 30124 𝒫 5216333.

🛳 to Lido - San Nicolò from piazzale Roma (Tronchetto) daily (35 mn) ; to Punta Sabbioni from
Riva degli Schiavoni daily (40 mn); to island of Pellestrina-Santa Maria del Mare from Lido Alberoni
daily (1 h 15 mn); to islands of Murano (10 mn), Burano (40 mn) and Torcello (45 mn) daily, from
Fondamenta Nuove ; to Treporti-Cavallino from Fondamenta Nuove daily (1 h 10 mn) – Information: ACTV - Venetian Transport Union, piazzale Roma ⊠ 30135 𝒫 5287880, Fax 5207135.

🄗 San Marco Ascensione 71/c ⊠ 30124 𝒫 5226356 – Santa Lucia Railway station ⊠ 30121
𝒫 715016.

A.C.I. fondamenta Santa Chiara 518/a ⊠ 30125 𝒫 5200300.
Roma 528 ① – Bologna 152 ① – Milano 267 ① – Trieste 158 ①.

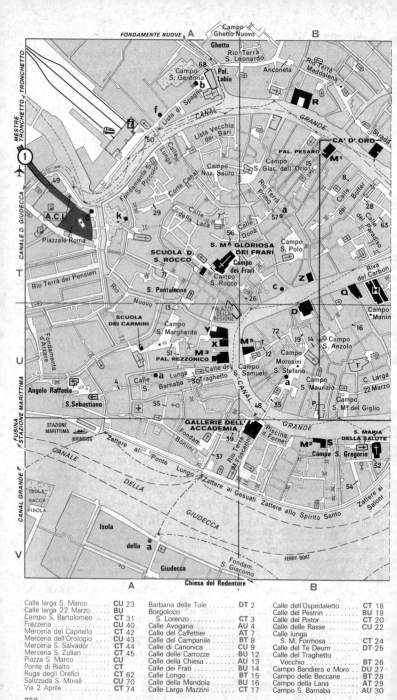

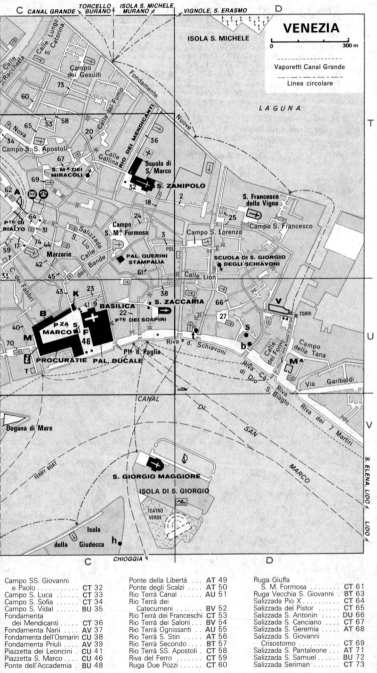

VENEZIA

0 ——————— 300 m

- - - - Vaporetti Canal Grande
—·—·— Linea circolare

🏨🏨🏨🏨 **Cipriani** ⚓, isola della Giudecca 10 ✉ 30133 ✆ 5207744, Telex 410162, Fax 5203930, ≤, 🚯, « Floral garden with heated ♨ », ≤s, ✵ – ⧈ ▤ 📺 ☎ – 🔬 100. 🆎 🆂 ⓞ ⋿ 𝗩𝗜𝗦𝗔. ✾
CV h
March-November – **M** a la carte 110/160000 – **95 rm** ⤓ 650/890000 suites 1200/2800000.

🏨🏨🏨🏨 **Gritti Palace**, campo Santa Maria del Giglio 2467 ✉ 30124 ✆ 794611, Telex 410125, Fax 5200942, ≤ Grand Canal, « Outdoor rest. service in summer on the Grand Canal » – ⧈ ▤ 📺 ☎ 🔥 – 🔬 50. 🆎 🆂 ⓞ ⋿ 𝗩𝗜𝗦𝗔. ✾
EZ a
M a la carte 120/170000 – ⤓ 31000 – **97 rm** 476/667000 suites 1369/1904000.

🏨🏨🏨🏨 **Danieli**, riva degli Schiavoni 4196 ✉ 30122 ✆ 5226480, Telex 410077, Fax 5200208, ≤ canale di San Marco, « Hall in a small Venetian style courtyard and summer rest. service on terrace with panoramic view » – ⧈ ▤ 📺 ☎ – 🔬 70-150. 🆎 🆂 ⓞ ⋿ 𝗩𝗜𝗦𝗔. ✾
GZ a
M a la carte 112/177000 – ⤓ 29000 – **222 rm** 373/619000 suites 1131/1785000.

🏨🏨🏨🏨 **Bauer Grünwald**, campo San Moisè 1459 ✉ 30124 ✆ 5231520, Telex 410075, Fax 5207557, ≤ Grand Canal, 🚯 – ⧈ ▤ 📺 ☎ – 🔬 25-180. 🆎 🆂 ⓞ ⋿ 𝗩𝗜𝗦𝗔. ✾ rest
FZ h
M a la carte 90/120000 – **214 rm** ⤓ 320/520000 suites 892/1190000.

VENEZIA

🏨🏨 **Londra Palace,** riva degli Schiavoni 4171 ⊠ 30122 ℰ 5200533, Telex 420681, Fax 5225032, ≤ San Marco canal – 🛗 🗏 📺 ☎ – 🔏 100. 🖭 🕙 ⓪ 🖪 𝗩𝗜𝗦𝗔 GZ **t**
M (see **Les Deux Lions** below) – ☲ 25000 – **69 rm** 245/385000.

🏨🏨 **Europa e Regina,** calle larga 22 Marzo 2159 ⊠ 30124 ℰ 5200477, Telex 410123, Fax 5231533, ≤ Grand Canal, « Outdoor rest. service in summer on the Grand Canal » – 🛗 🗏 📺 ☎ 🕭 – 🔏 30-140. 🖭 🕙 ⓪ 🖪 𝗩𝗜𝗦𝗔. 𝒮 rest FZ **d**
M 85/90000 – ☲ 26500 – **192 rm** 322/536000 suites 833/1071000.

🏨🏨 **Monaco e Grand Canal,** calle Vallaresso 1325 ⊠ 30124 ℰ 5200211, Telex 410450, Fax 5200501, ≤ Grand Canal and Santa Maria della Salute Church, « Outdoor rest. service in Summer on the Grand Canal » – 🛗 🗏 📺 ☎ 🕭 – 🔏 40. 🖭 🕙 🖪 𝗩𝗜𝗦𝗔. 𝒮 rest FZ **e**
M Grand Canal Rest. a la carte 85/130000 – **70 rm** ☲ 280/420000 suites 450/850000.

🏨🏨 **Metropole** without rest., riva degli Schiavoni 4149 ⊠ 30122 ℰ 5205044, Telex 410340, Fax 5223679, ≤ San Marco canal, « Collection of period bric-a-brac » – 🛗 🗏 📺 ☎ – 🔏 40. 🖭 🕙 ⓪ 🖪 𝗩𝗜𝗦𝗔 DU **t**
72 rm ☲ 299/360000.

🏨🏨 **Luna Hotel Baglioni,** calle larga dell'Ascensione 1243 ⊠ 30124 ℰ 5289840, Telex 410236, Fax 5287160 – 🛗 ❦ rm 🗏 📺 ☎ – 🔏 30-150. 🖭 🕙 ⓪ 🖪 𝗩𝗜𝗦𝗔. 𝒮 rest FZ **p**
M (closed January and February) a la carte 70/100000 – **109 rm** ☲ 270/490000 suites 700/1200000.

🏨🏨 **Pullman Park Hotel,** giardini Papadopoli ⊠ 30125 ℰ 5285394, Telex 410310, Fax 5230043 – 🛗 🗏 📺 ☎ – 🔏 60. 🖭 🕙 ⓪ 🖪 𝗩𝗜𝗦𝗔. 𝒮 rest AT **k**
M a la carte 58/89000 – **100 rm** ☲ 210/320000.

🏨🏨 **Starhotel Splendid-Suisse,** San Marco-Mercerie 760 ⊠ 30124 ℰ 5200755, Telex 410590, Fax 5286498 – 🛗 🗏 📺 ☎ – 🔏 80. 🖭 🕙 🖪 𝗩𝗜𝗦𝗔. 𝒮 rest FY **n**
M (residents only) a la carte 68/86000 – **157 rm** ☲ 290/430000.

🏨🏨 **Bellini** without rest., Cannaregio 116-lista di Spagna ⊠ 30121 ℰ 5242488, Fax 715193 – 🛗 🗏 📺 ☎. 🖭 🕙 ⓪ 🖪 𝗩𝗜𝗦𝗔 AT **f**
65 rm ☲ 200/290000 suites 240/360000.

🏨🏨 **Amadeus,** lista di Spagna 227 ⊠ 30121 ℰ 715300, Telex 420811, Fax 5240841, « Garden » – 🛗 🗏 📺 ☎ – 🔏 40-150. 🖭 🕙 🖪 𝗩𝗜𝗦𝗔. 𝒮 AT **b**
M (closed Wednesday) 50/70000 – ☲ 18000 – **63 rm** 220/310000 suites 350000.

🏨🏨 **Saturnia-International and Rest. Il Cortile,** calle larga 22 Marzo 2398 ⊠ 30124 ℰ 5208377, Telex 410355, Fax 5207131, 🌫, « 14C Patrician building » – 🛗 🗏 📺 ☎ – 🔏 60. 🖭 🕙 🖪 𝗩𝗜𝗦𝗔. 𝒮 rest EZ **n**
M (closed Wednesday) a la carte 64/99000 – **95 rm** ☲ 250/370000.

🏨🏨 **Gabrielli Sandwirth,** riva degli Schiavoni 4110 ⊠ 30122 ℰ 5231580, Telex 410228, Fax 5209455, ≤ San Marco canal, « Small courtyard and garden » – 🛗 🗏 📺 ☎. 🖭 🕙 ⓪ 🖪 𝗩𝗜𝗦𝗔. 𝒮 rest DU **b**
20 February-23 November – **M** 40/60000 – **100 rm** ☲ 225/370000.

🏨🏨 **La Fenice et des Artistes** without rest., campiello de la Fenice 1936 ⊠ 30124 ℰ 5232333, Telex 411150, Fax 5203721 – 🛗 🗏 📺 ☎. 🕙 🖪 𝗩𝗜𝗦𝗔. EZ **v**
65 rm ☲ 155/208000 suites 270/325000, 🗏 21000.

🏨🏨 **Cavalletto e Doge Orseolo,** calle del Cavalletto 1107 ⊠ 30124 ℰ 5200955, Telex 410684, Fax 5238184, ≤ – 🛗 🗏 📺 ☎. 🖭 🕙 🖪 𝗩𝗜𝗦𝗔. 𝒮 rest FZ **f**
M a la carte 55/85000 – **80 rm** ☲ 210/354000.

🏨 **Rialto,** riva del Ferro 5149 ⊠ 30124 ℰ 5209166, Telex 420809, Fax 5238958 – 🗏 📺 ☎. 🖭 🕙 ⓪ 🖪 𝗩𝗜𝗦𝗔. 𝒮 FY **v**
M (closed Thursday and November-15 March) a la carte 32/70000 (12 %) – **71 rm** ☲ 163/224000, 🗏 22500.

🏨 **Concordia** without rest., calle larga San Marco 367 ⊠ 30124 ℰ 5206866, Telex 411069, Fax 5206775 – 🛗 🗏 📺 ☎. 🖭 🕙 🖪 𝗩𝗜𝗦𝗔. 𝒮 GZ **r**
55 rm ☲ 215/320000.

🏨 **Flora** without rest., calle larga 22 Marzo 2283/a ⊠ 30124 ℰ 5205844, Telex 410401, Fax 5228217, « Small flower garden » – 🛗 🗏 ☎. 🖭 🕙 ⓪ 🖪 𝗩𝗜𝗦𝗔 EZ **t**
closed 20 November-1 February – **44 rm** ☲ 150/200000, 🗏 16000.

🏨 **Santa Chiara** without rest., Santa Croce 548 ⊠ 30125 ℰ 5206955, Telex 420690, Fax 5228799 – 🛗 🗏 📺 ☎. 🖭 🕙 🖪 𝗩𝗜𝗦𝗔. 𝒮 AT **c**
☲ 17000 – **28 rm** 135/170000.

🏨 **San Cassiano** without rest., Santa Croce 2232 ⊠ 30125 ℰ 5241768, Telex 420810, Fax 721033, ≤ – 🛗 🗏 📺 ☎. 🖭 🕙 ⓪ 🖪 𝗩𝗜𝗦𝗔 EX **f**
35 rm ☲ 157/212000.

🏨 **Ala** without rest., campo Santa Maria del Giglio 2494 ⊠ 30124 ℰ 5208333, Telex 410275, Fax 5206390 – 🛗 🗏 📺 ☎. 🖭 🕙 🖪 𝗩𝗜𝗦𝗔 EZ **e**
77 rm ☲ 150/212000.

🏨 **Pausania** without rest., Dorsoduro 2824-fondamenta Gherardini ⊠ 30123 ℰ 5222083, Telex 420178 – 🗏 📺 ☎. 🖭 🕙 🖪 𝗩𝗜𝗦𝗔 AU **a**
24 rm ☲ 150/200000.

🏛 **San Moisè** without rest., San Marco 2058 ⌧ 30124 ℰ 5203755, Telex 420655 – 🔲 📺 ☎.
🖭 🖻 🖫 🕡 🖻 *VISA*   EZ **b**
16 rm ⌧ 156/212000.

🏛 **Ateneo** without rest., San Marco 1876, calle Minelli ⌧ 30124 ℰ 5200777, Fax 5228550 –
🔲🔲 📺 ☎. 🖭 🖫 🖻 *VISA*   EZ **d**
20 rm ⌧ 156/212000.

🏛 **Nuovo Teson** without rest., calle de la Pescaria 3980 ⌧ 30122 ℰ 5205555, Fax 5285335
– ☎. 🖭 🖻 *VISA*   DU **s**
30 rm ⌧ 105/118000.

🏛 **Carpaccio** without rest., San Polo-calle Corner 2765 ⌧ 30125 ℰ 5235946, Fax 5242134,
≤ Grand Canal – ☎. 🖫 🖻 *VISA*   BT **c**
20 March-15 November – **17 rm** ⌧ 130/195000.

🏛 **San Stefano** without rest., San Marco, campo San Stefano 2957 ⌧ 30124 ℰ 5200166,
Fax 5224460 – 🛗 🔲 📺 ☎. 🖫 🖻 *VISA*. 🛠   BU **a**
closed 15 January-15 February – **11 rm** ⌧ 140/190000, 🔲 15000.

XXXX **Caffè Quadri**, piazza San Marco 120 ⌧ 30124 ℰ 5289299, Fax 5208041 – 🖭 🖫 🕡 🖻
VISA. 🛠   FZ **y**
closed Monday and 30 July-25 August – **M** a la carte 74/112000.

XXXX **Antico Martini,** campo San Fantin 1983 ⌧ 30124 ℰ 5224121, Fax 5289857, 🛱 – 🔲. 🖭
🖫 🕡 🖻 *VISA*. 🛠   EZ **x**
*closed Tuesday, Wednesday lunch, 8 January-24 March (except Carnival) and 27 November-21
December* – **M** a la carte 66/103000 (15 %).

XXX ۞ **Harry's Bar**, calle Vallaresso 1323 ⌧ 30124 ℰ 5285777, Fax 5208822, American bar
rest. – 🔲. 🖭 🖫 🕡 🖻 *VISA*   FZ **n**
closed Monday and 6 to 13 January – **M** a la carte 90/153000 (20 %)
Spec. Tagliardi al ragú, Scampi alla Thermidor, Pasticceria della Casa. Wines Tocai, Cabernet.

XXX **Les Deux Lions**, riva degli Schiavoni 4175 ⌧ 30122 ℰ 5200533, Fax 5225032, Elegant
rest., « Summer service on the canal bank » – 🔲. 🖭 🖫 🕡 🖻 *VISA*. 🛠   GZ **t**
closed lunch, Tuesday, 11 November-17 December and 10 to 25 January – **M** (booking essential) a la carte 61/92000.

XXX ۞ **La Caravella**, calle larga 22 Marzo 2397 ⌧ 30124 ℰ 5208901, Typical rest. – 🔲. 🖭
🖫 🕡 🖻 *VISA*. 🛠   EZ **m**
closed Wednesday – **M** (booking essential) a la carte 78/114000.
Spec. Bigoli in salsa, Scampi allo Champagne, Filetto di bue Caravella. Wines Sauvignon, Cabernet
Sauvignon.

XXX **Taverna la Fenice,** campiello de la Fenice ⌧ 30124 ℰ 5223856, « Outdoor Summer
service » – 🖭 🖫 🕡   EZ **v**
closed Wednesday – **M** a la carte 52/102000.

XXX **Al Campiello,** calle dei Fuseri 4346 ⌧ 30124 ℰ 5206396, American Bar rest.-late night
dinners – 🔲. 🖭 🖫 🕡 🖻 *VISA*   FZ **z**
closed Monday – **M** (booking essential) a la carte 59/87000 (13 %).

XXX La Colomba, piscina di Frezzeria 1665 ⌧ 30124 ℰ 5221175, Fax 5221175, 🛱, « Collection
of contemporary art » – 🔲 – 🏛 60   FZ **m**

XX **Do Forni,** calle dei Specchieri 457/468 ⌧ 30124 ℰ 5237729, Telex 420832, Fax 5288132
– 🔲. 🖭 🖫 🕡 🖻 *VISA*   GY **c**
closed 22 November-5 December and Thursday except June-October – **M** a la carte 55/77000
(12 %).

XX **Al Graspo de Ua,** calle dei Bombaseri 5094 ⌧ 30124 ℰ 5223647, Fax 5211187, Typical
tavern – 🔲. 🖭 🖫 🕡 🖻 *VISA*   FY **x**
closed Monday, Tuesday, 25 July-10 August and 20 December-13 January – **M** a la carte
56/86000 (16 %).

XX **Harry's Dolci,** Giudecca 773 ⌧ 30133 ℰ 5224844, Fax 5222322, « Outdoor Summer service on the Giudecca canal » – 🔲. 🖭 🖫 🕡 🖻 *VISA*   AV **a**
closed 7 November-7 March and Tuesday except September – **M** a la carte 37/76000 (15 %).

XX **Osteria da Fiore,** San Polo-calle del Scaleter 2202 ⌧ 30125 ℰ 721308 – 🔲. 🖭 🖫 🕡
🖻 *VISA*. 🛠   BT **a**
closed Sunday, Monday, 7 to 30 August and Christmas-6 January – **M** (fish only) (booking
essential) a la carte 47/76000 (10 %).

X **Madonna,** calle della Madonna 594 ⌧ 30125 ℰ 5223824, Venetian trattoria – 🔲. 🖭 🖫
🖻 *VISA*. 🛠   EY **e**
closed Wednesday, 4 to 17 August and 24 December-31 January – M a la carte 29/46000
(12 %).

X **Antica Carbonera,** calle Bembo 4648 ⌧ 30124 ℰ 5225479, Venetian trattoria – 🔲. 🖭
🖫 🕡 🖻 *VISA*   FY **q**
closed 20 July-10 August, 8 January-2 February, Tuesday and Sunday July-August – **M** a la
carte 34/68000 (12 %).

X **Antica Trattoria Poste Vecie,** Pescheria 1608 ⌧ 30125 ℰ 721822, 🛱, Typical venetian
trattoria – 🔲. 🖭 🖫 🕡 🖻 *VISA*. 🛠   EX **a**
closed Tuesday except September-October – **M** a la carte 46/84000.

in Lido : 15 mn by boat from San Marco FZ – ⊠ 30126 Venezia Lido.

🖪 Gran Viale S. M. Elisabetta 6 ☎ 5265721 :

Excelsior, lungomare Marconi 41 ☎ 5260201, Telex 410023, Fax 5267276, ≤, 🔨, 🐎, ⚓,
🏊 – 🛗 🍴 📺 ☎ & 🚗 🅿 – 🔬 40-600. 🆎 🕃 ⓞ 🗲 *VISA*. 🛇 rest
April-October – **M** a la carte 91/148000 – 🖙 27500 – **196 rm** 536000 suites 1190/1547000.

Des Bains, lungomare Marconi 17 ☎ 5265921, Telex 410142, Fax 5260113, ≤, 🍴,
« Floral park with heated 🏊 and 🐎 », ≋s, ⚓ – 🛗 🍴 📺 ☎ 🅿 – 🔬 90-380. 🆎 🕃 ⓞ
🗲 *VISA*. 🛇 rest
April-October – **M** 85/110000 – **191 rm** 🖙 449/473000 suite 1029000.

Quattro Fontane 🕭, via 4 Fontane 16 ☎ 5260227, Telex 411006, Fax 5260726, 🍴, 🌳,
🐎 – 🍴 📺 ☎ 🅿 – 🔬 40. 🆎 🕃 ⓞ 🗲 *VISA*. 🛇 rest
21 April-15 October – **M** a la carte 66/100000 – 🖙 220/330000.

Le Boulevard without rest., Gran Viale S. M. Elisabetta 41 ☎ 5261990, Telex 410185,
Fax 5261917, 🍴 – 🛗 🍴 📺 ☎ 🅿 – 🔬 60. 🆎 🕃 ⓞ 🗲 *VISA*
closed January – **45 rm** 🖙 272/355000.

Villa Mabapa, riviera San Nicolò 16 ☎ 5260590, Telex 410357, Fax 5269441, « Summer
rest. in garden », 🌳 – 🛗 🍴 🍴 📺 ☎ & – 🔬 60. 🆎 🕃 ⓞ 🗲 *VISA*. 🛇 rest
M *(closed 3 November-15 March)* a la carte 41/59000 – **62 rm** 🖙 170/290000.

Villa Laguna, via San Gallo 6 ☎ 5260342, Fax 5268922, ≤ laguna of San Marco, 🍴 – 🛗
🍴 📺 ☎ 🅿 – 🔬 25
34 rm.

Villa Otello, without rest., via Lepanto 12 ☎ 5260048, Fax 5261084 – 🛗 🐾 🅿
season – **34 rm.**

Helvetia without rest., Gran Viale S.M. Elisabetta 4/6 ☎ 5260105, Telex 420045,
Fax 5268903, 🌳 – 🛗 🐾 🅿. 🕃 🗲 *VISA*. 🛇
April-October – **56 rm** 🖙 157/210000.

Rigel without rest., viale Dandolo 13 ☎ 5268810, Fax 5204083 – 🛗 🍴 ☎. 🆎 🕃 ⓞ 🗲 *VISA*
February-October – **42 rm** 🖙 122/181000.

Vianello, località Alberoni ⊠ 30011 Alberoni ☎ 731072, 🌳
15 March-15 October – **M** *(closed September-June)* 25000 – 🖙 10000 – **20 rm** 73/91000.

Ai Murazzi, località Cà Bianca ☎ 5267278, ≤ – 🍴 🅿
season.

Trattoria da Ciccio, via S. Gallo 241-in direction of Malamocco ☎ 5265489, 🍴 – 🅿. 🕃
🗲 *VISA*
closed Tuesday and 15 to 30 November – **M** a la carte 26/42000 (12 %).

in Torcello 45 mn by boat from fondamenta Nuove CT – ⊠ 30012 Burano :

Locanda Cipriani, ☎ 730150, Fax 735433, « Summer service in garden » – 🍴. 🆎 🕃 ⓞ
🗲 *VISA*
19 March-10 November ; closed Tuesday – **M** a la carte 80/113000 (15 %).

Ostaria al Ponte del Diavolo, ☎ 730401, Fax 730250, 🍴, 🌳 – 🆎 🕃 🗲 *VISA*
March-15 November ; closed Thursday and dinner (except Saturday) – **M** a la carte 51/72000
(10 %).

Norway

Norge

OSLO

PRATICAL INFORMATION

LOCAL CURRENCY

Norwegian Kroner: 100 N-Kr = 16.78 US $ (Jan. 92)

TOURIST INFORMATION

The telephone number and address of the Tourist Information office is given in the text under **⌖**.

FOREIGN EXCHANGE

In the Oslo area banks are usually open between 8.15am and 3.30pm, but in summertime, 15.5 - 31/8, they close at 3pm. Thursdays they are open till 5pm. Saturdays and Sundays closed.
Most large hotels, main airports and railway stations have exchange facilities. At Fornebu Airport the bank is open from 6.30am to 10.30pm on weekdays and 7.00am to 10pm on Sundays, all the year round.

MEALS

At lunchtime, follow the custom of the country and try the typical buffets of Scandinavian specialities.
At dinner, the a la carte and the menus will offer you more conventional cooking.

SHOPPING IN OSLO

(Knitted ware - silver ware)
Your hotel porter should be able to help you and give you information.

CAR HIRE

The international car hire companies have branches in each major city.
Your hotel porter should be able to give details and help you with your arrangements.

TIPPING IN NORWAY

A service charge is included in hotel and restaurant bills and it is up to the customer to give something in addition if he wants to.
The cloakroom is sometimes included in the bill, sometimes you pay a certain amount.
Taxi drivers and baggage porters have no claim to be tipped. It is up to you if you want to give a gratuity.

SPEED LIMITS

The maximum permitted speed within congested areas is 50 km/h - 31mph. Outside congested areas it is 80 km/h - 50mph. Where there are other speed limits (lower or higher) they are signposted.

SEAT BELTS

The wearing of seat belts in Norway is compulsory for drivers and passengers. All cars registered in Norway after 1/1-84 must have seat belts in the back seat too, and it is compulsory to use them.

ANIMALS

Very strict quarantine regulations for animals from all countries except Sweden. NO dispensations.

Oslo

Norge **985** M 7 – pop. 450 800 – ⚙ 02.

See : Bygdøy AZ – Viking Ships★★★ (Vikingeskipene), Folk Museum (Norsk Folkemuseum), Kon-Tiki and RA Museum★ (Kon-Tiki Museet), Polarship Fram★ (Fram Museet), Maritime Museum★ (Norsk Sjøfartsmuseum) ; Frognerparken★ (Vigeland Sculptures★★) AX – City-Hall★ (Rådhuset) BY **H** – Munch Museum★ (Munchmuseet) CY – National Gallery★ (Nasjonalgalleriet) BY **M1** – Akershus Castle★ (Akershus Festning) BZ – Historical Museum★ (Historisk Museum) BY **M2**.

Outskirts : Holmenkollen★★ (NW : 10 km) – Ski Jump★, Ski Museum★ AX – Tryvann Tower★★ (Tryvannstårnet) (NW : 14 km) : ⚹★★ AX – Sonja Henie-Onstad Art Centre★ (Henie-Onstads Kultursenter) (W : 12 km) AY.

🏌 Oslo Golfklubb 🖉 50 44 02.

✈ Fornebu SW : 8 km 🖉 59 67 16 – SAS : Oslo City, Stenersg. 1 a 🖉 Business travel : 17 00 10 (Europe and Overseas) 17 00 20 (Domestics and Scandinavia), Vacation travel : 42 77 60 – Air Terminal : Havnegata, main railway station, seaside.

🚢 Copenhagen, Frederikshavn, Kiel : contact tourist information centre (see below).

🛈 Norwegian Information Centre Vestbaneplassen 1 🖉 83 00 50, Fax 83 91 50, Telex 71969 and main railway station – KNA (Kongelig Norsk Automobilklub) Royal Norwegian Automobile Club, Drammensveien 20C 🖉 56 19 00 – NAF (Norges Automobil Forbund), Storg. 2 🖉 34 14 00.

Hamburg 888 – København 583 – Stockholm 522.

365

OSLO

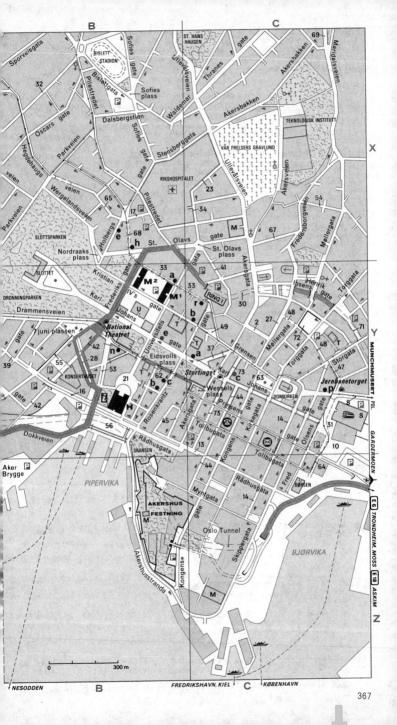

Grand, Karl Johansgate 31, 0159 Oslo 1, 𝄞 42 93 90, Telex 71683, Fax 42 12 25, ⊜s, ☒
– |₿| ⇄ rm ☰ ☑ ☎ ⇔ – ⚑ 300. 🗚 ⓞ ᴇ 𝗩𝗜𝗦𝗔. ⌘
CY **a**
M (see also **Grand Café** below) – **Etoile** (closed Sunday lunch and Saturday) 160/245 and dinner
a la carte 341/438 – **283 rm** � 1450/1850, **6 suites** 4500/10000.

Oslo Plaza Ⓜ, Sonja Henie Plass 3, 0107 Oslo 1, 𝄞 17 10 00, Telex 11241, Fax 17 73 00,
≤ City and Fjord, 𝄁ᴪ, ⊜s, ☒ – |₿| ⇄ rm ☰ ☑ ☎ ᴠ ⇔ – ⚑ 900. 🗚 ⓞ ᴇ
𝗩𝗜𝗦𝗔
by Biskop Gunnerus' Gate   CY
M 275/475 and a la carte – **655 rm** ⊊ 1295/1895, **20 suites** 2200/8500.

Continental, Stortingsgaten 24-26, 0161 Oslo 1, 𝄞 41 90 60, Telex 71012, Fax 42 96 89 –
|₿| ⇄ rm ☰ ☑ ☎ ⇔ – ⚑ 300. 🗚 ⓞ ᴇ 𝗩𝗜𝗦𝗔. ⌘
BY **n**
closed Christmas – **M** (see also **Theatercaféen** below) – **Annen Etage** (closed Saturday, Sunday,
Easter, 3 weeks July, Christmas and Bank Holidays) (dinner only) a la carte 389/587 – **152 rm**
⊊ 1450/1800, **8 suites** 2400/3900.

Royal Christiana, Biskop Gunnerus gate 3, 0106 Oslo 1, 𝄞 42 94 10, Fax 42 46 22, 𝄁ᴪ,
⊜s, ☒ – |₿| ⇄ rm ☰ ☑ ☎ ᴠ ⇔ – ⚑ 400. 🗚 ⓞ ᴇ 𝗩𝗜𝗦𝗔. ⌘
CY **p**
M a la carte 42/115 – **383 rm** ⊊ 1450/1650, **73 suites** 1795/3000.

SAS Scandinavia, Holbergsgate 30, 0166 Oslo 1, 𝄞 11 30 00, Telex 79090, Fax 11 30 17,
≤ City and Fjord, 𝄁ᴪ, ⊜s, ☒ – |₿| ⇄ rm ☰ ☑ ☎ ᴠ ⇔ – ⚑ 800. 🗚 ⓞ ᴇ
𝗩𝗜𝗦𝗔
BX **e**
M Holberg (closed Sunday, Monday, 12 to 20 April, 5 July-3 August and 20 December-
5 January) (dinner only) 385/550 and a la carte – **487 rm** ⊊ 1495/1745, **4 suites** 3000/10000.

Bristol, Kristian IV's des gate 7, 0130 Oslo 1, 𝄞 41 58 40, Telex 71668, Fax 42 86 51 – |₿|
⇄ rm ☰ rest ☑ ☎ – ⚑ 200. 🗚 ⓞ ᴇ 𝗩𝗜𝗦𝗔. ⌘
CY **b**
M (closed Sunday lunch) (buffet lunch) 160 and dinner a la carte – **138 rm** ⊊ 1170/1490, **3 suites**
2500.

Scandic Crown Ⓜ, Parkveien 68, 0254 Oslo 2, 𝄞 44 69 70, Telex 71763, Fax 44 26 01, 𝄁ᴪ,
⊜s – |₿| ⇄ rm ☰ rest ☑ ☎ – ⚑ 100. 🗚 ⓞ ᴇ 𝗩𝗜𝗦𝗔
AY **f**
closed Easter and Christmas – **M** 195/200 and a la carte – **185 rm** ⊊ 1195/1395.

Ambassadeur ⑊, Camilla Colletts vei 15, 0258 Oslo 2, 𝄞 44 18 35, Fax 44 47 91,
« Distinctively themed bedrooms », ⊜s, ☒ – |₿| ☰ rest ☑ ☎. 🗚 ⓞ ᴇ 𝗩𝗜𝗦𝗔. ⌘ AX **t**
closed Easter, Christmas and New Year – **M** (see **Ambassadeur** below) – **34 rm** ⊊ 945/1395,
8 suites 1445/1645.

Rica Victoria, Rosenkrantzgate 13, 0160, Oslo 1, 𝄞 42 99 40, Fax 42 99 43 – |₿| ⇄ rm ☰
☑ ☎ ᴠ ⇔. 🗚 ⓞ ᴇ 𝗩𝗜𝗦𝗔. ⌘
BY **b**
closed 24 to 26 December – **M** (closed Sunday lunch) 79/98 dinner and a la carte – **153 rm**
⊊ 795/1100, **3 suites** 1675/1850.

Gabelshus ⑊, Gabelsgate 16, 0272 Oslo 2, 𝄞 55 22 60, Telex 74073, Fax 44 27 30,
« Antique furniture, paintings » – |₿| ⇄ rm ☰ ☑ ☎ Ⓟ – ⚑ 60. 🗚 ⓞ ᴇ 𝗩𝗜𝗦𝗔. ⌘
closed 1 week Easter and 22 December-2 January – **M** 300/460 (dinner) and a la carte – **45 rm**
⊊ 750/1000.
AY **m**

Stefan, Rosenkrantzgate 1, 0159 Oslo 1, 𝄞 42 92 50, Telex 19809, Fax 33 70 22 – |₿| ⇄ rm
☰ ☑ ☎ ᴠ – ⚑ 70. 🗚 ⓞ ᴇ 𝗩𝗜𝗦𝗔. ⌘
CY **r**
closed 21 December-2 January – **M** (unlicensed) (buffet lunch)/dinner – **131 rm** ⊊ 1075/1175.

Ritz ⑊, Frederik Stangs Gate 3, 0272 Oslo 2, 𝄞 44 39 60, Fax 44 67 13 – |₿| ⇄ rm ☑ ☎
Ⓟ – ⚑ 60. 🗚 ⓞ ᴇ 𝗩𝗜𝗦𝗔
AY **e**
closed 22 December-2 January – **M** 200 and a la carte – **50 rm** ⊊ 770/970.

Europa without rest., St. Olavsgate 31, 0166 Oslo 1, 𝄞 20 99 90, Telex 71512, Fax 11 27 27
– |₿| ⇄ rm ☑ ☎. 🗚 ⓞ ᴇ 𝗩𝗜𝗦𝗔. ⌘
BX **h**
closed 10 to 21 April and 23 December-2 January – **156 rm** ⊊ 1045/1250, **2 suites** 1990.

Cecil without rest., Stortingsgatan 8, 0161 Oslo 1, 𝄞 42 70 00, Telex 11228, Fax 42 26 70
– |₿| ⇄ rm ☑ ☎ ᴠ ⇔. 🗚 ⓞ ᴇ 𝗩𝗜𝗦𝗔. ⌘
BY **c**
closed 15 to 21 April and 23 December-2 January – **112 rm** ⊊ 755/1240.

Saga, Eilert Sundtsgt. 39, 0259, Oslo 2 𝄞 43 04 85, Fax 44 08 63 – ☑ ☎ Ⓟ – ⚑ 30. 🗚
ⓞ ᴇ 𝗩𝗜𝗦𝗔
AX **b**
closed 20 December-1 January and Easter – **M** 130/210 – **37 rm** ⊊ 845/995.

Savoy, Universitetsgt. 11, 0164 Oslo 1, 𝄞 20 26 55, Telex 76418, Fax 11 24 80 – |₿| ☑ ☎
– ⚑ 90 – **77 rm**.
BY **a**

Norum, Bygdøy Allé 53, 0265 Oslo 2, 𝄞 44 79 90, Telex 79315, Fax 44 92 39 – |₿| ⇄ rm
☰ rest ☑ ☎ – ⚑ 65. 🗚 ⓞ ᴇ 𝗩𝗜𝗦𝗔. ⌘
AX **s**
closed 23 December-2 January – **M** (closed Sunday) 185/450 and a la carte – **55 rm** ⊊
⊊ 690/790.

XXX ✿ **D'Artagnan** (Nielsen), Øvre Slottsgate 16, 0157 Oslo 1, 𝄞 41 50 62 – ☰. 🗚 ⓞ ᴇ 𝗩𝗜𝗦𝗔
closed Saturday except October-December, Sunday, 4 July-4 August and 20 December-
8 January – **M** (dinner only) 465/575 and a la carte 465/535
CY **d**
Spec. Salade de crabe et émince d'avocat, Roulade de sole et saumon, Confit de cuisses de
canard.

XXX ✿ **Bagatelle** (Hellstrøm), Bygdøy Allé 3, 0257 Oslo 2, 𝄞 44 63 97, Fax 55 35 92 – 🗚 ⓞ ᴇ 𝗩𝗜𝗦𝗔
closed lunch Saturday and Monday, Sunday, Easter and Christmas – **M** 350/650 and a la carte
400/555
AY **x**
Spec. Bouillon de langoustines aux épices douces, Brochette de Pétoncles, Bar rôti en peau.

XXX **Ambassadeur** (at Ambassadeur H.) Camilla Colletts vei 15, 0208 Oslo 2, 𝒫 44 18 35, Fax 44 47 91, « Elegant decor, paintings » – 🍽. 🆎 ⓪ Ɛ 𝘝𝘐𝘚𝘈   AX **t**
closed Saturday, Sunday, Easter, July, Christmas and New Year – **M** (dinner only) 370/450.

XX ✿ **Feinschmecker,** Balchensgate 5, Box 3165, 0265 Oslo 2, 𝒫 44 17 77 – 🍽. 🆎 ⓪ Ɛ
𝘝𝘐𝘚𝘈   AX **n**
closed Sunday, 5 July - 3 August and 23 December - 5 January – **M** 395 and a la carte 372/427
Spec. Monkfish with cabbage and a ginger cream sauce, Medallions of reindeer with an apple and cowberry compote, Walnut parfait with a coffee sauce.

XX **Det Blå Kjøkken,** Drammensveien 30, 0255 Oslo 2, 𝒫 44 26 50, Fax 55 71 56 – 🍽. 🆎 ⓪
Ɛ 𝘝𝘐𝘚𝘈   AY **k**
closed Sunday and Christmas – **M** (dinner only) 415/525 and a la carte.

XX **Blom,** Karl Johansgate 41b, 0162 Oslo 1, 𝒫 42 73 00, Fax 42 04 28, « Collectin of heraldic shields and international art » – 🍽. 🆎 ⓪ Ɛ 𝘝𝘐𝘚𝘈   BY **e**
closed Sunday and Christmas – **M** 195/525 and a la carte.

XX **Kastanjen,** Bygdøy Allé 18, 0262 Oslo 2, 𝒫 43 44 67, Fax 55 48 72 – 🆎 ⓪ Ɛ 𝘝𝘐𝘚𝘈 AY **a**
closed Sunday – **M** (booking essential) (dinner only) a la carte 245/405.

XX **Theatercaféen** (at Continental H.), Stortingsgaten 24, 0161 Oslo 1, 𝒫 33 32 00, Telex 71012, Fax 42 96 89 – 🆎 ⓪ Ɛ 𝘝𝘐𝘚𝘈   BY **n**
M (buffet lunch) 75 and a la carte 191/429.

X **A Touch of France,** Øvre Slottsgate 16, 0157, Oslo 1 𝒫 42 56 97, Fax 42 77 41 – 🍽. 🆎 ⓪ Ɛ 𝘝𝘐𝘚𝘈   CY **c**
closed Sunday lunch and 22 December-2 January – **M** a la carte 210/315.

X **Grand Café** (at Grand H.), Karl Johansgt. 31, 0159 Oslo 1, 𝒫 42 93 90, Telex 71683, Fax 42 12 25 – 🍽. 🆎 ⓪ Ɛ 𝘝𝘐𝘚𝘈   CY **a**
M a la carte 186/309.

at Fornebu Airport SW : 8 km by E 18 AY and Snarøyveien – ✉ ✪ 02 Oslo :

🏨 **SAS Park Royal,** Fornebuparken, Box 185, Oslo-N-1324, Lysaker 𝒫 12 02 20, Telex 78745, Fax 12 00 11, « Private beach and park », ↖, ⇌, ✕ – ▯ ⇌ rm 🍽 📺 ☎ ♿ 🅿 – 🛉 180.
🆎 ⓪ Ɛ 𝘝𝘐𝘚𝘈, ✕
M 145/245 and a la carte – **254 rm** ⌕ 1550/1875.

at Sandvika SW : 14 km by E 18 Exit E 68 – ✉ ✪ 02 Oslo :

🏨 **Rica H.Oslofjord** Ⓜ, Sandviksveien 184, 1301 Sandvika, 𝒫 54 57 00, Telex 74345, Fax 54 27 33, ↖, ⇌ – ▯ ⇌ rm 🍽 📺 ☎ ♿ ⇦ 🅿 – 🛉 500. 🆎 ⓪ Ɛ 𝘝𝘐𝘚𝘈
M Orchidee a la carte approx. 389 – **245 rm** ⌕ 1190/1470, **3 suites** 2650/4750.

at Holmenkollen NW : 10 km by Bogstadveien, Sørkedalsveien and Holmenkollveien – ✉ ✪ 02 Oslo :

🏨 **Holmenkollen Park H. Rica** ⌂, Kongeveien 26, 𝒫 14 60 90, Telex 72094, Fax 14 61 92, ≼ Oslo city and Fjord, ⇌, ▧ – ⇌ rm 🍽 📺 ☎ ♿ ⇦ 🅿 – 🛉 400. 🆎 ⓪ Ɛ 𝘝𝘐𝘚𝘈
closed 23 to 29 December – **M** De Fem Stuer (buffet lunch) 210/1000 and a la carte 385/525
– **183 rm** ⌕ 1345/1445, **8 suites** 1990/1995.

Portugal

PRATICAL INFORMATION

LOCAL CURRENCY

Escudo: 100 Esc. = 0.75 US $ (Jan. 92).

FOREIGN EXCHANGE

Hotels, restaurants and shops do not always accept foreign currencies and the tourist is therefore advised to change cheques and currency at banks, saving banks and exchange offices - The general opening times are as follows: banks 8.30am to noon and 1 to 2.45pm (closed on Saturdays), money changers 9.30am to 6pm (usually closed on Saturday afternoons and Sundays).

TRANSPORT

Taxis may be hailed when showing the green light or sign "Livre" on the windscreen.

Metro (subway) network. In each station complete information and plans will be found.

SHOPPING IN LISBON

Shops and boutiques are generally open from 9am to 1pm and 3 to 7pm - In Lisbon, the main shopping streets are: Rua Augusta, Rua do Carmo, Rua Garrett (Chiado), Rua do Ouro, Rua da Prata, Av. da Roma.

TIPPING

A service charge is added to all bills in hotels, restaurants and cafés; it is usual, however, to give an additional tip for personal service; 10 % of the fare or ticket price is also the usual amount given to taxi drivers and cinema and theatre usherettes.

SPEED LIMITS

The speed limit on motorways is 120 km/h - 74 mph, on other roads 90 km/h - 56 mph and in built up areas 60 km/h - 37 mph.

SEAT BELTS

Out of cities, it is compulsory for drivers and front seat passengers to wear seat belts.

THE FADO

The Lisbon Fado (songs) can be heard in restaurants in old parts of the town such as the Alfama, the Bairro Alto and the Mouraria. A selection of fado cabarets will be found at the end of the Lisbon restaurant list.

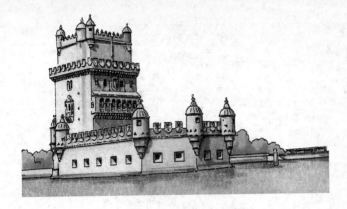

Lisbon

(LISBOA) 1100 437 P 2 – Pop. 826 140 – alt. 111 – ✪ 01.

SEE :

View : ★★ from the Suspension Bridge (Ponte de 25 Abril), ★★ from Christ in Majesty (Cristo-Rei) S : 3,5 km.

CENTRE : POMBALINE LISBON

See : Rossio★ (square) GY – Avenida da Liberdade★ FX – Edward VII Park★ (Cold Greenhouse★) EX – St. Rock★ (Igreja São Roque) FY **M¹** – Terreiro do Paço★ (square) GZ – São Pedro de Alcantara Belvedere★ FY **A**.

MEDIEVAL LISBON

See : St. George's Castle★★ (Castelo de São Jorge) GY – Cathedral★ (Sé) GZ – Santa Luzia Belvedere★ (Miradouro de Santa Luzia) – Alfama★★ (Beco do Carmeiro★ and Rua de São Pedro★) HYZ.

MANUELINE LISBON

See : Hieronymite Monastery★★ (Mosteiro dos Jerónimos : church★★, cloister★★★) – Belém Tower★★ (Torre de Belém) – Monument to the Discoveries★ (Padrão dos Descobrimentos).

MUSEUMS

Museum of Ancient Art★★ (Museu Nacional de Arte Antiga : polyptych by Nuno Gonçalves★★★, Portuguese Primitive paintings★★) – Calouste Gulbenkian Museum★★★ (Art collection) – Azulejo Museum★ – Coach Museum★★ (Museu Nacional dos Coches) – Maritime Museum★★ (Museu de Marinha) – Popular Art★.

OTHER CURIOSITIES

Church of the Mother of God★★ (Igreja da Madre de Deus : ínterior★★, altar★, chapter house★★, paintings★) – Modern Art Center★ – Zoologic Garden and climatizated★★ – Botanic Garden★ EX – Monsanto Park★ – Fronteira Palace Garden★ – Free waters aqueduct★ (Aqueduto das Águas Livres) EX.

🛇, 🏌 Estoril Golf Club W : 25 km 𝄢 468 01 76 Estoril – 🏌 Lisbon Sports Club NW : 20 km 𝄢 431 00 77 – 🏌 Club de Campo de Lisboa S : 15 km 𝄢 226 32 44 Aroeira, Monte da Caparica.

✈ Lisbon Airport N : 8 km from city centre 𝄢848 11 01 – T.A.P., Praça Marquês de Pombal 3, ✉ 1200, 𝄢 54 40 80 and airport 𝄢 848 91 81.

🚂 𝄢 87 75 09.

⛴ to Madeira : E.N.M., Rua de São Julião 5-1º, ✉ 1100, 𝄢 87 01 21 and Cais Rocha Conde de Óbidos, ✉ 1300 𝄢 396 25 47.

🅱 Palácio Foz, Praça dos Restaudores 𝄢 346 63 07 and airport 𝄢 89 42 48 – **A.C.P.** Rua Rosa Araújo 24, ✉ 1200, 𝄢 356 39 31, Telex 12581 – **A.C.P.** Av Barbosa do Bocage 23-1º, ✉ 1000, 𝄢 793 61 21, Fax 793 40 26.

Madrid 653 – Bilbao 904 – Paris 1817 – Porto 325 – Sevilla 411.

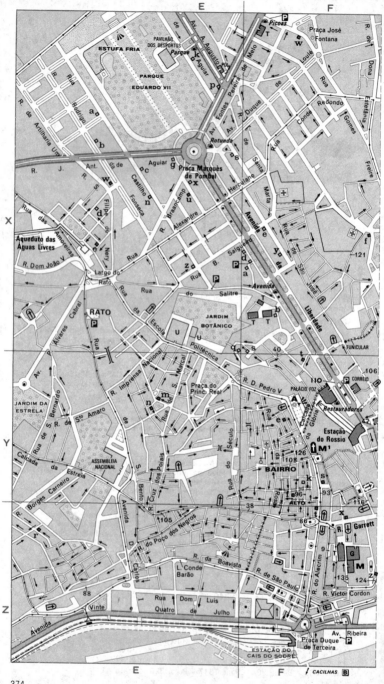

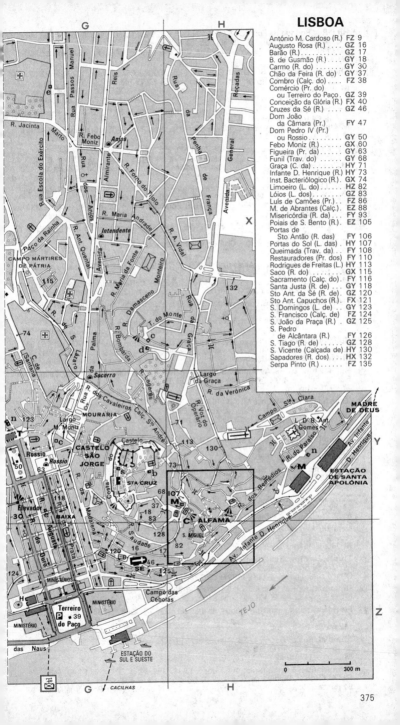

LISBOA

🏨🏨 **Ritz,** Rua Rodrigo da Fonseca 88, ⊠ 1093, 🅟 69 20 20, Telex 12589, Fax 69 17 83, ≤, 🌭
– 🛗 🖹 📺 ☎ ⇔ 🅟 – 🛣 25/600. 🖭 ⓘ 🆔 𝑉𝐼𝑆𝐴. 🕸 rest EX **b**
M Varanda a la carte 4350/5400 – **The Grill** a la carte 5700/8800 – **310 rm** � 40000/
44000.

🏨🏨 **Sheraton Lisboa H.,** Rua Latino Coelho 1, ⊠ 1097, 🅟 57 57 57, Telex 12774, Fax 54 71 64,
≤, 🗻 heated – 🛗 🖹 📺 ☎ ⇔ – 🛣 25/550. 🖭 ⓘ 🆔 𝑉𝐼𝑆𝐴. 🕸
M Alfama Grill *(closed Saturday and Sunday)* a la carte 4600/6200 – **Caravela** a la carte
3100/5100 – **384 rm** ⊏ 40000/45000. by Av. Fontes Pereira de Melo EFX

🏨🏨 **Le Meridien Lisboa,** Rua Castilho 149, ⊠ 1000, 🅟 69 09 00, Telex 64315, Fax 69 32 31,
≤ – 🛗 🖹 📺 ☎ 🕭 – 🛣 25/480. 🖭 ⓘ 🆔 𝑉𝐼𝑆𝐴. 🕸 EX **a**
M Atlantic *(closed Saturday Sunday August)* a la carte 6600/8700 – **Brasserie des Amis** a la
carte 4700/6950 – **331 rm** ⊏ 37000/42000.

🏨🏨 **Tívoli Lisboa,** Av. da Liberdade 185, ⊠ 1200, 🅟 52 11 01, Telex 12588, Fax 57 94 61, 🌭
« Terrace with ≤ town », 🗻 heated, 🕸 – 🛗 🖹 📺 ☎ 🕭 – 🛣. 🖭 ⓘ 🆔 𝑉𝐼𝑆𝐴. 🕸
M Grill Terraço a la carte approx. 7000 – **Zodíaco** a la carte approx. 4600 – **327 rm** ⊏ 34000/
40000. FX **d**

🏨🏨 **Alfa Lisboa,** Av. Columbano Bordalo Pinheiro, ⊠ 1000, 🅟 726 21 21, Telex 18477,
Fax 726 30 31, ≤ – 🛗 🖹 📺 ☎ 🕭 – 🛣 25/250. 🖭 ⓘ 🆔 𝑉𝐼𝑆𝐴. 🕸
M A Aldeia a la carte 3400/4150 – **Grill Pombalino** a la carte 3500/6600 – **350 rm**
⊏ 27500/33000. NW by Av. A. Augusto Aguiar EX

🏨🏨 **Altis,** Rua Castilho 11, ⊠ 1200, 🅟 52 24 96, Telex 13314, Fax 54 86 96, 𝄐, 🔲 – 🛗 🖹 📺
☎ 🕭 – 🛣 EX **z**
M Girasol *(lunch only)* 5000 – **Grill Dom Fernando** *(closed Sunday)* a la carte 6000/7000 –
307 rm ⊏ 30000/35000.

🏨🏨 **Continental,** Rua Laura Alves 9, ⊠ 1000, 🅟 793 50 05, Telex 65632, Fax 797 36 69 – 🛗
🖹 📺 ☎ 🕭 – 🛣 25/180. 🖭 ⓘ 🆔 𝑉𝐼𝑆𝐴.
M D. Miguel *(closed Sunday)* a la carte 5150/5350 – **Coffee Shop Continental** a la carte
3800/5100 – **220 rm** ⊏ 22000/26500. N by Av. Fontes Pereira de Melo EFX

🏨🏨 **Lisboa Penta,** Av. dos Combatentes, ⊠ 1600, 🅟 726 40 54, Telex 18437, Fax 726 42 81,
≤, 🗻 – 🛗 🖹 📺 ☎ 🕭 🅟 – 🛣 25/600. 🖭 ⓘ 🆔 𝑉𝐼𝑆𝐴. 🕸 rest
M 4000 Grill Passarola – rest. **Verde Pino** – **588 rm** ⊏ 19400/23600.
NW by Av. A. Augusto de Aguiar EX

🏨🏨 **Holiday Inn Crowne Plaza,** av. Marechal Craveiro Lopes 390, ⊠ 1700, 🅟 759 96 39,
Telex 61170, Fax 758 66 05, 𝄐 – 🛗 🖹 📺 ☎ 🕭 – 🛣 25/200. 🖭 ⓘ 🆔 𝑉𝐼𝑆𝐴. 🕸
M 4500 – **221 rm** 30000/35000. N by Av. Fontes Pereira de Melo EFX

🏨🏨 **Holiday Inn Lisboa,** Av. António José de Almeida 28 A, ⊠ 1000, 🅟 793 52 22, Telex 60330,
Fax 793 66 72 – 🛗 🖹 📺 ☎ 🕭 – 🛣. 🖭 ⓘ 🆔 𝑉𝐼𝑆𝐴. 🕸
M 4000 – **169 rm** ⊏ 29000/34500. N by Av. Fontes Pereira de Melo EFX

🏨🏨 **Novotel Lisboa,** Av. José Malhoa 1642, ⊠ 1000, 🅟 726 60 22, Telex 40114, Fax 726 64 96,
≤, 🗻 – 🛗 🖹 📺 ☎ 🕭 🕭 – 🛣 25/300. 🖭 ⓘ 🆔 𝑉𝐼𝑆𝐴. 🕸 rest
M a la carte approx. 3500 – ⊏ 850 – **246 rm** 13150/15500.
NW by Av. A. Augusto de Aguiar EX

🏨🏨 **Lisboa Plaza,** Travessa do Salitre 7, ⊠ 1200, 🅟 346 39 22, Telex 16402, Fax 347 16 30 –
🛗 🖹 📺 ☎. 🖭 ⓘ 🆔 𝑉𝐼𝑆𝐴. 🕸 FX **b**
M 4500 – **96 rm** ⊏ 25000/29500.

🏨🏨 **Fénix and Rest. el Bodegón,** Praça Marquês de Pombal 8, ⊠ 1200, 🅟 53 51 21,
Telex 12170, Fax 53 61 31 – 🛗 🖹 📺 ☎ 🕭 – 🛣 25/100. 🖭 ⓘ 🆔 𝑉𝐼𝑆𝐴. 🕸 EX **g**
M a la carte 3900/5150 – **123 rm** ⊏ 17500/19500.

🏨🏨 **Zurique,** Rua Ivone Silva, ⊠ 1000, 🅟 793 71 11, Fax 793 72 90 – 🛗 🖹 📺 ☎ 🕭 – 🛣 25/150.
🖭 🆔 𝑉𝐼𝑆𝐴. 🕸 N by Av. Fontes Pereira de Melo EFX
M 3000 – **252 rm** ⊏ 14000/16000.

🏨🏨 **Lutécia,** Av. Frei Miguel Contreiras 52, ⊠ 1700, 🅟 80 31 21, Telex 12457, Fax 80 78 18,
≤ – 🛗 🖹 📺 ☎. 🖭 ⓘ 🆔 𝑉𝐼𝑆𝐴. 🕸 N by Av. Almirante Reis EX
M 3600 – **151 rm** ⊏ 16000/19500.

🏨🏨 **Tivoli Jardim,** Rua Julio Cesar Machado 7, ⊠ 1200, 🅟 53 99 71, Telex 12172,
Fax 355 65 66, 🗻 heated, 🕸 – 🛗 🖹 📺 ☎ 🅟. 🖭 ⓘ 🆔 𝑉𝐼𝑆𝐴. 🕸 FX **a**
M a la carte approx. 4700 – **119 rm** ⊏ 19900/24500.

🏨🏨 **Diplomático,** Rua Castilho 74, ⊠ 1200, 🅟 356 20 41, Telex 13713, Fax 52 21 55 – 🛗 🖹
📺 ☎ – 🛣. 🖭 ⓘ 🆔 𝑉𝐼𝑆𝐴. 🕸 – **M** 3400 – **90 rm** ⊏ 17500/20000. EX **c**

🏨🏨 **Flórida** without rest, Rua Duque de Palmela 32, ⊠ 1200, 🅟 57 61 45, Telex 12256,
Fax 54 35 84 – 🛗 🖹 📺 ☎ – 🛣 25/100. 🖭 ⓘ 🆔 𝑉𝐼𝑆𝐴. 🕸 rest EX **x**
112 rm ⊏ 16500/20000.

🏨🏨 **Mundial,** Rua D. Duarte 4, ⊠ 1100, 🅟 86 31 01, Telex 12308, Fax 87 91 29, ≤ – 🛗 🖹 📺
☎ 🅟 – 🛣 25/140. 🖭 ⓘ 🆔 𝑉𝐼𝑆𝐴. 🕸 GY **c**
M 3200 – **147 rm** ⊏ 16500/20700.

🏨🏨 **Dom Manuel I** without rest, Av. Duque d'Ávila 189, ⊠ 1000, 🅟 57 61 60, Telex 43558,
Fax 57 69 85, « Tasteful decor » – 🛗 🖹 📺 ☎. 🖭 ⓘ 🆔 𝑉𝐼𝑆𝐴. 🕸
64 rm ⊏ 13500/15000. N by Av. Fontes Pereira de Melo EFX

🏨 **Lisboa Alif H.** without rest, av. João XXI-Campo Pequeno, ⊠ 1000, *𝒫* 795 24 64, Telex 64460, Fax 795 41 16 – |🛗| 🗏 📺 ☎ 🚗 – 🔬 25/40. 🆎 ⓞ Ɛ 𝘝𝘐𝘚𝘈. 🛠
115 rm 🖙 11500/13000.　　　　　　　　　 N by Av. Fontes Pereira de Melo EFX

🏨 **Lisboa** without rest, Rua Barata Salgueiro 5, ⊠ 1100, *𝒫* 355 41 31, Telex 60228, Fax 355 41 39 – |🛗| 🗏 📺 ☎ 🚗. 🆎 ⓞ Ɛ 𝘝𝘐𝘚𝘈.　　　　　　　　　 FX **e**
61 rm 🖙 19250/23000.

🏨 **Veneza** without rest, av. da Liberdade 189, ⊠ 1200, *𝒫* 352 26 18, Fax 352 66 78, « Old palace » – |🛗| 🗏 📺 ☎ 🅿. 🆎 ⓞ Ɛ 𝘝𝘐𝘚𝘈. 🛠　　　　　　　　　 FX **d**
38 rm 🖙 15000/20000.

🏨 **Lisboa Carlton** without rest, av. Conde Valbom 56, ⊠ 1000, *𝒫* 795 11 57, Telex 65815, Fax 795 11 66 – |🛗| 🗏 📺 ☎ 🚗. 🆎 ⓞ Ɛ 𝘝𝘐𝘚𝘈. 🛠 N by Av. Augusto de Aguiar EX
72 rm 🖙 13500/16000.

🏨 **Amazónia H.,** Travessa Fábrica dos pentes 12, ⊠ 1200, *𝒫* 387 70 06, Telex 66361, Fax 387 90 90, ⅃ heated – |🛗| 🗏 📺 ☎ 🚗 – 🔬 25/150. 🆎 ⓞ Ɛ 𝘝𝘐𝘚𝘈. 🛠　　　 EX **d**
M 2700 – **192 rm** 🖙 9900/12550.

🏨 **Roma,** Av. de Roma 33, ⊠ 1700, *𝒫* 76 77 61, Telex 16586, Fax 793 29 81, ≼, ▨ – |🛗| 🗏 ☎ – 🔬 25/230. 🆎 ⓞ Ɛ 𝘝𝘐𝘚𝘈. 🛠　　　　　　　 N by Av. Almirante Reis GX
M 2600 – **265 rm** 🖙 10000/15000.

🏨 **Eduardo VII,** Av. Fontes Pereira de Melo 5, ⊠ 1000, *𝒫* 53 01 41, Telex 18340, Fax 53 38 79, ≼ – |🛗| 🗏 📺 ☎ – 🔬 25/60. 🆎 ⓞ Ɛ 𝘝𝘐𝘚𝘈. 🛠　　　　　　 EX **p**
M 3900 – **121 rm** 🖙 14200/16200.

🏨 **Dom Carlos** without rest, Av. Duque de Loulé 121, ⊠ 1000, *𝒫* 53 90 71, Telex 16468, Fax 352 07 28 – |🛗| 🗏 📺 ☎. 🆎 ⓞ Ɛ 𝘝𝘐𝘚𝘈. 🛠　　　　　　　　 EX **s**
73 rm 🖙 13800/17400.

🏨 **Miraparque,** Av. Sidónio Pais 12, ⊠ 1000, *𝒫* 57 80 70, Telex 16745, Fax 57 89 20 – |🛗| 🗏 🚗. 🆎 ⓞ Ɛ 𝘝𝘐𝘚𝘈. 🛠　　　　　　　　　　　　　　　　　 EX **k**
M 2750 – **100 rm** 🖙 9000/11000.

🏨 **Príncipe Real,** Rua da Alegria 53, ⊠ 1200, *𝒫* 346 01 16, Telex 44571, Fax 342 21 04 – |🛗| 🗏 📺 ☎. 🆎 ⓞ Ɛ 𝘝𝘐𝘚𝘈. 🛠　　　　　　　　　　　　　　　 EX **q**
M a la carte approx. 3200 – **24 rm** 🖙 18000/21000.

🏨 **Britânia** without rest, Rua Rodrigues Sampaio 17, ⊠ 1100, *𝒫* 315 50 16, Telex 13733, Fax 315 50 21 – |🛗| 🗏 📺 ☎. 🆎 ⓞ Ɛ 𝘝𝘐𝘚𝘈. 🛠　　　　　　　　 FX **y**
30 rm 🖙 12800/15800.

🏨 **York House,** Rua das Janelas Verdes 32, ⊠ 1200, *𝒫* 396 25 44, Telex 16791, Fax 67 27 93, ⏞, « Former 16C convent, portuguese decor » – ☎. 🆎 ⓞ Ɛ 𝘝𝘐𝘚𝘈. 🛠
M *(closed Sunday)* a la carte approx. 4500 – **36 rm** 🖙 17700/19500.
　　　　　　　　　　　　　　　　　　 W by Calçada M. de Abrantes EZ

🏨 **As Janelas Verdes** without rest, Rua das Janelas Verdes 47, ⊠ 1200, *𝒫* 396 81 43, Telex 16791, Fax 67 27 93 – 🚗. 🆎 ⓞ Ɛ 𝘝𝘐𝘚𝘈. 🛠　　　 W by Av. 24 de Julho EZ
17 rm 🖙 17700/19500.

🏨 **Botânico** without rest, Rua Mãe de Agua 16, ⊠ 1200, *𝒫* 342 03 92, Telex 16174, Fax 342 01 25 – |🛗| 🗏 📺 ☎. 🆎 ⓞ Ɛ 𝘝𝘐𝘚𝘈. 🛠　　　　　　　　 FX **s**
30 rm 🖙 9200/13000.

🏨 **Da Torre,** Rua dos Jerónimos 8, ⊠ 1400, *𝒫* 363 62 62, Fax 64 59 95 – |🛗| 📺 ☎ – 🔬. 🆎 ⓞ Ɛ 𝘝𝘐𝘚𝘈　　　　　　　　　　　　　　 W by Av. 24 de Julho EZ
M (see São Jerónimo below) – **50 rm** 🖙 9750/12250.

🏨 **Flamingo,** Rua Castilho 41, ⊠ 1200, *𝒫* 53 21 91, Telex 14736, Fax 352 12 16 – |🛗| 🗏 📺 ☎. 🆎 ⓞ Ɛ 𝘝𝘐𝘚𝘈. 🛠　　　　　　　　　　　　　　　　　 EX **n**
M 3000 – **39 rm** 🖙 13200/15700.

🏨 **Berna** without rest, Av. António Serpa 13, ⊠ 1000, *𝒫* 793 67 67, Telex 62516, Fax 793 62 78 – |🛗| 🗏 📺 ☎ 🚗 – 🔬 25/140. 🆎 ⓞ Ɛ 𝘝𝘐𝘚𝘈. 🛠　 N by Av. Fontes Pereira de Melo EFX
240 rm 🖙 10000/12000.

🏨 **Albergaria Senhora do Monte** without rest, Calçada do Monte 39, ⊠ 1100, *𝒫* 86 60 02, Fax 87 77 83, ≼ São Jorge castle, town and river Tejo – |🛗| 🗏 📺 ☎. 🆎 ⓞ Ɛ 𝘝𝘐𝘚𝘈. 🛠　　　　　　　　　　　　　　　　　　　　　　　　　　　　 GX **c**
28 rm 🖙 10500/14000.

🏨 **Fonte Luminosa** without rest, Alameda D. Afonso Enriques 70 6°, ⊠ 1000, *𝒫* 80 81 69, Telex 15063, Fax 80 90 03 – |🛗| ☎. Ɛ 𝘝𝘐𝘚𝘈. 🛠　　　 N by Av. Almirante Reis GX
37 rm 🖙 6000/8500.

🏨 **São Pedro** without rest, Rua Pascoal de Melo 130, ⊠ 1000, *𝒫* 57 87 65 – |🛗| 🚗. Ɛ 𝘝𝘐𝘚𝘈. 🛠　　　　　　　　　　　　　　　　　　 N by Av. Almirante Reis GX
85 rm 🖙 7560/8760.

🏨 **Insulana** without rest, Rua da Assunção 52, ⊠ 1100, *𝒫* 342 76 25 – |🛗| 📺 ☎. 🆎 ⓞ Ɛ 𝘝𝘐𝘚𝘈. 🛠　　　　　　　　　　　　　　　　　　　　　　　　 GY **e**
32 rm 🖙 8500/10000.

🏨 **Dom Joao** without rest, Rua José Estevao 43, ⊠ 1100, *𝒫* 54 30 64 – |🛗| ☎. 🆎 ⓞ Ɛ 𝘝𝘐𝘚𝘈. 🛠　　　　　　　　　　　　　　　　　　　　　　　　　 GX **e**
18 rm 🖙 9000/10000.

🏨 **Imperador** without rest, Av. 5 de Outubro 55, ⊠ 1000, *𝒫* 352 48 84, Fax 352 65 37 – |🛗| ☎. 🆎 ⓞ Ɛ 𝘝𝘐𝘚𝘈. 🛠 – **43 rm** 🖙 7000/8000.　 N by Av. Fontes Pereira de Melo EFX

XXXX ❀ **Tágide,** Largo da Academia Nacional de Belas Artes 18, ✉ 1200, ℰ 32 07 20, Fax 347 18 80, ≪ – 🗐. 🖭 ☺ **E** *VISA*. ❀ FZ **z**
closed Saturday, Sunday and Bank Holidays – **M** a la carte 6000/7800
Spec. Salmão marinado, Crepes de Santolà à Tágide, Lombos de robalo à portuguesa.

XXXX **Antonio Clara - Clube de Empresários,** Av. da República 38, ✉ 1000, ℰ 76 63 80, Telex 62506, Fax 797 41 44, « Former old palace » – 🗐 🅿. 🖭 ☺ **E** *VISA*. ❀
closed Sunday – **M** a la carte 3700/6750. N by Av. Fontes Pereira de Melo EFX

XXXX **Clara,** Campo dos Mártires da Patria 49, ✉ 1100, ℰ 355 73 41, 🈝 – 🗐. 🖭 ☺ **E** *VISA*. FX **f**
closed Saturday lunch and Sunday – **M** a la carte 5600/6500.

XXXX **Aviz,** Rua Serpa Pinto 12-B, ✉ 1200, ℰ 342 83 91 – 🗐. 🖭 ☺ **E** *VISA*. ❀ FZ **x**
closed Saturday, Sunday and Bank Holidays
M a la carte approx. 7000.

XXXX **Tavares,** Rua da Misericórdia 37, ✉ 1200, ℰ 32 11 12, Late 19C decor – 🗐. 🖭 ☺ **E** *VISA*. FZ **t**
closed Saturday, and Sunday lunch – **M** a la carte 5600/7100.

XXX **Gare Marítima-Michel** (Hotel School), Gare Marítima de Alcantara-Alcantara Sul ℰ 397 85 76, « On the side of the river Tejo with ≪ » – 🗐. 🖭 ☺ **E** *VISA*. ❀
closed Saturday lunch, Sunday and Bank Holidays – **M** a la carte approx. 6000.
W by Av. 24 de Julho EZ

XXX **Gambrinus,** Rua das Portas de Santo Antão 25, ✉ 1100, ℰ 32 14 66, Fax 346 50 32 – 🗐. 🖭 *VISA*. ❀ GY **n**
M a la carte 8800/11600.

XXX **Escorial,** Rua das Portas de Santo Antão 47, ✉ 1100, ℰ 346 44 29, Fax 346 37 58 – 🗐. 🖭 ☺ **E** *VISA*. GY **n**
M a la carte approx. 6000.

XXX ❀ **Casa da Comida,** Travessa das Amoreiras 1, ✉ 1200, ℰ 68 53 76, Fax 387 51 32, « Patio with plants » – 🗐. 🖭 ☺ **E** *VISA*. EX **e**
closed Saturday lunch and Sunday – **M** a la carte 6000/9000
Spec. Casquinhas de caranguejo, Lagosta con vegetais, Perdiz ou faisão à convento de Alcântara.

XXX **Mister Cook** with coffee shop, Av. Guerra Junqueiro 1, ✉ 1000, ℰ 80 72 37, Fax 793 71 52, « Original decor » – 🗐. 🖭 ☺ **E** *VISA*. ❀ N by Av. Fontes Pereira de Melo EFX
closed Sunday – **M** a la carte 3270/5400.

XXX **Pabe,** Rua Duque de Palmela 27-A, ✉ 1200, ℰ 53 74 84, English pub style – 🗐. 🖭 ☺ **E** *VISA*. ❀ EX **u**
M a la carte 5100/6600.

XXX **Chester,** Rua Rodrigo da Fonseca 87-D, ✉ 1200, ℰ 65 73 47, meat specialities – 🗐. 🖭 ☺ **E** *VISA*. EX **w**
closed Sunday – **M** a la carte 5150/6700.

XXX **Saraiva's,** Rua Eng. Canto Resende 3, ✉ 1000, ℰ 53 19 87, Modern decor – 🗐. 🖭 ☺ **E** *VISA*. ❀ N by Av. Augusto de Aguiar EX
closed Saturday and Bank Holidays – **M** a la carte 4050/5850.

XXX **Bachus,** Largo da Trindade 9, ✉ 1200, ℰ 32 28 28 – 🗐. 🖭 ☺ **E** *VISA*. ❀ FY **s**
M a la carte 4900/7400.

XXX ❀ **Conventual,** Praça das Flores 45, ✉ 1200, ℰ 60 91 96 – 🗐. 🖭 ☺ **E** *VISA* EY **m**
closed Saturday lunch and Sunday – **M** a la carte 3300/5300
Spec. Concha de mariscos gratinada, Bacalhau de coentrada, Pato com champagne e pimenta rosa.

XXX **O Faz Figura,** Rua do Paraiso 15 B, ✉ 1100, ℰ 86 89 81, ≪, 🈝 – 🗐. 🖭 ☺ **E** *VISA*. ❀ HY **n**
closed Sunday and Bank Holidays – **M** a la carte 4000/6000.

XX **Via Graça,** Rua Damasceno Monteiro 9 B, ✉ 1100, ℰ 87 08 30, ≪ São Jorge castle, town and river Tejo – 🗐. 🖭 ☺ **E** *VISA*. ❀ GX **d**
closed Saturday lunch, Sunday, 15 to 31 August and 23 December-2 January – **M** a la carte 2850/5150.

XX **Casa do Leão,** Castelo de São Jorge, ✉ 1100, ℰ 888 01 54, Fax 87 63 29, ≪ – 🗐. 🖭 ☺ *VISA*. ❀ GY **s**
M (lunch only) a la carte 4500/8100.

XX **Santa Cruz - Michel,** Largo de Santa Cruz do Castelo 5, ✉ 1100, ℰ 86 43 38 – 🗐. 🖭 ☺ **E** *VISA* GY **b**
closed Saturday lunch, Sunday and Bank Holidays – **M** a la carte 3000/5000.

XX **São Jerónimo,** Rua dos Jerónimos 12, ✉ 1400, ℰ 64 87 96 – 🗐. 🖭 ☺ **E** *VISA*. ❀
closed Saturday lunch and Sunday – **M** a la carte 2850/4450. W by Av. 24 de Julho EZ

XX **Espelho d'Água,** Av. de Brasilia, ✉ 1400, ℰ 301 73 73, Fax 363 26 92, ≪, 🈝, Artificial lake side setting. Modern decor – 🗐. 🖭 ☺ **E** *VISA*. ❀
closed Sunday – **M** a la carte 2800/5400. W 3 km by Av. 24 de Julho EZ

XX **Sancho,** Travessa da Glória 14, ✉ 1200, ℰ 346 97 80 – 🗐. 🖭 **E** *VISA*. ❀ FXY **t**
closed Sunday and Bank Holidays – **M** a la carte 1540/3800.

XX **Saddle Room,** Praça José Fontana 17C, ✉ 1000, ℘ 352 31 57, Telex 64269, Fax 54 09 61,
Rustic English style decor – 🍽. 𝔸𝔼 ⓪ 𝐄 𝗩𝗜𝗦𝗔 · FX **w**
closed Saturday lunch and Sunday – **M** a la carte 2630/4830.

XX **Adega Tía Matilde,** Rua da Beneficencia 77, ✉ 1600, ℘ 797 21 72 – 🍽. 𝔸𝔼 ⓪ 𝐄 𝗩𝗜𝗦𝗔.
❀ N by Av. Fontes Pereira de Melo EFX
closed Sunday – **M** a la carte 3975/5850.

X **Xêlê Bananas,** Praça das Flores 29, ✉ 1200, ℘ 395 25 15, Tropical style decor – 🍽. 𝔸𝔼
⓪ 𝐄 𝗩𝗜𝗦𝗔 EY **n**
closed Saturday lunch and Sunday – **M** a la carte 2300/4050.

X **Sua Excelencia,** Rua do Conde 42, ✉ 1200, ℘ 60 36 14 – 🍽. 𝔸𝔼 ⓪ 𝐄 𝗩𝗜𝗦𝗔 · **M** a la carte 3075/
5475. W by Av. 24 de Julho EZ

X **Chez Armand,** Rua Carlos Mardel 38, ✉ 1900, ℘ 52 07 70, Fax 52 42 57, French rest., meat
specialities – 🍽. 𝔸𝔼 ⓪ 𝐄 𝗩𝗜𝗦𝗔 N by Av. Almirante Reis GX
closed Saturday lunch, Sunday and 3 August-10 September – **M** a la carte 2540/3110.

X **Porta Branca,** Rua do Teixeira 35, ✉ 1200, ℘ 32 10 24 – 🍽. 𝔸𝔼 ⓪ 𝐄 𝗩𝗜𝗦𝗔. ❀ FY **e**
closed Saturday lunch, Sunday and June – **M** a la carte 3500/4700.

Typical atmosphere :

XX **Arcadas do Faia,** Rua da Barroca 56, ✉ 1200, ℘ 342 67 42, Telex 13649, Fax 342 19 23,
Fado cabaret – 🍽. 𝔸𝔼 ⓪ 𝐄 𝗩𝗜𝗦𝗔. ❀ FY **f**
closed Sunday – **M** (dinner only) a la carte 6000/6650.

XX **Sr. Vinho,** Rua do Meio -à- Lapa 18, ✉ 1200, ℘ 67 74 56, Fax 67 74 56, Fado cabaret –
🍽. 𝔸𝔼 ⓪ 𝐄 𝗩𝗜𝗦𝗔. ❀ EZ **r**
closed Sunday – **M** (dinner only) a la carte 4070/6860.

X **Adega Machado,** Rua do Norte 91, ✉ 1200, ℘ 342 87 13, Fax 346 75 07, Fado cabaret
– 🍽. 𝔸𝔼 ⓪ 𝐄 𝗩𝗜𝗦𝗔. ❀ FY **k**
closed Monday and November-March – **M** (dinner only) a la carte 6400/8000.

379

Spain

España

MADRID - BARCELONA - MALAGA
MARBELLA - SEVILLA - VALENCIA

PRACTICAL INFORMATION

LOCAL CURRENCY

Peseta: 100 ptas = 1,03 US $ (Jan. 92)

TOURIST INFORMATION

The telephone number and address of the Tourist Information offices is given in the text of the towns under ⓘ.

FOREIGN EXCHANGE

Banks are usually open fron 9am to 2pm (12.30pm on Saturdays).
Exchange offices in Sevilla and Valencia airports open from 9am to 2pm, in Barcelone airport from 9am to 2pm and 7 to 11pm. In Madrid and Málaga airports, offices operate a 24 hour service.

TRANSPORT

Taxis may be hailed when showing the green light or sign "Libre" on the windscreen.
Madrid, Barcelona and Valencia have a Metro (subway) network. In each station complete information and plans will be found.

SHOPPING

In the index of street names, those printed in red are where the principal shops are found.
The big stores are easy to find in town centres; they are open from 10am to 8pm.
Exclusive shops and boutiques are open from 10am to 2pm and 5 to 8pm - In Madrid they will be found in Serrano, Princesa and the Centre; in Barcelona, Passeig de Gracia, Diagonal and the Rambla de Catalunya.
Second-hand goods and antiques: El Rastro (Flea Market), Las Cortes, Serrano in Madrid; in Barcelona, Los Encantes (Flea Market), Barrio Gótico.

TIPPING

Hotel, restaurant and café bills always include service in the total charge. Nevertheless it is usual to leave the staff a small gratuity which may vary with the district and the service given. Doormen, porters and taxi-drivers are used to being tipped.

SPEED LIMITS

The maximum permitted speed on motorways is 120 km/h - 74 mph, and 90 km/h - 56 mph on other roads.

SEAT BELTS

The wearing of seat belts is compulsory for drivers and passengers.

"TAPAS"

Bars serving "tapas" (typical spanish food to be eaten with a glass of wine or an aperitif) will usually be found in central, busy or old quarters of towns. In Madrid, idle your way to the Calle de Cuchilleros (Plaza Mayor) or to the Calle Cardenal Cisnero (Glorieta de Bilbao).

Madrid

Madrid 28000 **444** y **447** K 19 – Pop. 3 188 297 – alt. 646 – ✪ 91.

See : The Prado Museum★★★ (Museo del Prado) NY – The Old Madrid★ : Plaza Mayor★★ KY, Plaza de la Villa★ KY, Bishop Chapel★ KZ, Vistillas Gardens KYZ panorama★, San Francisco El Grande Church (chairs★, sacristy chair★) KZ – Oriente Quarter★★ : Royal Palace (Palacio Real)★★★ KX (Real Armería★★, Royal Carriage Museum★ DY **M1**), Descalzas Reales Convent★★ KLX (Convento de las Descalzas, Reales), Encarnación Royal Monastery★ KX (Real Monasterio de la Encarnación), University City★ (Ciudad Universitaria) DV, West Park★ (Parque del Oeste) DV, Country House★ (Casa de Campo) DX, Zoo★★ – El Madrid de los Borbones★★ : Plaza de la Cibeles★ MNX, Paseo del Prado★ MNXZ, Palacio de Villahermosa (colección Thysse-Bornemisza★★) MY **M6**, Casón del Buen Retiro★ NY, Reina Sofia Art Center★ MZ, Puerta de Alcalá★ NX, Parque del Buen Retiro★★ NYZ.

Other Museums : Archeological Museum★★ (Museo Arqueológico Nacional : Dama de Elche★★★) NV – Lázaro Galdiano Museum★★ HV **M4** – Real Academia de Bellas Artes de San Fernando★ LX **M2** – San Antonio de la Florida (Frescos★★) DX – Wax Museum★ (Museo de Cera) NV – Sorolla Museum★ GV **M5** – Plaza Monumental de las Ventas★ JV **B** – Army Museum★ (Museo del Ejército) NY.

Envir. : El Pardo (Palacio★) NW : 13 km by C 601.

Racecourse of the Zarzuela – ⌕, ⌕ Puerta de Hierro ✆ 216 17 45 – ⌕, ⌕ Club de Campo ✆ 357 21 32 – ⌕ La Moraleja N : 11 km ✆ 650 07 00 – ⌕ Club Barberán S : 10 km ✆ 218 85 05 – ⌕ Las Lomas, El Bosque SW : 18 km ✆ 616 21 70 – ⌕ Real Automóvil Club de España N : 28 km ✆ 652 26 00 – ⌕ Nuevo Club de Madrid, Las Matas W : 26 km ✆ 630 08 20 – ⌕ Somosaguas W : 10 km by Casa de Campo ✆ 212 16 47.

🛪 Madrid-Barajas by ② : 13 km ✆ 305 83 44 – Iberia : pl. de Cánovas del Castillo 5, ✉ 28014, ✆ 587 81 36 NZ and Aviaco, Modesto Lafuente 76, ✉ 28003, ✆ 534 42 00 FV.

🚅 Chamartin ✆ 733 11 22 – Principe Pio ✆ 248 87 16.

Shipping Companies : Cia. Trasmediterránea, Pedro Munõz Seca 2 NX, ✉ 28001, ✆ 431 07 00, Fax 431 08 04.

🛈 Princesa 1, ✉ 28008, ✆ 541 23 25, Duque de Medinaceli 2, ✉ 28014, ✆ 429 49 51 pl. Mayor 3, ✉ 28012, ✆ 266 54 77, Chamartin Station, ✉ 28036, ✆ 315 99 76 and Barajas airport ✆ 305 86 56 – R.A.C.E. José Abascal 10, ✉ 28003, ✆ 447 32 00, Fax 447 79 48.

Paris (by Irún) 1310 – Barcelona 627 – Bilbao 397 – La Coruña 603 – Lisboa 653 – Málaga 548 – Porto 599 – Sevilla 550 – Valencia 351 – Zaragoza 322.

Centre : Paseo del Prado, Puerta del Sol, Gran Vía, Alcalá, Paseo de Recoletos, Plaza Mayor, (plan pp. 6 and 7) :

Palace, pl. de las Cortes 7, ⊠ 28014, ℰ 429 75 51, Telex 23903, Fax 429 82 66 – |🛗| 🗏 📺
🕿 🔥 ⇌ – 🔬 25/500. 🖭 ⓞ ⋶ 𝘝𝘐𝘚𝘈. ⋘ rest　　　　　　　　　　　　　MY　e
M 6250 **Grill Neptuno** *(closed August)* a la carte 5050/6800 – ⊡ 2150 – **500 rm** 35000/43000.

Princesa, Princesa 40, ⊠ 28008, ℰ 542 21 00, Telex 44377, Fax 542 35 01 – |🛗| 🗏 📺 ⇌
– 🔬 25/750. 🖭 ⓞ ⋶ 𝘝𝘐𝘚𝘈. ⋘　　　　　　　　　　　　　　　　　plan p. 6　EV　c
⊡ 1900 – **406 rm** 23100/28900.

Villa Real coffee shop only, Pl. de las Cortes, 10, ⊠ 28014, ℰ 420 37 67, Telex 44600,
Fax 420 25 47, « Tasteful decor » – |🛗| 🗏 📺 🕿 ⇌ – 🔬 25/150. 🖭 ⓞ ⋶ 𝘝𝘐𝘚𝘈. ⋘　　MY　c
⊡ 1650 – **96 rm** 24200/35000.

Tryp Plaza, Pl. de España, ⊠ 28013, ℰ 247 12 00, Telex 27383, Fax 248 23 89, ≼, ⊼ –
|🛗| 🗏 📺 🕿 – 🔬 25/300. 🖭 ⓞ ⋶ 𝘝𝘐𝘚𝘈. ⋘　　　　　　　　　　　　　　　　　KV　s
M 3200 – ⊡ 1200 – **306 rm** 17450/21850.

Tryp Ambassador, Cuesta de Santo Domingo 5, ⊠ 28013, ℰ 541 67 00, Telex 49538,
Fax 559 10 40 – |🛗| 🗏 📺 🕿 – 🔬 25/280. 🖭 ⓞ ⋶ 𝘝𝘐𝘚𝘈. ⋘　　　　　　　　　　　KX　k
M a la carte 5000/6000 – ⊡ 1200 – **181 rm** 17450/21850.

G.H. Reina Victoria, Pl. del Ángel 7, ⊠ 28012, ℰ 531 45 00, Telex 47547, Fax 522 03 07
– |🛗| 🕿. 🖭 ⓞ 𝘝𝘐𝘚𝘈. ⋘　　　　　　　　　　　　　　　　　　　　　　　　　　　LY　s
M 3000 – ⊡ 1200 – **201 rm** 17450/21850.

Liabeny, Salud 3, ⊠ 28013, ℰ 532 53 06, Telex 49024, Fax 532 74 21 – |🛗| 🗏 📺 🕿 ⇌.
🖭 ⋶ 𝘝𝘐𝘚𝘈. ⋘ – **M** 2400 – ⊡ 800 – **219 rm** 8400/13000.　　　　　　　　　　　LX　c

Suecia and Rest. Las Tres Fuentes, Marqués de Casa Riera 4, ⊠ 28014, ℰ 531 69 00,
Telex 22313, Fax 521 71 41 – |🛗| 🗏 📺 🕿 – 🔬 25/150. 🖭 ⓞ ⋶ 𝘝𝘐𝘚𝘈. ⋘　　　　MX　r
M *(closed Saturday lunch, Sunday, Bank Holidays and August)* a la carte 4500/5300 – ⊡ 1375
– **128 rm** 15000/23500.

Emperador without rest, Gran Vía 53, ⊠ 28013, ℰ 247 28 00, Telex 46261, Fax 247 28 17,
⊼ – |🛗| 🗏 📺 🕿 – 🔬 25/300. ⋘　　　　　　　　　　　　　　　　　　　　　　KX　n
232 rm 12240/15300.

Arosa coffee shop only, Salud 21, ⊠ 28013, ℰ 532 16 00, Telex 43618, Fax 531 31 27 –
|🛗| 🗏 📺 🕿 ⇌. 🖭 ⓞ ⋶ 𝘝𝘐𝘚𝘈　　　　　　　　　　　　　　　　　　　　　　　　LX　q
⊡ 1150 – **139 rm** 11900/16500.

Mayorazgo, Flor Baja 3, ⊠ 28013, ℰ 247 26 00, Telex 45647, Fax 541 24 85 – |🛗| 🗏 📺
🕿 ⇌ – 🔬 25/250. 🖭 ⓞ ⋶ 𝘝𝘐𝘚𝘈. ⋘　　　　　　　　　　　　　　　　　　　　KV　c
M 3300 – ⊡ 900 – **200 rm** 9300/12900.

Tryp Menfis, Gran Vía 74, ⊠ 28013, ℰ 247 09 00, Telex 48773, Fax 247 51 99 – |🛗| 🗏 📺
🕿. 🖭 ⓞ ⋶ 𝘝𝘐𝘚𝘈. ⋘　　　　　　　　　　　　　　　　　　　　　　　　　　　KV　u
M 2200 – ⊡ 825 – **116 rm** 12850/16100.

Tryp Washington without rest, Gran Vía 72, ⊠ 28013, ℰ 541 72 27, Telex 48773,
Fax 247 51 99 – |🛗| 🗏 📺 🕿. 🖭 ⓞ ⋶ 𝘝𝘐𝘚𝘈. ⋘　　　　　　　　　　　　　　　　KV　u
M (at hotel Tryp Menfis) – ⊡ 825 – **120 rm** 11050/13800.

El Coloso, Leganitos 13, ⊠ 28013, ℰ 248 76 00, Telex 47017, Fax 247 49 68 – |🛗| 🗏 📺
🕿 ⇌ – 🔬 25/175. 🖭 ⓞ ⋶ 𝘝𝘐𝘚𝘈. ⋘　　　　　　　　　　　　　　　　　　　　KX　y
M 2500 – ⊡ 1150 – **84 rm** 14360/17950.

Regina without rest, Alcalá 19, ⊠ 28014, ℰ 521 47 25, Telex 27500, Fax 521 47 25 – |🛗|
🗏 📺 🕿. 🖭 ⋶ 𝘝𝘐𝘚𝘈. ⋘ – ⊡ 750 – **142 rm** 8700/10900.　　　　　　　　　　　LX　v

Casón del Tormes without rest, Río 7, ⊠ 28013, ℰ 541 97 46, Fax 541 18 52 – |🛗| 🗏 📺
🕿. ⋶ 𝘝𝘐𝘚𝘈. ⋘ – ⊡ 525 – **63 rm** 6500/9600.　　　　　　　　　　　　　　　　KV　v

Mercator coffee shop only, Atocha 123, ⊠ 28012, ℰ 429 05 00, Telex 46129, Fax 369 12 52
– |🛗| 📺 🕿 🅿. 🖭 ⋶ 𝘝𝘐𝘚𝘈　　　　　　　　　　　　　　　　　　　　　　　　　　NZ　b
⊡ 700 – **89 rm** 7200/9800.

Los Condes without rest, Los Libreros 7, ⊠ 28004, ℰ 521 54 55, Telex 42730,
Fax 521 78 82 – |🛗| 🗏 📺 🕿. 🖭 ⋶ 𝘝𝘐𝘚𝘈. ⋘ – ⊡ 590 – **68 rm** 5950/10100.　　　KV　g

Tryp Capitol without rest, Gran Vía 41, ⊠ 28013, ℰ 521 83 91, Telex 41499 – |🛗| 🗏 📺
⇌. 🖭 ⓞ ⋶ 𝘝𝘐𝘚𝘈. ⋘　　　　　　　　　　　　　　　　　　　　　　　　　　　KLX　t
⊡ 825 – **144 rm** 11050/13800.

Carlos V without rest, Maestro Vitoria 5, ⊠ 28013, ℰ 531 41 00, Telex 48547, Fax 531 37 61
– |🛗| 🗏 📺 🕿. 🖭 ⓞ ⋶ 𝘝𝘐𝘚𝘈. ⋘　　　　　　　　　　　　　　　　　　　　　　LX　f
⊡ 600 – **67 rm** 8400/10500.

Atlántico without rest, Gran Vía 38 - 3º, ⊠ 28013, ℰ 522 64 80, Telex 43142, Fax 531 02 10
– |🛗| 🗏 🕿. 🖭 ⓞ ⋶ 𝘝𝘐𝘚𝘈. ⋘　　　　　　　　　　　　　　　　　　　　　　　　LX　e
⊡ 440 – **62 rm** 6770/9500.

Anaco coffee shop only, Tres Cruces 3, ⊠ 28013, ℰ 522 46 04, Fax 531 64 84 – |🛗| 🗏 📺
🕿. 🖭 ⓞ ⋶ 𝘝𝘐𝘚𝘈. ⋘　　　　　　　　　　　　　　　　　　　　　　　　　　　LX　a
⊡ 655 – **39 rm** 6800/10500.

California without rest, Gran Vía 38, ⊠ 28013, ℰ 522 47 03 – |🛗| 🕿. 🖭 ⓞ ⋶ 𝘝𝘐𝘚𝘈. ⋘
⊡ 350 – **26 rm** 4900/6500.　　　　　　　　　　　　　　　　　　　　　　　　　LX　e

Alexandra without rest, San Bernardo 29, ⊠ 28015, ℰ 542 04 00, Fax 559 28 25 – |🛗| 🕿.
🖭 ⋶ 𝘝𝘐𝘚𝘈 – ⊡ 530 – **69 rm** 5515/7420.　　　　　　　　　　　　　　　　　　KV　z

MADRID

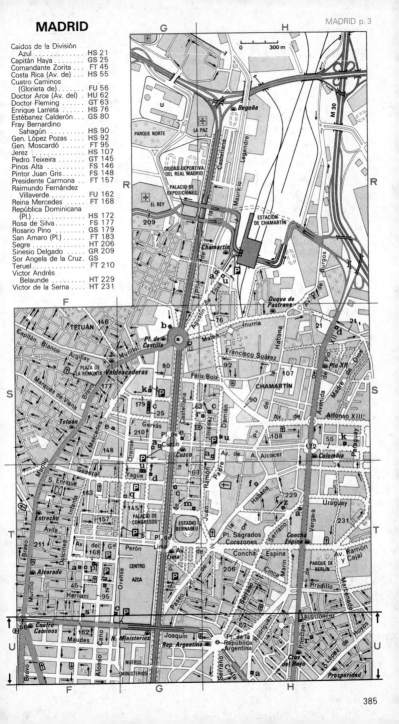

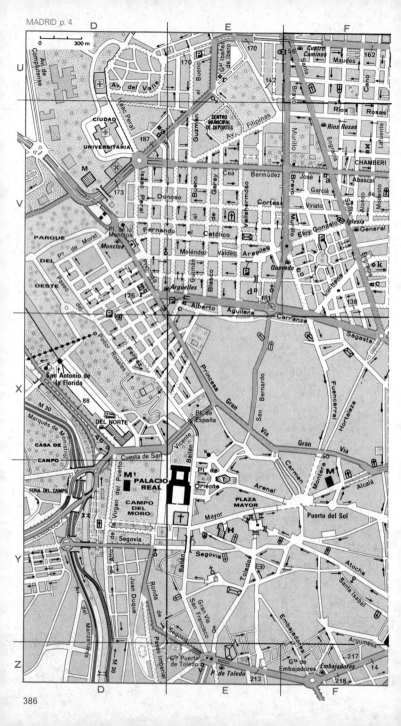

MADRID

387

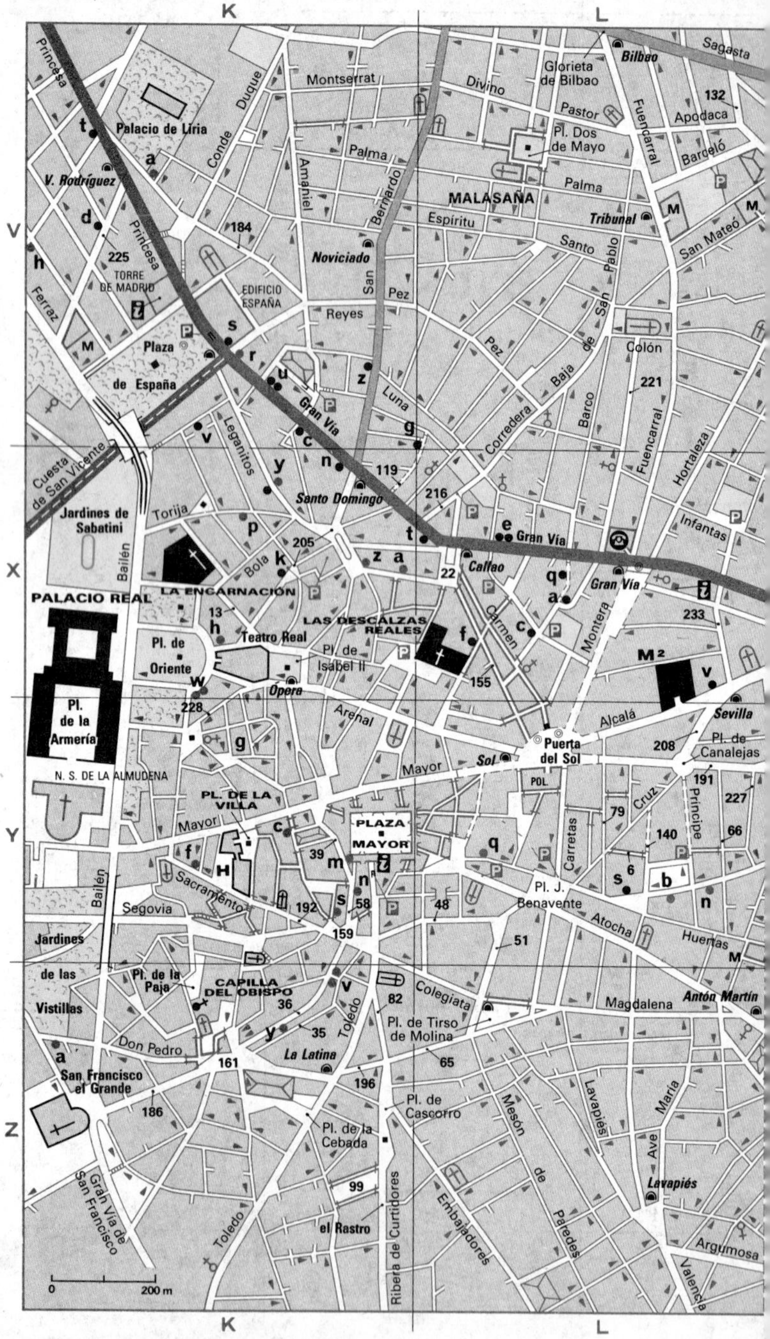

K L

Principe Pío
Palacio de Liria
Montserrat
Divino
Glorieta de Bilbao
Bilbao
Sagasta
t
a
Conde Duque
Palma
Pastor
Pl. Dos de Mayo
132
Apodaca
V. Rodríguez
d
Amaniel
San Bernardo
Palma
MALASAÑA
Fuencarral
Barceló
h
Princesa
184
Noviciado
San
Espíritu
Santo
Tribunal
M
San Mateo
225
TORRE DE MADRID
EDIFICIO ESPAÑA
Pez
Reyes
Pez
Baja
San Pablo
Santo
Colón
221
Ferraz
M
s
Plaza
de España
r
u
Gran Vía
Luna
z
g
Corredera
Barco
Fuencarral
Hortaleza
Cuesta de San Vicente
v
Leganitos
c
n
119
216
Infantas
Jardines de Sabatini
Torija
y
Santo Domingo
t
e
Gran Vía
Callao
22
Gran Vía
233
Bailén
p
Bola
k
205
z a
q
a
c
C
Montera
PALACIO REAL
LA ENCARNACIÓN
h
13
Teatro Real
LAS DESCALZAS REALES
Pl. de Isabel II
f
Carmen
M²
v
Sevilla
PL. de Oriente
w
228
Ópera
Arenal
155
Alcalá
Pl. de Canalejas
208
N. S. DE LA ALMUDENA
g
Pl. de la Armería
PL. DE LA VILLA
Mayor
Puerta del Sol
Sol
PDL
191
Príncipe
227
66
Bailén
f
H
c
39
m
PLAZA MAYOR
q
Carretas
79
Cruz
140
s
6
b
n
Sacramento
192
n
58
Pl. J. Benavente
Atocha
48
Huertas
M
Segovia
159
51
Jardines
Pl. de la Paja
CAPILLA DEL OBISPO
36
V
82
Colegiata
Magdalena
Antón Martín
de las
Don Pedro
y
35
161
Toledo
Pl. de Tirso de Molina
65
Lavapiés
Mira
Vistillas
a
La Latina
196
Pl. de Cascorro
Mesón
Ave.
San Francisco el Grande
186
Pl. de la Cebada
de
Lavapiés
Gran Vía de San Francisco
99
el Rastro
Ribera de Curtidores
Embajadores
Peñuelas
Argumosa
Lavapiés
Valencia

0   200 m

MADRID

*The names
of main shopping streets
are indicated in red
at the beginning
of the list of streets.*

XXXX ✿ **El Cenador del Prado,** Prado 4, ⊠ 28014, ℘ 429 15 61 – 🗏. 🖭 ⓪ ⋿ 𝗩𝗜𝗦𝗔. ✸LY **n**
closed Saturday lunch, Sunday and 15 days in August – **M** a la carte 6000/6900
Spec. Patatas a la importancia con almejas, Solomillo sobre hojaldre a la pera, Helado de plátano con salsa de chocolate caliente..

XXX ✿ **Café de Oriente,** pl. de Oriente 2, ⊠ 28013, ℘ 541 39 74, Basque and French rest. –
🗏. 🖭 ⓪ ⋿ 𝗩𝗜𝗦𝗔. ✸ KXY **w**
closed Saturday lunch, Sunday, Holy Week and August – **M** a la carte 5100/6800
Spec. Polente de sesos con huevos mollet, Rodaballo bordalesa con setas moriles, Hígado de oca al jengibre..

XXX **Paradis Madrid,** Marqués de Cubas 14, ⊠ 28014, ℘ 429 73 03, Fax 429 32 95 – 🗏. 🖭
⓪ 𝗩𝗜𝗦𝗔. ✸ MY **v**
closed Sunday dinner – **M** a la carte 3850/4950.

XXX **Jaun de Alzate,** Princesa 18, ⊠ 28008, ℘ 547 00 10, Fax 559 49 39 – 🗏. 🖭 ⓪ ⋿ 𝗩𝗜𝗦𝗔
closed Saturday lunch, Sunday and August – **M** a la carte 4850/6500. KV **a**

XXX **La Basílica,** Bolsa 12, ⊠ 28012, ℘ 521 86 23, Fax 522 22 25, « In an 18C Church » – 🗏.
🖭 ⓪ ⋿ 𝗩𝗜𝗦𝗔. ✸ LY **q**
closed Saturday lunch and Sunday – **M** a la carte approx. 6000.

XXX **Korynto,** Preciados 36, ⊠ 28013, ℘ 521 59 65, Seafood – 🗏. 🖭 ⓪ ⋿ 𝗩𝗜𝗦𝗔. ✸ KX **a**
M a la carte 5350/7600.

XXX **Bajamar,** Gran Vía 78, ⊠ 28013, ℘ 248 48 18, Fax 248 90 90, Seafood – 🗏. 🖭 ⓪ ⋿ 𝗩𝗜𝗦𝗔
✸ – **M** a la carte 3550/6200. KV **r**

XXX **Irizar,** Jovellanos 3, ⊠ 28014, ℘ 531 45 69, Basque and French rest – 🗏. 🖭 ⓪ ⋿ 𝗩𝗜𝗦𝗔
✸ MY **d**
closed Saturday lunch, Sunday and Holy Week – **M** a la carte 3975/5225.

XXX **El Landó,** pl. Gabriel Miró 8, ⊠ 28005, ℘ 266 76 81, Tasteful decor – 🗏. 🖭 ⓪ ⋿ 𝗩𝗜𝗦𝗔
✸ KZ **a**
closed Sunday, Bank Holidays and August – **M** a la carte 4200/5600.

XX **El Espejo,** paseo de Recoletos 31, ⊠ 28004, ℘ 308 23 47, Fax 593 22 23, « Old Parisian style café » – 🗏. 🖭 ⓪ ⋿ 𝗩𝗜𝗦𝗔. ✸ NV **a**
M a la carte 3500/4500.

XX **Ainhoa,** Bárbara de Braganza 12, ⊠ 28004, ℘ 308 27 26, Basque rest – 🗏. ✸ NV **s**
closed Sunday and August – **M** a la carte 3300/6900.

XX **Horno de Santa Teresa,** Santa Teresa 12, ⊠ 28004, ℘ 319 10 61 – 🗏. 🖭 ⋿ 𝗩𝗜𝗦𝗔.
MV **t**
closed Saturday, Sunday and August – **M** a la carte 4000/5450.

XX **Café de Oriente (Horno de Leña),** pl. de Oriente 2, ⊠ 28013, ℘ 247 15 64, Fax 247 77 07,
In a cellar – 🗏. 🖭 ⓪ ⋿ 𝗩𝗜𝗦𝗔. ✸ KXY **w**
M a la carte 2725/4200.

XX **Platerías,** pl. de Santa Ana 11, ⊠ 28012, ℘ 429 70 48, Early 20C café style – 🗏. 🖭 ⓪
⋿ 𝗩𝗜𝗦𝗔. ✸ LY **b**
closed Sunday – **M** a la carte approx. 4500.

XX **El Asador de Aranda,** Preciados 44, ⊠ 28013, ℘ 247 21 56, Roast lamb, « Castilian decor » – 🗏. ⋿ 𝗩𝗜𝗦𝗔. ✸ KX **z**
closed Monday dinner and 27 July-16 August – **M** a la carte 2450/2925.

XX **Arce,** Augusto Figueroa 32, ⊠ 28004, ℘ 522 59 13, Fax 522 04 40 – 🗏. 🖭 ⓪ ⋿ 𝗩𝗜𝗦𝗔
✸ MV **c**
closed Saturday lunch, Sunday, Holy Week and 15 to 30 August – **M** a la carte 5500/6600.

XX **El Mentidero de la Villa,** Santo Tomé 6, ⊠ 28004, ℘ 308 12 85, « Original decor » – 🗏.
🖭 ⓪ ⋿ 𝗩𝗜𝗦𝗔. ✸ MV **b**
closed Saturday lunch, Sunday and 15 to 31 August – **M** a la carte approx. 5000.

XX **Casa Gallega,** pl. de San Miguel 8, ⊠ 28005, ℘ 2473055, Galician rest. – 🗏. 🖭 ⓪ ⋿
𝗩𝗜𝗦𝗔. KY **c**
M a la carte 3600/5300.

XX **La Ópera de Madrid,** Amnistía 5, ⊠ 28013, ℘ 248 50 92 – 🗏. 🖭 ⓪ ⋿ 𝗩𝗜𝗦𝗔. ✸ KY **g**
closed Sunday, Bank Holidays and August – **M** a la carte 2900/4075.

X **El Schotis,** Cava Baja 11, ⊠ 28005, ℘ 265 32 30 – 🗏. 🖭 ⓪ ⋿ 𝗩𝗜𝗦𝗔. ✸ KZ **v**
closed Monday and August – **M** a la carte 3175/4800.

X **Casa Paco,** Puerta Cerrada 11, ⊠ 28005, ℘ 266 31 66 – 🗏. ⓪ 𝗩𝗜𝗦𝗔. ✸ KY **s**
closed Sunday and August – **M** a la carte 3900/4400.

X **El Ingenio,** Leganitos 10, ⊠ 28013, ℘ 541 91 33 – 🗏. 🖭 ⓪ ⋿ 𝗩𝗜𝗦𝗔. ✸ KX **y**
M a la carte 2075/3100.

Typical atmosphere :

XX **Posada de la Villa,** Cava Baja 9, ⊠ 28005, ℘ 266 18 80, Fax 266 18 80, « Castilian decor »
– 🗏. 🖭 ⓪ ⋿ 𝗩𝗜𝗦𝗔. KZ **v**
closed Sunday dinner and August – **M** a la carte 2775/4625.

XX **Botín,** Cuchilleros 17, ⊠ 28005, ℘ 266 42 17, Fax 266 84 94, Old Madrid decor, typical bodega – 🗏. 🖭 ⓪ ⋿ 𝗩𝗜𝗦𝗔 KY **n**
M a la carte 2750/4450.

XX **Sixto Gran Mesón,** Cervantes 28, ⊠ 28014, ℰ 429 22 55, Castilian decor – ▤. 𝔸𝔼 ⓞ 𝔼
𝘝𝘐𝘚𝘈. ⅏ – closed Sunday dinner – **M** a la carte 2400/3850.   MY **n**

XX **Café de Chinitas,** Torija 7, ⊠ 28013, ℰ 248 51 35, Fax 247 04 63, Flamenco cabaret –
▤. 𝔸𝔼 𝔼.   KX **p**
closed Sunday – **M** (dinner only, charge for show) a la carte 5950/7000.

X **Casa Lucio,** Cava Baja 35, ⊠ 28005, ℰ 265 32 52, Fax 266 48 66, Castilian decor – ▤. 𝔸𝔼
ⓞ **𝘝𝘐𝘚𝘈**. ⅏ – closed Saturday lunch and August – **M** a la carte 3600/4100.   KZ **y**

X **Las Cuevas de Luis Candelas,** Cuchilleros 1, ⊠ 28012, ℰ 266 54 28, Old Madrid decor–
Staff in bandit costume – ▤. 𝔸𝔼 ⓞ 𝔼 **𝘝𝘐𝘚𝘈**.   KY **m**
M a la carte 2775/4625.

X **Taberna del Alabardero,** Felipe V - 6, ⊠ 28013, ℰ 247 25 77, Fax 247 77 07, Typical
tavern – ▤. 𝔸𝔼 ⓞ 𝔼 **𝘝𝘐𝘚𝘈**. ⅏ – **M** a la carte 3075/4350.   KX **h**

Retiro-Salamanca-Ciudad Lineal : Castellana, Velázquez, Serrano, Goya, Príncipe de Vergara, Narváez, (plan p.5 except where otherwise stated) :

🏚🏚 **Ritz,** pl. de la Lealtad 5, ⊠ 28014, ℰ 521 28 57, Telex 43986, Fax 532 87 76, 🍴 – 🕴 ▤
📺 ☎ – 🔏 25/280. 𝔸𝔼 ⓞ 𝔼 **𝘝𝘐𝘚𝘈**. ⅏ rest   plan p. 7   NY **k**
M 9000 – ⊒ 2600 – **156 rm** 55000/65000.

🏚🏚 **Villa Magna,** paseo de la Castellana 22, ⊠ 28046, ℰ 578 20 00, Telex 22914, Fax 575 31 58
– 🕴 ▤ 📺 ☎ ら ⇐⇒ – 🔏 25/250. 𝔸𝔼 ⓞ 𝔼 **𝘝𝘐𝘚𝘈**. ⅏   GV **y**
M a la carte 7250/10000 – ⊒ 2750 – **182 rm** 45000/55000.

🏚🏚 **Wellington,** Velázquez 8, ⊠ 28001, ℰ 575 44 00, Telex 22700, Fax 576 41 64, 🏊 – 🕴 ▤
📺 ☎ ⇐⇒ – 🔏 25/300. 𝔸𝔼 ⓞ 𝔼 **𝘝𝘐𝘚𝘈**. ⅏   HX **t**
M (see rest. **El Fogón** below) – ⊒ 1950 – **258 rm** 18240/28500.

🏚🏚 **Tryp Fénix,** Hermosilla 2, ⊠ 28001, ℰ 431 67 00, Telex 45639, Fax 576 06 61 – 🕴 ▤ 📺
☎ – 🔏 25/100. 𝔸𝔼 ⓞ 𝔼 **𝘝𝘐𝘚𝘈**. ⅏   plan p. 7   NV **c**
M a la carte 5600/7900 – ⊒ 1375 – **226 rm** 21000/26300.

🏚🏚 **Sol Los Galgos and Rest. Diábolo,** Claudio Coello 139, ⊠ 28006, ℰ 262 66 00,
Telex 43957, Fax 261 76 62 – 🕴 ▤ 📺 ☎ ⇐⇒ – 🔏 25/300. 𝔸𝔼 ⓞ 𝔼 **𝘝𝘐𝘚𝘈**. ⅏   HV **a**
M a la carte 3250/5150 – ⊒ 1375 – **358 rm** 16100/20200.

🏚🏚 **Príncipe de Vergara,** Príncipe de Vergara 92, ⊠ 28001, ℰ 563 26 95, Telex 27064,
Fax 563 72 53 – 🕴 ▤ 📺 ☎ ⇐⇒ – 🔏 25/300. 𝔸𝔼 ⓞ 𝔼 **𝘝𝘐𝘚𝘈**. ⅏   HV **c**
M a la carte 4100/6600 – ⊒ 1600 – **170 rm** 15900/22800.

🏚🏚 **Sanvy,** Goya 3, ⊠ 28001, ℰ 576 08 00, Telex 44994, Fax 575 24 43 – 🕴 ▤ 📺 ☎ –
🔏 25/120. 𝔸𝔼 ⓞ 𝔼 **𝘝𝘐𝘚𝘈**. ⅏   plan p. 7   NV **r**
M (closed August) a la carte 4500/5500 – ⊒ 1600 – **141 rm** 15900/22800.

🏚🏚 **Tryp G.H. Velázquez,** Velázquez 62, ⊠ 28001, ℰ 575 28 00, Telex 22779, Fax 575 28 09
– 🕴 ▤ 📺 ☎ ⇐⇒ – 🔏 25/280. 𝔸𝔼 ⓞ 𝔼 **𝘝𝘐𝘚𝘈**. ⅏ rest   HX **s**
M 3425 – ⊒ 1000 – **144 rm** 13800/17250.

🏚🏚 **Agumar** coffee shop only, paseo Reina Cristina 7, ⊠ 28014, ℰ 552 69 00, Telex 22814,
Fax 433 60 95 – 🕴 ▤ 📺 ☎ – 🔏 25/150. 𝔸𝔼 ⓞ 𝔼 **𝘝𝘐𝘚𝘈**. ⅏   HZ **a**
⊒ 975 – **252 rm** 11950/14950.

🏚🏚 **Novotel Madrid,** Albacete 1, ⊠ 28027, ℰ 405 46 00, Telex 41862, Fax 404 11 05, 🍴, 🏊
– 🕴 ▤ 📺 ☎ ら ⇐⇒ ℗ – 🔏 25/250. 𝔸𝔼 ⓞ 𝔼 **𝘝𝘐𝘚𝘈**   E : by M 30   JY
M 3600 – ⊒ 1050 – **236 rm** 13000/16500.

🏚🏚 **Convención** coffee shop only, O'Donnell 53, ⊠ 28009, ℰ 574 84 00, Telex 23944,
Fax 574 56 01 – 🕴 ▤ 📺 ☎ ⇐⇒ – 🔏 25/1000. 𝔸𝔼 ⓞ 𝔼 **𝘝𝘐𝘚𝘈**. ⅏   JX **a**
⊒ 1000 – **790 rm** 11700/14575.

🏚🏚 **Alcalá and Rest. Basque,** Alcalá 66, ⊠ 28009, ℰ 435 10 60, Telex 48094, Fax 435 11 05
– 🕴 ▤ 📺 ☎ ⇐⇒ – 🔏 25/60. 𝔸𝔼 ⓞ 𝔼 **𝘝𝘐𝘚𝘈**. ⅏   HX **w**
M (closed Saturday and Sunday) a la carte 2575/3975 – ⊒ 900 – **153 rm** 11525/16835.

🏚🏚 **Pintor,** Goya 79, ⊠ 28001, ℰ 435 75 45, Telex 23281, Fax 576 81 57 – 🕴 ▤ 📺 ☎ ⇐⇒
– 🔏 25/350. 𝔸𝔼 𝔼 **𝘝𝘐𝘚𝘈**. ⅏   HX **c**
M a la carte 2880/4925 – ⊒ 1100 – **176 rm** 12800/16720.

🏚🏚 **Conde de Orgaz,** av. Moscatelar 24, ⊠ 28043, ℰ 388 40 99, Fax 388 00 09 – 🕴 ▤ 📺
☎ ⇐⇒ – 🔏 25/100. 𝔸𝔼 ⓞ 𝔼 **𝘝𝘐𝘚𝘈**. ⅏   NE : by López de Hoyos   HU
M 2000 – ⊒ 1000 – **91 rm** 14800/18500.

🏚🏚 **G. H. Colón,** Pez Volador 11, ⊠ 28007, ℰ 573 59 00, Telex 22984, Fax 573 08 89, 🏊, 🍴
– 🕴 ▤ 📺 ☎ ⇐⇒ – 🔏 25/130. 𝔸𝔼 ⓞ 𝔼 **𝘝𝘐𝘚𝘈**   JY **x**
M 3000 – ⊒ 700 – **390 rm** 9500/14000.

🏚🏚 **Emperatriz,** López de Hoyos 4, ⊠ 28006, ℰ 563 80 88, Telex 43640, Fax 563 98 04 – 🕴
▤ 📺 ☎ ら – 🔏 25/150. 𝔸𝔼 ⓞ 𝔼 **𝘝𝘐𝘚𝘈**. ⅏   GV **z**
M 2900 – ⊒ 1300 – **170 rm** 11000/17500.

🏚🏚 **Serrano** without rest, Marqués de Villamejor 8, ⊠ 28006, ℰ 435 52 00, Fax 435 48 49 –
🕴 ▤ 📺 ☎. 𝔸𝔼 ⓞ 𝔼 **𝘝𝘐𝘚𝘈**. ⅏   GHV **k**
⊒ 850 – **34 rm** 8500/14000.

🏚🏚 **Balboa,** Núñez de Balboa 112, ⊠ 28006, ℰ 563 03 24, Telex 27063, Fax 262 69 80 – 🕴 ▤
📺 ☎ ⇐⇒ – 🔏 25/30. 𝔸𝔼 ⓞ 𝔼 **𝘝𝘐𝘚𝘈**. ⅏   HV **n**
M 4000 – ⊒ 1200 – **122 rm** 14800/20000.

🏥 **Sur** without rest. coffee shop only, paseo Infanta Isabel 9, ⊠ 28014, ℰ 539 94 00, Telex 47494, Fax 467 09 96 – 🗏 – 🔏 25/45. 🖭 ⓞ 🗲 𝗩𝗜𝗦𝗔. ⅏
🚄 950 – **67 rm** 11700/16100.   plan p. 7   NZ   **a**

🏥 **Abeba** without rest, Alcántara 63, ⊠ 28006, ℰ 401 16 50, Fax 402 75 91 – 🗏 🗏 🖭 🕸
🚗. 🖭 ⓞ 🗲 𝗩𝗜𝗦𝗔.   HV   **r**
🚄 550 – **90 rm** 8200/10750.

🟦🟦🟦 **Club 31,** Alcalá 58, ⊠ 28014, ℰ 531 00 92 – 🗏. 🖭 ⓞ 🗲 𝗩𝗜𝗦𝗔. ⅏   plan p. 7   NX   **e**
M a la carte 5500/7800.

🟦🟦🟦 ❀ **El Amparo,** Callejón de Puigcerdá 8, ⊠ 28001, ℰ 431 64 56, Fax 575 54 91, « Original decor » – 🗏. 🖭 🗲 𝗩𝗜𝗦𝗔. ⅏   HX   **h**
closed Saturday lunch, Sunday, Holy Week and August – **M** a la carte 5375/7800
Spec. Lomos de salmonete al vino con tuétano y puerros, Pichón a las dos pimientas con puré de apio e higos, Dátiles rellenos de chantilly, helado de almendras.

🟦🟦🟦 **Suntory,** Castellana 36, ⊠ 28046, ℰ 577 37 33, Fax 577 75 05, Japanese rest. – 🗏 🚗.
🖭 ⓞ 𝗩𝗜𝗦𝗔. ⅏   GV   **d**
closed Sunday and Bank Holidays – **M** a la carte 6000/8000.

🟦🟦🟦 **Villa y Corte de Madrid,** Serrano 110, ⊠ 28006, ℰ 564 50 19, Fax 564 50 91, Tasteful decor – 🗏. 🖭 ⓞ 𝗩𝗜𝗦𝗔   HV   **a**
closed Sunday and August – **M** a la carte 3575/4800.

🟦🟦🟦 **El Gran Chambelán,** Ayala 46, ⊠ 28001, ℰ 431 77 45 – 🗏. 🖭 ⓞ 𝗩𝗜𝗦𝗔. ⅏   HX   **r**
closed Sunday – **M** a la carte 3400/4200.

🟦🟦🟦 **Sorolla,** Hermosilla 4, ⊠ 28001, ℰ 576 08 00, Telex 44994, Fax 575 24 43 – 🗏. 🖭 ⓞ 🗲
𝗩𝗜𝗦𝗔. ⅏   plan p. 7   NV   **r**
closed August – **M** a la carte 4500/5500.

🟦🟦🟦 **Balzac,** Moreto 7, ⊠ 28014, ℰ 420 01 77, 🍽 – 🗏. 🖭 ⓞ 🗲 𝗩𝗜𝗦𝗔. ⅏ plan p. 7   NY   **a**
closed Saturday lunch, Sunday and August – **M** a la carte approx. 6000.

🟦🟦🟦 **El Comedor,** Montalbán 9, ⊠ 28014, ℰ 531 69 68, Fax 531 61 91, 🍽 – 🗏. 🖭 ⓞ 🗲 𝗩𝗜𝗦𝗔.
                                             plan p. 7   NX   **a**
closed Saturday lunch and Sunday – **M** a la carte 3550/6200.

🟦🟦 **El Fogón,** Villanueva 34, ⊠ 28001, ℰ 575 44 00, Telex 22700, Fax 576 41 64 – 🗏. 🖭 ⓞ
🗲 𝗩𝗜𝗦𝗔. ⅏ – closed August – **M** a la carte 4650/5275.   HX   **t**

🟦🟦 **Ponteareas,** Claudio Coello 96, ⊠ 28006, ℰ 575 58 73, Fax 541 65 98, Galician rest – 🗏
🚗. 🖭 ⓞ 𝗩𝗜𝗦𝗔. ⅏   HV   **w**
closed Sunday, Bank Holidays and August – **M** a la carte 4180/6035.

🟦🟦 **St.-James,** Juan Bravo 26, ⊠ 28006, ℰ 575 00 69, 🍽, Rice dishes – 🗏. 🖭 ⅏ HV   **t**
closed Sunday – **M** a la carte 3100/4900.

🟦🟦 **Al Mounia,** Recoletos 5, ⊠ 28001, ℰ 435 08 28, North African rest., « Oriental atmosphere » – 🗏. 🖭 ⓞ 🗲 𝗩𝗜𝗦𝗔. ⅏   plan p. 7   NV   **u**
closed Sunday, Monday and August – **M** a la carte 3050/3900.

🟦🟦 **La Fonda,** Lagasca 11, ⊠ 28001, ℰ 577 79 24, Catalonian rest. – 🗏. 🖭 ⓞ 🗲 𝗩𝗜𝗦𝗔. ⅏
closed Sunday dinner – **M** a la carte 2425/3525.   HX   **f**

🟦🟦 ❀ **Casa d'a Troya,** Emiliano Barral 14, ⊠ 28043, ℰ 416 44 55 Galician rest. – 🗏. 𝗩𝗜𝗦𝗔. ⅏
closed Sunday, Bank Holidays and 15 July-1 September – **M** (booking essential) a la carte 2225/4300   E by M 30   JY
Spec. Pulpo a la gallega, Merluza a la gallega, Tarta de Santiago.

🟦 **Asador Velate,** Jorge Juan 91, ⊠ 28009, ℰ 435 10 24, Basque rest. – 🗏. 🖭 ⓞ 🗲 𝗩𝗜𝗦𝗔.
⅏   HJX   **x**
closed Sunday, Bank Holidays and August – **M** a la carte 3685/4885.

🟦 ❀ **La Trainera,** Lagasca 60, ⊠ 28001, ℰ 576 05 75, Fax 575 47 17, Seafood – 🗏. 🗲 𝗩𝗜𝗦𝗔.
⅏   HX   **k**
closed Sunday and August – **M** a la carte 4100/4800
Spec. Salpicón de mariscos. Pescados y mariscos cocidos, plancha y a la americana. Bonito encebollado (summer).

🟦 ❀ **El Pescador,** José Ortega y Gasset 75, ⊠ 28006, ℰ 402 12 90, Seafood – 🗏. 🗲 𝗩𝗜𝗦𝗔. ⅏
closed Sunday and August – **M** a la carte 3900/5050   JV   **t**
Spec. Angulas de Aguinaga, Lenguado "Evaristo", Bogavante a la americana.

🟦 ❀ **Viridiana,** Fundadores 23, ⊠ 28028, ℰ 356 90 40 – 🗏. ⅏   JX   **c**
closed Sunday and August – **M** a la carte 3300/5500
Spec. Marinado de lubina al jengibre sobre aguacate y mango, Salteado de lomo de buey con boletus edulis, Sorbete de bayas rojas al aguardiente de tapaculos..

Arganzuela, Carabanchel Villaverde : Antonio López, paseo de Las Delicias, paseo de Santa María de la Cabeza (plan p. 4 except where otherwise Stated)

🏨 **Carlton,** paseo de las Delicias 26, ⊠ 28045, ℰ 539 71 00, Telex 44571, Fax 527 85 10 –
🗏 🗏 🖭 ☎. 🖭 ⓞ 🗲 𝗩𝗜𝗦𝗔. ⅏   plan p. 5   GZ   **n**
M 2500 – 🚄 950 – **112 rm** 14400/19500.

🏨 **Praga** without rest. coffee shop only, Antonio López 65, ⊠ 28019, ℰ 469 06 00, Telex 22823, Fax 469 83 25 – 🗏 🗏 ☎ 🚗 – 🔏 25/350. 🖭 ⓞ 🗲 𝗩𝗜𝗦𝗔. ⅏
🚄 625 – **428 rm** 8000/10500.   by Pl. Emperador Carlos V   NZ

🏨🏨 **Aramo,** paseo Santa María de la Cabeza 73, ⊠ 28045, 𝒫 473 91 11, Telex 45885, Fax 473 92 14 – |⧆| 🗏 ☎ ⟷ 🔄 ⃞ E 🗺 ❄ rest   by Pl. Emperador Carlos V   NZ
M 2500 – ⟳ 800 – **105 rm** 11000/15000.

🏨🏨 **Puerta de Toledo,** glorieta Puerta de Toledo 4, ⊠ 28005, 𝒫 474 71 00, Telex 22291, Fax 474 07 47 – |⧆| 🗏 📺 ☎ ⟷ ⃞ E 🗺 ❄   EZ **v**
M (see rest. **Puerta de Toledo** below) – ⟳ 650 – **152 rm** 5850/9800.

🞩🞩 **Puerta de Toledo,** glorieta Puerta de Toledo 4 𝒫 474 76 75, Telex 22291, Fax 474 30 35 – 🗏 ⃞ E 🗺 ❄   plan p. 4 EZ **v**
M a la carte approx. 3775.

Moncloa : Princesa, paseo del Pintor Rosales, paseo de la Florida, Casa de Campo (plan p. 4 except where otherwise stated)

🏨🏨🏨 **Meliá Madrid,** Princesa 27, ⊠ 28008, 𝒫 541 82 00, Telex 22537, Fax 541 19 88 – |⧆| 🗏 📺 ☎ – 🔏 25/200. ⃞ ⓞ E 🗺 ❄   plan p. 6 KV **t**
M a la carte 3850/7100 – ⟳ 1875 – **266 rm** 23000/28750.

🏨🏨 **Tryp Monte Real** ⟆, Arroyofresno 17 𝒫 316 21 40, Telex 22089, Fax 316 21 40, 🌳, « Garden », 🏊, – |⧆| 🗏 ☎ ⟷ 🅿 – 🔏 25/200. ⃞ ⓞ E 🗺 ❄
M 6000 – ⟳ 1320 – **80 rm** 16700/26500.
          NW : 8 km by Av. Puerta de Hierro and C 601

🏨🏨 **Florida Norte,** paseo de la Florida 5, ⊠ 28008, 𝒫 542 83 00, Telex 23675, Fax 247 78 33 – |⧆| 🗏 📺 ☎ ⟷ ⃞ ⓞ 🗺 ❄   DX **v**
M 2100 – ⟳ 700 – **399 rm** 10500/14500.

🏨🏨 **Pullman Calatrava** without rest, Tutor 1, ⊠ 28008, 𝒫 541 98 80, Telex 43190, Fax 248 51 26 – |⧆| 🗏 📺 ☎ ⟷ ⃞ E 🗺 ❄   plan p. 6 KV **d**
⟳ 1200 – **98 rm** 14500/17950.

🏨 **Tirol** without shop only, Marqués de Urquijo 4, ⊠ 28008, 𝒫 248 19 00 – |⧆| 🗏 ☎. E 🗺 ❄   DV **r**
97 rm 7000/9000.

🞩🞩🞩 **Café Viena,** Luisa Fernanda 23, ⊠ 28008, 𝒫 248 15 91, « Old style café » – 🗏. ⃞ ⓞ E 🗺 ❄   plan p. 6 KV **h**
closed Sunday and August – **M** a la carte 4125/5600.

🞩 **Currito,** Casa de Campo - Pabellón de Vizcaya, ⊠ 28011, 𝒫 464 57 04, Fax 479 72 54, 🌳, Basque rest. – ⃞ ⓞ E 🗺 ❄   by Segovia DY
M a la carte 3800/5700.

Chamberí : San Bernardo, Fuencarral, Alberto Aguilera, Santa Engracia (plan p. 4 to 7) :

🏨🏨🏨 **Santo Mauro and Rest. Belagua,** Zurbano 36, ⊠ 28010, 𝒫 319 69 00, Fax 308 54 77, 🌳, « Elegant palace with garden », 🔲, – |⧆| 🗏 📺 ☎ ⟷ ⃞ ⓞ E 🗺 ❄ rest   GV **g**
M (closed Sunday, Bank Holidays and August) a la carte 6200/8200 – ⟳ 2500 – **36 rm** 35200/52800.

🏨🏨🏨 **Miguel Ángel,** Miguel Ángel 31, ⊠ 28010, 𝒫 442 00 22, Telex 44235, Fax 442 53 20, 🔲 – |⧆| 🗏 📺 ☎ ⟷ – 🔏 25/300. ⃞ ⓞ E 🗺 ❄   GV **c**
M 6000 – ⟳ 1700 – **278 rm** 24800/31000.

🏨🏨 **Mindanao,** San Francisco de Sales 15, ⊠ 28003, 𝒫 549 55 00, Telex 22631, Fax 544 55 96, 🏊, – |⧆| 🗏 📺 ☎ ⟷ – 🔏 25/200. ⃞ ⓞ E 🗺 ❄   DV **a**
M a la carte 3350/5350 – ⟳ 1750 – **289 rm** 22000/27500.

🏨🏨 **Castellana Inter-Continental,** paseo de la Castellana 49, ⊠ 28046, 𝒫 308 18 10, Telex 27686, Fax 319 58 53, 🌳 – |⧆| 🗏 📺 ☎ ⟷ – 🔏 25/550. ⃞ ⓞ E 🗺 ❄ GV **a**
M 5000 – ⟳ 2100 – **305 rm** 31200/39200.

🏨🏨 **Escultor,** Miguel Ángel 3, ⊠ 28010, 𝒫 410 42 03, Telex 44285, Fax 319 25 84 – |⧆| 🗏 📺 ☎. ⃞ ⓞ E 🗺 ❄   GV **s**
M (see rest. **Señorío de Errazu** below) – ⟳ 1050 – **82 rm** 10900/18150.

🏨🏨 **Sol Alondras** coffee shop only, José Abascal 8, ⊠ 28003, 𝒫 447 40 00, Telex 49454, Fax 593 88 00 – |⧆| 🗏 📺 ☎. ⃞ ⓞ E 🗺 ❄   FV **a**
⟳ 900 – **72 rm** 12700/15900.

🏨🏨 **Gran Versalles** without rest, Covarrubias 4, ⊠ 28010, 𝒫 447 57 00, Telex 49150, Fax 446 39 87 – 🗏 – 🔏 25/140. ⃞ ⓞ E 🗺 ❄   MV **a**
⟳ 975 – **145 rm** 13250/18250.

🏨🏨 **Zurbano,** Zurbano 79, ⊠ 28003, 𝒫 441 45 00, Telex 27578, Fax 441 32 24 – |⧆| 🗏 ☎ ⟷ – 🔏 25/100. ⃞ ⓞ E 🗺 ❄   GV **x**
M 4500 – ⟳ 1200 – **269 rm** 16000/20000.

🏨 **G.H. Conde Duque** without rest, pl. Conde Valle de Suchil 5, ⊠ 28015, 𝒫 447 70 00, Telex 22058, Fax 448 35 69 – |⧆| 🗏 📺 ☎ – 🔏 25/160. ⃞ ⓞ E 🗺 ❄   EV **d**
⟳ 1450 – **136 rm** 13250/19850.

🞩🞩🞩🞩🞩 ❀ **Fortuny,** Fortuny 34, ⊠ 28010, 𝒫 308 32 67, Fax 593 22 23, 🌳, « Former palace, tastefully decorated » – 🗏. ⃞ ⓞ E 🗺 ❄   GV **n**
closed Saturday lunch, Sunday and Bank Holidays – **M** a la carte 5500/7000
Spec. Raviolis de cigalitas y trufas, Lubina al vapor de laurel con aceite al coral de bogavante, Milhojas de mollejas de ternera, hongos y trufas.

XXXXX ✿ **Jockey,** Amador de los Ríos 6, ☒ 28010, ℘ 319 24 35, Fax 319 24 35 – 🗐. 🆎 ① 🖃 *VISA*.
    NV **k**
    closed Saturday, Sunday, Bank Holidays and August – **M** a la carte 7100/8700
    Spec. Ensalada de ventresca con pimientos rojos asados, Langostinos con verduras a la japonesa, Pichón de Talavera relleno al estilo Jockey..

XXXXX ✿ **Lúculo,** Génova 19, ☒ 28004, ℘ 319 40 29, 😋 – 🗐. 🆎 ① 🖃 *VISA*. ⚬⚬
    NV **d**
    closed Saturday lunch, Sunday, Bank Holidays, 1 to 6 January, Holy Week and 10 to 31 August
    – **M** a la carte 6400/8800
    Spec. Escabeche de foie de pato, Lasaña de morcilla, Cocido de pescados.

XXXX ✿ **Las Cuatro Estaciones,** General Ibáñez Ibero 5, ☒ 28003, ℘ 553 63 05, Telex 43709,
    Fax 553 32 98, Modern decor – 🗐. 🆎 ① 🖃 *VISA*. ⚬⚬
    EU **r**
    closed Saturday, Sunday and August – **M** a la carte 4300/5575
    Spec. Ensalada tibia de bogavante al vinagre de sidra, Hojaldre de bacalao a la crema de ajo, Noisette de cordero lechal salsa al tomillo.

XXX **Lur Maitea,** Fernando el Santo 4, ☒ 28010, ℘ 308 03 50, Basque rest. – 🗐. 🆎 ① 🖃 *VISA*.
    ⚬⚬
    MNV **u**
    closed Saturday lunch, Sunday, Bank Holidays and August – **M** a la carte approx. 5500.

XXX **Annapurna,** Zurbano 5, ☒ 28010, ℘ 410 77 27, Indian rest. – 🗐. 🆎 ① 🖃 *VISA*.
    ⚬⚬
    MV **w**
    closed Saturday lunch in Summer, Sunday and Bank Holidays – **M** a la carte 2950/4050.

XXX **Cortegrande,** Sagasta 27, ☒ 28004, ℘ 445 55 43 – 🗐. 🆎 ① 🖃 *VISA*. ⚬⚬
    MV **a**
    closed Saturday lunch, Sunday, Bank Holidays and August – **M** a la carte 3800/6200.

XXX **Señorío de Errazu,** Miguel Ángel 3, ☒ 28010, ℘ 308 24 25 – 🗐. 🆎 ① 🖃 *VISA*.
    GV **s**
    closed Saturday lunch, Sunday and August – **M** a la carte 4050/5150.

XX **Aymar,** Fuencarral 138, ☒ 28010, ℘ 445 57 67, Seafood – 🗐. 🆎 ① 🖃 *VISA*. ⚬⚬
    FV **e**
    M a la carte 3950/4750.

XX **La Plaza de Chamberí,** pl. de Chamberí 10, ☒ 28010, ℘ 446 06 97, 😋 – 🗐. 🆎 ① 🖃
    VISA. ⚬⚬
    FV **k**
    closed Sunday and Holy Week – **M** a la carte 3475/4000.

X **La Gran Tasca,** Santa Engracia 24, ☒ 28010, ℘ 448 77 79, Castilian decor – 🗐. 🆎 ①
    🖃 *VISA*. ⚬⚬
    FV **c**
    closed Sunday and Holy Week – **M** a la carte 2975/5575.

X **Casa Félix,** Bretón de los Herreros 39, ☒ 28003, ℘ 441 24 79 – 🗐 🅿. 🆎 🖃 *VISA*. ⚬⚬
    FV **x**
    M a la carte 2650/4200.

Chamartín, Tetuán : Capitán Haya, Orense, Alberto Alcocer, paseo de la Habana (plan p. 3 except where otherwise stated) :

🏨🏨 **Eurobuilding,** Padre Damián 23, ☒ 28036, ℘ 457 31 00, Telex 22548, Fax 457 97 29,
    « Garden and terrace with 🏊 » – 📶 🗐 📺 ☎ 🚗 – 🕍 25/900. 🆎 ① 🖃 *VISA*. ⚬⚬
    M 3950 **La Taberna** a la carte 5225/6987 – **Le Relais** (buffet) a la carte 4535/5120 – ⥱ 1800
    – **520 rm** 22300/28800.
    HS **a**

🏨🏨 **Meliá Castilla,** Capitán Haya 43, ☒ 28020, ℘ 571 22 11, Telex 23142, Fax 571 22 10, 🏊
    – 📶 🗐 📺 ☎ 🕭 🚗 – 🕍 25/800. 🆎 ① 🖃 *VISA*. ⚬⚬
    GS **c**
    M (see **L'Albufera** – **La Fragata** – **El Hidalgo** below) – ⥱ 1950 – **907 rm** 22150/27200.

🏨 **Holiday Inn,** pl. Carlos Trías Beltrán 4 (entrance by Orense 22-24), ☒ 28020, ℘ 597 01 02,
    Telex 44709, Fax 597 02 92, 🏊 – 📶 🗐 📺 ☎ 🕭 – 🕍 25/400. 🆎 ① 🖃 *VISA*. ⚬⚬ rest
    M Rib Room – **La Terraza** a la carte 4075/6050 – ⥱ 1600 – **313 rm** 23500/29500.
    GT **z**

🏨 **Cuzco** without rest. coffee shop only, paseo de la Castellana 133, ☒ 28046, ℘ 556 06 00,
    Telex 22464, Fax 556 03 72 – 📶 🗐 📺 ☎ 🚗 🅿 – 🕍 25/500. 🆎 ① 🖃 *VISA*. ⚬⚬
    GS **a**
    ⥱ 1200 – **330 rm** 15840/19800.

🏨 **Chamartín,** Chamartín railway station, ☒ 28036, ℘ 323 18 33, Telex 49201, Fax 733 02 14
    – 📶 🗐 📺 ☎ – 🕍 25/500. 🆎 ① 🖃 *VISA*. ⚬⚬
    HR
    M (see Rest. **Cota 13** below) – ⥱ 1000 – **378 rm** 12000/16300.

🏨 **La Habana,** paseo de la Habana 73, ☒ 28036, ℘ 345 82 84, Telex 41869, Fax 259 79 81
    – 📶 🗐 📺 ☎ 🚗 – 🕍 25/250. 🆎 ① 🖃 *VISA*. ⚬⚬
    HT **f**
    M a la carte 3950/5400 – ⥱ 1600 – **157 rm** 15900/22800.

🏨 **Orense 38** coffee shop only, Pedro Teixeira 5, ☒ 28020, ℘ 597 15 68, Fax 597 12 95 – 📶
    🗐 📺 ☎ 🚗. 🆎 ① 🖃 *VISA*. ⚬⚬
    GT **q**
    ⥱ 900 – **140 rm** 22000.

🏨 **Foxá 32** coffee shop only, Agustín de Foxá 32, ☒ 28036, ℘ 733 10 60, Telex 49366,
    Fax 314 11 65 – 📶 🗐 📺 ☎ 🚗 – 🕍 25/250. 🆎 ① 🖃 *VISA*. ⚬⚬
    HR **u**
    ⥱ 875 – **161 rm** 15050/18590.

🏨 **Foxá 25** coffee shop only, Agustín de Foxá 25, ☒ 28036, ℘ 323 11 19, Telex 44911,
    Fax 314 11 65 – 📶 🗐 📺 ☎ 🚗. 🆎 ① 🖃 *VISA*. ⚬⚬
    HR **a**
    ⥱ 875 – **121 rm** 15050/18590.

🏨 **El Gran Atlanta** without rest, Comandante Zorita 34, ☒ 28020, ℘ 553 59 00, Telex 45210,
    Fax 533 08 58 – 📶 🗐 📺 ☎ 🚗 – 🕍 25/120. 🆎 ① 🖃 *VISA*
    FT **p**
    ⥱ 975 – **180 rm** 14600/18250.

🏨 **Apartotel El Jardín** without rest. carret. N I km 5'7 (service lane), ✉ 28050, 𝒫 202 83 36, Fax 766 86 91, 🛴, 🐎, 🎾 – 🛗 🗏 📺 ☎ 🚗 🅿. 🆎 ⓘ 🆅🆂🅰. 🕸   by ① RH
🔲 800 38 suites 19000

🏨 **Aitana** without rest. coffee shop only, paseo de la Castellana 152, ✉ 28046, 𝒫 250 71 07, Telex 49186, Fax 457 07 81 – 🛗 🗏 📺 ☎. 🆎 ⓘ 🗲 🆅🆂🅰. 🕸   GT **c**
🔲 750 – **111 rm** 9700/14000.

🏨 **Aristos and Rest. El Chaflán**, av. Pío XII-34, ✉ 28016, 𝒫 457 04 50, Fax 457 10 23, �
– 🛗 🗏 📺 🚗. 🆎 ⓘ 🗲 🆅🆂🅰. 🕸   HS **d**
M *(closed Sunday)* a la carte 3550/4250 – 🔲 550 – **24 rm** 7700/11900.

🎞🎞🎞🎞🎞 ❀❀❀ **Zalacaín**, Álvarez de Baena 4, ✉ 28006, 𝒫 261 48 40, Fax 261 47 32, 🌿 – 🗏. 🆎
ⓘ 🗲 🆅🆂🅰. 🕸   plan p. 7 GV **b**
colsed Saturday lunch, Sunday, Holy Week and August – **M** a la carte 7050/9400
Spec. Crema fría de hongos con caviar en gelatina, Lomos de salmonete a las finas hierbas, bucles de rabo de vaca al tomillo.

🎞🎞🎞🎞🎞 **Príncipe y Serrano**, Serrano 240, ✉ 28016, 𝒫 250 41 03, Fax 259 60 79 – 🗏. 🆎 ⓘ 🗲
🆅🆂🅰. 🕸   HT **a**
colsed Saturday lunch, Sunday and August – **M** a la carte 5500/7000.

🎞🎞🎞🎞 **El Bodegón**, Pinar 15, ✉ 28006, 𝒫 262 31 37 – 🗏. 🆎 ⓘ 🗲 🆅🆂🅰. 🕸   plan p. 7 GV **q**
closed Saturday lunch, Sunday, Bank Holidays and August – **M** a la carte 5500/7650.

🎞🎞🎞🎞 ❀ **Príncipe de Viana**, Manuel de Falla 5, ✉ 28036, 𝒫 259 14 48, Fax 259 53 92, 🌿 – 🗏.
🆎 ⓘ 🗲 🆅🆂🅰. 🕸   GT **c**
closed Saturday lunch, Sunday, Holy Week and August – **M** a la carte 6000/7200
Spec. Menestra de verduras, Escalopes de lubina a la albahaca, Estofado de rabo de vaca a la salvia.

🎞🎞🎞 **Nicolasa**, Velázquez 150, ✉ 28002, 𝒫 563 17 35, Fax 564 32 75 – 🗏. 🆎 ⓘ 🗲 🆅🆂🅰. 🕸
closed Sunday and August – **M** a la carte 4800/6000.   HU **a**

🎞🎞🎞 **L'Albufera**, Capitán Haya 45, ✉ 28020, 𝒫 279 63 74, Telex 23142, Fax 571 22 10, Rice dishes – 🆎 🗲 🆅🆂🅰. 🕸   GS **c**
M a la carte 3960/7365.

🎞🎞🎞 **La Fragata**, Capitán Haya 45, ✉ 28020, 𝒫 570 98 34 – 🆎 ⓘ 🗲 🆅🆂🅰. 🕸   GS **c**
closed August – **M** a la carte 4300/4800.

🎞🎞🎞 **El Hidalgo**, Capitán Haya 45 𝒫 570 68 16, Regional rest. – 🗏 🅿. 🆎 ⓘ 🗲 🆅🆂🅰. 🕸
closed August – **M** a la carte 2800/3400.   GS **c**

🎞🎞🎞 **La Máquina**, Sor Ángela de la Cruz 22, ✉ 28020, 𝒫 572 33 18, Fax 572 33 19 – 🗏. 🆎
ⓘ 🆅🆂🅰. 🕸   FS **e**
closed Sunday – **M** a la carte 4400/5300.

🎞🎞🎞 **O'Pazo**, Reina Mercedes 20, ✉ 28020, 𝒫 553 23 33, Seafood – 🗏. 🗲 🆅🆂🅰. 🕸   FT **p**
closed Sunday and August – **M** a la carte 3900/5500.

🎞🎞🎞 **José Luis**, Rafael Salgado 11, ✉ 28036, 𝒫 250 02 42, Telex 41779, Fax 250 99 11 – 🗏.
🆎 ⓘ 🗲 🆅🆂🅰. 🕸   GT **m**
closed Sunday and August – **M** a la carte 3900/5850.

🎞🎞🎞 ❀ **Señorío de Bertiz**, Comandante Zorita 6, ✉ 28020, 𝒫 533 27 57 – 🗏. 🆎 ⓘ 🆅🆂🅰. 🕸
closed Saturday lunch, Sunday and August – **M** a la carte 3750/7075   FT **s**
Spec. Lasagna de espinacas almejas y gambas, Sauté de hojaldre relleno de langostinos y carabineros, Pechugas de pichón asadas en hoja de coll y mousse de hongos.

🎞🎞🎞 **Cota 13**, Chamartín railway station, ✉ 28036, 𝒫 315 10 83, Telex 49201, Fax 733 02 14
– 🗏. 🆎 ⓘ 🗲 🆅🆂🅰. 🕸   HR
closed Saturday, Sunday, Bank Holidays and August – **M** a la carte approx. 4000.

🎞🎞🎞 **Bogavante**, Capitán Haya 20, ✉ 28020, 𝒫 556 21 14, Fax 597 00 79, Seafood – 🗏. 🆎 ⓘ
🗲 🆅🆂🅰. 🕸   GT **d**
closed Sunday – **M** a la carte 4100/6100.

🎞🎞🎞 **Señorío de Alcocer**, Alberto Alcocer 1, ✉ 28036, 𝒫 457 16 96 – 🗏. 🆎 ⓘ 🗲 🆅🆂🅰. 🕸
closed Sunday, Bank Holidays and August – **M** a la carte approx. 7000.   GS **e**

🎞🎞🎞 ❀ **El Olivo**, General Gallegos 1 𝒫 259 15 35 – 🗏. 🆎 ⓘ 🗲 🆅🆂🅰. 🕸   HS **c**
closed Sunday, Monday and August – **M** a la carte 3800/5050.
Spec. Hongos marinados al sabor de trufas (autumn), Rape sobre compota de tomate en salsa aceitunas negras, Foie gras caliente con uvas al vino de Pedro Ximénez.

🎞🎞🎞 **La Boucade**, Capitán Haya 30, ✉ 28020, 𝒫 556 02 45 – 🗏. 🆅🆂🅰. 🕸   GS **a**
closed Sunday and August – **M** a la carte approx. 4000.

🎞🎞🎞 ❀ **Goizeko Kabi**, Comandante Zorita 37, ✉ 28020, 𝒫 533 01 85, Fax 533 02 14, Basque rest. – 🗏. 🆎 ⓘ 🗲 🆅🆂🅰. 🕸   FT **a**
closed Saturday lunch and Sunday – **M** a la carte approx. 7000
Spec. Lomo de lubina al horno con patatitas y cebolla, Solomillo en hojaldre en salsa Périgord, Mousse fría de naranja en lágrima de chocolate.

🎞🎞🎞 ❀ **Cabo Mayor**, Juan Ramón Jiménez 37, ✉ 28036, 𝒫 250 87 76, Fax 458 16 21 – 🗏. 🆎
ⓘ 🆅🆂🅰. 🕸   GHS **r**
closed Sunday, Holy Week and 10 days in August – **M** a la carte 4850/7000
Spec. Ajedrez de melón y foie-gras, Kokotxas con huevos de codorniz, Charlota de pichón con salsa de hongos.

XXX **El Foque de Quiñones,** Suero de Quiñones 22, ⊠ 28002, ℰ 519 25 72 – 🍽. 🖭 ⓞ ⅀
VISA. ✂   HU   **r**
closed Sunday – **M** a la carte 4200/5250.

XXX **Lutecia,** Corazón de María 78, ⊠ 28002, ℰ 519 34 15 – 🍽. 🖭 ⓞ *VISA*. ✂
closed Saturday lunch, Sunday and August – **M** a la carte 2900/3500.
                                                                      by Lopez de Hoyos   HU

XX **Rugantino,** Velazquez 136, ⊠ 28006, ℰ 261 02 22, Italian rest – 🍽. 🖭 ⓞ ⅀ *VISA*.
✂   plan p. 5   HV   **e**
M a la carte approx. 3900.

XX **De Funy,** Serrano 213, ⊠ 28016, ℰ 259 72 25, Telex 44885, Fax 250 72 54, ☂, Lebanese
rest. – 🍽. 🖭 ⓞ ⅀ *VISA*. ✂   HT   **z**
closed Monday – **M** a la carte 3350/5700.

XX **Rheinfall,** Padre Damián 44, ⊠ 28036, ℰ 457 82 88, German rest., « Regional German
decor » – 🍽. 🖭 ⓞ ⅀ *VISA*. ✂   HS   **u**
M a la carte 2700/3900.

XX **La Tahona,** Capitán Haya 21 (lateral), ⊠ 28020, ℰ 555 04 41, Roast lamb,
« Medieval Castillan decor » – 🍽. ⅀ *VISA*. ✂   GT   **u**
closed Sunday dinner and August – **M** a la carte 2450/2925.

XX **Serramar,** Rosario Pino 12, ⊠ 28020, ℰ 570 07 90, Seafood – 🍽. 🖭 ⓞ ⅀ *VISA*. ✂
closed Sunday – **M** a la carte 4175/4975.   GS   **k**

XX **House of Ming,** paseo de la Castellana 74, ⊠ 28046, ℰ 261 10 13, Chinese rest. – 🍽.
🖭 ⓞ ⅀ *VISA*. ✂   GV   **f**
M a la carte 2430/3085.

X **El Asador de Aranda,** pl. de Castilla 3, ⊠ 28046, ℰ 733 87 02, Roast lamb, Castilian decor
– 🍽. ⅀ *VISA*. ✂   GS   **b**
closed Sunday dinner and 16 August-15 September – **M** a la carte 2450/3325.

on the road to the Airport E : 12,5 km – ⊠ 28042 Madrid – ☎ 91 :

🏯 **Diana and Rest. Asador Duque de Osuna,** Galeón 27 (Alameda de Osuna) ℰ 747 13 55,
Telex 45688, Fax 747 97 97, ☒ – 🛗 🍽 📺 ☎ – 🔬 25/220. 🖭 ⓞ ⅀ *VISA*. ✂
M *(closed Sunday)* a la carte 2900/5200 – ⊡ 750 – **271 rm** 11900/14900.

Environs

at El Plantío NW : 13 km – ⊠ 28023 El Plantío – ☎ 91 :

XX **Los Remos,** carret. N VI : 13 km ℰ 307 72 30, Seafood, Terrace – 🍽 ⓟ. ⅀ *VISA*.
✂
closed Sunday, Bank Holidays dinner and 15 to 31 August – **M** a la carte 3800/4900.

at Barajas E : 14 km – 28042 Madrid – ☎ 91 :

🏨 **Barajas,** av. de Logroño 305 ℰ 747 77 00, Telex 22255, Fax 747 87 17, ☂, ☒, ☞ – 🛗
🍽 📺 ☎ ⓞ – 🔬 25/675. 🖭 ⓞ ⅀ *VISA*. ✂ rest
M 5125 – ⊡ 1750 – **230 rm** 21600/27000.

🏨 **Alameda,** av. de Logroño 100 ℰ 747 48 00, Telex 43809, Fax 747 89 28, ☒, ▨ – 🛗 🍽 📺
☎ ⓐ ⓞ – 🔬 25/280. 🖭 ⓞ ⅀ *VISA*. ✂ rest
M 4400 – ⊡ 1200 – **145 rm** 16800/21000.

at San Sebastián de los Reyes N : 17 km – ⊠ 28700 San Sebastián de los Reyes – ☎ 91 :

XXX **Mesón Tejas Verdes,** ℰ 652 73 07, ☂, Castilian decor, ☞ – 🍽 ⓟ. 🖭 ⓞ ⅀ *VISA*. ✂
closed Sunday dinner, Bank Holidays dinner and August – **M** a la carte 2950/4700.

Moralzarzal 28411 Madrid 👭👭👭 J 18 – pop. – ☎ 91 :
♦Madrid 42.

XXX ⊛ **El Cenador de Salvador,** av. de España 30 ℰ 857 77 22, Fax 857 77 80, ☂, « Garden
terrace » – ⓟ. 🖭 ⓞ ⅀ *VISA*. ✂
closed Sunday dinner, Monday and 15 to 30 October – **M** a la carte 6400/8100
Spec. Cardos breseados con endivias (winter), Charlota de perdiz con berenjenas (season), Souflé
de chocolate cremoso.

Michelin Green Guides in English

		New York City
Austria	Greece	Portugal
Canada	Italy	Rome
England : The West Country	London	Scotland
France	Mexico	Spain
Germany	Netherlands	Switzerland
Great Britain	New England	Washington

See : Gothic Quarter★★ (Barri Gotic) : Cathedral★★ MX, Plaça del Rei★ MX 149, Frederic Marés Museum★★ (Museu F. Marès) MX – La Rambla★ LX, MY : Atarazanas and Maritim Museum★★ MY, Plaça Reial★ MY – Montcada st.★ (carrer de Montcada) NVX : Picasso Museum★ NV, Santa María del Mar Church★ NX – Montjuich★ (Montjuïc) : Museum of Catalonian Art★★★ (romanic and gothic collections★★★), Spanish Village★ (Poble espanyol), Joan Miró Foundation★ – Archeological Museum★ (Museo Arqueológico) – El Eixample : Holy Family★★ (Sagrada Familia) JU, Passeig de Gràcia★ HV, Casa Batlló★ HV B, La Pedrera or Casa Milà★ HV P – Güell Park★★ (Parque Güell) – Catalonian Music Palace★ (Palau de la Mùsica Catalana) MVY, Antoni Tàpies Foundation★ HV S.

Other curiosities : Pedralbes Monastery★. Zoo★ (Parc zoologic) KX Tibidabo (☀★★).

🏌, 🏌 of Prat S : 16 km ✆ 379 02 78 – 🏌 of Sant Cugat NW : 20 km ✆ 674 39 58 – 🏌 of Vallromanas NW : 25 km ✆ 568 03 62.

✈ Barcelona S : 12 km ✆ 317 10 11 – Iberia : Paseo de Gracia 30, ✉ 08007, ✆ 301 68 00 HV – and Aviaco : aeropuerto ✆ 379 24 58.

🚗 Sants ✆ 490 75 91.

⛴. to the Balearic islands : Cía. Trasmediterránea, muelle Barcelona-Estación Marítima 1, ✉ 08039, ✆ 317 42 62, Fax 412 28 42.

🛈 Gran Vía de les Corts Catalanes 658, ✉ 08010, ✆ 301 74 43, and at airport ✆ 325 58 29 – R.A.C.C. Santaló 8, ✉ 08021, ✆ 200 33 11, Fax 200 39 64.

Madrid 627 – Bilbao 607 – Lérida/Lleida 169 – Perpignan 187 – Tarragona 109 – Toulouse 388 – Valencia 361 – Zaragoza 307.

Plans on following pages

Old Town and the Gothic Quarter Ramblas, pl. S. Jaume, via Laietana, Passeig Nacional, Passeig de Colom

🏨 **Le Meridien Barcelona,** Ramblas 111, ✉ 08002, ✆ 318 62 00, Telex 54634, Fax 301 77 76 – 🛗 🗏 📺 🕭 👃 🚗 – 🛋 25/200. 🝏 ⓪ 🝏 🝏. 🛇   LX **b**
M 3700 – ⛛ 2000 – **209 rm** 29800/37300.

🏨 **Colón,** av. de la Catedral 7, ✉ 08002, ✆ 301 14 04, Telex 52654, Fax 317 29 15 – 🛗 🗏 📺 🕭 – 🛋 25/200. 🝏 ⓪ 🝏 🝏. 🛇 rest   MV **e**
M 3200 – ⛛ 1250 – **155 rm** 27000/31000.

🏨 **Rivoli Rambla,** Rambla dels Estudis 128, ✉ 08002, ✆ 302 66 43, Telex 99222, Fax 317 50 53 – 🛗 🗏 📺 🕭 👃 – 🛋 25/180. 🝏 ⓪ 🝏 🝏. 🛇   LX **r**
M a la carte 4000/5000 – ⛛ 1900 – **90 rm** 19200/24000.

🏨 **Royal** coffee shop only, Rambla dels Estudis 117, ✉ 08002, ✆ 301 94 00, Telex 97565, Fax 317 31 79 – 🛗 🗏 📺 🕭 🚗 – 🛋 25/100. 🝏 ⓪ 🝏 🝏.   LX **e**
⛛ 1200 – **108 rm** 13500/21800.

🏨 **Almirante** without rest, Via Laietana 42, ✉ 08003, ✆ 268 30 20, Fax 268 31 92 – 🛗 🗏 📺 🕭 🚗 – 🛋 25/40. 🝏 ⓪ 🝏 🝏. 🛇   MV **d**
⛛ 1500 – **76 rm** 16000/22500.

🏨 **Gravina** coffee shop only, Gravina 12, ✉ 08001, ✆ 301 68 68, Telex 99370, Fax 317 28 38 – 🛗 🗏 📺 🕭 – 🛋 25/50. 🝏 ⓪ 🝏 🝏. 🛇   HX **d**
⛛ 700 – **60 rm** 9900/13900.

🏨 **Montecarlo** without rest, Rambla dels Estudis 124, ✉ 08002, ✆ 317 58 00, Telex 93345, Fax 317 57 50 – 🛗 🗏 📺 🕭 👃 🚗. 🝏 ⓪ 🝏 🝏   LX **r**
⛛ 595 – **75 rm** 7900/11900.

🏨 **Reding,** Gravina 5, ✉ 08001, ✆ 412 10 97, Fax 268 34 82 – 🛗 🗏 📺 🕭 🚗. 🝏 ⓪ 🝏 🝏 🝏. 🛇   HX **d**
M 1500 – ⛛ 850 – **44 rm** 16500.

🏨 **Atlantis** without rest, Pelai 20, ✉ 08001, ✆ 318 90 12, Fax 412 09 14 – 🛗 🗏 📺 🕭. 🝏 🝏 🝏. 🛇 – ⛛ 850 – **42 rm** 12000/16000.   HX **a**

🏨 **Metropol** without rest, Ample 31, ✉ 08002, ✆ 315 40 11, Fax 319 12 76 – 🛗 🗏 📺 🕭. 🝏 ⓪ 🝏 🝏. 🛇   NY **r**
⛛ 800 – **68 rm** 7700/10800.

🏨 **Regencia Colón** without rest, Sagristans 13, ✉ 08002, ✆ 318 98 58, Telex 98175, Fax 317 28 22 – 🛗 🗏 📺 🕭. 🝏 ⓪ 🝏 🝏. 🛇   MV **r**
⛛ 950 – **55 rm** 8700/12700.

🏨 **Rialto** coffee shop only, Ferrán 42, ✉ 08002, ✆ 318 52 12, Telex 97206, Fax 315 38 19 – 🛗 🗏 📺 🕭 – 🛋 25/50. 🝏 ⓪ 🝏 🝏   MX **s**
⛛ 675 – **132 rm** 9880/13500.

🏨 **Lleó** without rest, Pelai 24, ✉ 08001, ✆ 318 13 12, Telex 98338, Fax 412 26 57 – 🛗 🗏 📺 🕭 👃. ⓪ 🝏 🝏. 🛇   HX **a**
⛛ 850 – **75 rm** 8000/11000.

🏨 **Turín,** Pintor Fortuny 9, ✉ 08001, ✆ 302 48 12 – 🛗 🗏 📺 🕭 👃. 🝏 ⓪ 🝏 🝏. 🛇 rest   LX **v**
M 990 – ⛛ 600 – **60 rm** 9900/14000.

🏨 **Park H.,** av. Marqués de l'Argentera 11, ✉ 08003, ✆ 319 60 00, Telex 99883, Fax 319 45 19 – 🛗 🗏 📺 🕭 👃 🚗. 🝏 ⓪ 🝏 🝏. 🛇   NX **e**
M 2250 – ⛛ 1150 – **87 rm** 11000/14500.

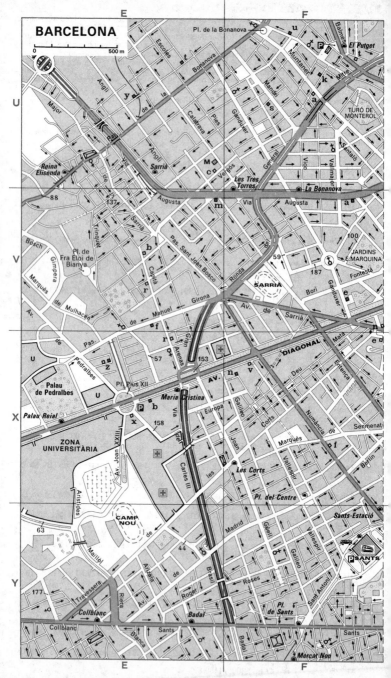

BARCELONA

0   500 m

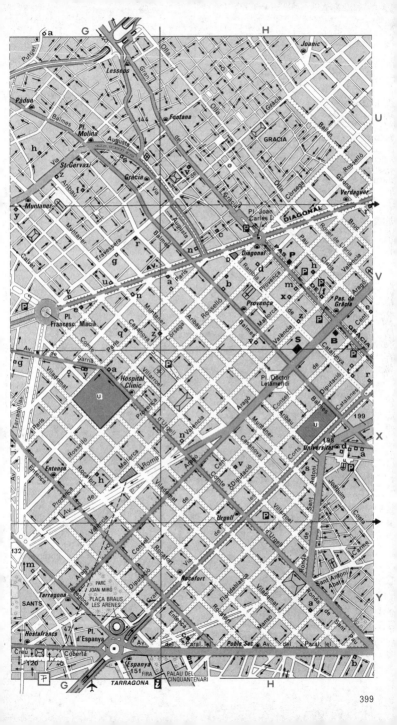

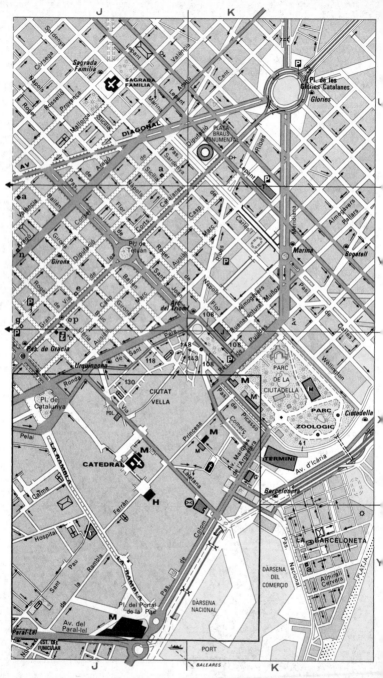

STREET INDEX TO BARCELONA TOWN PLAN

BARCELONA

We suggest:

For a successful tour,
that you prepare it
in advance.

Michelin maps and guides
will give you much useful
information on route planning,
places of interest,
accommodation, prices etc.

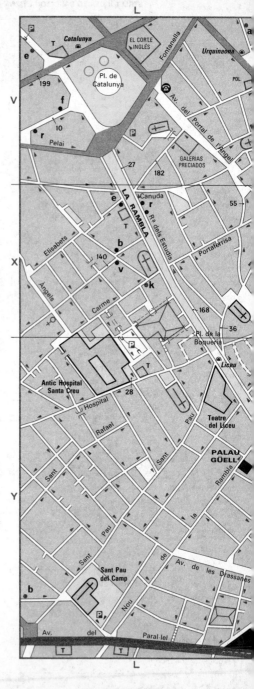

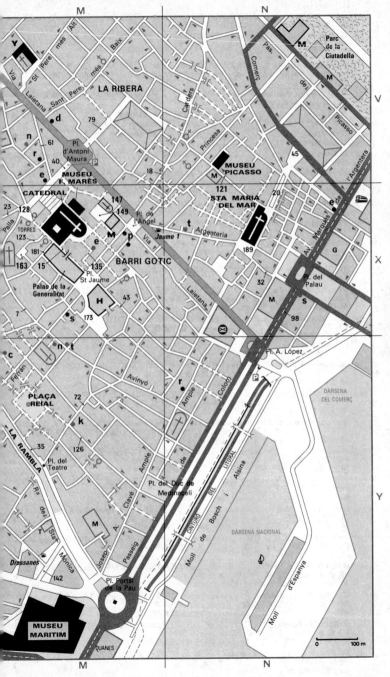

🏨 **Suizo,** pl. del Angel 12, ⊠ 08002, ℰ 315 41 11, Telex 97206, Fax 315 38 19 – 📳 🗐 📺 ☎.
ᴬᴱ ⓞ 🖙 𝘝𝘐𝘚𝘈 – **M** 2750 – ⊑ 675 – **48 rm** 9880/13500. MX **p**

🏨 **Gótico** without rest, Jaume I-14, ⊠ 08002, ℰ 315 22 11, Telex 97206, Fax 315 38 19 – 📳
🗐 📺 ☎. ᴬᴱ ⓞ 🖙 𝘝𝘐𝘚𝘈
⊑ 675 – **70 rm** 9330/12950. MX **p**

XXX **La Odisea,** Copons 7, ⊠ 08002, ℰ 302 36 92, Fax 412 32 67 – 🗐. ᴬᴱ ⓞ 🖙 𝘝𝘐𝘚𝘈 MV **n**
closed Saturday lunch, Sunday, Holy Week and 9 August-9 September – **M** a la carte
3725/6400.

XX **Agut d'Avignon,** Trinitat 3, ⊠ 08002, ℰ 302 60 34, Fax 302 53 18 – 🗐. ᴬᴱ ⓞ 🖙 𝘝𝘐𝘚𝘈. ⋙
M a la carte 4270/6180. MY **n**

XX **Nostromo,** Ripoll 16, ⊠ 08002, ℰ 412 24 55 – 🗐. ᴬᴱ ⓞ 🖙 𝘝𝘐𝘚𝘈. ⋙ MV **r**
closed Sunday and 15 August-9 September – **M** a la carte 3475/3900.

XX **Quo Vadis,** Carmen 7, ⊠ 08001, ℰ 302 40 72 – 🗐. ᴬᴱ ⓞ 🖙 𝘝𝘐𝘚𝘈 LX **k**
closed Sunday – **M** a la carte 4150/5675.

XX **El Gran Café,** Avinyó 9, ⊠ 08002, ℰ 318 79 86, « Early 20C style » – 🗐. ᴬᴱ ⓞ 🖙 𝘝𝘐𝘚𝘈.
⋙ MY **t**
closed Saturday lunch, Sunday and 25 August-15 September – **M** a la carte 3675/5275.

XX **Brasserie Flo,** Junqueres 10, ⊠ 08003, ℰ 319 31 02, Fax 317 35 48 – 🗐. ᴬᴱ ⓞ 🖙 𝘝𝘐𝘚𝘈
M a la carte approx. 3800. LV **a**

XX **Senyor Parellada,** Argentería 37, ⊠ 08003, ℰ 315 40 10 – 🗐. ᴬᴱ ⓞ 🖙 𝘝𝘐𝘚𝘈. ⋙ NX **t**
closed Sunday and Bank Holidays – **M** a la carte 2350/3400.

XX **7 Portes,** passeig d'Isabel II - 14, ⊠ 08003, ℰ 319 30 33, Fax 319 46 62 – 🗐. ᴬᴱ ⓞ 🖙 𝘝𝘐𝘚𝘈. ⋙
M a la carte 2605/3550. NX **s**

X **Can Solé,** Sant Carles 4, ⊠ 08003, ℰ 319 50 12, Seafood – 🗐. ᴬᴱ ⓞ 🖙 𝘝𝘐𝘚𝘈. ⋙ KY **a**
closed Saturday dinner and Sunday – **M** a la carte 3700/4800.

South of Av. Diagonal pl. de Catalunya, Gran Vía de les Corts Catalanes, Passeig de Gràcia,
Balmes, Muntaner, Aragó

🏨🏨🏨 **Ritz,** Gran Vía de les Corts Catalanes 668, ⊠ 08010, ℰ 318 52 00, Telex 52739,
Fax 318 01 48 – 📳 🗐 📺 ☎ – 🛗 25/350. ᴬᴱ ⓞ 🖙 𝘝𝘐𝘚𝘈. ⋙ JV **p**
M 6950 – ⊑ 2050 – **158 rm** 32800/41000.

🏨🏨🏨 **Princesa Sofía,** pl. de Pius XII 4, ⊠ 08028, ℰ 330 71 11, Telex 51032, Fax 330 76 21, ⟨,
📳, 🔲 – 📳 🗐 📺 ☎ ⟸ – 🛗 25/1200. ᴬᴱ ⓞ 🖙 𝘝𝘐𝘚𝘈. ⋙ EX **x**
M 4400 rest. **Le Gourmet** (closed Sunday, Monday and August) a la carte 3750/5250 and rest.
L'Empordá (closed Saturday, Sunday and July) a la carte 3450/5000 – ⊑ 1700 – **505 rm**
21500/34500.

🏨🏨 **Barcelona Hilton,** av. Diagonal 589, ⊠ 08014, ℰ 419 22 33, Telex 99623, Fax 322 52 91,
🖙 – 📳 🗐 📺 🕭 – 🛗 25/800. ᴬᴱ ⓞ 🖙 𝘝𝘐𝘚𝘈. ⋙ FX **v**
M 3250 – ⊑ 2300 – **290 rm** 31000/40000.

🏨🏨 **Meliá Barcelona Sarriá,** av. de Sarriá 50, ⊠ 08029, ℰ 410 60 60, Telex 51638,
Fax 321 51 79, ⟨ – 📳 🗐 📺 ☎ ⟸ – 🛗 25/900. ᴬᴱ ⓞ 🖙 𝘝𝘐𝘚𝘈. ⋙ FV **n**
M 5000 – ⊑ 2000 – **291 rm** 24000/30000.

🏨🏨 **Havana Palace and Rest. Grand Place,** Gran Vía de les Corts Catalanes 647, ⊠ 08010,
ℰ 412 11 15, Telex 51531, Fax 412 26 11 – 📳 🗐 📺 ☎ ⟸ – 🛗 25/200. ᴬᴱ ⓞ 🖙 𝘝𝘐𝘚𝘈. ⋙ JV **e**
M 4300 – ⊑ 1800 – **145 rm** 25250/31600.

🏨🏨 **Majestic,** passeig de Gràcia 70, ⊠ 08008, ℰ 488 17 17, Telex 52211, Fax 488 18 80, 🔳
– 📳 🗐 📺 ☎ – 🛗 25/600. ᴬᴱ ⓞ 🖙 𝘝𝘐𝘚𝘈 HV **f**
M 3300 – ⊑ 1400 – **335 rm** 14300/23800.

🏨🏨 **Diplomatic and Rest. La Salsa,** Pau Claris 122, ⊠ 08009, ℰ 317 31 00, Telex 54701,
Fax 318 65 31, 🔳 – 📳 🗐 📺 ☎ – 🛗 25/250. ᴬᴱ. HV **e**
M (closed Sunday) 5700 – ⊑ 1750 – **217 rm** 21200/26500.

🏨🏨 **Calderón,** Rambla de Catalunya 26, ⊠ 08007, ℰ 301 00 00, Telex 99529, Fax 317 31 57,
🔳, 🔲 – 📳 🗐 📺 ☎ ⟸ – 🛗 25/200. ᴬᴱ ⓞ 🖙 𝘝𝘐𝘚𝘈. ⋙ HX **t**
M a la carte 4500/7000 – ⊑ 1400 – **248 rm** 19400/24200.

🏨🏨 **Avenida Palace,** Gran Vía de les Corts Catalanes 605, ⊠ 08007, ℰ 301 96 00, Telex 54734,
Fax 318 12 34 – 📳 🗐 📺 ☎ – 🛗 25/300. ᴬᴱ ⓞ 🖙 𝘝𝘐𝘚𝘈 HX **r**
M 5100 – ⊑ 1400 – **211 rm** 35000/41000.

🏨🏨 **G.H. Catalonia,** Balmes 142, ⊠ 08008, ℰ 415 90 90, Telex 97532, Fax 415 22 09 – 📳 🗐
📺 ☎ 🕭 ⟸ – 🛗 48/260. ᴬᴱ ⓞ 🖙 𝘝𝘐𝘚𝘈. ⋙ HV **b**
M 2450 – ⊑ 1500 – **84 rm** 18900/24900.

🏨🏨 **Condes de Barcelona,** Passeig de Gràcia 75, ⊠ 08008, ℰ 487 37 37, Telex 51531,
Fax 216 08 35 – 📳 🗐 📺 ☎ – 🛗 25/300. ᴬᴱ ⓞ 🖙 𝘝𝘐𝘚𝘈. ⋙ HV **m**
M a la carte 4700/3200 – ⊑ 1500 – **109 rm** 17900/28000.

🏨🏨 **Gallery H.,** Rosselló 249, ⊠ 08008, ℰ 415 99 11, Telex 97518, Fax 415 91 84, 🕿 – 📳 🗐
📺 ☎ 🕭 ⟸ – 🛗 25/200. ᴬᴱ ⓞ 🖙 𝘝𝘐𝘚𝘈. ⋙ HV **d**
M a la carte 2840/4875 – ⊑ 1400 – **115 rm** 20000/25000.

🏨🏨 **St. Moritz** without rest, Diputació, 262 bis, ⊠ 08007, ℰ 412 15 00, Fax 412 12 36 – 📳 🗐
📺 ☎ 🕭 ⟸ – 🛗 25/140. ᴬᴱ ⓞ 𝘝𝘐𝘚𝘈. ⋙ JV **g**
⊑ 1300 – **92 rm** 15800/24000.

🏨🏨 **Gran Derby** without rest, Loreto 28, ✉ 08029, 𝄐 322 20 62, Telex 97429, Fax 419 68 20 - |🛗| 🗏 📺 ☎ 🚗 - 🔬 25/100. 🆎 ⓸ 🛦 𝗩𝗜𝗦𝗔   GX **g**
⫩ 1250 - **42 rm** 23000.

🏨🏨 **Balmes** without rest, coffee shop only, Mallorca 216, ✉ 08008, 𝄐 451 19 14, Fax 451 00 49, Terrace with ⊇ ⟩ - |🛗| 🗏 📺 ☎ - 🔬 25/70. 🆎 ⓸ 🛦 𝗩𝗜𝗦𝗔   HV **v**
⫩ 975 - **96 rm** 12000/16500.

🏨🏨 **Derby** without rest, coffee shop only, Loreto 21, ✉ 08029, 𝄐 322 32 15, Telex 97429, Fax 410 08 62 - |🛗| 🗏 📺 ☎ 🚗 - 🔬 25/100. 🆎 ⓸ 🛦 𝗩𝗜𝗦𝗔   FX **e**
⫩ 1250 - **116 rm** 14500/22000.

🏨🏨 **Alexandra,** Mallorca 251, ✉ 08008, 𝄐 487 05 05, Telex 81107, Fax 216 06 06 - |🛗| 🗏 📺 ☎ 🚗 - 🔬 25/100. 🆎 ⓸ 🛦 𝗩𝗜𝗦𝗔   HV **x**
M 3850 - ⫩ 1350 - **75 rm** 18400/22900.

🏨🏨 **Astoria** without rest, Paris 203, ✉ 08036, 𝄐 209 83 11, Telex 81129, Fax 202 30 08 - |🛗| 🗏 📺 ☎ - 🔬 25/30. 🆎 ⓸ 🛦 𝗩𝗜𝗦𝗔   HV **a**
⫩ 975 - **114 rm** 9500/15400.

🏨🏨 **Master,** Valencia 105, ✉ 08011, 𝄐 323 62 15, Telex 81258, Fax 323 43 89 - |🛗| 🗏 📺 ☎ 🚗 - 🔬 25/170. 🆎 ⓸ 🛦 𝗩𝗜𝗦𝗔 ⁑ rest   HX **n**
M 3500 - ⫩ 1200 - **81 rm** 16800/21200.

🏨🏨 **Cristal,** Diputació 257, ✉ 08007, 𝄐 487 87 78, Telex 54560, Fax 487 90 30 - |🛗| 🗏 📺 ☎ 🚗 - 🔬 25/70. 🆎 ⓸ 🛦 𝗩𝗜𝗦𝗔 ⁑   HX **t**
M 3300 - ⫩ 925 - **148 rm** 13600/22000.

🏨🏨 **Numancia,** Numancia 74, ✉ 08029, 𝄐 322 44 51, Fax 410 76 42 - |🛗| 🗏 📺 ☎ 🚗 - 🔬 25/70. 🆎 ⓸ 🛦 𝗩𝗜𝗦𝗔 ⁑   FX **f**
⫩ 900 - **140 rm** 12100/16700.

🏨🏨 **Grand Passage Suites H.,** Muntaner 212, ✉ 08036, 𝄐 201 03 06, Fax 201 00 04 - |🛗| 🗏 📺 ☎ - 🔬 25/80. 🆎 ⓸ 🛦 𝗩𝗜𝗦𝗔 ⁑   GV **n**
M (closed Sunday)) 3850 - ⫩ 1350 - **41 rm** 18400/22900.

🏨🏨 **Núñez Urgel,** Comte d'Urgell 232, ✉ 08036, 𝄐 322 41 53, Fax 419 01 06 - |🛗| 🗏 📺 ☎ 🚗 - 🔬 25/100. 🆎 ⓸ 🛦 𝗩𝗜𝗦𝗔 ⁑ rest   GX **a**
M a la carte 3200/5300 - ⫩ 1000 - **120 rm** 13500/20000.

🏨🏨 **Regente,** rambla de Catalunya 76, ✉ 08008, 𝄐 215 25 70, Telex 51939, Fax 487 32 27, ⊇ - |🛗| 🗏 ☎ - 🔬 25/30. 🆎 ⓸ 🛦 𝗩𝗜𝗦𝗔   HV **z**
M 3000 - ⫩ 1100 - **78 rm** 14300/21500.

🏨🏨 **Expo H.,** Mallorca 1, ✉ 08014, 𝄐 325 12 12, Telex 54147, Fax 325 11 44, ⊇ - |🛗| 🗏 📺 ☎ 🚗 - 🔬 25/800. 🆎 ⓸ 🛦 𝗩𝗜𝗦𝗔 ⁑   GY **m**
M 2225 - ⫩ 1000 - **432 rm** 18400/23750.

🏨🏨 **Duques de Bergara,** Bergara 11, ✉ 08002, 𝄐 301 51 51, Telex 81257, Fax 317 34 42 - |🛗| 🗏 📺 ☎ - 🔬 25/80. 🆎 ⓸ 🛦 𝗩𝗜𝗦𝗔 ⁑   LV **f**
M 2310 - ⫩ 1200 - **56 rm** 14500/21900.

🏨 **Regina** without rest, coffee shop only, Bergara 2, ✉ 08002, 𝄐 301 32 32, Telex 59380, Fax 318 23 26 - |🛗| 🗏 📺 ☎. 🆎 ⓸ 🛦 𝗩𝗜𝗦𝗔 ⁑   LV **r**
⫩ 950 - **102 rm** 9800/14600.

🏨 **Paral·lel** without rest, no ⫩, Poeta Cabanyes 7, ✉ 08004, 𝄐 329 11 04, Fax 442 16 56 - |🛗| 🗏 📺 ☎. 🆎 ⓸ 𝗩𝗜𝗦𝗔   HY **b**
66 rm 6250/9500.

🏵🏵🏵🏵🏵 **Beltxenea,** Mallorca 275, ✉ 08008, 𝄐 215 30 24, Fax 487 00 81, ⊞, « Garden terrace » - 🗏. 🆎 ⓸ 🛦 𝗩𝗜𝗦𝗔 ⁑ - closed Saturday lunch and Sunday - **M** a la carte approx. 7000.   HV **h**

🏵🏵🏵🏵 ✿ **La Dama,** av. Diagonal 423, ✉ 08036, 𝄐 202 06 86, Fax 200 72 99 - 🗏. 🆎 ⓸ 🛦 𝗩𝗜𝗦𝗔 ⁑ **M** a la carte 4300/6400   HV **a**
Spec. Ensalada tibia de cigalas al vinagre de naranja, Gratén de bogavante sobre lecho de espinacas, Carro de pasteleria y de quesos artesanos.

🏵🏵🏵🏵 **Finisterre,** av. Diagonal 469, ✉ 08036, 𝄐 439 55 76 - 🗏. 🆎 ⓸ 𝗩𝗜𝗦𝗔 ⁑   GV **e**
closed Sunday in July and August - **M** a la carte 4650/5800.

🏵🏵🏵 **Oliver y Hardy,** av. Diagonal 593, ✉ 08014, 𝄐 419 31 81, ⊞ - 🗏. 🆎 ⓸ 🛦 𝗩𝗜𝗦𝗔 FX **n**
closed Sunday - **M** a la carte 4100/5600.

🏵🏵🏵 ✿ **Jaume de Provença,** Provença 88, ✉ 08029, 𝄐 430 00 29, Fax 439 29 50 - 🗏. 🆎 ⓸ 🛦 𝗩𝗜𝗦𝗔   GX **h**
closed Sunday dinner, Monday, Holy Week and August - **M** a la carte 4100/5450
Spec. ''Panellets'' de foie-gras, Turbot sobre caviar de sanfaina, Pastel de manitas de cerdo con ciruelas.

🏵🏵🏵 **Bel Air,** Córsega 286, ✉ 08008, 𝄐 237 75 88, Fax 237 95 26, Rice dishes - 🗏. 🆎 ⓸ 🛦 𝗩𝗜𝗦𝗔   HV **b**
closed Sunday - **M** a la carte 5000/6300.

🏵🏵🏵 **Tikal,** Rambla de Catalunya 5, ✉ 08007, 𝄐 302 22 21 - 🗏. 🆎 ⓸ 🛦 𝗩𝗜𝗦𝗔 ⁑   LV **e**
closed Sunday - **M** a la carte 3400/5200.

🏵🏵 **Rías de Galicia,** Lleida 7, ✉ 08004, 𝄐 424 81 52, Fax 426 13 07, Seafood - 🗏. 🆎 ⓸ 🛦 𝗩𝗜𝗦𝗔 ⁑ - **M** a la carte 4000/6000.   HY **e**

🏵🏵 **Vinya Rosa - Magí,** av. de Sarriá 17, ✉ 08029, 𝄐 430 00 03, Fax 430 00 41 - 🗏. 🆎 ⓸ 🛦 𝗩𝗜𝗦𝗔 - closed Saturday lunch, Sunday and Holy Week - **M** a la carte 3080/5170.   GX **y**

XX **Gorría,** Diputació 421, ✉ 08013, ☎ 245 11 64, Basque rest. – ▤. AE ⓓ E VISA — JU **a**
closed Sunday and 15 to 31 August – **M** a la carte 3640/5025.

XX **La Sopeta,** Muntaner 6, ✉ 08011, ☎ 323 56 32 – ▤. AE ⓓ E VISA. ✻ — HX **s**
closed Sunday and 15 to 30 August – **M** a la carte 2950/4500.

XX ✿ **Ca l'Isidre,** Les Flors 12, ✉ 08001, ☎ 441 11 39 – ▤. AE VISA — LY **b**
closed Sunday and Bank Holidays – **M** a la carte 3800/5500
Spec. Terrina de foie gras trufado, Sesos a la manteca negra, Solomillo al bañuls y trufa.

XX **Casa Chus,** av. Diagonal 339 bis, ✉ 08037, ☎ 207 02 15 – ▤. AE ⓓ E VISA — HV **r**
closed Sunday dinner – **M** a la carte 3625/5850.

XX **Alt Berlín,** Sabino Arana 54, ✉ 08028, ☎ 339 01 66, Fax 339 05 58, German rest. – ▤. AE ⓓ E VISA — EX **b**
M a la carte 3450/5075.

X **L'Aram,** Aragó 305 ☎ 207 01 88 – ▤. AE ⓓ E VISA. ✻ — JV **n**
closed Saturday lunch, Sunday, Holy Week and 14 August-14 September – **M** a la carte 3750/4775.

X **El Pescador,** Mallorca 314, ✉ 08037, ☎ 207 10 24, Seafood – ▤. AE ⓓ E VISA. ✻ – *closed Sunday* – **M** a la carte 4250/5700. — JV **a**

X **Els Perols de l'Empordá,** Villarroel 88, ✉ 08011, ☎ 323 10 33, Ampurdan rest – ▤. AE ⓓ E VISA — HX **v**
closed Sunday dinner, Monday, Holy Week and 15 to 30 August – **M** a la carte 2400/3900.

X **Azpiolea,** Casanova 167, ✉ 08036, ☎ 430 90 30, Basque rest. – ▤. ⓓ E VISA. ✻ — GV **q**
closed Sunday and 15 August-15 September – **M** a la carte 3450/4175.

North of Av. Diagonal vía Augusta, Capitá Arenas, ronda General Mitre, passeig de la Bonanova, av. de Pedralbes

🏨 **Presidente,** av. Diagonal 570, ✉ 08021, ☎ 200 21 11, Telex 52180, Fax 209 51 06, ⛱ – |‡| ▤ TV ☎ – 🎤 25/420. AE ⓓ E VISA. ✻ — GV **u**
M 3750 – ☕ 1500 – **152 rm** 35000/41000.

🏨 **Hesperia** coffee shop only, Vergós 20, ✉ 08017, ☎ 204 55 51, Telex 98403, Fax 204 43 92 – |‡| ▤ TV ☎ 🚗 – 🎤 25/150. AE ⓓ E VISA. ✻ — EU **c**
☕ 1200 – **139 rm** 15700/19625.

🏨 **Suite H.,** Muntaner 505, ✉ 08022, ☎ 212 80 12, Telex 99077, Fax 211 23 17 – |‡| ▤ TV ☎ 🚗 – 🎤 25/90. AE ⓓ E VISA. ✻ — FU **a**
M 2420 – ☕ 1500 – **70 rm** 18500/24900.

🏨 **Balmoral** without rest, vía Augusta 5, ✉ 08006, ☎ 217 87 00, Telex 54087, Fax 415 14 21 – |‡| ▤ TV ☎ 🚗 – 🎤 25/250. AE ⓓ E VISA. ✻ — HV **n**
☕ 900 – **94 rm** 14300/22000.

🏨 **Cóndor,** via Augusta 127, ✉ 08006, ☎ 209 45 11, Telex 52925, Fax 202 27 13 – |‡| ▤ TV ☎ – 🎤 25/50. AE ⓓ E VISA. ✻ — GU **z**
M 2400 – ☕ 1200 – **78 rm** 13900/19200.

🏨 **Arenas** coffee shop dinner only, Capitá Arenas 20, ✉ 08034, ☎ 280 03 03, Telex 54990, Fax 280 33 92 – |‡| ▤ TV ☎ – 🎤 25/50. AE ⓓ E VISA. ✻ — EX **r**
☕ 925 – **59 rm** 17600/22000.

🏨 **Victoria,** av. de Pedralbes 16 bis, ✉ 08034, ☎ 280 15 15, Telex 98302, Fax 280 52 67, 🌴, ⛱ – |‡| ▤ TV ☎ 🚗. AE E VISA. ✻ — EX **z**
M 1500 – ☕ 1250 – **79 suites** 19400/24250

🏨 **Park Putxet,** Putxet 68, ✉ 08023, ☎ 212 51 58, Telex 98718, Fax 418 58 17 – |‡| ▤ TV ☎ 🚗 – 🎤 25/200. AE ⓓ E VISA. ✻ — GU **a**
M 1815 – ☕ 950 – **141 rm** 11500/14500.

🏨 **Belagua,** vía Augusta 89, ✉ 08006, ☎ 237 39 40, Telex 99643, Fax 415 30 62 – |‡| ▤ TV ☎ – 🎤 25 /90. AE ⓓ E VISA. ✻ rest — GU **s**
M 3200 – ☕ 900 – **72 rm** 13300/16700.

🏨 **Mitre** without rest, Bertrán 9, ✉ 08023, ☎ 212 11 04, Telex 98671, Fax 418 94 81 – |‡| ▤ TV ☎. AE ⓓ E VISA — FU **t**
☕ 725 – **57 rm** 13200/16500.

🏨 **Condado,** Aribau 201, ✉ 08021, ☎ 200 23 11, Telex 54546, Fax 200 25 86 – |‡| ▤ TV ☎. AE ⓓ E VISA. ✻ rest — GV **g**
M 1850 – ☕ 900 – **88 rm** 12800/16000.

🏨 **Pedralbes** coffee shop dinner only, Fontcuberta 4, ✉ 08034, ☎ 203 71 12, Telex 99850, Fax 205 70 65 – |‡| ▤ TV ☎ – 🎤 25/35. AE ⓓ E VISA. ✻ — EV **b**
☕ 900 – **28 rm** 12800/15950.

🏨 **Covadonga** without rest, av. Diagonal 596, ✉ 08021, ☎ 209 55 11, Telex 93394, Fax 209 58 33 – |‡| ▤ TV ☎. AE ⓓ E VISA. ✻ — GV **v**
☕ 500 – **85 rm** 8200/10600.

🏨 **Bonanova Park** without rest, Capitá Arenas, 51, ✉ 08034, ☎ 204 09 00, Telex 98671, Fax 204 50 14 – |‡| TV ☎ – 🎤 25/35. AE ⓓ E VISA. ✻ — EV **r**
☕ 550 – **60 rm** 10000/12500.

XXXX ✿ **Via Veneto,** Ganduxer 10, ✉ 08021, ℰ 200 72 44, Fax 201 60 95, « Early 20C decor »
– ■. 🅰🅴 ⓞ 🄴 *VISA*. ✍ FV **e**
closed Saturday lunch and Sunday except July-August – **M** a la carte 4590/6130
Spec. Mil-hojas de trufas negras con higado de pato fresco, puerros y col, Rodaballo a la vinagreta
de anchoas, Tarta de mango sobre fondo de coco rallado.

XXXX **Reno,** Tuset 27, ✉ 08006, ℰ 200 91 29, Fax 414 41 14 – ■. 🅰🅴 ⓞ 🄴 *VISA*. ✍ GV **r**
M a la carte 5500/7500.

XXX ✿✿ **Neichel,** av. de Pedralbes 16 bis, ✉ 08034, ℰ 203 84 08, Fax 205 63 69 – ■. 🅰🅴 ⓞ
🄴 *VISA* EX **z**
closed Sunday, Bank Holidays, Holy Week, 15 August-15 September and Christmas – **M** a la
carte 5600/6700
Spec. Ensalada de bacalao y salmón al aceite de cep y sésamo, Salmonetes "Rotie" al hinojo
braseado, Lomo de corderito relleno con setas de trufas negras y su jugo.

XXX ✿ **Botafumeiro,** Major de Gràcia, 81, ✉ 08012, ℰ 218 42 30, Fax 415 58 48, Seafood –
■. 🅰🅴 ⓞ 🄴 *VISA*. ✍ HU **v**
closed Sunday dinner, Monday, and Holy Week – **M** a la carte 3700/5400.
Spec. Arroz a la marinera, Salpicón de merluza, Rodaballo a las brasas con salsa de limón.

XXX ✿ **Eldorado Petit,** Dolors Monserdá 51, ✉ 08017, ℰ 204 51 53, Fax 280 57 02, 🍴 – ■.
🅰🅴 🄴 *VISA*. ✍ EU **y**
closed Sunday and 15 days in August – **M** a la carte 4200/6750
Spec. Ensalada templada de salmonetes en escabeche de "Russinyols", Lomo de lubina en "papillote", Rabo de buey relleno con setas de bosque (autumn).

XXX ✿ **Azulete,** Vía Augusta 281, ✉ 08017, ℰ 203 59 43, 🍴 – 🅰🅴 ⓞ 🄴 *VISA* EV **m**
closed Saturday lunch, Sunday and 20 August-8 September – **M** a la carte 4500/6400.
Spec. Ensalada de gambas a la vinagreta de rúcola, Turbot justo salteado con salsifies y albahaca
frita, Pichón asado con cebollitas y rossinyols.

XXX **El Túnel de Muntaner,** Sant Màrius 22, ✉ 08022, ℰ 212 60 74 – ■. 🅰🅴 ⓞ 🄴 *VISA*
closed Sunday – **M** a la carte 3900/4700. FU **k**

XXX **Paradis Roncesvalles,** vía Augusta 201, ✉ 08021, ℰ 209 01 25, Fax 209 12 95 – ■. 🅰🅴
ⓞ 🄴 *VISA*. ✍ FV **a**
closed Sunday dinner – **M** a la carte 3700/4950.

XX **La Petite Marmite,** Madrazo 68, ✉ 08006, ℰ 201 48 79 – ■. 🅰🅴 ⓞ 🄴 *VISA*. ✍ GU **f**
closed Sunday, Bank Holidays, Holy Week and August – **M** a la carte 2825/3375.

XX ✿ **Florián,** Bertrand i Serra 20, ✉ 08022, ℰ 212 46 27, Fax 418 72 30 – ■. ⓞ 🄴 *VISA*. ✍
closed Sunday and 15 August-15 September – **M** a la carte 4900/7000 FU **s**
Spec. Una trufa entera asada al horno y envuelta en tocino, Rodaballo al horno con pimientos
verdes, Rabo de buey al Cabernet Sauvignon.

XX **El Trapío,** Esperanza 25, ✉ 08017, ℰ 211 58 17, 🍴, « Terrace » – 🅰🅴 ⓞ 🄴 *VISA*. ✍
closed Sunday and Monday lunch – **M** a la carte approx. 5000. EU **t**

XX **El Asador de Aranda,** av. del Tibidabo 31, ✉ 08022, ℰ 417 01 15, 🍴, Roast lamb,
« Former palace » – *VISA*. ✍ by Balmes FU
closed Sunday dinner – **M** a la carte approx. 4000.

XX ✿ **El Racó d'En Freixa,** Sant Elíes 22, ✉ 08006, ℰ 209 75 59 – ■. 🅰🅴 ⓞ 🄴 *VISA*. ✍
closed Bank Holiday dinner, Monday, Holy Week and 15 August-15 September – **M** a la carte
3400/5400 GU **h**
Spec. Armonía de frutos de mar al caviar, Bacalao fresco con hortalizas a la griega, Pichón de
masía en hábito verde.

XX **Gaig,** passeig de Maragall 402, ✉ 08031, ℰ 429 10 17 – ■. 🅰🅴 ⓞ 🄴 *VISA*
closed Bank Holidays dinner, Monday, Holy Week and August – **M** a la carte 2800/3975.
N : by Travessera de Gràcia HU

XX **Roig Robi,** Séneca 20, ✉ 08006, ℰ 218 92 22, 🍴, « Patio - Terrace » – ■. 🅰🅴 ⓞ 🄴 *VISA*.
✍ HV **c**
closed Sunday and Bank Holidays – **M** a la carte 3900/5000.

XX **Arcs de Sant Gervasi,** Santaló 103, ✉ 08021, ℰ 201 92 77 – ■. 🅰🅴 ⓞ 🄴 *VISA*. ✍
M a la carte approx. 3500. GV **y**

X **Es Plá,** Sant Gervasi de Cassoles 86, ✉ 08022, ℰ 212 65 54, Seafood – ■. 🅰🅴 ⓞ 🄴 *VISA*.
✍ FU **u**
closed Sunday dinner – **M** a la carte 4000/7600.

Typical atmosphere :

XX **Font del Gat,** passeig Santa Madrona, Montjuic, ✉ 08004, ℰ 424 02 24, 🍴, Regional
decor – Ⓟ. 🅰🅴 ⓞ 🄴 *VISA*. ✍ by Av. Reina María Cristina GY
M a la carte 3300/4200.

X **La Cuineta,** Paradis 4, ✉ 08002, ℰ 315 01 11, Fax 315 07 98, « In a 17C cellar » – ■. 🅰🅴
ⓞ 🄴 *VISA* – **M** a la carte 2800/5725. MX **e**

X **Can Culleretes,** Quintana 5, ✉ 08002, ℰ 317 64 85 – ■. 🄴 *VISA* MY **c**
closed Sunday dinner, Monday and 17 August-7 September – **M** a la carte 1850/2700.

X **Los Caracoles,** Escudellers 14, ✉ 08002, ℰ 302 31 85, Fax 302 07 43, Rustic regional
decor – ■. 🅰🅴 ⓞ 🄴 *VISA*. ✍ MY **k**
M a la carte 2500/4350.

X **Pá i Trago,** Parlament 41, ✉ 08015, ☎ 441 13 20, Fax 441 13 20 – ▤. E VISA. ✻
closed Monday and February – **M** a la carte 2250/3800 HY **a**

X **A la Menta,** passeig Manuel Girona 50, ✉ 08034, ☎ 204 15 49, Tavern – ▤. AE ⓓ E VISA. ✻ EV **f**
closed Sunday dinner – **M** a la carte 3950/4950.

Environs

at Esplugues de Llobregat W : 5 km – ✉ 08950 Esplugues de Llobregat – ☎ 93 :

XXX **La Masía,** av. Paisos Catalans 58 ☎ 371 00 09, Fax 372 84 00, 🍴, « Terrace under pine trees » – ▤ P. AE ⓓ E VISA. ✻
closed Sunday dinner – **M** a la carte 3100/5425.

X ✿ **Quirze,** Laureá Miró 202 ☎ 371 10 84, 🍴 – ▤ P. AE ⓓ E VISA
closed Sunday dinner, Monday and August – **M** a la carte 3900/5100
Spec. Ensalada de sesos de cordero a la vinagreta de nuez, Turbo a la crema con colmenillas, Civet de ciervo (15 October-15 March).

at Sant Just Desvern W : 6 km – ✉ 08960 Sant Just Desvern – ☎ 93

Sant Just, Frederic Mompou 1 ☎ 473 25 17, Fax 473 24 50 – |♦| ▤ TV ☎ 🚗 – 🏛 25/450. AE ⓓ E VISA. ✻
M 2500 – ☕ 1200 – **150 rm** 17100/21400.

San Celoni Barcelona 443 G37 – pop. 11929 alt. 152 – ☎ 93.
Barcelona 49.

XX ✿✿ **El Racó de Can Fabes,** Sant Joan 6 ☎ 867 28 51, Fax 867 38 61, Rustic decor – ▤. AE ⓓ E VISA. ✻
closed Sunday dinner, Monday, 27 January-10 February and 29 June-13 July – **M** a la carte 5250/6550
Spec. Canapés de queso del Montseny con remolacha y su vinagreta, Parmentier de alcachofas y almejas, Foie-gras Rossini en homenaje a Escoffier.

MÁLAGA - MARBELLA

Málaga 29000 446 V16 – pop. 503 251 – ☎ 952 – Seaside resort.
See : Gibralfaro : ≤★★ DY – Alcazaba★ (museum ★) CDY.
Envir. : Finca de la Concepción★ N : 7 km – Road★ from Málaga to Antequera ≤★★
⛳18 Club de Campo of Málaga S : 9 km ☎ 38 11 20 – ⛳9 of El Candado E : 5 km.
✈ Málaga S : 9 km ☎ 32 20 00 – Iberia : Molina Larios 13, ✉ 29015, ☎ 21 37 31 and – Aviaco : airport ☎ 31 78 58.
🚆 ☎ 31 62 49.
⛴ to Melilla : Cía Trasmediterránea, Estación Marítima, ✉ 29016 (CZ), ☎ 22 43 93, Fax 22 48 83.
ℹ Pasaje de Chinitas 4, ✉ 29015, ☎ 21 34 45 and Císter 11 (first floor), ✉ 29015, ☎ 22 79 07 – R.A.C.E. Calderería 1, ✉ 29008, ☎ 21 42 60, Fax 38 77 42.
Madrid 548 – Algeciras 133 – Córdoba 175 – Sevilla 217 – Valencia 651.

Plan opposite

Centre :

Málaga Palacio without rest, Av. Cortina del Muelle 1, ✉ 29015, ☎ 21 51 85, Telex 77021, Fax 21 51 85, ≤, 🏊 – |♦| ▤ TV ☎ – 🏛 25/300. AE ⓓ E VISA. ✻ CZ **b**
☕ 950 – **223 rm** 13390/14500.

Don Curro without rest, coffee shop only, Sancha de Lara 7, ✉ 29015, ☎ 22 72 00, Telex 77366, Fax 21 59 46 – |♦| ▤ TV ☎. AE ⓓ E VISA CZ **e**
☕ 600 – **105 rm** 7130/10165.

Suburbs :

Parador de Málaga-Gibralfaro ⛰ (might close due to refurbishment), ✉ 29016, ☎ 22 19 03, Fax 22 19 02, « Magnificent setting with ≤ Málaga and sea » – AE ⓓ E VISA. ✻ au Gibralfaro DY
M 3200 – ☕ 1100 – **12 rm** 11500.

XXX **Café de París,** Vélez Málaga 8, ✉ 29016, ☎ 22 50 43, Fax 22 50 43 – ▤. AE ⓓ E VISA. ✻ by Pas. Cánovas del Castillo DZ
closed Sunday and 1 to 20 July – **M** a la carte 4050/5350.

XX **Antonio Martín,** paseo Marítimo 4, ✉ 29016, ☎ 22 21 13, Fax 21 10 18, ≤, 🍴, Large terrace by the sea – ▤ P. AE ⓓ E VISA by Pas. Cánovas del Castillo DZ
closed Sunday dinner in winter – **M** a la carte approx. 4000.

X **La Taberna del Pintor,** Maestranza 6, ✉ 29016, ☎ 21 53 15, Typical decor, Meat dishes – ▤. AE ⓓ E VISA by Pas. Cánovas del Castillo DZ
closed Sunday – **M** a la carte 2615/3900.

MÁLAGA

Constitución . . . . CY 40
Granada . . . . CDY
Marqués de Larios . . . . . CYZ 84
Nueva . . . . CYZ
Santa Lucia . . . . CY 123

Aduana (Pl. de la) . . . . . . DY 2
Arriola (Pl. de la) . . . . CZ 5
Atocha (Pasillo) . . . . CZ 8
Calderena . . . . CY 13
Cánovas del Castillo (Pas.) . DZ 18
Cárcer . . . . CY 27
Casapalma . . . . CY 30
Colón (Alameda de) . . . . . . CZ 32
Comandante Benitez (Av. del) . . . . CZ 35
Compañia . . . . CY 37
Cortina del Muelle . . . . CZ 42
Especerias . . . . CY 56
Frailes . . . . CDY 61
Huerto del Conde . . . . DY 67
Mariblanca . . . . CY 77
Martinez . . . . CZ 86
Molina Larios . . . . CYZ 95
Postigo de los Abades . . . CDZ 106
Reding (Paseo de) . . . . . . DY 110
Santa Isabel (Pasillo de) . . CYZ 120
Santa Mariá . . . . CY 125
Sebastián Souvirón . . . . . . CZ 130
Strachan . . . . CZ 133
Teatro (Pl. del) . . . . CY 135
Tejón y Rodriguez . . . . CY 138
Tetuán (Puente de) . . . . . . CZ 140

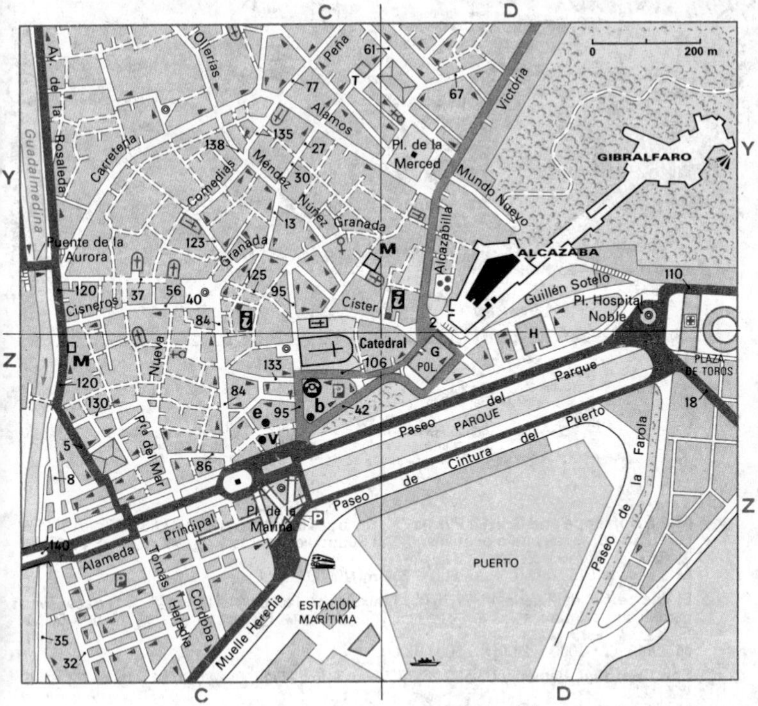

at Club de Campo E : 9 km – ✉ 29000 Málaga – ☎ 952 :

Parador de Málaga del Golf, ✉ apartado 324 - 29080 Málaga, ✆ 38 12 55, Fax 38 21 41, ≤, 🏔, « Overlooking the golf course », 🏊, 🎾, 🏌18 – ▤ 📺 ☎ 🅟 – 🏃 25/70. AE ⓓ E VISA. 🚫
M 3200 – ☕ 1100 – **60 rm** 14000.

at Urbanización Mijas Golf by N 340 SW : 30 km – ✉ 29640 Fuengirola – ☎ 952 :

Byblos Andaluz 🐚, ✆ 47 30 50, Telex 79713, Fax 47 67 83, ≤ golf course and mountains, 🏔, Talassotherapy facilities, « Andalusian style, situated between two golf courses », 🏊, 🏊, 🏔, 🎾, 🏌18 🏌18 – 🛗 ▤ 📺 ☎ 🅟 – 🏃 30/200. AE ⓓ E VISA. 🚫 rest
M 5000 **Le Nailhac** *(dinner only, closed Wednesday)* a la carte approx. 8000 – **El Andaluz** a la carte 3100/5100 – ☕ 1700 – **144 rm** 18000/22000.

Marbella **29600** Málaga 446 W 15 – pop. 67 882 – ☎ 952 – Beach.

🏌18 Río Real-Los Monteros by ① : 5 km ✆ 77 37 76 – 🏌18 Nueva Andalucía by ② : 5 kmÜ072 ✆ 78 72 00 – 🏌18 Aloha golf, urbanización Aloha by ② : 8 km ✆ 81 23 88 – 🏌18 golf Las Brisas, Nueva Andalucía by ② ✆ 81 08 75 – Iberia : paseo Marítimo ✆ 77 02 84.

ℹ Miguel Cano 1 ✆ 77 14 42.

Madrid 602 ① – Algeciras 77 ② – Málaga 56 ①.

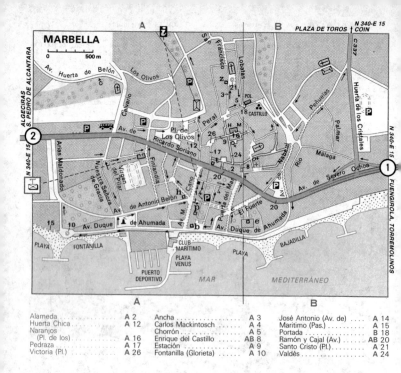

🏨🏨🏨 **Meliá Don Pepe and Grill La Farola** ⑤, Finca Las Merinas by ② 𝒞 77 03 00, Telex 77055, Fax 77 03 00, ≤ sea and mountains, 🛋, « Subtropical plants », 🏊, 🏖, 🍴 – 🛗 🗏 📺 ☎ 👌 🅿 – 🔬 25/400. ⴰ Ⓞ Ε 𝓥𝓘𝓢𝓐. 🛎
M a la carte 5150/8650 – 🍽 1600 – **204 rm** 26600/33200.

🏨🏨 **El Fuerte**, av. del Fuerte 𝒞 77 15 00, Telex 77523, Fax 82 44 11, ≤, 🛋, « Terraces with garden and palm trees », 🎣, 🏊 heated, 🏊, 🍴 – 🛗 🗏 📺 ☎ 👌 🏎 🅿 – 🔬 25/600. ⴰ Ⓞ Ε 𝓥𝓘𝓢𝓐. 🛎 rest AB **e**
M 3950 – 🍽 1000 – **263 rm** 8500/16000.

🏨 **San Cristóbal,** Ramón y Cajal 3 𝒞 77 12 50, Telex 77712, Fax 86 20 44 – 🛗 🗏 📺 ☎. Ε 𝓥𝓘𝓢𝓐. 🛎 A **t**
M 1350 – 🍽 400 – **97 rm** 5300/7400.

🏨 **Lima** without rest, av. Antonio Belón 2 𝒞 77 05 00, Fax 86 30 91 – 🛗 ☎. ⴰ Ⓞ Ε 𝓥𝓘𝓢𝓐. 🛎 A **h**
🍽 425 – **64 rm** 5040/6300.

🏯🏯🏯 ✿ **La Fonda,** pl. Santo Cristo 10 𝒞 77 25 12, 🛋, « Andalusian patio » – ⴰ Ⓞ Ε 𝓥𝓘𝓢𝓐. 🛎 A **z**
closed Sunday – **M** (dinner only) a la carte 4350/5600
Spec. Ensalada de sardinas marinadas, Dorada al estilo Fonda, Escalopines de ternera al vino Málaga.

🏯🏯 **Santiago,** av. Duque de Ahumada 5 𝒞 77 43 39, Fax 82 45 03, 🛋, Seafood – 🗏. ⴰ Ⓞ Ε 𝓥𝓘𝓢𝓐. 🛎 A **b**
M a la carte 3550/4850.

🏯 **Mesón del Conde,** av. del Mar 18 𝒞 77 10 57, Rustic decor, Swiss rest – 🗏. ⴰ Ⓞ Ε 𝓥𝓘𝓢𝓐 A **p**
closed Monday, Tuesday lunch and November-15 december – **M** a la carte 2370/3950.

on the road to Cádiz by ② – ✉ 29600 Marbella – ✪ 952 :

🏨🏨🏨 **Marbella Club** ⑤, 3 km 𝒞 77 13 00, Telex 77319, Fax 82 98 84, 🛋, « Elegant decor ; garden », 🏊 heated, 🍴 – 🗏 📺 ☎ 🅿 – 🔬 25/200. ⴰ Ⓞ Ε 𝓥𝓘𝓢𝓐. 🛎
M 4900 – 🍽 1900 – **90 rm** 24000/30000.

🏨🏨🏨 **Puente Romano** ⑤, 3,5 km 𝒞 77 01 00, Telex 77399, Fax 77 57 66, 🛋, « Elegant Andalusian complex in attractive garden », 🏊 heated, 🍴 – 🛗 🗏 📺 ☎ 🅿 – 🔬 25/160. ⴰ Ⓞ Ε 𝓥𝓘𝓢𝓐. 🛎 rest
M a la carte 3500/5650 – 🍽 1500 – **218 rm** 22000/31000.

Coral Beach, 5 km ✆ 82 45 00, Telex 79816, Fax 82 62 57, ⊾, ⇌ – ▯▮ ▤ 📺 🕿 🅟 – 🚗
🔬 – ⚹ 25/300. 🄰🄴 ⓞ 🄴 *VISA*. 🕸
March-October – **M** 4000 – ⊡ 1500 – **170 rm** 18000/23000 – PA 8000.

Andalucía Plaza, 7,5 km - urb. Nueva Andalucía, ⊠ 29660 Nueva Andalucía, ✆ 81 20 00,
Telex 77086, Fax 81 47 92, �, ⊾, ▣, ⇌, 🕸 – ▯▮ ▤ 📺 🕿 🅟 – 🔬 25/800. 🄰🄴 ⓞ 🄴
VISA. 🕸 rest
M 3350 – ⊡ 900 – **415 rm** 11895/14800.

Marbella Dinamar Club 24, 6 km, ⊠ 29660 Nueva Andalucía, ✆ 81 05 00, Telex 77656,
Fax 81 23 46, ≼, 🌆, « Garden with ⊾ », ▣, 🕸 – ▯▮ ▤ 🕿 🅟 – 🔬 25/150. 🄰🄴 ⓞ 🄴 *VISA*.
🕸
M 2750 – ⊡ 950 – **117 rm** 12000/15000.

Guadalpin, 1,5 km ✆ 77 11 00, 🌆, ⊾, ⇌ – 🕿 🅟. 🄰🄴 ⓞ 🄴 *VISA*. 🕸 rest
M 1725 – ⊡ 425 – **110 rm** 6100/8700.

Las Fuentes del Rodeo, 8 km, ⊠ 29660 Nueva Andalucía, ✆ 81 40 17, Telex 77340,
Fax 81 15 01, 🌆, « Garden », ⊾, ⇌ – 🕿 🅟. 🄰🄴 ⓞ 🄴 *VISA*. 🕸 rest
April-December – **M** 2500 – ⊡ 750 – **100 rm** 5300/10600.

Nagüeles without rest, 3,5 km ✆ 77 16 88 – 🅟. 🕸
March-15 October – ⊡ 350 – **17 rm** 2300/3800.

La Meridiana, 3,5 km - camino de la Cruz-urb Lomas del Virrey ✆ 77 61 90, Fax 82 60 24,
≼, 🌆, « Garden terrace », ⊾ – 🅟. 🄰🄴 ⓞ 🄴 *VISA*.
closed Monday and 10 January-February – **M** (dinner only in Summer) a la carte 4100/
5850.

on the road to Málaga by ① – ⊠ 29600 Marbella – ✪ 952 :

Los Monteros ⑤, 5,5 km ✆ 77 17 00, Telex 77059, Fax 82 58 46, ≼, 🌆, « Subtropical
garden », ⊾, ▣, 🕸, 🛝 – ▯▮ ▤ 📺 🕿 🅟 – 🔬 25/50. 🄰🄴 ⓞ 🄴 *VISA*. 🕸
M 5500 (see also **El Corzo** below) – ⊡ 1700 – **170 rm** 23100/29600.

Don Carlos ⑤, 10 km ✆ 83 11 40, Telex 77481, Fax 83 34 29, ≼, 🌆, « Large garden »,
⊾ heated, 🕸 – ▯▮ ▤ 📺 🕿 🅟 – 🔬 25/1200. 🄰🄴 *VISA*. 🕸
M 4650 – ⊡ 1200 – **238 rm** 18600/23600.

Artola without rest, 12,5 km ✆ 83 13 90, Fax 83 04 50, ≼, « On a golf course », ⊾, ⇌,
🛝 – 🅟. 🄰🄴 *VISA*. 🕸
⊡ 600 – **31 rm** 6500/8750.

El Corzo, 5,5 km - Hotel Los Monteros ✆ 77 17 00, Telex 77059, Fax 82 58 46, 🌆 –
🅟. 🄰🄴 ⓞ 🄴 *VISA*. 🕸
M (dinner only) a la carte 6750/7500
Spec. Mousse de salmón con caviar de Beluga, Entrecote a la bordalesa, Tarta de
limón.

La Hacienda, 11,5 km and detour 1,5 km ✆ 83 12 67, Fax 83 33 28, 🌆, « Rustic
decor-Patio » – 🅟. 🄰🄴 ⓞ 🄴 *VISA*. 🕸
*closed Monday lunch in August, Monday and Tuesday the rest of the year and 15 November-
20 December* – **M** a la carte 4850/6000.

at Puerto Banús W : 8 km – ⊠ 29660 Nueva Andalucía – ✪ 952 :

Taberna del Alabardero, Muelle Benabola ✆ 81 27 94, Fax 81 86 30, 🌆 – ▤. 🄰🄴 ⓞ 🄴
VISA. 🕸
closed Sunday except in Summer and February – **M** a la carte 3800/5800.

Michel's, muelle Ribera 48 ✆ 81 55 59, 🌆 – ▤. 🄰🄴 ⓞ 🄴 *VISA*
closed February – **M** a la carte 3450/4700.

Cipriano, Edificio Levante - local 4 and 5 ✆ 81 10 77, 🌆, Seafood – ▤. 🄰🄴 ⓞ 🄴 *VISA*
M a la carte 3300/5650.

SEVILLA 41000 🄿 🄰🄴🄶 T 11 12 – pop. 653 833 alt. 12 – ✪ 954.

See : Giralda★★★ BX – Cathedral★★★ (Capilla mayor altarpiece★★, Capilla Real★★) BX – Reales
Alcázares★★★ (Admiral Apartment : Virgin of the Mareantes altarpiece★, Palacio de Pedro El
Cruel★★★ : Ambassadors room - vault★★, Carlos V Palace : tapices★★, gardens★) BXY – Santa
Cruz Quarter BCX – Fine Arts Museum★★ AV – Pilate's House★★ (Azulejos★★, Cupule of the
staircase★) CX – María Luisa Park★★ – Archeological Museum (Carambolo tresor★) Charity
Hospital★ BY.

Envir. : Itálica ≼★ N : 9 km.

🏌 and Racecourse Club Pineda : 3 km ✆ 461 14 00 ; 🏌 Club Las Miras (Aznalcázar) SW : 25 km
✆ 5750414.

✈ Sevilla - San Pablo : 14 km ✆ 455 61 11 – Iberia : Almirante Lobo 3, ⊠ 41001, ✆ 421 88 00
BX.

🚉 Santa Justa ✆ 453 86 86.

🄸 av. de la Constitución 21 B ⊠ 41004, ✆ 422 14 04, and paseo de las Delicias ⊠ 41012,
✆ 423 44 65 – **R.A.C.E.** (R.A.C. de Andalucía) av. Eduardo Dato 22, ⊠ 41002, ✆ 463 13 50.

Madrid 550 – La Coruña 950 – Lisboa 417 – Málaga 217 – Valencia 682.

SEVILLA

Inclusion in the
Michelin Guide
cannot be achieved
by pulling strings
or by offering favours.

412

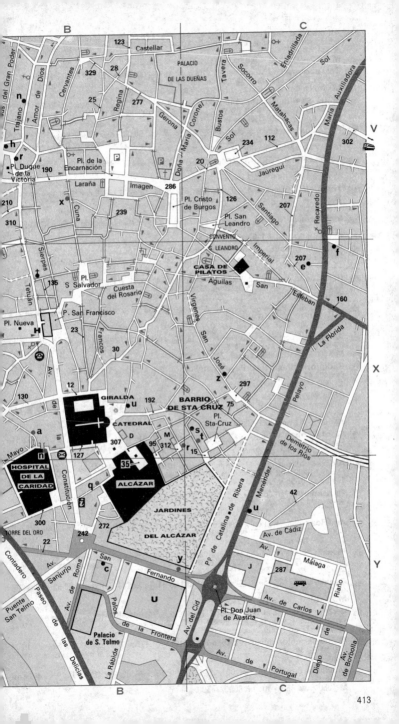

Alfonso XIII, San Fernando 2, ⊠ 41004, ℰ 422 28 50, Telex 72725, Fax 421 60 33, ⌖, « Magnificient Andalusian building », ⅁, ⌲ – ⌷ ▤ ⊡ ☎ ⇔ ℗ – ⚗ 25/500. ⒶⒺ ⓪ Ⓔ 𝑉𝐼𝑆𝐴.
M 5750 – 𝔼 1850 – **149 rm** 45000/60000.
BY c

Sol Lebreros, Luis Morales 2, ⊠ 41005, ℰ 457 94 00, Telex 72772, Fax 458 23 09, ℟, ⅁ – ⌷ ▤ ⊡ ☎ ⇔ ℗ – ⚗ 25/500. ⒶⒺ ⓪ Ⓔ 𝑉𝐼𝑆𝐴. ℠
by Luis Montoto CX
M (see La Dehesa below) – 𝔼 1500 – **439 rm** 36800/46000.

Meliá Sevilla, Doctor Pedro de Castro 1, ⊠ 41004, ℰ 442 26 11, Telex 73094, Fax 442 16 08, ⅁ – ⌷ ▤ ⊡ ☎ ⅁ ⇔ – ⚗ 25/100. ⒶⒺ ⓪ Ⓔ 𝑉𝐼𝑆𝐴. ℠
by Av. de Portugal CY
M 3500 – 𝔼 1500 – **366 rm** 36800/46000.

Porta Coeli, av. Eduardo Dato 49, ⊠ 41018, ℰ 453 35 00, Telex 72913, Fax 457 85 80, ⌧ – ⌷ ▤ ⊡ ☎ – ⚗. ⒶⒺ ⓪ Ⓔ 𝑉𝐼𝑆𝐴. ℠
by Demetrio de los Rios CXY
M (see Florencia below) – 𝔼 1200 – **243 rm** 18000/30000.

Sol Macarena, San Juan de Ribera 2, ⊠ 41009, ℰ 437 58 00, Telex 72815, Fax 438 18 03, ⅁ – ⌷ ▤ ⊡ ☎ – ⚗ 25/700. ⒶⒺ ⓪ Ⓔ 𝑉𝐼𝑆𝐴. ℠
N Barrio La Macarena
M 4200 – 𝔼 1500 – **327 rm** 36800/46000.

Tryp Colón, Canalejas 1, ⊠ 41001, ℰ 422 29 00, Telex 72726, Fax 422 09 38 – ⌷ ▤ ⊡ ☎ ⅁ ⇔ – ⚗ 25/80. ⒶⒺ ⓪ Ⓔ 𝑉𝐼𝑆𝐴. ℠
AX s
M 5200 – 𝔼 1950 – **218 rm** 43200/54000.

Inglaterra, pl. Nueva 7, ⊠ 41001, ℰ 422 49 70, Telex 72244, Fax 456 13 36 – ⌷ ▤ ⊡ ☎ ⇔. ⒶⒺ ⓪ Ⓔ 𝑉𝐼𝑆𝐴. ℠ rest
AX r
M 3000 – 𝔼 750 – **116 rm** 20000/30000.

Pasarela without rest, av. de la Borbolla 11, ⊠ 41004, ℰ 441 55 11, Telex 72486, Fax 442 07 27 – ⌷ ▤ ⊡ ☎. ⒶⒺ ⓪ Ⓔ 𝑉𝐼𝑆𝐴. ℠
by Av. de Portugal CY
𝔼 900 – **82 rm** 20000/34000.

G. H. Lar, pl. Carmen Benítez 3, ⊠ 41003, ℰ 441 03 61, Telex 72816, Fax 441 04 52 – ⌷ ▤ ⊡ ☎ ⇔ – ⚗ 25/250. ⒶⒺ ⓪ Ⓔ 𝑉𝐼𝑆𝐴. ℠
CX f
M 2600 – 𝔼 1000 – **137 rm** 21000/30000.

Husa Sevilla, Pagés del Corro 90, ⊠ 41010, ℰ 434 24 12, Fax 434 27 07 – ⌷ ▤ ☎ ⇔ – ⚗ 25/220. ⒶⒺ ⓪ Ⓔ 𝑉𝐼𝑆𝐴. ℠
AY a
M 3250 – 𝔼 1100 – **128 rm** 11800/18000.

Armendariz, carret. de Su Eminencia 15, ⊠ 41013, ℰ 423 29 60, Fax 423 42 30 – ⌷ ⊡ ☎ ℗ – ⚗ 25/40. ⒶⒺ ⓪ Ⓔ 𝑉𝐼𝑆𝐴. ℠
S : by Pas. de las Delicias BY
M 4500 – 𝔼 1200, **90 suites** 24000/55000

Becquer without rest, Reyes Católicos 4, ⊠ 41001, ℰ 422 89 00, Telex 72884, Fax 421 44 00 – ⌷ ▤ ⊡ ☎ ⇔. ⒶⒺ ⓪ Ⓔ 𝑉𝐼𝑆𝐴. ℠
AX v
𝔼 500 – **120 rm** 13000/20000.

Doña María without rest, Don Remondo 19, ⊠ 41004, ℰ 422 49 90, Fax 421 95 46, « Elegant classic decor, terrace with ⅁ and ≼ » – ⌷ ▤ ⊡ ☎ – ⚗ 25/40. ⒶⒺ ⓪ Ⓔ 𝑉𝐼𝑆𝐴. ℠
BX u
𝔼 1000 – **61 rm** 22000/32000.

Monte Triana without rest, Clara de Jesús Montero 24, ⊠ 41010, ℰ 434 31 11, Fax 434 33 28 – ▤ ⇔ – ⚗ 25/50. ⒶⒺ Ⓔ 𝑉𝐼𝑆𝐴. ℠
W by Puente Isabel II AX
𝔼 500 – **117 rm** 16000/20000.

Alcázar without rest, Menéndez Pelayo 10, ⊠ 41004, ℰ 441 20 11, Telex 72360, Fax 442 16 59 – ⌷ ▤ ⊡ ☎ ⇔. ⒶⒺ ⓪ Ⓔ 𝑉𝐼𝑆𝐴. ℠
CY u
100 rm 𝔼 15550/21100.

Fernando III, San José 21, ⊠ 41004, ℰ 421 77 08, Telex 72491, Fax 422 02 46, ⅁ – ⌷ ▤ ☎ ⇔ – ⚗ 25/250. ⒶⒺ ⓪ 𝑉𝐼𝑆𝐴
CX z
M 3000 – 𝔼 850 – **157 rm** 17600/22000.

América coffee shop only, Jesús del Gran Poder 2, ⊠ 41002, ℰ 422 09 51, Telex 72709, Fax 421 06 26 – ⌷ ▤ ⊡ ☎. ⒶⒺ ⓪ Ⓔ 𝑉𝐼𝑆𝐴. ℠
BV h
𝔼 750 – **100 rm** 17000/25000.

Hispalis, av. de Andalucía 52, ⊠ 41006, ℰ 452 94 33, Telex 73208, Fax 467 53 13 – ⌷ ▤ ⊡ ☎ ⇔ – ⚗ 25/40. ⒶⒺ ⓪ Ⓔ 𝑉𝐼𝑆𝐴. ℠
by Luis Montoto CX
M 1350 – 𝔼 950 – **68 rm** 25500/32000.

Giralda, Sierra Nevada 3, ⊠ 41003, ℰ 441 66 61, Telex 72417, Fax 441 93 52 – ⌷ ▤ ⊡ ☎. ⒶⒺ ⓪ Ⓔ 𝑉𝐼𝑆𝐴. ℠
CX e
M 2500 – 𝔼 950 – **111 rm** 24000/30000.

Derby without rest, pl. del Duque 13, ⊠ 41002, ℰ 456 10 88, Telex 72709, Fax 421 33 91, Terrace with ≼ – ⌷ ▤ ⊡ ☎. ⒶⒺ ⓪ Ⓔ 𝑉𝐼𝑆𝐴. ℠
BV r
𝔼 750 – **75 rm** 17000/25000.

Monte Carmelo without rest, Turia 7, ⊠ 41011, ℰ 427 90 00, Telex 73195, Fax 427 10 04 – ⌷ ▤ ⊡ ☎ ⇔. ℠
SW by Pl. de Cuba AY
68 rm 12000/20000.

La Rábida, Castelar 24, ⊠ 41001, ℰ 422 09 60, Telex 73062, Fax 422 43 75, ⌖ – ⌷ ▤ rm ⊡ ☎. ℠ rest
AX d
M 1650 – 𝔼 350 – **100 rm** 8000/14500.

🏦 **Venecia** without rest, Trajano 31, ✉ 41002, ☎ 438 11 61, Fax 490 19 55 – 🛗 🗐 📺 ☎ ⇌.
⟋ BV **n**
🖴 400 – **26 rm** 10000/20000.

🏛 **Murillo** without rest, Lope de Rueda 7 y 9, ✉ 41004, ☎ 421 60 95, Fax 421 96 16 – 🛗
☎ 🖭 ⑩ ⼚ 𝘝𝘐𝘚𝘈. ⟋ CX **s**
🖴 400 – **57 rm** 8000/14500, 14 suites 7500/23000

🏛 **Montecarlo**, Gravina 51, ✉ 41001, ☎ 421 75 03, Telex 72729 – 🛗 ☎. 🖭 ⑩ ⼚ 𝘝𝘐𝘚𝘈.
⟋ AX **e**
M 1700 – 🖴 500 – **51 rm** 9000/18000.

🏛 **Reyes Católicos** without rest, no 🖴, Gravina 57, ✉ 41001, ☎ 421 12 00, Fax 421 63 12
– 🛗 🗐 ☎. 🖭 ⑩ ⼚ 𝘝𝘐𝘚𝘈. ⟋ AX **n**
27 rm 9000/18000.

XXX ✿ **Egaña Oriza**, San Fernando 41, ✉ 41004, ☎ 422 72 11, Fax 421 04 29, « Winter
garden » – 🗐. 🖭 ⑩ ⼚ 𝘝𝘐𝘚𝘈. ⟋ BY **y**
closed Saturday and Sunday – **M** a la carte 5200/6400
Spec. Tosta de foie gras gratinada con cebollitas a la miel, Lomo de merluza con kokotxas en
salsa verde, Becada flambeada al Armagnac.

XXX **Florencia**, av. Eduardo Dato 49, ✉ 41018, ☎ 453 35 00, Telex 72913, Fax 457 85 80, Tasteful decor – 🗐. by Demetrio de los Rios CXY
closed August
M a la carte 2800/4725.

XXX **El Burladero**, Canalejas 1, ✉ 41001, ☎ 422 29 00, Telex 72726, Fax 422 09 38, Bullfighting
theme – 🗐. 🖭 ⑩ ⼚ 𝘝𝘐𝘚𝘈. AX **a**
M a la carte approx. 5000.

XXX **San Marco**, Cuna 6, ✉ 41004, ☎ 421 24 40 – 🗐. 🖭 ⑩ ⼚ 𝘝𝘐𝘚𝘈. ⟋ BV **x**
closed Sunday – **M** a la carte 4080/4900.

XXX **Pello Roteta**, Farmacéutico Murillo Herrera 10, ✉ 41010, ☎ 427 84 17, Basque rest – 🗐.
🖭 ⑩ ⼚ 𝘝𝘐𝘚𝘈. ⟋ AY **y**
closed Saturday lunch, Sunday and 15 August-15 September – **M** a la carte 3100/4600.

XXX **La Dehesa**, Luis Morales 2, ✉ 41005, ☎ 457 94 00, Telex 72772, Typical Andalusian decor,
– 🗐. 🖭 ⑩ ⼚ 𝘝𝘐𝘚𝘈. by Luis Montoto CX
M (Grill) – a la carte 3125/4575.

XXX **Rincón de Curro**, Virgen de Luján 45, ✉ 41011, ☎ 445 02 38 – 🗐. 🖭 ⑩ ⼚ 𝘝𝘐𝘚𝘈.
⟋ by pl. de Cuba AY
M a la carte approx. 5000.

XXX **Río Grande**, Betis, ✉ 41010, ☎ 427 39 56, Fax 427 98 46, ≼, 🌲, « Large terrace on
riverside » – 🗐. 🖭 ⑩ ⼚ 𝘝𝘐𝘚𝘈 AY **r**
M a la carte 3250/4250.

XXX **Ox's**, Betis 61, ✉ 41010, ☎ 427 95 85, Basque rest – 🗐. 🖭 ⑩ ⼚ 𝘝𝘐𝘚𝘈. ⟋ AY **b**
closed Sunday dinner and August – **M** a la carte 3300/5400.

XX **Jamaica**, Jamaica 16, ✉ 41012, ☎ 461 12 44, Fax 461 10 50 – 🗐. 🖭 ⑩ ⼚ 𝘝𝘐𝘚𝘈.
⟋ by Pas. de las Delicias BCY
closed Sunday dinner and August – **M** a la carte 2850/4400.

XX **La Encina**, Virgen de Aguas Santas 6 acceso E, ✉ 41011, ☎ 445 93 22 – 🗐. 🖭 ⑩ ⼚
𝘝𝘐𝘚𝘈 by Pl. de Cuba AY
closed Sunday and 15 August-15 September – **M** a la carte 3500/4400.

XX **La Albahaca**, pl. Santa Cruz 12, ✉ 41004, ☎ 422 07 14, « Former manor house » – 🗐.
🖭 ⑩ ⼚ 𝘝𝘐𝘚𝘈. ⟋ CX **t**
closed Sunday – **M** a la carte 4000/5500.

XX **Rincón de Casana**, Santo Domingo de la Calzada 13, ✉ 41018, ☎ 453 17 10, Regional
decor – 🗐. 🖭 ⑩ ⼚ 𝘝𝘐𝘚𝘈. ⟋ by Av. E. Dato DX
closed Sunday in Summer – **M** a la carte 3255/4215.

XX **La Isla**, Arfe 25, ✉ 41001, ☎ 421 26 31 – 🗐. 🖭 ⑩ ⼚ 𝘝𝘐𝘚𝘈. ⟋ BX **a**
M a la carte 3250/4600.

X **Los Alcázares**, Miguel de Mañara 10, ✉ 41004, ☎ 421 31 03, Fax 456 18 29, 🌲, Regional
decor – 🗐. ⼚ 𝘝𝘐𝘚𝘈. ⟋ BY **q**
closed Sunday – **M** a la carte 3125/3650.

X **Hostería del Laurel** with rm, pl. de los Venerables 5, ✉ 41004, ☎ 422 02 95, Fax 421 04 50,
Typical decor – 🛗 🗐 📺 ☎. 🖭 ⑩ ⼚ 𝘝𝘐𝘚𝘈. ⟋ BCX **r**
M a la carte 2150/3050 – 🖴 450 – **21 rm** 12800/16000.

at San Juan de Aznalfarache W : 4 km – ✉ 41920 – ✿ 95 :

🏯 **Alcora** ⑤, carret. de Tomares ☎ 476 94 00, Fax 476 94 98, ≼, « Patio with plants », 🛋,
🔁 – 🛗 🗐 📺 🖚 ⇌ 🅿 – 🕍 25/700. 🖭 ⑩ ⼚ 𝘝𝘐𝘚𝘈. ⟋
M 3000 – 🖴 1500 – **421 rm** 18500/26500.

🏛 **Betania**, cerro del Sagrado Corazón ☎ 476 80 33, Fax 476 44 99, ≼, Former convent,
« Garden terrace with 🔁 » – 🗐 📺 ☎ 🅿 – 🕍 25/120. 🖭 ⑩ ⼚ 𝘝𝘐𝘚𝘈. ⟋ rest
M 4200 – 🖴 1000 – **97 rm** 30400/38000.

415

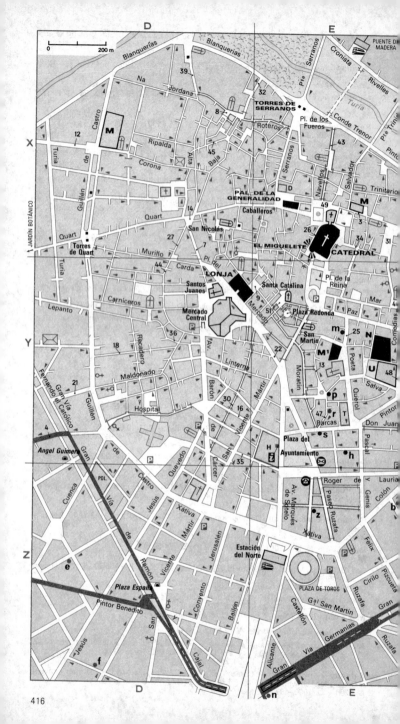

VALENCIA

We suggest:
For a successful tour,
that you prepare it
in advance.
Michelin maps and guides
will give you much useful
information on
route planning,
places of interest,
accommodation, prices, etc.

See : The Old town★ : Cathedral★ (El Miguelete★) EX – Palacio de la Generalidad★ (ceilings★) EX – Lonja★ (silkhall★★, Maritime consulate hall : ceiling★) DY – Ceramics Museum★★ (Museo de Cerámica : palacio del Marqués de Dos Aguas★) EY M1 – San Pío V Museum★ (valencian primitifs★★) FX – Patriarc College or of the Corpus Christi★ (museum : Passion triptych★) EY N – Serranos Towers★ EX.

🏌 of Manises W : 12 km 𝒫 379 08 50 – 🏌 Club Escorpión NW : 19 km by Liria Road 𝒫 160 12 11 – 🏌 El Saler, Parador Luis Vives E : 15 km 𝒫 161 11 86.

✈ Valencia - Manises Airport W : 9,5 km 𝒫 152 14 51 – Iberia : Paz 14, ⊠ 46003, 𝒫 351 37 39.
🚂 𝒫 351 00 43.

⛴. To the Balearic and Canary Islands : Cía. Trasmediterránea, av. Manuel Soto Ingeniero 15, ⊠ 46024, 𝒫 367 07 04, Fax 367 33 45.

🄱 pl. del Ayuntamiento 1, ⊠ 46002, 𝒫 351 04 17, Paz 48, ⊠ 46003, 𝒫 352 28 97, and Airport, 𝒫 370 95 00 – R.A.C.E. (R.A.C. de Valencia) av. Jacinto Benavente 25, ⊠ 46005, 𝒫 374 94 05.

Madrid 351 – Albacete 183 – Alicante (by coast) 174 – Barcelona 361 – Bilbao 606 – Castellón de la Plana 75 – Málaga 654 – Sevilla 682 – Zaragoza 330.

Plan on preceding pages

🏨 **Meliá Valencia,** av. Baleares 2, ⊠ 46023, 𝒫 360 73 00, Telex 64252, Fax 360 89 21, ⅏ – 🛗 🗏 📺 ☎ – 🛦 25/250. 🖭 ⓞ 🇪 𝐕𝐈𝐒𝐀. ⋘   by Puente de Aragón   FZ
M 3500 – ⊒ 1325 – **314 rm** 14300/19000.

🏨 **Astoria Palace,** pl. Rodrigo Botet 5, ⊠ 46002, 𝒫 352 67 37, Telex 62733, Fax 352 80 78 – 🛗 🗏 📺 ☎ – 🛦 25/500. 🖭 ⓞ 🇪 𝐕𝐈𝐒𝐀. ⋘   EY **p**
M 3500 – ⊒ 900 – **207 rm** 13700/18000.

🏨 **Reina Victoria,** Barcas 4, ⊠ 46002, 𝒫 352 04 87, Telex 64755, Fax 352 04 87 – 🛗 🗏 📺 ☎ – 🛦 25/50. 🖭 ⓞ 🇪 𝐕𝐈𝐒𝐀.   EY **s**
M 2800 – ⊒ 825 – **97 rm** 11350/18600.

🏨 **Dimar** without rest, coffee shop only, Gran Vía Marqués del Turia 80, ⊠ 46005, 𝒫 395 10 30, Telex 62952, Fax 373 09 26 – 🛗 🗏 📺 ☎ 🚗 – 🛦 25/80. 🖭 ⓞ 🇪 𝐕𝐈𝐒𝐀. ⋘
⊒ 1000 – **95 rm** 8625/14375.   FZ **q**

🏨 **Ciudad de Valencia,** av. del Puerto 214, ⊠ 46023, 𝒫 367 75 00, Telex 63069, Fax 367 98 64 – 🛗 🗏 📺 ☎ 🚗 – 🛦 30/80. 🖭 ⓞ 🇪 𝐕𝐈𝐒𝐀. ⋘ SE by Puente de Aragón FZ
M a la carte appox. 3500 – ⊒ 900 – **149 rm** 11100/13800.

🏨 **Abashiri,** av. Ausias March 59, ⊠ 46013, 𝒫 373 28 52, Telex 63017, Fax 373 49 66 – 🛗 🗏 📺 ☎ 🚗 – 🛦 30/250. 🖭 ⓞ 𝐕𝐈𝐒𝐀. ⋘   S by Castellón
M 2500 – ⊒ 900 – **105 rm** 9200/13800.

🏨 **Expo H.** without rest, coffee shop only, av. Pio XII-4, ⊠ 46009, 𝒫 347 09 09, Telex 63212, Fax 348 31 81, ⅏ – 🛗 🗏 📺 ☎ – 🛦 25/500. 🖭 ⓞ 🇪 𝐕𝐈𝐒𝐀. ⋘   by Cuart DX
⊒ 850 – **396 rm** 10240/12800.

🏨 **Inglés,** Marqués de Dos Aguas 6, ⊠ 46002, 𝒫 351 64 26, Telex 62228, Fax 394 02 51 – 🛗 🗏 📺 ☎. 🖭 🇪 𝐕𝐈𝐒𝐀. ⋘   EY **m**
M 1650 – ⊒ 650 – **62 rm** 7000/13000.

🏨 **Renasa** without rest, coffee shop only, av. Cataluña 5, ⊠ 46010, 𝒫 369 24 50, Fax 393 18 24 – 🛗 🗏 📺 ☎. 🖭 ⓞ 🇪 𝐕𝐈𝐒𝐀   W by Puente del Real FX
⊒ 525 – **73 rm** 8500/10500.

🏨 **Llar** without rest, Colón 46, ⊠ 46004, 𝒫 352 84 60, Fax 351 90 00 – 🛗 🗏 ☎. 🖭 ⓞ 🇪 𝐕𝐈𝐒𝐀
⊒ 450 – **50 rm** 5900/8200.   FZ **u**

🏨 **Sorolla** without rest, no ⊒, Convento de Santa Clara 5, ⊠ 46002, 𝒫 352 33 92, Fax 352 14 65 – 🛗 🗏 📼. 🖭 🇪 𝐕𝐈𝐒𝐀. ⋘   EZ **z**
50 rm 4300/8100.

🏨 **Continental** without rest, Correos 8, ⊠ 46002, 𝒫 351 09 26, Fax 351 09 26 – 🛗 🗏 ☎. 🖭 🇪 𝐕𝐈𝐒𝐀. ⋘   EY **h**
⊒ 400 – **43 rm** 4750/7500.

XXX **Eladio,** Chiva 40, ⊠ 46018, 𝒫 384 22 44 – 🗏. 🖭 ⓞ 🇪 𝐕𝐈𝐒𝐀. ⋘   by Cuart DX
closed Sunday and August – M a la carte 4200/5350.

XXX 🟢 **Oscar Torrijos,** Dr. Sumsi 4, ⊠ 46005, 𝒫 373 29 49 – 🗏. 🖭 ⓞ 🇪 𝐕𝐈𝐒𝐀. ⋘
closed Sunday and 15 August-15 September – M a la carte 3700/4800
Spec. Terrina de higado de pato (April-October), Arroz de langosta, Mousse de chocolate.
    by Av. Antic Regne de Valencia EF

XXX **La Hacienda,** Navarro Reverter 12, ⊠ 46004, 𝒫 373 18 59 – 🗏. 🖭 ⓞ 🇪 𝐕𝐈𝐒𝐀. ⋘FY **y**
closed Saturday lunch, Sunday and Holy Week – M a la carte 3300/6200.

XXX **Larrad,** Navarro Reverter 16, ⊠ 46004, 𝒫 334 86 02 – 🗏. 🖭 ⓞ 🇪 𝐕𝐈𝐒𝐀   FY **a**
closed Saturday lunch, and Sunday – M a la carte 4300/5700.

XXX Ma Cuina, Gran Vía Germanías 49, ⊠ 46006, 𝒫 341 77 99 – 🗏 🚗   EZ **n**

XXX **Versalles,** Dolores Alcayde 14 𝒫 342 37 38, Fax 342 18 04, 🌤, « In a villa » – 🗏. 🖭 ⓞ 🇪 𝐕𝐈𝐒𝐀. ⋘   by S. Vincente Mártir DZ
closed Sunday and 15 August-15 September – M a la carte 3130/5830.

XXX ✿ **Galbis,** Marvá 28, ✉ 46007, ✆ 380 94 73, Fax 380 06 54 – 🍽, 🔲 VISA. 🕸   DZ **f**
closed Saturday lunch, Sunday and 2 August-6 September – **M** a la carte 3225/4575
Spec. El arroz del día (lunch only), Suquet de pescados con almejas estilo pescador, Fritada de
cabrito con ajos tiernos (October-April).

XXX **Lionel,** Pizarro 9, ✉ 46004, ✆ 351 65 66 – 🍽. 🔲 ① E VISA. 🕸   EZ **b**
closed Sunday and 15 August-15 September – **M** a la carte 2100/2870.

XXX Comodoro, Transits 3, ✉ 46002, ✆ 351 38 15 – 🍽   EY **r**

XX **El Gourmet,** Taquígrafo Martí 3, ✉ 46005, ✆ 395 25 09 – 🍽. 🔲 E VISA. 🕸   FZ **b**
closed Sunday and August – **M** a la carte 2300/3050.

XX **El Gastrónomo,** av. Primado Reig 149, ✉ 46020, ✆ 369 70 36 – 🍽. 🔲 E VISA.
🕸   by Puente del Real   FX
closed Sunday, Holy Week and August – **M** a la carte 2900/3800.

XX **Civera,** Lérida 11, ✉ 46009, ✆ 347 59 17, Seafood – 🍽. 🔲 ① E VISA. 🕸
closed Monday and August – **M** a la carte 2700/4600.   by pl. de Santa Mónica   EX

XX **Mey Mey,** Historiador Diago 19, ✉ 46007, ✆ 384 07 47, Chinese rest. – 🍽. 🔲 VISA. 🕸
closed Sunday dinner, Monday lunch, Holy Week and 15 days in August – **M** a la carte
2300/3400.   DZ **e**

X **Eguzki,** av. Baleares, 1, ✉ 46023, ✆ 369 90 60, Basque rest. – 🍽. E VISA. 🕸
closed Sunday, Bank Holydays, Holy Week and August – **M** a la carte 3375/4300.
by Puente Aragón   FZ

X **El Plat,** Conde de Altea 41, ✉ 46005, ✆ 395 15 11, Rice dishes – 🍽. 🔲 E VISA   FZ **v**
closed Monday, Bank Holydays dinner and 1 to 10 September – **M** a la carte 2850/3950.

X **Palace Fesol,** Hernán Cortés 7, ✉ 46004, ✆ 352 93 23, « Regional decor » – 🍽. 🔲 ①
E VISA. 🕸   FZ **s**
closed Saturday and Sunday in Summer, Sunday dinner and Monday the rest of the year – **M**
a la carte 2900/3600.

by road C 234 NW : 8,5 km – ✉ 46035 Valencia – 🕿 96 :

🏨 **Feria,** av. de las Ferias 2 ✆ 364 44 11, Fax 364 54 83 – 🛗 🍽 📺 ☎ 🚗 – 🔬 25/60. 🔲
① E VISA. 🕸 rest
M 3475 – 🖵 800 – **136 rm** 10000/23000.

at El Saler SE : 8 km – ✉ 46012 Valencia – 🕿 96 :

🏨 Sidi Saler 🦢, SE : 3 km ✆ 161 04 11, Telex 64208, Fax 161 08 38, ≤, 🔬, 🔲, 🌊, 🎾 – 🛗
🍽 📺 ☎ 🅿 – 🔬 25/300
276 rm.

🏨 **Parador Luis Vives** 🦢, SE : 7 km ✆ 161 11 86, Telex 61069, Fax 162 70 16, ≤, « In the
middle of the golf course », 🔬, 🎾, ℼ₈ – 🛗 🍽 📺 ☎ 🅿 – 🔬 25/300. 🔲 ① E VISA. 🕸
M 3500 – 🖵 1200 – **58 rm** 14000.

at Manises – on the Airport road NW : 9,5 km – ✉ 46940 Manises – 🕿 96 :

🏨 **Sol Azafata,** Autopista del aeropuerto ✆ 154 61 00, Telex 61451, Fax 153 20 19 – 🛗 🍽
📺 ☎ 🚗 🅿 – 🔬 25/300. 🔲 ① E VISA
M 2800 – 🖵 900 – **130 rm** 8100/10150.

at Puçol N : 25 km by motorway A 7 – ✉ 46760 Puçol – 🕿 96 :

🏨 **Monte Picayo** 🦢, Urbanización Monte Picayo ✆ 142 01 00, Telex 62087, Fax 142 21 68,
🍴, « On a hillside with ≤ », 🔬, 🌊, 🎾 – 🛗 🍽 📺 ☎ 🅿 – 🔬 25/600. 🔲 ① E VISA.
🕸
M a la carte 3500/4200 – 🖵 1250 – **82 rm** 15950/19950.

Sweden

Sverige

STOCKHOLM - GOTHENBURG

PRACTICAL INFORMATION

LOCAL CURRENCY

Swedish Kronor: 100 SEK = 18.09 US $ (Jan. 92).

TOURIST INFORMATION

In Stockholm, the Tourist Centre is situated in the Sweden House, entrance from Kungsträdgården at Hamngatan. Open Mon-Fri 9am-5pm. Sat. and Sun. 9am-2pm. Telephone weekdays 08/789 20 00, weekends to Excursion Shop and Tourist Centre 08/789 24 28 or 789 24 29. For Gothenburg, see information in the text of the town under 🔢.

FOREIGN EXCHANGE

Banks are open between 9.00am and 3.00pm on weekdays only. Some banks in the centre of the city are usually open weekdays 9am to 5.30pm. Most large hotels have exchange facilities, and Arlanda airport has banking facilities between 7am to 10pm seven days a week.

MEALS

At lunchtime, follow the custom of the country and try the typical buffets of Scandinavian specialities.
At dinner, the a la carte and the menus will offer you more conventional cooking.

SHOPPING

In the index of street names, those printed in red are where the principal shops are found.
The main shopping streets in the centre of Stockholm are: Hamngatan, Biblioteksgatan, Drottninggatan.
In the Old Town mainly Västerlånggatan.

THEATRE BOOKINGS

Your hotel porter will be able to make your arrangements or direct you to Theatre Booking Agents.

CAR HIRE

The international car hire companies have branches in Stockholm, Gothenburg, Arlanda and Landvetter airports. Your hotel porter should be able to give details and help you with your arrangements.

TIPPING

Hotels and restaurants normally include a service charge of 15 per cent. Doormen, baggage porters etc. are generally given a gratuity.
Taxi included 10 % tip in the amount shown on the meter.

SPEED LIMITS - SEAT BELTS

The maximum permitted speed on motorways and dual carriageways is 110 km/h - 68 mph and 90 km/h - 56 mph on other roads except where a lower speed limit is signposted.
The wearing of seat belts is compulsory for drivers and passengers.

Stockholm

Sverige 985 M 15 – pop. 674 459 Greater Stockholm 1 491 726 – ✪ 08.

See : Old Town★★★ (Gamla Stan) : Stortorget★★, AZ, Köpmangatan★★ AZ **35**, Österlånggatan★★ AZ ; Royal Warship Vasa★★★ (Wasavarset) DY, Skansen Open-Air Museum★★★ DY.
Royal Palace★★ (Kungliga Slottet) AZ ; Changing of the Guard★★ ; Apartments★★, Royal Armoury★★, Treasury★ ; Museum★ ; Great Church★★ (Storkyrkan) AZ ; Riddarholmen Church★★ (Riddarholmskyrkan) AZ ; Town Hall★★ (Stadshuset) BYH ; ☀★★★, Djurgården DYZ ; Waldemarsudde House★★, Rosendal Palace★, Thiel Gallery★ ; Gröna Lunds Tivoli★ DZ.
Kaknäs TV Tower★ (Kaknäs Tornet) ☀★★★ DY ; Gustav Adolf Square★ (Gustav Adolfs Torg) CY **16** ; Kings Gardens★ (Kungsträdgården) CY ; Riddarhouse★ (Riddarhuset) AZ ; German Church★ (Tyska Kyrkan) AZ ; Fjällgatan★ DZ ; Sergels Torg CY **54** – Hötorget★ CY **20**.

Museums : Museum of National Antiquities★★★ (Historiska Museet) DY ; National Art Gallery★★ (National Museum) DY **M1** ; Nordic Museum★★ (Nordiska Museet) DY **M2** ; Museum of Far Eastern Antiquities★★ (Ostasiastiska Museet) DY **M3** ; Museum of Modern Art (Moderna Museet) DYZ **M4** ; National Maritime Museum★★ (Sjöhistoriska Museet) DY ; Halwyl Museum★ (Halwylska Museet) CY **M5** ; City Museum★ (Stads Museet) CZ **M6** ; Strindberg Museum★ BX **M7** ; Museum of Medieval Stockholm★ (Stockholms Medeltidsmuseum) CY **M8**.

Outskirts : Drottningholm Palace★★ (Drottningholms Slott) W : 12 km BY ; Apartments★★, Gardens★★, Court Theatre★, Chinese Pavilion★ ; Tours by boat★★ (in summer) : Under the Bridges★★ ; Archipelago★★ (Vaxholm, Möja, Sandhamn, Utö), Mälarenlake★ (Gripsholm, Skokloster) ; Haga Park and Pavilion of Gustav III★ (N : 4 km) BX ; Millesgården★ (E : 4 km) DX.

🛅 Svenska Golfförbundet ✆ 753 02 65.

✈ Stockholm-Arlanda N : 41 km ✆ 797 60 00 – SAS : Flygcity, Klarabergsviadukten 72 ✆ 020/797 40 58 – Air-Terminal : opposite main railway station.

🚃 Motorail for Southern Europe : SJ Travel-Agency, Vasagatan 22 ✆ 23 21 70.

🚢 To Finland : contact Silja Line ✆ 22 21 40 or Viking Line ✆ 714 56 00 – Excursions by boat : contact Stockholm Information Service (see below).

🅸 Stockholm Information Service, Tourist Centre, Sverigehuset, Hamngatan 27 ✆ 789 20 00 – Motormännens Riksförbund ✆ 782 38 00 – Kungl. Automobilkluben (Royal Automobile Club) ✆ 660 00 55.

Hamburg 935 – København 630 – Oslo 522.

STOCKHOLM

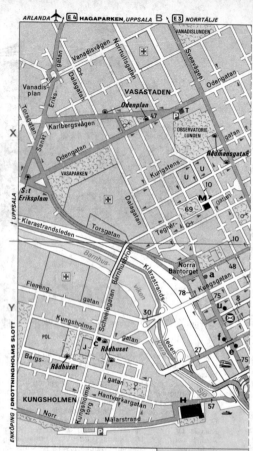

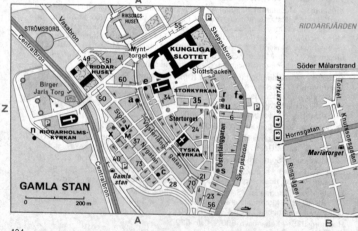

GAMLA STAN

0   200 m

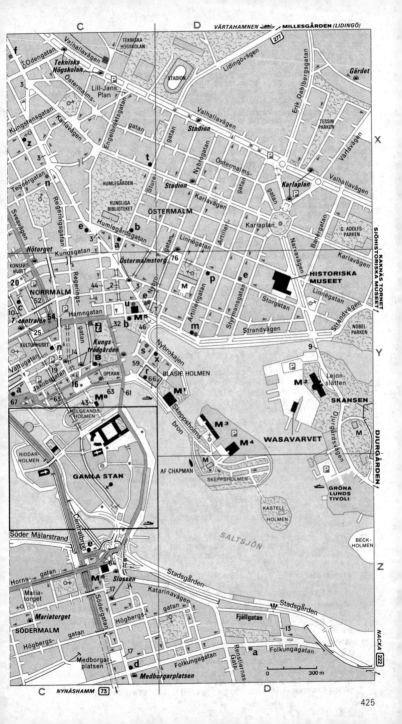

Grand H., Södra Blasieholmshamnen 8, Box 16424, S-103 27, ℰ 22 10 20, Telex 19500, Fax 21 86 86, ≤, ≘s – 🛗 ⅍ rm 🗏 rest 📺 ☎ ᵫ – 🛦 400. 🝏 ⑩ 🔚 𝘝𝘐𝘚𝘈. ⑁ CY **r**
M Verandan 145/300 and a la carte – (see also **Franska Matsalen** below) – **302 rm** ⊇ 1890/2890, **19 suites** 5590/19170.

Sheraton-Stockholm, Tegelbacken 6, Box 195, S-101 23, ℰ 14 26 00, Telex 17750, Fax 21 70 26, ≤, ≘s – 🛗 ⅍ rm 🗏 📺 ☎ ᵫ ⇦ 🄿 – 🛦 400. 🝏 ⑩ 🔚 𝘝𝘐𝘚𝘈 CY **a**
M Premiere (Seafood) (closed Saturday, Sunday and Bank Holidays) 275/300 and a la carte – Bistro – **449 rm** ⊇ 1280/2390, **10 suites** 3050/6250.

SAS Royal Viking, Vasagatan 1, Box 234, S-101 24, ℰ 14 10 00, Telex 13900, Fax 14 10 00, ≘s, ◹, – 🛗 ⅍ rm 🗏 📺 ☎ ᵫ ⇦ – 🛦 250. 🝏 ⑩ 🔚 𝘝𝘐𝘚𝘈. ⑁ BY **f**
closed 23 to 27 December – **M** (Italian rest.) 210 (lunch) and a la carte 195/377 – **315 rm** ⊇ 1245/1985, **4 suites** 1995/3500.

Scandic Crown, Guldgränd 8, Box 15270, S-104 65, ℰ 702 25 00, Telex 11019, Fax 642 83 58, ≘s, ◹, – 🛗 ⅍ rm 🗏 📺 ☎ ᵫ ⇦ – 🛦 285. 🝏 ⑩ 🔚 𝘝𝘐𝘚𝘈 CZ **e**
M La Couronne d'Or (closed Saturday lunch, Sunday and Bank Holidays) 230/370 and a la carte – **246 rm** ⊇ 1188/1788, **18 suites** 1750/3400.

Sergel Plaza, Brunkebergstorg 9, Box 16411, S-103 27, ℰ 22 66 00, Telex 16700, Fax 21 50 70, ≘s – 🛗 ⅍ rm 🗏 📺 ☎ ᵫ – 🛦 150. 🝏 ⑩ 🔚 𝘝𝘐𝘚𝘈 CY **n**
M Anna Rella (closed Sunday dinner) a la carte 220/315 – **394 rm** ⊇ 1195/1910, **12 suites** 2350/5800.

Globe, Arenaslingan 7, Box 10004, S-121 26, S : 1 ½ km by Rd 73 ℰ 725 90 00, Telex 12630, Fax 649 08 80, ≘s – 🛗 ⅍ rm 🗏 📺 ☎ ᵫ – 🛦 220. 🝏 ⑩ 🔚 𝘝𝘐𝘚𝘈 CZ
M 180/350 and a la carte – **279 rm** ⊇ 920/1300, **9 suites** 2250/3840.

SAS Strand, Nybrokajen 9, Box 16396, S-103 27, ℰ 678 78 00, Telex 10504, Fax 611 24 36, ≤, ≘s – 🛗 ⅍ rm 📺 ☎ ᵫ – 🛦 30. 🝏 ⑩ 🔚 𝘝𝘐𝘚𝘈. ⑁ CDY **x**
M 175/610 and a la carte – **120 rm** ⊇ 1595/2300, **18 suites** 2600/3800.

Amaranten, Kungsholmsgatan 31, Box 8054, S-104 20, ℰ 654 10 60, Telex 17498, Fax 652 62 48, ≘s, ◹, – 🛗 ⅍ rm 🗏 📺 ☎ ᵫ – 🛦 170. 🝏 ⑩ 🔚 𝘝𝘐𝘚𝘈 BY **c**
M 100/180 and a la carte – **404 rm** ⊇ 900/1595, **6 suites** 2200/4500.

Continental, Klara Vattugränd 4, corner of Vasagatan, S-101 22, ℰ 24 40 20, Telex 10100, Fax 11 36 95, ≘s – 🛗 ⅍ rm 📺 ☎ ᵫ – 🛦 70. 🝏 ⑩ 🔚 𝘝𝘐𝘚𝘈 BY **e**
M (closed Sunday) 130/360 and a la carte – **235 rm** ⊇ 1250/1970, **2 suites** 2500/3000.

Diplomat, Strandvägen 7c, Box 14059, S-104 40, ℰ 663 58 00, Telex 17119, Fax 783 66 34, ≘s – 🛗 ⅍ rm 🗏 rest 📺 ☎. 🝏 ⑩ 🔚 𝘝𝘐𝘚𝘈 DY **m**
closed Christmas – **M** (closed Saturday dinner and Sunday) 125/165 and a la carte – **130 rm** ⊇ 1250/1990, **3 suites** 2750/5150.

Anglais, Humlegårdsgatan 23, Box 5178, S-102 44, ℰ 614 16 00, Telex 19475, Fax 611 09 72 – 🛗 ⅍ rm 🗏 📺 ☎ – 🛦 250. 🝏 ⑩ 🔚 𝘝𝘐𝘚𝘈 CX **a**
closed Christmas – **M** 69/245 and a la carte – **161 rm** ⊇ 690/1950, **9 suites** 3380.

Stockholm Plaza, Birger Jarlsgatan 29, Box 7707, S-103 95, ℰ 14 51 20, Telex 13982, Fax 10 34 92, ≘s – 🛗 ⅍ rm 📺 ☎ – 🛦 40. 🝏 ⑩ 🔚 𝘝𝘐𝘚𝘈 CX **e**
closed Christmas – **M** (closed Saturday lunch and Sunday) a la carte 170/250 – **147 rm** ⊇ 1095/1450, **4 suites** 1850/2750.

Berns, Näckströmsgatan 8, Berzelii Park, S-111 47, ℰ 614 07 00, Telex 12132, Fax 611 51 75, « Modern interior decor » – 🛗 ⅍ rm 🗏 rm 📺 ☎ – 🛦 500. 🝏 ⑩ 🔚 𝘝𝘐𝘚𝘈. ⑁ CY **b**
closed 23 to 30 December – **M Röda Rummet** (closed Sunday lunch) 250 and a la carte – **60 rm** ⊇ 1495/1995, **3 suites** 2800/4000.

Park, Karlavägen 43, Box 5255, S-102 45, ℰ 22 96 20, Telex 10666, Fax 21 62 68, ≘s – 🛗 ⅍ rm 🗏 📺 ☎ ᵫ – 🛦 120. 🝏 ⑩ 🔚 𝘝𝘐𝘚𝘈. ⑁ CX **t**
closed Christmas – **M** (closed lunch Saturday and Sunday) 150/260 – **194 rm** ⊇ 1325/1860, **8 suites** 2500/3500.

City, Slöjdgatan 7, Hötorget, Box 1132, S-111 81, ℰ 22 22 40, Telex 12487, Fax 20 82 24, ≘s – 🛗 ⅍ rm 🗏 📺 ☎ ᵫ – 🛦 70. 🝏 ⑩ 🔚 𝘝𝘐𝘚𝘈 CY **c**
closed Christmas-New Year – **M** (closed Sunday) (unlicensed) (lunch only) 150 and a la carte – **300 rm** ⊇ 1015/1140.

Birger Jarl without rest. (unlicensed), Tulegatan 8, Box 19016, S-104 32, ℰ 15 10 20, Telex 11843, Fax 673 73 66, ≘s – 🛗 ⅍ rm 🗏 📺 ☎ ᵫ – 🛦 150. 🝏 ⑩ 🔚 𝘝𝘐𝘚𝘈 CX **z**
closed Christmas-New Year – **226 rm** ⊇ 880/1150, **6 suites** 1300/1450.

Malmen, Götgatan 49-51, Box 4274, S-102 61, ℰ 22 60 80, Telex 119489, Fax 641 11 48, – 🛗 ⅍ rm 📺 ☎ ᵫ – 🛦 110. 🝏 ⑩ 🔚 𝘝𝘐𝘚𝘈 CZ **d**
closed 20 December-2 January – **M** (closed Sunday) 45 (lunch) and dinner a la carte – **280 rm** ⊇ 995/1450, **2 suites** 2000/2415.

Wellington without rest., Storgatan 6, S-114 51, ℰ 667 09 10, Telex 17963, Fax 667 12 54, ≘s – 🛗 ⅍ rm 📺 ☎. 🝏 ⑩ 🔚 𝘝𝘐𝘚𝘈 DY **p**
closed 23 December-2 January – **50 rm** ⊇ 1020/1400, **1 suite** 1800.

Freys, Bryggargatan 12b, Box 70439, S-107 25, ℰ 20 13 00, Telex 16750, Fax 24 22 24 – 🛗 ⅍ rm 🗏 📺 ☎ ᵫ. 🝏 ⑩ 🔚 𝘝𝘐𝘚𝘈 BY **u**
closed Christmas – **M** (closed Sunday lunch) 95/150 – **99 rm** ⊇ 895/1040.

XXXX **Operakällaren** (at Opera House), Operahuset, Box 1616, S-111 86, ✆ 676 58 00, Fax 20 95 92, « Opulent classical decor » – 🆎 ⓪ 🅴 𝗩𝗜𝗦𝗔   CY
closed Sunday lunch and 1 July-2 August – **M** 220/670 and a la carte 465/735.

XXXX **Franska Matsalen** (at Grand H.), Södra Blasieholmshamnen 8, Box 16424, S-103 27, ✆ 611 52 14, Telex 19500, Fax 21 86 86, ≼ – 🆎 ⓪ 🅴 𝗩𝗜𝗦𝗔   r
closed Saturday, Sunday, 13 July-9 August and 23 December-6 January – **M** (dinner only) a la carte 335/685.

XX ❀ **Paul and Norbert** (Lang), Strandvägen 9, S-114 56, ✆ 663 81 83 – 🆎 ⓪ 🅴 𝗩𝗜𝗦𝗔
closed Saturday, Sunday, July, Christmas, Easter and Bank Holidays – **M** (booking essential) (dinner only) 450/940 and a la carte 470/600   DY **m**
Spec. Consommé de renne au vieux madère en croûte, langue de jeune renne pochée, le suprême de gelinotte sautée, lentilles à la crème au vinaigre de Xérès, La crème blanc-manger au cardemome frappé aux pommes.

XX **Coq Blanc**, Regeringsgatan 111, S-111 39, ✆ 11 61 53, Fax 10 76 35 – 🍽. 🆎 ⓪ 🅴 𝗩𝗜𝗦𝗔
closed Saturday lunch and 29 June-2 August – **M** 190/410 and a la carte.   CX **n**

XX **Teatergrillen**, Nybrogatan 4, S-114 34, ✆ 611 70 44, Fax 611 32 06, « Theatre atmosphere » – 🆎 ⓪ 🅴 𝗩𝗜𝗦𝗔   CY **e**
closed Saturday lunch and Sunday – **M** 220/380 and a la carte.

XX **Nils Emil**, Folkungagatan 122, S-116 30, ✆ 640 72 09 – 🍽. 🆎 ⓪ 🅴 𝗩𝗜𝗦𝗔   DZ **a**
closed Saturday lunch, Sunday, 1 to 30 July and Bank Holidays – **M** (booking essential) 175 (lunch) and a la carte 230/420.

XX **Clas På Hörnet** with rm, Surbrunnsgatan 20, S-113 48, ✆ 16 51 30, Fax 612 53 15, « 18C atmosphere » – 📶 📺 ☎. 🆎 ⓪ 🅴 𝗩𝗜𝗦𝗔. ✼   CX **f**
closed 21 June, 24 to 26 and 31 December – **M** (closed lunch Saturday, Sunday and Bank Holidays) 185/385 and a la carte - **10 rm** ⌑ 900.

XX **La Brochette**, Storgatan 27, S-114 55, ✆ 662 20 00, Fax 622 37 75, 🌱 – 🍽. 🆎 ⓪ 🅴
𝗩𝗜𝗦𝗔   DY **e**
M Ma Cave ✆ 60 25 28 (basement, with cellar) (closed lunch Saturday and Sunday, 1 June and 31 August) 160/350 and a la carte - **Brasserie** (ground floor).

XX **Wärdshuset Stallmästaregården**, Norrtull, S-113 47, N : 2 km by Sveavägen (at beginning of E 4) ✆ 610 13 01, Fax 31 50 16, ≼, 🌱, « 17C inn, waterside setting », 🌿 – Ⓟ
M (lunch only).   by Sveavägen BX

X ❀ **Wedholms Fisk** (Wedholm), Nybrokajen 17, S-111 48, ✆ 611 78 74, Seafood – 🆎 ⓪ 🅴
𝗩𝗜𝗦𝗔   CY **s**
closed Sunday, 4 July-3 August and Bank Holidays – **M** 130/285 and a la carte 215/565
Spec. Tartar of salmon and salmon roe with crème fraîche, Grilled turbot with snow-peas and Dijon hollandaise, Fricassé of sole, turbot, lobster, and scallops with a Champagne sauce.

X ❀ **KB**, Smålandsgatan 7, S-111 46, ✆ 679 60 32, Fax 611 82 83 – 🆎 ⓪ 🅴 𝗩𝗜𝗦𝗔   CY **u**
closed Saturday lunch, Sunday, mid June-mid August and Bank Holidays – **M** 395 (dinner) and a la carte 205/465
Spec. Assorted marinated herring on ice, Poached turbot with horseradish and nut-brown butter, Rack of lamb with creamed leeks and morel mushrooms.

X **Greitz**, Vasagatan 50, S-111 20, ✆ 23 48 20, Fax 24 20 93 – 🆎 ⓪ 🅴 𝗩𝗜𝗦𝗔   BY **a**
closed Saturday lunch, Sunday dinner and 20 June-20 August – **M** 195 and a la carte.

X **Riche**, Birger Jarlsgatan 4, S-114 34, ✆ 611 70 22, Fax 611 05 13 – 🍽. 🆎 ⓪ 🅴 𝗩𝗜𝗦𝗔
closed lunch Saturday and Sunday – **M** 206/325 and a la carte.   CY **e**

Gamla Stan (Old Stockholm) :

🏨 **Reisen**, Skeppsbron 12-14, S-111 30, ✆ 22 32 60, Telex 17494, Fax 20 15 59, ≼, « Original maritime decor », 📶 – 📶 🕒 rm 🍽 rest 📺 ☎ – 🔺 60. 🆎 ⓪ 🅴 𝗩𝗜𝗦𝗔   AZ **f**
closed Christmas – **M** (closed lunch Saturday and Sunday) 310/550 and a la carte - **111 rm** ⌑ 1350/2750, **3 suites** 3900/4500.

🏨 **Victory**, Lilla Nygatan 5, S-111 28, ✆ 14 30 90, Telex 14050, Fax 20 21 77, « Swedish rural furnishings, maritime antiques », 📶 – 📶 🕒 rm 🍽 📺 ☎ – 🔺 90. 🆎 ⓪ 🅴 𝗩𝗜𝗦𝗔. ✼
closed 18 December-4 January – **M** (see also **Leijontornet** below) – **44 rm** ⌑ 950/2600, **4 suites** 3600/6195.   AZ **v**

🏨 **Gamla Stan** without rest., Lilla Nygatan 25, S-111 28, ✆ 24 44 50, Telex 13896, Fax 21 64 83 –
📶 🕒 rm 📺 ☎ – 🔺 25. 🆎 ⓪ 🅴 𝗩𝗜𝗦𝗔   AZ **c**
closed 20 December-2 January – **51 rm** ⌑ 885/1520.

🏨 **Lady Hamilton** without rest., Storkyrkobrinken 5, S-111 28, ✆ 23 46 80, Telex 10434, Fax 11 11 48, « Swedish rural antiques », 📶 – 📶 📺 ☎. 🆎 ⓪ 🅴 𝗩𝗜𝗦𝗔. ✼   AZ **e**
34 rm ⌑ 1550/1940.

🏨 **Mälardrottningen**, Riddarholmen, S-111 28, ✆ 24 36 00, Telex 15864, Fax 24 36 76, « Formerly Barbara Hutton's yacht », 📶 – 🍽 📺 ☎. 🆎 ⓪ 🅴 𝗩𝗜𝗦𝗔   AZ **n**
closed 24 to 26 December – **M** (closed Sunday in winter except December) 75/200 and a la carte - **58 rm** (cabins) ⌑ 750/1050, **1 suite** 1850/1950.

🏨 **Lord Nelson** without rest., Västerlånggatan 22, S-111 29, ✆ 23 23 90, Telex 10434, Fax 10 10 89, « Ship style installation, maritime antiques », 📶 – 📶 📺 ☎. 🆎 ⓪ 🅴 𝗩𝗜𝗦𝗔.
✼ – **31 rm** ⌑ 1355/1560.   AZ **a**

XXX ✿ **Eriks** (Lallerstedt) with rm, 1st floor, Österlånggatan 17, S-111 31, ✆ 23 85 00, Fax 796 60 69, Seafood – ▤ TV ☎. AE ⓓ E VISA AZ **u**
closed Sunday, July and Christmas-New Year – **M** a la carte 438/590 – **2 rm** 2100, **4 suites** 2900/3500
Spec. Grilled duck liver with shallots, grapes and a port wine sauce, Poached turbot with fried butter and horseradish, Fudge pie with whipped cream.

XX ✿ **Leijontornet** (at Victory H.), Lilla Nygatan 5, S-111 28, ✆ 14 23 55, Telex 14050, Fax 20 21 77, ☂, « Remains of a 14C fortification tower in the dining room » – AE ⓓ E VISA AZ **v**
closed lunch Sunday and Bank Holidays and July – **M** 220/580 and a la carte 330/580
Spec. Poached oysters on a bed of cucumber with a Sauterne sabayon, Salmon and turbot in pastry with artichokes and a buttery mussel sauce, Cloudberry paté with stracciatella ice cream.

XX **Den Gyldene Freden,** Österlånggatan 51, Box 2269, S-103 17, ✆ 24 97 60, Fax 21 38 70 – AE ⓓ E VISA AZ **s**
closed Sunday – **M** 180/400 and a la carte.

XX **Källaren Aurora,** Munkbron 11, S-111 28, ✆ 21 93 59, Fax 11 16 22, « In the cellars of a 17C house » – ▤. AE ⓓ E VISA AZ **x**
closed Sunday – **M** 275/420 and a la carte.

XX **Fem Små Hus,** Nygränd 10, S-111 30, ✆ 10 87 75, Fax 14 96 95, « 17C Cellars, antiques » – ▤. AE ⓓ E VISA AZ **r**
M 177/360 and a la carte.

to the E :

at Djurgården E : 3 km by Strandvägen DY – ✉ ⊕ 08 Stockholm :

XXX **Villa Källhagen** ⛵ with rm, Djurgårdsbrunnsvägen 10, S-115 27, ✆ 667 60 60, Fax 667 60 43, ≤, « Waterside setting, garden », ≘s – ⫶ ✈ rm ▤ TV ☎ Ⓟ – 🏃 40. AE ⓓ E VISA DY
closed Christmas-New Year – **M** 210/565 and a la carte 201/435 – **18 rm** ☕ 1150/1400, **2 suites** 2200.

to the NW :

at Solna 5 km by Sveavägen BX and E4 – ✉ Solna – ⊕ 08 Stockholm :

XXX ✿ **Ulriksdals Wärdshus** (Krücken), 171 71 Solna, Exit E 18/E 3 from E4 ✆ 85 08 15, Fax 85 08 58, ≤, « Former inn in Royal Park », ⛺ – Ⓟ. AE ⓓ E VISA
closed dinner Sunday and Bank Holidays and 24 to 26 December – **M** 590/640 and a la carte 510/640
Spec. Papillon d'avocat et œufs d'ablette, Noisettes de renne, sauce Cognac, Cerises chaudes, glace a la canelle.

XX **Finsmakaren,** Råsundavägen 9, 171 52 Solna, ✆ 27 67 71 – AE ⓓ E VISA
closed Saturday, Sunday, 1 July-6 August, 21 December-8 January – **M** 415/475 and a la carte.

at Sollentuna 15 km by Sveavägen BX and E4 – ✉ Sollentuna – ⊕ 08 Stockholm :

XX ✿ **Edsbacka Krog** (Lingström), Sollentunavägen 220, 191 47, ✆ 96 33 00, Fax 96 40 19, « 17C inn » – Ⓟ. AE ⓓ E VISA
closed Saturday lunch, Monday dinner, Sunday and 12 July-9 August – **M** 250/475 and a la carte 254/387
Spec. Grilled scallops with a lemon butter sauce and basil, Roast saddle of roe deer with a black-currant sauce, potatoes and leek cake, Cloudberry parfait with almond biscuits.

at Upplands Väsby NW : 29 km by Sveavägen and E 4 – ✉ Upplands Väsby – ⊕ 0760 Arlanda :

🏨 **Scandic Crown,** Kanalvägen 10, GLG Center, S-194 61, E 4 - Bredden Exit ✆ 955 00, Telex 10565, Fax 955 10, 🏋, ≘s, 🏊 – ⫶ ✈ rm ▤ TV ☎ ♿ 🚗 – 🏃 320. AE ⓓ E VISA
M 143/175 and a la carte – **228 rm** ☕ 950/1140, **8 suites** 2000.

at Arlanda Airport 40 km by Sveavägen BX and E4 – ⊕ 0760 Arlanda :

🏨 **SAS Arlandia,** Box 103, 190 45 Stockholm - Arlanda ✆ 618 00, Telex 13018, Fax 619 70, ≘s, 🏊 – ⫶ ✈ rm ▤ TV ☎ ♿ Ⓟ – 🏃 244. AE ⓓ E VISA
M 248/300 and a la carte – **335 rm** ☕ 1495/1945, **8 suites** 2125.

Do not mix up :

Comfort of hotels	: 🏨🏨 ... 🏠, ☂
Comfort of restaurants	: XXXXX ... X
Quality of the cuisine	: ✿✿✿, ✿✿, ✿

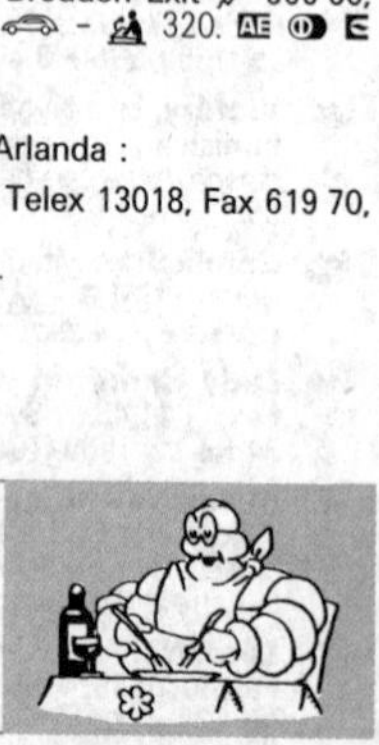

See : Art Gallery★★★ (Konstmuseum) CX **M1** – Castle Park★★★ (Slottsskogen) AX – Botanical Gardens★★ (Botaniska Trädgården) AX – East India House★★ (Ostindiska Huset) BU **M2** – Liseberg Amusement Park★★ (Lisebergs Nöjespark) DX – Natural History Museum★★ (Naturhistoriska Museet) AX – Röhss Museum of Arts and Crafts★★ (Röhsska Konstslöjdmuseet) BV **M3** – Älvsborg Bridge★ (Älvsborgsbron) AV – Maritime Centre★ (Maritime Centrum) CVX **22** – Maritime Center★ (Maritime Centrum) (Viking★) BT – Maritime Museum★ (Sjöfartsmuseet) AV – New Älvsborg Fortress★ (Nya Älvsborgs Fästning) AU – Götaplatsen (Carl Milles Poseidon★★) CX – Seaman's Tower (Sjömanstornet) (✸★★) AV – Masthugg Church (Masthuggskyrkran) (inside★) AV.

Envir. : Northern and southern archipelago★ (Hönö, Öckerö, Vrångö) – Kungsbacka : Tjolöholms Castle★, S : 40 km by E6.

🞖 Albatross, Lillbagsvägen Hisings Backa, R 15 🖉 55 04 40 – 🞖 Delsjö, Kallebäck, H 7 🖉 40 69 59 – 🞖 Göteborgs, Golfbanevägen, Hovås, R 23 🖉 28 24 44.

✈ Scandinavian Airlines System : Norra Hamngatan 20-22 🖉 94 20 00/63 85 00 Landvetter Airport : 🖉 94 10 00.

⚓ To Denmark : contact Stena Line A/B, Telex 20886, Fax 24 10 38 – To continent : contact Scandinavian Seaways 🖉 65 06 00, Telex 21724.

🖪 Basargatan 10 (vid Kungsportsplatsen), 🖉 10 07 40 – Kungsportsplatsen 2 🖉 17 11 70.

Copenhague 279 – Oslo 322 – Stockholm 500.

Plans on following pages

🏨 **Sheraton and restaurant Madeleine,** Södra Hamngatan 59-65, Box 288, S-401 24, 🖉 80 60 00, Telex 28250, Fax 15 98 88, 🖪, 🛋, 🖼 – 🛊 ⇆ 🖩 🖵 ☎ ఓ ⬟ – 🕍 450. 🖭 ⓞ 🗉 𝘝𝘐𝘚𝘈. 🕉 – closed 23 December-3 January – **M** Madeleine (closed Sunday and Monday) (dinner only) a la carte approx. 435 – **Frascati** (closed Sunday lunch) a la carte approx. 430 – **323 rm** ⚏ 1590/1960. **17 suites** 2250/7100. BU **b**

🏨 **Park Avenue and restaurant Belle Avenue,** Kungsportsavenyn 36-38, Box 53 233, S-400 16, 🖉 17 65 20, Telex 2320, Fax 16 95 68, 🖪, 🖼 – 🛊 ⇆ rm 🖵 ☎ ⬟ – 🕍 550. CX **f** 🗉 𝘝𝘐𝘚𝘈
M (closed Sunday) (buffet lunch) 125 and dinner a la carte – **301 rm** ⚏ 1340/1970. **17 suites** 2320/3400.

🏨 **Scandic Crown,** Polhemsplatsen 3, S-411 11, 🖉 80 09 00, Fax 15 45 88, 🖪 – 🛊 ⇆ rm 🖵 ☎ ఓ ⬟ – 🕍 200. 🖭 ⓞ 🗉 𝘝𝘐𝘚𝘈 – closed 21 to 27 December – **M** 48/168 lunch and a la carte approx. 347 – **310 rm** ⚏ 1190/1425. **10 suites** 2900. CU **d**

🏨 **Europa,** Köpmansgatan 38, Box 264, S-401 24, 🖉 80 12 80, Telex 21374, Fax 15 47 55, 🖪, 🖼 – 🛊 ⇆ rm 🖩 🖵 ☎ ఓ – 🕍 140. 🖭 ⓞ 🗉 𝘝𝘐𝘚𝘈 BU **a**
M 110/265 and a la carte – **455 rm** ⚏ 1295/1470. **5 suites** 1750/2500.

🏨 **Gothia,** Mässans Gata 24, Box 5184, S-402 26, 🖉 40 93 00, Telex 21941, Fax 18 98 04, ≤, « Panoramic restaurant on 18th floor » – 🛊 ⇆ rm 🖩 🖵 ☎ ఓ – 🕍 40. 🖭 ⓞ 🗉 𝘝𝘐𝘚𝘈 DX **k**
M Gemini Sky 200/300 – **290 rm** ⚏ 1250/1500. **2 suites** 3200.

🏨 **Rubinen,** Kungsportsavenyn 24, Box 53097, S-400 14, 🖉 81 08 00, Telex 20837, Fax 16 75 86 – 🛊 ⇆ rm 🖩 🖵 ☎ ఓ – 🕍 60. 🖭 ⓞ 🗉 𝘝𝘐𝘚𝘈 – closed 23 to 27 December – **M** 85/95 and dinner a la carte – **184 rm** ⚏ 1085/1485. **1 suite** 1690/2590. CV **c**

🏨 **Panorama,** Eklandagatan 51-53, Box 24037, S-400 22, 🖉 81 08 00, Telex 27716, Fax 81 42 37, 🖪 – 🛊 ⇆ rm 🖩 🖵 ☎ ⬟ – 🕍 120. 🖭 ⓞ 🗉 𝘝𝘐𝘚𝘈 DX **s** closed 2 weeks Christmas-New Year – **M** (closed Saturday lunch and Sunday) 165/200 and a la carte – **341 rm** ⚏ 990/1320.

🏨 **Opalen,** Engelbreksgatan, Box 5106, S-402 23, 🖉 81 03 00, Telex 2215, Fax 18 76 22, 🖪 – 🛊 ⇆ rm 🖩 🖵 ☎ ఓ ⬟ – 🕍 180. 🕉 DV **u** **237 rm, 4 suites.**

🏨 **Riverton,** Stora Badhusgatan 26, S-411 21, 🖉 10 12 00, Fax 13 08 66, « Roof garden restaurant with ≤ harbour », 🖪 – 🛊 🖩 🖵 ☎ ఓ ⬟ – 🕍 120. 🖭 ⓞ 🗉 𝘝𝘐𝘚𝘈. 🕉 AV **c** closed 23 to 27 December – **M** (closed Sunday) a la carte 210/310 – **190 rm** ⚏ 1120/1220.

🏨 **Victors** without rest., Skeppsbroplatsen 1, S-411 18, 🖉 17 41 80, Telex 20076, Fax 13 96 10, ≤ harbour, 🖪 – 🛊 🖩 🖵 ☎ ⬟ – 🕍 40 AU **b** **35 rm, 9 suites.**

🏨 **Windsor and Brasserie Lipp,** Kungsportsavenyn 6-8, S-411 36, 🖉 17 65 40, Telex 21014, Fax 11 34 39, 🖪 – 🛊 ⇆ rm 🖩 🖵 ☎ ఓ ⬟ – 🕍 40. 🖭 ⓞ 🗉 𝘝𝘐𝘚𝘈 CV **e** closed 20 December-2 January – **M** (closed Sunday in winter, 24-25 and 31 December) 200/350 and a la carte – **91 rm** ⚏ 990/1500.

🏨 **Tidbloms,** Olskroksgatan 23, Box 6162, S-416 66, NE : 2 ½ km 🖉 19 20 70, Telex 27369, Fax 19 78 35, 🖪 – 🛊 ⇆ rm 🖩 🖵 ☎ ⬟ – 🕍 80. 🖭 ⓞ 🗉 𝘝𝘐𝘚𝘈. 🕉 by Redbergsvägen DT **M** 200/300 and a la carte – **42 rm** ⚏ 930/1080.

🏨 **Novotel,** Klippan 1, S-414 51, SW : 3 ½ km 🖉 14 90 00, Telex 28181, Fax 42 22 32, ≤, 🖪 – 🛊 ⇆ rm 🖩 🖵 ☎ ⬟ – 🕍 150. 🖭 ⓞ 🗉 𝘝𝘐𝘚𝘈 by E 3 AV **M** (buffet lunch) 105/120 and a la carte – ⚏ 52 – **145 rm** ⚏ 1050/1190. **4 suites** 1590.

🏨 **Eggers** without rest., Drottningtorget, Box 323, S-401 25, 🖉 80 60 70, Group Telex 27273, Fax 15 42 43 – 🛊 ⇆ 🖵 ☎ – 🕍 25. 🖭 ⓞ 🗉 𝘝𝘐𝘚𝘈 BU **e** closed 23 to 26 December – **77 rm** ⚏ 790/1295.

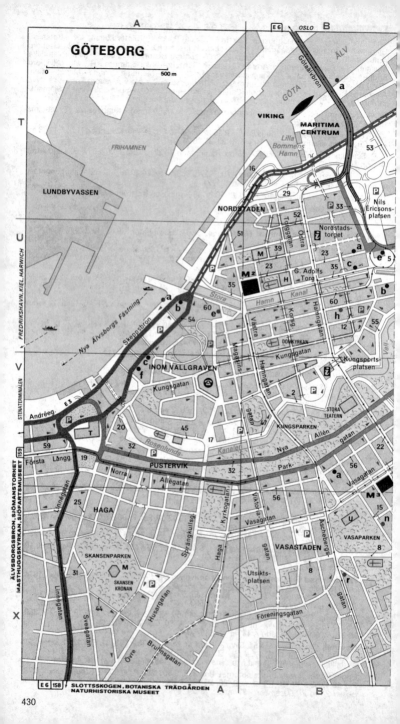

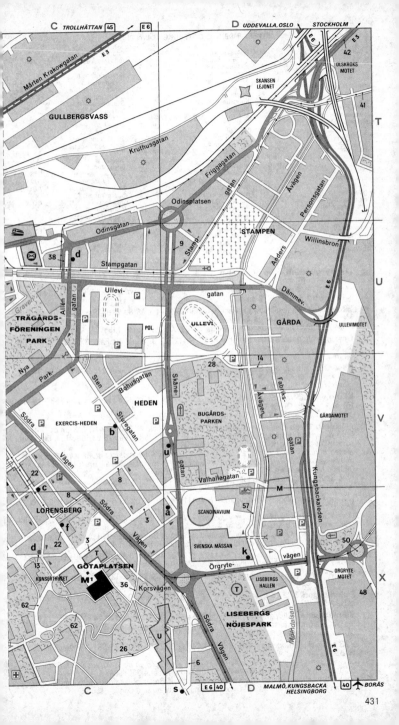

STREET INDEX TO GÖTEBORG TOWN PLAN

Fredsgatan .... **BU** 12
Korsgatan .... **BU**
Kungsgatan .... **ABV**
Köpmansgatan .... **BU** 23
Postgatan .... **BU** 39
Spannmålsgatan .... **BTU** 52
Torggatan .... **BTU**

Anders Personsg .... **DTU**
Andréegatan .... **AV**
Basargatan .... **BV** 2
Berzeliigatan .... **CX** 3
Bohusgatan .... **CV**
Brunnsgatan .... **AX**
Drottningtorget .... **BU** 5
Dämmevägen .... **DU**
Eklandagatan .... **DX** 6
Engelbrektsgatan .... **BCVX** 8
Fabriksgatan .... **DV**
Folkungagatan .... **DU** 9
Friggagatan .... **DT**
Föreningsgatan .... **BX**
Första Långgatan .... **AV**
Geijersgatan .... **CX** 13
Gustaf Adolfs Torg .... **BU**
Gårdavägen .... **DV** 14
Götabergsgatan .... **BX** 15
Götaleden .... **BT** 16
Götaplatsen .... **CX**
Götaälvbron .... **BT**
Haga Kyrkogata .... **AX**
Hvitfeldtsplatsen .... **AV** 17
Järntorget .... **AV** 19
Järntorgsgatan .... **AV** 20
Korsvägen .... **CDX**
Kruthusgatan .... **CT**
Kungsbackaleden .... **DVX**
Kungsports Avenyn .... **BCUX** 22
Kungsportsplatsen .... **BV**
Landsvägsgatan .... **AX** 25
Lennart Torstenssonsgatan .... **CX** 26
Levgrensvägen .... **DV** 28
Lilla Bommen .... **BT** 29
Lilla Risåsgatan .... **AX** 31
Magasinsgatan .... **ABV**
Masthamnsgatan .... **AV** 32
Mårten Krakowgatan .... **CT**
Nils Ericsonsgatan .... **BT** 33
Nils Ericsonsplatsen .... **BT**
Norra Allégatan .... **AV**
Norra Hamngatan .... **ABU** 35
Nya Allén .... **BCV**
Odinsgatan .... **CU**
Odinsplatsen .... **DT**
Olof Wijksgatan .... **CX** 36
Parkgatan .... **BCV**
Polhemsplatsen .... **CU** 38
Redbergsvägen .... **DT** 41
Riddaregatan .... **DT** 42
Risåsgatan .... **AX** 44
Rosenlundsgatan .... **AV** 45
Sahlgrensgatan .... **BV** 47
Sankt Sigfridsgatan .... **DX** 48
Sankt Sigfrids Plan .... **DX** 50
Skeppsbron .... **AU**
Skånegatan .... **DV**
Smedjegatan .... **AU** 51
Stadstjänaregatan .... **BT** 53
Stampgatan .... **CDU**
Sten Sturegatan .... **CV**
Stora Badhusgatan .... **AU** 54
Stora Nygatan .... **BU** 55
Storgatan .... **BVX** 56
Sveagatan .... **AX**
Sven Rydells Gata .... **DX** 57
Södra Allégatan .... **AV** 59
Södra Hamngatan .... **ABU** 60
Södra Vägen .... **CDX**
Ullevigatan .... **CDU**
Valhallagatan .... **DV**
Viktor Rydbergsgatan .... **CX** 62
Willinsbron .... **DU**
Västra Hamngatan .... **BUV**
Åvagen .... **DTV**
Örgrytevägen .... **DX**
Östra Hamngatan .... **BU**

Liseberg Heden, Sten Sturegatan, S-411 38, ✆ 20 02 80, Telex 27450, Fax 16 52 83, – rm – 80. AE E VISA CV **b**
closed 23 December-4 January – **M** *(closed lunch Saturday and Sunday)* 130/140 and a la carte – **157 rm** 880/1120, **2 suites** 1520.

Ekoxen without rest., Norra Hamnagatan 38, S-411 06, ✆ 80 50 80, Fax 15 33 70, – – 15. AE E VISA BU **c**
closed 18 December-3 January – **74 rm** 895/1195, **1 suite** 1195.

Onyxen without rest., Sten Sturegatan 23, S-412 53, ✆ 81 08 45, Fax 16 56 72 – DX **a**
34 rm.

Poseidon without rest., Storgatan 33, S-411 38, ✆ 10 05 50, Telex 27663, Fax 13 83 91, – . AE E VISA BV **a**
closed Christmas – **49 rm** 940/1200.

Klang without rest., Stora Badhusgatan 28b, S-403 13, ✆ 17 40 50, Fax 17 40 58 – – 20. AE E VISA. AV **f**
closed 20 December-3 January – **49 rm** 500/850.

XXX ✿ **Westra Piren** (Öster), at Eriksberg, Docks (on Pier No 4), S-402 79, NW : 3 km by Götaälvbron or by boat from Lilla Bommens Hamn BT ✆ 51 95 55, Fax 23 99 40, , « Dockside setting, overlooking the harbour » – AE E VISA
closed 5 July-6 August and 19 December - 7 January – **M** *(closed Saturday lunch, Saturday dinner January - March, Sunday and Bank Holidays)* (booking essential) 199/510 and a la carte 390/560 – **Brasserie** 159 (lunch) and a la carte 220/340
Spec. Soupe d'étrilles et de coques parfumée à l'anis, Flétan grillé sur une fondue d'oignons, sauce romarin et orange, Charlotte aux châtaignes sur une sauce au chocolat.

XXX ✿ **The Place** (Wagner), Arkivgatan 7, S-411 34, ✆ 16 03 33, Fax 16 78 54 – AE E VISA CX **d**
closed Sunday and 22 December-7 January – **M** (booking essential) (dinner only) 345/595 and a la carte 300/550 – **Grill** a la carte
Spec. Consommé with saltwater crayfish and asparagus, Grilled fillet of turbot with lobster crepes, red wine sauce (Sept-Apr), Fillet of deer with a wild strawberry and Armagnac sauce (Sept-Jan).

XX **Le Chablis,** Aschebergsgatan 22, S-411 27, ✆ 20 35 45, Fax 20 82 01, Seafood – AE E VISA
closed Saturday lunch and Sunday – **M** 165/475 and a la carte. BX **r**

XX S/S Marieholm, Skeppsbroplatsen, Stenpiren, S-403 20, ✆ 13 88 80, Fax 13 65 70, ←, Seafood, « Converted Ship » – 120 AU **a**

XX **Fiskekrogen,** Lilla Torget 1, S-411 18, ✆ 11 21 84, Fax 74 04 83, Seafood – AE E VISA
closed Sunday, July and Bank Holidays – **M** 250 and a la carte 190/320. AU **e**

XX **Sjömagasinet,** Klippans Kulturreservat 1, S-414 51, SW : 3,5 km ✆ 24 65 10, Fax 24 55 39, ←, , « Former East India company warehouse » – . AE E VISA by E 3 AV
closed Sunday – **M** 350/400 and a la carte.

XX ✿ **28 +** (Lyxell), Götabergsgatan 28, S-411 34, ✆ 20 21 61, Fax 81 97 57, « Cellar » – AE E VISA
closed Saturday lunch, Sunday, 17 to 20 April, 28 June-2 August, 23 December-5 January and Bank Holidays – **M** 125/455 and a la carte 280/506 BX **n**
Spec. Goat's cheese with a crayfish and tomato salad, Breast of wild duck with bacon, cabbage and an orange mustard sauce, Chocolate and cherry tureen, Cognac sauce.

XX **Stallgården,** Kyrkogatan 33, S-404 25, ℘ 13 03 16, Fax 11 59 39, « Interior courtyard » –
BU **h**
ᴀᴇ ⓞ ᴇ ᴠɪsᴀ
M 69/262 and a la carte.

X **Eriksbergsfärjan,** Gullbergskajen, Plats 212, S-411 04, ℘ 15 35 05, 🏠 – ᴀᴇ ⓞ ᴇ
BT **a**
ᴠɪsᴀ
closed dinner Monday to Friday and Saturday – **M** (buffet lunch) 169/250 and lunch a la
carte.

at Landvetter Airport E : 30 km – ⊠ S-438 02 Landvetter :

🏨 Landvetter Airport Hotel, Box 2103, ⊠ S-438 02, ℘ 94 64 10, Telex 28733, Fax 94 64 70,
⇌ – 📶 ⤬ rm 📺 ☎ ᾧ ℗ – 🛡 20. ᴀᴇ ⓞ ᴇ ᴠɪsᴀ. ⚘
by Rd 40 DX
M 220 and a la carte – **37 rm** ⊑ 830/950, **7 suites** 1250/1375.

Switzerland

Suisse
Schweiz
Svizzera

BASLE - GENEVA - ZÜRICH

PRACTICAL INFORMATION

LOCAL CURRENCY

Swiss Franc: 100 F = 73.80 US $ (Jan. 92).

LANGUAGES SPOKEN

German, French and italian are usually spoken in all administrative departments, shops, hotels and restaurants.

AIRLINES

A large number of international airlines operate out of the main Swiss airports. For general information ring the number given after the airport symbol and name in the text of each town.

POSTAL SERVICES

In large towns, post offices are open from 7.30am to noon and 1.45pm to 6pm, and Saturdays untill 11am. The telephone system is fully automatic.

SHOPPING

Department stores are generally open from 8.30am to 6pm, except on Saturdays when they close at 4 or 5pm and Monday morning.
In the index of street names, those printed in red are where the principal shops are found.

TIPPING

In hotels, restaurants and cafés the service charge is generally included in the prices.

SPEED LIMITS – MOTORWAYS

The speed limit on motorways is 120 km/h - 74 mph, on other roads 80 km/h - 50 mph, and in built up areas 50 km/h - 31 mph.
Driving on Swiss motorways is subject to the purchase of a single rate vignette (one per car) obtainable from frontier posts, tourist offices and post offices.

SEAT BELTS

The wearing of seat belts is compulsory in all Swiss cantons for front seat passengers.

Town plans of Basle, Geneva and Zürich : with the permission of Federal directorate for cadastral surveys, 2 January 1992

BASLE **(BASEL) 4000** Switzerland 166 ⑩, 216 ④ – pop. 171 036 alt. 273 – ✪ Basle and environs from France 19-41-61 from Switzerland 061.

See : Cathedral (Munster)★★ : ⇐★ CY – Zoological Garden★★★ AZ – The Port (Hafen) ※★, Exposition★ CX – Fish Market Fountain★ (Fischmarktbrunnen) BY – Old Streets★ BY – Oberer Rheinweg ⇐★ CY – Museums : Fine Arts★★★ (Kunstmuseum) CY, Historical★ (Historisches Museum) CY, Ethnographic (Museum für Völkerkunde)★ CY **M1** – Haus zum Kirschgarten★ CZ, Antiquities (Antikenmuseum)★ CY – ※★ from Bruderholz Water Tower 3,5 km by ⑥.

18 private ✆ 89 68 50 91 at Hagenthal-le-Bas (68-France) SW : 10 km.

✈ Basle-Mulhouse ✆ 325 31 11 at Basle (Switzerland) by Zollfreie Strasse 8 km and at Saint-Louis (68-France) ✆ 89 69 00 00.

ℹ Office de Tourisme Blumenrain 2/Schifflände ✆ 261 50 50, Telex 963318 and at Railway Station (Bahnhof) ✆ 261 36 84 – A.C. Suisse, Birsigstr. 4 ✆ 272 39 33 – T.C.S., Petrihof, Steinentorstr. 13 ✆ 272 19 55.

Paris 554 ⑧ – Bern 95 ⑤ – Freiburg 71 ① – Lyon 400 ⑧ – Mulhouse 35 ⑧ – Strasbourg 145 ①.

Plan on following pages

Trois Rois, Blumenrain 8 ✉ 4001 ✆ 261 52 52, Telex 962937, Fax 261 21 53, ⇐, 🏞 – 🛗 ▤ 📺 ☎ 🅟 – 🏠 80. AE ⓓ GB. ✻ rest BY **a**
Rôtisserie des Rois M 77/140 – **Rhy-Deck M** 22/45 – ☕ 26 – **80 rm** 250/480, 8 suites.

Plaza Ⓜ, Riehenring 45 ✉ 4058 ✆ 692 33 33, Telex 964439, Fax 691 56 33, 🏊 – 🛗 ⇔ ▤ 📺 ☎ ♿ 🚗 – 🏠 50. AE ⓓ GB JCB. ✻ rest DX **r**
Rôtisserie Plaza *(closed 12 July-16 August and Sunday)* **M** 65/120 – **Grand Café M** a la carte 25/50 – **223 rm** ☕ 420, 26 suites.

International Ⓜ, Steinentorstrasse 25 ✉ 4001 ✆ 281 75 85, Telex 962370, Fax 281 76 27, 🏊 – 🛗 ⇔ rm ▤ rm 📺 ☎ ♿ – 🏠 230. AE ⓓ GB JCB. ✻ rest BZ **b**
Steinenpick M a la carte 40/80 🍷 – **Rôtisserie Charolaise M** a la carte 70/95 – **210 rm** ☕ 195/420, 5 suites.

Euler, Centralbahnplatz 14 ✉ 4002 ✆ 272 45 00, Telex 962215, Fax 271 50 00 – 🛗 ▤ rest 📺 ☎ 🚗 – 🏠 160. AE ⓓ GB. ✻ rest CZ **a**
M a la carte 90/115 🍷 – ☕ 17 – **55 rm** 245/425, 9 suites 470/850.

Hilton Ⓜ, Aeschengraben 31 ✉ 4002 ✆ 271 66 22, Telex 965555, Fax 271 52 20, 🏊 – 🛗 ⇔ rm ▤ 📺 ☎ ♿ – 🏠 50 - 300. AE ⓓ GB JCB. ✻ rest CZ **d**
M 44 – ☕ 26 – **207 rm** 195/340, 10 suites.

✿ **Europe and rest. Quatre Saisons** Ⓜ, Clarastrasse 43 ✉ 4005 ✆ 691 80 80, Telex 964103, Fax 691 82 01 – 🛗 ⇔ rm ▤ 📺 ☎ 🚗 – 🏠 40 - 100. AE ⓓ GB JCB. ✻ rest CX **k**
M *(closed Sunday)* 75/160 🍷 – **170 rm** ☕ 150/290
Spec. Soufflé de panais en salade à la truffe noire, Soupe à l'orge perlé aux capuns de turbotin, Jalousie de joue de porc aux lentilles. Wines Maispracher.

Schweizerhof, Centralbahnplatz 1 ✉ 4002 ✆ 271 28 33, Telex 962373, Fax 271 29 19, 🏞 – 🛗 ▤ 📺 ☎ 🅟 – 🏠 100. AE ⓓ GB CZ **n**
M a la carte 50/115 🍷 – **75 rm** ☕ 150/250.

Mérian, Rheingasse 2 ✉ 4058 ✆ 681 00 00, Telex 963537, Fax 681 11 01, ⇐, 🏞 – 🛗 📺 ☎ ♿ 🚗 – 🏠 25 - 100. AE ⓓ GB CY **b**
M 28/45 🍷 – **63 rm** ☕ 175/230.

Basel, Münzgasse 12 ✉ 4051 ✆ 261 24 23, Telex 964199, Fax 261 25 95 – 🛗 ▤ rest 📺 ☎. AE ⓓ GB BY **x**
M a la carte 70/110 🍷 – **71 rm** ☕ 155/210.

Métropol without rest, Elisabethenanlage 5 ✉ 4002 ✆ 271 77 21, Telex 962268, Fax 271 78 82 – 🛗 📺 ☎ – 🏠 40 - 120. AE ⓓ GB JCB CZ **a**
46 rm ☕ 160/265.

Krafft am Rhein 🐚, Rheingasse 12 ✉ 4058 ✆ 691 88 77, Telex 964360, Fax 691 09 07, ⇐, 🏞 – 🛗 📺 ☎. AE ⓓ GB CY **z**
M 14/50 – **52 rm** ☕ 100/260.

Muenchnerhof, Riehenring 75 ✉ 4058 ✆ 691 77 80, Telex 964476, Fax 691 14 90 – 🛗 📺 ☎. AE ⓓ GB CX **u**
M 14/60 🍷 – **40 rm** ☕ 50/240.

XXXX ✿✿ **Stucki,** Bruderholzallee 42 ✉ 4059 ✆ 35 82 22, Fax 35 82 03, 🏞, « Floral garden » – 🅟. AE ⓓ GB by ⑥
closed 26 July-17 August, Sunday and Monday – **M** 100/165 and a la carte
Spec. Gratin de topinambours aux truffes blanches (autumn-winter), Lotte au curry, Ris de veau braisé à la sauge. Wines Pinot noir de Pratteln, Riesling de Kaisten.

XXX **Zum Schützenhaus,** Schützenmattstrasse 56 ✉ 4051 ✆ 272 67 60, Fax 272 65 86, 🏞, « Converted 16C hunting lodge » – 🅟. AE ⓓ GB JCB AY **e**
closed Sunday and Bank Holidays – **Garten Saal M** 49/115 🍷 – **Brasserie Le Schluuch M** 25/35 🍷.

XX **Donati,** St-Johannsvorstadt 48 ✉ 4056 ✆ 322 09 19, 🏞, Italian rest. BX **p**
closed July, Monday and Tuesday – **M** a la carte 70/100 🍷.

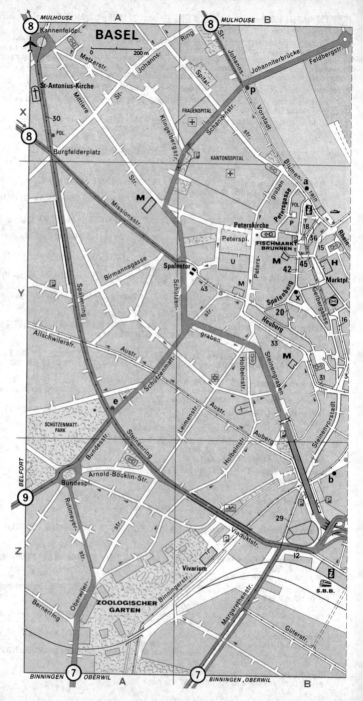

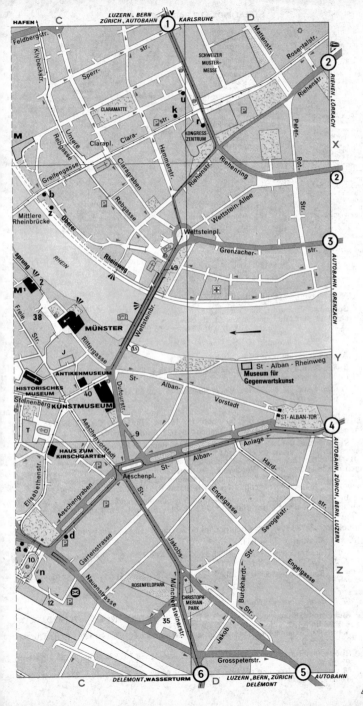

STREET INDEX TO BASEL TOWN PLAN

Aeschenvorstadt . . . . CYZ
Barfüsserpl. . . . . BY 3
Centralbahnpl. . . . . CZ 10
Clarapl. CX
Eisengasse . . . . BY 15
Falknerstr. . . . . BY 16
Freie Str. . . . . CY
Gerbergasse . . . . BY
Greifengasse . . . . CY
Marktpl. . . . . BY
Steinenvorstadt . . . . BY

Aeschengraben . . . . CZ
Aeschenpl. . . . . CZ
Allschwilerstr. . . . . AY
Arnold Böcklin-Str. . . . . . . AZ
Auberg . . . . BYZ
Augustinergasse . . . . CY 2
Austr. . . . . ABY
Bernerring . . . . AZ
Birmannsgasse . . . . AY
Blumenrain . . . . BY
Brunngässlein . . . . CY 9
Bundespl. . . . . AZ
Bundesstr. . . . . AYZ
Burgfelderpl. . . . . AX
Centralbahnstr. . . . . CZ 12
Claragraben . . . . CY
Clarastr. CX
Dufourstr. . . . . CY
Elisabethenstr. . . . . CZ
Engelgasse . . . . DZ
Feldbergstr. . . . . BCX
Fischmarktpl. . . . . BY 18
Gemsberg . . . . BY 20
Grenzacherstr. . . . . DY
Grosspeterstr. . . . . DZ
Güterstr. . . . . BZ
Hammerstr. . . . . CXY
Hardstr. . . . . DZ
Heuberg . . . . BY
Holbeinstr. . . . . BYZ
Innere-
  Margarethenstr. . . . . BZ 29
Jacob Burckhardt-Str. . . . . DZ
Johanniterbrücke . . . . BX
Kannenfeldpl. . . . . AX
Kannenfeldstr. . . . . AX 30
Klingelbergstr. . . . . AX
Kohlenberg . . . . BY 31
Leimenstr. . . . . BY
Leonhardsgraben . . . . BY 33
Lindenhofstr. . . . . CZ 35
Margarethenstr. . . . . BZ
Marktgasse . . . . BY 36
Mattenstr. . . . . DX
Metzerstr. . . . . AX
Missionsstr. . . . . AY
Mittlere-Rheinbrücke . . . . . CY
Mittlere-Str. . . . . AXY
Münchensteinerstr. . . . . . . CZ
Münsterpl. . . . . CY 38
Nauenstr. . . . . CZ
Oberer-Rheinweg . . . . CY
Oberwilerstr. . . . . AZ
Peter Rot-Str. . . . . DXY
Petersgasse . . . . BY
Petersgraben . . . . BY
Peterspl. . . . . BY
Rebgasse . . . . CY
Rheinsprung . . . . BCY
Riehenring . . . . DY
Riehenstr. . . . . DY
Rittergasse . . . . CY
Rosentalstr. . . . . DX
Rutimeyerstr. . . . . AZ
St-Alban-Anlage . . . . CDZ
St-Alban-Graben . . . . CY 40
St-Alban-Vorstadt . . . . CDY
St-Jakobs-Str. . . . . CDZ
St-Johanns-Ring . . . . ABX
St-Johanns-Vorstadt . . . . . BX
Schanzenstr. . . . . BX
Schneidergasse . . . . BY 42
Schützengraben . . . . ABY
Schützenmattstr. . . . . ABY
Sevogelstr. . . . . DZ
Spalenberg . . . . BY
Spalenring . . . . AY
Spalenvorstadt . . . . BY 43
Sperrstr. CX
Spitalstr. . . . . BX
Stadthausgasse . . . . BY 45
Steinenberg . . . . CY
Steinengraben . . . . BY
Steinenring . . . . AYZ
Untere-Rebgasse CX
Viaduktstr. . . . . BZ
Wettsteinallee . . . . DY
Wettsteinbrücke . . . . CY
Wettsteinpl. . . . . CDY
Wettsteinstr. . . . . CY 49

at Binningen by ⑧ : 8 km - ✉ 4102 :

XXX **Schloss Binningen,** Schlossgasse 5 ✆ 47 20 55, Fax 47 06 35, 余, « 16C mansion, elegantly decorated, garden » - Ⓟ. AE GB
closed 19 July-10 August, Sunday and Monday - **M** 95/125 ♂.

at the Basle-Mulhouse airport : by ⑧ : 8 km :

XX **Airport rest,** 5th floor in the airport, ≤ - ▤.

Swiss Side, ✉ 4030 Bâle ✆ 325 32 32, Fax 325 32 65 - AE ① GB
M 50 ♂.

French Side, ✉ 68300 St-Louis ✆ 89 69 77 48, Fax 89 69 15 19 - AE ① GB
M (in FF) 175 ♂.

GENEVA

Switzerland 74 ⑥, 217 ⑪ - pop. 167 167 alt. 375 Greater Geneva 395 238 - Casino - ✪ Geneva, environs : from France 19-41-22, from Switzerland 022.

See : The Shores of the lake ≤★★★ - Parks★★ : Mon Repos, la Perle du Lac and Villa Barton - Botanical Garden★ : alpine rock-garden★★ - Cathedral★ : ☼★★ FY - Reformation Monument★ FYZ **D** - Palais des Nations★ ≤★★ - Parc de la Grange★ GY - Parc des Eaux-Vives★ - Nave★ of Church of Christ the King - Woodwork★ in the Historical Museum of the Swiss Abroad - Museums : Art and History★★★ GZ, Ariana★★, Natural History★★ GZ - Petit Palais : Modern Art Museum★ GZ **M1** - Baur Collection★ (in 19C mansion) GZ, Old Musical Instruments★ GZ.

Exc. : by boat on the lake. Rens. Cie Gén. de Nav., Jardin Anglais ✆ 21 25 21 - Mouettes genevoises, 8 quai du Mont-Blanc ✆ 732 29 44 - Swiss Boat, 4 quai du Mont-Blanc ✆ 736 79 35.

18 at Cologny ✆ 735 75 40 ; 18 Country Club de Bossey ✆ 50 43 75 25, by road to Troinex.

✈ Genève-Cointrin ✆ 799 31 11.

ℹ Office de Tourisme Cornavin station ✆ 738 52 00, Telex 412679 - A.C. Suisse, 21 r. de la Fontenette ✆ 42 22 33 - T.C. Suisse, 9 r. P.-Fatio ✆ 737 12 12.

Paris 538 ⑦ - Bern 154 ② - Bourg-en-B. 101 ⑦ - Lausanne 63 ② - Lyon 151 ⑦ - Torino 252 ⑥.

Plan on following pages

Right Bank (Cornavin Railway Station - Les Quais) :

Richemond, Brunswick garden ✉ 1211 ✆ 731 14 00, Telex 412560, Fax 731 67 09, ≤, 余 - |‡| ▤ rm ▣ ☎ ⇔ - 🏛 250. AE ① GB JCB FY **u**
M (see also **Le Gentilhomme** below) - **Le Jardin M** a la carte 60/90 ♂ - ☕ 28 - **67 rm** 320/600, 31 suites 800.

Rhône, quai Turrettini ✉ 1201 ✆ 731 98 31, Telex 412559, Fax 732 45 58, ≤, 余 - |‡| ⊁ rm ▤ ▣ ☎ ♿ ⇔ - 🏛 40 - 150. AE ① GB JCB. ✂ rest EY **r**
M (see also **Le Neptune** below) - **Café Rafael M** 65/80 ♂ - ☕ 23 - **212 rm** 268/680, 8 suites.

Les Bergues, 33 quai Bergues ✉ 1201 ☎ 731 50 50, Telex 412540, Fax 732 19 89, ←, – 🛗 ▤ rm 📺 ☎ ♿ – 🏛 40 - 350. AE ⓓ GB JCB FY **k**
M (see also **Amphitryon** below) - **Le Pavillon M** 50 🍷 – ☕ 25 – **123 rm** 280/530, 10 suites.

Noga Hilton Ⓜ, 19 quai Mt-Blanc ✉ 1201 ☎ 731 98 11, Telex 412337, Fax 738 64 32, ←, , – 🛗 ⇄ ▤ rm 📺 ☎ ♿ – 🏛 850. AE ⓓ GB JCB GY **y**
M (see also **Le Cygne** below) - **La Grignotière M** a la carte 45/80 🍷 – **Le Bistroquai M** a la carte approx. 30 🍷 – ☕ 26 – **377 rm** 345/550, 36 suites.

Beau Rivage, 13 quai Mt-Blanc ✉ 1201 ☎ 731 02 21, Telex 412539, Fax 738 98 47, ←, – 🛗 ⇄ rm 📺 ☎ – 🏛 30 - 350. AE ⓓ GB JCB FY **d**
M (see also **Le Chat Botté** below) - **Le Quai 13** ☎ 731 31 82 **M** a la carte 45/85 🍷 – ☕ 22 – **98 rm** 300/600, 6 suites.

Président Ⓜ, 17 quai Wilson ✉ 1211 ☎ 731 10 00, Telex 412328, Fax 731 22 06, ← lake – 🛗 ⇄ rm ▤ rm 📺 ☎ ♿ 🚗 – 🏛 25 - 80. AE ⓓ GB JCB. ✻ rest GX **d**
M a la carte 75/120 – ☕ 22 – **152 rm** 280/400, 28 suites.

Paix, 11 quai Mt-Blanc ✉ 1201 ☎ 732 61 50, Telex 412554, Fax 738 87 94, ← – 🛗 ▤ 📺 ☎ – 🏛 70. AE ⓓ GB JCB FY **s**
M a la carte 60/110 🍷 – ☕ 24 – **86 rm** 250/500, 14 suites 500/800.

Ramada Renaissance Ⓜ, 19 r. Zürich ✉ 1201 ☎ 731 02 41, Telex 412557, Fax 738 75 14 – 🛗 ⇄ rm ▤ 📺 ☎ ♿ 🚗 – 🏛 150. AE ⓓ GB JCB FX **s**
La Cortille M 50/95 – **Café Ragueneau M** 50/95 – ☕ 23 – **212 rm** 240/335, 7 suites.

Bristol Ⓜ, 10 r. Mt-Blanc ✉ 1201 ☎ 732 38 00, Telex 412544, Fax 738 90 39, 🏋 – 🛗 ▤ rest 📺 ☎ ♿ – 🏛 30 - 100. AE ⓓ GB FY **w**
M 18/95 🍷 – ☕ 18 – **95 rm** 240/380, 4 suites 700.

Pullman Rotary Ⓜ, 18 r. Cendrier ✉ 1201 ☎ 731 52 00, Telex 412704, Fax 731 91 69, – 🛗 ▤ 📺 ☎. AE ⓓ GB. ✻ rest FY **t**
M *(closed Saturday and Sunday)* a la carte approx. 50 🍷 – ☕ 24 – **84 rm** 240/270, 10 duplex 380.

Warwick Ⓜ, 14 r. Lausanne ✉ 1201 ☎ 731 62 50, Telex 412731, Fax 738 99 35 – 🛗 ⇄ rm ▤ 📺 ☎ – 🏛 25 - 300. AE ⓓ GB JCB. ✻ rest FY **n**
Les 4 Saisons *(closed Saturday and Sunday)* **M** 60/65 – ☕ 19 – **169 rm** 260/330.

Berne, 26 r. Berne ✉ 1201 ☎ 731 60 00, Telex 412542, Fax 731 11 73 – 🛗 ▤ 📺 ☎ – 🏛 30 - 100. AE ⓓ GB JCB. ✻ rest FY **x**
M 35 🍷 – **84 rm** ☕ 190/260, 4 suites 340.

Cornavin without rest, 33 bd James Fazy ✉ 1211 ☎ 732 21 00, Telex 412548, Fax 732 88 43 – 🛗 ▤ 📺 ☎. AE ⓓ GB JCB EY **t**
115 rm ☕ 185/260.

Ambassador, 21 quai Bergues ✉ 1201 ☎ 731 72 00, Telex 412533, Fax 738 90 80, – 🛗 ▤ rm 📺 ☎ – 🏛 40. AE ⓓ GB FY **p**
M 46/55 🍷 – ☕ 12 – **86 rm** 145/313.

Carlton, 22 r. Amat ✉ 1202 ☎ 731 68 50, Telex 412546, Fax 732 82 47 – 🛗 kitchenette 📺 ☎ 🚗. AE ⓓ GB JCB FX **a**
M *(closed Sunday lunch and Saturday)* 42 🍷 – **123 rm** ☕ 160/285.

Grand Pré without rest, 35 r. Gd Pré ✉ 1202 ☎ 733 91 50, Telex 414210, Fax 734 76 91 – 🛗 ⇄ 📺 ☎ – 🏛 30. AE ⓓ GB EX **s**
80 rm ☕ 175/260.

Midi Ⓜ, pl. Chevelu ✉ 1201 ☎ 731 78 00, Telex 412552, Fax 731 00 20, – 🛗 ▤ rest 📺 ☎. AE ⓓ GB FY **r**
M *(closed Sunday)* 27 🍷 – **85 rm** ☕ 160/240.

XXXX **Le Gentilhomme** - Hôtel Richemond, Brunswick garden ✉ 1211 ☎ 731 14 00, Telex 412560, Fax 731 67 09 – ▤. AE ⓓ GB JCB FY **u**
M (dinner only) 95/135.

XXXX ✿ **Le Chat Botté** - Hôtel Beau Rivage, 13 quai Mt-Blanc ✉ 1201 ☎ 731 65 32, Telex 412539, Fax 738 98 47 – ▤. AE ⓓ GB JCB FY **d**
closed 11 to 26 April, 19 December-3 January, Saturday, Sunday and Bank Holidays – **M** 105/135
Spec. Filets de perche du lac poêlés au beurre d'épice (summer), Filets de rouget en soupe de roche, Rouelles de rognon de veau et galettes de pommes de terre. Wines Satigny, Dardagny.

XXXX ✿ **Le Cygne** - Hôtel Noga Hilton, 19 quai Mt-Blanc ✉ 1201 ☎ 731 98 11, Telex 412337, Fax 738 64 32, ← – ▤. AE ⓓ GB JCB. ✻ GY **y**
M 130/150
Spec. Bar à la fumée de bois et vinaigrette de truffe, Gratinée de poularde de Bresse au chou truffé, Croustillants de langoustines. Wines Lully, Dardagny.

XXXX **Amphitryon** - Hôtel Les Bergues, 33 quai Bergues ✉ 1201 ☎ 731 50 50, Fax 732 19 89 – AE ⓓ GB JCB FY **k**
closed Saturday and Sunday – **M** a la carte 75/95.

XXX **Le Neptune** - Hôtel du Rhône, quai Turrettini ✉ 1201 ☎ 731 98 31, Telex 412559, Fax 732 45 58, – ▤. AE ⓓ GB JCB. ✻ EY **r**
closed Saturday, Sunday and Bank Holidays – **M** a la carte 75/120.

X **Bœuf Rouge,** 17 r. A. Vincent ✉ 1201 ☎ 732 75 37, lyonnaise cuisine – GB FY **z**
closed Saturday and Sunday – **M** a la carte 55/85 🍷.

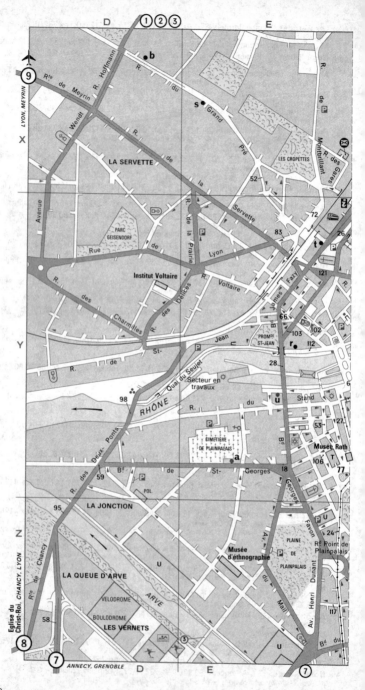

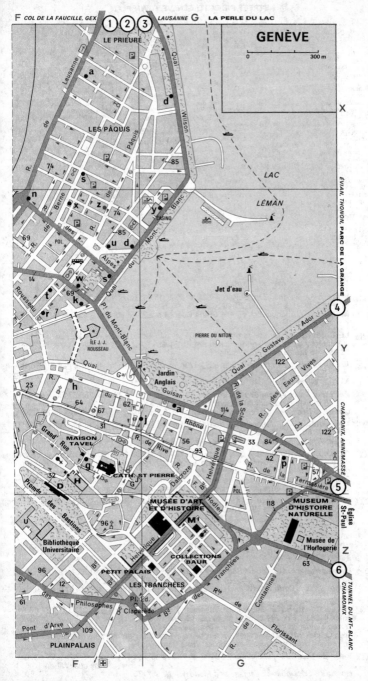

GENÈVE

0   300 m

F COL DE LA FAUCILLE, GEX   LAUSANNE   G   LA PERLE DU LAC

① ② ③

LE PRIEURÉ

a

d

LES PÂQUIS

s

n   x   z

y   CASINO

u   d

w   s

t

r   k

r   7

ÎLE J. J. ROUSSEAU

LAC

LÉMAN

Jet d'eau

PIERRE DU NITON

h

64   67   62

i

31   a

Rhône

MAISON
TAVEL

g

CATH. ST PIERRE

D   H

96

MUSÉE D'ART
ET D'HISTOIRE

M

COLLECTIONS
BAUR

Bibliothèque
Universitaire

PETIT PALAIS

LES TRANCHÉES

96   12

61   Philosophes

Pl. Éd.
Claparède

Pont d'Arve   109

PLAINPALAIS

Jardin
Anglais

Guisan

114

93   56

33   84

42   P   57

Termassière

118

MUSEUM
D'HISTOIRE
NATURELLE

Musée de
l'Horlogerie

63

Église
St-Paul

ÉVIAN, THONON, PARC DE LA GRANGE

CHAMONIX, ANNEMASSE

TUNNEL DU MT-BLANC
CHAMONIX

X

Y

Z

④ ⑤ ⑥

443

STREET INDEX TO GENEVE TOWN PLAN

Confédération (R.) .... FY 23
Marché (R. du) .... FY 64
Mont-Blanc (R. du) .... FY 69
Rhône (R. du) .... FGY
Rive (R. de) .... GY

Ador (Quai G.) .... GY
Alpes (R. des) .... FY
Bel-Air (Pl.) .... EY 6
Bergues (Q. des) .... FY 7
Berne (R. de) .... FY
Candolle (R. de) .... FZ 12
Chantepoulet (R.) .... FY 14
Charmilles (R. des) ...... DY
Cirque (Pl. du) .... EY 18
Claparède (Pl. Ed.) .... FGZ
Conseil-Général (R.) ...... EZ 24
Contamines (R. de) .... GZ
Cornavin (Pl. de) .... EY 26
Corraterie (R. de) .... EY 27
Coulouvrenière (Pt) ...... EY 28
Croix-d'Or (R. de la) ...... FY 31
Croix-Rouge (R.) .... FY 32
Délices (R. des) .... DEY
Deux-Ponts (R. des) .... DY
Dunant (Av. H.) .... EZ
Eaux-Vives (Pl.) .... GY 33
Eaux-Vives (R.) .... GY
Favon (Bd G.) .... EYZ
Fazy (Bd James) .... EY
Frontenex (Av. de) ...... GY 42

Grand-Pré (R. du) .... DEX
Grand-Rue .... FY
Grottes (R. des) .... EX 52
Guisan (Q. Gén.) .... FGY
Helvétique (Bd) .... FGZ
Hodler (R. F.) .... GYZ
Hoffmann (R.) .... DX
Hollande (R. de) .... EY 53
Italie (R. d') .... GY 56
J.-Dalcroze (Bd) .... FGZ
Jargonnant (R. de) ...... GY 57
Jeunes (Rte des) .... DZ 58
Jonction (Rd-Pt) .... DY 59
Lausanne (R. de) .... FX
Leschot (R.) .... FZ 61
Longemalle (Pl.) .... FY 62
Lyon (R. de) .... DEY
Mail (Av. du) .... EZ
Malagnou (Rte de) .... GZ 63
Mercier (Pl. Isaac) ...... EY 66
Meyrin (Rte de) .... DX
Molard (Pl. du) .... FY 67
Mont-Blanc (Pt) .... FY
Mont-Blanc (Q.) .... FGY
Montbrillant (Pl.) .... EY 72
Montbrillant (R.) .... EX
Monthoux (R. de) .... FXY 74
Neuve (Pl.) .... EY 77
Pâquis (R. des) .... FXY
Pépinière (R. de la) ...... EY 83
Philosophes (Bd) .... FZ
Pictet de Rochemont (Av.) GY 84

Plainpalais (Rd-Pt) ...... EZ
Plantamour (R. Ph.) ..... FGY 85
Pont d'Arve (Bd du) .... EFZ
Prairie (R. de la) .... EY
Rive (Rd-Pt de) .... GY 93
Rousseau (R.) .... EFY
St-Georges (Bd de) ..... DEY
St-Georges (Pt de) ..... DZ 95
St-Jean (R. de) .... DEY
St-Léger (R.) .... FZ 96
Scie (R. de la) .... GY
Servette (R. de la) ...... DEY
Seujet (Quai du) .... DEY
Sous-Terre (Pt) .... DY 98
Stand (R. du) .... EY
Temple (R. du) .... EY 102
Terrassière (R.) .... GY
Terreaux-du-Temple (R. des) ...... EY 103
Théâtre (Bd du) .... EY 106
Tour (Bd de la) .... FZ 109
Tranchées (Bd des) ..... GZ
Turrettini (Q. Th.) ...... EY 112
Versonnex (R.) .... GY 114
Vignier (R.) .... EZ 117
Villereuse (R. de) ...... GZ 118
Voltaire (R.) .... EY
Wendt (Av.) .... DXY
Wilson (Quai) .... GX
22-Cantons (Pl.) .... EY 121
31-Décembre (R. du) .... GY 122

Left Bank (Commercial Centre) :

Métropole, 34 quai Gén. Guisan ✉ 1204 ☎ 21 13 44, Telex 421550, Fax 21 13 50, ≤ – ⎮ ▤ TV ☎ – 🏛 50 - 200. AE ① GB JCB. ✂ rest GY **a**
M (see also **L'Arlequin** below) - **Le Grand Quai M** a la carte 60/100 – **121 rm** ⊇ 230/550, 6 suites 800/900.

La Cigogne, 17 pl. Longemalle ✉ 1204 ☎ 311 42 42, Telex 421748, Fax 311 40 65, « Tastefully decorated and furnished » – ⎮ TV ☎ – 🏛 25. AE ① GB. ✂ rest FGY **j**
M 96 – **45 rm** ⊇ 240/425, 5 suites 720.

Armures [M] 🐎, 1 r. Puits-St-Pierre ✉ 1204 ☎ 310 91 72, Telex 421129, Fax 310 98 46 – ⎮ ▤ TV ☎. AE ① GB JCB FY **g**
M 40 – **24 rm** ⊇ 220/340, 4 suites 440.

XXXX **Parc des Eaux-Vives,** 82 quai G. Ador ✉ 1207 ☎ 735 41 40, Fax 786 87 65, « Pleasant setting in extensive park, attractive ≤ » – Ⓟ. AE ① GB by ④
closed 26 December-15 February, Tuesday lunch, Sunday dinner and Monday – **M** 80/130 🍷.

XXXX **L'Arlequin** - Hôtel Métropole, 34 quai Gén. Guisan ✉ 1204 ☎ 21 13 44, Telex 421550, Fax 21 13 50 – ▤. AE ① GB JCB. ✂ GY **a**
closed August, Saturday and Sunday – **M** 90/110.

XXX ✿✿ **Le Béarn** (Goddard), 4 quai Poste ✉ 1204 ☎ 321 00 28 – ▤. ① GB EY **u**
closed 19 July-23 August, February Holidays, Saturday (except dinner October-April) and Sunday – **M** 110/140 and a la carte
Spec. Croustillant de truffe et foie gras (15 December-15 February), Oursins fourrés aux coquilles Saint-Jacques, Petite marmite de homard "Célestine". Wines Pinot gris et noir.

XXX **Baron de la Mouette (Mövenpick Fusterie),** 40 r. Rhône ✉ 1204 ☎ 21 88 55, Fax 28 93 22, ≤ – ▤. AE ① GB FY **h**
M a la carte 55/95 🍷.

Environs

to the N :

Palais des Nations :

Intercontinental [M], 7 petit Saconnex ✉ 1211 ☎ 734 60 91, Telex 412921, Fax 734 28 64, ≤, ≤, 🏊 – ⎮ ▤ TV ☎ 🚗 Ⓟ – 🏛 25 - 600. AE ① GB JCB. ✂ rest by ①
M (see also **Les Continents** below) - **La Pergola M** a la carte 60/85 🍷 – ⊇ 23 – **271 rm** 300/450, 60 suites.

XXXX ✿ **Les Continents** - Hôtel Intercontinental, 7 petit Saconnex ✉ 1211 ☎ 734 60 91, Telex 412921, Fax 734 28 64 – ▤ Ⓟ. AE ① GB JCB. ✂ by ①
closed Sunday lunch and Saturday – **M** a la carte 90/130
Spec. Cannelloni de langoustines aux artichauts, Filets de rougets aux agrumes, Lapereau sauté au coulis d'oignons et mijoté de lentilles. Wines Dardagny, Peissy.

XXX **Perle du Lac,** 128 r. Lausanne ✉ 1202 ☎ 731 79 35, Fax 731 49 79, ≤, ≤ – AE ① GB. ✂ by quai Wilson GX
closed 22 December-22 January and Monday – **M** 95/135.

at Palais des Expositions : 5 km - 1218 Grand Saconnex :

Holiday Inn Crowne Plaza M, 26 voie Moëns 791 00 11, Telex 415695, Fax 798 92 73, - 40 - 160. AE GB JCB
M a la carte 55/90 - 22 - **288 rm** 250/330.

at Bellevue by ③ and road to Lausanne : 6 km - 1293 :

La Réserve M, 301 rte Lausanne 774 17 41, Telex 419117, Fax 774 25 71, « Set in a park near the lake, marina », - 80. AE GB
M (see also **Tsé Fung** below) - 25 - **114 rm** 270/450, 15 suites.

Tsé Fung - Hôtel La Réserve, 301 rte Lausanne 774 17 41, Telex 419117, Fax 774 25 71, Chinese rest. - AE GB
M 75/125.

at Genthod by ③ and road to Lausanne : 7 km - 1294 :

Rest. du Château de Genthod (Leisibach), 1 rte Rennex 774 19 72, - GB
closed 16 to 24 August, 20 December-10 January, Sunday and Monday - **M** 42/85
Spec. Papet vaudois (October-March), Truite saumonée à l'aneth, Fricassée de porc. Wines Pinot noir, Russin.

to the E by road to Evian :

at Cologny by ④ : 3,5 km - 1223 :

Aub. du Lion d'Or (Large), au Village 736 44 32, « Overlooking the lake and Geneva » - AE GB
closed 18 to 26 April, 20 December-20 January, Saturday and Sunday - **M** 130/165 and a la carte
Spec. Filets de rougets poêlés au caramel de légumes, Turbot rôti à la marjolaine, Chariot de pâtisseries. Wines Lully, Pinot noir du Valais.

to the S :

at Petit-Lancy by ⑧ : 3 km - 1213 :

Host. de la Vendée, 28 chemin Vendée 792 04 11, Telex 421304, Fax 792 05 46, - 80. AE GB
closed 21 December-4 January - **M** *(closed Saturday lunch and Sunday)* 72/105 - **33 rm** 145/245
Spec. Filet de Saint-Pierre en pétales dorés et jus de viande, Spirale de filet de sole au beurre de Sauternes, Coquelet en pie aux truffes et Champagne. Wines Aligoté, Dôle.

at Grand-Lancy by ⑦ : 3 km - 1212 Lancy :

Marignac (Pelletier), 32 av. E. Lance 794 04 24, Fax 794 34 83, park - GB
closed 2 to 17 August, Saturday lunch and Sunday - **M** 45/115
Spec. Fines tranches de saumon et son tartare sur mesclin, Escalopes de foie gras frais de canard sur pommes-en-l'air. Wines Pinot gris, Gamay.

to the W :

at Peney-Dessus by road to Peney : 10 km - 1242 Staigny :

Domaine de Châteauvieux (Chevrier) with rm, 753 15 11, Fax 753 19 24, « Old manor farmhouse », - 30. GB
closed 2 to 17 August and 20 December-7 January - **M** *(closed Sunday and Monday)* 95/110 - **18 rm** 120/190
Spec. Suprêmes de grouse rôtis au chou et foie gras (October-November), St-Jacques poêlées aux lentilles vertes (December-March), Canette rôtie (September-April). Wines Satigny.

at Cointrin by road to Lyon : 4 km - 1216 :

Mövenpick Radisson M, 20 rte Pré Bois 798 75 75, Telex 415701, Fax 791 02 84 - rm - 270. AE GB JCB
M a la carte 35/55 - **La Belle Époque** *(closed Saturday lunch and Sunday)* **M** a la carte 55/95 - **Kikkoman** *(closed Sunday)* **M** 79/98 - 18 - **336 rm** 210/330, 14 suites.

Penta M, 75 av. L. Casaï 798 47 00, Telex 415571, Fax 798 77 58, - 700. AE GB JCB. rest
La Récolte M a la carte approx. 70 - 22 - **308 rm** 180/260.

Rôtisserie Plein Ciel (at the airport), 717 76 76, Telex 415775, Fax 798 77 68, - . AE GB
M 39/43.

In this Guide,
a symbol or a character, printed in red or black,
does not have the same meaning.
Please read the explanatory pages carefully.

See : The Quays★★ BYZ – Fraumünster cloisters★ (Alter Kreuzgang des Fraumünsters) BZ **D** –
View of the town from the Zürichhorn Gardens★ V – Church of SS. Felix and Regula★ ∪ **E** – Church
of Zürich-Altstetten★ ∪ **F** – Zoological Gardens★ (Zoo Dolder) ∪ – Museums : Swiss National
Museum★★★ (Schweizerisches Landesmuseum) BY – Fine Arts Museum★★ (Kunsthaus) CZ –
Rietberg Museum★★ V **M2** – Buhrle Collection★★ (Sammlung Buhrle) V **M3**.

✈ Kloten ✆ 812 71 11.

🗓 Offizielles Verkehrsbüro, Bahnhofplatz 15 ✉ 8023 ✆ 211 40 00, Telex 813 744 – A.C.S. Forchstrasse
95 ✉ 8032 ✆ 55 15 00 – T.C.S. Alfred-Escher-Strasse 38 ✉ 8002 ✆ 201 25 36.

Basle 109 ⑥ – Bern 125 ⑥ – Geneva 278 ⑥ – Innsbruck 288 ① – Milan 304 ⑤.

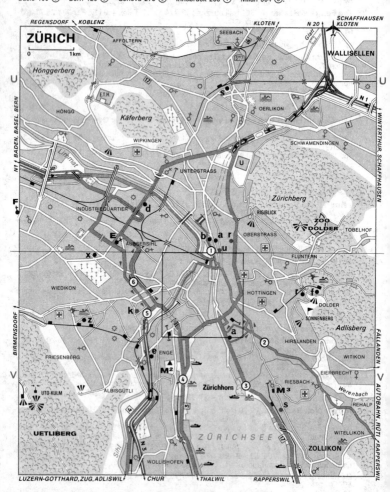

On the right bank of river Limmat (University, Fine Arts Museum) :

🏨🏨🏨 Dolder Grand Hotel ⑤, Kurhausstr. 65, ✉ 8032, ✆ 251 62 31, Telex 816416, Fax 251 88 29,
≼ Zürich and lake, 🌣, ⚖, 🏌, park, ✗ – 🛗 🗐 📺 ☎ 🖙 🅿 – 🕍 200. 🖭 ⑨ 🖪 *VISA*. 🛰 rest
M 70/75 and a la carte 89/125 – **La Rotonde** 108/125 and a la carte 82/128 – **165 rm**
⊆ 280/490, **11 suites** 530/2500.
V **f**

🏨🏨🏨 **Zurich et la Residence**, Neumühlequai 42, ✉ 8001, ✆ 363 63 63, Telex 817587,
Fax 363 60 15, ≼, 🎰, 🚠, 🖾 – 🛗 ❄ rm 🗐 📺 ☎ 🖙 – 🕍 250. 🖭 ⑨ 🖪 *VISA*
M (buffet lunch) 18/29 and a la carte – **Tourne Broche** – **White Elephant** *(Thai rest.)* – **263 rm**
⊆ 280/360, **10 suites** 650/1100.
∪ **b**

Eden au Lac, Utoquai 45, ⊠ 8023, 𝒫 261 94 04, Telex 816339, Fax 261 94 09, ←, 🆘 –
|🛗| ⓔ 🕿 ℗ – ⚖ 25. 🅰🅴 ⓞ ⋿ 𝘝𝘐𝘚𝘈   V a
M 120 and a la carte 72/95 – **52 rm** ⊑ 250/480, **3 suites** 850/950.

Waldhaus Dolder ♨, Kurhausstr. 20, ⊠ 8030, 𝒫 251 93 60, Telex 816460, Fax 251 00 29,
← Zürich and lake, 🎬, 🆘, ☒, 1g, ⚘, ⚒ – |🛗| ✗ rest ▤ 📺 🕿 🚗 ℗ – ⚖ 35. 🅰🅴 ⓞ ⋿
𝘝𝘐𝘚𝘈   V r
M 20/50 (lunch) and a la carte 53/82 – ⊑ 15 – **97 rm** 180/420, **3 suites** 400/600.

Central Plaza, Central 1, ⊠ 8001, 𝒫 251 55 55, Telex 817152, Fax 251 85 35 – |🛗| ▤ 📺
– ⚖ 45. 🅰🅴 ⓞ ⋿ 𝘝𝘐𝘚𝘈   BY z
M Cascade *(closed Saturday and Sunday)* 32/42 and a la carte – ⊑ 18 – **94 rm** 250/370, **4 suites**
450/550.

Pullman Continental, Stampfenbachstr. 60, ⊠ 8035, 𝒫 363 33 63, Telex 817089,
Fax 363 33 18 – |🛗| ▤ 📺 🕿 ⚓, 🚗 – ⚖ 70. 🅰🅴 ⓞ ⋿ 𝘝𝘐𝘚𝘈   U a
M Diff *(closed Sunday)* (dinner only) 68 and a la carte 60/100 – **Coq d'Or** 48/52 and a la carte
50/80 – ⊑ 22 – **180 rm** 240/320.

Opera without rest., Dufourstr. 5, ⊠ 8008, 𝒫 251 90 90, Telex 816480, Fax 251 90 01 – |🛗|
▤ 📺 🕿 – ⚖ 12. 🅰🅴 ⓞ ⋿ 𝘝𝘐𝘚𝘈   CZ b
closed 21 December-8 January – **67 rm** ⊑ 190/290.

Europe without rest., Dufourstr. 4, ⊠ 8008, 𝒫 261 10 30, Telex 816461, Fax 251 03 67 –
|🛗| ▤ 📺 🕿. 🅰🅴 ⓞ ⋿ 𝘝𝘐𝘚𝘈   CZ a
40 rm ⊑ 250/450, **2 suites** 560/780.

Tiefenau, Steimweisstr. 8-10, ⊠ 8032, 𝒫 251 24 09, Telex 816395, Fax 251 24 76, 🎬
|🛗| ⓔ rest 📺 🕿 ℗ – ⚖ 35. 🅰🅴 ⓞ ⋿ 𝘝𝘐𝘚𝘈   CZ h
closed 18 December-4 January – **M** 40 and a la carte – **25 rm** ⊑ 180/360, **3 suites** 400/460.

Ambassador, Falkenstr. 6, ⊠ 8008, 𝒫 261 76 00, Telex 816508, Fax 251 23 94 – |🛗| ▤ 📺
🕿. 🅰🅴 ⓞ ⋿ 𝘝𝘐𝘚𝘈   CZ a
M 29/49 and a la carte – **45 rm** ⊑ 190/290.

Wellenberg without rest., Niederdorfstr. 10, ⊠ 8001, 𝒫 262 43 00, Fax 251 31 30 – |🛗| 📺
🕿 &.   BY s
46 rm.

Zürcherhof, Zähringerstr. 21, ⊠ 8025, 𝒫 262 10 40, Telex 816490, Fax 262 04 84 – |🛗|
▤ rest 📺 🕿. 🅰🅴 ⓞ ⋿ 𝘝𝘐𝘚𝘈. ⚒   CY q
M *(closed Saturday and Sunday)* 18,50/38,50 and a la carte – **35 rm** ⊑ 130/240.

Rütli without rest., Zähringerstr. 43, ⊠ 8001, 𝒫 251 54 26, Telex 816037, Fax 261 21 53 –
|🛗| 📺 🕿. 🅰🅴 ⋿ 𝘝𝘐𝘚𝘈. ⚒   CY a
62 rm ⊑ 130/215.

Franziskaner, Niederdorfstr. 1, ⊠ 8001, 𝒫 252 01 20, Telex 816431, Fax 252 61 78 – 📺
🕿 – ⚖ 100. 🅰🅴 ⓞ ⋿ 𝘝𝘐𝘚𝘈   BY x
M 15/32 and a la carte 30/51 – **20 rm** ⊑ 150/220.

Ammann without rest., Kirchgasse 4, ⊠ 8001, 𝒫 252 72 40, Telex 817137, Fax 262 43 70
– 📺 🕿. 🅰🅴 ⋿ 𝘝𝘐𝘚𝘈   BCZ n
22 rm ⊑ 170/262, **1 suite** 250/300.

Helmhaus without rest., Schiffländeplatz 30, ⊠ 8001, 𝒫 251 88 10, Telex 816525,
Fax 251 04 30 – |🛗| ✗ rest 📺 🕿. 🅰🅴 ⓞ ⋿ 𝘝𝘐𝘚𝘈. ⚒   BCZ s
closed until 1 May due to refurbishment – **25 rm** ⊑ 135/225.

XXX **Agnès Amberg,** Hottingerstr. 5, ⊠ 8032, 𝒫 251 26 26, Fax 252 50 62 – 🅰🅴 ⓞ ⋿ 𝘝𝘐𝘚𝘈
closed lunch Monday and Saturday, Sunday, last week July, 2 weeks August and 24 Decem-
ber-7 January – **M** 47/175 and a la carte approx. 106   CY d

XXX **Zunfthaus Zur Schmiden,** Marktgasse 20, ⊠ 8001, 𝒫 251 52 87, Fax 261 12 67, « 15C
blacksmith's guild house » – ▤ rest – ⚖ 60. 🅰🅴 ⓞ ⋿ 𝘝𝘐𝘚𝘈   BY f
closed mid July-mid August – **M** 28/73 and a la carte 55/86.

XX **Kronenhalle,** Rämistrasse 4, ⊠ 8001, 𝒫 251 02 56, « Café de luxe, fine art collection »
– ▤. 🅰🅴 ⓞ ⋿ 𝘝𝘐𝘚𝘈   CZ r
M a la carte 62/115.

XX **Wirtschaft Flühgass,** Zollikerstr. 214, Riesbach, ⊠ 8008, 𝒫 53 12 15, Fax 55 75 32, « 16C
inn » – ℗. 🅰🅴 ⓞ ⋿ 𝘝𝘐𝘚𝘈   V s
closed Saturday, Sunday, 11 July-10 August and 25 December-4 January – **M** (booking essential) 85/130 and a la carte.

XX **Haus Zum Rüden,** Limmatquai 42 (1st floor), ⊠ 8001, 𝒫 261 95 66, Fax 261 18 04, « 13C
guild house » – |🛗| ▤. 🅰🅴 ⓞ ⋿ 𝘝𝘐𝘚𝘈   BY m
M *(closed Sunday)* 140 and a la carte.

XX **Zunfthaus Zur Saffran,** Limmatquai 54, (1st floor), ⊠ 8001, 𝒫 261 65 65, Fax 252 21 32,
« 14C saffron guild house » 🅰🅴 ⓞ ⋿ 𝘝𝘐𝘚𝘈   BY c
closed Sunday, Monday and 19 July - 17 August – **M** 22,50/35 and a la carte.

XX **Köngistuhl,** Stüssihofstatt 3, ⊠ 8001, 𝒫 261 76 18, Fax 252 61 78 – 🅰🅴 ⓞ ⋿ 𝘝𝘐𝘚𝘈   BY r
M 110/120 and a la carte.

ZÜRICH

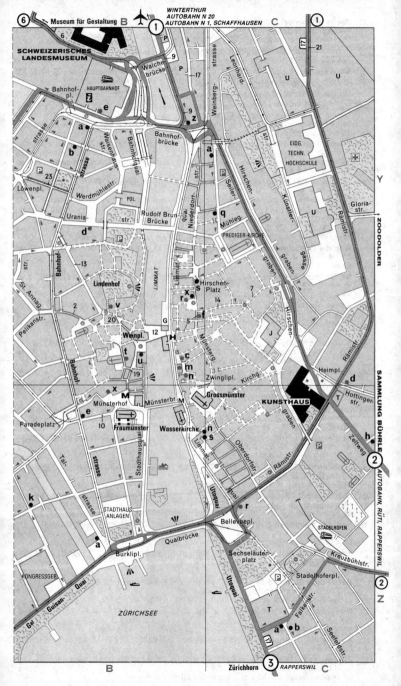

XX **Jacky's Stapferstube,** Culmannstr. 45, ⊠ 8033, 𝒫 361 37 48, Veal and beef specialities – 🗐 **🅿. AE ⊙ E VISA** U r
closed Sunday and Monday – **M** a la carte approx. 106.

XX Zunfthaus Zum Zimmerleuten, Limmatquay 40, (1st floor), ⊠ 8001, 𝒫 252 08 34, Fax 252 08 48, « 18C guild house » BY n

X **Casa Ferlin,** Stampfenbachstr. 38, ⊠ 8006, 𝒫 362 35 09, Italian rest. – 🗐. **AE ⊙ E VISA**
closed Saturday, Sunday and mid July-mid August – **M** a la carte 61,50/81,50. U u

On the left bank of River Limmat (Main railway station, Business centre) :

🏨🏨 **Baur au Lac,** Talstr. 1, ⊠ 8022, 𝒫 221 16 50, Telex 813567, Fax 211 81 39, ㈜, « Lakeside setting and gardens » – 🛗 🗐 🔟 🕿 ⬅ 🅿 – 🛆 150. **AE ⊙ E VISA**. ℅ rest BZ **a**
M Le Pavillon *(summer only)* 55/69 and a la carte 55/130 – Le Grill – **123 rm** 🍽 320/520, **16 suites** 950/1700.

🏨 **Savoy Baur en Ville,** Paradeplatz, ⊠ 8001, 𝒫 211 53 60, Telex 812845, Fax 221 14 67 – 🛗 🗐 🔟 🕿 ⬅ – 🛆 135. **AE ⊙ E VISA**. ℅ BZ **e**
M Orsini (Italian rest.) 52/85 and a la carte – **Savoy Grill** 56/95 and a la carte – **104 rm** 🍽 350/650, **8 suites** 950/1100.

🏨 **Schweizerhof,** Bahnhofplatz 7, ⊠ 8023, 𝒫 211 86 40, Telex 813754, Fax 211 35 05 – 🛗 🗐 🔟 🕿 – 🛆 40. **AE ⊙ E VISA** BY **a**
M La Soupière *(closed Sunday)* 80/135 and a la carte – **114 rm** 🍽 200/420 Bb, **1 suite** 450/780.

🏨 **Atlantis Sheraton** ⟨⟩, Döltschiweg 234, ⊠ 8055, 𝒫 463 00 00, Telex 813338, Fax 463 03 88, ≤ countryside and city, ㈜, 🏋, ⊗, ⊠, park – 🛗 ½⇆ rm 🗐 rest 🔟 🕿 ⬅ 🅿 – 🛆 200. **AE ⊙ E VISA** V **z**
M *(closed Saturday lunch)* a la carte 36/76 – **159 rm** 🍽 340/400, **2 suites** 1200.

Annexe Guesthouse ⟨⟩, 𝒫 463 00 00, Telex 813338, Fax 463 03 88 – 🛗 ½⇆ rm 🔟 🕿. **AE ⊙ E VISA**
61 rm 🍽 175/240.

🏨 **St. Gothard,** Bahnhofstr. 87, ⊠ 8023, 𝒫 211 55 00, Telex 812420, Fax 211 24 19, ⊗ – 🛗 ½⇆ 🗐 🔟 🕿 – 🛆 40. **AE ⊙ E VISA** BY **b**
M 40/95 and a la carte – 🍽 22 – **128 rm** 250/450, **7 suites** 520/780.

🏨 **Ascot,** Tessinerplatz 9, ⊠ 8002, 𝒫 201 18 00, Telex 815454, Fax 202 72 10 – 🛗 🗐 🔟 🕿 – 🛆 50. **AE ⊙ E VISA**. ℅ AZ **a**
M Jockey Club *(closed Saturday, Sunday, 1 August, 15 September and Christmas)* 65/86 and a la carte – **73 rm** 🍽 200/470.

🏨 **Splügenschloss,** Splügenstr. 2, ⊠ 8002, 𝒫 201 08 00, Telex 815553, Fax 201 42 86 – 🛗 ½⇆ rm 🗐 🔟 🕿 🅿 – 🛆 20. **AE ⊙ E VISA**. ℅ rest AZ **e**
M 110 and a la carte – **49 rm** 🍽 240/450, **1 suite** 500/550.

🏨 **Neues Schloss,** Stockerstr. 17, ⊠ 8022, 𝒫 201 65 50, Telex 815560, Fax 201 64 18 – 🛗 🔟 🕿 🅿 – 🛆 25. **AE ⊙ E VISA**. ℅ rest AZ **m**
M Le Jardin *(closed Sunday lunch)* (Sunday dinner, residents only) 57/90 and a la carte – **57 rm** 🍽 210/440, **1 suite** 500/600.

🏨 **Zum Storchen,** Weinplatz 2, ⊠ 8022, 𝒫 211 55 10, Telex 813354, Fax 211 64 51, ≤ River Limmat and city, ㈜, « Riverside setting » – 🛗 🔟 🕿 – 🛆 40. **AE ⊙ E VISA** BY **u**
M a la carte 58/84 – **77 rm** 🍽 210/450 Bb, **1 suite** 600/800.

🏨 **Stoller,** Badenerstr. 357, ⊠ 8040, 𝒫 492 65 00, Telex 822460, Fax 492 65 01, ㈜ – 🛗 🔟 🕿 ⬅ 🅿 – 🛆 50. **AE ⊙ E VISA** V **x**
M 26 (dinner) and a la carte 39/66 – **79 rm** 🍽 200/320.

🏨 **Glockenhof,** Sihlstr. 31, ⊠ 8023, 𝒫 211 56 50, Telex 812466, Fax 211 56 60, ㈜ – 🛗 🗐 rest 🔟. **AE ⊙ E VISA** AY **e**
M 27/38 and a la carte – **108 rm** 🍽 180/268.

🏨 **Glärnischhof,** Claridenstr. 30, ⊠ 8022, 𝒫 202 47 47, Telex 815366, Fax 201 01 64 – 🛗 🗐 rest 🔟 🕿 🅿 – 🛆 35. **AE ⊙ E VISA** BZ **k**
M 42 (lunch) and a la carte 31/62 – **70 rm** 🍽 260/500.

🏨 **Senator,** Heinrichstr. 254, ⊠ 8005, 𝒫 272 20 21, Fax 272 25 85, ㈜ – 🛗 🔟 🕿 ⬅ – 🛆 35. **AE ⊙ E VISA** U **d**
M *(closed Saturday and Sunday)* 16/30 and a la carte 49/62 – **102 rm** 175/230.

🏨 **Engematthof** ⟨⟩, Engimattstr. 14, ⊠ 8002, 𝒫 201 25 04, Telex 817273, Fax 201 25 16, ㈜, ㈜ – 🛗 🔟 🕿 ⬅ – 🛆 20. **AE ⊙ E VISA**. ℅ V **e**
M 14/35 and a la carte – **79 rm** 🍽 142/290.

XXX **Baron de la Mouette** (Mövenpick Dreikönighaus), Beethovenstr. 32, Dreikönigstr., ⊠ 8002, 𝒫 286 53 53, Fax 286 53 55 – 🗐. **AE ⊙ E VISA** AZ **r**
closed Saturday, Sunday and 11 July - 23 August – **M** a la carte 63/80.

XX **Nouvelle,** Erlachstr. 46, ⊠ 8003, 𝒫 462 63 63, Fax 462 81 55 – 🗐 – 🛆 10. **AE ⊙ E VISA** V **k**
closed Saturday, Sunday and mid June-mid July – **M** 125/145 a la carte.

XXX Au Premier, Bahnhofbuffet, Hauptbahnhof, ⊠ 8023, 𝒫 211 15 10, Telex 812552, Fax 212 04 25. BY **e**

XX **Zunfthaus zur Waag,** Münsterhof 8, ⊠ 8001, 𝒫 211 07 30, Fax 212 01 69, « 17C weavers' guild house » – **AE ⊙ E VISA** BZ **x**
M (booking essential) 150 and a la carte 44,50/99,10.

XX **Veltliner Keller**, Schlüsselgasse 8, ⊠ 8001, ℰ 221 32 28, Fax 212 20 94, « 14Chouse » BY **t**

XX **Rotisserie Lindenhofkeller,** Pfalzgasse 4, ⊠ 8001, ℰ 211 70 71, Fax 212 33 37, 🌲 –
▤. AE ① E VISA BY **v**
closed Saturday, Sunday, 3 weeks August-September – **M** 20/36 (lunch) and a la carte 66/92.

X **Brasserie Lipp,** Uraniastr. 9, ⊠ 8001, ℰ 211 11 55, Fax 212 17 26 – AE ① E VISA
closed Sunday and 1 July-31 August – **M** 45/55 and a la carte. BY **d**

Environs North

at Zurich-Oerlikon : by ① – ⊠ 8050 Zurich-Oerlikon :

🏛 **International,** Am Marktplatz, ⊠ 8050, ℰ 311 43 41, Telex 823251, Fax 312 44 68, 🖘,
🟦 – 🛊 🎇 ▤ 🆀 🕾 ☎ – 🔬 650. AE ① E VISA. 🛠 U **s**
M Panorama Grill *(30th floor)* ≤ Zurich 13/17 and a la carte 25/60 – **Lotus Garden** *(Chinese rest.)* – ⌸ 15 – **334 rm** 260/290, **11 suites** 550/950.

at Zürich-Kloten (Airport) : 10 km by ① :

🏛 **Ramada Renaissance,** Talackerstr. 1, ⊠ 8152, Glattbrugg ℰ 810 85 00, Telex 825003,
Fax 810 87 55, 🕰, 🖘, 🟦 – 🛊 🎇 rm ▤ 🆀 🕾 – 🔬 300. AE ① E VISA
M – **Asian Place** *(closed lunch Saturday and Sunday and Monday)* 20/30 and a la carte –
⌸ 25 – **197 rm** 225/275, **7 suites** 315/560.

🏛 **Hilton,** Hohenbühlstr. 10, ⊠ 8058, ℰ 810 31 31, Telex 825428, Fax 810 93 66, 🌲, 🖘 –
🛊 🎇 rm ▤ 🆀 🕾 ☎ ♿, – 🔬 280. AE ① E VISA. 🛠 rest
M Harvest Grill a la carte approx. 81,50 – **Taverne** a la carte approx. 66,50 – ⌸ 26 – **276 rm**
350/390, **10 suites** 575/995.

🏛 **Novotel,** Talackerstr. 21 ⊠ 8152 Glattbrugg, ℰ 810 31 11, Telex 828770, Fax 810 81 85,
🌲 – 🛊 🎇 rm ▤ 🆀 🕾 ♿, – 🔬 150. AE ① E VISA
M a la carte 32,50/52,80 – **256 rm** ⌸ 140/180, **1 suite** 290.

🏠 **Fly Away,** Marktgasse 19, ⊠ 8302, Kloten ℰ 813 66 13, Fax 813 51 25, 🌲 – 🛊 ▤ 🕾 ♿,
🖘 🅿. AE ① E VISA
M 24,50/46,50 and a la carte – ⌸ 9 – **42 rm** 130/165.

🏠 Welcome Inn, Holbergstr. 1, ⊠ 8302 Kloten, ℰ 814 07 27, Telex 825527, Fax 813 56 16, 🌲
– 🛊 🕾 🖘 🅿 – 🔬 17 – **96 rm**.

at Unterengstringen : 7 km by ① – ⊠ 8103 Unterengstringen :

XXX **Witschi's,** Zurcherstr. 55, ⊠ 8103, ℰ 750 44 60, Fax 750 19 68, 🌲 – 🖘. AE ① E VISA
closed Sunday, Monday, 3 weeks July and 3 weeks December-January – **M** 65/190 and a la carte.

at Dielsdorf : NW : 15,5 km by ① and B 17 – ⊠ 8157 Dielsdorf :

XX **Bienengarten** with rm., Regensbergerstr. 9, ℰ 853 12 17, Fax 853 24 41, 🌲, « Modern
lithographs », 🌲 – 🛊 ▤ 🆀 🕾 🅿. AE ① E VISA
M 40/110 and a la carte – **8 rm** ⌸ 160/320.

at Nürensdorf : 17 km by ① via Kloten – ⊠ 8309 Nürensdorf :

XXX ✿ **Gasthof Zum Bären** with rm, ℰ 836 42 12 – 🛊 ▤ rest 🆀 🕾 🖘 🅿. AE ① E VISA
closed 23 December - 7 January – **M** *(closed Sunday and Monday)* 65/150 and a la carte –
14 rm ⌸ 80/200
Spec. Cassoulet de scampis et légumes, sauce au gingembre et aux oignons, Filets de perche,
sauce mousseline, Poitrine de canard Challandais, sauce aux échalotes.

Environs South

at Küsnacht : 6 km by ③ – ⊠ 8700 Küsnacht :

🏠 **Ermitage,** Seestr. 80, ⊠ 8700, ℰ 910 52 22, Telex 825707, Fax 910 52 44, ≤ lake, 🌲,
« lakeside setting, terrace and garden » – 🛊 ▤ 🕾 🅿 – 🔬 20. AE ① E VISA
M 110 (dinner) and a la carte 63/109 – ⌸ 18 – **20 rm** 150/260, **6 suites** 360/700.

XXX ✿✿ **Petermann's Kunststube** (Petermann), Seestr. 160, ⊠ 8700, ℰ 910 07 15,
Fax 910 04 95 – ▤ 🅿. AE ① E VISA
closed Sunday, Monday, 9 to 24 February and 19 August-10 September – **M** 65/185 and a
la carte 92/110
Spec. Le Pot au feu de la mer à l'infusion de coriandre, La poularde de Bresse à la crème d'estragon
et aux carottes fondantes, Le soufflé au fromage blanc et à la vanille sur une compote de rhubarbe.

at Rüschlikon : 9 km by ④ – ⊠ 8803 Rüschlikon :

🏠 Belvoir 🦢, Säumerstr. 37, ⊠ 8803, ℰ 724 02 02, Fax 724 11 76, ≤ lake, 🌲 – 🛊 ▤ rest
🆀 🕾 🖘 🅿 – 🔬 150. 🛠 rest – **25 rm**.

at Gattikon : 13,5 km by ⑤ – ⊠ 8136 Gattikon-Thalwil :

XXX ✿ **Sihlhalde,** Sihlhaldenstr. 70, ⊠ 8136, ℰ 720 09 27, 🌲 – ▤ E VISA
closed Sunday, Monday and 20 July-12 August – **M** 48/85 and a la carte
Spec. Ravioli aux truffes, Chasse été (June-August), Escalope de saumon avec choucroute.

at Wädenswil : 22 km by ⑤ – ⊠ 8820 Wädenswil :

XX **Eichmühle,** by N3, exit Richterswil, ℰ 780 34 44, Fax 780 48 64, ≤, 🌲 – AE E VISA
closed Sunday dinner, Monday, 15 to 30 February and 1 to 15 October – **M** 98/125.

United Kingdom

LONDON - BIRMINGHAM - EDINBURGH
GLASGOW - LEEDS - LIVERPOOL
MANCHESTER

PRACTICAL INFORMATION

LOCAL CURRENCY

Pound Sterling: £ 1 = 1.87 US $ (Jan. 92).

TOURIST INFORMATION

Tourist information offices exist in each city included in the Guide. The telephone number and address is given in each text under ⒵

FOREIGN EXCHANGE

Banks are open between 9.30am and 3pm on weekdays only and some open on Saturdays. Most large hotels have exchange facilities, and Heathrow and Gatwick Airports have 24-hour banking facilities.

SHOPPING

In London: Oxford St./Regent St. (department stores, exclusive shops)
Bond St. (exclusive shops, antiques)
Knightsbridge area (department stores, exclusive shops, boutiques)
For other towns see the index of street names: those printed in red are where the principal shops are found.

THEATRE BOOKINGS IN LONDON

Your hotel porter will be able to make your arrangements or direct you to Theatre Booking Agents.
In addition there is a kiosk in Leicester Square selling tickets for the same day's performances at half price plus booking fee. It is open 12-6.30pm.

CAR HIRE

The international car hire companies have branches in each major city. Your hotel porter should be able to give details and help you with your arrangements.

TIPPING

Many hotels and restaurants include a service charge but where this is not the case an amount equivalent to between 10 and 15 per cent of the bill is customary. Additionally doormen, baggage porters and cloakroom attendants are generally given a gratuity.
Taxi drivers are customarily tipped between 10 and 15 per cent of the amount shown on the meter in addition to the fare.

SPEED LIMITS

The maximum permitted speed on motorways and dual carriageways is 70 mph (113 km/h.) and 60 mph (97 km/h.) on other roads except where a lower speed limit is signposted.

SEAT BELTS

The wearing of seat belts in the United Kingdom is compulsory for drivers, front seat passengers and rear seat passengers where seat belts are fitted. It is illegal for front seat passengers to carry children on their lap.

ANIMALS

It is forbidden to bring domestic animals (dogs, cats...) into the United Kingdom.

London

404 folds ㊷ to ㊹ – pop. 7 566 620 – ☎ 071 or 081.

✈ Heathrow, ℰ (081) 759 4321, Telex 934892 – Terminal : Airbus (A1) from Victoria, Airbus (A2) from Paddington – Underground (Piccadilly line) frequent service daily.

✈ Gatwick, ℰ 0293 (Crawley) 28822 and ℰ 081 (London) 668 4211, Telex 877725, by A 23 and M 23 – Terminal : Coach service from Victoria Coach Station (Flightline 777, hourly service) – Railink (Gatwick Express) from Victoria (24 h service).

✈ London City Airport, ℰ (071) 589 55 99, Telex 264731.

✈ Stansted, at Bishop's Storford, ℰ 0279 (Bishop's Stortford) 680800, Telex 818708, NE : 34 m. off M 11 and A 120.

British Airways, Victoria Air Terminal : 115 Buckingham Palace Rd., SW1, ℰ (071) 834 9411, p. 16 BX.

🚃 Euston and Paddington ℰ 0345 090700.

🛈 London Tourist Board and Convention Bureau, Telephone Information Services ℰ (071) 730 3488.
British Travel Centre, 12 Regent St. Piccadilly Circus, SW1, ℰ (071) 730 3400.
National Tourist Information Centre, Victoria Station Forecourt, SW1, ℰ (071) 730 3488.

Sights

HISTORIC BUILDINGS AND MONUMENTS

Palace of Westminster★★★ p. 10 LY – Tower of London★★★ p. 11 PVX – Banqueting House★★ p. 10 LX – Buckingham Palace★★ p. 16 BVX – Kensington Palace★★ p. 8 FX – Lincoln's Inn★★ p. 17 EV – London Bridge★ p. 11 PVX – Royal Hospital Chelsea★★ p. 15 FU – St. James's Palace★★ p. 13 EP – South Bank Arts Centre★★ p. 10 MX – The Temple★★ p. 6 MV – Tower Bridge★★ p. 11 PX – Albert Memorial★ p. 14 CQ – Apsley House★ p. 12 BP – George Inn★, Southwark p. 11 PX – Guildhall★ p. 7 OU – Dr Johnson's House★ p. 6 NUV **A** – Leighton House★ p. 8 EY – The Monument★ (❋★) p. 7 PV **G** – Royal Opera Arcade★ p. 13 FGN – Stample Inn★ p. 6 MU **Y** – Theatre Royal★ (Haymarket) p. 13 GM.

CHURCHES

The City Churches

St. Paul's Cathedral★★★ p. 7 NOV – St. Bartholomew the Great★★ p. 7 OU **K** – St. Mary-at-Hill★★ p. 7 PV **B** – Temple Church★★ p. 6 MV – All Hallows-by-the-Tower (font cover★★, brasses★) p. 7 PV **Y** – St. Bride's (steeple★★) p. 7 NV **J** – St. Giles Cripplegate★ p. 7 OU **N** – St. Helen Bishopsgate★ (monuments★★) p. 7 PUV **R** – St. James Garlickhythe (tower and spire★, sword rest★) p. 7 OV **R** – St. Margaret Lothbury p. 7 PU **S** – St. Margaret Pattens (woodwork★) p. 7 PV **N** – St. Mary Abchurch★ p. 7 PV **X** – St. Mary-le-Bow (tower and steeple★★) p. 7 OV **G** – St. Michael Paternoster Royal (tower and spire★) p. 7 OV **D** – St. Olave★ p. 7 PV **S**.

Other Churches

Westminster Abbey★★★ p. 10 LY – Southwark Cathedral★★ p. 11 PX – Queen's Chapel★ p. 13 EP – St. Clement Danes★ p. 17 EX – St. James's★ p. 13 EM – St. Margaret's★ p. 10 LY **A** – St. Martin in-the-Fields★ p. 17 DY – St. Paul's★ (Covent Garden) p. 17 DX – Westminster Roman Catholic Cathedral★ p. 10 KY **B**.

STREETS – SQUARES – PARKS

The City★★★ p. 7 NV – Regent's Park★★★ (Terraces★★, Zoo★★★) p. 5 HIT – Belgrave Square★★ p. 16 AVX – Burlington Arcade★★ p. 13 DM – Hyde Park★★ p. 9 GHVX – The Mall★★ p. 13 FF – Piccadilly★★ p. 13 EM — St. James's Park★★ p. 10 KXY – Trafalgar Square★★ p. 17 DXY – Whitehall★★ (Horse Guards★) p. 10 LX – Barbican★ p. 7 OU – Bloomsbury★ p. 6 LMU – Bond Street★ pp. 12-13 CK-DM – Charing Cross★ p. 17 DY – Cheyne Walk★ p. 9 GHZ – Jermyn Street★ p. 13 EN – Piccadilly Arcade★ p. 13 DEN – Queen Anne's Gate★ p. 10 KY – Regent Street★ p. 13 EM – St. James's Square★ p. 13 FN – St. James's Street★ p. 13 EN – Shepherd Market★ p. 12 CN – Strand★ p. 17 DY – Victoria Embankment★ p. 17 DEXY – Waterloo Place★ p. 13 FN.

MUSEUMS

British Museum★★★ p. 6 LU – National Gallery★★★ p. 13 GM – Science Museum★★★ p. 14 CR – Tate Gallery★★★ p. 10 LZ – Victoria and Albert Museum★★★ p. 15 DR – Courtauld Institute Galleries★★ p. 6 KLU **M** – Museum of London★★ p. 7 OU **M** – National Portrait Gallery★★ p. 13 GM – Natural History Museum★★ p. 14 CS – Queen's Gallery★★ p. 16 BV – Wallace Collection★★ p. 12 AH – Imperial War Museum★ p. 10 NY – London Transport Museum★ p. 17 DX – Madame Tussaud's★ p. 5 IU **M** – Sir John Soane's Museum★ p. 6 MU **M** – Wellington Museum★ p. 12 BP.

Alphabetical list of areas included

LONDON CENTRE

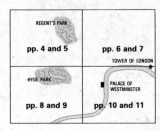

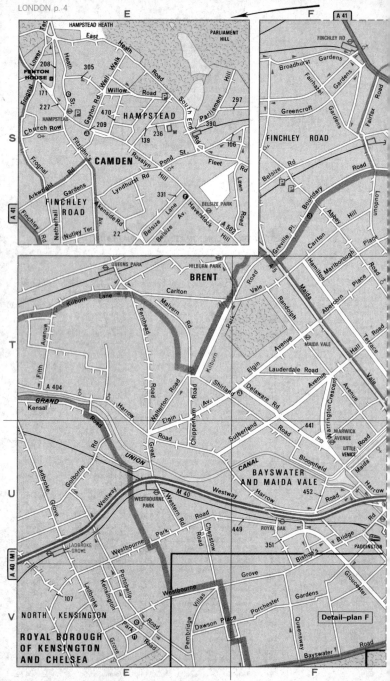

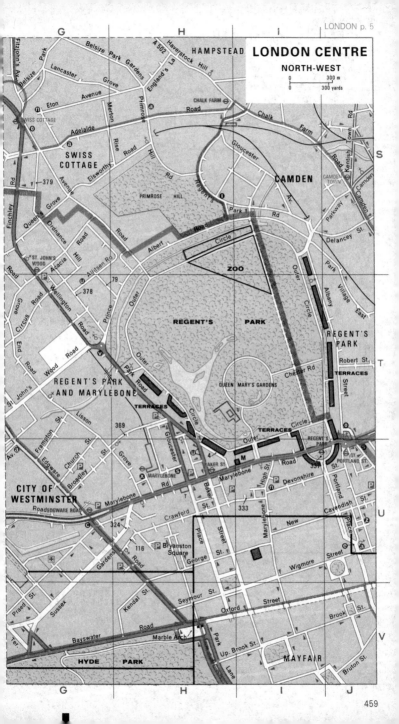

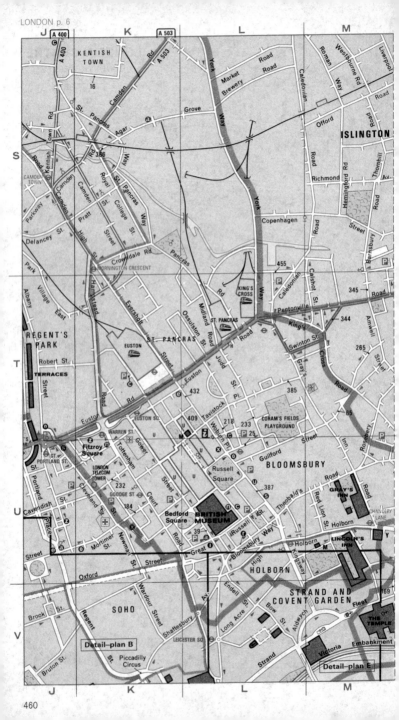

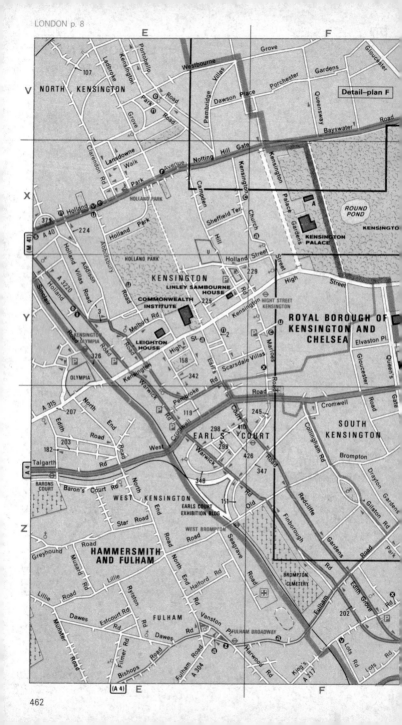

LONDON CENTRE
SOUTH-WEST

MAYFAIR

CITY OF WESTMINSTER

HYDE PARK

THE LONG WATER

THE SERPENTINE

GARDENS

HYDE PARK AND KNIGHTSBRIDGE

Kensington

GREEN PARK

HYDE PARK CORNER

BUCKINGHAM PALACE

Belgrave Square

Detail–plan D

BELGRAVIA

VICTORIA

Detail–plan C

CHELSEA

BATTERSEA PARK

WANDSWORTH

Mon–Fri. Tidal traffic flow

463

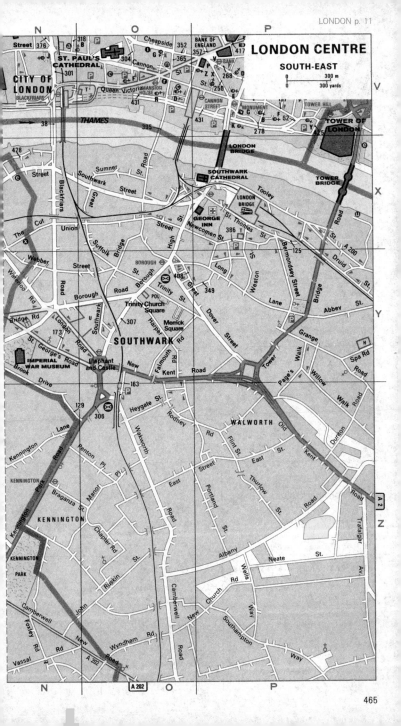

LONDON CENTRE

SOUTH-EAST

| 0 | 300 m |
| 0 | 300 yards |

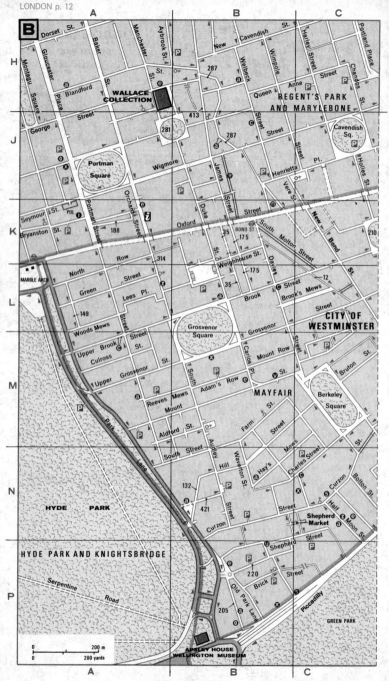

B

Oxford Street is closed to private traffic, Mondays to Saturdays :
from 7 am to 7 pm between Portman Street and St. Giles Circus

467

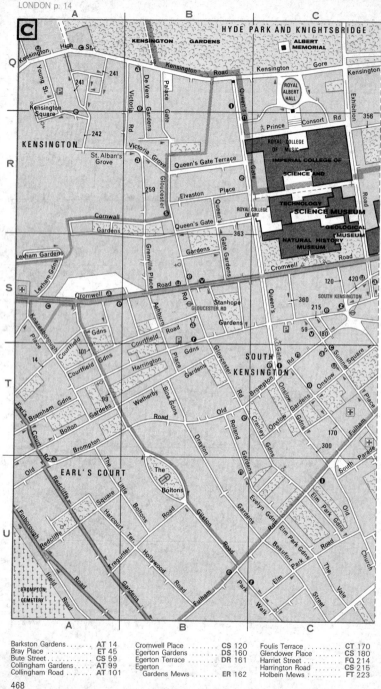

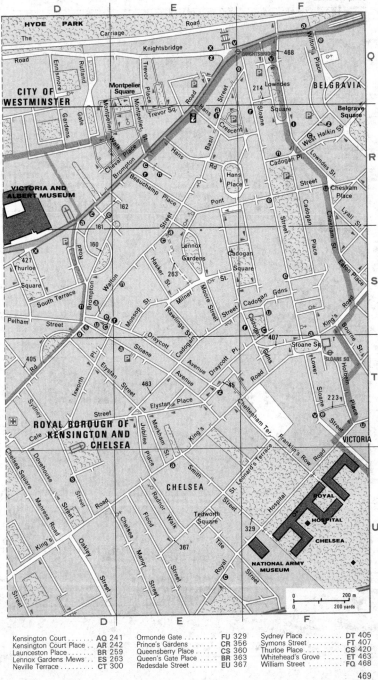

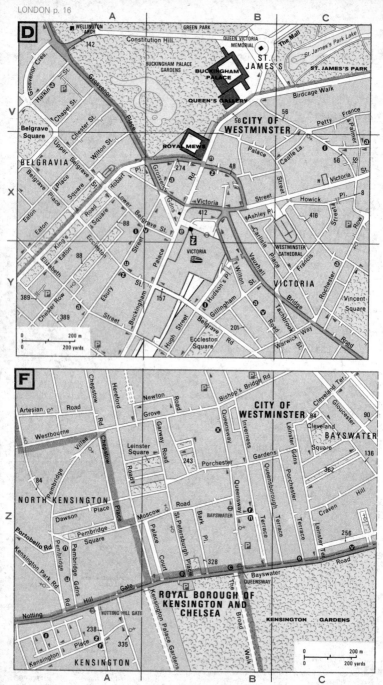

D

WELLINGTON ARCH

GREEN PARK

Constitution Hill

142

BUCKINGHAM PALACE GARDENS

QUEEN VICTORIA MEMORIAL

ST. JAMES'S

The Mall

St. James's Park Lake

BUCKINGHAM PALACE

ST. JAMES'S PARK

Grosvenor Cres.

QUEEN'S GALLERY

Birdcage Walk

V

Halkin St.

Chapel St.

Chester St.

Grosvenor Place

56

CITY OF WESTMINSTER

Petty France

Palmer St.

Belgrave Square

Upper Belgrave

Wilton St.

ROYAL MEWS

Palace

Castle La.

56

Victoria

St.

BELGRAVIA

Belgrave Place

Belgrave Square

Hobart Pl.

Grosvenor Gdns.

274

Rd

48

Street

Howick

Pl.

8

X

Eaton Place

Lower Belgrave St.

Victoria

Street

412

Street

Ashley Pl.

416

Row

Eaton Square

88

Eccleston

Street

Carlisle Place

King's Road

88

Palace

WESTMINSTER CATHEDRAL

Francis

Elizabeth

Eaton

Eccleston

Street

VICTORIA

VICTORIA

Rochester

Y

389

Chester Row

Ebury

St.

Buckingham

Hudson's Pl.

Wilton St.

Vincent Square

389

Street

157

Gillingham

Vauxhall Bridge

Tachbrook

Vincent Square

Hugh Street

Belgrave Rd

201

Warwick Way

Road

Eccleston Square

0 — 200 m
0 — 200 yards

F

Chepstow

Hereford

Newton

Bishop's Bridge Rd

Cleveland Ter.

Gloucester

Artesian

Road

Chepstow Rd

Grove

Garway

Road

Queensway

Inverness

Leinster Gdns

94

Cleveland

90

CITY OF WESTMINSTER

BAYSWATER

Westbourne

Villas

Chepstow

Leinster Square

Porchester

Gardens

Porchester

Square

136

84

Road

243

Queensborough

362

NORTH KENSINGTON

Moscow

Bark

BAYSWATER

Terrace

Terrace

Craven

Z

Dawson

Place

St. Petersburgh Place

Road

Queensway

Hill

256

Pembridge Square

Palace

Queensway

Leinster

Portobello Rd

Pembridge Gdns

328

Bayswater

KENSINGTON GARDENS

Kensington Park Rd

Pembridge

Gate

Kensington Gate

QUEENSWAY

Bayswater

Road

Broad

ROYAL BOROUGH OF KENSINGTON AND CHELSEA

Notting

Hill

NOTTING HILL GATE

Kensington Palace Gardens

Walk

238

Place

335

KENSINGTON

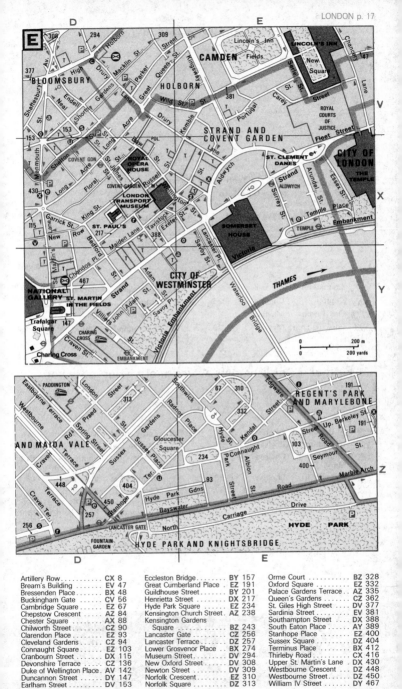

Starred establishments in London

✿✿✿

		Area	Page
XXXX	Le Gavroche	Mayfair	33

✿✿

		Area	Page
XXXX	La Tante Claire	Chelsea	26
XXXX	Chez Nico	Regent's Park and Marylebone	35
XXX	Harvey's	Wandsworth	31

✿

		Area	Page			Area	Page
🏠	Connaught	Mayfair	32	XXXX	L'Arlequin	Battersea	30
🏠	Capital	Chelsea	26	XXX	Suntory	St. James's	36
XXXXX	Oak Room	Mayfair	33	XXX	Tatsuso	City	25
XXXX	Four Seasons	Mayfair	33	XX	Sutherlands	Soho	36

Further establishments which merit your attention

M

XXX	Al Bustan	Belgravia	32	XXX	Zen Central	Mayfair	34
XXX	Bibendum	Chelsea	26	XX	Caprice (Le)	St. James's	36
XXX	Chutney Mary	Chelsea	27	XX	Hilaire	South Kensington	30
XXX	Dynasty II	Chelsea	26	XX	Simply Nico	Victoria	38
XXX	Now and Zen	Strand and Covent Garden	37	X	Chinon	Shepherd's Bush	25
XXX	Red Fort	Soho	36	X	Kensington Place	Kensington	28
XXX	Turner's	Chelsea	26	X	Vijay	Kilburn	23

Restaurants classified acording to type

Seafood

XX **Hippocampe (L')** (City of Westminster – *Soho*) 37

XX **Seppia (La)** (City of Westminster – *Mayfair*) 34

XX **Sheekey's** (City of Westminster – *Strand & Covent Garden*) 37

XX **Suquet (Le)** (Royal Borough of Kensington & Chelsea – *Chelsea*) 27

Chinese

XXXX **Oriental** (City of Westminster – *Mayfair*) 33

XXX **Empress Garden** (City of Westminster – *Mayfair*) 34

XXX **Inn of Happiness** (City of Westminster – *Victoria*) 38

XXX **Now and Zen** (City of Westminster – *Strand & Covent Garden*) 37

XXX **Princess Garden** (City of Westminster – *Mayfair*) 34

XXX **Zen** (Royal Borough of Kensington & Chelsea – *Chelsea*) 27

XXX **Zen Central** (City of Westminster – *Mayfair*) 34

XX **Chin's** (Hammersmith – *Fulham*) . 25

XX **Gallery Rendez-Vous** (City of Westminster – *Soho*) 37

XX **Good Earth** (Royal Borough of Kensington & Chelsea – *Chelsea*) 27

XX **Hsing** (City of Westminster – *Bayswater & Maida Vale*) 31

XX **Hunan** (City of Westminster – *Victoria*) 38

XX **I Ching** (Royal Borough of Kensington & Chelsea – *Kensington*) 28

XX **Ken Lo's Memories of China** (City of Westminster – *Victoria*) 38

XX **Kym's** (City of Westminster – *Victoria*) 38

XX **Magic Dragon** (Royal Borough of Kensington & Chelsea – *Chelsea*) 27

XX **Mao Tai** (Hammersmith – *Fulham*) 25

XX **Ming** (City of Westminster – *Soho*) 37

XX **Mr Wing** (Royal Borough of Kensington & Chelsea – *South Kensington*) 30

XX **Poons** (City of Westminster – *Bayswater & Maida Vale*) 31

XX **Poons of Russell Square** (Camden – *Bloomsbury*) 24

XX **Princess Garden** (Royal Borough of Kensington & Chelsea – *Kensington*) 28

XX **Sailing Junk** (Royal Borough of Kensington & Chelsea – *Kensington*) 28

XX **Shanghai** (Royal Borough of Kensington & Chelsea – *Kensington*) 28

XX **Zen W 3** (Camden-Hampstead) .. 24

English

XXX **Simpson's-in-the-Strand** (City of Westminster – *Strand & Covent Garden*) 37

XXX **Chutney Mary** (anglo Indian) (Royal Borough of Kensington & Chelsea – *Chelsea*) 27

XX **English Garden** (Royal Borough of Kensington & Chelsea – *Chelsea*) 27

XX **Green's** (City of Westminster – *St.-James's*) 36

XX **Green's** (City of Westminster – *Victoria*) 38

X **Auntie's** (Camden – *Bloomsbury*) 24

X **Tate Gallery** (City of Westminster – *Victoria*) 38

French

Hungarian

Indian & Pakistani

Italian

XXX **Incontro (L')** (City of Westminster – *Victoria*) 38

XXX **Santini** (City of Westminster – *Victoria*) 38

XX **Amico (L')** (City of Westminster – *Victoria*) 38

XX **Beccofino** (Royal Borough of Kensington & Chelsea – *Chelsea*) ... 27

XX **Dell Arte** (City of Westminster – *Hyde Park and Knightsbridge*) ... 32

XX **Eleven Park Walk** (Royal Borough of Kensington & Chelsea – *Chelsea*) 27

XX **Fenice (La)** (Royal Borough of Kensington & Chelsea – *Chelsea*) . 28

XX **Finezza (La)** (Royal Borough of Kensington & Chelsea – Chelsea) . 27

XX **Fontana Amorosa** (City of Westminster – *Regent's Park & Marylebone*) 36

XX **Gran Paradiso** (City of Westminster – *Victoria*) 38

XX **Gritti** (City of Westminster – *Strand & Covent Garden*) 37

XX **Loggia (La)** (City of Westminster – *Regent's Park & Marylebone*) 36

XX **Orso** (City of Westminster – *Strand & Covent Garden*) 37

XX **Paesana (La)** (Royal Borough of Kensington & Chelsea – *Kensington*) 28

XX **Salotto** (Royal Borough of Kensington & Chelsea – *Chelsea*) ... 27

XX **Sandrini** (Royal Borough of Kensington & Chelsea – *Chelsea*) ... 27

XX **San Marino** (City of Westminster – *Bayswater & Maida Vale*) 31

XX **Toto's** (Royal Borough of Kensington & Chelsea – *Chelsea*) ... 27

X **Al San Vicenzo** (City of Westminster – *Bayswater & Maida Vale*) .. 31

X **Cibo** (Royal Borough of Kensington & Chelsea – *South Kensington*) ... 28

Japanese

XXX ✿ **Suntory** (City of Westminster – *St. James's*) 36

XXX **Benihana** (Camden – *Hampstead*) 24

XXX ✿ **Tatsuso** (City of London – *City of London*) 25

XX **Asuka** (City of Westminster – *Regent's Park & Marylebone*) ... 35

XX **Hiroko** (Royal Borough of Kensington & Chelsea – *Kensington*) ... 28

XX **Hot Gossip** (Hammersmith – *Fulham*) 25

XX **Masako** (City of Westminster – *Regent's Park & Marylebone*) ... 35

XX **Miyama** (City of London – *City of London*) 25

XX **Miyama** (City of Westminster – *Mayfair*) 34

XX **Mon** (City of Westminster – *Regent's Park Marylebone*) 35

XX **Nakano** (Royal Borough of Kensington & Chelsea – *Chelsea*) ... 27

XX **Shogun** (City of Westminster – *Mayfair*) 34

Korean

XX **Kaya** (City of Westminster – *Soho*) 37

Lebanese

XXX **Al Bustan** (City of Westminster – *Belgravia*) 32

XX **Maroush III** (City of Westminster – *Regent's Park & Marylebone*) 35

XX **Phoenicia** (Royal Borough of Kensington & Chelsea – *Kensington*) 28

Oriental

XXX **Dynasty II** (Royal Borough of Kensington & Chelsea – *Chelsea*) 26

XX **Ho-Ho** (City of Westminster – *Mayfair*) 34

XX **Penang** (Royal Borough of Kensington & Chelsea – *Chelsea*) 27

Thai

XX **Blue Elephant** (Hammersmith – *Fulham*) 25

XX **Busabong Too** (Royal Borough of Kensington & Chelsea – *Chelsea*) 27

XX **Chada** (Wandsworth – *Battersea*) 30

XX **Lena's** (Wandsworth – *Battersea*) 30

XX **Tui** (Royal Borough of Kensington & Chelsea – South Kensington) . 30

X **Sri Sian** (City of Westminster – *Soho*) 37

Greater London is divided, for administrative purposes, into 32 boroughs plus the City; these sub-divide naturally into minor areas, usually grouped around former villages or quarters, which often maintain a distinctive character.

✪ of Greater London: **071** or **081** except special cases.

LONDON AIRPORTS

Heathrow Middx. W : 17 m. by A 4, M 4 – **Underground** Piccadilly line direct – 404 – ✪ 081.

✈ ℰ 759 4321, Telex 934892.

Edwardian International, 140 Bath Rd, UB3 5AW, ℰ 759 6311, Telex 23935, Fax 759 4559, ℔, ⇌, ▣ – 🛗 ⊁ rm ▤ ▧ ☎ & 🅿 – ⚖ 500. ⚡ 🄰🄴 ⓪ VISA. ⚘
M *(closed Saturday lunch)* 27.00/33.00 **st.** and a la carte ⅄ 6.50 – **442 rm**, **17 suites.**

Excelsior Heathrow (Forte), Bath Rd, West Drayton, UB7 0DU, ℰ 759 6611, Telex 24525, Fax 759 3421, ℔, ⇌, ▣ – 🛗 ⊁ rm ▤ ▧ ☎ & 🅿 – ⚖ 700. ⚡ 🄰🄴 ⓪ VISA
M *(closed Saturday lunch)* 14.95/21.50 **st.** and a la carte ⅄ 4.35 – ⌷ 9.50 – **523 rm** 105.00/145.00 **st.**, **16 suites** 215.00 **st.** – SB (weekends only) 118.00 **st.**

Sheraton Skyline, Bath Rd, Hayes, UB3 5BP, ℰ 759 2535, Telex 934254, Fax 750 9150, « Exotic indoor garden », ▣ – 🛗 ⊁ rm ▤ ▧ ☎ & 🅿 – ⚖ 500. ⚡ 🄰🄴 ⓪ VISA
M 23.70/35.70 **t.** and a la carte ⅄ 6.00 – ⌷ 10.75 – **347 rm** 125.00/160.00 **s.**, **5 suites** 310.00/700.00 **st.** – SB (weekends only) 241.00/299.80 **st.**

Sterling, Terminal 4, TW6 3AF, ℰ 759 7755, Telex 925094, Fax 759 7579, ℔, ⇌, ▣ – 🛗 ⊁ rm ▤ ▧ ☎ & 🅿 – ⚖ 240 – **393 rm**, **4 suites.**

Holiday Inn, Stockley Rd, West Drayton, UB7 9NA, ℰ 0895 (West Drayton) 445555, Telex 934518, Fax 445122, ℔, ⇌, ▣, ℡₉ – 🛗 ⊁ rm ▤ ▧ ☎ & 🅿 – ⚖ 120. ⚡ 🄰🄴 ⓪ VISA
M 15.70/19.95 **t.** and a la carte ⅄ 6.05 – ⌷ 9.50 – **379 rm** 98.00/113.00 **st.**, **1 suite** 250.00/485.00 **st.** – SB (weekends only) 94.00/188.00 **st.**

Sheraton Heathrow, Colnbrook by-pass, West Drayton, UB7 0HJ, ℰ 759 2424, Telex 934331, Fax 759 2091, ▣ – 🛗 ⊁ rm ▤ ▧ ☎ 🅿 – ⚖ 70. ⚡ 🄰🄴 ⓪ VISA. ⚘
M 14.00 **st.** and a la carte ⅄ 3.50 – ⌷ 10.00 – **414 rm** 95.00/160.00 **st.**, **1 suite** 125.00 **st.**

Forte Crest, Sipson Rd, West Drayton, UB7 0JU, ℰ 759 2323, Telex 934280, Fax 897 8659, ℔, ⇌ – 🛗 ⊁ rm ▤ ▧ ☎ 🅿 – ⚖ 200. ⚡ 🄰🄴 ⓪ VISA
M 14.95 **st.** and a la carte ⅄ 4.50 – ⌷ 9.50 – **565 rm** 85.00/110.00 **st.**, **4 suites** 170.00 **st.** – SB (weekends only) 98.00 **st.**

Heathrow Penta, Bath Rd, Hounslow, TW6 2AQ, ℰ 897 6363, Telex 934660, Fax 897 1113, ≤, ℔, ⇌, ▣ – 🛗 ▤ ▧ ☎ 🅿 – ⚖ 450. ⚡ 🄰🄴 ⓪ VISA. ⚘
M *(bar lunch Saturday and Sunday)* 15.00/16.00 **st.** and a la carte – ⌷ 9.00 – **627 rm** 95.00/142.50 **st.**, **9 suites** 185.00/425.00 **st.**

Heathrow Park (Mt. Charlotte Thistle), Bath Rd, Longford, West Drayton, UB7 0EQ, ℰ 759 2400, Telex 934093, Fax 759 5278 – ⊁ rm ▤ ▧ ☎ 🅿 – ⚖ 600. ⚡ 🄰🄴 ⓪ VISA
M (bar meals Saturday lunch and Sunday) (carving lunch Monday to Friday) /dinner 15.25 **st.** and a la carte ⅄ 5.70 – ⌷ 8.25 – **306 rm** 85.00/145.00 **st.**

Forte Posthouse, Bath Rd, Hayes, UB3 5AJ, ℰ 759 2552, Telex 21777, Fax 564 9265 – 🛗 ⊁ rm ▤ ▧ ☎ 🅿. ⚡ 🄰🄴 ⓪ VISA
M (carving rest.) 10.50/17.00 **st.** ⅄ 3.95 – ⌷ 7.95 – **180 rm** 65.00 **st.** – SB (weekends only) 78.00 **st.**

Yiewsley – ⊠ Middx. – ✪ 081.

XXX **L'Esprit**, The Arena, Stockley Park, UB11 1AA, ℰ 573 7333, Fax 561 0550 – ▤ 🅿. ⚡ 🄰🄴 ⓪ VISA
closed Saturday lunch, dinner Monday to Wednesday, Sunday, 24 December-1 January and Bank Holidays – **M** 16.25 **st.** (lunch) and a la carte 16.15/25.95 **st.** ⅄ 6.00.

Gatwick West Sussex S : 28 m. by A 23 and M 23 – **Train** from Victoria : Gatwick Express – 404 T 30 – ⊠ West Sussex – ✪ 0293 Gatwick.

✈ ℰ 28822 (general information)/31299 (flight information) and ℰ 081 (London) 759 4321.

🛈 International Arrivals Concourse ℰ 560108.

London Gatwick Airport Hilton, Gatwick Airport, (South Terminal), RH6 0LL, ℰ 518080, Telex 877021, Fax 528980, ℔, ⇌, ▣ – 🛗 ⊁ rm ▤ ▧ ☎ & – ⚖ 360. ⚡ 🄰🄴 ⓪ VISA
M 15.50/20.00 **st.** and a la carte ⅄ 7.25 – ⌷ 10.75 – **547 rm** 117.00/158.00 **st.**, **3 suites** 206.00/350.00 **st.** – SB (weekends only) 160.00 **st.**

🏨🏨 **Gatwick Penta,** Povey Cross Rd, ⊠ Horley (Surrey), RH6 0BE, ℰ 820169, Telex 87440, Fax 820259, ℔, ⇌, ⬛, squash – 🛗 ⇔ rm ▤ 📺 ☎ 🅿 – 🔬 150. 🔼 🅰🅴 ⓪ 𝗩𝗜𝗦𝗔
M 15.00/17.25 **st.** and a la carte ⬧ 4.00 – ⊊ 8.75 – **255 rm** 95.00/110.00 **st., 5 suites** 205.00/220.00 **st.** – SB 112.00/124.00 **st.**

🏨🏨 **Sterling,** Gatwick Airport (North Terminal), RH6 0PH, ℰ 567070, Telex 87202, Fax 567739, ℔, ⇌, ⬛ – 🛗 ⇔ rm ▤ 📺 ☎ 🐾 – 🔬 300. 🔼 🅰🅴 ⓪ 𝗩𝗜𝗦𝗔. ⋇
M 15.00 **st.** and a la carte ⬧ 5.00 – ⊊ 10.00 – **460 rm** 110.00/120.00 **st., 14 suites** 180.00/250.00 **st.**

🏨 **Forte Crest,** Povey Cross Rd, ⊠ Horley (Surrey), RH6 0BA, ℰ 771621, Fax 771054, ⬛,
🛗 ⇔ rm ▤ 📺 ☎ 🐾 – 🔬 120. 🔼 🅰🅴 ⓪ 𝗩𝗜𝗦𝗔
M (closed Saturday lunch) 12.50/14.50 **st.** and a la carte ⬧ 5.15 – ⊊ 8.50 – **215 rm** 75.00/85.00 **st.** – SB (weekends only) 98.00 **st.**

BRENT

Kilburn – ⊠ NW6 – ✆ 071.

✗ **Vijay,** 49 Willesden Lane, NW6 7RF, ℰ 328 1087, South Indian rest. – ▤. 🔼 🅰🅴 ⓪ 𝗩𝗜𝗦𝗔
M a la carte 14.00 **st.**

CAMDEN Except where otherwise stated see pp. 4-7.

Bloomsbury – ⊠ NW1/W1/WC1 – ✆ 071.

🛈 35-36 Woburn Pl. WC1 ℰ 580 4599.

🏨🏨🏨 **Russell** (Forte), Russell Sq., WC1B 5BE, ℰ 837 6470, Telex 24615, Fax 837 2857 – 🛗 ⇔ rm 📺 ☎ – 🔬 450. 🔼 🅰🅴 ⓪ 𝗩𝗜𝗦𝗔   LU **o**
M (carving rest.) 15.50 **st.** and a la carte ⬧ 5.50 – ⊊ 9.85 – **324 rm** 95.00/170.00 **st., 3 suites** 145.00/190.00 **st.** – SB (weekends only) 118.00 **st.**

🏨🏨 **Mountbatten** (Edwardian), 20 Monmouth St., WC2H 9HD, ℰ 836 4300, Telex 298087, Fax 240 3540 – 🛗 ⇔ rm ▤ rest 📺 ☎ – 🔬 75. 🔼 🅰🅴 ⓪ 𝗩𝗜𝗦𝗔   p. 17 DV **o**
M (closed lunch Saturday, Sunday and Bank Holidays) 16.50/22.50 **st.** – ⊊ 12.00 – **121 rm** 163.00/181.00 **st., 6 suites** 150.00/398.00 **st.**

🏨🏨 **Marlborough** (Edwardian), Bloomsbury St., WC1B 3QD, ℰ 636 5601, Telex 298274, Fax 636 0532 – 🛗 ⇔ rm ▤ rest 📺 ☎ – 🔬 200. 🔼 🅰🅴 ⓪ 𝗩𝗜𝗦𝗔. ⋇   LU **i**
M (closed Sunday lunch) 14.50/18.50 **st.** and a la carte ⬧ 5.00 – ⊊ 10.50 – **167 rm** 120.00/167.00 **st., 2 suites** 200.00/385.00 **st.** – SB (weekends only) 160.00 **st.**

🏨🏨 **Grafton** (Edwardian), 130 Tottenham Court Rd, W1P 9HP, ℰ 388 4131, Telex 297234, Fax 387 7394 – 🛗 ▤ rest 📺 ☎ – 🔬 100. 🔼 🅰🅴 ⓪ 𝗩𝗜𝗦𝗔. ⋇   KU **n**
M (closed Saturday lunch) 12.00/15.00 **st.** and a la carte ⬧ 6.50 – ⊊ 10.00 – **233 rm** 119.00/180.00 **st., 4 suites** 230.00/250.00 **st.**

🏨🏨 **Montague Park,** 12-20 Montague St., WC1B 5BJ, ℰ 637 1001, Telex 23307, Fax 637 2506 – 🛗 ▤ 📺 ☎ 🐾 – 🔬 80. 🔼 🅰🅴 ⓪ 𝗩𝗜𝗦𝗔. ⋇   LU **c**
M (closed lunch Saturday and Sunday) 13.50/16.50 **st.** and a la carte ⬧ 5.75 – ⊊ 9.50 – **109 rm** 91.00/157.00 **st.**

🏨🏨 **Kenilworth** (Edwardian), 97 Great Russell St., WC1B 3LB, ℰ 637 3477, Telex 25842, Fax 631 3133 – 🛗 ▤ rest 📺 ☎ – 🔬 100. 🔼 🅰🅴 ⓪ 𝗩𝗜𝗦𝗔   LU **a**
M 16.95 **st.** and a la carte ⬧ 5.00 – ⊊ 10.00 – **191 rm** 111.00/152.00 **st., 1 suite** 186.00/255.00 **st.**

🏨🏨 **Forte Crest,** Coram St., WC1N 1HT, ℰ 837 1200, Fax 837 5374 – 🛗 ⇔ rm ▤ rest 📺 ☎ – 🔬 700. 🔼 🅰🅴 ⓪ 𝗩𝗜𝗦𝗔   LT **c**
M (carving lunch)/dinner 16.50 and a la carte ⬧ 9.95 – ⊊ 10.25 – **281 rm** 95.00/105.00 **st., 3 suites** 250.00 **st.** – SB (weekends only) 98.00 **st.**

🏨 **Portland,** 7 Montague St., WC1B 5BP, ℰ 323 1717, Fax 636 6498 – 🛗 ▤ rest 📺 ☎. 🔼 🅰🅴 ⓪ 𝗩𝗜𝗦𝗔. ⋇   LU **w**
M (closed Saturday lunch and Sunday) (Italian rest.) 13.50 **t.** and a la carte ⬧ 4.90 – **25 rm** ⊊ 75.00/110.00 **st., 1 suite** 190.00 **st.** – SB (January, July-August and weekends) 90.00 **st.**

🏨 **Bonnington,** 92 Southampton Row, WC1B 4BH, ℰ 242 2828, Telex 261591, Fax 831 9170 – 🛗 ⇔ rm ▤ rest 📺 ☎ 🐾 – 🔬 120. 🔼 🅰🅴 ⓪ 𝗩𝗜𝗦𝗔   LU **s**
M 15.00 **st.** and a la carte ⬧ 3.20 – **215 rm** ⊊ 92.00/116.00 **st.** – SB (weekends only) 120.00/150.00 **st.**

🏨 **Kingsley** (Mt. Charlotte Thistle), Bloomsbury Way, WC1A 2SD, ℰ 242 5881, Telex 21157, Fax 831 0225 – 🛗 📺 ☎ – 🔬 100. 🔼 🅰🅴 ⓪ 𝗩𝗜𝗦𝗔. ⋇   LU **r**
M (closed lunch Saturday, Sunday and Bank Holidays) 15.25 **t.** and a la carte ⬧ 4.55 – ⊊ 8.50 – **98 rm** 69.00/79.00 **st., 2 suites** 225.00 **st.**

🏨 **Bloomsbury Park** (Mt. Charlotte Thistle), 126 Southampton Row, WC1B 5AD, ℰ 430 0434, Telex 25757, Fax 242 0665 – 🛗 📺 ☎ – 🔬 30. 🔼 🅰🅴 ⓪ 𝗩𝗜𝗦𝗔. ⋇   LU **u**
M (closed Friday dinner, Saturday, Sunday and Bank Holidays) (bar lunch)/dinner 13.95 **t.** and a la carte ⬧ 4.60 – ⊊ 8.40 – **95 rm** 84.00/120.00 **st.**

XX **Neal Street,** 26 Neal St., WC2 9PH, ☞ 836 8368 – ▤. ◨ AE ⓞ VISA   p. 17 DV **s**
   closed Saturday, Sunday, Christmas-New Year and Bank Holidays – **M** a la carte 30.00/36.00 **t.**
   🍸 7.50.

XX **Mon Plaisir,** 21 Monmouth St., WC2H 9DD, ☞ 836 7243, French rest.   DV **a**

XX **Poons of Russell Square,** 50 Woburn Pl., WC1H 0JE, ☞ 580 1188, Chinese rest. – ▤   LU **x**

XX **Kanishka,** 161 Whitfield St., W1P 5RY, ☞ 388 0860, Indian rest. – ▤. ◨ ⓞ VISA   KTU **z**
   closed lunch Saturday and Bank Holiday and Sunday – **M** 6.95/12.00 **t.** and a la carte.

X **Smith's,** 33 Shelton St., WC2H 9PU, ☞ 379 0310, Fax 836 8395 – ◨ AE ⓞ VISA
   closed Sunday and Bank Holidays – **M** 10.50 **st.** (dinner) and a la carte 19.25/23.00
   st. 🍸 4.50.   p. 17 DVX **u**

X **Auntie's,** 126 Cleveland St., W1P 5DN, ☞ 387 1548, English rest. – ◨ AE ⓞ VISA JU **s**
   closed Saturday lunch and Sunday – **M** approx. 18.40 **t.** 🍸 5.20.

Camden Town – ✉ NW1 – ✆ 071.

X **La Bougie,** 7 Murray St., NW1 9RE, ☞ 485 6400, Bistro   KS **a**
   *closed Saturday lunch, Monday, last 2 weeks August, 2 weeks Christmas and Bank Holiday
   Sundays* – **M** a la carte 12.75/14.50 **t.** 🍸 3.75.

Euston – ✉ WC1 – ✆ 071.

🏨 **Scandic Crown,** 17/18 Upper Woburn Pl., WC1 0HT, ☞ 383 4105, Fax 412 0047, ⇔ – 🛗
   ✳ rm ▤ TV ☎ &. – 🔏 120. ◨ AE ⓞ VISA   KT **e**
   M 10.75/14.50 **st.** – **149 rm** 100.00/137.50 **st.**, **1 suite** 219.00 **st.**

Hampstead – ✉ NW3 – ✆ 071.

🏨 **Forte Posthouse,** 215 Haverstock Hill, NW3 4RB, ☞ 794 8121, Fax 435 5586 – 🛗 ✳ rm
   TV ☎ P – 🔏 30. ◨ AE ⓞ VISA   ES **r**
   M a la carte 9.55/20.90 **st.** 🍸 3.95 – ⊊ 5.95 – **138 rm** 49.00 **st.**

🏨 **Clive** (Hilton), Primrose Hill Rd, NW3 3NA, ☞ 586 2233, Telex 22759, Fax 586 1659 – 🛗 TV
   ☎ P – 🔏 300. ◨ AE ⓞ VISA. ✁   HS **a**
   M *(closed Saturday lunch)* 9.95/12.95 **st.** and a la carte 🍸 5.10 – **93 rm** 45.00/71.00 **s.**, **3 suites**
   81.00 **s.** – SB (weekends only) 72.00/106.00 **st.**

🏨 **Swiss Cottage,** 4 Adamson Rd, NW3 3HP, ☞ 722 2281, Telex 297232, Fax 483 4588,
   « Antique furniture collection » – 🛗 TV ☎ P – 🔏 60. ◨ AE ⓞ VISA. ✁   GS **n**
   M 14.95 **t.** and a la carte 🍸 4.75 – **61 rm** ⊊ 50.00/140.00 **t.**, **3 suites** 118.00/140.00 **t.**

XXX Benihana, 100 Avenue Rd, NW3 3HF, ☞ 586 9508, Fax 586 6740, Japanese Teppan-Yaki rest.
   – ▤   GS **o**

XX **Carapace,** 118 Heath St., NW3 1DR, ☞ 435 8000 – ◨ AE ⓞ VISA   ES **e**
   closed 26 December and 1 January – **M** (dinner only and Sunday lunch)/dinner 25.00 **t.** and
   a la carte 🍸 4.00.

XX **Zen W3,** 83-84 Hampstead High St., NW3 1RE, ☞ 794 7863, Chinese rest. – ◨ AE ⓞ VISA
   closed 3 days at Christmas – **M** a la carte 21.10/31.00 **t.** 🍸 4.50.   ES **a**

Holborn – ✉ WC2 – ✆ 071.

🏨 **Drury Lane Moat House** (Q.M.H.), 10 Drury Lane, High Holborn, WC2B 5RE, ☞ 836 6666,
   Telex 8811395, Fax 831 1548 – 🛗 ✳ rm ▤ TV ☎ – 🔏 100. ◨ AE ⓞ VISA
   M 13.25 **t.** and a la carte 🍸 9.00 – ⊊ 9.50 – **151 rm** 123.00/173.00 **st.**, **2 suites** 300.00 **st.** –
   SB (weekends only) 140.00 **st.**   p. 17 DV **c**

Kentish Town – ✉ NW5 – ✆ 071.

XX **Bengal Lancer,** 253 Kentish Town Rd, NW5 2JT, ☞ 485 6688, Fax 482 4523 – ▤. ◨ AE
   ⓞ VISA   JS **c**
   closed Saturday lunch and 25-26 December – **M** a la carte 10.50/18.00 **t.**

Regent's Park – ✉ NW1 – ✆ 071.

🏨 **White House** (Rank), Albany St., NW1 3UP, ☞ 387 1200, Telex 24111, Fax 388 0091, 🕼
   – 🛗 ✳ rm ▤ TV ☎ &. – 🔏 100. ◨ AE ⓞ VISA. ✁   JT **o**
   M 22.50 **st.** and a la carte 🍸 6.50 – ⊊ 10.75 – **561 rm** 118.00/153.00 **st.**, **15 suites**
   198.00/355.00 **st.** – SB (weekends only) 84.00/92.00 **st.**

XX **Odette's,** 130 Regent's Park Rd, NW1 8XL, ☞ 586 5486 – ◨ AE ⓞ VISA   HS **i**
   closed Saturday lunch, Sunday, last 2 weeks August, 1 week Christmas and Bank Holidays –
   M a la carte 23.40/28.00 **t.** 🍸 5.95.

Swiss Cottage – ✉ NW3 – ✆ 071.

🏨 **Holiday Inn,** 128 King Henry's Rd, NW3 3ST, ☞ 722 7711, Telex 267396, Fax 586 5822, 🕼,
   ⇔, 🏊 – 🛗 ✳ rm ▤ TV ☎ &. P – 🔏 400. ◨ AE ⓞ VISA   GS **a**
   M 18.00 **t.** (lunch) and a la carte 17.75/27.95 **t.** 🍸 6.50 – ⊊ 11.25 – **295 rm** 135.00/157.50 **st.**,
   8 suites 169.00/518.00 **st.**

CITY OF LONDON – ☺ 071 Except where otherwise stated see p. 7.

XXX ☺ **Tatsuso,** 32 Broadgate Circle, EC2M 2QS, ✆ 638 5863, Fax 638 5864, Japanese rest. –
■, ⚑ ⚑ ⓞ ⱽ⌶ⱽⱭ
PU u
closed Saturday, Sunday, 24 December-3 January and Bank Holidays – **M** (booking essential)
60.00/65.00 **t.** and a la carte 29.10/49.10 **t.**
Spec. Assorted marinated seaweed, Shabu-Shabu, Green Tea ice cream.

XX **Candlewick Room,** 45 Old Broad St., EC2N 1HT, ✆ 628 7929, French rest. – ⚑ ⚑ ⓞ
ⱽ⌶ⱽⱭ
PU n
closed Saturday, Sunday and Bank Holidays – **M** (lunch only) 24.95 **t.** and a la carte ⚑ 5.95.

XX **Le Poulbot** (basement), 45 Cheapside, EC2V 6AR, ✆ 236 4379, French rest. – ■, ⚑ ⚑
ⓞ ⱽ⌶ⱽⱭ
OV i
closed Saturday, Sunday and Bank Holidays – **M** (lunch only) 31.50 **st.**

XX **Corney and Barrow,** 109 Old Broad St., EC2N 1AP, ✆ 638 9308 – ■, ⚑ ⚑ ⓞ
ⱽ⌶ⱽⱭ
PU c
closed Saturday, Sunday and Bank Holidays – **M** (lunch only) 24.95 **t.** and a la carte ⚑ 6.30.

XX Corney and Barrow, 118 Moorgate, EC2M 6UR, ✆ 628 2898 – ■
PU o

XX **Corney and Barrow,** 44 Cannon St., EC4N 6JJ, ✆ 248 1700 – ■, ⚑ ⚑ ⓞ
ⱽ⌶ⱽⱭ
OV r
closed Saturday, Sunday and Bank Holidays – **M** (lunch only) 19.50 **t.** and a la carte ⚑ 7.95.

XX **Le Sous Sol,** 32 Old Bailey, EC4M 7HS, ✆ 236 4379, French rest. – ⚑ ⚑ ⱽ⌶ⱽⱭ NV a
closed Saturday, Sunday and Bank Holidays – **M** (lunch only) 24.50 **t.** ⚑ 5.95.

XX Shares, Beehive Passage, off Lime St., EC3M 7AA, ✆ 623 1843 – ■
PV s

XX **Miyama,** 17 Godliman St., EC4V 5BD, ✆ 489 1937, Japanese rest. – ■, ⚑ ⚑ ⓞ
ⱽ⌶ⱽⱭ
OV e
closed Saturday, Sunday and Bank Holidays – **M** 16.00/38.00 **t.** and a la carte ⚑ 5.00.

X **Bubb's,** 329 Central Market, Farringdon St., EC1A 9NB, ✆ 236 2435, French rest. NU a
closed Saturday, Sunday, 2 weeks August, 1 week Christmas and Bank Holidays – **M** (booking
essential) (lunch only) a la carte approx. 25.40 **st.** ⚑ 4.85.

X **Whittington's,** 21 College Hill, EC4R 2RP, ✆ 248 5855 – ■, ⚑ ⚑ ⓞ ⱽ⌶ⱽⱭ OV c
closed Saturday, Sunday and Bank Holidays – **M** (lunch only) a la carte 20.20/24.35 **st.** ⚑ 4.50.

HAMMERSMITH AND FULHAM p. 8.

Fulham – ✉ SW6 – ☺ 071.

🏨 **La Reserve,** 422-428 Fulham Rd, SW6 1DU, ✆ 385 8561, Fax 385 7662, « Contemporary
decor » – 🛗 ⤢ rm �📺 ☎, ⚑ ⚑ ⓞ ⱽ⌶ⱽⱭ. ⌘ FZ a
M 25.00/30.00 **t.** and a la carte – ⌑ 3.00 – **40 rm** 75.00/110.00 **st.**

XX Hiders, 755 Fulham Rd, SW6, ✆ 736 2331

XX **Blue Elephant,** 4-6 Fulham Broadway, SW6 1AA, ✆ 385 6595, Fax 386 7665, Thai rest. –
■, ⚑ ⚑ ⓞ ⱽ⌶ⱽⱭ
EZ z
closed Saturday lunch and 24 to 27 December – **M** (booking essential) 25.00/28.00 **t.** and a
la carte ⚑ 5.35.

XX **Hot Gossip,** 593-599 Fulham Rd, SW6 5VA, ✆ 386 0506, Fax 386 0467, Japanese, Teppan-
yaki and Chinese rests. – ■
EZ a

XX **Chin's,** 311-313 New Kings Rd, SW6 4RF, ✆ 736 8833, Chinese rest. – ■, ⚑ ⚑ ⓞ ⱽ⌶ⱽⱭ
M 19.00/29.00 **st.** and a la carte ⚑ 4.60.

XX **Mao Tai,** 58 New Kings Rd, Parsons Green, SW6 4UG, ✆ 731 2520, Chinese (Szechuan)
rest. – ■, ⚑ ⚑ ⓞ ⱽ⌶ⱽⱭ
M 17.50 **t.** and a la carte ⚑ 7.50.

XX **Nayab,** 309 New Kings Rd, SW6 4RF, ✆ 731 6993, Indian rest. – ⚑ ⚑ ⓞ ⱽ⌶ⱽⱭ
closed 25 to 26 December and 1 January – **M** a la carte 11.20/16.35 **t.**

Shepherd's Bush – ✉ W12/W14 – ☺ 071.

X **Chinon,** 25 Richmond Way, W14 0AS, ✆ 602 5968 – ■, ⚑ ⚑ ⱽ⌶ⱽⱭ
closed Sunday, Easter, 2 weeks August-September and Bank Holidays – **M** 18.50 **t.** and a la
carte 35.00/39.50 **t.**

KENSINGTON and CHELSEA (Royal Borough of).

Chelsea – ✉ SW1/SW3/SW10 – ☺ 071 – Except where otherwise stated see pp. 14
and 15.

🏨 **Hyatt Carlton Tower,** 2 Cadogan Pl., SW1X 9PY, ✆ 235 5411, Telex 21944, Fax 245 6570,
≤, ♨, ⌚, ⌘, ✂ – 🛗 ⤢ rm ■ �📺 ☎ ⟲ Ⓟ – 🔏 300. ⚑ ⚑ ⓞ ⱽ⌶ⱽⱭ. ⌘ FR n
M Chelsea Room 25.50/32.00 **st.** and a la carte – **Rib Room** 22.50/32.00 **st.** and a la carte
⚑ 7.50 – ⌑ 12.75 – **194 rm** 220.00 **s.**, **30 suites** 320.00/2000.00 **s.**

Conrad Chelsea Harbour, Chelsea Harbour, SW1D 0XG, ℰ 823 3000, Telex 919222, Fàx 351 6525, ≤, ⅃₅, ⌿s, ⌷ – 🛊 ⌷ ⇔ rm 🔲 – 🔬 180. 🔼 🖭 ⓞ 𝘝𝘐𝘚𝘈 ⌿※
M 16.00 **t.** (lunch) and a la carte 19.50/26.00 **t.** –, **160 suites** 195.00/1000.00 **s.**

Sheraton Park Tower, 101 Knightsbridge, SW1X 7RN, ℰ 235 8050, Telex 917222, Fax 235 8231, ≤ – 🛊 ⇔ rm 🔲 ⌷ 🔼 ⇔ 🖳 – 🔬 80. 🔼 🖭 ⓞ 𝘝𝘐𝘚𝘈 ⌿※   FQ **v**
M 22.00/25.00 **st.** and a la carte ⋈ 7.50 – ⌷ 14.50 – **267 rm** 195.00/280.00 **s.**, **22 suites** 395.00/1050.00 **s.**

Durley House, 115 Sloane St., SW1X 9PJ, ℰ 235 5537, Telex 919235, Fax 259 6977, « Tastefully furnished Georgian town house », ⌿※ – 🛊 🔲 🕾. 🔼 🖭 𝘝𝘐𝘚𝘈 ⌿※   FS **e**
M (room service only) a la carte 12.00/22.50 **t.** ⋈ 6.00 – ⌷ 10.50 –, **11 suites** 250.00/300.00 **t.**

Capital, 22-24 Basil St., SW3 1AT, ℰ 589 5171, Telex 919042, Fax 225 0011 – 🛊 🔲 🔲   ER **a**
M 20.00/25.00 **st.** and a la carte 36.00/40.50 **st.** – ⌷ 10.50 – **48 rm** 165.00/285.00 **st.**
Spec. Composed salad of french leaves with crab, peppers and caviar, Poêlé of rabbit, truffle, leek and carrots, Parfait of Poire William with a warm pear Pithivier.

Cadogan, 75 Sloane St., SW1X 9SG, ℰ 235 7141, Telex 267893, Fax 245 0994 – 🛊 ⇔ rm 🔲 rest 🔲 🕾 – 🔬 40. 🔼 🖭 ⓞ 𝘝𝘐𝘚𝘈 ⌿※   FR **e**
closed until mid 1992 for refurbishment – **M** 24.00/29.00 **st.** and a la carte ⋈ 6.50 – ⌷ 10.50 – **64 rm** 159.00/199.00 **st.**, **5 suites** 275.00/325.00 **st.**

Draycott, 24-26 Cadogan Gdns, SW3 2RP, ℰ 730 6466, Fax 730 0236 – 🛊 🔲 🕾. 🔼 🖭 ⓞ 𝘝𝘐𝘚𝘈 ⌿※   FS **c**
M (room service only) – ⌷ 9.25 – **24 rm** 75.00/250.00 **t.**

Fenja without rest., 69 Cadogan Gdns, SW3 2RB, ℰ 589 7333, Telex 934272, Fax 581 4958 – 🛊 🔲 🕾. 🔼 𝘝𝘐𝘚𝘈 ⌿※   FS **r**
⌷ 10.50 – **13 rm** 105.00/210.00 **st.**

Chelsea, 17-25 Sloane St., SW1X 9NU, ℰ 235 4377, Telex 919111, Fax 235 3705 – 🛊 ⇔ rm 🔲 🕾 – 🔬 120. 🔼 🖭 ⓞ 𝘝𝘐𝘚𝘈 ⌿※   FR **r**
M (closed Bank Holidays) 15.00/25.00 **st.** and a la carte ⋈ 5.00 – ⌷ 9.75 – **218 rm** 141.00/172.00 **st.**, **7 suites** 195.00/280.00 **st.**

Basil Street, 8 Basil St., SW3 1AH, ℰ 581 3311, Telex 28379, Fax 581 3693 – 🛊 🔲 🕾 – 🔬 55. 🔼 🖭 𝘝𝘐𝘚𝘈 ⌿※   FQ **o**
M 15.25 **t.** and a la carte ⋈ 5.00 – ⌷ 9.20 – **91 rm** 105.25/141.00 **st.**, **1 suite** 226.25 **st.**

Egerton House, 17-19 Egerton Terr., SW3 2BX, ℰ 589 2412, Fax 584 6540 – 🛊 🔲 🔲 🕾. 🔼 🖭 𝘝𝘐𝘚𝘈 ⌿※   DR **e**
M (room service only) a la carte 15.00/38.00 **st.** – ⌷ 12.50 – **27 rm** 98.00/190.00 **st.**, **1 suite** 230.00 **st.**

Beaufort, 33 Beaufort Gdns, SW3 1PP, ℰ 584 5252, Telex 929200, Fax 589 2834, « English floral watercolour collection » – 🛊 ⇔ rm 🔲 🔲 🕾. 🔼 🖭 ⓞ 𝘝𝘐𝘚𝘈 ⌿※   ER **n**
closed 22 December-2 January – **M** (room service only) – **28 rm** ⌷ 150.00/250.00 **st.** – SB (November-April) (weekends only) 80.00/110.00 **st.**

Royal Court (Q.M.H.), Sloane Sq., SW1W 8EG, ℰ 730 9191, Telex 296818, Fax 824 8381 – 🛊 🔲 rest 🔲 🕾 – 🔬 40. 🔼 🖭 ⓞ 𝘝𝘐𝘚𝘈   FST **a**
M (closed Saturday lunch and Sunday dinner) 12.50 **st.** and a la carte ⋈ 5.00 – ⌷ 9.25 – **102 rm** 92.00/117.00 **st.** – SB (weekends only) 130.00 **st.**

Eleven Cadogan Gardens without rest., 11 Cadogan Gdns, SW3 2RJ, ℰ 730 3426, Fax 730 5217 – 🛊 🕾. 🔼 𝘝𝘐𝘚𝘈 ⌿※   FS **u**
M (room service only) – ⌷ 8.50 – **56 rm** 89.00/200.00 **st.**, **5 suites** 200.00/350.00 **st.**

L'Hotel without rest., 28 Basil St., SW3 1AT, ℰ 589 6286, Telex 919042, Fax 225 0011 – 🛊 🔲 🕾. 🔼 🖭 𝘝𝘐𝘚𝘈 – **12 rm** 110.00/145.00 **t.**   ER **i**

Parkes without rest., 41-43 Beaufort Gdns, SW3 1PW, ℰ 581 9944, Telex 922488, Fax 225 3447 – 🛊 🔲 🔲 🖭 ⓞ 𝘝𝘐𝘚𝘈 ⌿※   ER **c**
17 rm ⌷ 103.00/138.00, **16 suites** 230.00.

La Tante Claire (Koffmann), 68-69 Royal Hospital Rd, SW3 4HP, ℰ 352 6045, Fax 352 3257, French rest. – 🔲. 🔼 🖭 ⓞ 𝘝𝘐𝘚𝘈   EU **c**
closed Saturday, Sunday, Christmas-New Year and Bank Holidays – **M** 23.50 **st.** (lunch) and a la carte 49.00/60.50 **st.** ⋈ 7.80
Spec. Coquilles St. Jacques rôties, sauce encre, Assiette canardière, Saumon confit à l'huile d'olive et pipérade.

Waltons, 121 Walton St., SW3 2HP, ℰ 584 0204 – 🔲. 🔼 🖭 ⓞ 𝘝𝘐𝘚𝘈   DS **a**
closed 25 and 26 December – **M** 14.75/21.00 **t.** and a la carte ⋈ 4.50.

Dynasty II, Chelsea Wharf, 15 Lots Rd, SW10 0QJ, ℰ 351 1020, ≤, Oriental Cuisine, « Riverside setting » – 🔲 🅿. 🔼 🖭 ⓞ 𝘝𝘐𝘚𝘈   p. 9 GZ **n**
M 25.00/35.00 **t.** and a la carte 20.00/31.00 **t.** ⋈ 5.00.

Turners, 87-89 Walton St., SW3 2HP, ℰ 584 6711, Fax 584 4441 – 🔲. 🔼 🖭 ⓞ 𝘝𝘐𝘚𝘈   ES **n**
closed Saturday lunch, 25 to 30 December and Bank Holidays – **M** 18.50/29.50 **st.** and a la carte ⋈ 8.00.

Bibendum, Michelin House, 81 Fulham Rd, SW3 6RD, ℰ 581 5817, Fax 823 7925 – 🔲. 🔼 𝘝𝘐𝘚𝘈   DS **s**
closed 3 days Christmas – **M** 26.00 **t.** (lunch) and a la carte 26.25/50.00 **t.** ⋈ 5.25.

XXX Zen, Chelsea Cloisters, Sloane Av., SW3 3DW, ☎ 589 1781, Chinese rest. – 🍽 ET **a**

XXX **Chutney Mary,** 535 Kings Rd, SW10 0SZ, ☎ 351 3113, Anglo-Indian rest. – 🍽
M a la carte 20.20/29.95. FZ **v**

XX **Daphne's,** 110-112 Draycott Av., SW3 3AE, ☎ 589 4257 – 🍽 🔼 🗚 ⑪ 𝑉𝐼𝑆𝐴 DS **e**
closed Saturday lunch, Sunday dinner and Bank Holidays – **M** 18.00/28.00 **t.** and a la carte
⑧ 4.50.

XX Salotto, 257-259 Fulham Rd, SW3 6HY, ☎ 351 1383, Italian rest. CU **i**

XX La Finezza, 62-64 Lower Sloane St., SW1N 8BP, ☎ 730 8639, Italian rest. – 🍽 FT **v**

XX **English Garden,** 10 Lincoln St., SW3 2TS, ☎ 584 7272, English rest. – 🍽 🔼 🗚 ⑪
𝑉𝐼𝑆𝐴 ET **x**
closed 25 and 26 December – **M** 16.25 **t.** (lunch) and a la carte 19.25/25.95 ⑧ 4.50.

XX **Gavvers,** 61-63 Lower Sloane St., SW1W 8DH, ☎ 730 5983, French rest. – 🍽 🔼 ⑪
𝑉𝐼𝑆𝐴 FT **e**
closed Saturday lunch, Sunday and Bank Holidays – **M** 16.25/30.75 **st.** and a la carte **st.** ⑧ 5.95.

XX **Busabong Too,** 1a Langton St., SW1D 0JL, ☎ 352 7517, Thai rest. – 🍽 🔼 🗚 ⑪ 𝑉𝐼𝑆𝐴
closed Bank Holiday lunch and 24 to 27 December – **M** (booking essential) 14.95/19.50 **t.** and
a la carte. FZ **x**

XX **Nakano,** 11 Beauchamp Pl., SW3 1NQ, ☎ 581 3837, Japanese rest. – 🍽 🔼 🗚 ⑪ 𝑉𝐼𝑆𝐴
closed Sunday lunch, Monday, Easter, 1 week August and 23 December-6 January – **M**
18.00/42.50 **t.** and a la carte. ER **r**

XX Sandrini, 260-262a Brompton Rd, SW3 2AS, ☎ 584 1724, Italian rest. DS **n**

XX **Poissonnerie de l'Avenue,** 82 Sloane Av., SW3 3DZ, ☎ 589 2457, Fax 581 3360, French
Seafood rest. – 🍽 🔼 🗚 ⑪ 𝑉𝐼𝑆𝐴 DS **u**
closed Sunday, 24 December-3 January, Easter and Bank Holidays – **M** a la carte 20.25/27.25 **t.**
⑧ 4.50.

XX **St. Quentin,** 243 Brompton Rd, SW3 2EP, ☎ 589 8005, Fax 584 6064, French rest. – 🍽.
🔼 🗚 ⑪ 𝑉𝐼𝑆𝐴 DR **a**
M 12.50/15.25 **t.** and a la carte ⑧ 5.10.

XX Penang, 294 Fulham Rd, SW10 9EW, ☎ 351 2599, Malaysian rest. – 🍽 BU **e**

XX Eleven Park Walk, 11 Park Walk, SW10 0PZ, ☎ 352 3449, Italian rest. – 🍽 CU **r**

XX **Magic Dragon,** 99-103 Fulham Rd, SW3 6RH, ☎ 225 2244, Fax 929 5689, Chinese rest. –
🍽. 🔼 🗚 ⑪ 𝑉𝐼𝑆𝐴 DS **o**
closed Monday and Bank Holidays – **M** 10.00/28.00 **st.** and a la carte.

XX **Good Earth,** 233 Brompton Rd, SW3 2EP, ☎ 584 3658, Fax 823 8769, Chinese rest. –
🔼 🗚 ⑪ 𝑉𝐼𝑆𝐴 DR **c**
closed 24 to 27 December – **M** 10.00/25.00 **t.** and a la carte ⑧ 3.50.

XX **Good Earth,** 91 King's Rd, SW3 4PA, ☎ 352 9231, Chinese rest. – 🍽. 🔼 🗚 ⑪ 𝑉𝐼𝑆𝐴
M 11.50/30.00 **t.** and a la carte ⑧ 3.50. EU **a**

XX **Toto's,** Walton House, Walton St., SW3 2JH, ☎ 589 0075, Italian rest. – 🔼 🗚 𝑉𝐼𝑆𝐴 ES **a**
closed 2 days Easter and 3 days Christmas – **M** 18.00/25.00 **st.** and a la carte ⑧ 6.50.

XX **Beccofino,** 100 Draycott Av., SW3 3AD, ☎ 584 3600, Italian rest. – 🔼 🗚 𝑉𝐼𝑆𝐴 ES **r**
closed Sunday – **M** a la carte 14.90/28.10 **t.** ⑧ 3.70.

XX **Le Suquet,** 104 Draycott Av., SW3 3AE, ☎ 581 1785, French Seafood rest. – 🔼 🗚 ⑪ 𝑉𝐼𝑆𝐴
M a la carte approx. 21.00 **t.** DS **c**

XX **Dan's,** 119 Sydney St., SW3 6NR, ☎ 352 2718, Fax 352 3265 – 🔼 🗚 ⑪ 𝑉𝐼𝑆𝐴 DU **s**
closed Saturday lunch, Sunday, Christmas-New Year and Bank Holidays – **M** 22.00 **t.** (dinner)
and lunch a la carte 16.40/19.30 **t.** ⑧ 4.50.

Kensington – ✉ SW7/W8/W11/W14 – ☎ 071 – Except where otherwise stated see
pp. 8-11.

🏨 **Royal Garden** (Rank), Kensington High St., W8 4PT, ☎ 937 8000, Telex 263151,
Fax 938 4532, ≤ Kensington Gardens – 🛗 ⇔ rm 🍽 📺 🕿 🅿 – 🔏 800. 🔼 🗚 ⑪ 𝑉𝐼𝑆𝐴. ⨯
M Royal Roof *(closed Saturday lunch and Sunday)* (dancing Saturday) 18.95/33.00 **st.** and a
la carte – ☲ 11.95 – **383 rm** 175.00/195.00 **st.**, **15 suites** 275.00/950.00 **st.** – SB (weekends
only) 132.00/154.00 **st.** p. 14 AQ **c**

🏨 **Halcyon,** 81 Holland Park, W11 3RZ, ☎ 727 7288, Telex 266721, Fax 229 8516 – 🛗 📺
🕿. 🔼 🗚 ⑪ 𝑉𝐼𝑆𝐴. ⨯ EX **u**
M – Kingfisher a la carte 12.50/21.75 **s.** ⑧ 6.50 – ☲ 12.50 – **41 rm** 165.00/235.00 **st.**, **3 suites**
250.00/550.00 **st.** – SB (weekends only) 195.00 **st.**

🏨 **Copthorne Tara,** Scarsdale Pl., W8 5SR, ☎ 937 7211, Telex 918834, Fax 937 7100 – 🛗
⨯ rm 🍽 📺 🕿 🕹 🅿 – 🔏 500. 🔼 🗚 ⑪ 𝑉𝐼𝑆𝐴. ⨯ FY **u**
M 12.15/22.50 **st.** and a la carte ⑧ 8.40 – ☲ 8.95 – **820 rm** 99.00/140.00 **st.**, **8 suites**
235.00/355.00 **st.**

🏨 **London Kensington Hilton,** 179-199 Holland Park Av., W11 4UL, ☎ 603 3355,
Telex 919763, Fax 602 9397 – 🛗 ⨯ rm 🍽 📺 🕿 🕹 🅿 – 🔏 200. 🔼 🗚 ⑪ 𝑉𝐼𝑆𝐴. ⨯
M (carving lunch) 18.95/35.00 **st.** and a la carte ⑧ 5.50 (see also **Hiroko** below) – ☲ 11.75
– **596 rm** 108.00/165.00 **st.**, **7 suites** 230.00/300.00 **st.** EX **s**

🏨🏨 **Kensington Park,** 16-32 De Vere Gardens, W8 5AG, ℰ 937 8080, Telex 929643, Fax 937 7616 – 🛗 📺 ☎ ⅙ – 🔬 120. 🅰 🆎 ⓞ 𝘝𝘐𝘚𝘈. ⅙   p. 14 BQ **e**
M 13.80 **t.** and a la carte ⅙ 5.40 – ☲ 9.95 – **325 rm** 99.00/120.00 st., **7 suites** 240.00/275.00 st.

🏨🏨 **Kensington Palace Thistle** (Mt. Charlotte Thistle), 8 De Vere Gdns, W8 5AF, ℰ 937 8121, Telex 262422, Fax 937 2816 – 🛗 ⅙ rm 🍽 rest 📺 ☎ – 🔬 180. 🅰 🆎 ⓞ 𝘝𝘐𝘚𝘈. ⅙   p. 14 BQ **a**
M 10.50/17.00 st. and a la carte ⅙ 6.95 – ☲ 9.95 – **297 rm** 95.00/130.00 st., **1 suite** 250.00 st. – SB 119.00/217.00 st.

🏨🏨 **Kensington Close** (Forte), Wrights Lane, W8 5SP, ℰ 937 8170, Fax 937 8289, 🔗, 🚡, 🅽, 🏊, squash – 🛗 ⅙ rm 🍽 rest 📺 ☎ 🅿 – 🔬 150. 🅰 🆎 ⓞ 𝘝𝘐𝘚𝘈   FY **c**
M 14.25 **t.** and a la carte ⅙ 5.00 – ☲ 7.50 – **530 rm** 85.00/95.00 st. – SB 98.00 st.

❌❌❌ **Belvedere in Holland Park,** Holland House, off Abbotsbury Rd, W8 6LU, ℰ 602 1238, « 19C orangery in park » – 🍽. 🅰 🆎 ⓞ 𝘝𝘐𝘚𝘈   EY **u**
closed Saturday lunch, Sunday dinner and 25 December – **M** (booking essential) a la carte 16.10/23.60 **t.**

❌❌ **Clarke's,** 124 Kensington Church St., W8 4BH, ℰ 221 9225, Fax 229 4564 – 🍽. 🅰 𝘝𝘐𝘚𝘈   EX **c**

❌❌ **La Pomme d'Amour,** 128 Holland Park Av., W11 4UE, ℰ 229 8532, French rest. – 🍽. 🆎 ⓞ 𝘝𝘐𝘚𝘈   EX **e**
closed Saturday lunch, Sunday and Bank Holidays – **M** 12.50/19.50 **t.** and a la carte ⅙ 4.50.

❌❌ **L'Escargot Doré,** 2-4 Thackeray St., W8 5ET, ℰ 937 8508, French rest. – 🍽. 🅰 🆎 ⓞ 𝘝𝘐𝘚𝘈   AR **e**
closed Saturday lunch, Sunday, last 2 weeks August and Bank Holidays – **M** 13.90 **t.** and a la carte ⅙ 4.80.

❌❌ **Shanghai,** 38c-d Kensington Church St., W8 4BX, ℰ 938 2501, Chinese rest. – 🍽. 🅰 🆎 ⓞ 𝘝𝘐𝘚𝘈   FX **a**
closed 24 to 26 December and Bank Holidays – **M** 16.50/23.00 **t.** and a la carte ⅙ 4.00.

❌❌ **La Fenice,** 148 Holland Park Av., W11 4UE, ℰ 221 6090, Italian rest. – 🍽. 🅰 🆎 𝘝𝘐𝘚𝘈   EX **v**
closed Saturday lunch, Monday and Bank Holidays – **M** 11.50 **t.** and a la carte ⅙ 3.20.

❌❌ **Launceston Place,** 1a Launceston Pl., W8 5RL, ℰ 937 6912, Fax 938 2412 – 🍽. 🅰 𝘝𝘐𝘚𝘈
closed Saturday lunch and Sunday dinner – **M** 14.95 **t.** (lunch) and a la carte 21.00/26.00 **t.** ⅙ 4.00.   p. 14 BR **a**

❌❌ **Hiroko** (at London Kensington Hilton H.), 179-199 Holland Park Av., W11 4UL, ℰ 603 5003, Japanese rest. – 🅿. 🅰 🆎 ⓞ 𝘝𝘐𝘚𝘈   EX **s**

❌❌ **Princess Garden,** 11 Russell Gdns, W14 8EZ, ℰ 602 0312, Chinese rest. 🍽   EY **i**

❌❌ **Phoenicia,** 11-13 Abingdon Rd, W8 6AH, ℰ 937 0120, Lebanese rest. – 🍽. 🅰 🆎 ⓞ 𝘝𝘐𝘚𝘈   EY **n**
closed 25 and 26 December – **M** 8.95/26.20 **t.** and a la carte.

❌❌ **Boyd's,** 135 Kensington Church St., W8 7LP, ℰ 727 5452 – 🅰 🆎 𝘝𝘐𝘚𝘈   p. 16 AZ **r**
M 14.85 **t.** (lunch) and a la carte 19.25/32.45 **t.** ⅙ 6.75.

❌❌ **La Paesana,** 50 Uxbridge St., W8 7TA, ℰ 229 4332, Italian rest. – 🍽. 🆎 ⓞ 𝘝𝘐𝘚𝘈
closed Sunday, Easter and Bank Holidays – **M** a la carte 13.90/16.40 **t.** ⅙ 3.80.   p. 16 AZ **i**

❌❌ **Sailing Junk,** 59 Marloes Rd, W8 6LE, ℰ 937 2589, Chinese rest. – 🍽. 🅰 🆎 ⓞ 𝘝𝘐𝘚𝘈   FY **x**
closed Sunday lunch – **M** 4.80/19.80 st. and a la carte ⅙ 3.50.

❌❌ **I Ching,** 40 Earls Court Rd, W8 6EJ, ℰ 937 0409, Chinese (Peking, Szechuan) rest. – 🍽   EY **a**

❌ **Kensington Place,** 201 Kensington Church St., W8 7LX, ℰ 727 3184, Fax 229 2025 – 🍽. 🅰 𝘝𝘐𝘚𝘈   p. 16 AZ **z**
M 12.50 **t.** (lunch) and a la carte 15.00/24.50 **t.** ⅙ 4.00.

❌ **Café Kensington,** 2 Lancer Sq., Kensington Church St., W8 4EH, ℰ 938 2211 – 🍽. 🅰 🆎 ⓞ 𝘝𝘐𝘚𝘈   AQ **u**
closed Bank Holidays – **M** a la carte 13.00/20.00 **t.** ⅙ 3.75.

❌ **Cibo,** 3 Russell Gdns, W14 8EZ, ℰ 371 6271, Italian rest. – 🅰 🆎 ⓞ 𝘝𝘐𝘚𝘈   EY **o**
closed Sunday dinner – **M** a la carte 17.00/38.90 **t.** ⅙ 4.75.

  North Kensington – ✉ W2/W10/W11 – ☎ 071 – Except where otherwise stated see pp. 4-7.

🏨 **Abbey Court** without rest., 20 Pembridge Gdns, W2 4DU, ℰ 221 7518, Telex 262167, Fax 792 0858, « Tastefully furnished Victorian town house » – 📺 ☎. 🅰 🆎 ⓞ 𝘝𝘐𝘚𝘈. ⅙   p. 16 AZ **u**
☲ 7.00 – **22 rm** 84.00/150.00 **t.**

🏨 **Pembridge Court,** 34 Pembridge Gdns, W2 4DX, ℰ 229 9977, Telex 298363, Fax 727 4982 – 🛗 ⅙ rest 🍽 rest 📺 ☎. 🅰 🆎 ⓞ 𝘝𝘐𝘚𝘈   p.18 AZ **n**
M *(closed Sunday and Bank Holidays)* (dinner only) a la carte 12.00/18.50 **t.** ⅙ 4.80 – **25 rm** ☲ 65.00/110.00 **t.**

🏨 **Portobello,** 22 Stanley Gdns, W11 2NG, ℰ 727 2777, Telex 268349, Fax 792 9641, « Attractive town house in Victorian terrace » – 📺 ☎. 🅰 🆎 ⓞ 𝘝𝘐𝘚𝘈. ⅙   EV **n**
closed 23 December-2 January – **M** (residents only) 15.00/20.00 st. and a la carte ⅙ 4.50 – ☲ 6.95 – **24 rm** 70.50/125.75 st., **1 suite** 170.40 st.

XXX **Leith's,** 92 Kensington Park Rd, W11 2PN, ✆ 229 4481 – ▤. 🖭 AE ⓪ VISA EV **e**
closed 30-31 August and 24 to 27 December – **M** (dinner only) 23.50/44.00 **st.** ⓘ 6.75.

XX **Chez Moi,** 1 Addison Av., Holland Park, W11 4QS, ✆ 603 8267, French rest. – 🖭 AE ⓪
VISA p. 8 EX **n**
closed Saturday lunch, Sunday, Christmas-New Year and Bank Holidays – **M** 14.00 **t.** (lunch)
and a la carte 18.25/27.25 **t.** ⓘ 4.75.

South Kensington – ✉ SW5/SW7/W8 – ✪ 071 – pp.14 and 15.

🏛️ **Blakes,** 33 Roland Gdns, SW7 3PF, ✆ 370 6701, Telex 8813500, Fax 373 0442, « Antique
oriental furnishings » – 🛗 ▤ rest 📺 ☎. 🖭 AE VISA BU **n**
M 28.50 **st.** (lunch) and a la carte 31.75/53.50 **t.** ⓘ 7.00 – ☷ 14.50 – **46 rm** 150.00/270.00 **t.**,
6 suites 220.00/600.00 **t.**

🏛️ **Pelham,** 15 Cromwell Pl., SW7 2LA, ✆ 589 8288, Telex 8814714, Fax 584 8444, « Tastefully
furnished Victorian town house » – 🛗 ▤ 📺 ☎. 🖭 AE VISA CS **z**
M 14.95/17.95 **st.** and a la carte ⓘ 9.50 – **34 rm** ☷ 115.00/165.00 **t.**, **3 suites** 200.00/265.00 **t.**

🏛️ **Gloucester** (Rank), 4-19 Harrington Gdns, SW7 4LH, ✆ 373 6030, Telex 917505,
Fax 373 0409 – 🛗 ※ rm ▤ 📺 ☎ ℗ – 🔬 400. 🖭 AE ⓪ VISA. ✸ BS **r**
M 21.40 **t.** (dinner) and a la carte 19.95/30.25 **t.** ⓘ 8.00 – ☷ 11.50 – **544 rm** 150.00/180.00 **st.**,
6 suites 210.00/750.00 **st.**

🏛️ **Rembrandt,** 11 Thurloe Pl., SW7 2RS, ✆ 589 8100, Telex 295828, Fax 225 3363, ▮▮, ≋,
🖭 – 🛗 ※ rm ▤ rest 📺 ☎ – 🔬 250. 🖭 AE ⓪ VISA. ✸ DS **x**
M 16.75 **st.** and a la carte ⓘ 6.50 – ☷ 9.20 – **196 rm** 97.00/260.00 **st.** – SB (weekends only)
127.90/147.90 **st.**

🏛️ **Swallow International,** Cromwell Rd, SW5 0TH, ✆ 973 1000, Telex 27260, Fax 244 8194,
▮▮, ≋, 🖭 – 🛗 ※ rm ▤ rest 📺 ☎ ℗ – 🔬 200. 🖭 AE ⓪ VISA. ✸ AS **c**
closed 3 days at Christmas – **M** 15.00/20.00 **st.** and a la carte ⓘ 6.00 – ☷ 8.25 – **415 rm**
95.00/120.00 **st.**, **1 suite** 150.00/250.00 **st.** – SB 183.00/240.00 **st.**

🏛️ **Holiday Inn,** 94-106 Cromwell Rd, SW7 4ER, ✆ 373 2222, Telex 911311, Fax 373 0559, ▮▮,
≋, 🖭 – 🛗 ※ rm ▤ 📺 ☎ – 🔬 125. 🖭 AE ⓪ VISA. ✸ BS **u**
M 9.95/15.95 **t.** and a la carte – ☷ 10.95 – **143 rm** 118.00/145.00 **st.**, **19 suites**
190.00/250.00 **st.** – SB (weekends only) 94.00/112.00 **st.**

🏛️ **Gore,** 189-190 Queen's Gate, SW7 5EX, ✆ 584 6601, Telex 296244, Fax 589 8127,
« Attractive decor » – 🛗 📺 ☎. 🖭 AE ⓪ VISA. ✸ BR **n**
M (only members and residents may book) a la carte 12.25/20.80 **t.** – ☷ 9.40 – **58 rm**
87.00/109.00 **s.**

🏛️ **Regency,** 100 Queen's Gate, SW7 5AG, ✆ 370 4595, Telex 267594, Fax 370 5555, ▮▮, ≋
– 🛗 ※ rm ▤ rest 📺 ☎ – 🔬 100. 🖭 AE ⓪ VISA. ✸ CT **e**
M *(closed lunch Saturday and Sunday)* 15.00/25.00 **st.** and a la carte – ☷ 12.00 – **204 rm**
111.00/131.00 **st.**, **6 suites** 190.00/225.00 **st.** – SB (weekends only) 140.00/180.00 **st.**

🏛️ **John Howard,** 4 Queen's Gate, SW7 5EH, ✆ 581 3011, Telex 8813397, Fax 589 8403 – 🛗
▤ 📺 ☎. 🖭 AE ⓪ VISA. ✸ BQ **i**
M 15.75 **st.** and a la carte ⓘ 4.50 – ☷ 9.75 – **52 rm** 85.00/175.00 **st.**

🏛️ **Onslow,** 109-113 Queen's Gate, SW7 5LR, ✆ 589 6300, Telex 262180, Fax 581 1492 – 🛗
▤ rest 📺 ☎ – 🔬 80. 🖭 AE ⓪ VISA. ✸ CT **i**
M 13.50/15.00 **t.** and a la carte ⓘ 5.00 – ☷ 8.50 – **173 rm** 99.00/125.00 **t.**

🏛️ Baileys, 140 Gloucester Rd, SW7 4QH, ✆ 373 6000, Telex 264221, Fax 370 3760 – 🛗 📺
☎ – 🔬 70. 🖭 AE ⓪ VISA. ✸ BS **a**
☷ 11.00 – **162 rm** 140.00/450.00 **st.**

🏛️ **Cranley** without rest., 8-12 Bina Gardens, SW5 0LA, ✆ 373 0123, Fax 373 9497, « Tasteful
decor, antiques » – 🛗 📺 ☎. 🖭 AE ⓪ VISA BT **c**
☷ 11.45 – **31 rm** 99.00/160.00 **st.**, **4 suites** 205.00/277.00 **st.**

🏛️ Vanderbilt (Edwardian), 68-86 Cromwell Rd, SW7 5BT, ✆ 589 2424, Telex 946944,
Fax 225 2293 – 🛗 ▤ rest 📺 ☎ – 🔬 120 BS **v**
223 rm.

🏛️ Park International, 117-125 Cromwell Rd, SW7 4DS, ✆ 370 5711, Telex 296822,
Fax 244 9211 – 🛗 📺 ☎ – 🔬 45 AS **e**
117 rm.

🏛️ Embassy House (Jarvis) 31-33 Queen's Gate, SW7 5JA, ✆ 584 7222, Telex 914893,
Fax 589 8193 – 🛗 📺 ☎. 🖭 AE ⓪ VISA BR **e**
M *(closed lunch Saturday and Sunday)* (buffet lunch)/dinner 22.00 **t.** and a la carte – **67 rm**,
1 suite.

🏛️ Norfolk (Q.M.H.), 2-10 Harrington Rd, SW7 3ER, ✆ 589 8191, Telex 268852, Fax 581 1874,
▮▮, ≋ – 🛗 📺 ☎ – 🔬 60. 🖭 AE ⓪ VISA. ✸ CS **e**
M – Brasserie de la Paix *(closed Saturday lunch)* 11.95/18.00 **t.** and a la carte ⓘ 6.50 – ☷
9.00 – **93 rm** 115.00/145.00 **st.**, **3 suites** 165.00/185.00 **st.** – SB 130.00 **st.**

🏛️ Kensington Plaza, 61 Gloucester Rd, SW7 4PE, ✆ 584 8100, Telex 8950993, Fax 823 9175,
≋ – 🛗 📺 ☎ – 🔬 50. 🖭 AE ⓪ VISA. ✸ BS **e**
M (Indian rest.) 15.00/20.00 **st.** and a la carte ⓘ 7.95 – ☷ 7.50 – **90 rm** 70.00/120.00 **st.**

🏠 **Number Sixteen** without rest., 14-17 Sumner Pl., SW7 3EG, ℰ 589 5232, Telex 266638, Fax 584 8615, « Attractively furnished Victorian town houses », 🚗 – 🖨 📺 ☎. 🔄 AE ⓪ VISA. ⚡
⚡ 8.00 – **36 rm** 60.00/160.00 **t.**
CT **c**

🏠 **Cranley Place** without rest., 1 Cranley Pl., SW7 3AB, ℰ 589 7944, Fax 225 3931, « Tasteful decor » – 📺 ☎
10 rm.
CT **o**

🏠 **Five Sumner Place** without rest., 5 Sumner Pl., SW7 3EE, ℰ 584 7586, Fax 823 9962 – 🖨
📺 ☎. 🔄 AE ⓪ VISA. ⚡
13 rm ⚡ 55.00/95.00 **st.**
CT **a**

🏠 **Cranley Gardens** without rest. 8 Cranley Gdns, SW7 3DB, ℰ 373 3232, Telex 894489, Fax 373 7944 – 🖨 📺 ☎. 🔄 AE ⓪ VISA
⚡ 5.50 – **85 rm** 63.00/89.00 **st.**
BT **e**

🏠 **Alexander** without rest., 9 Sumner Pl., SW7 3EE, ℰ 581 1591, Telex 917133, Fax 581 0824, « Attractively furnished Victorian town houses », 🚗 – 🖨 📺 ☎. 🔄 AE ⓪ VISA. ⚡CT **a**
36 rm ⚡ 85.00/155.00, **1 suite** 195.00.

🏠 **Aster House,** 3 Sumner Pl., SW7 3EE, ℰ 581 5888, Fax 584 4925, 🚗 – ⚡ 📺 ☎. 🔄 AE
⓪ VISA. ⚡
12 rm ⚡ 52.00/79.00 **s.**
CT **u**

XXX **Bombay Brasserie,** Courtfield Close, 140 Gloucester Rd, SW7 4QH, ℰ 370 4040, Indian rest., « Raj- style decor, conservatory garden » – 🍽. 🔄 VISA
BS **a**
closed 25 and 26 December – **M** (buffet lunch) 13.50 **t.** and dinner a la carte approx. 17.30 **t.**
⚡ 4.95.

XX **Hilaire,** 68 Old Brompton Rd, SW7 3LQ, ℰ 584 8993 – 🍽. 🔄 AE ⓪ VISA
CT **n**
closed Sunday, 1 week Easter, 2 weeks August, 1 week Christmas and Bank Holidays –
M (booking essential) 20.95/34.00 **t.** and a la carte 29.50/37.00 **t.** ⚡ 7.00.

XX **Nizam,** 152 Old Brompton Rd, SW5 0BE, ℰ 373 0024, Indian rest. – 🍽
BT **a**
M a la carte 13.10/17.55 **t.**

XX **Mr Wing,** 242-244 Old Brompton Rd, SW5 0DE, ℰ 370 4450, Chinese rest. – ⚡. 🔄 AE
AV **a**
closed 25 to 30 December – **M** 15.00/20.00 **t.** and a la carte.

XX **Tui,** 19 Exhibition Rd, SW7 2HE, ℰ 584 8359, Fax 352 8343, Thai rest. – 🔄 AE ⓪ VISA
CS **u**
closed Bank Holidays – **M** a la carte 12.15/20.05 **t.**

XX **Delhi Brasserie,** 134 Cromwell Rd, SW7 4HA, ℰ 370 7617, Indian rest. – 🍽. 🔄 AE ⓪
VISA
AS **a**
closed 25 and 26 December – **M** 14.25 **t.** and a la carte.

XX **Memories of India,** 18 Gloucester Rd, SW7 4RB, ℰ 589 6450, Telex 265196, Fax 581 5980, Indian rest. – 🍽. 🔄 AE ⓪ VISA
BR **s**
closed 25 and 26 December – **M** 14.50/15.00 **t.** and a la carte.

MERTON

Wimbledon – ✉ SW19 – 📞 081.

🏠 **Cannizaro House** (Mt. Charlotte Thistle) ⚡, West Side, Wimbledon Common, SW19 4UF, ℰ 879 1464, Telex 9413837, Fax 879 7338, ⚡, « 18C country house overlooking Cannizaro Park », 🚗 – 🖨 📺 ☎ 📞 – ⚡ 40. 🔄 AE ⓪ VISA
DXY **x**
M 28.00 **st.** and a la carte – ⚡ 8.75 – **44 rm** 110.00/160.00 **t.**, **2 suites** 210.00/285.00 **t.** –
SB 160.00/250.00 **st.**

WANDSWORTH

Battersea – ✉ SW8/SW11 – 📞 071.

XXX ⚡ **L'Arlequin** (Delteil), 123 Queenstown Rd, SW8 3RH, ℰ 622 0555, Fax 498 0715, French rest. – 🍽. 🔄 AE ⓪ VISA
HZ **o**
closed Saturday, Sunday and 3 weeks summer – **M** (booking essential) 20.50 **st.** (lunch) and a la carte 35.00/51.50 **st.** ⚡ 6.00
Spec. Petits choux farcis à l'ancienne, Gibier en saison, Soufflé chaud "Genevieve".

XX **Le Chausson,** Ransome's Dock, 35-37 Parkgate Rd, SW11 4NP, ℰ 223 1611, French rest. – 📞. 🔄 AE ⓪ VISA
HZ **e**
closed Saturday lunch, Sunday, last 3 weeks August and Christmas-New Year – **M** 17.00/25.00 **t.** and a la carte ⚡ 4.50.

XX **Chada,** 208-210 Battersea Park Rd, SW11 4ND, ℰ 622 2209, Thai rest. – 🍽. 🔄 AE ⓪ VISA
closed Saturday lunch, Sunday and Bank Holidays – **M** a la carte 11.30/21.60 **t.**

XX **Lena's,** 196 Lavender Hill, SW11 1JA, ℰ 228 3735, Thai rest. – 🍽. 🔄 AE ⓪ VISA
closed Sunday lunch, Easter, 25 December and 1 January – **M** 15.00/25.00 **st.** and a la carte ⚡ 4.95.

Wandsworth – ⊠ SW17 – ☎ 081.

XXX ✿✿ **Harvey's** (White), 2 Bellevue Rd, SW17 7EG, ℰ 672 0114 – ☲. 🖎 VISA
closed Sunday, Monday, first 2 weeks August and 2 weeks Christmas – **M** (booking essential)
24.00/48.00 **t.** ⊿ 10.00
Spec. Foie gras poché aux lentilles, Tête de porc braisée aux épices, Tarte Tatin aux poires.

WESTMINSTER (City of)

Bayswater and Maida Vale – ⊠ W2/W9 – ☎ 071 – Except where otherwise stated
see pp. 16 and 17.

▲▲▲ **Royal Lancaster** (Rank), Lancaster Terr., W2 2TY, ℰ 262 6737, Telex 24822, Fax 724 3191,
<ul>❬ – ⟨≣⟩ ⋈ rm ☰ ☲ TV ☎ ℗ – 🕭 1 400. 🖎 ᴁ ⓪ VISA. ⅍</ul> DZ **e**
M 20.50/23.00 **t.** and a la carte – ⥯ 12.00 – **398 rm** 148.00/188.00 **st.**, **20 suites**
395.00/850.00 **st.**

▲▲ **Whites** (Mt. Charlotte Thistle), Bayswater Rd, 90-92 Lancaster Gate, W2 3NR, ℰ 262 2711,
Telex 24771, Fax 262 2147 – ⟨≣⟩ ⋈ rm ☰ ☲ TV ☎ ℗. 🖎 ᴁ ⓪ VISA. ⅍ CZ **v**
M *(closed Saturday lunch)* 16.00/21.50 **t.** and a la carte ⊿ 7.15 – ⥯ 10.00 – **52 rm**
135.00/225.00 **st.**, **2 suites** 225.00/350.00 **st.** – SB 158.00/220.00 **st.**

▲▲ **London Metropole**, Edgware Rd, W2 1JU, ℰ 402 4141, Telex 23711, Fax 724 8866, ❬, ☞,
🖾 – ⟨≣⟩ ☰ TV ☎ – 🕭 1 250. 🖎 ᴁ ⓪ VISA p. 5 GU **c**
M 13.95/45.00 **st.** and a la carte ⊿ 8.75 – ⥯ 9.75 – **742 rm** 115.00/145.00 **st.**, **24 suites**
150.00/550.00 **st.**

▲ **Plaza on Hyde Park** (Hilton), Lancaster Gate, W2 3NA, ℰ 262 5022, Telex 8954372,
Fax 724 8666 – ⟨≣⟩ ⋈ rm TV ☎ – 🕭 70 DZ **r**
402 rm.

▲ **Coburg**, 129 Bayswater Rd, W2 4RJ, ℰ 221 2217, Telex 268235, Fax 229 0557 – ⟨≣⟩ TV ☎.
🖎 ᴁ ⓪ VISA. ⅍ BZ **c**
M (see **Spice Merchant** below) – **131 rm** ⥯ 79.50/129.50, **1 suite** 180.00.

▲ **Hyde Park Towers**, 41-51 Inverness Terr., W2 3JN, ℰ 221 8484, Group Telex 263260,
Fax 221 2286 – ⟨≣⟩ ☰ rest TV ☎ – 🕭 40 BZ **r**
115 rm.

▲ **Eden Park**, 35-39 Inverness Terr., W2 3JS, ℰ 221 2220, Group Telex 263260, Fax 221 2286
– ⋈ rm ☰ rest TV ☎ BZ **n**
137 rm.

▲ **London Embassy** (Jarvis), 150 Bayswater Rd, W2 4RT, ℰ 229 1212, Telex 27727,
Fax 229 2623 – ⟨≣⟩ ⋈ rm ☰ TV ☎ ℗ – 🕭 60. 🖎 ᴁ ⓪ VISA. ⅍ BZ **o**
M (carving rest.) 19.00 **t.** and a la carte ⊿ 6.00 – ⥯ 9.50 – **192 rm** 100.00/138.00 **t.**, **1 suite**
195.00 **t.** – SB (weekends only) 105.00/121.00 **st.**

▲ **Hospitality Inn** (Mt. Charlotte Thistle), 104 Bayswater Rd, W2 3HL, ℰ 262 4461,
Telex 22667, Fax 706 4560 – ⟨≣⟩ ☰ TV ☎ ℗ – 🕭 40. 🖎 ᴁ ⓪ VISA CZ **o**
M (bar lunch)/dinner 13.25 **st.** and a la carte ⊿ 4.75 – ⥯ 8.15 – **174 rm** 78.50/105.00 **st.**,
1 suite.

▲ **Mornington** without rest., 12 Lancaster Gate, W2 3LG, ℰ 262 7361, Telex 24281,
Fax 706 1028, ☞ – ⟨≣⟩ TV ☎ 🖎 ᴁ ⓪ VISA DZ **s**
closed 23 December-2 January – ⥯ 5.00 – **68 rm** 75.00/103.00 **st.**

▲ **Pavilion**, 35-39 Leinster Gdns, W2 3AR, ℰ 258 0269, Telex 268613, Fax 723 7295, ☞ –
⟨≣⟩ TV ☎ – 🕭 80. 🖎 ᴁ ⓪ VISA. ⅍ CZ
M (dinner only) 15.00 **st.** and a la carte ⊿ 4.00 – ⥯ 5.00 – **97 rm** 50.00/110.00 **st.** – SB 80.00 **st.**

XX **Spice Merchant** (at Coburg H.), 130 Bayswater Rd, W2 4RJ, ℰ 221 2442, Fax 229 0557,
Indian rest. – ☰. 🖎 ᴁ ⓪ VISA BZ **c**
M (buffet lunch)/dinner a la carte 9.00/15.00 **t.** ⊿ 5.50.

XX **Poons**, Whiteleys, Queensway, W2 4YN, ℰ 792 2884, Chinese rest. – ☰. 🖎 ᴁ ⓪
VISA BZ **x**
closed Christmas – **M** 5.00/10.00 **st.** and a la carte.

XX **San Marino**, 26 Sussex Pl., W2 2TH, ℰ 723 8395, Italian rest. – 🖎 ᴁ ⓪ VISA DZ **u**
closed Bank Holidays – **M** a la carte 17.20/22.50 **t.**

XX **Hsing**, 451 Edgware Rd, W2 1TH, ℰ 402 0904, Chinese rest. – 🖎 ᴁ ⓪ GU **a**
closed Sunday – **M** a la carte 13.75/20.00 **t.**

X **Al San Vincenzo**, 30 Connaught St., W2 2AE, ℰ 262 9623, Italian rest. – 🖎 VISA
closed Saturday lunch, Sunday, 2 weeks August, Christmas and Bank Holidays –
M 19.00/32.00 **t.** ⊿ 6.50. EZ **o**

Belgravia – ⊠ SW1 – ☎ 071 – Except where otherwise stated see pp. 14 and 15.

▲▲▲▲ **Berkeley**, Wilton Pl., SW1X 7RL, ℰ 235 6000, Telex 919252, Fax 235 4330, 𝄞, ☞, 🖾 –
⟨≣⟩ ☰ TV ☎ ⟵⟶ – 🕭 200. 🖎 ᴁ ⓪ VISA. ⅍ FQ **e**
M Restaurant *(closed Saturday)* 19.50 **st.** (lunch) and a la carte 25.70/39.25 **st.** ⊿ 5.35 – **Buttery**
(closed Sunday) 15.00 **st.** (lunch) and a la carte 21.00/30.00 **st.** ⊿ 5.35 – ⥯ 16.00 – **132 rm**
170.00/275.00 **st.**, **27 suites** 440.00/495.00 **st.**

🏨🏨 **Sheraton Belgravia,** 20 Chesham Pl., SW1X 8HQ, ℰ 235 6040, Telex 919020, Fax 259 6243
– ▮ ⇄ rm ▮ ▭ ☎ ▮ ▮ ⓪ 𝘝𝘐𝘚𝘈 ⅏
FR **u**
M (closed lunch Saturday and Bank Holidays) 18.50/19.75 **t.** and a la carte ▯ 5.00 – ⌘ 11.75
– **82 rm** 230.00/250.00 **s.**, **7 suites** 310.00 **s.**

🏨🏨 **Halkin,** 5 Halkin St., SW1X 7DJ, ℰ 333 1000, Telex 290308, Fax 333 1100 – ▮ ▮ ☎
– ▮ 25. ▮ ▮ ⓪ 𝘝𝘐𝘚𝘈 ⅏
AV **a**
M (Italian rest.) 22.50/35.00 **st.** and a la carte ▯ 9.00 – ⌘ 8.50 – **37 rm** 180.00/280.00 **s.**, **4 suites** 300.00/450.00 **s.**

🏨🏨 **Lowndes,** 21 Lowndes St., SW1X 9ES, ℰ 235 6020, Telex 919065, Fax 235 1154 – ▮ ⇄ rm
▮ rest ▭ ☎. ▮ ▮ ⓪ 𝘝𝘐𝘚𝘈 ⅏
FR **i**
M 15.50 **t.** (lunch) and a la carte 17.50/25.50 **st.** ▯ 10.00 – ⌘ 10.25 – **74 rm** 150.00 **s.**, **5 suites** 300.00/450.00 **s.**

XXX **Al Bustan,** 27 Motcomb St., SW1X 8JU, ℰ 235 8277, Lebanese rest. – ▮. ▮ ▮ 𝘝𝘐𝘚𝘈
closed 25 December and 1 January – **M** a la carte 20.25/26.75.
FR **z**

XX **Motcombs,** 26 Motcomb St., SW1X 8JU, ℰ 235 6382, Fax 245 6351 – ▮. ▮ ▮ ⓪ 𝘝𝘐𝘚𝘈 FR **z**
closed Sunday and Bank Holidays – **M** 15.00 **t.** (lunch) and a la carte approx. 14.90 **t.**

▮ Hyde Park and Knightsbridge ▮ – ✉ SW1/SW7 – ☎ 071 – pp. 14 and 15.
🛈 Harrods (Basement Banking hall), Knightsbridge, SW1 ℰ 730 3488/824 8844.

🏨🏨🏨 **Hyde Park** (Forte), 66 Knightsbridge, SW1Y 7LA, ℰ 235 2000, Telex 262057, Fax 235 4552,
⇔ – ▮ ⇄ rm ▮ ▭ ☎ ▮ ▮ ⓪ 𝘝𝘐𝘚𝘈 ⅏
EQ **v**
M Park Room 24.50/35.00 **st.** ▯ 10.00 – **Grill room** (closed Saturday and Sunday) 34.50/48.50 **st.** ▯ 10.00 – ▯ 14.00 – **166 rm** 199.00/285.00 **st.**, **19 suites** 525.00/1 400.00 **st.**

🏨 **Knightsbridge Green** without rest., 159 Knightsbridge, SW1X 7PD, ℰ 584 6274,
Fax 225 1635 – ▮ ▭ ☎. ▮ ▮ ⓪ 𝘝𝘐𝘚𝘈
EQ **z**
closed Christmas – ⌘ 8.50 – **10 rm** 85.00/100.00 **st.**, **14 suites** 115.00 **st.**

XX **Lucullus,** 48 Knightsbridge, SW1X 7JN, ℰ 245 6622, Fax 245 6625, Seafood – ▮
FQ **a**
M 12.50 **t.** (lunch) and dinner a la carte approx. 33.00 **t.** ▯ 5.00.

XX **Dell Arte,** 116 Knightsbridge, SW1X 7PJ, ℰ 225 3512, Italian rest. – ▮ ▮ ⓪ 𝘝𝘐𝘚𝘈
EQ **x**
closed Sunday – **M** 12.50/26.00 **t.** and a la carte ▯ 4.00.

▮ Mayfair ▮ – ✉ W1 – ☎ 071 – pp. 12 and 13.

🏨🏨🏨 **Claridge's,** Brook St., W1A 2JQ, ℰ 629 8860, Telex 21872, Fax 499 2210 – ▮ ▮ ▭ ☎
▮. ▮ ▮ ⓪ 𝘝𝘐𝘚𝘈 ⅏
BL **c**
M 48.00/58.00 **st.** and a la carte 34.50/63.50 **st.** ▯ 5.80 – **Causerie** (closed Saturday) 18.50/30.00 **st.** and a la carte 29.50/47.50 **st.** ▯ 5.80 – ⌘ 15.75 – **137 rm** 190.00/290.00 **st.**, **53 suites** 490.00/1125.00 **st.**

🏨🏨🏨 **Dorchester,** Park Lane, W1A 2HJ, ℰ 629 8888, Telex 887704, Fax 409 0114, 𝑓ᵢ, ⇌ ▭
☎ ▮ ⇔ – ▮ 500. ▮ ▮ ⓪ 𝘝𝘐𝘚𝘈 ⅏
BN **a**
M – Terrace (closed Sunday, Monday and 26 December) (dinner only) 35.00 **st.** and a la carte 32.50/48.50 **st.** ▯ 9.00 – **Grill** 25.00/45.00 **st.** and a la carte 22.00/31.00 **st.** ▯ 9.00 (see also **Oriental** below) – ⌘ 12.50 – **202 rm** 180.00/240.00 **s.**, **50 suites** 380.00/1000.00 **s.**

🏨🏨🏨 **Four Seasons Inn on the Park,** Hamilton Pl., Park Lane, W1A 1AZ, ℰ 499 0888,
Telex 22771, Fax 493 1895 – ▮ ⇄ rm ▮ ▭ ☎ ⇔ – ▮ 400. ▮ ▮ ⓪ 𝘝𝘐𝘚𝘈 ⅏
M – Lanes 26.10/30.80 **st.** and dinner a la carte 30.80/36.85 **st.** (see also **Four Seasons** below) – ⌘ 7.45 – **209 rm** 209.00/260.00 **s.**, **19 suites** 308.00/1045.00 **s.**
BP **a**

🏨🏨🏨 **Le Meridien London,** 21 Piccadilly, W1V 0BH, ℰ 734 8000, Telex 25795, Fax 437 3574,
𝑓ᵢ, ⇌, ▮, squash – ▮ ▮ ▭ ☎ ▮ – ▮ 200. ▮ ▮ ⓪ 𝘝𝘐𝘚𝘈 ⅏
EM **a**
M Terrace Garden 19.00 **t.** (lunch) and a la carte 15.70/24.35 **t.** ▯ 8.20 – (see also **Oak Room** below) – ⌘ 11.50 – **210 rm** 190.00/230.00, **50 suites** 300.00/550.00.

🏨🏨🏨 **Grosvenor House** (Forte), Park Lane, W1A 3AA, ℰ 499 6363, Telex 24871, Fax 493 3341,
𝑓ᵢ, ▮, ⇄ rm ▮ ▭ ☎ ▮ – ▮ 1 000. ▮ ▮ ⓪ 𝘝𝘐𝘚𝘈 ⅏
AM **a**
M 15.50/19.50 **st.** and a la carte – (see also **90 Park Lane** below) – ⌘ 11.75 – **384 rm** 160.00/210.00 **st.**, **163 suites** 285.00/690.00 **st.** – SB (weekends only) 198.00 **st.**

🏨🏨 ✿ **Connaught,** Carlos Pl., W1Y 6AL, ℰ 499 7070, Fax 495 3262 – ▮ ▮ rest ▭ ☎ ▮
𝘝𝘐𝘚𝘈
BM **e**
M (booking essential) 22.80/55.80 **t.** and a la carte 28.10/59.00 **t.** ▯ 5.00 – **66 rm**, **24 suites**
Spec. Galette Connaught aux diamants noirs, salade Aphrodite, Homard et langoustines grillés aux herbes, Crème brûlée d'un soir.

🏨🏨 **Le Gavroche at Fortyseven Park,** 47 Park St., W1Y 4EB, ℰ 491 7282, Telex 22116,
Fax 491 7281 – ▮ ▮ ▭ ☎ – ▮ 30. ▮ ▮ ⓪ 𝘝𝘐𝘚𝘈 ⅏
AM **c**
M (see **Le Gavroche** below) – ⌘ 15.50 – **52 suites** 225.00/430.00 **s.**

🏨🏨 **Britannia** (Inter-Con.), Grosvenor Sq., W1A 3AN, ℰ 629 9400, Telex 23941, Fax 629 7736
– ▮ ▮ ⇄ rm ▮ ▭ ☎ – ▮ 80. ▮ ▮ ⓪ 𝘝𝘐𝘚𝘈 ⅏
BM **x**
M 21.30 **st.** and a la carte ▯ 12.00 – (see also **Shogun** below) – ⌘ 10.75 – **314 rm** 175.00/210.00, **12 suites** 375.00/500.00.

🏨🏨 **Park Lane,** Piccadilly, W1Y 8BX, ℰ 499 6321, Telex 21533, Fax 499 1965, 𝑓ᵢ, – ▮ ▮ ⇄ rm
▭ ☎ ▮ – ▮ 500. ▮ ▮ ⓪ 𝘝𝘐𝘚𝘈 ⅏
BP **x**
M closed Sunday and Bank Holidays 16.00/22.00 **st.** and a la carte ▯ 10.00 – ⌘ 10.75 – **266 rm** 147.00/175.00 **s.**, **54 suites** 205.00 **s.**

London Hilton on Park Lane, 22 Park Lane, W1A 2HH, ✆ 493 8000, Telex 24873, Fax 493 4957, « ≤ London from Window on the World Restaurant », ≤s – |≑| ⋙ rm ▤ 🖂 ☎ & – 🔏 1 000. 🔼 AE ⓪ VISA. ✸
BP **e**
M 36.00/55.00 **t.** and a la carte ♦ 14.00 – ☲ 13.95 – **396 rm**, **52 suites**.

Inter-Continental, 1 Hamilton Pl., Hyde Park Corner, W1V 0QY, ✆ 409 3131, Telex 25853, Fax 409 7460, *Ⅰ₆*, ≤s – |≑| ⋙ rm ▤ 🖂 ☎ & ⇔ – 🔏 700. 🔼 AE ⓪ VISA. ✸ BP **o**
M 20.50 **t.** and a la carte ♦ 7.50 (see also **Le Soufflé** below) – ☲ 14.95 – **438 rm** 190.00/250.00 **s.**, **29 suites** 270.00/1200.00 **s.**

May Fair Inter-Continental, Stratton St., W1A 2AN, ✆ 629 7777, Telex 262526, Fax 629 1459, *Ⅰ₆*, ≤s – ▣ – |≑| ⋙ rm ▤ 🖂 ☎ & – 🔏 270. 🔼 AE ⓪ VISA. ✸ DN **z**
M (see **Le Chateau** below) – ☲ 10.50 – **269 rm** 140.00/235.00 **st.**, **24 suites** 400.00/1400.00 – SB (weekends only) 238.00/250.00 **st.**

Brown's (Forte), 29-34 Albemarle St., W1A 4SW, ✆ 493 6020, Fax 493 9381 – |≑| ⋙ rm ▤ rest 🖂 ☎ – 🔏 80. 🔼 AE ⓪ VISA. ✸ DM **e**
M 23.00 **st.** and a la carte ♦ 7.00 – ☲ 10.75 – **127 rm** 160.00/198.00 **st.**, **6 suites** 330.00/400.00 **st.** – SB (weekends only) 198.00 **st.**

Marriott, Duke St., Grosvenor Sq., W1A 4AW, ✆ 493 1232, Telex 268101, Fax 491 3201 – |≑| ▤ 🖂 ☎ & – 🔏 375. 🔼 AE ⓪ VISA. ✸ BL **a**
M (closed Saturday lunch) 25.00 **t.** (lunch) and a la carte 21.75/28.45 **t.** – ☲ 9.75 – **206 rm** 100.00/230.00 **s.**, **17 suites** 290.00 **s.**

Athenaeum (Rank), 116 Piccadilly, W1V 0BJ, ✆ 499 3464, Telex 261589, Fax 493 1860 – |≑| ⋙ rm ▤ 🖂 ☎ – 🔏 55. 🔼 AE ⓪ VISA. ✸ CP **s**
M (closed Saturday lunch) 22.50 **st.** and a la carte ♦ 8.15 – ☲ 12.85 – **90 rm** 178.00/213.00 **st.**, **22 suites** 330.00 **st.**

Westbury (Forte), Conduit St., W1A 4UH, ✆ 629 7755, Telex 24378, Fax 495 1163 – |≑| ⋙ rm ▤ 🖂 ☎ – 🔏 110. 🔼 AE ⓪ VISA DM **a**
M 15.00/22.00 **st.** and a la carte ♦ 7.45 – ☲ 11.50 – **229 rm** 155.00/180.00 **st.**, **14 suites** 255.00/555.00 **st.** – SB (weekends only) 138.00 **st.**

Holiday Inn, 3 Berkeley St., W1X 6NE, ✆ 493 8282, Telex 24561, Fax 629 2827 – |≑| ⋙ rm ▤ 🖂 ☎ – 🔏 70. 🔼 AE ⓪ VISA. ✸ DN **r**
M (bar lunch Saturday) 17.00/23.00 **t.** and a la carte ♦ 8.95 – ☲ 11.75 – **178 rm** 164.00/220.00 **st.**, **7 suites** 330.00/600.00 **st.**

Washington, Curzon St., W1 8DT, ✆ 499 7000, Telex 24540, Fax 495 6172 – |≑| ⋙ rm ▤ 🖂 ☎ – 🔏 80. 🔼 AE ⓪ VISA. ✸ CN **s**
M 20.00 25.00 **st.** ♦ 7.00 – ☲ 10.50 – **169 rm** 141.00/172.00 **st.**, **4 suites** 230.00/385.00 **st.**

Chesterfield, 35 Charles St., W1X 8LX, ✆ 491 2622, Telex 269394, Fax 491 4793 – |≑| ⋙ rm 🖂 ☎ – 🔏 100. 🔼 AE ⓪ VISA. ✸ CN **c**
M 22.50/24.00 **t.** and a la carte ♦ 6.00 – ☲ 9.95 – **109 rm** 115.00/170.00 **st.**, **4 suites** 150.00/300.00 **st.**

Green Park, Half Moon St., W1Y 8BP, ✆ 629 7522, Telex 28856, Fax 491 8971 – |≑| ⋙ rm ▤ rest 🖂 ☎ – 🔏 70. 🔼 AE ⓪ VISA. ✸ CN **a**
M 16.50 **st.** and a la carte ♦ 5.10 – ☲ 9.75 – **161 rm** 104.00/174.00 **st.**

Flemings, 7-12 Half Moon St., W1 7RA, ✆ 499 2964, Telex 27510, Fax 499 1817 – |≑| 🖂 ☎ – 🔏 45. 🔼 AE ⓪ VISA. ✸ CN **z**
M 15.50 **st.** and a la carte ♦ 5.75 – ☲ 10.20 – **132 rm** 97.00/184.00 **st.**, **11 suites** 184.00/230.00 **st.** – SB 130.00 **st.**

London Mews Hilton without rest., 2 Stanhope Row, W1Y 7HE, ✆ 493 7222, Telex 24665, Fax 629 9423 – |≑| ⋙ rm ▤ 🖂 ☎ ⇔ – 🔏 50. 🔼 AE ⓪ VISA. ✸ BP **u**
71 rm ☲ 146.00/174.00 **st.**, **1 suite** 350.00 **st.**

XXXXX ✿ **Oak Room** (at Le Meridien London H.), 21 Piccadilly, W1V 0BH, ✆ 734 8000, Telex 25795, Fax 437 3574, French rest. – ▤. 🔼 AE ⓪ VISA EM **a**
closed Saturday lunch and Sunday – **M** 23.00/44.00 **t.** and a la carte 30.00/40.00 **t.** ♦ 9.50
Spec. Gazpacho de langoustines à la crème de courgettes, Suprême de bar au beurre de truffe, Canard sauce Arabica.

XXXXX **90 Park Lane** (at Grosvenor House H.), Park Lane, W1A 3AA, ✆ 409 1290, Fax 493 3341 – ▤. 🔼 AE ⓪ VISA AM **a**
M 15.50/19.50 **st.** and a la carte ♦ 14.50.

XXXX ✿✿✿ **Le Gavroche** (Roux), 43 Upper Brook St., W1Y 1PF, ✆ 408 0881, Fax 409 0939, French rest. – ▤. 🔼 AE ⓪ VISA AM **c**
closed Saturday, Sunday, 21 December-2 January and Bank Holidays – **M** (booking essential) 30.00/60.00 **st.** and a la carte 41.50/76.10 **st.** ♦ 13.00
Spec. Soufflé suissesse, Tournedos gratiné aux poivres, Sablé aux fraises.

XXXX ✿ **Oriental** (at Dorchester H.), Park Lane, W1A 2HJ, ✆ 629 8888, Telex 887704, Fax 409 0114, Chinese (Canton) rest. – ▤. 🔼 AE ⓪ VISA BN **a**
closed Saturday lunch, Sunday, Christmas Day and New Year's Day – **M** 20.00/30.00 **st.** and a la carte 23.00/31.00 **st.** ♦ 9.00.

XXXX ✿ **Four Seasons** (at Inn on the Park H.) Hamilton Pl., Park Lane, W1A 1AZ, ✆ 499 0888, Telex 22771, Fax 493 1895, French rest. – ▤. 🔼 AE ⓪ VISA BP **a**
M 24.75/44.00 **st.** and a la carte 33.80/53.10 **st.** ♦ 7.45
Spec. Délices du Sud-Ouest, Baron de lapereau, étuvée de carottes au gingembre, Parfait glacé à l'orange et à la cardamome, sauce chocolat.

487

XXXX **Le Soufflé** (at Inter-Continental H.), 1 Hamilton Pl., Hyde Park Corner, W1V 0QY, ℘ 409 3131, Telex 25853, Fax 409 7460 – ⬛ ⟵⟶ ⬛ AE ⑩ VISA
closed Saturday lunch – **M** 25.50/43.00 **t.** and a la carte 33.20/58.20 **t.** ⑂ 9.00.
BP o

XXXX **Le Chateau** (at May Fair Inter-Continental H.), Stratton St., W1A 2AN, ℘ 629 7777, Telex 262526, Fax 629 1459, French rest. – ⬛ ⬛ AE ⑩ VISA
closed Saturday lunch – **M** 20.00/32.50 **t.** and a la carte.
DN z

XXX **Princess Garden,** 8-10 North Audley St., W1Y 1WF, ℘ 493 3223, Fax 491 2655, Chinese (Peking) rest. – ⬛ ⬛ AE ⑩ VISA
closed 1 week Christmas – **M** 20.00/35.00 **t.** and a la carte ⑂ 8.00.
AL z

XXX **Empress Garden,** 15-16 Berkeley St., W1X 5AE, ℘ 493 1381, Chinese (Peking, Canton) rest. – ⬛ ⬛ AE ⑩ VISA
closed 25 and 26 December – **M** 20.00/70.00 **t.** and a la carte ⑂ 7.50.
DN i

XXX **Zen Central,** 20-22 Queen St., W1X 7PJ, ℘ 629 8089, Chinese rest. – ⬛ ℗. ⬛ AE ⑩ VISA
M a la carte approx. 18.50 **t.** ⑂ 6.00.
CN x

XX **Greenhouse,** 27a Hay's Mews, W1X 7RJ, ℘ 499 3331 ⬛. ⬛ AE ⑩ VISA
closed Saturday lunch, Sunday dinner and 24 December-2 January – **M** a la carte 19.50/26.00 **t.** ⑂ 5.00.
BN x

XX **Copper Chimney,** 13 Heddon St., W1R 7LF, ℘ 439 2004, Indian rest. – ⬛. ⬛ AE ⑩ VISA
closed 25 December and 1 January – **M** 18.50 **t.** (dinner) and a la carte 19.00/25.00 **t.**
EM x

XX **Ho-Ho,** 29 Maddox St., W1R 9LD, ℘ 493 1228, Oriental cuisine – ⬛. ⬛ AE ⑩ VISA
closed Sunday and Bank Holidays – **M** 17.80/23.00 **t.** and a la carte.
DL x

XX **Langan's Brasserie,** Stratton St., W1X 5FD, ℘ 491 8822 – ⬛
DN e

XX **Shogun** (at Britannia H.), Adams Row, W1Y 5DE, ℘ 493 1255, Japanese rest. – ⬛. ⬛ AE ⑩ VISA
closed Monday and Christmas-New Year – **M** (dinner only) 30.50 **t.** and a la carte ⑂ 5.00.
BM x

XX **Miyama,** 38 Clarges St., W1Y 7PJ, ℘ 499 2443, Japanese rest. – ⬛. ⬛ AE ⑩ VISA
closed Saturday lunch, Sunday and Bank Holidays – **M** 15.00/32.00 **t.** and a la carte ⑂ 7.00.
CN e

XX **La Seppia,** 8a Mount St., W1, ℘ 499 3385, Italian Seafood rest. – ⬛ AE ⑩ VISA
closed Saturday, Sunday, last 3 weeks August, 10 days at Christmas and Bank Holidays – **M** 20.50 **t.** and a la carte ⑂ 5.50.
BM v

Regent's Park and Marylebone – ✉ NW1/NW6/NW8/W1 – ☎ 071 – Except where otherwise stated see pp. 12 and 13.

🅱 Selfridges Store, Oxford St., W1 ℘ 730 3488.

🏨🏨 **Churchill,** 30 Portman Sq., W1A 4ZX, ℘ 486 5800, Telex 264831, Fax 935 0431, ✂ – ⬛
⬛ ☎ ⬛ – ⬛ 200. ⬛ ⬛ AE ⑩ VISA ✂
M 29.00 **t.** (lunch) and a la carte 22.75/36.70 **t.** ⑂ 4.50 – ⟷ 15.00 – **403 rm** 185.00/200.00 **s.,** **49 suites** 300.00/995.00 **s.**
AJ x

🏨🏨 **Portman Intercontinental,** 22 Portman Sq., W1H 9FL, ℘ 486 5844, Telex 261526, Fax 935 0537, ✂ – ⬛ ✤ rm ⬛ ⬛ ☎ ⑂ ℗ – ⬛ 380. ⬛ AE ⑩ VISA. ✂
M 19.50/26.50 **t.** and a la carte ⑂ 10.50 – ⟷ 12.50 – **262 rm** 153.00/185.00 **t.,** **10 suites** 400.00/700.00 **t.**
AJ o

🏨🏨 **Langham Hilton,** 1 Portland Place, W1N 3AA, ℘ 636 1000, Telex 21113, Fax 323 2340 – ⬛ ✤ rm ⬛ ⬛ ☎ ⑂ ℗ – ⬛ 360. ⬛ AE ⑩ VISA
p. 5 JU e
M 22.00/29.50 **t.** and a la carte ⑂ 7.00 – ⟷ 15.50 – **365 rm** 170.00/255.00, **20 suites** 380.00/1 100.00.

🏨🏨 **Selfridge** (Mt. Charlotte Thistle), 400 Orchard St., W1H 0JS, ℘ 408 2080, Telex 22361, Fax 629 8849 – ⬛ ✤ rm ⬛ ⬛ ☎ – ⬛ 220. ⬛ AE ⑩ VISA. ✂
AK e
M *(closed Saturday lunch and Sunday)* 19.75 **st.** and a la carte ⑂ 5.25 – ⟷ 10.20 – **294 rm** 135.00/160.00 **st.,** **2 suites** 350.00 **st.**

🏨🏨 **Berkshire** (Edwardian), 350 Oxford St., W1N 0BY, ℘ 629 7474, Telex 22270, Fax 629 8156 – ⬛ ✤ rm ⬛ ⬛ ☎ – ⬛ 40. ⬛ AE ⑩ VISA. ✂
BK n
M *(closed Saturday lunch)* 28.00/35.00 **st.** and a la carte ⑂ 6.00 – ⟷ 13.50 – **145 rm** 158.00/245.00 **st.,** **2 suites** 300.00/450.00 **st.**

🏨🏨 **Clifton Ford,** 47 Welbeck St., W1M 8DN, ℘ 486 6600, Telex 22569, Fax 486 7492 – ⬛ ✤ rm ⬛ ☎ – ⬛ 80. ⬛ AE ⑩ VISA
BH a
M 21.50/29.00 **st.** and a la carte ⑂ 5.00 – ⟷ 12.95 – **196 rm** 120.00/135.00 **s.,** **4 suites** 300.00 **s.**

🏨🏨 **Ramada H. London,** 10 Berners St., W1A 3BE, ℘ 636 1629, Telex 25759, Fax 580 3972 – ⬛ ✤ rm ⬛ rest ⬛ ☎ ⑂ – ⬛ 120. ⬛ AE ⑩ VISA
EJ r
M *(closed Saturday lunch)* 13.50/15.75 **st.** and a la carte ⑂ 5.00 – ⟷ 9.75 – **232 rm** 100.00/150.00 **st.,** **3 suites** 300.00/450.00 **st.** – SB (weekends only) 150.00/198.00 **s.**

🏨🏨 **London Regent's Park Hilton,** 18 Lodge Rd, NW8 7JT, ℘ 722 7722, Telex 23101, Fax 483 2408 – ⬛ ⬛ ⬛ ☎ ⑂ – ⬛ 150. ⬛ AE ⑩ VISA. ✂
p. 5 GT v
M *(closed Saturday lunch)* (carving rest.) 20.00/30.00 **st.** and a la carte ⑂ 7.25 – ⟷ 11.30 – **376 rm** 119.50/159.50 **st.,** **1 suite** 191.00/251.00 **st.**

🏨🏨 **Montcalm,** Great Cumberland Pl., W1A 2LF, ℘ 402 4288, Telex 28710, Fax 724 9180 – ⬛ ⬛ rm ⬛ ☎ – ⬛ 60. ⬛ AE ⑩ VISA. ✂
p. 17 EZ x
M *(closed lunch Saturday, Sunday and Bank Holidays)* 17.75/21.95 **t.** and a la carte ⑂ 6.00 – ⟷ 12.00 – **101 rm** 167.00/215.00 **st.,** **14 suites** 270.00/600.00 **st.**

🏨🏨 **St. George's** (Forte), Langham Pl., W1N 8QS, ℰ 580 0111, Fax 436 7997, ≼ – 🛗 ⅙⊁ rm
🔳 rest 🔟 ☎ – 🕍 35. 🔼 🕮 ① 𝗩𝗜𝗦𝗔 p. 5 JU **a**
M *(closed lunch Saturday and Sunday)* 15.50 **st.** and a la carte ┆ 7.00 – ⊒ 10.95 – **83 rm**
95.00/120.00 **st.**, **3 suites** 200.00 **st.** – SB (weekends only) 118.00 **st.**

🏨🏨 **Holiday Inn,** 134 George St., W1H 6DN, ℰ 723 1277, Telex 27983, Fax 402 0666, ℐ𝟝, ≋,
🔳 – 🛗 ⅙⊁ rm 🔳 🔟 ☎ ⅊ Ⓟ – 🕍 120. 🔼 🕮 ① 𝗩𝗜𝗦𝗔 ⚘ p. 17 EZ **i**
M 15.00/25.00 **st.** and a la carte ┆ 7.40 – ⊒ 11.25 – **239 rm** 152.00/180.00 **st.**, **2 suites**
495.00/595.00 **st.**

🏨🏨 **Forte Crest,** Carburton St., W1P 8EE, ℰ 388 2300, Fax 387 2806 – 🛗 🔳 rest 🔟 ☎ Ⓟ –
🕍 500. 🔼 🕮 ① 𝗩𝗜𝗦𝗔 p. 5 JU **i**
M 7.50/14.50 **st.** and a la carte ┆ 5.00 – ⊒ 8.25 – **312 rm** 95.00/105.00 **st.**, **5 suites**
150.00/175.00 **st.** – SB (weekends only) 98.00 **st.**

🏨 **Dorset Square,** 39-40 Dorset Sq., NW1 6QN, ℰ 723 7874, Telex 263964, Fax 724 3328,
« Attractively furnished Regency town houses » – 🛗 🔳 🔟 ☎. 🔼 🕮 𝗩𝗜𝗦𝗔 ⚘
M *(closed Sunday lunch and Saturday)* 27.00 **t.** ┆ 14.95 – ⊒ 9.50 – **37 rm** 90.00/
165.00 **st.** p. 5 HU **s**

🏨 **Durrants,** 26-32 George St., W1H 6BJ, ℰ 935 8131, Telex 894919, Fax 487 5510,
« Converted Georgian houses with Regency facade » – 🛗 🔟 ☎ – 🕍 40. 🔼 🕮 𝗩𝗜𝗦𝗔
⚘ AH **e**
M 25.00/35.00 **st.** and a la carte ┆ 4.50 – ⊒ 8.25 – **93 rm** 58.00/135.00 **st.**, **3 suites**
136.00/185.00 **st.**

🏨 Londoner, 57-59 Welbeck St., W1M 8HS, ℰ 935 4442, Telex 894630, Fax 487 3782 – 🛗
⅙⊁ rm 🔟 ☎ – 🕍 90 BJ **c**
144 rm.

🏨 **Rathbone,** Rathbone St., W1P 1AJ, ℰ 636 2001, Telex 28728, Fax 636 3882 – 🛗 ⅙⊁ rm
🔳 🔟 ☎ p. 6 KU **x**
M *(closed Sunday lunch, Saturday and Bank Holidays)* 12.50/15.50 **st.** and a la carte ┆ 5.60
– ⊒ 9.50 – **68 rm** 95.00/140.00 **st.**, **4 suites** 150.00/185.00 **st.**

🏨 Langham Court, 31-35 Langham St., W1N 5RE, ℰ 436 6622, Telex 21331, Fax 436 2303 –
🛗 🔟 ☎ – 🕍 50 JU **z**
56 rm.

🏨 **Mostyn,** 4 Bryanston St., W1H 0DE, ℰ 935 2361, Fax 487 2759 – 🛗 🔟 ☎ – 🕍 150. 🔼
🕮 ① 𝗩𝗜𝗦𝗔. ⚘ AK **i**
M 25.00 **st.** (lunch) and a la carte 16.00/22.50 **st.** ┆ 5.00 – ⊒ 8.75 – **118 rm** 92.00/124.00 **st.**,
3 suites 160.00/200.00 **st.**

🏨 Harewood, Harewood Row, NW1 6SE, ℰ 262 2707, Telex 297225, Fax 262 2975 – 🛗 ⅙⊁ rm
🔳 rest 🔟 ☎ – 🕍 100 p. 5 HU **x**
93 rm.

❌❌❌❌ ✿✿ **Chez Nico** (Ladenis), 35 Great Portland St., W1N 5DD, ℰ 436 8846, French rest. – 🔳.
🔼 ① 𝗩𝗜𝗦𝗔 DJ **c**
closed Bank Holiday lunch, Saturday, Sunday, Easter and 10 days Christmas – **M** (booking
essential) 27.75/60.00 **st.**
Spec. Grillade de St. Jacques, Loup de mer au fenouil, Rouget au parfum de romarin purée au
basilic.

❌❌❌ **Rue St. Jacques,** 5 Charlotte St., W1P 1HD, ℰ 637 0222, French rest. – 🔳. 🔼 🕮 ① 𝗩𝗜𝗦𝗔
closed Saturday lunch, Sunday, Easter, Christmas-New Year and Bank Holidays –
M 25.00/38.00 **t.** ┆ 6.25. p. 6 KU **c**

❌❌❌ **Martin's,** 239 Baker St., NW1 6XE, ℰ 935 3130 – 🔳. 🔼 🕮 ① 𝗩𝗜𝗦𝗔 p. 5 HU **u**
closed Saturday, Sunday, Christmas and Bank Holidays – **M** a la carte 27.00/44.50 **t.** ┆ 6.75.

❌❌❌ Odins, 27 Devonshire St., W1N 1RJ, ℰ 935 7296 p. 5 IU **n**

❌❌ **Masako,** 6-8 St. Christopher's Pl., W1M 5HB, ℰ 935 1579, Japanese rest. BJ **e**
closed Sunday, 4 May, 31 August, Christmas and New Year – **M** 35.00/60.00 **t.** and a la carte.

❌❌ **Gaylord,** 79-81 Mortimer St., W1N 7TB, ℰ 580 3615, Indian and Pakistani rest. – 🔳. 🔼
🕮 ① 𝗩𝗜𝗦𝗔 p. 6 KU **o**
M 11.50/15.00 **t.** and a la carte ┆ 3.50.

❌❌ Maroush III, 62 Seymour St., W1H 5AF, ℰ 724 5024, Lebanese rest. – 🔳 EZ **a**

❌❌ **Stephen Bull,** 5-7 Blandford St., W1H 3AA, ℰ 486 9696 – 🔼 𝗩𝗜𝗦𝗔 AH **a**
closed Saturday lunch, Sunday and 23 December-2 January – **M** a la carte approx. 22.50 **t.**
┆ 5.00.

❌❌ Mon, (at Cumberland H.), Marble Arch, W1A 4RF, ℰ 262 6528, Japanese rest. – 🔳AK **n**

❌❌ **The Restaurant,** Jason Court, 76 Wigmore St., W1H 9DQ, ℰ 224 2992 – 🔳. 🔼 🕮 𝗩𝗜𝗦𝗔
closed Saturday lunch, Sunday, 1 week August, 2 weeks Christmas-New Year and Bank Holidays
– **M** 16.00/18.00 **t.** (lunch) and a la carte ┆ 4.50. BJ **a**

❌❌ **Asuka,** Berkeley Arcade, 209a Baker St., NW1 6AB, ℰ 486 5026, Fax 262 1456, Japanese
rest. – 🔼 🕮 ① 𝗩𝗜𝗦𝗔 p. 5 HU **u**
closed Saturday lunch, Sunday, and Bank Holidays – **M** 15.50/55.00 **st.** and a la carte ┆ 6.00.

❌❌ Le P'tit Montmartre, 15-17 Marylebone Lane, W1M 5FE, ℰ 935 9226, French rest. – 🔳.
🔼 🕮 ① 𝗩𝗜𝗦𝗔 BJ **a**
closed Saturday lunch, Sunday, Easter, 4 days Christmas and Bank Holidays – **M** 16.95 **t.** and
a la carte ┆ 4.50.

XX **Fontana Amorosa,** 1 Blenheim Terr., NW8 0EH, ☎ 328 5014, Italian rest. – 🔌 AE ⓪ VISA
closed Monday lunch, Sunday, mid August-mid September and Bank Holidays – **M** a la carte
17.90/27.20 **t.**   p. 4 FS **s**

XX **Tino's,** 128 Allitsen Rd, NW8 7AU, ☎ 586 6264 – 🔌 AE VISA   p. 5 GT **u**
closed 17 April, 25 December and 1 January – **M** 13.50 **t.** (lunch) and a la carte 15.30/21.35 **t.**
 4.95.

XX **La Loggia,** 68 Edgware Rd, W2 2EG, ☎ 723 0554, Italian rest. – 🍽. 🔌 AE ⓪
VISA   p. 17 EZ **a**
closed Saturday lunch, Sunday and Bank Holidays – **M** a la carte 18.00/27.70 **t.** 4.00.

St. James's – ✉ W1/SW1/WC2 – ☎ 071 – pp. 12 and 13.

🏨🏨🏨 **Ritz,** Piccadilly, W1V 9DG, ☎ 493 8181, Telex 267200, Fax 493 2687, « Elegant restaurant
in Louis XV style » – 🛗 ⌷ TV ☎. 🔌 AE ⓪ VISA. ✂   DN **n**
M 26.50/35.00 **st.** and a la carte 32.00/40.00 **st.** 7.00 – 🍽 13.50 – **115 rm** 190.00/265.00 **st.**,
14 suites 505.00/640.00 st.

🏨🏨 **Dukes** ⑤, 35 St. James's Pl., SW1A 1NY, ☎ 491 4840, Telex 28283, Fax 493 1264 – 🛗
🍽 rest TV ☎ – 🔏 30. 🔌 AE ⓪ VISA. ✂   EP **x**
M *(closed Saturday lunch)* 19.95/28.50 **t.** and a la carte 29.35/60.40 **t.** – 🍽 11.75 – **36 rm**
180.00/215.00 **t.**, **26 suites** 420.00 **t.**

🏨🏨 **22 Jermyn Street,** 22 Jermyn St., SW1Y 6HL, ☎ 734 2353, Fax 734 0750 – 🛗 TV ☎. 🔌
AE ⓪ VISA. ✂   FM **e**
M (room service only) a la carte 18.50/23.50 **t.** 5.50 – 🍽 10.50 – **5 rm** 165.00 **st.**, **13 suites**
230.00/275.00 **st.**

🏨🏨 Stafford ⑤, 16-18 St. James's Pl., SW1A 1NJ, ☎ 493 0111, Telex 28602, Fax 493 7121 –
🛗 🍽 rest TV ☎ – 🔏 40   DN **u**
56 rm, 6 suites.

🏨🏨 **Forte Crest,** 81 Jermyn St., SW1Y 6JF, ☎ 930 2111, Fax 839 2125 – 🛗 ✂ rm 🍽 rest TV
☎ ⌷ – 🔏 90. 🔌 AE ⓪ VISA. ✂   EN **i**
M a la carte 22.50/40.00 **st.** – 🍽 8.50 – **255 rm** 135.00/160.00 **st.** – SB (weekends only)
118.00 **st.**

🏨 **Hospitality Inn Piccadilly** (Mt. Charlotte Thistle), 31-39 Coventry St., W1V 8EL, ☎ 930 4033,
Telex 8950058, Fax 925 2586 – 🛗 ✂ TV ☎. 🔌 AE ⓪ VISA. ✂   FGM **a**
M (room service only) – 🍽 9.50 – **92 rm** 107.00/120.00 **st.**

🏨 **Royal Trafalgar Thistle** (Mt. Charlotte Thistle), Whitcomb St., WC2H 7HG, ☎ 930 4477,
Telex 298564, Fax 925 2149 – 🛗 ✂ rm TV ☎. 🔌 AE ⓪ VISA. ✂   GM **r**
M 15.75 **st.** and a la carte 5.75 – 🍽 9.75 – **108 rm** 94.00/123.00 **st.**

XXX ❀ **Suntory,** 72-73 St. James's St., SW1A 1PH, ☎ 409 0201, Fax 499 7993, Japanese rest.
– 🍽. 🔌 AE ⓪ VISA   EP **z**
closed Sunday, New Year and Bank Holidays – **M** 22.00/64.00 **st.** and a la carte 30.80/51.50 **st.**
 7.00
Spec. Teppan-Yaki, Shabu-Shabu, Sashimi.

XX **Le Caprice,** Arlington House, Arlington St., SW1A 1RT, ☎ 629 2239, Fax 493 9040 – 🍽.
🔌 AE ⓪ VISA   DN **c**
closed 24 December-1 January – **M** a la carte 17.50/32.50 **t.** 5.75.

XX **Green's,** 36 Duke St. St. James's, SW1Y 6DF, ☎ 930 4566, Fax 930 1383, English rest. –
🍽. 🔌 AE ⓪ VISA   EN **n**
closed Sunday dinner, Christmas, New Year and Bank Holidays – **M** a la carte 16.25/46.50 **t.**

Soho – ✉ W1/WC2 – ☎ 071 – pp. 12 and 13.

🏨🏨 **Hampshire** (Edwardian), Leicester Sq., WC2H 7LH, ☎ 839 9399, Telex 914848, Fax 930 8122
– 🛗 🍽 TV ☎ – 🔏 80. 🔌 AE ⓪ VISA. ✂   GM **s**
M 17.50/24.00 **st.** and a la carte 6.00 – 🍽 13.00 – **118 rm** 198.00/237.00 **st.**, **5 suites**
270.00/648.00 **st.**

XXX **Lindsay House,** 21 Romilly St., W1V 5TG, ☎ 439 0450, Fax 581 2848 – 🍽. 🔌 AE ⓪ VISA GL **i**
closed 25 and 26 December – **M** 14.75 **t.** (lunch) and a la carte 29.50/34.40 **t.** 4.50.

XXX **Au Jardin des Gourmets,** 5 Greek St., W1V 5LA, ☎ 437 1816, Fax 437 0043, French rest.
– 🍽. 🔌 AE ⓪ VISA   GJ **a**
closed Saturday lunch, Sunday, Easter, Christmas and Bank Holidays – **M** (booking essential)
17.95/18.50 **t.** and a la carte 3.75.

XXX **Red Fort,** 77 Dean St., W1V 5HA, ☎ 437 2525, Indian rest. – 🍽. 🔌 AE ⓪ VISA FJK **r**
closed Christmas Day – **M** a la carte 15.90/25.20 **st.**

XXX **La Bastide,** 50 Greek St., W1V 5LQ, ☎ 734 3300, French rest. – 🔌 AE ⓪ VISA GK **e**
closed Saturday lunch, Sunday, Christmas-New Year and Bank Holidays – **M** 23.00 **t.** (lunch)
and a la carte 24.70/30.90 **t.** 7.00.

XX ❀ **Sutherlands,** 45 Lexington St., W1R 3LG, ☎ 434 3401, Fax 287 2997 – 🍽. 🔌 AE VISA
closed Saturday lunch, Sunday and Bank Holidays – **M** 24.00/39.50 **t.** 5.75   EK **u**
Spec. Terrine of scallops, oysters and leeks with a Chardonnay and saffron stock, Baked sea bass
with braised endive and a dark fennel sauce, Tournedos of beef wrapped in Parma ham with
a rich thyme sauce.

XX **L'Escargot,** 48 Greek St., W1V 5LQ, ℰ 437 2679, Fax 437 0790, French rest. – 🗏 🔜 AE ⓪ VISA
closed Saturday lunch, Sunday, Easter, Christmas and Bank Holidays – **M** (booking essential)
12.50 **t.** (dinner) and a la carte 15.25/24.00 **t.** 👌 4.40.   GK **e**

XX **L'Hippocampe,** 63 Frith St., W1V 5TA, ℰ 734 4545, French Seafood rest. – 🗏 🔜 AE ⓪ VISA
closed Saturday lunch, Sunday, Easter, Christmas-New Year and Bank Holiday Saturdays –
M 16.50 **t.** and a la carte 👌 4.75.   FK **z**

XX **Ming,** 35-36 Greek St., W1V 5LN, ℰ 734 2721, Chinese rest. – 🔜 AE ⓪ VISA   GK **c**
closed Sunday and 25-26 December – **M** 13.00/19.00 **t.** and a la carte 👌 6.00.

XX **Gopal's,** 12 Bateman St., W1V 5TD, ℰ 434 0840, Indian rest. – 🗏. 🔜 AE ⓪ VISA GK **e**
M 10.50/15.00 **t.** and a la carte 👌 3.25.

XX **Kaya,** 22-25 Dean St., W1V 5AL, ℰ 437 6630, Korean rest. – 🗏   FJ **i**

XX **Gay Hussar,** 2 Greek St., W1V 6NB, ℰ 437 0973, Hungarian rest. – 🗏. AE   GJ **c**
closed Sunday – **M** 15.00 **t.** (lunch) and a la carte 16.20/23.50 **st.** 👌 3.00.

XX **Gallery Rendez-Vous,** 53-55 Beak St., W1R 3LF, ℰ 734 0455, Chinese (Peking) rest. – 🗏.
🔜 AE ⓪ VISA – **M** 12.50/38.00 **t.** and a la carte 👌 5.00.   EL **a**

X **Sri Siam,** 14 Old Compton St., W1V 5PE, ℰ 434 3544, Thai rest. – 🗏. 🔜 AE ⓪
GK **r**
closed Sunday lunch, 24 to 26 December and 1 January – **M** 9.50/15.50 **t.** and a la carte 👌 3.95.

X **Alastair Little,** 49 Frith St., W1V 5TE, ℰ 734 5183 – 🔜 VISA   FK **o**
closed Saturday lunch, Sunday and Bank Holidays – **M** 23.00 **t.** (lunch) and a la carte
28.00/39.00 **t.**

Strand and Covent Garden – ✉ WC2 - ☎ 071 - p. 17.

🏨 **Savoy,** Strand, WC2R 0EU, ℰ 836 4343, Telex 24234, Fax 240 6040 – 🛗 ⇔ rm 🗏 TV ☎
⇔ – 🔜 450. 🔜 AE ⓪ VISA. ⇔   DEY **a**
M Grill *(closed Saturday lunch, Sunday, 5 and 31 August and Bank Holidays)* 29.75 **t.** (dinner)
and a la carte 29.60/41.45 **t.** 👌 5.35 – **River** 24.95/38.50 **st.** and a la carte 35.50/45.10 **st.** 👌 5.35
– 🖵 15.75 – **150 rm** 180.00/275.00 **st.**, **50 suites** 300.00/650.00 **st.** – SB (weekends only)
310.00/530.00 **st.**

🏨 **Howard,** 12 Temple Pl., WC2R 2PR, ℰ 836 3555, Telex 268047, Fax 379 4547 – 🛗 🗏 TV
☎ – 🔜 100. 🔜 AE ⓪ VISA   EX **e**
M 15.00/25.00 **st.** and a la carte 👌 4.50 – 🖵 13.85 – **133 rm** 200.00/226.00 **st.**, **2 suites**
270.00/465.00 **st.**

🏨 **Waldorf** (Forte), Aldwych, WC2B 4DD, ℰ 836 2400, Telex 24574, Fax 836 7244 – 🛗 ⇔ rm
TV ☎ – 🔜 400. 🔜 AE ⓪ VISA – **M** 15.50/18.00 **st.** and a la carte 👌 7.95 – 🖵 11.00 – **291 rm** 125.00/155.00 **st.**, **19 suites**
240.00/425.00 **st.** – SB (weekends only) 108.00/278.00 **st.**   EX **x**

XXXX **Boulestin,** 1a Henrietta St., WC2E 8PS, ℰ 836 7061, Fax 836 1283, French rest. – 🗏. 🔜
AE ⓪ VISA – *closed Saturday lunch, Sunday, last 2 weeks August and Bank Holidays* – **M** 18.75
st. (lunch) and a la carte 27.50/32.00 **st.** 👌 6.50.   DX **a**

XXX **Now and Zen,** 4a Upper St. Martin's Lane, WC2H 9EA, ℰ 497 0376, Chinese rest. – 🗏
closed 3 days at Christmas – **M** a la carte 25.30/50.30 **t.**   DX **x**

XXX **Simpson's-in-the-Strand,** 100 Strand, WC2R 0EW, ℰ 836 9112, Fax 836 1381, English
rest. – 🗏. 🔜 AE ⓪ VISA   EX **o**
closed Sunday and Bank Holidays – **M** (booking essential) 18.50 **t.** and a la carte 👌 4.95.

XXX **Ivy,** 1 West St., WC2H 9NE, ℰ 836 4751, Fax 497 3644 – 🗏. 🔜 AE ⓪ VISA   GK **z**
closed 25 and 26 December – **M** a la carte 19.00/32.25 **t.** 👌 5.75.

XX **Orso,** 27 Wellington St., WC2E 7DA, ℰ 240 5269, Fax 497 2148, Italian rest. – 🗏 EX **z**
closed 25 and 26 December – **M** (booking essential) a la carte 19.00/23.50 **t.** 👌 5.00.

XX **Gritti,** 11 Upper St. Martin's Lane, WC2, ℰ 836 5121, Italian rest. – 🗏. 🔜 AE ⓪ VISA
closed Sunday and Bank Holidays – **M** 14.75/20.75 **t.** and a la carte 👌 8.50.   DX **e**

XX **Sheekey's,** 28-32 St. Martin's Court, WC2N 4AL, ℰ 240 2565, Seafood – 🗏. 🔜 AE ⓪
VISA
DX **v**
closed Saturday lunch, Sunday and Bank Holidays – **M** 19.00/25.00 **t.** and a la carte 👌 4.50.

Victoria – ✉ SW1 - ☎ 071 - Except where otherwise stated see p. 16.
🗎 Victoria Station Forecourt ℰ 730 3488.

🏨 **St. James Court,** Buckingham Gate, SW1E 6AF, ℰ 834 6655, Telex 938075, Fax 630 7587,
🛁, ⇔ – 🛗 ⇔ rm 🗏 rest TV ☎ – 🔜 180. 🔜 AE ⓪ VISA. ⇔   CX **i**
M (see **Auberge de Provence** and **Inn of Happiness** below) – 🖵 12.50 – **363 rm**
150.00/190.00 **s.**, **27 suites** 250.00/700.00 **s.**

🏨 **Royal Horseguards Thistle** (Mt. Charlotte Thistle), 2 Whitehall Court, SW1A 2EJ,
ℰ 839 3400, Telex 917096, Fax 925 2263 – 🛗 ⇔ rm 🗏 TV ☎ – 🔜 60. 🔜 AE ⓪ VISA. ⇔
M *(closed Saturday, Sunday and Bank Holidays)* 17.50/22.45 **st.** and a la carte 👌 7.50 – 🖵
10.25 – **368 rm** 99.00/110.00 **st.**, **8 suites** 385.00 **st.**   p. 10 LX **a**

🏨 **Stakis St. Ermin's,** 2 Caxton St., SW1H 0QW, ℰ 222 7888, Telex 917731, Fax 222 6914
– 🛗 ⇔ rm 🗏 rest TV ☎ – 🔜 150. 🔜 AE ⓪ VISA   CX **a**
M (carving rest.) 15.00/17.50 **st.** and a la carte 👌 5.95 – 🖵 9.75 – **282 rm** 127.60/161.70 **st.**,
8 suites 295.00 **st.** – SB (weekends only) 92.00/104.00 **st.**

Goring, 15 Beeston Pl., Grosvenor Gdns, SW1W 0JW, ✆ 834 8211, Telex 919166, Fax 834 4393 – 🛗 📺 ☎ – 🛄 50. 🔼 🆎 ⓞ 𝐕𝐈𝐒𝐀. ⛿ BX e
M 19.50/23.00 **t.** and a la carte 🍷 6.50 – ⌾ 10.50 – **80 rm** 120.00/175.00 **st.**, **4 suites** 205.00 **st.**

Royal Westminster Thistle (Mt. Charlotte Thistle), 49 Buckingham Palace Rd, SW1W 0QT, ✆ 834 1821, Telex 916821, Fax 931 7542 – 🛗 ⇆ rm 🔲 📺 ☎ – 🛄 150. 🔼 🆎 ⓞ 𝐕𝐈𝐒𝐀. ⛿ BX z
⌾ 9.95 – **134 rm** 118.00/180.00 **st.**

Grosvenor (Mt. Charlotte Thistle), 101 Buckingham Palace Rd, SW1W 0SJ, ✆ 834 9494, Telex 916006, Fax 630 1978 – 🛗 ⇆ rm 🔲 rest 📺 ☎ – 🛄 150. 🔼 🆎 ⓞ 𝐕𝐈𝐒𝐀. ⛿ BX e
M (carving rest.) 15.35 **st.** and a la carte 🍷 4.80 – ⌾ 8.75 – **363 rm** 98.00/190.00 **st.**, **3 suites** 245.00/325.00 **st.**

Rubens, 39-41 Buckingham Palace Rd, SW1W 0PS, ✆ 834 6600, Telex 916577, Fax 828 5401 – 🛗 ⇆ rm 🔲 rest 📺 ☎ – 🛄 60. 🔼 🆎 ⓞ 𝐕𝐈𝐒𝐀. ⛿ BX n
M (buffet lunch Saturday and Sunday) 14.20/15.75 **st.** and a la carte – ⌾ 9.40 – **189 rm** 97.00/215.00 **st.**

Scandic Crown, 2 Bridge Pl., SW1V 0QA, ✆ 834 8123, Telex 914973, Fax 828 1099, 𝑓₆, ⇆₆, 🔲 – 🛗 ⇆ rm 🔲 📺 ☎ – 🛄 200. 🔼 🆎 ⓞ 𝐕𝐈𝐒𝐀. ⛿ BY i
M 16.75 **st.** (lunch) and a la carte 14.75/23.70 **st.** 🍷 5.00 – ⌾ 8.50 – **205 rm** 107.00/137.50 **st.**, **5 suites** 219.50 **st.**

Ebury Court, 26 Ebury St., SW1W 0LU, ✆ 730 8147, Fax 823 5966 – 🛗 📺 ☎. 🔼 🆎 ⓞ 𝐕𝐈𝐒𝐀 AX i
closed 2 weeks Christmas-New Year – **M** (closed Saturday lunch) 16.50 **t.** 🍷 4.00 – **45 rm** ⌾ 70.00/150.00 **st.**

XXX **Inn of Happiness** (at St. James Court H.), Buckingham Gate, SW1E 6AF, ✆ 821 1931, Telex 938075, Fax 630 7587, Chinese rest. – 🔲. 🔼 🆎 ⓞ 𝐕𝐈𝐒𝐀 CX i
closed lunch Saturday and Bank Holidays – **M** 20.00/30.00 **t.** and a la carte.

XXX **Auberge de Provence** (at St. James Court H.), Buckingham Gate, SW1E 6AF, ✆ 821 1899, Telex 938075, Fax 630 7587, French rest. – 🔲. 🔼 🆎 ⓞ 𝐕𝐈𝐒𝐀 CX i
closed Saturday lunch, Sunday and Bank Holidays – **M** 25.00/30.00 **t.** and a la carte 🍷 5.00.

XXX **Santini,** 29 Ebury St., SW1W 0NZ, ✆ 730 4094, Fax 730 0544, Italian rest. – 🔲. 🔼 🆎 ⓞ 𝐕𝐈𝐒𝐀 ABX v
closed Saturday and Sunday lunch and Bank Holidays – **M** 18.25 **t.** (lunch) and a la carte 24.60/52.25 **t.**

XXX **L'Incontro,** 87 Pimlico Rd, SW1W 8PH, ✆ 730 6327, Fax 730 5062, Italian rest. – 🔲. 🔼 🆎 𝐕𝐈𝐒𝐀 p. 15 FT u
closed Sunday lunch and Bank Holidays – **M** 18.25 **t.** (lunch) and a la carte 23.55/45.65 **t.**

XX **Green's,** Marsham Court, Marsham St., SW1P 4JY, ✆ 834 9552, English rest. – 🔲. 🔼 🆎 ⓞ 𝐕𝐈𝐒𝐀 p. 10 LZ z
closed Sunday lunch, Saturday and Bank Holidays – **M** (booking essential) a la carte 17.50/79.50 **t.**

XX **Ken Lo's Memories of China,** 67-69 Ebury St., SW1W 0NZ, ✆ 730 7734, Chinese rest. – 🔲. 🔼 🆎 ⓞ 𝐕𝐈𝐒𝐀 AY u
closed Sunday and Bank Holidays – **M** 20.00/40.00 **t.** and a la carte.

XX **Ciboure,** 21 Eccleston St., SW1W 9LX, ✆ 730 2505, French rest. – 🔲. 🔼 🆎 ⓞ 𝐕𝐈𝐒𝐀 AY z
closed Saturday lunch, Sunday dinner and 2 August-2 September – **M** 13.00/15.00 **t.**

XX **Simply Nico,** 48a Rochester Row, SW1P 1JU, ✆ 630 8061 – 🔼 ⓞ 𝐕𝐈𝐒𝐀 CY a
closed lunch Saturday and Bank Holidays, Sunday, 4 days at Easter and 10 days at Christmas – **M** (booking essential) 27.00/29.00 **st.**

XX **Kym's,** 70-71 Wilton Rd, SW1V 1DE, ✆ 828 8931, Chinese (Szechuan, Hunan) rest. – 🔲. 🔼 🆎 ⓞ 𝐕𝐈𝐒𝐀 BY v
M 7.50/12.50 **t.** and a la carte 🍷 4.00.

XX **Hunan,** 51 Pimlico Rd, SW1W 8NE, ✆ 730 5712, Chinese (Hunan) rest. – 🔼 🆎 𝐕𝐈𝐒𝐀 p. 9 IZ a
M 10.00/18.50 **t.** and a la carte 🍷 4.00.

XX **Eatons,** 49 Elizabeth St., SW1W 9PP, ✆ 730 0074 – 🔼 🆎 ⓞ 𝐕𝐈𝐒𝐀 AY a
closed Saturday, Sunday and Bank Holidays – **M** 11.80 **s.** and a la carte 🍷 4.40.

XX **L'Amico,** 44 Horseferry Rd, SW1P 2AF, ✆ 222 4680, Italian rest. – 🔼 🆎 ⓞ 𝐕𝐈𝐒𝐀 p. 10 LY e
closed Saturday and Sunday – **M** (booking essential) a la carte 18.00/32.60 **st.** 🍷 4.40.

XX **Gran Paradiso,** 52 Wilton Rd, SW1V 1DE, ✆ 828 5818, Italian rest. – 🔼 🆎 ⓞ 𝐕𝐈𝐒𝐀 BY a
closed Saturday lunch, Sunday, last 2 weeks August and Bank Holidays – **M** a la carte 16.00/20.80 **t.** 🍷 2.80.

X **Tate Gallery,** Tate Gallery, Millbank, SW1P 4RG, ✆ 834 6754, English rest., « Rex Whistler murals » – 🔲. 🔼 𝐕𝐈𝐒𝐀 p. 10 LZ c
closed Sunday, 17 April, 1 May, 24 to 26 December and 1 January – **M** (lunch only) (booking essential) a la carte 16.80/22.20 **t.** 🍷 5.40.

X **La Poule au Pot,** 231 Ebury St., SW1W 8UT, ✆ 730 7763, French rest.
closed Saturday lunch and Sunday – **M** 12.25/25.00 **st.** and a la carte. p. 9 IZ n

Bray-on-Thames Berks W : 34 m. by M 4 (junction 8-9) and A 308 404 R 29 – pop. 9 427
– ⊠ ✆ 0628 Maidenhead

ⅩⅩⅩⅩ ✿✿✿ **Waterside Inn** (Roux), Ferry Rd, SL6 2AT, ✆ 20691, Fax 784710, French rest.,
« ≼ Thames-side setting », 🐟 – ▤ 🄿 ⚠ AE ① VISA
closed 26 December - 7 February and Bank Holidays – **M** *(closed Tuesday lunch, Sunday dinner
from 3rd weekend October - 2nd weekend April and Monday)* 26.50/52.00 **st.** and a la carte
43.10/59.70 **st.** ⅟ 10.50
Spec. Tronçonnettes de homard poêlées minute au porto blanc, Filets de lapereau grillés aux
marrons glacés, Soufflé chaud aux framboises (summer).

Reading

at Shinfield Berks. W : 43 m. on A 327 403 404 Q 29 – pop. 194 727 – ✆ 0734.

ⅩⅩⅩ ✿✿ **L'Ortolan** (Burton-Race), The Old Vicarage, Church Lane, RG2 9BY, ✆ 883783,
Fax 885391, French rest., 🐟 – 🄿 ⚠ AE ① VISA
closed Sunday dinner, Monday, last 2 weeks August and last 2 weeks September –
M 29.50/55.00 **t.**
Spec. Blancs de rouget grillés, crème de romarin et pâtes fraîches (Apr-Oct), Pigeonneau rôti au
miel, petits oignons glacés et girolles (June-Oct), Tarte soufflée à la poire rosemonde (June-Sept).

Oxford

at Great Milton Oxon NW : 49 m. by M 40 (junction 7) and A 329 403 404 Q 28 – ⊠ ✆ 0844
Great Milton :

🏨 ✿✿ **Le Manoir aux Quat'Saisons** (Blanc) 🌸, Church St., OX9 7PD, ✆ 278881,
Telex 837552, Fax 278847, ≼, « Part 15C and 16C manor house », 🔾 heated, 🐟, park, 🎾
– ⅍ rest ▤ ☎ ﻻ 🄿 – 🕍 40. ⚠ AE ① VISA. ⅙
M 26.50/59.50 **st.** and a la carte 58.50/75.00 **st.** ⅟ 11.50 – ⌇ 14.50 – **16 rm** 165.00/275.00 **st.**,
3 suites 375.00 **st.** – SB (weekends only) 255.00/340.00 **st.**
Spec. Queue de Homard rôtie et bavarois de tomates à la vinaigrette de corail, Epaule de lapin
au pinot noir et filet rôti dans sa panoufle à l'estragon, Le "café crème".

BIRMINGHAM West Midlands 403 404 O 26 – pop. 1 013 995 – ECD : Wednesday – ✆ 021.

See : Museum and Art Gallery★★ JZ **M2** – Barber Institute of fine Arts★★ (at Birmingham
University) EX – Museum of Science and Industry★ JY **M3** – Cathedral of St. Philip (stained
glass portrayals★) KYZ. Envir. : Aston Hall ★★ FV **M**.

🏌 Cocks Moor Woods, Alcester Rd, South, King's Heath ✆ 444 3584, S : 6 ½ m. by A 435 FX
– 🏌 Edgbaston, Church Rd ✆ 454 1736, S : 1 m. FX – 🏌 Warley, Lightwoods Hill, ✆ 429 2440,
W : 5 m. by A 456.

✈ Birmingham Airport : ✆ 767 7145, E : 6 ½ m. by A 45.

🛈 2 City Arcade, ✆ 643 2514, Fax 616 1038 – Convention Visitor Bureau, National Exhibition Centre
✆ 780 4321, Fax 780 4260 – Birmingham Airport ✆ 767 5511.

London 122 – Bristol 91 – Liverpool 103 – Manchester 86 – Nottingham 50.

Plans on following pages

🏨 **Hyatt Regency,** 2 Bridge St., B1 2JZ, ✆ 643 1234, Telex 335097, Fax 616 2323, ≼, Ⅰ₆, ≋,
🔲 – 🛗 ⅍ rm ▤ ▤ ☎ – 🕍 180. ⚠ AE ① VISA   JZ **a**
M a la carte 10.50/19.50 **st.** ⅟ 4.00 – ⌇ 11.00 – **315 rm** 110.00 **st.**, **4 suites** 180.00/650.00 **st.**

🏨 **Swallow,** 12 Hagley Rd, B16 8SJ, ✆ 452 1144, Telex 333806, Fax 456 3442, Ⅰ₆, ≋, 🔲
– 🛗 ⅍ rm ▤ ☎ ﻻ 🄿 – 🕍 25. ⚠ ① VISA   FX **c**
M – Langtrys a la carte 28.50/39.50 **st.** ⅟ 7.75 – (see also **Sir Edward Elgar's** below) – **94 rm**
⌇ 97.50/120.00 **st.**, **4 suites** 195.00/250.00 **st.** – SB (weekends only) 132.60 **st.**

🏨 **Plough and Harrow** (Forte), 135 Hagley Rd, Edgbaston, B16 8LS, ✆ 454 4111,
Telex 338074, Fax 454 1868, ≋, 🐟 – 🛗 ⅍ rm ▤ ☎ 🄿 – 🕍 60. ⚠ AE ① VISA ⅙
M *(closed lunch Bank Holidays)* 17.00/18.00 **t.** and a la carte – ⌇ 10.25 – **41 rm** 75.00/95.00 **st.**,
3 suites 120.00/140.00 **st.** – SB (weekends only) 118.00 **st.**   EX **a**

🏨 **Holiday Inn,** Central Sq., Holliday St., B1 1HH, ✆ 631 2000, Telex 337272, Fax 643 9018,
Ⅰ₆, ≋, 🔲 – 🛗 ⅍ rm ▤ ☎ ﻻ 🄿 – 🕍 150. ⚠ AE ① VISA ⅙   JZ **z**
M *(closed Saturday lunch)* 14.95/15.95 **st.** and a la carte – ⌇ 9.50 – **291 rm** 96.00/105.00 **st.**,
4 suites 225.00/295.00 **st.** – SB (weekends only) 94.00/114.00 **st.**

🏨 **Copthorne,** Paradise Circus, B3 3HJ, ✆ 200 2727, Telex 339026, Fax 200 1197, Ⅰ₆, ≋,
– 🛗 ⅍ rm ▤ rest ▤ ☎ ﻻ 🄿 – 🕍 150. ⚠ AE ① VISA. ⅙   JZ **e**
M *(bar lunch Saturday)* 12.95/14.95 **t.** and a la carte ⅟ 6.50 – ⌇ 8.95 – **210 rm** 89.00/99.00 **st.**,
2 suites 215.00 **st.**

🏨 **Midland,** 128 New St., B2 4JT, ✆ 643 2601, Telex 338419, Fax 643 5075 – 🛗 ▤ ☎ – 🕍 200.
⚠ AE ① VISA   KZ **r**
M *(closed lunch Saturday and Sunday)* 15.00 **t.** and a la carte ⅟ 8.95 – **109 rm** 65.00/99.00 **st.**,
2 suites 95.00/135.00 **st.**

🏨 Grand (Q.M.H.), Colmore Row, B3 2DA, ✆ 236 7951, Telex 338174, Fax 233 1465 – 🛗 ▤ rest
▤ ☎ – 🕍 450 – **173 rm**, **3 suites.**   JKY **c**

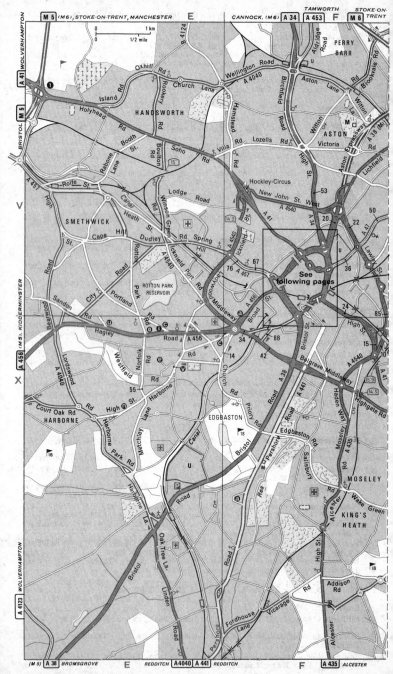

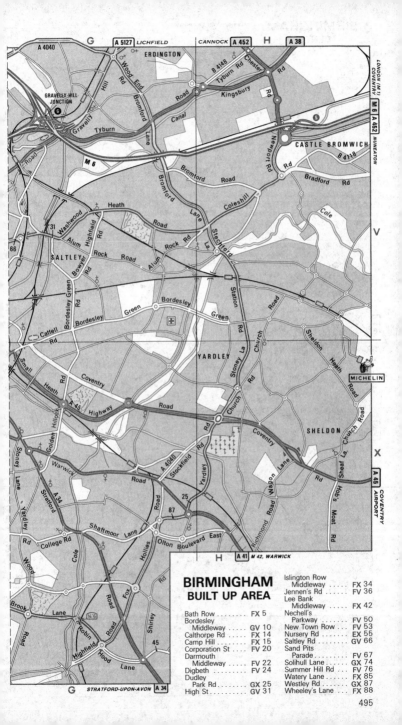

BIRMINGHAM
BUILT UP AREA

BIRMINGHAM
CENTRE

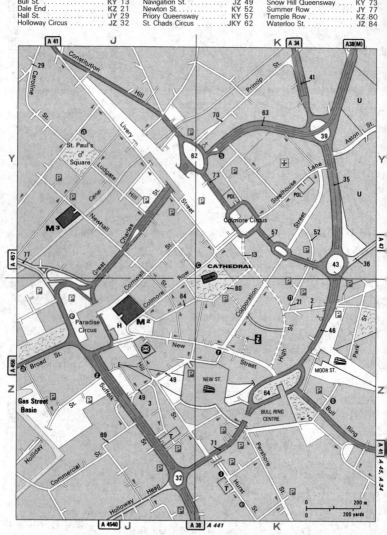

GREEN TOURIST GUIDES

Picturesque scenery, buildings

Attractive route

Touring programmes

Plans of towns and buildings.

STREET INDEX TO BIRMINGHAM TOWN PLANS

In this Guide,

a Symbol or a character,
printed in black or another colour,
in light or bold type,
does not have the same meaning.
Please read the explanatory pages carefully.

🏨🏨 **Royal Angus Thistle** (Mt. Charlotte Thistle), St. Chad's, Queensway, B4 6HY, ℰ 236 4211, Telex 336889, Fax 233 2195 – |🛗| 🖐 rm 📺 ☎ 🅿 – 🛎 140. 🖪 🖭 ⑩ 𝘝𝘐𝘚𝘈   KY **s**
M *(closed Saturday lunch)* 12.95/16.50 **st.** and a la carte ⅄ 5.10 – ☑ 8.50 – **131 rm** 75.00/95.00 **st., 2 suites** 120.00 **st.** – SB 90.00/180.00 **st.**

🏨🏨 **Strathallan Thistle** (Mt. Charlotte Thistle), 225 Hagley Rd, Edgbaston, B16 9RY, ℰ 455 9777, Telex 336680, Fax 454 9432 – |🛗| 🖐 rm 🍽 rest 📺 ☎ 🅿 – 🛎 200. 🖪 🖭 ⑩ 𝘝𝘐𝘚𝘈   EX **i**
M *(closed Saturday lunch)* 10.25/17.25 **t.** and a la carte ⅄ 4.95 – ☑ 8.75 – **163 rm** 85.00/98.00 **t., 4 suites** 115.00 **t.**

🏨 **Jonathan's with rm**, 16-24 Wolverhampton Rd, B68 0LH, W : 4 m. by A 456 ℰ 429 3757, Fax 434 3107, English rest., « Victoriana » – 📺 ☎ 🅿 – 🛎 30
21 rm, 5 suites.

🏨 **Apollo** (Mt. Charlotte Thistle), 243 Hagley Rd, Edgbaston, B16 9RA, ℰ 455 0271, Telex 336759, Fax 456 2394 – |🛗| 🖐 rm 🍽 rest 📺 ☎ 🅿 – 🛎 150. 🖪 🖭 ⑩ 𝘝𝘐𝘚𝘈   EX **o**
M *(closed Saturday lunch)* 9.50/16.00 **st.** and a la carte ⅄ 5.00 – ☑ 8.15 – **124 rm** 72.00/78.00 **st., 2 suites** 85.00 **st.** – SB (weekends only) 68.00/74.00 **st.**

🏨 **Novotel**, 70 Broad St., B1 2HT, ℰ 643 2000, Telex 335556, Fax 643 9796, 🛋, 🍴 – |🛗| 🖐 rm 🍽 rest 📺 ☎ 🕭 🅿 – 🛎 300. 🖪 🖭 ⑩ 𝘝𝘐𝘚𝘈 𝘚𝘗   FV **a**
M a la carte 15.45/17.75 **t.** ⅄ 5.50 – ☑ 7.00 – **148 rm** 40.00/70.00 **st.**

🏨 **Asquith House**, 19 Portland Rd, off Hagley Rd, Edgbaston, B16 9HN, W : 2 m. by A 456 ℰ 454 5282, Fax 456 4668, « Attractive furnishings », 🌳 – 📺 ⊛. 🖪 🖭 𝘝𝘐𝘚𝘈   EX **c**
closed Christmas and Easter – **M** (dinner only) 20.35/33.05 **st.** ⅄ 3.25 – **10 rm** ☑ 50.60/61.80 **st.**

🏨 **Fountain Court**, 339-343 Hagley Rd, Edgbaston, B17 8NH, ℰ 429 1754, Fax 429 1209, 🌳 – 📺 ☎ 🅿. 🖪 🖭 𝘝𝘐𝘚𝘈   EX **u**
closed 1 week Christmas-New Year – **M** (weekends by arrangement) (bar lunch)/dinner 13.50 **st.** ⅄ 5.95 – **25 rm** ☑ 40.50/58.00 **st.** – SB (weekends only) 70.00/100.00 **st.**

🏨 **Copperfield House** 60 Upland Rd, Selly Park, B29 7JS, ℰ 472 8344, 🌳 – 🖐 rest 📺 ☎ 🅿. 🖪 𝘝𝘐𝘚𝘈   FX **a**
M *(by arrangement Friday to Sunday)* 13.95 **st.** – **14 rm** ☑ 40.00/50.00 **st.** – SB (April-October) (weekends only) 50.00 **st.**

XXXX **Sir Edward Elgar's**, (at Swallow H.), 12 Hagley Rd, B16 8SJ, ℰ 452 1144, Telex 333806, Fax 456 3442 – 🍽 🅿. 🖪 🖭 ⑩ 𝘝𝘐𝘚𝘈   FX **c**
M 17.50/28.50 **st.** and a la carte ⅄ 7.75.

XXX **Sloans**, 27-29 Chad Sq., Hawthorne Rd, Edgbaston B15 3TQ, ℰ 455 6697 – 🖪 🖭 𝘝𝘐𝘚𝘈
closed Saturday lunch, Sunday, 26 to 31 December and Bank Holidays – **M** 15.50/18.00 **t.** and a la carte ⅄ 4.50.   EX **v**

XX **Days of the Raj**, 51 Dale End, B4 7LS, ℰ 236 0445, Indian rest. – 🍽. 🖪 🖭 ⑩ 𝘝𝘐𝘚𝘈
closed lunch Saturday and Sunday and 25-26 December – **M** (buffet lunch)/dinner a la carte 15.55/21.30 **st.**   KZ **n**

XX **Maharaja**, 23-25 Hurst St., B5 4AS, ℰ 622 2641, North Indian rest. – 🍽. 🖪 🖭 ⑩ 𝘝𝘐𝘚𝘈
closed Sunday and Bank Holidays – **M** 10.75/14.50 **t.** and a la carte.   KZ **i**

XX **Henry's**, 27 St. Paul's Sq., B3 1RB, ℰ 200 1136, Chinese (Canton) rest. – 🖪 🖭 ⑩ 𝘝𝘐𝘚𝘈   JY **a**
closed Sunday and Bank Holidays – **M** 12.00/18.00 **t.** and a la carte ⅄ 4.00.

XX **Henry Wong**, 283 High St., Harborne, B17 9QH, W : 3 ¾ m. by A 456 ℰ 427 9799, Chinese (Canton) rest. – 🖪 🖭 ⑩ 𝘝𝘐𝘚𝘈   EX **n**
closed Sunday, last week August and Bank Holidays – **M** 10.00/13.00 **t.** and a la carte ⅄ 4.50.

XX **Dynasty**, 93-103 Hurst St., B5 4TE, ℰ 622 1410, Chinese rest. – 🖪 🖭 𝘝𝘐𝘚𝘈   KZ **e**
M 9.00/11.50 **st.** and a la carte.

XX **Lorenzo**, 3 Park St., Digbeth, B5 5JD, ℰ 643 0541, Italian rest. – 🖪 🖭 ⑩ 𝘝𝘐𝘚𝘈   KZ **o**
closed Saturday lunch, Sunday and Bank Holidays – **M** 12.00/30.00 **t.** and a la carte ⅄ 7.80.

at Birmingham Airport SE : 7 ½ m. by A 45 – ✉ ⊛ 021 Birmingham :

🏨 **Novotel**, Passenger Terminal, B26 3QL, ℰ 782 7000, Telex 338158, Fax 782 0445 – |🛗| 🖐 rm 🍽 rest 📺 ☎ 🕭 – 🛎 30
195 rm.

🏨 **Forte Posthouse**, Coventry Rd, Elmdon, B26 3QW, on A 45 ℰ 782 8141, Telex 338005, Fax 782 2476 – 🖐 rm 📺 ☎ 🅿 – 🛎 150. 🖪 🖭 ⑩ 𝘝𝘐𝘚𝘈
M 10.00/13.95 **st.** and a la carte ⅄ 3.95 – ☑ 5.95 – **136 rm** 49.50 **st.** – SB (weekends only) 78.00 **st.**

at National Exhibition Centre SE : 9 ½ m. on A 45 – ✉⊛ 021 Birmingham :

🏨🏨 **Birmingham Metropole**, Bickenhill, B40 1PP, ℰ 780 4242, Telex 336129, Fax 780 3923, 🍴, squash – |🛗| 🖐 rm 🍽 📺 ☎ 🕭 🅿 – 🛎 2 000. 🖪 🖭 ⑩ 𝘝𝘐𝘚𝘈
M 17.35 **t.** and a la carte – **797 rm** ☑ 112.00/173.00 **t., 9 suites** 310.00/460.00 **t.**

🏨 **Arden**, Coventry Rd, B92 0EH, ℰ 0675 (Hampton-in-Arden) 443221, Telex 334913, Fax 443225, 🛋, 🍴, 🖪 – |🛗| 📺 ☎ 🕭 🅿 – 🛎 130. 🖪 🖭 ⑩ 𝘝𝘐𝘚𝘈
M (bar lunch Saturday) 11.45/12.75 **t.** and a la carte ⅄ 4.95 – ☑ 7.00 – **76 rm** 65.00/72.50 **t.**

at Kings Norton SW : 7 m. by A 441 – FX – ✉ ☎ 021 Birmingham :

Norton Place (at The Patrick Collection), 180 Lifford Lane, B30 3NT, ✆ 433 5656, Fax 433 3048, « Collection of classic motor cars », ℒ, 🚗 – ⇔ rm TV ☎ ♿ P – 🎤 140. AE ① VISA. ✻
M (see **Lombard Room** below) – ☕ 9.00 – **9 rm** 90.00/175.00 **st.**, **1 suite** 225.00 **st.** – SB (weekends only) 150.00 **st.**

XXX **Lombard Room** (at The Patrick Collection), 180 Lifford Lane, B30 3NT, ✆ 451 3991, Fax 433 3048, « Collection of classic motor cars », 🚗 – ⇔ ▤ P. AE ① VISA
M 18.50/19.00 **t.** and a la carte 🍷 5.25.

at Great Barr NW : 6 m. on A 34 – ✉ ☎ 021 Birmingham :

Forte Posthouse, Chapel Lane, B43 7BG, ✆ 357 7444, Fax 357 7503, ℒ, ≘s, ⛱ heated, 🏊 – ⇔ rm TV ☎ P – 🎤 150. AE ① VISA CT **x**
M a la carte 12.20/22.95 **st.** 🍷 3.75 – ☕ 5.95 – **192 rm** 49.50 **st.** – SB (weekends only) 79.00/99.00 **st.**

Great Barr, Pear Tree Drive, Newton Rd, B43 6HS, W : 1 m. by A 4041 ✆ 357 1141, Telex 336406, Fax 357 7557, 🚗 – TV ☎ P – 🎤 120. AE ① VISA. ✻ CT **z**
M *(closed Bank Holidays)* 12.00/15.00 **st.** and a la carte 🍷 5.50 – **114 rm** ☕ 60.00/72.00 **st.**

at West Bromwich NW : 6 m. on A 41 – ✉ ☎ 021 Birmingham :

West Bromwich Moat House (Q.M.H.), Birmingham Rd, B70 6RS, ✆ 553 6111, Telex 336232, Fax 525 7403 – |‡| ⇔ rm ▤ rest TV ☎ P – 🎤 120. AE ① VISA BU **c**
closed 1 to 5 January – **M** 11.50/13.50 **t.** – ☕ 5.00 – **180 rm** 55.00/65.00 **t.** – SB (weekends only) 88.90 **st.**

Prices — For full details of the prices quoted in this Guide, consult the introduction.

EDINBURGH Midlothian. (Lothian) 401 K 16 – pop. 408 822 – ☎ 031.

See : International Festival★★★ (August) – National Gallery of Scotland★★★ DY **M4** – Castle★★ – Lock★★ DZ – Abbey and Palace of Holyroodhouse★★ (Plasterwork ceilings★★★) – Gladstone's Land★ EYZ **A**, St. Giles' Cathedral★★ (Crown Spire★★★) EZ – Canongate Tolbooth★ EY **B**, Victoria Street★ EZ **84** – Royal Museum of Scotland★★ EZ **M2** – New Town★★ : Charlotte Square★★★ CY **14**, Royal Museum of Scotland (Antiquities★★) EY **M3**, The Georgian House★ CY **D** – National Portrait Gallery★ EY **M3** – Scott Monument★ EY **F**, Calton Hill EY : ✳★★★ from Nelson Monument – Royal Botanic Gardens★★★ – Edinburgh Zoo★★ – Scottish Agricultural Museum★ by A 90 – Craigmillar Castle★.

Envir. : Rosslyn Chapel★★, S : 7 m. by A 701 – Hopetoun House★★, W : 10 ½ m. by A 90 – Forth Bridges★★, W : 7 ½ m. by A 90 – Dalmeny (House★, Church★, Doorway★★) W : 7 m. by A 90.

⛳18 Silverknowes, Parkway, ✆ 336 3843, W : 4 m. – ⛳18 Liberton, Gilmerton Rd ✆ 664 8580, SE : 3 m. on A 7 – ⛳18 Craigmillar Park, Observatory Rd ✆ 667 2837 – ⛳18 Carrick Knowe, Glendevon Park ✆ 337 1096, W : 5 m. – ⛳18 Swanston Rd, Fairmilehead ✆ 445 2239, S : 4 m. by A 702 – ⛳18 Lothianburn, Biggar Rd ✆ 445 2206, S : 4 ½ m. by A 702.

✈ ✆ 333 1000, Telex 727615, W : 6 m. by A 8 – **Terminal** : Waverley Bridge.

🚗 ✆ 0345 090700.

ℹ Travel Centre, 3 Princes St., ✆ 557 1700 – Edinburgh Airport ✆ 333 2167.

Glasgow 46 – Newcastle upon Tyne 105.

Plan on next page

Caledonian (Q.M.H.), Princes St., EH1 2AB, ✆ 225 2433, Telex 72179, Fax 225 6632 – |‡| ⇔ rm TV ☎ ♿ P – 🎤 300. AE ① VISA. ✻ CY **n**
M Carriages 16.75/24.00 **t.** and a la carte 🍷 7.75 (see also **Pompadour** below) – ☕ 13.00 – **226 rm** 125.00/195.00 **t.**, **11 suites** 295.00/650.00 **t.** – SB (except Christmas-New Year) (weekends only) 160.00/200.00 **st.**

Balmoral, Princes St., EH2 2EQ, ✆ 556 2414, Telex 727282, Fax 557 3747, ℒ, ≘s, 🏊 – |‡| ⇔ rm ▤ rest TV ☎ ♿ P – 🎤 200. AE VISA. ✻ EY **n**
M 10.50 **t.** (lunch) and a la carte approx. 12.90 **t.** 🍷 5.75 – (see also **Grill** below) – ☕ 9.75 – **168 rm** 105.00/195.00 **t.**, **21 suites** 245.00/550.00 **t.**

Sheraton, 1 Festival Square, EH3 9SR, ✆ 229 9131, Telex 72398, Fax 228 4510, ℒ, ≘s, 🏊 – |‡| ⇔ rm ▤ TV ☎ ♿ P – 🎤 450. AE ① VISA. ✻ CDZ **v**
M 18.25/23.75 **st.** and a la carte 🍷 5.00 – ☕ 12.00 – **247 rm** 95.00/175.00 **st.**, **16 suites** 285.00/320.00 **st.**

George (Inter-Continental), 19-21 George St., EH2 2PB, ✆ 225 1251, Telex 72570, Fax 226 5644 – |‡| ⇔ rm ▤ rest TV ☎ P – 🎤 180. AE ① VISA DY **z**
M 25.00/30.00 **t.** and a la carte 🍷 6.00 – ☕ 10.50 – **193 rm** 105.00/145.00 **t.**, **2 suites** 225.00/374.00 **t.**

Carlton Highland, 1-29 North Bridge, EH1 1SD, ✆ 556 7277, Telex 727001, Fax 556 2691, ℒ, ≘s, 🏊, squash – |‡| ▤ rest TV ☎ ♿ – 🎤 350. AE ① VISA. ✻ EY **s**
M 13.00/17.50 **t.** and a la carte 🍷 5.50 – **196 rm** ☕ 99.00/146.00 **t.**, **4 suites** 295.00 **t.** – SB (weekends only) 118.00/126.00 **st.**

EDINBURGH

500

Howard, 32-36 Gt. King St., EH3 6QH, ✆ 557 3500, Fax 557 6515, « Georgian town houses » – ▮ 📺 ☎ 😊 – 🔏 35. 🅰 🆎 ⓞ 🆅🆂🅰. ✖ DY **s**
M – No 36 17.00/30.00 t. – **16 rm** � 97.00/255.00 t. – SB (except August and October) (weekends only) 140.00 **st.**

Dalmahoy H. Golf & Country Club 🏌, Kirknewtown, EH27 8EB, SW : 7 m. on A 71 ✆ 333 1845, Telex 772205, Fax 335 3203, ≤, ℉₆, ≘, 🔲, ℉₈, 🐎, park, ✖, squash – ▮ ✸ rm ≡ rest 📺 ☎ & 😊 – 🔏 250. 🅰 🆎 ⓞ 🆅🆂🅰.
M 12.50/17.50 t. and a la carte – **114 rm** �](98.00/115.00 **st.**, **1 suite** 125.00/150.00 **st.** – SB (weekends only) 92.00/170.00 **st.**

Hilton National, Bells Mills, 69 Belford Rd, EH4 3DG, ✆ 332 2545, Telex 727979, Fax 332 3805 – ▮ ✸ rm 📺 ☎ & 😊 – 🔏 120. 🅰 🆎 ⓞ 🆅🆂🅰. CY **i**
M (closed Saturday lunch) 16.00/20.00 **t.** and a la carte ₰ 6.95 – ⍺ 9.50 – **143 rm** 97.50/130.00 **t.**, **1 suite** 195.00 **t.** – SB (weekends only) 86.00/162.00 **st.**

Scandic Crown, 80 High St., EH1 1TH, ✆ 557 9797, Telex 727298, Fax 557 9789, ℉₆, ≘, 🔲 – ▮ ✸ rm ≡ rest 📺 ☎ & 😊 – 🔏 200. 🅰 🆎 ⓞ 🆅🆂🅰. ✖ EY **z**
M 13.95 **st.** and a la carte – ⍺ 8.50 – **228 rm** 89.00/160.00 **st.**, **10 suites** 230.00/280.00 **st.**

Capital Moat House (Q.M.H.), Clermiston Rd, EH12 6UG, ✆ 334 3391, Telex 728284, Fax 334 9712, ℉₆, ≘, 🔲 – ▮ ✸ rm 📺 ☎ & 😊 – 🔏 300. 🅰 🆎 ⓞ 🆅🆂🅰
M (buffet lunch)/dinner 14.95 **st.** and a la carte – ⍺ 7.25 – **98 rm** 73.00/123.00 **st.** – SB (weekends only) 90.00 **st.**

Roxburghe, 38 Charlotte Sq., EH2 4HG, ✆ 225 3921, Telex 727054, Fax 220 2518 – ▮ 📺 ☎ & – 🔏 200. 🅰 🆎 ⓞ 🆅🆂🅰 DY **o**
M (closed Saturday lunch) 10.00/17.90 **st.** and a la carte ₰ 4.75 – **74 rm** ⍺ 85.00/140.00 **st.**, **1 suite** 130.00/160.00 **st.**

Swallow Royal Scott, 111 Glasgow Rd, EH12 8NF, W : 4 ½ m. on A 8 ✆ 334 9191, Telex 727197, Fax 316 4507, ℉₆, ≘, 🔲 – ▮ ✸ rm 📺 ☎ 😊 – 🔏 250. 🅰 🆎 ⓞ 🆅🆂🅰 by A 8 CZ
M 14.50/32.00 **st.** and a la carte – **254 rm** ⍺ 92.00/117.50 **st.**, **4 suites** 163.50 **st.** – SB (weekends only) 107.10 **st.**

Royal Terrace, 18 Royal Terrace, EH7 5AQ, ✆ 557 3222, Telex 727182, Fax 557 5334, ℉₆, ≘, 🐎 – ▮ 📺 ☎ – 🔏 60. 🅰 🆎 ⓞ 🆅🆂🅰 EY **i**
M (bar lunch Saturday and Sunday) a la carte 18.95/26.00 **st.** – ⍺ 10.00 – **94 rm** 95.00/140.00 **st.**, **1 suite** 185.00 **st.**

King James Thistle (Mt. Charlotte Thistle), 107 Leith St., EH1 3SW, ✆ 556 0111, Telex 727200, Fax 557 5333 – ▮ ✸ rm 📺 ☎ 😊 – 🔏 200. 🅰 🆎 ⓞ 🆅🆂🅰 EY **u**
M (closed lunch Saturday and Sunday) 10.50 **t.** (lunch) and a la carte 16.50/25.00 **t.** ₰ 5.50 – ⍺ 8.50 – **142 rm** 72.00/90.00 **st.**, **5 suites** 140.00/170.00 **t.** – SB 82.00 **st.**

Bruntsfield, 69-74 Bruntsfield Pl., EH10 4HH, ✆ 229 1393, Telex 727897, Fax 229 5634 – ▮ 📺 ☎ 😊 – 🔏 25. 🅰 🆎 ⓞ 🆅🆂🅰 DZ **e**
M 9.50/18.50 **st.** and a la carte ₰ 4.00 – **50 rm** 66.50/105.00 **st.** – SB 90.00/110.00 **st.**

Ellersly Country House (Jarvis), 4 Ellersly Rd, EH12 6HZ, ✆ 337 6888, Telex 727239, Fax 313 2543, 🐎 – ✸ rm 📺 ☎ 😊 – 🔏 40. 🅰 🆎 ⓞ 🆅🆂🅰
M (closed Saturday lunch) 9.95/17.95 **t.** and a la carte ₰ 4.95 – ⍺ 7.95 – **54 rm** 83.00/99.00 **st.** – SB (weekends only) 65.00/99.00 **st.**

Holiday Inn Garden Court, Queensferry Rd, EH4 3HL, ✆ 332 2442, Telex 72541, Fax 332 3408, ≤ – ▮ ✸ rm ≡ rest 📺 ☎ 😊 – 🔏 60. 🅰 🆎 ⓞ 🆅🆂🅰.
M (dinner only) 20.00 **st.** and a la carte ₰ 4.00 – ⍺ 7.45 – **118 rm** 60.00/80.00 **st.**, **1 suite** 60.00/150.00 **st.** – SB 72.00/82.00 **st.**

Barnton Thistle (Mt. Charlotte Thistle), 562 Queensferry Rd, EH4 6AS, ✆ 339 1144, Telex 727928, Fax 339 5521, ≘ – ▮ 📺 ☎ 😊 – 🔏 100. 🅰 🆎 ⓞ 🆅🆂🅰
M 9.75/15.75 **t.** and a la carte ₰ 4.00 – ⍺ 8.45 – **47 rm** 72.00/104.00 **t.**, **3 suites** 120.00 **t.**

Stakis Grosvenor, Grosvenor St., EH12 5EF, ✆ 226 6001, Telex 72445, Fax 220 2387 – ▮ ✸ rm 📺 ☎ 😊 – 🔏 160. 🅰 🆎 ⓞ 🆅🆂🅰 CZ **a**
M (grill rest.) 19.00/22.50 **t.** and a la carte ₰ 3.20 – ⍺ 8.50 – **135 rm** 82.00/105.00 **t.**, **1 suite** 105.00/135.00 **t.** – SB 72.00/120.00 **st.**

Mount Royal (Jarvis), 53 Princes St., EH2 2DG, ✆ 225 7161, Telex 727641, Fax 220 4671 – ▮ 📺 ☎ – 🔏 50. 🅰 🆎 🆅🆂🅰 DY **a**
M 9.50/15.00 **st.** and a la carte – ⍺ 8.50 – **159 rm** 85.00/122.50 **st.** – SB 80.00/100.00 **st.**

Lady Nairne, 228 Willowbrae Rd, EH8 7NG, ✆ 661 3396, Fax 652 2789 – ▮ 📺 ☎ 😊 – 🔏 100. 🅰 🆎 ⓞ 🆅🆂🅰
33 rm ⍺ 49.50/75.00 **st.**

Pompadour (at Caledonian H.) Princes St., EH1 2AB, ✆ 225 2433, Telex 72179, Fax 225 6632 – 😊. 🅰 🆎 ⓞ 🆅🆂🅰 CY **n**
M (closed lunch Saturday and Sunday) 18.50/40.00 **t.** and a la carte ₰ 8.75.

Grill (at Balmoral H.), Princes St., EH2 2EQ, ✆ 556 2414, Telex 72332, Fax 557 3747 – ≡ 😊. 🅰 🆎 ⓞ 🆅🆂🅰
closed Saturday lunch and Sunday – **M** 17.75/27.50 **t.** and a la carte ₰ 5.75. EY **n**

XX **Vintners Room,** The Vaults, 87 Giles St., Leith, EH6 6BZ, ℰ 554 6767 – ⅔ ▤. AE VISA
closed Sunday and 2 weeks Christmas-New Year – M 12.00 **t.** (lunch) and a la carte 18.50/26.00 **t.** 4.00.

XX **Martins,** 70 Rose St., North Lane, EH2 3DX, ℰ 225 3106 – ⅔. AE ◑ VISA DY **n**
closed Saturday lunch, Sunday, Monday and 25 December-20 January – **M** (booking essential) 15.00 **t.** (lunch) and a la carte 20.75/27.60 **t.** 4.70.

XX **L'Auberge,** 56 St. Mary's St., EH1 1SX, ℰ 556 5888, French rest. – ▤. AE ◑ VISA EYZ **c**
closed Monday November-March, 26 December, 1 to 15 January and 1 week Easter – **M** 12.95/19.50 **t.** and a la carte 4.50.

XX **Raffaelli,** 10-11 Randolph Pl., EH3 7TA, ℰ 225 6060, Fax 225 8830, Italian rest. – AE ◑ VISA CY **c**
closed Saturday lunch, Sunday, 25-26 December and 1-2 January – **M** a la carte 15.00/22.75 **t.**

XX **Lancer's Brasserie,** 5 Hamilton Pl., Stockbridge, EH3 5BA, ℰ 332 3444, North Indian rest. – AE ◑ VISA – **M** (buffet lunch)/dinner 15.00 **t.** and a la carte. CY **r**

XX **Umberto,** 29-33 Dublin St., EH3 6NL, ℰ 556 2231, Italian rest. – AE ◑ VISA EY **e**
closed lunch Saturday and Sunday – **M** 8.95 **t.** (lunch) and a la carte 15.85/18.05 **t.** 4.25.

XX **Merchants,** 17 Merchants St., (under bridge), EH1 2QD, ℰ 225 4009 – AE ◑ VISA
closed Sunday, 25-26 December and 1 January – **M** (booking essential) 15.00 **t.** and a la carte 4.70. EZ **x**

XX **Indian Cavalry Club,** 3 Atholl Pl., EH3 8HP, ℰ 228 3282, Indian rest. – AE ◑ VISA
M 7.95/14.95 **t.** and a la carte. CZ **c**

XX **Cosmo,** 58a North Castle St., EH2 3LU, ℰ 226 6743, Italian rest. – VISA DY **r**
closed Saturday lunch, Sunday and Monday – **M** a la carte 16.40/25.10 **t.** 4.50.

XX **Denzler's 121,** 121 Constitution St., EH6 7AE, ℰ 554 3268 – VISA
closed Saturday lunch, Sunday, Monday, 2 days at Christmas and 5 days at New Year – **M** 11.00/22.00 **st.** and a la carte 5.20.

at Ingliston W : 7 ¾ m. on A 8 – ✉ 031 Edinburgh :

Norton House ⚘,, EH28 8LY, on A 8 ℰ 333 1275, Telex 727232, Fax 333 5305, ←, park – TV ☎ ♿ P – 250. AE ◑ VISA
M *(closed Saturday lunch)* 35.00 **st.** and a la carte 5.00 – **44 rm** 85.00/102.00 **st., 2 suites** 160.00 **st.** – SB 120.00/150.00 **st.**

When in a hurry use the **Michelin Main Road Maps** *:*

970 *Europe,* 980 *Greece,* 984 *Germany,* 985 *Scandinavia-Finland,*

986 *Great Britain and Ireland,* 987 *Germany-Austria-Benelux,* 988 *Italy,*

989 *France,* 990 *Spain-Portugal and* 991 *Yugoslavia.*

GLASGOW Lanark. (Strathclyde) 401 402 H 16 – pop. 754 586 – ☏ 041.

See : Burrell Collection★★★ – Cathedral★★★ DYZ – Tolbooth Steeple★ DZ **A** – Hunterian Art Gallery★★ CY **M2** - Art Gallery and Museum Kelvingrove★★ CY – City Chambers★ DZ **C** – Glasgow School of Art★ CY **B** – Museum of Transport★★ – Pollok House★ (Spanish paintings★★).

Envir. : Trossachs★★★, N : by A 739 and A 81 – Loch Lomond★★, NW : by A 82 – Clyde Estuary★ (Dumbarton Castle Site★, Hill House★, Helensburgh★) by A 82 – Bothwell Castle★ and David Livingstone Centre (Museum★) SE : 9 m. by A 724.

18 Linn Park, Simshill Rd ℰ 637 5871, S : 4 m. – 18 Lethamhill, Cumbernauld Rd ℰ 770 6220 – 9 Knightswood, Lincoln Av. ℰ 959 2131, W : 4 m. – 9 Kings Park, Croftpark Av., S : 4m. by B 766 – 9 Alexandra Park, Alexandra Par. ℰ 556 3211.

Access to Oban by helicopter.

✈ Glasgow Airport : ℰ 887 1111, W : 8 m. by M 8 – **Terminal** : Coach service from Glasgow Central and Queen Street main line Railway Stations and from Anderston Cross and Buchanan Bus Stationssee also Prestwick.

☐ 35 St. Vincent Pl. ℰ 204 4400 – Glasgow Airport, Paisley ℰ 848 4440.

Edinburgh 46 – Manchester 221.

Plan on following pages

Holiday Inn, 500 Argyle St., Anderston, G3 8RR, ℰ 226 5577, Telex 776355, Fax 221 9202, Lō, ≘s, ☐, squash – ▮ ⅔ rm ▤ TV ☎ ♿ P – 700. AE ◑ VISA CZ **a**
M 18.95/27.00 **t.** and a la carte 5.95 – ☐ 9.95 – **293 rm** 105.00/140.00 **st., 5 suites** 215.00 **st.** – SB (weekends only) 90.00/200.00 **st.**

Forte Crest, Bothwell St., G2 7EN, ℰ 248 2656, Telex 77440, Fax 221 8986, ← – ▮ ⅔ rm ▤ TV ☎ P – 800. AE ◑ VISA CZ **z**
M 18.15/22.45 **st.** and a la carte 6.95 – ☐ 8.50 – **251 rm** 90.00/100.00 **st., 3 suites** 170.00/210.00 **st.** – SB (weekends only) 98.00/104.00 **st.**

One Devonshire Gardens, 1 Devonshire Gdns, G12 OUX, ℰ 339 2001, Fax 337 1663, « Opulent interior design » – 📺 ☎ 🔼 AE ① VISA
M *(closed Saturday lunch)* 18.00/30.00 **t.** 🛦 8.00 – � 6.75 – **25 rm** 100.00/145.00 **t.**, **2 suites** 165.00 **t.**

Moat House International (Q.M.H.), Congress Rd, G3 8QT, ℰ 204 0733, Telex 776244, Fax 221 2022, ⩽, 🔥, ⇆, 🔼 – 🔋 📺 ☎ rm ▦ 📺 ☎ ᶑ 🅿 – 🕰 750. 🔼 AE ① VISA
M 18.00/30.00 **st.** and a la carte – ⊊ 9.50 – **269 rm** 89.00/99.00 **st.**, **15 suites** 175.00 **st.** –
SB (weekends only) 67.00/85.00 **st.**   CZ **r**

Hospitality Inn (Mt. Charlotte Thistle), 36 Cambridge St., G2 3HN, ℰ 332 3311, Telex 777334, Fax 332 4050 – 🔋 📺 ☎ ᶑ 🅿 – 🕰 1 500. 🔼 AE ① VISA   DY **z**
M *(closed Saturday lunch and Sunday)* 13.75/19.25 **st.** and a la carte 21.30/34.00 **st.** – ⊊ 10.50
– **304 rm** 85.00/110.00 **t.**, **3 suites** 185.00/195.00 **t.** – SB (weekends only) 100.00/120.00 **st.**

Stakis Grosvenor, Grosvenor Terr., Great Western Rd, G12 OTA, ℰ 339 8811, Telex 776247, Fax 334 0710 – 🔋 ⇆ 📺 ☎ 🅿 – 🕰 250   CY **r**
93 rm, **2 suites.**

Copthorne, George Sq., G2 1DS, ℰ 332 6711, Telex 778147, Fax 332 4264 – 🔋 ⇆ rm 📺 ☎ – 🕰 100. 🔼 AE ① VISA. ⅏   DZ **n**
M *(closed lunch Saturday, Sunday, and Bank Holidays)* (carving rest.) 16.00/17.00 **st.** and a la carte 🛦 5.95 – ⊊ 9.50 – **135 rm** 86.00/102.00 **st.**, **5 suites** 128.00/150.00 **st.** – SB (weekends only) 100.00/108.00 **st.**

Devonshire, 5 Devonshire Gardens, G12 OUX, ℰ 339 7878, Fax 339 3980 – 📺 ☎ – 🕰 40. 🔼 AE ①
M (lunch residents only) 25.00/29.00 **st.** and a la carte 🛦 4.75 – ⊊ 5.95 – **14 rm** 85.00/140.00 **st.** – SB (weekends only) 170.00/200.00 **st.**

Swallow, 517 Paisley Rd West, G51 1RW, ℰ 427 3146, Telex 778795, Fax 427 4059, 🔥, ⇆, 🔼 – 🔋 ⇆ rm ▦ rest 📺 ☎ 🅿 – 🕰 250. 🔼 AE ① VISA
M *(closed lunch Saturday and Bank Holidays)* 10.00/14.50 **st.** and a la carte 🛦 6.50 – **119 rm** ⊊ 77.00/130.00 **st.** – SB 86.70 **st.**

Tinto Firs Thistle (Mt. Charlotte Thistle), 470 Kilmarnock Rd, G43 2BB, ℰ 637 2353, Telex 778329, Fax 633 1340 – 📺 ☎ 🅿 – 🕰 60. 🔼 AE ① VISA
M *(closed Saturday lunch)* 7.95/15.00 **t.** and a la carte 🛦 4.50 – ⊊ 8.25 – **25 rm** 75.00/90.00 **st.**, **2 suites** 150.00/175.00 **st.** – SB (weekends only) 66.00 **st.**

Kelvin Park Lorne (Q.M.H.), 923 Sauchiehall St., G3 7TE, ℰ 334 4891, Telex 778935, Fax 337 1659 – 🔋 📺 ☎ 🅿 – 🕰 175. 🔼 AE ① VISA   CY **a**
M *(closed Saturday lunch)* 9.95/15.95 **st.** and a la carte 🛦 4.00 – ⊊ 7.50 – **99 rm** 70.00/155.00 **st.** – SB (weekends only) 104.00 **st.**

Crest (Forte), 377 Argyle St., G2 8LL, ℰ 248 2355, Telex 779652, Fax 221 1014 – 🔋 ⇆ rm 📺 ☎ 🅿 – 🕰 80. 🔼 AE ① VISA   CZ **x**
M 13.95/22.00 **st.** and a la carte 🛦 5.50 – ⊊ 8.50 – **121 rm** 77.00/89.00 **st.** – SB (weekends only) 78.00 **st.**

Stakis Ingram, 201 Ingram St., G1 1DQ, ℰ 248 4401, Telex 776470, Fax 226 5149 – 🔋 ⇆ rm ▦ 📺 ☎ – 🕰 200 – **90 rm**   DZ **c**

XXX **North Rotunda,** 28 Tunnel St., (2nd floor), G3 8HL, ℰ 204 1238, Fax 226 4264, French rest. – 🅿. 🔼 AE ① VISA   CZ **u**
closed Sunday, Monday, 25 December and 1 January – **M** 10.95/16.95 **t.** a la carte 🛦 6.20.

XXX Killermont House, 2022 Maryhill Rd, Maryhill Park, G20 OAB, ℰ 946 5412, ⼞ – 🅿.   by A8

XXX **Fountain,** 2 Woodside Cres., G3 7UL, ℰ 332 6396 – 🔼 AE ① VISA   CY **c**
closed Saturday lunch and Sunday – **M** 9.00/22.00 **t.** and a la carte 🛦 4.50.

XX **Buttery,** 652 Argyle St., G3 8UF, ℰ 221 8188, Fax 204 4639 – 🅿. 🔼 AE ①
VISA   CZ **e**
closed Saturday lunch, Sunday and Bank Holidays – **M** 14.25 **st.** (lunch) and a la carte 20.50/27.10 **t.**

XX **Rogano,** 11 Exchange Pl., G1 3AN, ℰ 248 4055, Fax 248 2608, Seafood, « Art deco » – 🔼 AE ① VISA   DZ **i**
closed Sunday lunch and Bank Holidays – **M** a la carte 14.00/23.50 **t.**

XX Cafe India, 171 North St., G3 7DL, ℰ 248 4074, Indian rest. – 🅿   CY **e**

XX **Ho Wong,** 82 York St., G2 3LE, ℰ 221 3550, Chinese (Peking) rest. – ▦. 🔼 AE ①
VISA   CZ **v**
M 6.50/18.00 **t.** and a la carte 🛦 4.95.

XX **Amber Royale,** 336 Argyle St., G2 8LY, ℰ 221 2550, Chinese rest. – ▦. 🔼 AE ①
VISA   CZ **o**
closed Sunday – **M** 6.00/18.00 **t.** and a la carte 🛦 5.50.

at Glasgow Airport (Renfrew). (Strathclyde) W : 8 m. by M 8 – ⊠ ✪ 041 Glasgow :

Forte Crest, Abbotsinch, PA3 2TR, ℰ 887 1212, Telex 777733, Fax 887 3738 – 🔋 ⇆ rm ▦ 📺 ☎ 🅿 – 🕰 400. 🔼 AE ① VISA
M *(closed Saturday lunch)* (carving rest.) 13.95 **st.** and a la carte 🛦 4.50 – ⊊ 8.95 – **283 rm** 80.00/90.00 **st.**, **5 suites** 116.00 **st.** – SB 78.00 **st.**

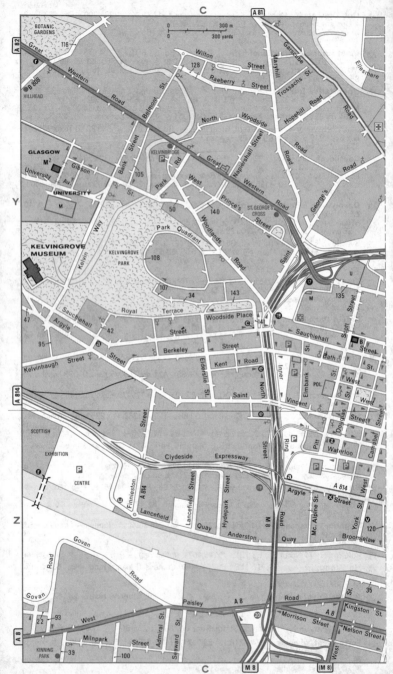

GLASGOW
CENTRE

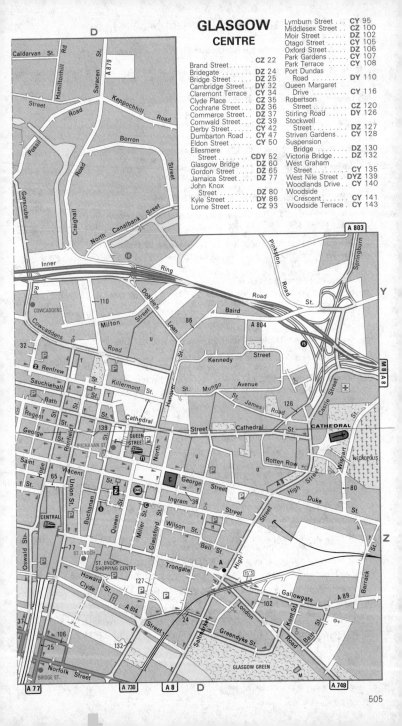

See : City Art Gallery ★ DZ M.

Envir. : Temple Newsam House★ (17C) (interior★★), E : 4 m. – Kirkstall Abbey★ (ruins 12C), NW : 3 m.

ⁿₛ, ⁿₛ The Temple Newsam, Temple Newsam Rd, Halton ⌀ 645624, E : 3 m. – ⁿₛ Gotts Park, Armley Ridge Rd, ⌀ 636600, W : 2 m. – ⁿₛ Middleton Park, Ring Rd., Middleton ⌀ 709506, S : 3 m. – ⁿₛ Roundhay, Park Lane ⌀ 662695, N : 4 m.

≼ Leeds - Bradford Airport : ⌀ 509696, Telex 557868 NW : 8 m. by A 65 and A 658.

🛈 19 Wellington St. ⌀ 462454/462455, Fax 421321.

London 204 – Liverpool 75 – Manchester 43 – Newcastle upon Tyne 95 – Nottingham 74.

Plan on next page

🏨🏨🏨 **42, The Calls,** 42 The Calls, LS2 7EW, ⌀ 440099, Fax 344100, ≼, « Converted riverside grain mill » – Ⓘ ⤬ rm 📺 ☎ 🅿 – 🔬 50. 🖅 🅰🅴 ⓪ 𝘝𝘐𝘚𝘈. ⋙ DZ **z**
M (see **Brasserie Forty Four** below) – ⍁ 10.00 – **36 rm** 95.00/115.00 **st.**, **3 suites** 120.00/185.00 **st.** – SB (weekends only) 120.00 **st.**

🏨🏨🏨 **Holiday Inn,** Wellington St., LS1 4DL, ⌀ 442200, Telex 557879, Fax 440460, ⑤ₛ, ⎕ – Ⓘ ⤬ rm 🍴 📺 ☎ & 🅿 – 🔬 200. 🖅 🅰🅴 ⓪ 𝘝𝘐𝘚𝘈. ⋙ CZ **c**
M (closed Saturday lunch) 14.50/18.50 **st.** and a la carte ⑨ 6.00 – ⍁ 9.50 – **120 rm** 130.00/146.00 **st.**, **5 suites** 178.00/305.00 **st.** – SB (weekends only) 116.00 **st.**

🏨🏨🏨 **Leeds Hilton,** Neville St., LS1 4BX, ⌀ 442000, Telex 557143, Fax 433577 – Ⓘ ⤬ rm 🍴 📺 ☎ & 🅿 – 🔬 400. 🖅 🅰🅴 ⓪ 𝘝𝘐𝘚𝘈 DZ **r**
M 11.50/17.50 **st.** and a la carte – ⍁ 9.95 – **186 rm, 20 suites.**

🏨🏨🏨 **Queen's** (Forte), City Sq., LS1 1PL, ⌀ 431323, Fax 425154 – Ⓘ ⤬ rm 🍴 rest 📺 ☎ & 🅿 – 🔬 700. 🖅 🅰🅴 ⓪ 𝘝𝘐𝘚𝘈 DZ **a**
M 12.25/22.50 **st.** and a la carte ⑨ 4.95 – ⍁ 8.70 – **183 rm** 85.00/115.00 **st.**, **5 suites** 163.00 **st.** – SB (weekends only) 104.00 **st.**

🏨🏨 **Haley's,** Shire Oak Rd, Headingly, LS6 2DE, NW : 2 m. off Otley Rd (A 660) ⌀ 784446, Fax 753342 – ⤬ rest 📺 ☎ 🅿. 🖅 🅰🅴 ⓪ 𝘝𝘐𝘚𝘈. ⋙
closed 26 to 30 December – M (closed Saturday lunch and Sunday dinner) 15.75/27.00 **st.** and a la carte – **22 rm** ⍁ 90.00/175.00 **st.** – SB (weekends only) 110.00/150.00 **st.**

🏨🏨 **Golden Lion** (Mt. Charlotte Thistle), 2 Lower Briggate, LS1 4AE, ⌀ 436454, Fax 429327 – Ⓘ 📺 ☎ – 🔬 120. 🖅 🅰🅴 ⓪ 𝘝𝘐𝘚𝘈. ⋙ DZ **v**
M (closed lunch Saturday and Bank Holidays) 12.95 **st.** (dinner) and a la carte 14.55/23.50 **st.** – **89 rm** ⍁ 70.00/90.00 **st.** – SB (weekends only) 75.00 **st.**

✕✕✕ Mandalay, 8 Harrison St., LS1 6PA, ⌀ 446453, Indian rest. – ⎕ DZ **e**

✕✕ **Brasserie Forty Four,** 42-44 The Calls, LS2 8AQ, ⌀ 342232, Fax 343332 – ⎕. 🖅 🅰🅴 𝘝𝘐𝘚𝘈 DZ **z**
closed Saturday lunch, Sunday, 25 to 30 December and Bank Holidays – M 9.40/23.35 **t.** and a la carte.

✕✕ Maxi's, 6 Bingley St., LS3 1LX, off Kirkstall Rd ⌀ 440552, Fax 343902, Chinese (Canton, Peking) rest., « Pagoda, ornate decor » – ⎕ 🅿. 🖅 🅰🅴 ⓪ 𝘝𝘐𝘚𝘈 AZ **a**

at Seacroft NE : 5 ½ m. at junction of A 64 and A 6120 – ✉ ✆ 0532 Leeds :

🏨🏨 **Stakis Leeds Windmill,** Ring Rd, LS14 5QP, ⌀ 732323, Telex 55452, Fax 323018 – Ⓘ ⤬ rm ⎕ rest 📺 ☎ 🅿 – 🔬 250. 🖅 🅰🅴 ⓪ 𝘝𝘐𝘚𝘈
M (closed Saturday lunch) (carving lunch) 9.00/15.95 **st.** ⑨ 4.50 – ⍁ 8.50 – **100 rm** 76.00/86.00 **st.** – SB (weekends only) 83.00 **st.**

at Garforth E : 6 m. at Junction of A 63 and A 642 – ✉ ✆ 0532 Leeds :

🏨🏨 **Hilton National,** Wakefield Rd, LS25 1LH, ⌀ 866556, Telex 556324, Fax 868326, ⑤, ⑤ₛ, ⎕ – ⤬ rm ⎕ rest 📺 ☎ & 🅿 – 🔬 250. 🖅 🅰🅴 ⓪ 𝘝𝘐𝘚𝘈
M (closed Saturday lunch) (carving lunch) 11.25/16.50 **st.** ⑨ 5.00 – ⍁ 9.45 – **144 rm** 83.75/117.25 **st.** – SB (weekends only) 94.00 **st.**

at Horsforth NW : 5 m. by A 65 off A 6120 – ✉ ✆ 0532 Leeds :

✕✕✕ Low Hall, Calverley Lane, LS18 5EF, ⌀ 588221, « Elizabethan manor », � – 🅿

at Bramhope NW : 8 m. on A 660 – ✉ ✆ 0532 Leeds :

🏨🏨 **Forte Crest,** Leeds Rd, LS16 9JJ, ⌀ 842911, Telex 556367, Fax 843451, ≼, ⑤, ⑤ₛ, ⎕, �, park – Ⓘ ⤬ rm 📺 ☎ 🅿 – 🔬 160. 🖅 🅰🅴 ⓪ 𝘝𝘐𝘚𝘈 – M 14.00/15.00 **st.** and a la carte ⑨ 4.00 – ⍁ 8.50 – **125 rm** 70.00/85.00 **st.**, **1 suite** 145.00/165.00 **st.**

🏨🏨 Parkway, Otley Rd, LS16 8AG, S : 2 m. on A 660 ⌀ 672551, Telex 556614, Fax 674410, ⑤, ⑤ₛ, ⎕, �, ✕ – Ⓘ 📺 ☎ & 🅿 – 🔬 250 – **103 rm.**

*If you intend staying in a resort or hotel
off the beaten track, telephone in advance,
especially during the season.*

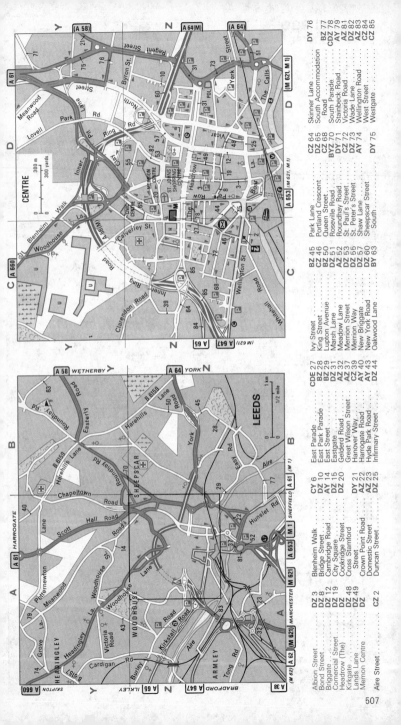

CENTRE

LEEDS

LIVERPOOL
CENTRE

*Great Britain and Ireland
is now covered
by a serie of Atlases
at a scale of 1 inch to 4.75 miles.
Three easy to use versions:
Paperback, Spiralbound, Hardback.*

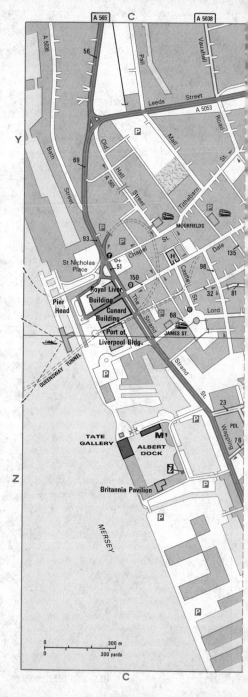

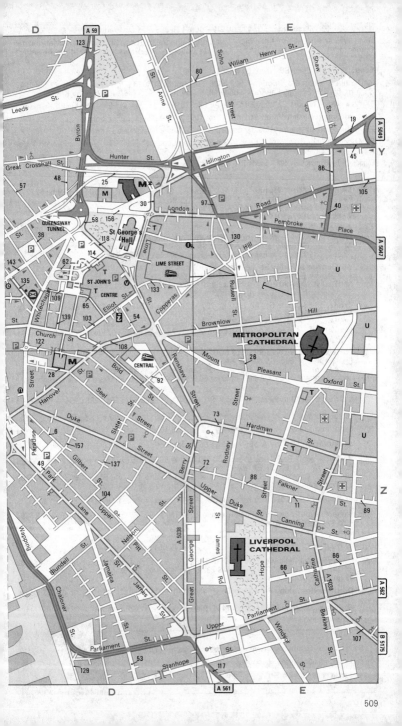

See : Walker Art Gallery★★ DY **M2** – Liverpool Cathedral★★ (Lady Chapel★) EZ – Metropolitan Cathedral★★ EYZ – Albert Dock★ CZ – Tate Gallery★ CZ – Merseyside Maritime Museum★ CZ **M1**.

Envir. : Speke Hall★ , SE : 8 m. by A 561.

🏌 Dunnings Bridge Rd, Bootle ℘ 928 6196, N : 5 m. by A 5036 – 🏌 Allerton Park ℘ 428 1046, S : 5 m. by B 5180 – 🏌 Lee Park Childwall, Valley Rd ℘ 487 9861, E : 7 m. by B 5178.

✈ Liverpool Airport : ℘ 486 8877, Telex 629323, SE : 6 m. by A 561 – **Terminal** : Pier Head.

⛴ to Douglas (Isle of Man Steam Packet Co.) 2-4 weekly (summer only) (4 h.).

⛴ to Birkenhead (Merseyside Transport) – to Wallasey (Merseyside Transport).

🛈 Merseyside Welcome Centre, Clayton Sq., Shopping Centre ℘ 709 3631 – Atlantic Pavilion, Albert Dock ℘ 708 8854.

London 219 – Birmingham 103 – Leeds 75 – Manchester 35.

Plan on preceding pages

🏨 **Liverpool Moat House** (Q.M.H.), Paradise St., L1 8JD, ℘ 709 0181, Telex 627270, Fax 709 2706, ♨, ⌊ₛ, 全ₛ, ▣ – ☒ ⟡ rm ▤ ▥ ☎ ℗ 🕭 – 🔬 400. ☒ 🄰🄴 ① **VISA** DZ **n** **M** *(closed Saturday lunch)* 16.00/18.00 **t.** and a la carte ⌡ 7.45 – **244 rm** 🖙 87.00/112.00 **t.**, **7 suites** 200.00/250.00 **t.** – SB (weekends only) 87.00/96.00 **st.**

🏨 **Atlantic Tower** (Mt. Charlotte Thistle), 30 Chapel St., L3 9RE, ℘ 227 4444, Telex 627070, Fax 236 3973, ≼ – |≣| ⟡ rm ▤ ▥ ☎ ℗ – 🔬 100. ☒ 🄰🄴 ① **VISA** CY **r** **M** *(closed Saturday lunch)* 15.50/15.95 **st.** and a la carte ⌡ 4.85 – 🖙 7.75 – **216 rm** 73.00/100.00 **st.**, **10 suites** 100.00/165.00 **st.** – SB 78.00/178.00 **st.**

🏨 **St. George's** (Forte), St. John's Precinct, Lime St., L1 1NQ, ℘ 709 7090, Fax 709 0137, ≼ – |≣| ⟡ rm ▥ ☎ ℗ – 🔬 200. ☒ 🄰🄴 ① **VISA** DY **v** **M** 12.50 **st.** and a la carte ⌡ 4.15 – 🖙 8.10 – **153 rm** 65.00/86.00 **st.**, **2 suites** 100.00/110.00 **st.** SB (weekends only) 75.00 **st.**

🏨 **Trials**, 56-62 Castle St., L2 7LQ, ℘ 227 1021, Telex 626125, Fax 236 0110 – |≣| ▥ ☎ ℗. ☒ 🄰🄴 ① **VISA**. ⬚ CY **e** **M** *(closed Saturday lunch, Sunday and Bank Holidays except lunch 25 December)* 17.50 **t.** (dinner) and a la carte 16.00/39.50 **t.** ⌡ 5.00 – 🖙 7.50 – **20 rm** 95.00/125.00 **t.**, **1 suite** 125.00 **t.** – SB (weekends only) 120.00 **st.**

🏨 **Forte Crest**, Lord Nelson St., L3 5QB, ℘ 709 7050, Telex 627954, Fax 709 2193 – |≣| ⟡ rm ▥ ☎ ℗ – 🔬 500. ☒ 🄰🄴 ① **VISA** DY **i** *closed 1 to 5 January* – **M** *(closed lunch Saturday, Sunday and Bank Holidays)* 8.50/13.30 **st.** and a la carte ⌡ 5.75 – 🖙 8.50 – **149 rm** 66.00/78.00 **st.**, **1 suite** 95.00 **st.** – SB (weekends only) 78.00 **st.**

XXX **L'Oriel**, Oriel Chambers, 14 Water St., L2 8TD, ℘ 236 5025, Fax 236 2794 – ☒ 🄰🄴 ① **VISA** CY **o** *closed Sunday, 25-26 December and 1 January* – **M** 12.95/15.50 **t.** and a la carte ⌡ 3.60.

XXX Ristorante Del Secolo, 36-40 Stanley St., ℘ 236 4004 DY **e**

at Bootle N : 5 m. by A 565 – ✉ ✆ 051 Liverpool :

🏨 **Park** (De Vere), Park Lane West, L30 3SU, on A 5036 ℘ 525 7555, Fax 525 2481 – |≣| ▥ ☎ ℗ – 🔬 100. ☒ 🄰🄴 ① **VISA** **M** *(closed Saturday lunch)* 10.50/12.00 **st.** and a la carte ⌡ 4.25 – **58 rm** 🖙 60.00/75.00 **st.** – SB (weekends only and weekdays May-August) 55.00/65.00 **st.**

at Blundellsands N : 6 ½ m. by A 565 – ✉ Crosby – ✆ 051 Liverpool :

🏨 Blundellsands (Lansbury), The Serpentine, L23 6TN, ℘ 924 6515, Telex 626270, Fax 931 5364 – |≣| ⟡ rm ▥ ☎ ℗ – 🔬 200 **43 rm**.

at Huyton E : 7 m. by M 62 on A 5058 – ✉ ✆ 051 Liverpool :

🏨 Logwood Mill, Fallows Way, L35 1RZ, SE : 3 ½ m. by A 5080 at junction with M 62 ℘ 449 2341, Telex 626243, Fax 449 3832, ⌊ₛ, 全ₛ – |≣| ▥ ☎ & ℗ – 🔬 250 **63 rm**.

🏨 **Derby Lodge,** Roby Rd, L36 4HD, ℘ 480 4440, Fax 480 8132, ⌲ – ▥ ☎ ℗. ☒ 🄰🄴 ① **VISA**. ⬚ **M** *(closed Saturday lunch)* 13.15/14.25 **t.** and a la carte ⌡ 3.75 – **16 rm** 🖙 69.00/100.00 **t.** – SB (weekends only) 109.90 **st.**

Send us your comments on the restaurants we recommend
and your opinion on the specialities
and local wines they offer.

See : Town Hall★ (19C) CZ – City Art Gallery★ CZ M² – Castlefield Heritage Parks★ CZ – Cathedral 15C (stalls and canopies★) CY.

Envir. : Heaton Hall★ (18C) , N : 5 m.

🏌 Heaton Park, ℰ 798 0295, N : by A 576 – 🏌 Fairfield Golf and Sailing, Booth Rd, Audenshaw, ℰ 370 1641, E : by A 635 – 🏌 Houldsworth, Wingate House, Higher Levenshulme N 224 5055.

✈ Manchester International Airport ℰ 489 3000 (British Airways) Tele – **Terminal :** Coach service from Victoria Station.

🛈 Town Hall Extension, Lloyd St. ℰ 234 3157/8 – Manchester International Airport, International Arrivals Hall ℰ 436 3344.

London 202 – Birmingham 86 – Glasgow 221 – Leeds 43 – Liverpool 35 – Nottingham 72.

Plan on next page

🏨 **Holiday Inn Crowne Plaza Midland,** Peter St., M60 2DS, ℰ 236 3333, Telex 667550, Fax 228 2241, 𝄞, ≘s, ⬚, squash – 🛗 ⇔ rm 🔟 ☎ 👌 – 🛐 400. 🌣 AE ⓞ VISA. ✀ **M** – French rest. *(closed Saturday lunch)* 17.95/28.50 **t.** and a la carte – **Trafford Room** *(closed Saturday lunch)* (carving rest.) 17.95 **t.** – ⌷ 10.50 – **296 rm** 118.00/138.00 **t.**, **7 suites** 199.00/399.00. – SB (weekends only) 106.00/120.00 **st.**   CZ **x**

🏨 **Ramada Renaissance,** Blackfriars St., Deansgate, M3 2EQ, ℰ 835 2555, Telex 669699, Fax 833 0731 – 🛗 ⇔ rm 🔲 rest 🔟 ☎ 👌 👤 – 🛐 350. 🌣 AE ⓞ VISA   CY **v** **M** 13.50/22.25 **t.** and a la carte 🍷 5.50 – ⌷ 9.25 – **200 rm** ⌷ 97.00/112.00 **t.**, **5 suites** 165.00 **t.** – SB 96.50/148.50 **st.**

🏨 **Copthorne Manchester,** Clippers Quay, Salford Quays, M5 3DL, ℰ 873 7321, Telex 669090, Fax 873 7318, 𝄞, ≘s, ⬚ – 🛗 ⇔ rm 🔲 rest 🔟 ☎ 👌 👤 – 🛐 150. 🌣 AE ⓞ VISA. ✀ **M** 11.50/14.25 **t.** and a la carte 🍷 5.00 – ⌷ 8.95 – **166 rm** 87.00/108.00 **st.**

🏨 Charterhouse, Oxford St., M60 7HA, ℰ 236 9999, Fax 236 0674 – 🛗 🔟 ☎ 👤 – 🛐 180 **45 rm**, **13 suites**.   CZ **o**

🏨 **Portland Thistle** (Mt. Charlotte Thistle), 3-5 Portland St., Piccadilly Gdns, M1 6DP, ℰ 228 3400, Telex 669157, Fax 228 6347, ≘s – 🛗 ⇔ rm 🔲 rest 🔟 ☎ 👤 – 🛐 200. 🌣 AE ⓞ VISA   CZ **a** **M** *(closed Saturday lunch)* 15.95/16.95 **t.** and a la carte 🍷 5.95 – ⌷ 10.50 – **203 rm** 85.00/105.00 **t.**, **3 suites** 146.00/302.50 **t.** – SB (weekends only) 99.00/213.40 **st.**

🏨 **Castlefield,** Liverpool Rd, M3 4JR, ℰ 832 7073, Fax 839 0326, 𝄞, ≘s, ⬚ – 🛗 ⇔ rm 🔲 rest 🔟 👌 👤 – 🛐 70. 🌣 VISA. ✀ **M** (bar lunch)/dinner 18.00 **st.** and a la carte 🍷 5.00 – **48 rm** ⌷ 60.00/79.00 **st.** – SB (weekends only) 55.00/80.00 **st.**

🏨 Cornelius, Manchester Rd, Chorlton-Cum-Hardy, M16 0ED, S : 5 m. by A 5103 on A 6010 ℰ 862 9595, Fax 862 9028 – 🔟 ☎ 👤 – 🛐 60 **15 rm**.

🍴 **Isola Bella,** Dolefield, Crown Sq., M3 3EN, ℰ 831 7099, Italian rest. – 🌣 AE VISA   CZ **e** *closed Sunday and Bank Holidays* – **M** a la carte 18.80/29.00 **st.** 🍷 5.20.

🍴 **Quan Ju De,** 44 Princess St., M1 6DE, ℰ 236 5236, Chinese (Canton) rest. – 🔲. 🌣 AE ⓞ VISA – *closed Saturday and Bank Holiday lunch* – **M** 9.50/18.50 **t.** and a la carte.   CZ **i**

🍴 **Giulio's Terrazza,** 14 Nicholas St., M1 4FE, ℰ 236 4033, Fax 236 0250, Italian rest. – 🌣 AE ⓞ VISA – *closed Sunday and Bank Holidays* – **M** 12.50/19.80 **t.** and a la carte 🍷 5.80.   CZ **r**

🍴 **Gaylord,** Amethyst House, Marriott's Court, Spring Gdns, M2 1EA, ℰ 832 6037, Indian rest. – 🔲. 🌣 AE ⓞ VISA   CZ **c** *closed 25 December and 1 January* – **M** a la carte 11.95/16.55 **t.** 🍷 5.30.

🍴 **Yang Sing,** 34 Princess St., M1 4JY, ℰ 236 2200, Fax 236 5934, Chinese (Canton) rest. – 🔲. 🌣 AE VISA   CZ **n** *closed 25 December* – **M** (booking essential) 12.25/20.00 **t.** and a la carte.

at Northenden S : 5 ¼ m. by A 5103 – ✉ ✆ 061 Manchester :

🏨 Forte Posthouse, Palatine Rd, M22 4FH, ℰ 998 7090, Telex 669248, Fax 946 0139 – 🛗 ⇔ rm 🔟 ☎ 👤 – 🛐 150 **196 rm**.

at Manchester Airport S : 9 m. by A 5103 off M 56 – ✉ ✆ 061 Manchester :

🏨 **Manchester Airport Hilton,** Outwood Lane, Ringway, M22 5WP, ℰ 436 4404, Telex 668361, Fax 436 1521, ≘s – 🛗 ⇔ rm 🔲 rest 🔟 ☎ 👤 – 🛐 130 **223 rm**.

🏨 **Forte Crest,** Ringway Rd, Wythenshawe, M22 5NS, ℰ 437 5811, Telex 668721, Fax 436 2340, 𝄞, ≘s, ⬚ – 🛗 ⇔ rm 🔲 rest 🔟 ☎ 👤 – 🛐 200. 🌣 AE ⓞ VISA **M** *(closed Saturday lunch)* 11.50/16.50 **st.** and a la carte 🍷 5.40 – ⌷ 8.50 – **295 rm** 85.00/95.00 **st.**, **3 suites** 159.00/259.00 **st.** – SB (weekends only) 90.00 **st.**

🏨 **Etrop Grange,** Outwood Lane, M22 5NR, ℰ 499 0500, Fax 499 0790 – 🔟 ☎ 👤 – 🛐 60. 🌣 AE ⓞ VISA. ✀ **M** *(closed Saturday lunch)* 14.25/26.50 **t.** – ⌷ 8.50 – **39 rm** 85.00/125.00 **t.**, **2 suites** 125.00/160.00 **t.** – SB 120.00/170.00 **st.**

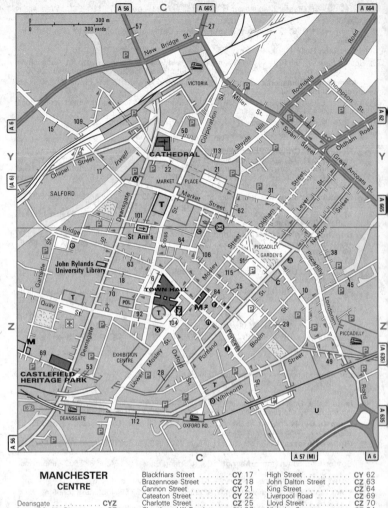

MANCHESTER
CENTRE

Deansgate . . . . **CYZ**
Lower Mosley Street . . . . . . **CZ**
Market Place . . . . **CY**
Market Street . . . . **CY**
Mosley Street . . . . **CZ**
Princess Street . . . . **CZ**

Addington Street . . . . **CY** 2
Albert Square . . . . **CZ** 6
Aytoun Street . . . . **CZ** 10
Blackfriars Road . . . . **CY** 15

Blackfriars Street . . . . **CY** 17
Brazennose Street . . . . **CZ** 18
Cannon Street . . . . **CY** 21
Cateaton Street . . . . **CY** 22
Charlotte Street . . . . **CZ** 25
Cheetham Hill Road . . . . . . **CY** 27
Chepstow Street . . . . **CZ** 28
Chorlton Street . . . . **CZ** 29
Church Street . . . . **CZ** 31
Dale Street . . . . **CZ** 38
Ducie Street . . . . **CZ** 45
Fairfield Street . . . . **CZ** 49
Fennel Street . . . . **CZ** 50
Great Bridgewater Street . . . **CZ** 53
Great Ducie Street . . . . **CY** 57

High Street . . . . **CY** 62
John Dalton Street . . . . **CZ** 63
King Street . . . . **CZ** 64
Liverpool Road . . . . **CZ** 69
Lloyd Street . . . . **CZ** 70
Nicholas Street . . . . **CZ** 84
Parker Street . . . . **CZ** 91
Peter Street . . . . **CZ** 92
St. Ann's Street . . . . **CZ** 101
St. Peter's Square . . . . **CZ** 104
Spring Gardens . . . . **CZ** 106
Viaduct Street . . . . **CY** 109
Whitworth Street West . . . . **CZ** 112
Withy Grove . . . . **CY** 113
York Street . . . . **CZ** 115

XXX **Moss Nook,** Ringwood Rd, Moss Nook, M22 5NA, ℰ 437 4778, Fax 498 8089 – **P**. **△** **AE** **VISA**
closed Saturday lunch, Sunday, Monday and 25 December-9 January – **M** 16.50/25.00 **t.** and a la carte ♦ 7.00.

at Worsley W : 7 ¼ m. by A 57 and M 602 off M 62 East – ⊠ ✆ 061 Manchester :

🏢 **Novotel Manchester West,** Worsley Brow, M28 4YA, at junction 13 of M 62 ℰ 799 3535, Telex 669586, Fax 703 8207, ⤢ heated – ▯ ⤢ rm **TV** ✆ & **P** – 🔏 200. **△** **AE** **①** **VISA**
M a la carte 10.80/19.40 **st.** – � 7.15 – **119 rm** 63.00/68.00 **st.**

512